D1090381

TECHNIQUE OF ORGANIC CHEMISTRY

ARNOLD WEISSBERGER, *Editor*

Volume IV

DISTILLATION

Second completely revised and augmented edition

TECHNIQUE OF ORGANIC CHEMISTRY

ARNOLD WEISSBERGER, ***Editor***

Volume I: Physical Methods of Organic Chemistry
Third Edition—in Four Parts

Volume II: Catalytic, Photochemical, and Electrolytic Reactions
Second Edition

Volume III: *Second Edition*
Part I. Separation and Purification
Part II. Laboratory Engineering

Volume IV: Distillation
Second Edition

Volume V: Adsorption and Chromatography

Volume VI: Micro and Semimicro Methods

Volume VII: Organic Solvents
Second Edition

Volume VIII: Investigation of Rates and Mechanisms of Reactions
Second Edition—in Two Parts

Volume IX: Chemical Applications of Spectroscopy

Volume X: Fundamentals of Chromatography

Volume XI: Elucidation of Structures by Physical and Chemical Methods
In Two Parts

TECHNIQUE OF ORGANIC CHEMISTRY

Volume IV

DISTILLATION

Second Completely Revised and Augmented Edition

Editors:

E. S. PERRY and A. WEISSBERGER

Authors:

C. S. Carlson
C. H. Deal
J. C. Hecker
D. E. Orgen
E. S. Perry
Arthur and Elizabeth Rose
J. Stewart
R. S. Tipson
F. E. Williams
T. J. Williams

1965

INTERSCIENCE PUBLISHERS
a division of John Wiley & Sons,
New York · London · Sydney

Library of Congress Catalog Card Number 45-8533

PRINTED IN THE UNITED STATES OF AMERICA

INTRODUCTION

Organic chemistry, from its very beginning, has used specific tools and techniques for the synthesis, isolation, and purification of compounds, and physical methods for the determination of their properties. Much of the success of the organic chemist depends upon a wise selection and a skillful application of these methods, tools, and techniques, which, with the progress of the science, have become numerous and often intricate.

The present series is devoted to a comprehensive presentation of the techniques which are used in the organic laboratory and which are available for the investigation of organic compounds The authors give the theoretical background for an understanding of the various methods and operations and describe the techniques and tools, their modifications, their merits and limitations, and their handling. It is hoped that the series will contribute to a better understanding and a more rational and effective application of the respective techniques. Reference is made to some investigations in the field of chemical engineering, so that the results may be of assistance in the laboratory and help the laboratory chemist to understand the problems which arise when his work is stepped up to a larger scale.

The field is broad and some of it is difficult to survey. Authors and editors hope that the volumes will be found useful and that many of the readers will let them have the benefit of their criticism and of suggestions for improvements.

A.W.

Research Laboratories
Eastman Kodak Company
Rochester, New York

TECHNIQUE OF ORGANIC CHEMISTRY

GENERAL PLAN OF THE SERIES

Volume I (Third Edition—in four parts). **Physical Methods of Organic Chemistry.** *Authors:* A. E. Alexander, D. H. Anderson, J. R. Anderson, J. C. Arthur, Jr., E. D. Bailey, N. Bauer, G. L. Beyer, E. R. Blout, L. O. Brockway, L. M. Corliss, A. H. Corwin, R. L. Custer, B. P. Dailey, G. Donnay, J. D. H. Donnay, K. Fajans, D. D. Fitts, G. K. Fraenkel, A. L. Geddes, H. S. Gutowsky, F. A. Hamm, W. D. Harkins, J. M. Hastings, W. Heller, E. E. Jelley, W. Klyne, C. G. Le Fevre, R. J. W. Le Fevre, S. Z. Lewin, W. N. Lipscomb, W. J. Mader, H. Mark, L. Meites, D. H. Moore, L. D. Moore, Jr., O. H. Muller, J. B. Nichols, W. C. Nixon, G. Oster, A. C. Parker, M. A. Peacock, R. B. Pontius, J. G. Powles, H. A. Scheraga, P. W. Selwood, T. Shedlowsky, R. Singer, D. R. Simonson, W. M. Siri, E. L. Skau, C. P. Smyth, M. Spiro, D. W. Stewart, J. M. Sturtevant, W. Swietoslawski, J. F. Swindells, C. Tanford, G. W. Thomson, B. M. Tolbert, R. Ullman, M. J. Vold, R. D. Vold, R. H. Wagner, H. Wakeham, C. E. Waring, S. Wawzonek, W. West, N. B. Woodall, and N. Wotherspoon

Volume II (Second Edition). **Catalytic Reactions,** V. I. Komarewsky, C. H. Riesz, and F. L. Morritz; **Photochemical Reactions,** C. R. Masson, V. Boekelheide, and W. A. Noyes, Jr.; **Electrolytic Reactions,** S. Swann, Jr.

Volume III (Second Edition).
Part I. Separation and Purification. C. M. Ambler, G. Broughton, D. Craig, L. C. Craig, A. B. Cummins, F. B. Hutto, Jr., A. L. Jones, K. Kammermeyer, F. W. Keith, Jr., E. MacWilliam, E. G. Scheibel, R. E. Stauffer, and R. S. Tipson.
Part II. Laboratory Engineering. J. W. Axelson, R. S. Egly, R. F. Eisenberg, M. P. Hofmann, R. R. Kraybill, G. H. Miller, J. H. Rushton, W. C. Streib

Volume IV (Second Edition). **Distillation.** C. S. Carlson, C. H. Deal, J. C. Hecker, D. E. Orgen, E. S. Perry, A. and E. Rose, J. Stewart, R. S. Tipson, F. E. Williams, and T. J. Williams

Volume V. Adsorption and Chromatography. H. G. Cassidy

Volume VI. Micro and Semimicro Methods. N. D. Cheronis. With contributions by A. R. Ronzio and T. S. Ma

Volume VII. Organic Solvents. A. Weissberger and E. S. Proskauer. *Second Edition* by J. A. Riddick and E. E. Toops, Jr.

Volume VIII (Second Edition—in two parts). **Investigations of Rates and Mechanisms of Reactions.** *Editors:* S. L. Friess, E. S. Lewis, and A. Weissberger. *Authors:* J. C. Balaceanu, M. L. Bender, S. A. Bernhard, C. E. Boozer, J. F. Bunnett, G. M. Burnett, B. Chance, L. DeMaeyer, M. Eigen, S. L. Friess, E. M. Grunwald, J. Higgins, F. M. Huennekens, J. C. Jungers, M. Kreevoy, E. S. Lewis, R. Livingston, A. Maccoll, E. F. MacNichol, Jr., H. W. Melville, B. K. Morse, R. M. Noyes, G. Porter, F. J. W. Roughton, G. A. Russell, W. H. Saunders, Jr., H. Strehlow, and A. Weller

Volume IX. Chemical Applications of Spectroscopy. *Editor:* W. West. *Authors:* A. B. F. Duncan, W. Gordy, R. N. Jones, F. A. Matsen, C. Sandorfy, and W. West

Volume X. Fundamentals of Chromatography. H. G. Cassidy

Volume XI (in two parts). **Elucidation of Structures by Physical and Chemical Methods.** *Editor:* K. W. Bentley. *Authors:* B. Belleau, K. W. Bentley, K. Biemann, J. C. D. Brand, A. R. H. Cole, J. K. N. Jones, J. F. King, E. Leete, P. de Mayo, S. McLean, F. J. McQuillin, K. H. Overton, M. B. Perry, N. Polgar, K. T. Potts, A. I. Scott, E. Y. Spencer, J. B. Stothers, G. A. Swan, Z. Valenta, and B. C. L. Weedon

Distillation

PREFACE TO THE SECOND EDITION

More than a decade has passed since *Distillation* was published in 1951, and many significant developments have taken place during this time. The volume is used not only as a reference book but also as an academic text, and the steadily continuing demand required a reprinting or a new edition. In view of the considerable amount of new information, of changed points of view in the discussion of some of the older material, and of the obsolescence of other items, it was decided to proceed with a new edition. This decision also afforded a welcome opportunity to include several areas germane to the use of the book, which were not treated in the first edition.

For the new edition, the chapters of the first edition were thoroughly revised by the original authors; some were expanded, others reduced in size. The chapter on "Distillation of Liquified Gases and Low Boiling Liquids" no longer appears as a separate chapter, because the use of chromatographic methods has diminished the practical importance of these operations. The discussion of theory is supplemented in the new edition by a special chapter (II) by Carl H. Deal emphasizing the importance of "Vapor–Liquid Equilibria" which are fundamental to all distillation processes. Chapter III, "Ordinary Fractional Distillation," by Frederick E. Williams, is a revision of the chapter in the first edition by A. L. Glasebrook and F. E. Williams, and "Extractive and Azeotropic Distillation" by Carl S. Carlson was revised by Joseph Stewart for the second edition (Chapter IV).

Batch distillation is commonly employed in the laboratory because of the simplicity and versatility of its equipment, but small scale continuous distillation is becoming increasingly important in the laboratory. It produces information under steady state conditions which is readily translatable to equipment on a larger scale. Moreover, it permits distillation of heat-sensitive materials which would not tolerate prolonged exposure in the batch still. "Continuous Distillation" is discussed in a new chapter (IX) by Frederick E. Williams.

While the present treatise is primarily concerned with laboratory techniques, it appeared desirable to include some information on the scaling up of operations in the pilot plant. We hope that Chapter X, "Pilot Plant Distillation," by Donald E. Orgen, will be of value in the communication between the laboratory and the pilot plant, and will help to feed back to the laboratory an understanding of some of the techniques which were developed for a larger scale. Chapter XI, "Automation in Distillation," by Theodore J. Williams has been added for similar reasons. It should be valuable for an understanding of larger scale operations, and alert the research worker to the techniques which were developed for commercial operations. Application of automation in the laboratory will, for instance, be important where the data obtained are to be used in the design of large-scale procedures.

The editor of the first edition acknowledges with gratitude the most valuable collaboration of Edmond S. Perry to whom should go the credit for the improvements in the second edition. We both thank the authors for their contributions, and the publishers and their staff for their expert handling of the publication of this treatise.

Research Laboratories
Eastman Kodak Company
Rochester, New York

EDMOND S. PERRY
ARNOLD WEISSBERGER

Distillation

PREFACE TO THE FIRST EDITION

Distillation is one of the chief operations used for the isolation and purification of volatile compounds. Much labor has been devoted to the understanding of the theory and to the perfection of the techniques of distillation at ordinary and reduced pressures, but the information thus obtained is not easy of access. The present volume gives a comprehensive account of the theory and practice of batch distillation on a laboratory scale. Its organization owes much to Dr. F. D. Rossini, to whom I express sincere thanks. I am grateful to the authors, not only for their contributions, but for many suggestions concerning chapters other than their own. Authors and editor acknowledge with gratitude the helpful suggestions, loan of materials, and assistance in the editorial work received from Miss M. W. Grafflin, Messrs. R. L. Bent and I. S. Bradley, and Drs. C. H. Bridges, E. M. Crane, M. R. Fenske, R. F. Marschner, W. J. Podbielniak, H. Skolnik, H. M. Spurlin, P. W. Vittum, and J. S. Whitaker. We are also indebted to Podbielniak, Inc., for assistance in the preparation of a number of the illustrations in Chapters II and IV. Arthur and Elizabeth Rose worked out the integrated list of symbols (shown on pages xviii–xxvii) following the approved list of the American Institute of Chemical Engineers as closely as possible. It did not prove feasible to use this for "Distillation under High Vacuum," and a separate list was made by Dr. J. C. Hecker for Chapter VI (pages 495 and 496), following the usage in the literature on high vacua. Dr. E. M. Crane prepared the subject index.

Certain phases of the subject matter of this book have been treated in preceding volumes of the series *Technique of Organic Chemistry*, particularly in the following volumes and chapters: VOLUME I, *Physical Methods of Organic Chemistry*, Part I, "Temperature Measurement" by J. M. Sturtevant, "Temperature Control" by J. M. Sturtevant, "Determination of Melting and Freezing Temperatures" by E. L. Skau and H. Wakeham, "Determination of Boiling and Condensation Temperatures" by W. Swietoslawski and J. R. Anderson, "Determination of Vapor Pressure" by G. W. Thomson, "Determination of Density" by N. Bauer, "Determination of Solubility" by R. D. Vold and M. J. Vold; VOLUME I, Part II, "Refractometry" by N. Bauer and K. Fajans; VOLUME III, "Heating and Cooling" by R. S. Egly. With few exceptions, the authors of *Distillation* have not repeated the information contained in these chapters. A cumulative index of the major topics covered in the first five volumes of this series is printed at the end of this volume.

During the preparation of *Distillation*, we suffered the loss of an author, Dr. J. K. Moore, who died suddenly in July, 1948. We had the benefit of his cooperation in the planning of the book as a whole and of Chapter II in particular. Dr. Moore was a scientist of great ability and a fine person who had become dear to everybody with whom he collaborated in the writing of this book.

To the publishers and their staff go the authors' and my thanks for their understanding, patient, and generous help in many problems.

A. W.

Research Laboratories
Eastman Kodak Company
Rochester, New York

TECHNIQUE OF ORGANIC CHEMISTRY

Volume IV

Distillation

CONTENTS

CHAPTER I

THEORY

ARTHUR and ELIZABETH ROSE, *State College, Pennsylvania*

I. INTRODUCTION

"Spare nat favorable reder to peruse and revolve to thy synguler helthe, conforte, and larnynge, thys book of distyllacion."(1527)[1]

"Now I am come to the arts and I shall begin from distillation, an invention of later times, a wonderful thing to be praised beyond the power of men; not that which the vulgar and unskilled men use, for they do but corrupt and destroy what is good; but that which is done by skillful artists. . . . Let one that loves learning and to search nature's secrets, enter upon this; for a dull fellow will never attain to this art of distilling."(1589)[2]

Distillation and organic chemistry have been closely associated for centuries. Long before organic chemistry was recognized as a distinct branch of science, the art of distillation was practiced in the preparation of what we now know as organic substances. The production of potable forms of ethyl alcohol is the example best known to the layman, and has in fact stimulated many improvements in apparatus. The distillation of such essential oils as turpentine and lemon, and of the many medicinal "waters" was likewise an early art. The alchemists stressed distillation as one of the processes necessary in the preparation of the philosopher's stone, and in their zodiac assigned to it the sign Virgo. By 1500 knowledge of distillation had become detailed enough to merit the publication of a comprehensive treatise on the subject, *Das kleine Distillierbuch*, by Brunswig, one of the earliest books on applied chemistry to appear in a language other than Latin.[3] This book and other publications of the period show that the early experts in the art carried out distillation operations of some complexity.

In the subsequent evolution of distillation apparatus, large-scale and industrial applications preceded its development in the laboratory. Early in the nineteenth century, ingenious stills for the manufacture of spirits were devised in France by Cellier-Blumenthal and Derosne[4, 5] and in Great Britain by Coffey.[6] These efficiently employed heat in bubble-plate towers that were little different from some of those used today. Later in the nineteenth centry, when organic chemistry emerged as a science, the development of the structural theory and the enormous amount of research on coal-tar derivatives were accompanied by marked refinements in laboratory stills. The raw-material shortages of the first world war and the extensive chemistry based on petroleum stimulated further improvements in apparatus, of which highly efficient packed columns of all sizes are the most important. The development has continued into the present with materials such as vitamins, close-boiling industrial solvents, fatty acids, liquefied air, sea water, and isotopes.

1. Terminology

Precise definitions of the terms used in this book are discussed in detail in the appropriate sections of the text. The purpose of the following section is to give the uninitiated reader a working knowledge of the terminology.

A. DEFINITIONS OF GENERAL TERMS AND THE APPARATUS

In broadest terms *distillation* is a process of separation based on the difference in composition between a liquid and the vapor formed from it. Condensation of the vapor and recovery of the resulting liquid are almost always implied. Distillation of a truly pure substance could yield no separation, but since truly pure substances are nonexistent, distillation of highly purified substances is of some interest as a partial proof that a sample is essentially a single, pure substance rather than a mixture. However, in general, discussions on distillation deal almost universally with the behavior of mixtures. *Simple distillation* involves the application of heat to vaporize the liquid and the subsequent cooling of the vapor formed until it condenses to a liquid at a different part of the apparatus. Such a process is effective in the separation of liquids from nonvolatile solids, as in the distillation of pure water from salt water, or the recovery of an organic solvent from mixtures with nonvolatile substances. In such cases the distinction from *evaporation* is not sharp.

A *simple distillation* also can serve as a means of partial separation of liquids of appreciably different boiling points or volatilities. Simple distillation is sometimes referred to as *differential distillation* because in general the composition of both vapor and residue changes gradually by differential amounts as the operation proceeds. In *flash distillation* or *equilibrium distillation,* a form of simple distillation, an appreciable proportion of a liquid is converted to vapor and maintained in contact with the residual liquid in such a way that equilibrium is reached.

The apparatus required for simple distillation consists of a pot, called a *still*, *retort*, or kettle, in which the liquid to be distilled (the distilland) is placed for heating, a *condenser*, and a receiver in which the *product*, or *distillate*, is collected. The term *still* is also used to refer to complete assemblages of apparatus or equipment for distillation. The earliest condensers were long tubes cooled by air. The famous Liebig condenser (actually adapted from large scale to laboratory use by Weigel before 1800[7]), in which the condenser tube is cooled by a countercurrent of cold water, came into common use about the middle of the nineteenth century, and must have served in many of the discoveries of that prolific period of organic chemistry.

Early in the art, simple distillation was found ineffective in the separation of liquids with close boiling points, and the first crude fractional distillations were devised. As originally practiced, fractional distillation meant the collection of the distillate in successive *fractions* or *cuts,* and was sometimes applied to the systematic recombination and redistillation of those cuts. Young,[8] for example, described in 1922 such a distillation of a benzene–toluene mixture, in which the original ten fractions were recombined and redistilled fourteen times, a process taking about 30 hours, in order to obtain appreciable proportions of nearly pure benzene and toluene. A similar procedure was used by Shepherd and Porter[9] in 1923 in the analysis of liquefied natural gas. As it is used today the term *fractional distillation* represents the whole process whereby the fractions are made as distinct in properties as possible. Especially included in this modern concept is the use of various devices to cause a partial condensation of the vapor over the still and return of the liquid condensate toward the still. In this sense, fractional distillation was introduced when the Alexandrian chemists[10] (about the fourth century A.D.) interposed between the still and condenser tube the first crude *still head,* thus foreshadowing the modern column or tower. Into the improvement of these early still heads has been put most of the effort of the subsequent centuries. The aim of fractional distillation is the achievement of the closest possible contact between rising vapor and descending liquid so that equilibrium will be approached and the distillate contain the highest possible proportion of the more volatile component. Such purification by the contact of countercurrent streams of liquid and vapor is generally referred to as *enrichment.*

The term rectification is closely associated with fractional distillation and had its origin in the distillation of spirits. Like any other concept involved in an art before it becomes a science, the term is still used with various meanings. In its general sense, it is almost a synonym for distillation, but in this chapter *rectification* will be defined as the enrichment, i.e., the purification, of the vapor in the head, tower, or column by contact with condensed liquid returning toward the still. Such liquid is known as *reflux.*

In the early still heads reflux was produced by the natural cooling effect of the surrounding air, or in some cases by the application of water to the outside of the still head. Here the reflux and vapor were in contact only on the inner surface of the head. In modern apparatus intimate contact is effected in an insulated or nearly adiabatic *column* or *tower*, supplied with *packing*, *plates*, or some other device for achieving a large liquid–gas interface. The reflux is produced in a condenser at the top of the column. The term *still head* is now applied also to the condenser and associated apparatus for taking off product and measuring temperature at the top of a laboratory column.

The term *contact rectification* is applied to all processes such as that described above in which rising vapor and descending liquid are brought into intimate contact, and mass transfer takes place from one phase to the other because of the fundamental tendency to approach equilibrium compositions. This process is usually carried out under adiabatic conditions, although much ordinary distillation is nonadiabatic and successful in the separation desired. Apparatus has been constructed in which the major portion of the enrichment is secured in a column that has an axial cooler and an external heater throughout the column length. The process involves repeated partial vaporization and condensation along the length of the column, and is called *thermal rectification*. The extent of the composition change depends upon the amount of heat added to the liquid and removed from the vapor. The process has advantages in vacuum distillation and is discussed in detail in Chapter V.

In *continuous distillation* (usual in large-scale operations) the material to be distilled (*feed*) is introduced continuously into the side of a tower and product is continuously withdrawn from the heater section (*boiler*) or still and from the condenser, and in some cases also from intermediate points above and below the point at which the feed enters. The portion of such a column above the point of entry of feed is called the *enriching section*, while the portion below the feed is called the *stripping* or *exhausting section*. In *batch distillation* the entire sample of the material to be distilled (the *charge*) is placed in the still before the distillation is begun and during the distillation the product is withdrawn only from the condenser. Both *partial* and *total condensers* are used. In the former, product is removed as vapor from the top of the condenser and another condenser is required to liquefy the vapor. Partial condensers are sometimes called *dephlegmators* and the liquid condensate is called *phlegm*. In total condensers, the more common arrangement, all the vapor is condensed and product is removed as liquid just below the condenser. This removal need not be complete and the remaining liquid supplies reflux. If all the condensate is returned down the column and no product is withdrawn, the column is said to be operating under *total* or *infinite reflux*. Such operation under total reflux is often used as a preliminary in order to bring the column as near equilibrium as possible before removing product. If the condensate is divided, the column is said to be operating under *partial* or *finite reflux*.

An infinity of variations of distillation are practiced. The broader types are discussed in later chapters, namely, ordinary fractional distillation, extractive and azeotropic distillation, moderate and high vacuum distillation, and sublimation. Related to extractive and azeotropic distillation, in that they are processes in which an attempt is made to modify the volatility of the material to be distilled, is a group of which *steam distillation* is best known. In this process, steam is introduced into the vapor stream either by formation from boiling water in the still pot or by a more direct means. Such a distillation may be either simple or fractional, as used in the latter case in the distillation of the less volatile fractions of petroleum. The more general term for this process, in which a substance other than steam may be used as the additive, is *codistillation*. *Carrier distillation* has a similar meaning, though the term *carrier gas distillation* implies that the gas sent through the process is not condensed in the distillate. *Amplified distillation* is codistillation in which the added component (or components) is miscible with the liquid being distilled, and in which the added component is also of about the same volatility as the charge (see p. 184). The terms defined here are all rather loosely used.

B. DEFINITIONS OF VARIABLES

Reflux Ratio, Holdup, Vapor Pressure, and Volatility. One of the major factors affecting the sharpness of separation and the time and cost of a distillation is the proportion of condensate returned as reflux. This proportion is measured by the *reflux ratio*, which may be expressed in various ways. In this chapter it is defined as the ratio of moles of reflux liquid per unit time to moles of product per unit time. A high reflux ratio means a large amount of reflux liquid for a given amount of product, and in general a better separation but a longer time for the distillation of a given charge than operation with a low reflux ratio. For some purposes it is advantageous to define reflux ratio as the ratio of descending reflux to rising vapor, both being measured in the same units. It is important to be certain which definition of reflux ratio is being used.

During any time period, a certain proportion of the liquid introduced into the apparatus is actually in the column or tower as reflux and rising vapor. This is known as *holdup*. The proportion of holdup to the total mixture being distilled is of consequence in batch distillation since it limits the percentage of the charge that can be distilled, and also has an effect on the sharpness of separation.

In any discussion of separation by distillation, vapor pressure is a basic concept. Every liquid evaporates into a closed space around it until the pressure of its vapor reaches a characteristic value called its *vapor pressure*. This is fixed for any liquid at a given temperature, increases with temperature, and varies from one liquid to another. It is an equilibrium value in the sense that, if the actual pressure of the vapor is greater or less than the characteristic value, condensation of vapor or evaporation of liquid will occur until the equilibrium value is established. This tendency for vapor and liquid to approach equilibrium constitutes the active driving force in all distillation operations.

A liquid that is a mixture of two or more substances will in general give a mixed vapor, the composition of which depends upon the values of the partial vapor pressures of the individual components. The factors determining these partial vapor pressures are complex and, in the case of distillation, are conveniently expressed in terms of the volatility and relative volatility. A further discussion of the concepts introduced here will be found in Section II. Although in practice mixtures of several substances are frequently distilled, and progress has been made in the theory of distillation of liquids of three or more components, the succeeding discussion in this chapter will be confined for convenience and simplicity to *binary* mixtures, unless specifically stated otherwise. The *volatility* of a substance is roughly proportional to its vapor pressure or inversely proportional to its boiling point. It must be emphasized that in mixtures the correspondence is only approximate, and that, particularly in the case of liquids with boiling points near one another, the correspondence may disappear altogether, and in certain cases the lower boiling component may have the smaller volatility. Volatility of substances in a mixture is usually expressed as the *relative volatility* which is assigned the symbol *alpha* (α). For materials which form an ideal solution, this is equal to the *vapor pressure ratio*, i.e., the ratio of the vapor pressures of the two pure materials at the same temperature. This may be expressed as

$$\alpha = p_1/p_2$$

where p_1 and p_2 are the vapor pressures (at the same temperature) of the pure substances whose separation is under consideration. The larger pressure is conventionally placed in the numerator. The more general definition of relative volatility in terms of the concentration in vapor and liquid phases at equilibrium is

$$\alpha = (y_1/y_2)/(x_1/x_2)$$

where x_1 and x_2 are the mole fractions of the two components in the liquid, and y_1 and y_2 are the corresponding mole fractions in the vapor. Pairs of components that have a relative volatility near unity are difficult to separate by distillation. A large relative volatility indicates a pair that can be separated easily.

Separating Power and Theoretical Plates. The degree of success in separating a mixture by distillation is also closely related to the inherent efficiency or effectiveness of the column and packing or plates. The terms theoretical plate, height equivalent to a theoretical plate (H.E.T.P.), plate efficiency, height of a transfer unit (H.T.U.), described in Sec. VI,

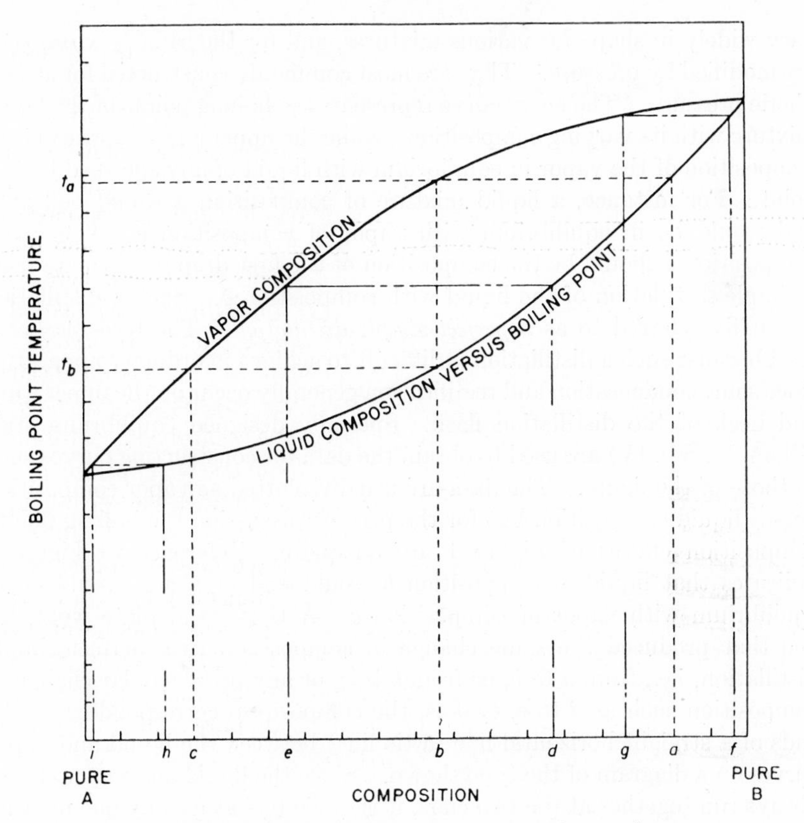

Fig. 1. Boiling point–composition diagram for binary mixtures.

and other concepts are used in expressing this inherent separating power of the apparatus. The H.E.T.P. standard was first introduced by Peters[11] and has been applied chiefly to packed columns, although it may also be used for plate columns. A *theoretical plate* may be defined as a device which produces the same difference in composition as exists at equilibrium between a liquid mixture and its vapor. The terms theoretical plate and *theoretical stage* are synonymous except that the latter is more general and applies also to any device that causes equilibrium separation in other separation processes, such as extraction, diffusion, chromatography, and crystallization.

The magnitude of the change in composition for one theoretical plate varies with the mixture under consideration, and for any one mixture it also varies with the composition. This may be illustrated by reference to the following graph of the composition of liquid and vapor plotted against the boiling points of a binary mixture (Fig. 1). Such boiling-point curves vary widely in shape for various mixtures, and for the same mixture they are modified by pressure. They are most commonly constructed for atmospheric pressure. The lower curve represents the boiling points of the liquid mixture with its varying compositions, while the upper curve represents the composition of the vapor in equilibrium with liquid of any specified boiling point. For instance, a liquid mixture of composition a would boil at t_a and would be in equilibrium with vapor of composition b. The vapor composition b should be the composition of the first drop of distillate from a simple distillation of the liquid with composition a. Such a distillation is usually referred to as a *perfect simple distillation*. The term *perfect* is used because such a distillation is difficult to achieve in ordinary apparatus, since some condensation and rectification generally occur on the upper walls and neck of the distillation flask. Specially designed equilibrium stills (Chap. II, Sec. IV) are used to obtain the data for constructing curves such as those of the figure. The data are usually plotted as vapor composition versus liquid composition but for the present discussion the boiling point–composition curves of Figure 1 are adequate. Reference to Figure 1 indicates that liquid of composition b would boil at t_b and would be in equilibrium with vapor of composition c. A theoretical plate would be one that produced the same change in composition as a perfect simple distillation, i.e., from a to b, or from b to c, or any other similar change in composition such as d to e, that is, the composition corresponding to the ends of a straight horizontal line (a tie line) between the liquid and vapor curves on a diagram of the type shown. Since the liquid and vapor curves always run together at the two ends, it is obvious that for any one mixture the composition differences corresponding to a theoretical plate will decrease toward zero as the liquid compositions approach those of the pure substances. It is also true that the closer the relative volatility approaches unity, the closer will the liquid and vapor curves approach one another, and the less will be the composition difference corresponding to a theoretical plate. A packed column (or any other rectifying device) that will produce a separation corresponding to two consecutive steps or units, such as from a to c, is said to have the equivalent of two theoretical plates. If the height of such a packed column is 10 in., the H.E.T.P. is 5 in. Similar reasoning applies to any number of plates, and any height of column. Columns have been constructed with hundreds of theoretical plates. A given column and packing may be expected to have about the same H.E.T.P. with different pairs of liquids if these are of the same general type as to chemical class, viscosity, and surface tension. If these characterisics vary to a great extent, the film thickness, area of gas–liquid interface, and rates of diffusion are presumably sufficiently changed so that the same column and packing may give markedly different H.E.T.P. values. Rapid progress is being made in expressing column performance in terms of the resistance to transfer of material across the film between the vapor and liquid (Sec. VI). However, the concept of theoretical plate and H.E.T.P. has been and still is of greater practical utility.

The term theoretical plate is based on the assumption that in a *plate* column the liquid on any plate should, under ideal conditions, give a vapor which would differ in composition by the amount indicated by the vapor–liquid composition diagram, and this vapor would condense to form the liquid on the plate above. Thus the composition difference from one plate to the next would correspond to that obtained by use of a vapor–liquid equilibrium diagram (Fig. 1). In actual operation the composition differences are usually less than this, and the term *plate efficiency* is used to represent the ratio of the actual concentration change to that expected from a theoretical or perfect plate.

The nature of the devices used to bring liquid and vapor into contact is the major factor determining H.E.T.P. and, in a given diameter column, also determines the maximum throughput. *Throughput,* or *vapor velocity,* or *boilup rate,* is the rate at which vapor is passing up the column and is usually expressed in terms of the quantity of liquid equivalent to the vapor passing up the column per unit time. As long as there is to be flow through the column there must be a difference in pressure between the still pot and the top of the column, and this must be sufficient to overcome the resistance between descending liquid and rising vapor as they pass through the interstices of the packing or through plates. There is a maximum throughput at which the *pressure drop* (difference in pressure between still pot and receiver) becomes so great that the velocity of the rising vapor is sufficient to prevent normal downward flow of the reflux. Under such circumstances excess liquid first collects in slugs and then is forced upward. This is usually called *flooding* and is not desirable during actual distillation but is regularly used to give increased efficiency by thoroughly wetting the packing for a short period prior to the start of a distillation in a packed column.

2. Relation of Distillation to Other Separation Processes—Fractionation

The term *fractionation* is often used to mean fractional distillation or rectification. Actually, distillation is one of a number of separation processes by means of which fractionation of mixtures may be achieved. In this broader sense fractionation implies any process for the systematic separation of a mixture into relatively pure fractions. Recombination of the similar fractions and repetition of the fundamental separation process are usually also implied. A widely known example of fractionation by a separation process other than distillation is the fractional-crystallization procedure. It was used extensively in the preparation of certain rare-earth elements.[12] A more recent important example of fractionation is the separation of isotopic uranium fluorides by diffusion barriers.[13] In this case a very ingenious system was devised for recombining certain fractions and repeating the fundamental separation with a minimum of handling. Each repetition of the fundamental separation is referred to as a *stage*, and an interconnected set of such stages is a *cascade*. Systematic fractional precipitation of high-polymer solutions is of interest as an aid in determining the distribution of molecular sizes. Extraction from one liquid to another through a multiplicity of discrete stages, as in a Craig unit,[14] has been extensively discussed and used as a means of separation and fractionation. Analogous procedures involving numerous repetitions of simple distillation and recombination of distillates are described in the older literature of distillation. In fact, some descriptions of such fractional separation are of such late date as to emphasize how recent is the development of efficient laboratory rectification equipment.

Distillation through a column is similar in principle to purification of a liquid mixture by countercurrent action of another suitably chosen liquid (continuous solvent extraction). A closely related case is purification of a gaseous mixture by countercurrent action of liquid solvent (ordinary absorption-tower action). These last three types of separation operations are alike in that a multiplicity of stages of repetition can be achieved by countercurrent gravity flow so that complex handling problems are entirely avoided. The effect of more than a thousand repetitions of the fundamental separation process has been claimed in a single packed column, and distillation columns with over one hundred stages are common. Gas–liquid chromatography is an example of a separation process in which very large numbers of stages are very easily obtained in a single column, while a single stage gas–liquid chromatography separation is almost unknown.

The principles and theory are essentially the same for all the different kinds of separation processes,[15] and more than one process is usually applicable for any one separation problem. If the relative volatility is near unity, consideration should be given to separation by modified distillation such as extractive or azeotropic distillation, described in Chapter IV or by methods other than distillation. However, distillation is frequently the best choice because of the simplicity of the apparatus and procedure. An absolutely pure product is not possible by any distillation process, but for all except azeotropic mixtures (Chap. II) such purity can be closely approached if sufficiently complex and elaborate processes and apparatus are used.

3. Distillation Curves

Like the apparatus, the theory of distillation has also developed largely around organic-chemical applications. The large-scale production of alcohols and of coal tar and petroleum derivatives stimulated extensive work on the theory of continuous distillation. Since this has been discussed exhaustively in many places,[16] this book concerns itself principally with batch distillation and specialized procedures, and the section on theory is written largely from the point of view of laboratory batch distillation and rectification.

The best method for expressing the results of a batch distillation is by means of a distillation curve in which the composition, boiling point, or some other property of the distillate collected during any brief time period is plotted against the total per cent of the charge distilled up to that time (Fig. 2). A perfect separation would result in curves with right-angle breaks. Such a situation is impossible theoretically, but is approached in the case of easily separable mixtures and sufficiently effective apparatus. The actual sharpness of the break in the curve gives an approximation of the sharpness of separation attained in any one case, since it is directly related to the purity of the fractions collected. The greater portion of the theory section of this book is a discussion of the various factors affecting the sharpness of separation as shown by distillation curves. The most important of these factors in fractional distillation are: (*1*) the difference in composition that can exist between liquid and vapor at equilibrium (vapor–liquid equilibrium relation or relative volatility); (*2*) the effectiveness of the contact of liquid and vapor, usually expressed as plate efficiency or height equivalent to a theoretical plate; and (*3*) the proportion of condensate directed back into the fractionating column (reflux ratio). Although they are interrelated, these factors refer, respectively, to the mixture under separation, the apparatus, and the method of operation. Addi-

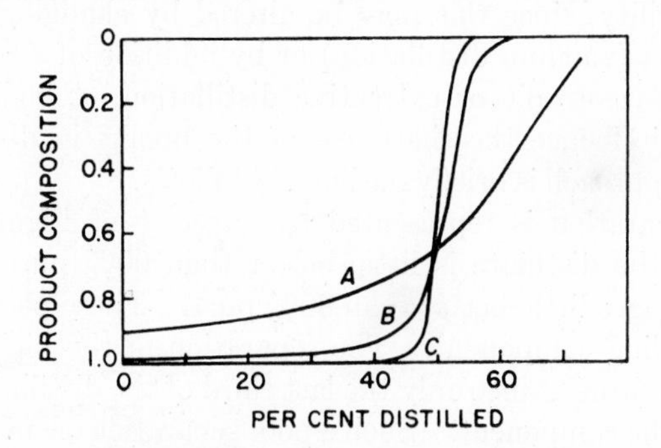

Fig. 2. Batch-fractionation curves.

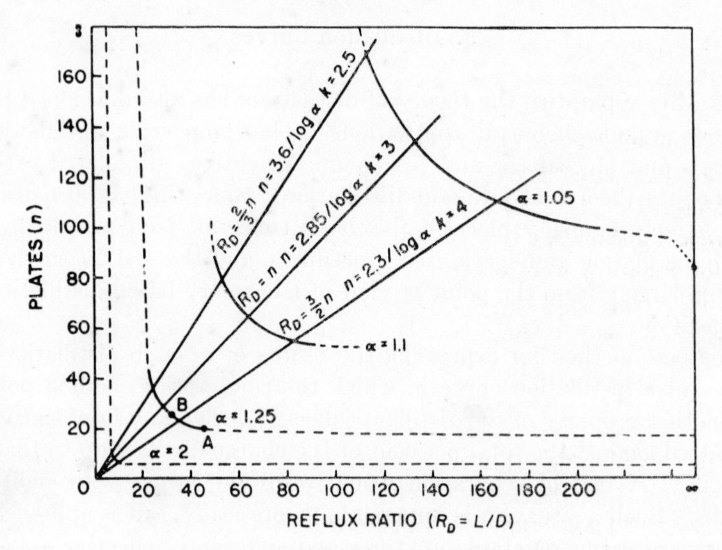

Fig. 3. Range of calculated plates and reflux ratios required for standard separation. Values of k as on p. 171.

tional factors are holdup, throughput, and the amount of excess or net condensation or vaporization occurring in the column itself, if it is not properly insulated from its surroundings—its adiabaticity. Simple distillation involves only the first of these factors, and the use of still heads presents an intermediate case. Variation in the operating procedure in fractionation allows considerable control of the results. The choice of reflux ratio together with the vapor velocity determines the time required for a batch distillation. These variables also play a part in determining the holdup and the number of theoretical plates. Choice of apparatus and packing determines the minimum and maximum values of the theoretical plates, the vapor velocity, and the holdup. There is even some control over the relative volatility, since this may be altered by changing the pressure of the distillation (vacuum distillation) or by addition of a new substance to the mixture (azeotropic or extractive distillation, or codistillation). All these effects influence the sharpness of the breaks in distillation curves. The general approach is briefly outlined as follows.

A poor separation is represented by curve *A* of Figure 2. Even the very first of the distillate is little better than 90% pure, and the entire first half averages little better than 80% pure. These percentages refer to the lower boiling component. The separation of the higher boiling component is even worse, since only the last third of the distillate contains more than 90% of the component. Such a poor separation occurs when materials are of nearly the same boiling point or volatility, and when either or both the reflux ratio and the equivalent number of theoretical plates are too low. Curve B indicates a reasonably good separation.

An approximate theoretical relationship between the sharpness of separation and the relative volatility, the reflux ratio, and the equivalent number of theoretical plates is given in Figure 3. This is based on the values of these factors calculated as necessary to obtain a good separation of a binary mixture as indicated by the distillation curve B of Figure 2. The relationships for Figure 3 were obtained by plotting values for the reflux ratio, R_D, and the number of theoretical plates, n, calculated to obtain the desired separation (p. 166). The same approximate relation is given by

$$n = R_D = \frac{2.85}{\log \alpha} = \frac{T_B + T_A}{3(T_B - T_A)}$$

where T_B and T_A are the absolute boiling points. These relations indicate that the reflux ratio should be numerically about equal to the number of theoretical plates. For substances boiling near 100°C. the expression becomes

$$R_D = n = \frac{250}{T_B - T_A}$$

It is, however, not necessary to specify exactly the number of theoretical plates required in order to achieve the desired separation. Any value of n within the range indicated by a solid curved line on the figure should be suitable. Within this range the lower values of n may be compensated for by a corresponding increase in R_D, and higher values of n allow use of a smaller R_D. It is essential that n remain approximately within the desired range since values that are too low cannot be compensated for by any increase in R_D, no matter how great, and values that are too high do not allow a corresponding decrease in R_D. Discrepancies of considerable magnitude must be expected in the practical use of these relations because of the many assumptions involved in the derivations. The chief of these are the assumptions of constant relative volatility and of negligible holdup. The limitations, derivations, and extension of these theoretical relations are discussed in detail in subsequent sections.

4. Conclusion

It is essential to emphasize that the theory of batch distillation is still only a partially developed field of knowledge. There are still large areas that are almost unexplored, as, for instance, that of multicomponent batch distillation. The theory is chiefly useful as a general guide rather than as a means of getting accurate numerical answers to specific detailed problems.

The number of variables is so great and their interrelations so complex that the theory, though imperfect, is essential in order to reduce necessary confirming experiments to a reasonable number.

The kind of information given by the theory may be likened to the view of a large unexplored region obtained from a high mountain top through imperfect lenses. One sees only the main features—a broad river, an open valley, a high plateau, or a forbidding peak and ridge with passes suggested here and there. It is inspiring, fascinating, and profitable to speculate on details, but it must be recognized that exact and useful knowledge will come only from the hard work of mile-by-mile exploration and development, with many disappointments and numerous difficulties and changes. The general methods of material balances, thermodynamics, fundamental rate concepts, higher mathematics, and automatic computation are akin to the use of field glasses and telescope and airplane photography. Painstaking experiment, like the careful work with compass, measuring tape, and plumb bob, must follow the more general approach. Those who venture into or are by necessity forced into such a region must proceed with a keen awareness of their situation. They may expect to discover easy short cuts and fertile areas for usefulness and achievement; they may also become involved in confusing morasses, great barrens, or impassable canyons. In any case it may confidently be expected that the main features of the original view will continue to remain as unchanged and reliable landmarks, and that the details will gradually build themselves into a continuous and coordinated whole.

II. THEORETICAL PLATES, REFLUX RATIO, AND COLUMN COMPOSITIONS

1. Importance of Vapor–Liquid Equilibrium Relations

A. BASIC LAWS AND DATA

Chapter II treats vapor–liquid equilibrium in detail, and the following paragraphs are intended merely to provide an elementary and general basis for the concepts discussed in this chapter. All separations by distillation depend upon the difference in composition between a liquid mixture and its vapor. In Sec. I a theoretical plate was defined as one that produces a perfect simple distillation, that is, the same difference in composition as exists at equilibrium between a liquid mixture and its vapor.

The composition of the vapor from any liquid mixture is determined by the actual vapor pressure (partial pressure) of each of the components under the conditions of the mixture. At any temperature, each pure liquid substance has its characteristic equilibrium vapor pressure, or saturation pressure, which it attains in a closed system with sufficient time for diffusion and opportunity for contact of liquid and vapor. In a mixture at equilibrium, the partial pressure of any one component depends on the characteristic vapor pressure of the pure substance, on the composition of the mixture, and on the effect of the other components in the mixture.

In actual distillation, equilibrium is usually not attained, since time for diffusion and opportunity for perfect contact between the countercurrent streams of liquid and vapor are seldom adequate. Complete theoretical analysis must therefore consider the time, rates, and surface areas involved in the diffusion of the components from liquid to vapor and vice versa. Such analyses are complex and still in process of development (see Sec. VI). In such complete analyses, as well as in the theoretical plate approach, vapor–liquid equilibrium composition relations, and their underlying vapor pressure concepts, are basic. For this reason the present section deals with the vapor pressure of liquid mixtures, and the difference in composition between liquid mixtures and their vapors.

Dalton's Law of Partial Pressures in a Vapor. The partial pressures of the individual components in a vapor mixture are related to the total pressure by Dalton's law of partial pressures, which states that the sum of the individual partial pressures in a mixture of gases or vapors is equal to the total pressure and that each individual gas exerts a pressure as if it were present alone in the volume occupied by the mixture. Except for discrepancies due to deviations from the perfect gas laws, these relations may be expressed by the mathematical formulas

$$\bar{p}_1 + \bar{p}_2 + \bar{p}_3 + \ldots = p$$

and, from the fundamental gas laws,

$$p = NRT/V$$

for the entire mixture, and

$$\bar{p}_1 = N_1RT/V$$

for a single component. Thus the partial pressure of any component in the vapor mixture divided by the total pressure of the mixture will approximate the mole fraction of the component in the vapor:

$$\frac{\bar{p}_1}{p} = \frac{N_1RT/V}{NRT/V} = \frac{N_1}{N} = y_1$$

This simple relation, $\bar{p}_1/p = y_1$, relates vapor pressure and vapor composition for the simplified discussion of distillation theory in this section.

Raoult's Law. With liquids that are completely miscible in one another, the vapor pressure of each component depends upon the composition of the liquid as well as the temperature. Each component affects the vapor pressure of the other. When there are two components and two phases, i.e., one liquid and one vapor, then the number of degrees of freedom is two. If the distilling temperature and the composition are fixed the total pressure is fixed. In the simplest cases, the ratio of the vapor pressure of a substance in such a mixture to its vapor pressure in the pure state is given by the mole fraction of the substance in the liquid mixture. For instance, the vapor pressure of pure benzene at 100°C. is 1344 mm. In a liquid mixture of 1 mole benzene and 9 moles toluene at the same temperature, the vapor pressure of benzene is 134 mm. Similarly the vapor pressure of toluene in this mixture is 504 mm., about 0.9 the value for pure toluene at this temperature (557 mm.). Mixtures in which this simple relation applies are called *ideal* and the relation is known as *Raoult's law.* It may be expressed mathematically as

$$\bar{p}_1 = p_1 x_1$$

in which $\bar{p}_1$ is the partial vapor pressure of component 1, p_1 is the vapor pressure of the pure substance, and x_1 is its mole fraction in the liquid. Ideal mixtures are usually made up of two or more closely similar compounds, and the law applies most closely to the component with mole fraction near unity. It also often applies to one component in a mixture but not to the others.

Henry's Law. In a limited number of instances the partial pressure ($\bar{p}_1$) of a particular component of a mixture can be related to the liquid composition by the expression

$$\bar{p}_1 = k x_1$$

in which x_1 is the mole fraction of the component in the liquid phase and k is the Henry's law constant for the mixture. This law usually applies for a component present in low concentration, but applies only rarely at appreciable concentrations. It is obvious that Raoult's law is a special case of Henry's law in which the constant k is replaced by the value for the vapor pressure of the pure component. The two laws apply best to opposite extremes of concentration—Henry's law for components having mole fractions near zero and Raoult's law for components having mole fractions near unity.

Vapor Pressures of Pure Substances at Various Temperatures. There are data in the literature on the vapor pressures of many substances at a variety of temperature (see Chap. II, General References, IV) but such information is often incomplete, and various procedures have been evolved for making the best use of the available data, and for expressing them concisely. The basic equation for the relation of vapor pressure to temperature is the Clausius–Clapeyron equation:

$$\frac{dp}{dT} = \frac{\lambda}{T\Delta V}$$

in which dp/dT is the rate of change of vapor pressure with absolute temperature, T, λ is the molar latent heat of vaporization, and ΔV is the difference in volume between a mole of liquid and a mole of vapor. If the volume of the liquid is assumed to be negligible, and the vapor is assumed to be ideal, so that $V = RT/p$, and λ is constant with respect to temperature, the above equation becomes

$$\frac{d \ln p}{dT} = \frac{\lambda}{RT^2} \text{ and } \ln p = -\frac{\lambda}{RT} + I$$

This is the basis for the empirical form in which vapor pressures are frequently recorded in the literature:

$$\log p = (A/T) + B$$

Here A and B are constants based on the experimental data obtained at two or more temperatures.

Dühring's Rule and Cox Charts. *Dühring's rule* is expressed by the relation

$$t_I = k_1 t_J + k_2$$

where t_I and t_J are boiling points of two different liquids at a particular pressure and k_1 and k_2 are constants. Thus values of t_I for various pressures give a straight line when plotted against the corresponding boiling points of t_J. This is equivalent to plotting against one another the temperatures at which a reference substance and another substance have the same vapor pressure. Once the reference line for substance I is established, only two points are needed to determine the position of the J line if the substances I and J are similar chemically.

Another method of expressing vapor-pressure data is the *Cox chart.*[17] This also gives straight lines, and often the entire vapor-pressure curve may be obtained from a single experimental value. The Cox chart makes use of a single reference substance, such as water or mercury. The vapor pressure–temperature data for the reference substance are plotted as a straight line with a slope of about 45°. This may be accomplished by using a logarithmic scale of pressure as ordinate, and marking the abscissa with the proper temperatures. The vapor pressure–temperature data for other substances will also form nearly straight lines when plotted in this way, and groups of related organic compounds give lines that join in a common point. Thus the normal boiling point of a hydrocarbon, alcohol, etc., will often suffice to establish the complete vapor pressure–temperature curve. Othmer[18] has presented valuable correlations of vapor pressure with latent heat and other data.

B. VOLATILITY AND RELATIVE VOLATILITY

The term *volatility* is commonly used in a broad sense to refer to the ease or difficulty of evaporation or vaporization of substances. For use in distillation it is desirable to define the volatility of any substance in a liquid mixture as its partial vapor pressure divided by its mole fraction in the liquid:

$$v_1 = \bar{p}_1/x_1 = y_1 p/x_1$$

For a pure liquid, $x_1 = 1$ and $v_1 = p_1$, that is, the volatility is identical with the vapor pressure. For a substance in an ideal mixture, the volatility is still equal to the vapor pressure of the pure material, since the equation may be rewritten as $\bar{p} = v_1 x_1$ and direct comparison to Raoult's law ($\bar{p}_1 = p_1 x_1$) indicates that v_1 must equal p_1.

Relative volatility, usually represented by the symbol α, is simply one volatility value divided by another. The larger volatility is conventionally placed in the numerator, so that the ratio is greater than one:

$$\alpha = v_1/v_2$$

The relation of the relative volatility to vapor and liquid composition may be derived by noting that

$$\frac{v_1}{v_2} = \frac{\bar{p}_1/x_1}{\bar{p}_2/x_2} = \frac{\bar{p}_1}{\bar{p}_2}\cdot\frac{x_2}{x_1}$$

But if Dalton's law applies, $\bar{p}_1/\bar{p}_2 = y_1/y_2$, since y_1 and y_2 are the mole fractions of the two components in the vapor phase, so that

$$\alpha = \frac{y_1}{y_2}\cdot\frac{x_2}{x_1}$$

or, for a binary mixture in which $x_2 = 1 - x_1$ and $y_2 = 1 - y_1$,

$$\alpha = \frac{y}{1-y}\cdot\frac{1-x}{x} = \frac{y/(1-y)}{x/(1-x)}$$

This relation is known as the *relative-volatility equation* and forms the basis for much of the current analysis of separation by distillation. It is conventional for x and y to refer to the more volatile component, unless otherwise stated. The equation is often written as

$$\frac{y}{1 - y} = \alpha \frac{x}{1 - x}$$

and used in the forms

$$y = \frac{\alpha x}{1 + x(\alpha - 1)}$$

and

$$x = \frac{y}{\alpha - y(\alpha - 1)}$$

When Raoult's law applies to the mixture, $v_1 = p_1$ and $v_2 = p_2$, so that

$$\alpha = p_1/p_2$$

Under these circumstances the relative volatility is identical with the vapor-pressure ratio.

Examination of the formula

$$\frac{y}{1 - y} = \alpha \frac{x}{1 - x}$$

indicates that, when relative volatility equals unity, no separation is possible, and that, when the value is near unity, very little difference in composition will exist between liquid and vapor that are in equilibrium. The relative volatility varies greatly for different mixtures. It often varies widely for different concentrations of the same mixture. The expression

$$\frac{y}{1 - y} = \frac{p_1}{p_2} \cdot \frac{x}{1 - x}$$

is strictly true only when Raoult's law applies, and the ideal gas laws hold for the vapor mixture, and then only at constant temperature. Most distillations are at constant pressure, but over a range of temperatures (Chap. II, Sec. I). The values of p_1 and p_2 vary with temperature according to the Clausius–Clapeyron equation

$$\frac{d \ln p}{dT} = \frac{\lambda}{RT^2}$$

so that p_1/p_2 is constant over a range of temperature only when the compounds concerned have equal molar heats of vaporization, λ. Only adjacent compounds in the same homologous series, or compounds with identical critical constants, would be expected to meet all the above requirements and behave as described by the equations with a constant relative-volatility value. However, for mixtures of similar liquids the variation with concentration is often not excessive, and use of an average value of the relative volatility is common practice when the variation is not over 10%. Much distillation is based on the assumption of a constant relative volatility for a particular mixture and distillation operation. This greatly simplifies the mathematical analysis and at the same time gives reasonable answers.

Relation between Relative Volatility and Boiling Points. By the use of Trouton's rule and the approximate Clapeyron equation it is possible to derive[19] a rough relation between relative volatility and the absolute boiling temperatures of two similar normal liquids:

$$\log \alpha = (8.9)\frac{T_2 - T_1}{T_2 + T_1} \text{ (see also Chap. II, Sec. I)}$$

For instance, the value of α for *n*-heptane–methylcyclohexane mixtures (b.p. 98.4 and 100.8°C., respectively) may be calculated by substituting the corresponding absolute temperatures in the equation:

$$\log \alpha = (8.9)\frac{373.8 - 371.4}{373.8 + 371.4} = 0.0286$$

Thus, $\alpha = 1.07$. The value obtained from the vapor-pressure ratio is 1.074.[20]

For liquid mixtures in which the boiling points of the components average about 100°C. the equation reduces to a simpler form (see p. 172).

C. VAPOR–LIQUID EQUILIBRIUM COMPOSITION DIAGRAMS

The discussion of H.E.T.P. (height equivalent to a theoretical plate) in Section I (see also Fig. 1) involved use of double curves relating the composition of a binary liquid mixture to its boiling point and vapor composition. It is also possible to use a single curve to relate liquid composition directly to vapor composition. Such a graph is called a vapor–liquid equilibrium composition diagram or curve (Fig. 4). These curves form the basis of most distillation calculations and theoretical analysis since they furnish the fundamental data of the relationship between any liquid and its vapor.

As indicated in the earlier discussion, in some cases the vapor–liquid equilibrium curve can be expressed by the relative-volatility equation (when α is constant):

$$\frac{y}{1 - y} = \alpha\frac{x}{1 - x}$$

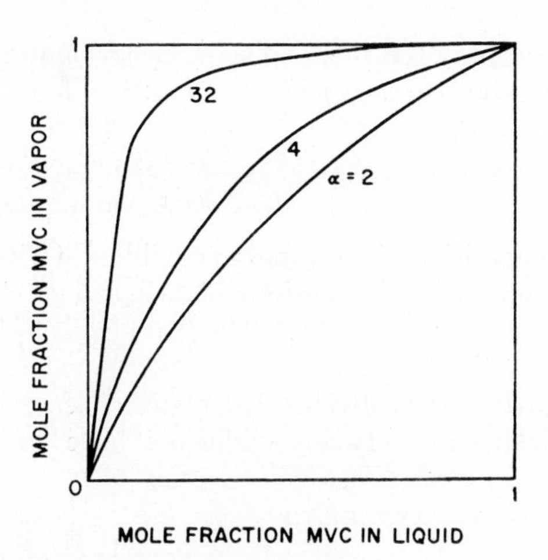

Fig. 4. Typical vapor–liquid equilibrium curves with constant relative volatilities.

This gives symmetrical curves closely resembling those in Figure 4. For any given pair of liquids the relative volatility generally decreases with increasing pressure.[21] Vapor–liquid equilibrium curves for nonideal mixtures may take on almost any shape (see Figs. 3 and 4, Chap. II).

2. Theoretical Plates and Plate Efficiency

A general description of the idea of a theoretical plate was given in Section I. The derivation was given from boiling point–composition curves, and the comparison of columns in terms of number of theoretical plates was indicated.

A. PLATE EFFICIENCY

In a plate column, a theoretical plate is one in which the vapor and liquid *leaving* the plate are of such composition as to be in equilibrium with one another. Thus each plate should theoretically give a perfect simple distillation. The separation on actual plates is usually somewhat less, due to imperfect mixing, foaming tendencies, entrainment, and the limitations of mechanical design for various column diameters. Numerous types of plates have been devised which vary widely in *plate efficiency.* The latter is a comparison of the actual separation with the theoretical, and may be expressed in two ways.

Overall plate efficiency is a simple percentage relation. Thus if a column with eight actual plates gives separation equivalent to only six theoretical plates, the plate efficiency is 75%. The efficiency of an individual plate is usually defined by the *Murphree plate efficiency*:[22]

$$e_m = \frac{y_n - y_{n-1}}{y_n^* - y_{n-1}} \tag{1}$$

in which y_n^* is composition of the vapor in equilibrium with liquid on plate n, y_n is actual composition of vapor from plate n, and y_{n-1} is actual composition of vapor from the plate below. The two kinds of plate efficiency are not identical, since the first represents an average value, but they usually do not differ greatly. It is obvious that plate efficiency is of great importance in industrial design, and many studies of it have been published.[23]

B. THEORETICAL PLATES AND H.E.T.P

Standards for *packed* columns have not been obtained so directly. Various shapes and types of packing are used, as well as various sizes of columns, and by trial and error the best combination of these for various scales of operation has been found. These packed columns and many plate columns as well are commonly evaluated in terms of height equivalent to a theoretical plate (H.E.T.P.)[24] or by the total number of theoretical plates in a given column. Since the change in composition in a packed column is gradual and continuous from top to bottom, whereas the concept of plates involves stepwise change from one plate to the next, the use of the theoretical-plate standard is basically unsound, and other standards and approaches avoiding this anomaly have been worked out (Sec. VI). The development of a fundamental diffusion picture for the theoretical-plate concept is making progress and will eventually result in an improved and comprehensive procedure for evaluating fractionating columns. However, the majority of existing experimental data and literature applicable to the distillation of organic materials is in terms of theoretical plates. This chapter therefore deals with this very useful and convenient standard.

The equations and procedures developed here are useful for calculating the number of theoretical plates in fractionating columns, and also for predicting distillate or product composition when still composition, number of plates, reflux ratio, and relative volatility are fixed. In general, the same methods may be used to estimate any one of these variables when the other four are known. Most of the detailed discussion in this chapter applies to binary mixtures. Multicomponent mixtures involve the same principles, but application is often complicated and laborious, although new lines of approach are reducing these difficulties (see p. 127 and Sec. V). However, the methods for binary mixtures indicate the general nature of the effect of reflux ratio, number of theoretical plates, and relative volatility in the distillation of multicomponent mixtures. The limitations and restrictions of the various methods are compared in the summary at the end of this section.

C. GENERAL PROCEDURE FOR DETERMINING NUMBER OF THEORETICAL PLATES AND H.E.T.P. FROM EXPERIMENTAL DATA

The most common procedure is that applied to ordinary batch-distillation apparatus operating at *total reflux*. The column to be evaluated is tested with a suitable binary mixture for which the vapor–liquid equilibrium curve is known (Chap. II). The necessary experimental data are the compositions at the bottom and top of the column after it is operating smoothly and compositions are no longer changing. For the usual batch-distillation apparatus having a total condenser, samples from the still and from the condenser or the distillate take-off line are used. The subsequent discussion assumes a total condenser is used.

When the two necessary compositions have been obtained, the number of theoretical plates is stepped off on the vapor–liquid equilibrium diagram (p. 27 and Fig. 6) or is calculated by the Fenske equation [eq. (3)]. The H.E.T.P. is then calculated by the formula

$$\text{H.E.T.P.} = Z/n \tag{2}$$

in which Z is the height of the packed section (in centimeters or inches) and n is the number of theoretical plates in the column itself, i.e., exclusive of the theoretical plate due to the difference in composition between the liquid in the still and the liquid leaving the bottom of the column. The divisor $n - 1$ is used when n signifies the total number of theoretical plates in the column and still taken together. The reasoning and equations are applicable between any two points in the column, provided proper compositions and the proper divisor are used.

The determination of number of plates and H.E.T.P. at *partial reflux* is a more complex matter. In both continuous and batch distillation at partial reflux, a material-balance study shows that the composition change from plate to plate is less than at total reflux because of the unequal quantities of liquid and vapor entering and leaving a plate during any given time interval. As a result, a different stepping off procedure or different equations must be used in estimating the number of theoretical plates at partial reflux. These methods (p. 34 *et seq.*) take into account the effect of unequal rates of flow of liquid and vapor on the material balance for a plate or section of packed column, as well as further complicating factors such as the gradual change in composition characteristic of batch distillation at partial reflux (p. 47).

Actual distillations are always carried out at partial reflux except when distillate is removed intermittently after periods of operation at total reflux.[25] Even this is probably equivalent to operation at partial reflux unless distillate removal is at widely spaced intervals. However, it has been generally assumed that the number of theoretical plates of any column at total reflux is indicative of the separation that will be obtained in actual distillation at partial reflux. The experimental procedure and calculations for total reflux are simpler, and it is possible to bring the various parts of the column into equilibrium in a more reproducible fashion. In other words, the total-reflux method of determining the number of theoretical

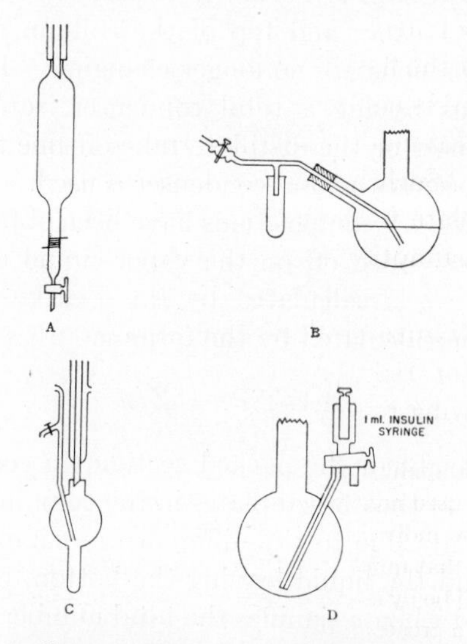

Fig. 5. Still-sampling arrangements: (A) Fenske.[26] (B) Morton.[27] (C) Rose.[28] (D) Prevost.[29]

plates furnishes a convenient way of comparing columns, even though the actual separations are always poorer at finite reflux.

Apparatus for Obtaining Distillate and Still Samples. There is now such a wealth of information available on types of columns and various packings that it is often unnecessary to make an experimental determination of the number of theoretical plates and H.E.T.P. However, in the absence of previous experience with experimental distillation, or upon dealing with systems of novel properties, experimental determination is essential.

Test samples of distillate may be taken from the condenser in the same manner as during a distillation, except that dead space or holdup in the sampling line must be a minimum. It is true that such holdup can be flushed out before a sample is collected, but this is not permissible because it is the equivalent of operation at finite reflux, whereas total reflux is usually desired and assumed.

For the still samples, the fractionating column to be tested must be equipped with a device for removing samples of the still liquid for analysis without interrupting the distillation and without evaporation of the more volatile component from the sample. It may be cooled by a small condenser on the sample line, or by immersing the sample container in a cooling bath before opening it to the air. The sample line should be of as small a volume as possible. It should be flushed with the still liquid just before the sample is taken. One practice is to incorporate a sampling line and valve draining from the lowest point of the still (Fig. 5A). For ordinary glass flasks, a siphon arrangement may be provided (Fig. 5B–D) if there is an extra opening at the top of the flask. The use of a pipet to remove samples from the boiling still liquid is not recommended. In some cases a small portion of the reflux liquid leaving the bottom of the column can be deflected into a sample container. Such liquid may be assumed to differ in composition by one theoretical plate from that in the still itself, but error may be introduced by this assumption.[30] Few experimental data are available as to its validity.

Choice of Test Mixture and Its Initial Composition. The ideal choice for a test mixture for H.E.T.P. determinations should come as close as possible to the following requirements:

(*1*) The vapor–liquid equilibrium diagram should be based on well established data. The data for commonly used mixtures are given in Tables I–VI, see Appendix (p. 62.)

(*2*) Purification of the individual components should be simple and certain, and the mixture should be such that quick and accurate analyses can be made on small samples. Final purification should be by distillation at high reflux through the column to be tested, or one with the same or a greater number of theoretical plates.

(*3*) The mixture must not seriously corrode the packing or the other parts of the apparatus.

(*4*) The mixture should be neither too easy nor too difficult to separate in the column to be tested. (See discussion of Tables I–VI in Appendix and the following discussion on choice of initial composition.)

(*5*) The components of the mixture should be similar chemically to those for which the column is to be used, and in the same general range of density, surface tension, and viscosity.

The initial composition of the test mixture must be such that the sample from the condenser contains an appreciable amount of the higher boiling component. This is necessary because the change in composition per theoretical plate becomes very small when the mixture is nearly pure in one or the other component. Thus, if a column with five theoretical plates is to be tested with benzene–toluene mixture, the initial composition should be near 20 mole-% benzene rather than 50 mole-%. The former mixture will give a condenser sample with about 89 mole-% benzene if there are four plates, 95 mole-% if there are five plates, and 98 mole-% for six plates. The corresponding compositions for the 50 mole-% initial test mixture would be about 97, 99, and 99+ mole-%. In the first case an uncertainty of 1% in analysis would not be serious, but in the second case such an uncertainty would make it impossible to do more than conclude that there must be four or more plates.

Much more serious is any uncertainty or inaccuracy in the position of the equilibrium curve itself. This affects the composition change of each plate or step and produces a cumulative error of increasing magnitude at the extremes of composition where the equilibrium line and the 45° line come close together (Fig. 6). Since even a 5 mole-% benzene–toluene mixture will give 95 mole-% benzene in the condenser of a seven- or eight-plate column, other test mixtures (see Appendix) are generally used for all except the shortest columns. It is of course possible to use any mixture that approximates the general requirements already mentioned.

D. OPERATION AT TOTAL REFLUX

Test Procedure. The column to be tested should be cleaned and dried and then charged with enough test mixture to fill at least half the still. For packed columns heat should be applied until flooding occurs throughout the column, and the heat input then reduced gradually to that desired for the test. If the packed section is equipped with heaters, these should be adjusted so that the column is operating adiabatically and the column then flooded again. It is important that the packing be kept wet when heat input is reduced after flooding, or the beneficial effect will be lost. The initial flooding generally makes subsequent behavior more reproducible, and also reduces the H.E.T.P. H.E.T.P. varies with throughput so that this must be kept at the chosen value throughout the test.

Operation at total reflux should continue until all parts of the apparatus are operating smoothly. This may best be tested by taking small samples from the condenser at intervals, until no further change in composition occurs. All samples should be withdrawn slowly and should be less than 1% of the charge, in order to minimize disturbances in column concentrations and reduce the intervals between samples. Small columns with few plates or open packing will return to a steady state quickly after removal of a sample, but large columns, and those with twenty or more plates, may require an hour or more. When the steady state is established, samples should be taken from both still and condenser, and used for analysis and a computation of the number of plates. It is preferable to repeat the removal of samples several times, allowing a suitable interval to elapse between each sampling operation to reestablish the steady state, and continuing until check results are obtained. A thorough test should include a complete shutdown and repetition of the experiment from the beginning. A test on a new packing should include emptying and repacking of the column and repeating the test.

Determination of Plates from Vapor–Liquid Equilibrium Diagrams. When the compositions of distillate and still are known, the vapor–liquid

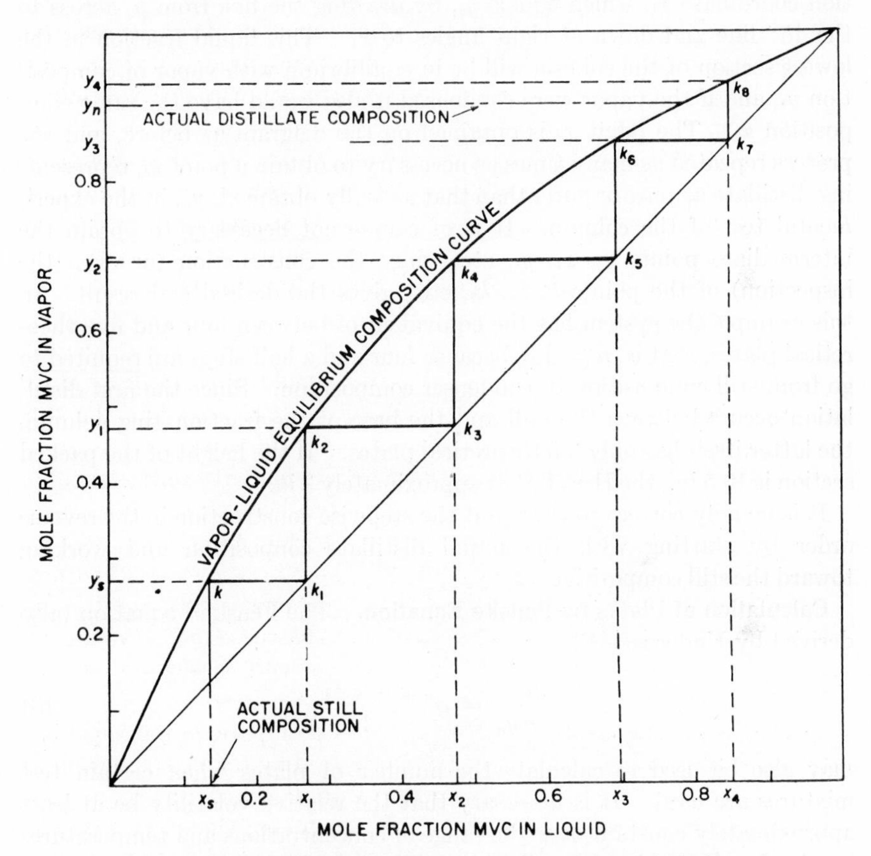

Fig. 6. Graphic method of obtaining number of theoretical plates.

composition diagram may be used to step off the number of theoretical plates. Such a stepping-off process was illustrated briefly in Section I with the use of a boiling point–composition diagram. It is more common to use a vapor–liquid composition diagram, since boiling points are not essential to the determination of the number of theoretical plates. The curves should be plotted on 24- or 36-in. square sheets of graph paper in order to reduce errors in plotting and reading.

The stepping-off process for a typical vapor–liquid equilibrium diagram involves the following reasoning (Fig. 6): If the actual still composition in the test is x_s, the vapor entering the bottom of the column would be of composition y_s. If all this vapor were condensed to complete a single, perfect, simple distillation, the distillate would also have the composition y_s. On the diagram, this value is now transposed to the liquid–composition coordinate x_1, which equals y_s, by drawing the line from y_s across to the 45° line and down at right angles to x_1. This liquid fraction in the lowest section of the column will be in equilibrium with vapor of composition y_1, and if the vapor were condensed it also would have the same composition x_2. The point x_2 is obtained on the diagram as before, and the process repeated as many times as necessary to obtain a point y_4, representing distillate as pure or purer than that actually obtained, y_n, in the experimental test of the column. It is of course not necessary to obtain the intermediate points y_s, x_1, y_1, etc., since the construction (or even the inspection) of the points k, k_1, k_2, etc., gives the desired end result. In this example the system has the equivalent of between four and five theoretical plates, that is, $n = 4.5$, because four and a half steps are required to go from still composition to condenser composition. Since the first distillation occurs between the still and the base of the fractionating column, the latter itself has only 3.5 theoretical plates. If the height of the packed section is 10.5 in., the H.E.T.P. is approximately 3 in.

It is equally correct to carry out the stepwise construction in the reverse order by starting with the actual distillate conposition and working toward the still composition.

Calculation of Plates by Fenske Equation. The Fenske[31] equation (also derived by Underwood[32])

$$\frac{y_n}{1 - y_n} = \alpha^{n+1} \frac{x_s}{1 - x_s} \tag{3}$$

may also be used to calculate the number of plates when certain test mixtures are used. It is necessary that the relative volatility be at least approximately constant over the range of concentrations and temperatures involved and that the vapor–liquid equilibrium follow the relative-volatility relation (p. 18)

$$\frac{y}{1 - y} = \alpha \frac{x}{1 - x} \tag{4}$$

An average value of α is used, and when α does not vary more than 10%, reasonable results may be expected. Methylcyclohexane–*n*-heptane, benzene–toluene, and benzene–ethylene dichloride mixtures meet the requirements.[33]

In the Fenske equation y_n is the mole fraction of the more volatile component in the distillate of a column operating at total reflux with a total condenser and with n theoretical plates and still composition x_s.

For purposes of calculation the equation may be written as

$$n = \frac{\log\left(\frac{y_n}{1 - y_n}\right) - \log\left(\frac{x_s}{1 - x_s}\right)}{\log \alpha} - 1 \tag{5}$$

For example, in Figure 6, where $y_n = 0.9$, $x_s = 0.135$, and $\alpha = 2.45$,

$$n = \frac{(0.954) - (9.193 - 10)}{0.389} - 1 = 3.5 \tag{6}$$

This is of course the same value that was obtained by the graphic procedure.

The *derivation* of the Fenske equation is merely the analytical equivalent of the graphic operations previously described for stepping off the number of theoretical plates. For the purpose of the derivation, the relative-volatility relation may be written as

$$\frac{y_s}{1 - y_s} = \alpha \frac{x_s}{1 - x_s} \tag{7}$$

The quantity $y_s/(1 - y_s)$ represents the molar ratio of the more volatile and less volatile components after liquid with molar ratio $x_s/(1 - x_s)$ is subjected to a single, perfect, simple, distillation. This corresponds closely to the degree of separation between the still pot and the vapor entering the base of the column; that is, when still composition is x_s, the vapor entering the bottom of the column has the composition y_s (Fig. 7A). If the column is assumed to be of the plate type, and if this vapor is completely condensed on the lowest plate of the column, the resulting liquid will be in equilibrium with new vapor having composition y_1, where

$$\frac{y_1}{1 - y_1} = \alpha \frac{y_s}{1 - y_s} = \alpha^2 \frac{x_s}{1 - x_s} \tag{8}$$

Complete condensation of this new vapor on the second plate from the bottom would give a liquid of composition y_1. Repetition of this reasoning shows that the new vapor rising from the second plate would have the molar ratio

$$\frac{y_2}{1 - y_2} = \alpha^3 \frac{x_s}{1 - x_s} \tag{9}$$

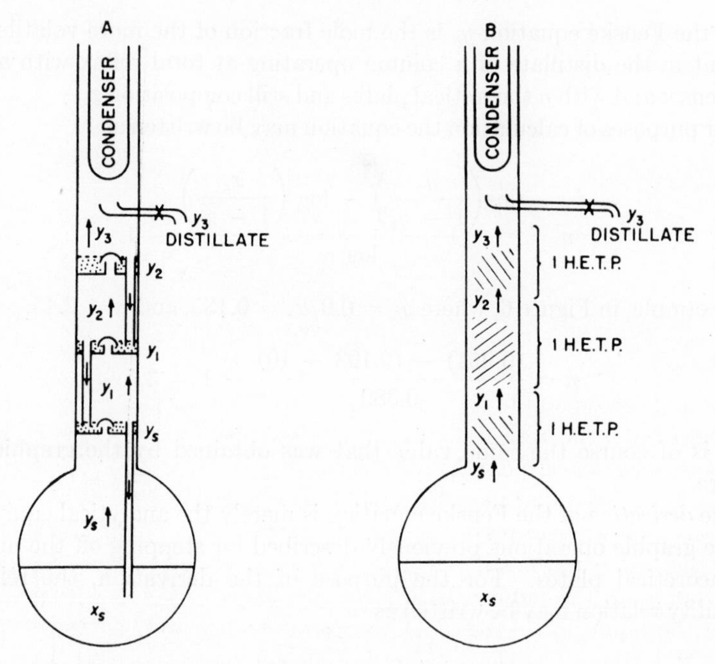

Fig. 7. Derivation of Fenske equation. Composition at various points in plate (A) and packed (B) columns at total reflux.

and, in general, the vapor from the nth plate would have the molar ratio

$$\frac{y_n}{1 - y_n} = \alpha^{n+1} \frac{x_s}{1 - x_s} \tag{10}$$

With a total condenser the distillate composition would also be y_n. Thus, if a column has n theoretical plates, a test under total reflux will give distillate composition y_n when still composition is x_s. Conversely, if these compositions are obtained in a test, the column must have n theoretical plates.

A somewhat similar situation exists in a packed column, and is represented approximately in Figure 7B. The end result is the same but the gradual change in composition requires a somewhat different analysis. By definition, the column height that produces a separation y_s to y_1 is the H.E.T.P., so that, at a distance equivalent to one H.E.T.P. unit above the base of the column, the vapor composition would be that corresponding to the molar ratio $y_1/(1 - y_1)$. Repetition of this reasoning shows that, at points distant from the base of the column by two, three, four, etc., times the H.E.T.P., the vapor composition would correspond to molar ratios of

$y_2/(1 - y_2)$, $y_3/(1 - y_3)$, $y_4/(1 - y_4)$, etc., and these are related as follows:

$$\frac{y_2}{1 - y_2} = \alpha \frac{y_1}{1 - y_1} = \alpha^3 \frac{x_s}{1 - x_s} \tag{11}$$

$$\frac{y_3}{1 - y_3} = \alpha \frac{y_2}{1 - y_2} = \alpha^4 \frac{x_s}{1 - x_s} \tag{12}$$

$$\frac{y_4}{1 - y_4} = \alpha^5 \frac{x_s}{1 - x_s} \tag{13}$$

At the distance n H.E.T.P. units the vapor and distillate composition (y_n) would correspond to eq. (3). Thus again, if a packed column has the equivalent of n theoretical plates, a test under total reflux will give product composition y_n when the still composition is x_s.

It is to be noted that in eqs. (3) and (10) the symbol n corresponds to the number of theoretical plates in the column proper, *excluding* a theoretical plate that exists in the still. Thus $n + 1$, the exponent in these equations, corresponds to the number of theoretical plates in the entire system between the liquid in the still and the vapor from plate n. However, confusion can arise when the Fenske equation is found as

$$\frac{y_n}{1 - y_n} = \alpha^n \frac{x_s}{1 - x_s} \tag{14}$$

This is acceptable and correct if it is recognized that in this case n must be taken as the total of the theoretical plates in the column *plus* that in the still pot. It behooves the reader to note carefully which meaning of n is being used. This may not be made explicit in the explanation of symbols, and it is frequently necessary to study the context in which the equation appears.

Another source of confusion is that the basic Fenske equation may be adapted for any section of a column that has n plates, and then appears as

$$\frac{y_n}{1 - y_n} = \alpha^n \frac{x_1}{1 - x_1} \tag{15}$$

in which x_1 is the composition of the liquid on the plate at the bottom of the section considered. A variation of this form (called the Fenske form) is written entirely in terms of liquid compositions (no y terms)

$$\frac{x_n}{1 - x_n} = \alpha^{n-1} \frac{x_1}{1 - x_1} \tag{16}$$

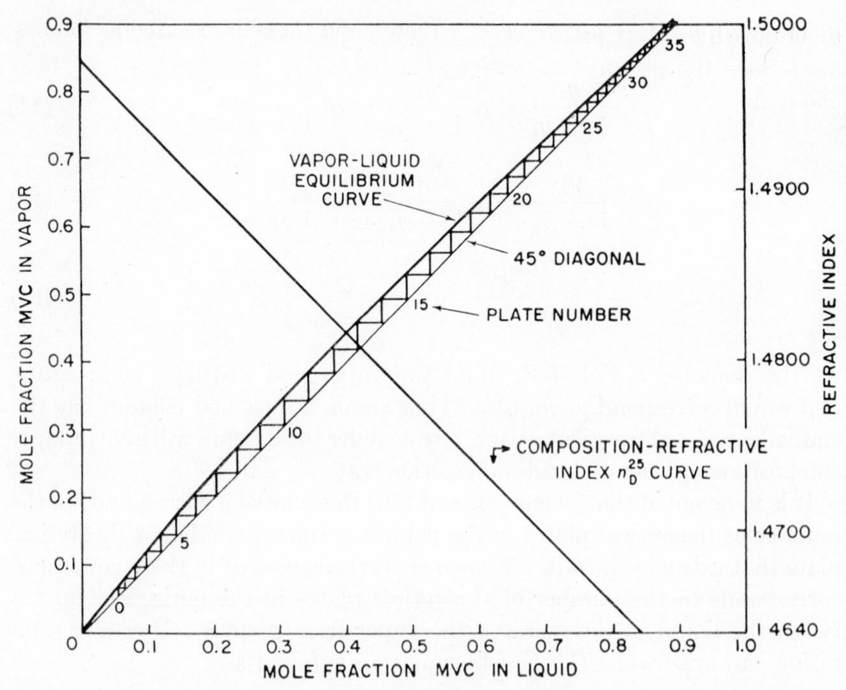

Fig. 8. Diagram for theoretical plates at total reflux. MVC = more volatile component.

This has the exponent $n - 1$ because one less stage of separation is involved in going from liquid on plate 1 to liquid on plate n. In both eqs. (15) and (16) n has the same meaning as in the basic eq. (10).

Determination of Plates by Simple Graphic and Tabular Methods. Simple graphic and tabular methods have also been developed for rapid routine calculation of H.E.T.P. These are particularly useful when the number of plates is large and the Fenske equation cannot be used because of variation in relative volatility. The following example will illustrate the method. Figure 8 shows a typical vapor–liquid equilibrium diagram with theoretical plates stepped off from the composition $x = 0.05$ to $x = 0.90$ (mole fraction more volatile component). These steps are numbered beginning with zero for the lowest value of x. Figure 9 shows enlarged sections of the same graph. The marked variation in composition change per plate is clearly brought out. Such a graph is used by reading off the plate numbers corresponding to the still and distillate compositions, and subtracting the smaller plate number from the larger. Inclusion of the refractive index curve in Figure 8 makes it possible to proceed directly from refractive index to composition to plate number. Large-scale graphs are desirable unless only a rough approximation is needed. Interpolation to obtain fractional plate numbers (tenths) is common practice, but in most cases the results of a test are not reproducible to better than one-half plate.

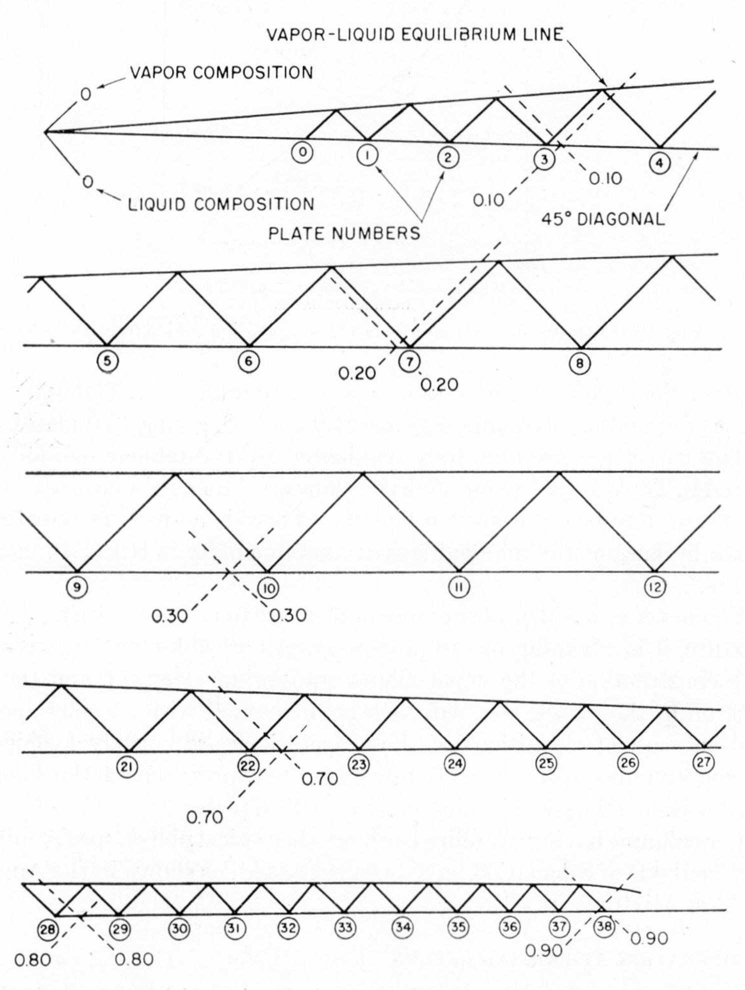

Fig. 9. Large-scale sections of Figure 8. Theoretical plates stepped-off from 0.05 to 0.90 mole fraction MVC.

The entire operation is facilitated by plotting plate numbers directly against composition and refractive index, as in Figure 10. Thus if still and distillate compositions are, respectively, 0.70 and 0.20 mole fraction more volatile component, the corresponding plate numbers are approximately 22.2 and 6.9. The number of plates is 15.3. If the refractive in-

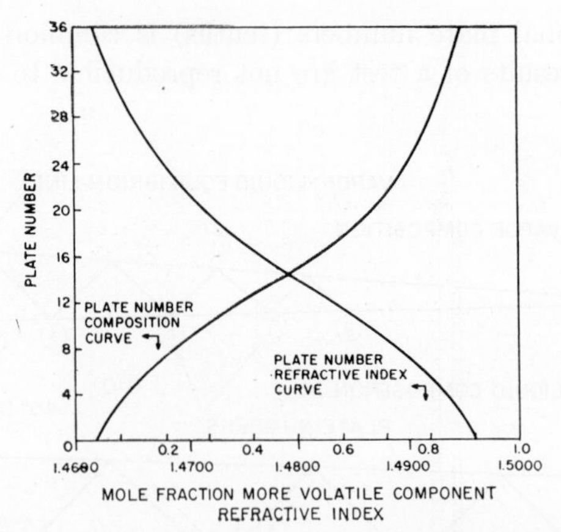

Fig. 10. Diagram of plate numbers vs. composition and refractive index.

dices of the samples from another test of a column are 1.4700 and 1.4900, the corresponding plate numbers are 21.9 and 6.9, giving 15.0 plates.

The use of graphs is entirely eliminated by the tabular method, illustrated in Table V (p. 68) for methylcyclohexane–toluene mixtures. Values are given only to the nearest 0.1 plate. There is no need for greater precision because of the inherent lack of reproducibility in H.E.T.P. measurements.

Whenever a considerable number of tests are to be made with a particular mixture, it is advantageous to prepare graphs or tables on the above plan. The construction of the vapor–liquid equilibrium diagram, and the stepping off of the plates, etc., can then be done once, with considerable care, and subsequent repetitions of these operations are entirely avoided. A nomograph may also be used to advantage to express the relations between composition, relative volatility, and theoretical plates.[34]

For columns having a hundred or more theoretical plates, special mixtures and methods of calculation have been suggested, as shown in the Appendix on Test Mixtures (p. 64).

E. OPERATION AT PARTIAL REFLUX

Test Procedures. In a continuous distillation with constant feed composition, duplicate samples may be obtained without difficulty, since the compositions of the still and product liquids should not change with time after the column is operating smoothly. Samples for analysis can then easily be withdrawn from any of the three lines. This steady-state situation can also be achieved in a batch distillation apparatus by return of the distillate continuously to the bottom of the still, as shown in Figure 11. Such an operation will also reach a steady state with compositions and flows

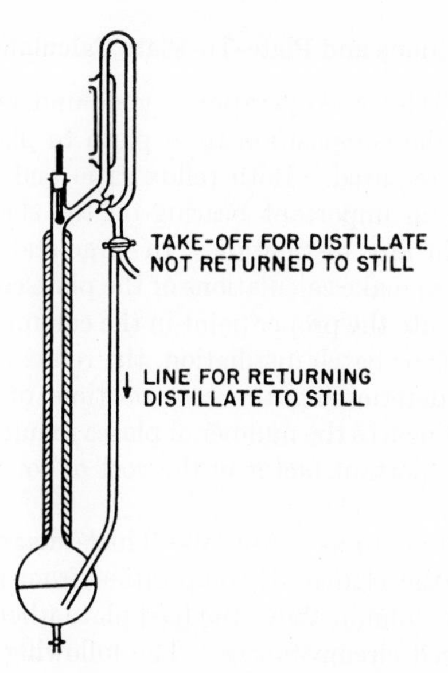

Fig. 11. Apparatus for returning distillate to still.

resembling in several respects those in the upper or enriching section of a continuous distillation unit. The return of distillate to the still "freezes" the compositions at a particular set of values so that replicate samples can be obtained. It is essential to ensure that the product stream is thoroughly mixed with the still liquid. When an adequate number of samples has been obtained, the distillate stream may be collected in a receiver for a limited time, and then again deflected into the still so that another group of samples can be obtained, with different still and distillate compositions.

This procedure is closely similar to that already described for total reflux operation in connection with Figure 6. The distillate and still compositions are determined by analysis of the samples taken from the column, and the number of plates then stepped off as already described, except that an additional line (the operating line) must be added to the diagram to take into account the effect of the partial reflux. Figure 13 shows such a diagram. If distillate composition is x_D and still composition x_{t-3}, the test would show a total of four plates for the system tested.

In practice, columns are not usually rated by the number of theoretical plates at partial reflux, so that the procedure just described is infrequently used. This return to still procedure is also not generally applicable to batch distillation. In batch distillation still samples of negligible size must be removed by the procedure already described for total-reflux tests. Distillate samples are obtained directly. Because of the change of compositions as the distillation progresses, duplicate samples cannot be obtained except by repeating an entire distillation from the beginning.

3. Column Compositions and Plate-To-Plate Calculations At Partial Reflux

For purposes of design and operation, a good understanding of the methods for predicting the composition from plate to plate or point to point at partial reflux is required. Both reflux ratio and the number of theoretical plates have an important bearing on the sharpness of separation actually resulting in any distillation. In large-scale continuous distillation, it is necessary to make calculations of the plate compositions at partial reflux in order to locate the proper point in the column for introducing feed. In either continuous or batch distillation, the reflux ratio chosen is an important factor in determining the cost or time of operation. Finally, since reflux ratio influences the number of plates required for a given separation, it is also an important factor in the cost of construction or choice of equipment.

Figure 13 is referred to as a McCabe–Thiele diagram[35] and is used for information about the change of composition from plate to plate in the part of a continuous column above the feed plate when operating at partial reflux under idealized circumstances. The following paragraphs give the equations on which the diagram is based, these being the basic relations between reflux ratio, number of theoretical plates, and still compositions. Various complicating factors will be introduced subsequently, but the simplified relations of the immediately following paragraphs are the basis for almost all other distillation calculations.

A. BASIS FOR PLATE-TO-PLATE CALCULATIONS

Sorel[36] was the first to show that a plate should not be expected to give as much separation under partial reflux as it does under total reflux, even though other conditions are identical. His method of estimating the degree of separation under any reflux ratio by means of material and heat balances has been thoroughly worked out for plate columns and continuous distillation. The same principles apply to packed columns and batch distillation, but two additional factors must be included in a careful theoretical analysis. As a batch distillation proceeds, there is a continual change in composition at any point in the column as the more volatile component is gradually removed. This adds to the system as worked out for continuous distillation a rate of change variable so that appreciably different relations may occur when holdup is not negligible (see p. 48). In the second place, in packed columns the gradual change of composition up the column requires a differential analysis which is necessarily more complex than the corresponding case for plate columns, for which the theory may be worked out step by step, corresponding to the distinct change in composition from plate to plate.

A number of different ways of approaching this problem have been proposed (Sec. VI) but there is much evidence that the relations derived for plate columns are reasonably satisfactory for packed columns. For these reasons and because the explanations and equations are basic and relatively simple, the next paragraph considers continuous or steady-state distillation in plate columns. It is assumed that the column is adiabatic, that the heat of mixing in vapor and liquid is negligible, and that the substances involved have similar thermal properties. Under these conditions the plates are operating at equimolal overflow. These simplifications are frequently applicable and are known as the *usual simplifying assumptions* (USA). The reasoning is based on the early work of Sorel, and the simplifications introduced by Lewis[37] and McCabe and Thiele.

B. CONTINUOUS AND STEADY-STATE DISTILLATION

Steady-state distillation may be defined as any distillation in which there is no change in column compositions with time. Examples are operation at total reflux or return-to-still operation with a batch column. A more pertinent example is ordinary continuous distillation, at partial reflux.

Plate-to-Plate Calculations by Method of Sorel and Lewis. With a total condenser in a continuous distillation at partial reflux it is reasonable to assume that the composition of the vapor leaving the top plate is the same as the distillate composition: $y_t = x_D$. With a partial condenser the composition of the vapor from the top plate is determined directly by experiment. In either case it is assumed that the vapor leaving the top plate is in equilibrium with the liquid on the top plate. When the relative-volatility equation applies, this liquid composition x_t can be calculated from the relation

$$\frac{x_t}{1 - x_t} = \frac{1}{\alpha} \cdot \frac{y_t}{1 - y_t} \tag{17}$$

For any binary mixture, x_t can also be found graphically from the vapor–liquid equilibrium diagram. The composition of vapor coming from plate $t - 1$ may then be found from the *operating-line equation* [eq. (23)]

$$y_{t-1} = \frac{L}{V} x_t + \frac{D}{V} x_D \tag{18}$$

The liquid composition x_{t-1} may be found as before from the vapor–liquid diagram and then used in another operating-line equation:

$$y_{t-2} = \frac{L}{V} x_{t-1} + \frac{D}{V} x_D \tag{19}$$

This process may be repeated as often as needed to obtain x_{t-2}, y_{t-3}, x_{t-3}, etc.

In order to derive the equation for the operating line, it is assumed that one has a plate column and that the reflux ratio is L/D, in which L represents moles reflux and D the moles distillate, both per unit time. (Re-

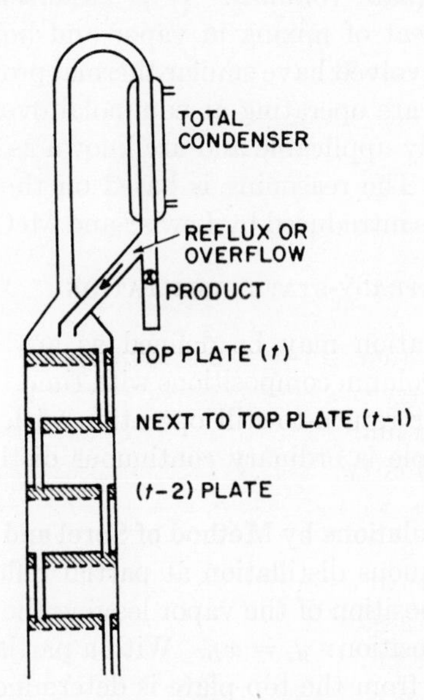

Fig. 12. Diagram of plate-to-plate calculations of composition, etc., by the method of Sorel, Lewis, and McCabe and Thiele.

flux ratio may be measured by a variety of means, as described in Chap. III.) The moles of vapor per unit time are then $V = L + D$. By a material balance about the top plate and condenser (as in Fig. 12) it is true that for any one component:

$$\left.\begin{matrix}\text{Moles of component}\\ \text{entering top plate } t\\ \text{in vapor from plate}\\ \text{below, } t-1\end{matrix}\right\} = \left\{\begin{matrix}\text{Moles of component}\\ \text{leaving top plate in}\\ \text{overflow to plate}\\ \text{below}\end{matrix}\right\} + \left\{\begin{matrix}\text{Moles of component}\\ \text{leaving system in dis-}\\ \text{tillate}\end{matrix}\right.$$

Expressed in symbols:

$$Vy_{t-1} = Lx_t + Dx_D \tag{20}$$

where y_{t-1} is the composition of the vapor from plate $t - 1$, x_t the composition of liquid from plate t, and x_D the distillate composition. This is usually written as eq. (18). A similar material balance may be made about the two uppermost plates, t and $t - 1$, and the condenser. In this case:

$$\left\{\begin{array}{l}\text{Moles of component}\\ \text{entering } t-1 \text{ plate}\\ \text{in vapor from } t-2\end{array}\right\} = \left\{\begin{array}{l}\text{Moles of component}\\ \text{leaving } t-1 \text{ plate in}\\ \text{overflow to } t-2\end{array}\right\} + \left\{\begin{array}{l}\text{Moles of component}\\ \text{leaving system in dis-}\\ \text{tillate}\end{array}\right\}$$

Or, in symbols:

$$Vy_{t-2} = Lx_{t-1} + Dx_D \tag{21}$$

In a similar manner it may be shown that

$$Vy_{t-3} = Lx_{t-2} + Dx_D \tag{22}$$

and, in general,

$$Vy_{n-1} = Lx_n + Dx_D \tag{23}$$

the *operating-line equation*, for any portion of a continuous-plate column above the point of entry of feed, or for any portion whatever of a batch-plate column operating under a steady state at finite reflux.

As shown above, this type of equation makes it possible to calculate the composition of the vapor from any particular plate from that of the liquid from the plate above, if the distillate composition and reflux ratio are known. A numerical example is given below in this section (p. 52). The above derivation assumes that there is no heat loss from the column and that the thermal properties of the mixture being distilled are such that a material balance will also produce a heat balance, and make $L_t = L_{t-1} = L_{t-2}$, etc., and $V_t = V_{t-1}$, etc. If the thermal properties such as heat of mixing are not negligible, and the latent heats and specific heats of the materials are not closely similar, the derivation must be based on a heat balance and the more complicated relations originally derived by Sorel must be used.

Lewis pointed out that liquids could be classified as either associating or nonassociating, and that when a mixture contained only liquids of one class the assumption of equimolal overflow ($L_t = L_{t-1} = L_{t-2}$, etc.) was reasonable. This has been substantiated by extensive use of the operating-line equation

$$y_{n-1} = \frac{L}{V}x_n + \frac{D}{V}x_D \tag{24}$$

in the design of large continuous-plate columns. When the liquids in a mixture are not of the same class, it is often possible to use the above equation by assigning fictitious molecular weights so that $L_t = L_{t-1}$, etc. This requires recalculation of the vapor–liquid equilibrium diagram in terms of the fictitious molecular weights. Graphic procedures have been developed by Ponchon[38] and Savarit[39] in order to apply the method of Sorel when heats of mixing, sensible heats, and latent heats vary so much that the simpler methods based on equimolal overflow are not satisfactory. Randall and Longtin[40] have generalized this procedure.

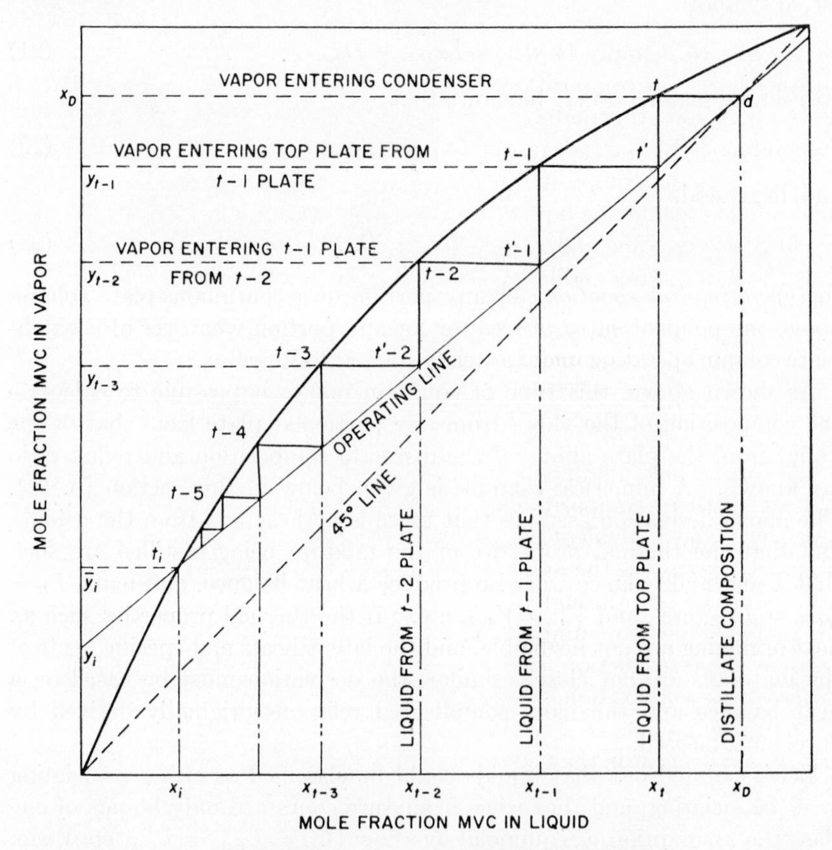

Fig. 13. Graphic construction of McCabe and Thiele.

It is important to recognize that for total-reflux conditions $D = 0$ and $L/V = 1$, so that the operating-line equation becomes

$$y_{n-1} = x_n \tag{25}$$

McCabe–Thiele Graphic Procedure. The following equivalent graphic method may also be used to calculate plate-to-plate compositions at partial reflux (Fig. 13). The first step is to draw on the vapor–liquid equilibrium diagram the so-called operating line, with eq. (24). This will pass through the point $d(x = x_D, y = y_t = x_D)$ and will have the slope L/V. Its intercept on the vertical axis ($x = 0$) will be

$$y_i = \frac{D}{V} x_D \tag{26}$$

so the line can simply be drawn through the points d and y_i. This line relates the liquid composition (x_n), from any plate to the composition of the vapor from the plate below (y_{n-1}). Therefore the value of y corresponding to the intersection of the operating line with the vertical line $x = x_t$ gives the composition of the vapor y_{t-1} leaving the $t - 1$ plate. The composition of the liquid from this plate may now be found by simply reading across from y_{t-1} to $t - 1$ on the equilibrium curve and then down to x_{t-1}. In a similar manner the following are located:

y_{t-2}, composition of vapor from $t - 2$ plate
x_{t-2}, composition of liquid from $t - 2$ plate
t_{t-3}, composition of vapor from $t - 3$ plate
x_{t-3}, composition of liquid from $t - 3$ plate

and so on. Thus, if still composition in a batch plate or packed column is x_{t-3} and distillate composition is x_D, it is obvious that the system as a whole must have the equivalent of four perfect plates.

In actual practice the number of plates is determined simply by drawing the operating line through the point d on the 45° diagonal representing distillate composition, and through the intercept [eq. (26)] and then stepping off the construction, of d, t, t', $t - 1$, $t' - 1$, etc., until a value of x near the still composition is reached. The equivalent number of theoretical plates is the number of steps less one if separation equivalent to one plate is assumed to occur in the still itself.

Figure 13 is plotted in terms of mole fractions of the more volatile component in the liquid and vapor. The graph may equally well be plotted in terms of weight fractions or weight per cent. It is sometimes convenient to show units of weight fractions or weight per cent along the other two sides of the graph, and to add a curve for the relation between the mole and weight fractions, so that either may be used with the diagram.[41] If the more volatile component is the higher in molecular weight the conversion curve should be plotted in terms of weight per cent along the horizontal axis (using the same scale as mole per cent more volatile component in the liquid) and in mole per cent along the vertical axis (coinciding with mole per cent more volatile component in the vapor). By reading from the weight per cent value to the conversion curve, then horizontally to the 45° line and then down to the horizontal scale the mole per cent liquid can be obtained. If the more volatile component has the lower molecular weight, the weight per cent scale should be plotted vertically. This type of plotting keeps the conversion curve below the 45° line and avoids confusion with the usual McCabe–Thiele construction above that line.

An entirely different graphical equivalent of the McCabe–Thiele procedure is based on the geometrical principle of similar triangles, and avoids the need for actual plotting of the vapor–liquid equilibrium diagram.[42]

When dealing with compositions near zero or unity, or with mixtures of relative volatility near unity, it is usually necessary to plot the x versus y diagram on an exaggerated scale in order to preserve a reasonable accuracy. Randall and Longtin,[43] as well as many others, have used graphs of $y - x$ versus x for mixtures having relative volatility very near unity. Sometimes a mere increase in the scale is sufficient, but in other cases plotting on logarithmic paper may be helpful. The equilibrium curve may appear as a straight line, and the operating line as a curve on such graphs. At very low or very high concentrations the two lines are nearly parallel. In some cases there are advantages in making the graph in terms of the less volatile component.[44]

When the equilibrium curve pinches the operating line a multiple cycle log–log graph paper allows plotting of the entire concentration range on one sheet of paper, while retaining the advantages of log–log plotting at both extremes of concentration. With this type of plot the $x = 0.5$ and $y = 0.5$ lines are placed about halfway along the two sides of the graph, and log cycles are added symmetrically in either direction from these starting points. As a result there are equal distances along the paper between $x = 0.5$, 0.05, 0.005, 0.0005, and also between $x = 0.5$, 0.95, 0.995, 0.9995, etc.[45, 46]

A special variety of normal probability paper also has the multiple cycle characteristics, and is commercially available.[47]

Minimum Reflux. It can be seen from inspection of Figure 13 that if the reflux ratio, L/D, is made higher and approaches total reflux, and if the ratio D/V and the intercept y_i approach zero, the operating line will approach the 45° diagonal and the entire operation approaches that for total reflux.

For any particular values of still composition, x_s, and product composition, x_D, there is also a minimum reflux ratio, $R_{D_{\min}}$, corresponding to the operating line which intersects the equilibrium curve at x_s. For example, such a situation would arise if still composition was x_i in Figure 13. Lower reflux ratios than correspond to the operating line shown cannot give a separation as great as from x_D to x_i, because for such lower reflux ratios the operating lines intersect the equilibrium curve to the *right* of t_i. It is clear that the stepping-off process cannot be continued to the left of t_i, and that the corresponding still composition is the minimum possible with the given vapor–liquid equilibrium curve, product composition, and operating line. Theoretically, an infinite number of plates is required to reach such a minimum composition. Actually those plates operating on material of composition near the minimum accomplish little or no separation, and increase in the number of plates does not improve the separation.

The minimum reflux ratio for the enriching section during distillation of a binary mixture when the usual simplifying assumptions are applicable is given by

$$R_{D\min} = \frac{x_D - y_s}{y_s - x_s} \tag{27}$$

This may be derived by noting that in Figure 13 if $x_s = x_i$, $y_s = \bar{y}_i$, and the slope of the operating line is

$$\frac{x_D - y_s}{x_D - x_s} = \left(\frac{L}{V}\right)_{\min} = \frac{(L/D)_{\min}}{(L/D)_{\min} + (D/D)} = \frac{R_{D\min}}{R_{D\min} + 1}$$

which then may be solved for $R_{D\min}$ to obtain eq. (27).

Smoker[48] has devised a nomograph for estimation of minimum reflux and theoretical plates corresponding to the equations of the preceding discussion.

The calculation of minimum reflux for the continuous distillation of multicomponent mixtures has been the subject of extensive study because of its practical importance in industrial distillation.[49]

Procedures When Usual Simplifying Assumptions Are Not Applicable. The original procedure of Sorel can be carried out by a graphic construction analogous to the McCabe–Thiele method just described. However, when the column is not adiabatic or the other usual simplifying assumptions are not applicable, the values of L and V are no longer equal on the different plates throughout the column. Their actual values depend on the thermal quantities (heats of vaporization, mixing, etc.) and, as a result, the operating line is curved; otherwise the stepwise procedure is unchanged. Modified but equivalent graphic methods are much used[50] for such calculations.

Equations for Stripping Section. In the section of a continuous column below the entry of the feed, the relation between the composition of the vapor coming up to a plate (y_{m-1}) and the liquid on the plate (x_m) is given by the equation

$$y_{m-1} = \frac{L}{V} x_m - \frac{B}{V} x_B$$

where L, V, and B are, respectively, the moles of overflow (reflux), vapor, and product withdrawn at the bottom of the column, all per unit time, and x_B is the composition of the last. For the bottom plate of a column, this is

$$y_s = \frac{L}{V} x_1 - \frac{B}{V} x_s$$

in which y_s and x_s are the compositions of the vapor from the still, and the liquid in the still, respectively, and x_1 is the composition of the liquid on the first plate. The values of x_s and x_B will be identical since the product is being withdrawn from the still. The value of y_s is obtainable from

$$\frac{y_s}{1 - y_s} = \alpha \frac{x_s}{1 - x_s}$$

or from the vapor–liquid equilibrium diagram for the mixture. The only remaining unknown is x_1, so its value can be calculated and the process repeated for the plates above to obtain values of x_2, x_3, etc. A graphic construction may be used, and a form of the Smoker equation has also been worked out for these operating conditions (see p. 46) and used as described on the following pages.

Location of Feed Plate in Continuous Distillation. In continuous distillation the point of introduction of the feed liquid should be on a plate where the composition is close to that of the feed. On McCabe–Thiele diagrams, the operating lines for enriching and stripping intersect at the feed composition. If the column and feed compositions were substantially different at the point where the feed enters, less separation would be achieved than if there is no difference in composition. This may be shown by constructing a number of different McCabe–Thiele diagrams with identical distillate compositions, reflux ratios, and number of theoretical plates, but with the two operating lines intersecting at various compositions.[51]

Application to Multicomponent Systems. The procedures just discussed are entirely valid for multicomponent mixtures, but application is complicated by the difficulty in finding x_{n-1} when y_{n-1} is known. This arises because in multicomponent mixtures the value of y_n will, in general, depend on the concentrations in the liquid of all the other components as well as on x_n. Thus, series of equilibrium curves or equivalent data are required, and trial and error, or specially developed methods must be used to find the correct solution.[49, 52]

Smoker and Other Equations. If the number of plates is large, or if very many McCabe–Thiele determinations are necessary, the graphic procedure becomes quite laborious, so that a number of algebraic methods have been devised. The most straightforward of these is the Smoker[53] equation, which is merely the algebraic or analytical equivalent of the McCabe–Thiele graphic procedure. As originally developed by Smoker it is useful only when relative volatility may be assumed to be constant. The same method may be applied to obtain equations for any case in which an algebraic statement for the equilibrium curve is known and can be solved for

x and y.[54] The derivation of the Smoker equation may be simply illustrated by the example of a column with one plate and a still operating with distillate return (Fig. 11). With the same reasoning used for the Lewis procedure one obtains eq. (18) or for this instance:

$$y_{\text{still}} = \frac{L}{V} x_{\text{plate}} + \frac{D}{V} x_D$$

It is also true that $x_D = y_{\text{plate}}$. Since the vapor from the plate (y_{plate}) is in equilibrium with the liquid on the plate (x_{plate}), these two compositions are related by the relative volatility equation

$$\frac{y_p}{1 - y_p} = \alpha \frac{x_p}{1 - x_p}$$

so that

$$x_p = \frac{y_p}{\alpha(1 - y_p) + y_p} = \frac{x_D}{\alpha(1 - x_D) + x_D}$$

This value of x_p may be substituted above to give

$$y_s = \frac{L}{V} \left[\frac{x_D}{\alpha(1 - x_D) + x_D} \right] + \frac{D}{V} x_D$$

Thus this equation gives directly the composition of vapor leaving the still in terms of the distillate composition, x_D, the reflux ratio, L/V and D/V, and the relative volatility α. No graphic operations are necessary. Since the vapor leaving the still, y_s, is in equilibrium with the liquid in the still, x_s, these are related by the relative volatility equation so that

$$x_s = \frac{y_s}{\alpha(1 - y_s) + y_s}$$

On substituting the value y_s in the above equation the still and product compositions are related by

$$x_s = \frac{\frac{L}{V} \left[\frac{x_D}{\alpha(1 - x_D) + x_D} \right] + \frac{D}{V} x_D}{\alpha - \alpha \left\{ \frac{L}{V} \left[\frac{x_D}{\alpha(1 - x_D) + x_D} \right] + \frac{D}{V} x_D \right\} + \frac{L}{V} \left[\frac{x_D}{\alpha(1 - x_D) + x_D} \right] + \frac{D}{V} x_D}$$

This final equation gives the still composition directly in terms of the distillate composition, without graphic operations. If the symbol ϕ_D is used to represent the quantity

$$\frac{L}{V} \left[\frac{x_D}{\alpha(1 - x_D) + x_D} \right] + \frac{D}{V} x_D$$

the equation appears much less formidable:

$$x_s = \frac{\phi_D}{\alpha(1 - \phi_D) + \phi_D}$$

For a continuous column the feed-plate composition replaces the still composition in the above reasoning so that

$$x_F = \frac{\phi_D}{\alpha(1 - \phi_D) + \phi_D}$$

In spite of the complexity of the relationship, Smoker has developed the equation for any number of plates in a relatively simple form, through the use of ingenious mathematical transformations. The most useful form for calculating the number of theoretical plates is

$$n = \log \left\{ \frac{[x_D - k][1 - M(x_s - k)]}{[x_s - k][1 - M(x_D - k)]} \right\} \bigg/ \log \frac{\alpha}{mc^2}$$

in which

$$M = \frac{mc(\alpha - 1)}{\alpha - mc^2} \tag{28}$$

and k is the root between 0 and 1 of

$$m(\alpha - 1)k^2 + [m + b(\alpha - 1) - \alpha]k + b = 0$$

with $m = R_D/(R_D + 1)$, $R_D = L/D$, $b = x_D/(R_D + 1)$, and $c = 1 + (\alpha - 1)k$. For calculating still composition from product composition when α, n, and R_D are known, it is convenient to use the form

$$x_s = k + \frac{(mc^2)^n(x_D - k)}{\alpha^n - (mc)(\alpha - 1)(x_D - k)\left[\dfrac{\alpha^n - (mc^2)^n}{\alpha - mc^2}\right]}$$

Bisesi[55] has furnished a nomograph for finding k in Smoker's equation. It can readily be shown that at total reflux the Smoker equation reduces to the Fenske equation.

The Smoker equations given in the preceding paragraphs are applicable only to the enriching section of a column, i.e., to an ordinary batch distillation (with negligible holdup), or to the portion of a continuous column above the feed entry. The equivalent equations applicable below the feed point—the equations for the stripping section—are

$$x_B = k + \frac{(mc^2)^n(x_F - k)}{\alpha^n - (mc)(\alpha - 1)(x_F - k)\left[\dfrac{\alpha^n - (mc^2)^n}{\alpha - mc^2}\right]}$$

and

$$n = \log \left\{ \frac{[x_F - k][1 - M(x_B - k)]}{[x_B - k][1 - M(x_F - k)]} \right\} \Big/ \log \frac{\alpha}{mc^2}$$

For the stripping section case, M remains as in eq. (28), but

$$m = \frac{R_D x_F + x_D - (R_D + 1)x_B}{(R_D + 1)(x_F - x_B)}$$

and

$$b = \frac{(x_F - x_D)x_B}{(R_D + 1)(x_F - x_B)}$$

Ramalho and Tiller[56] have combined the equations for the enriching and stripping sections.

Many other equations similar in objective to the Smoker equations have been published. A few of them are noted here. Underwood[57] derived relations for the case in which the distillate is near 100% purity, and for other special cases. Thomson and Beatty[58] and Clark[59] have also presented equations applicable under special circumstances. Later articles by Underwood give equations that are more generally useful.[60] Amundson and others[61] have each developed a system of theoretical plate equations by reasoning along lines similar to Smoker but using different mathematical transformations. Faasen[62] has worked out a nomograph for calculating number of theoretical plates and reflux ratio, but using a different approach from Smoker. All these relations are based on the stepwise graphic and algebraic procedure of Sorel as simplified by Lewis, and McCabe and Thiele. Various other methods of column evaluation have also been derived.[63]

C. BATCH DISTILLATION

Batch distillation apparatus has almost always been tested at total reflux rather than at partial reflux (p. 23) and there has been but little study of the composition differences to be expected under the latter circumstances. Collins and Lantz[64] have chosen to express the composition difference between still and product at partial reflux in terms of plate equivalents, a standard of column efficiency first suggested by Baker, Barkenbus, and Roswell.[65] Plate equivalents are a quantity numerically equal to the number of theoretical plates operating at total reflux which would give the separation obtained when the column is operating at a finite reflux ratio. The procedure is to step off between the vapor–liquid equilibrium curve and the 45° line the number of plates between still and distillate compositions in exactly the same way as for operation at total reflux. This simple, direct method of evaluation can serve admirably as a basis for comparison of columns,[66] but is not useful for predicting separation under new conditions. To avoid the sampling difficulty inherent in batch distillation because of the change of compositions with time, Collins and Lantz have used the method of returning the distillate to the still (Fig. 11) to "freeze" the compositions. However, this method gives results somewhat different from snap samples taken during a regular batch distillation because the return-to-still procedure involves steady state operations while batch distillation does not.

Colburn and Stearns[67] have pointed out that the Sorel–Lewis and McCabe–Thiele procedure cannot be depended upon to estimate the number of theoretical plates or composition differences for batch operation at finite reflux. This is because of the effect of constantly changing compositions and holdup on plate-to-plate compositions, even though the usual simplifying assumptions are valid. This may be shown by the following reasoning. For the top plate and condenser of a continuous distillation in which the usual simplifying assumptions are valid, the Sorel–Lewis equation is

$$Vy_{t-1} - Lx_t - Dx_D = 0$$

For the corresponding case of a batch distillation

$$Vy_{t-1} - Lx_t - Dx_D = -H_t\Delta x_t$$

in which H_t is the total holdup on the top plate and Δx_t is the change in composition on the top plate during the interval over which the distillate, D, is removed. Similar equations apply to other plates. The additional term necessarily results in a curved operating line for batch distillation. As a result it can be predicted that a given number of theoretical plates will result in a different separation in batch distillation from that in steady-state or continuous distillation.

In general, the equation for the operating line in batch distillation will be

$$Vy_{n-1} = Lx_n + Dx_D - \bar{H}_{n-1}\Delta x_h$$

in which $\bar{H}_{n-1}$ is the total holdup on all the plates above plate $n - 1$, and Δx_h is the change in composition of this material during the interval over which D is measured. This effect of changing composition has an important bearing on the role of reflux ratio and holdup in batch distillation. When holdup is negligible, or when the rate of change of composition of the holdup is small, the simpler laws of steady-state or continuous distillation may be adequate to predict the course of a batch distillation. The study to date of the much more complicated relationships that apply in batch distillation with finite reflux and large holdup leaves little doubt that in batch distillation appreciable holdup sometimes gives a sharper and better

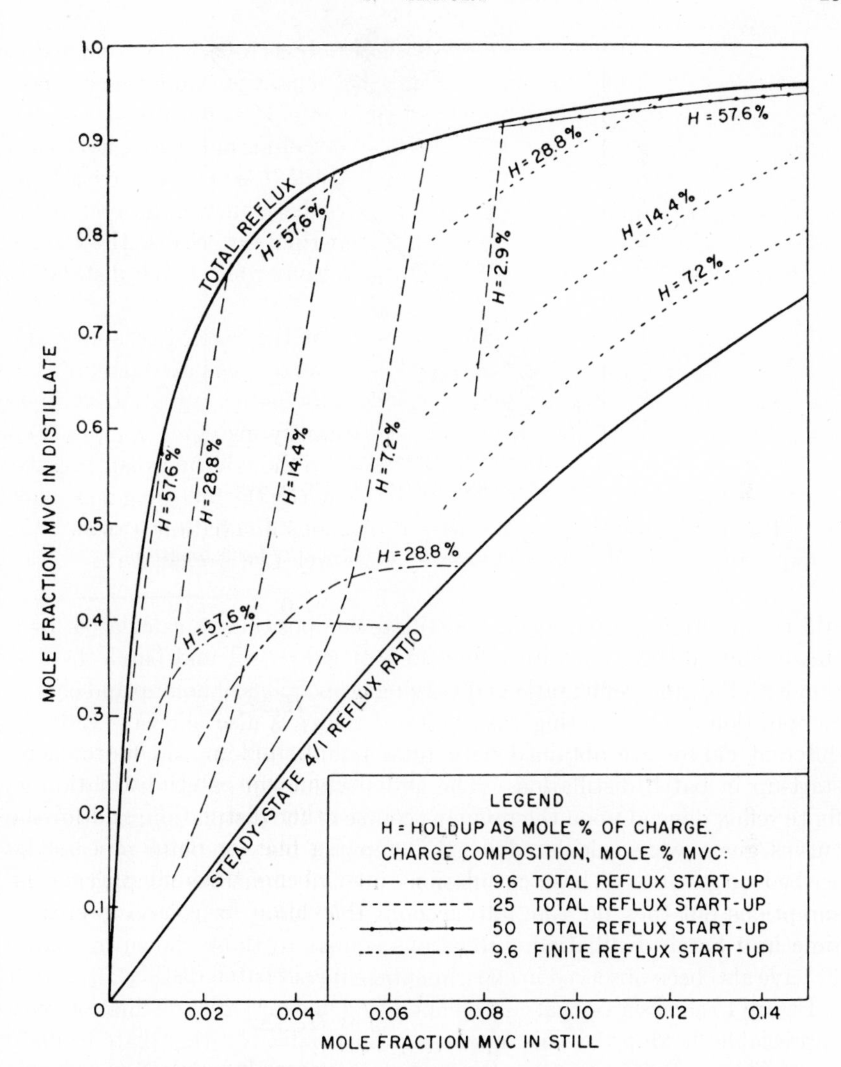

Fig. 14. Distillate composition vs. still composition from calculated batch-distillation curves.

separation than would be expected from the laws of continuous distillation. This is in addition to the improved separation near the beginning of a batch distillation commenced at total reflux. In contrast there are also combinations of operating conditions that cause larger holdup to give poorer separations in batch distillation.

The relation between still and distillate composition for various types of operation may best be shown by graphs such as Figure 14. This shows

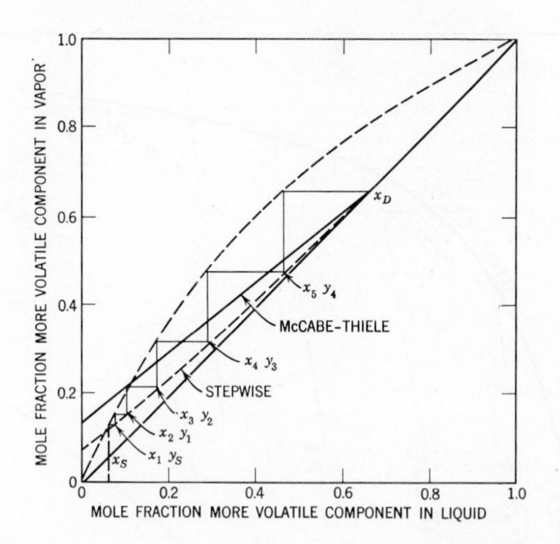

Fig. 15. Calculated operating line. Holdup = 7.2 mole-% of charge; x_D = 0.65. McCabe–Thiele operating line shown for comparison.[69]

still composition plotted against distillate composition as calculated for a steady-state distillation with reflux ratio of $R_D = 4/1$ and batch distillation with the same reflux ratio and varying proportions of holdup and charge composition. The limiting case of total reflux is also shown. Entirely different curves are obtained with total reflux start-up and finite reflux start-up in batch distillation. The actual values in batch distillation at finite reflux depend upon the previous course of the distillation, and for the curves given were calculated by the stepwise plate-to-plate process described on p. 101. These calculations involve numerous simplifying assumptions but they do take into account the change of composition with time in a batch distillation. Relations similar to those shown in Figure 14 have also been observed in experimental curves.[68]

Figure 15 shows a typical curved operating line for batch distillation with appreciable holdup.[69] This operating line indicates the plate-to-plate composition relations that are the underlying reason for the effect of holdup on separation in batch distillation.

4. Still and Product Composition Relations

A. UNDER PARTIAL REFLUX

The preceding part of this chapter has dealt with methods of determining the number of theoretical plates when still and product compositions are known. The same methods may be used to estimate product composition from still composition, or vice versa, when the number of plates is known. For steady-state distillation, or for batch distillation with negligible holdup, the McCabe–Thiele and Smoker procedures are the simplest that may be used for obtaining still and distillate compositions from one another. The results of a number of calculations of this kind are shown in

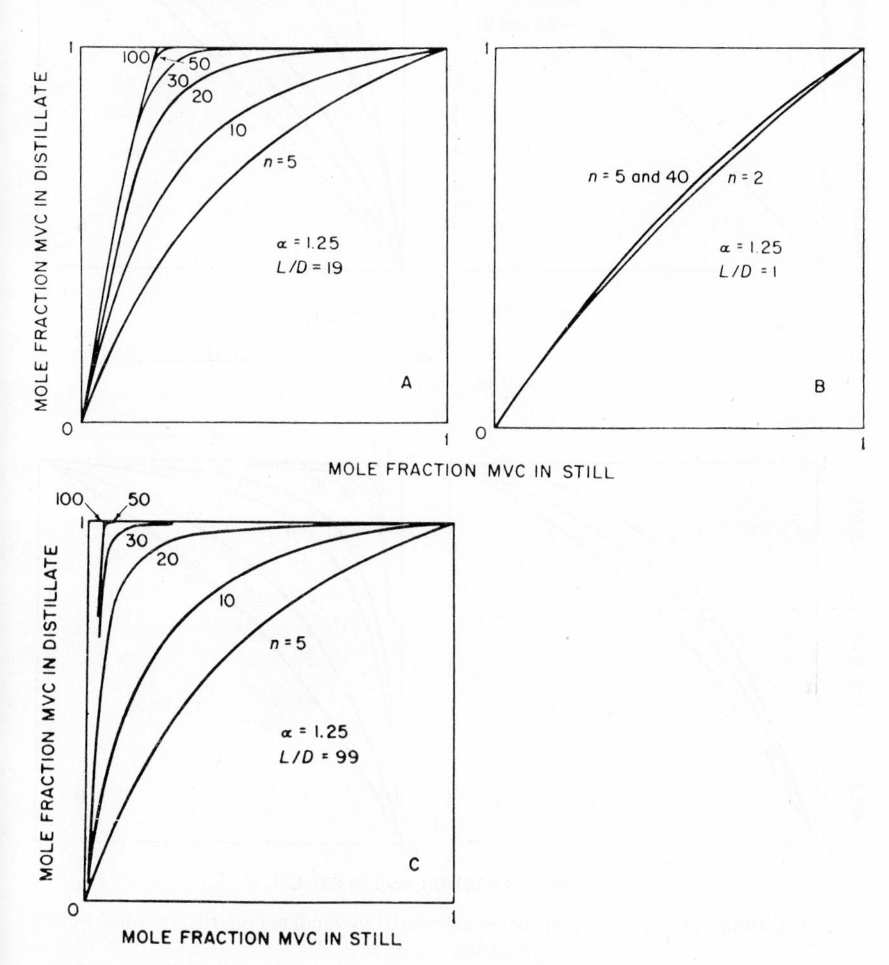

Fig. 16. Still-product composition curves calculated by McCabe–Thiele procedure for ideal binary mixture. $\alpha = 1.25$. Note in B that the same curve is obtained for all values of n greater than 5.

Figures 16–18. For example, in Figure 16A the product compositions corresponding to various calculated still compositions are summarized for a binary mixture having $\alpha = 1.25$, when distilled with reflux ratio $R_D = 19$ in columns with 5, 10, 20, 30, 50, and 100 theoretical plates.

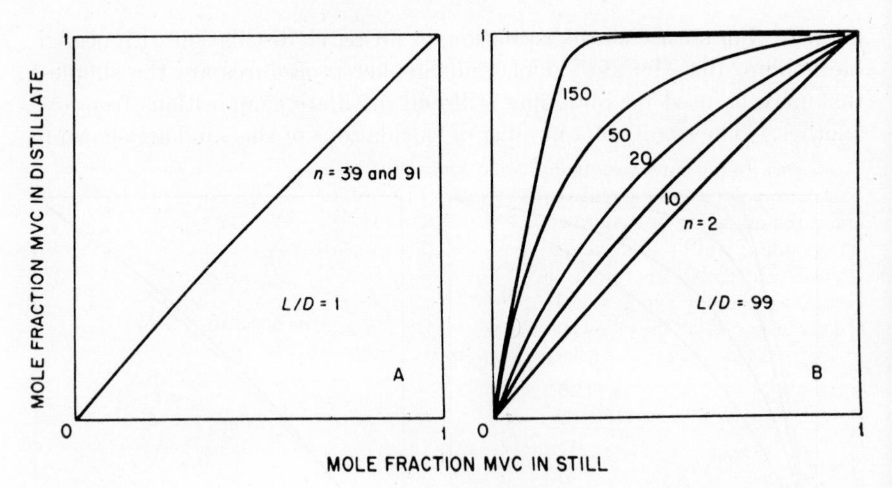

Fig. 17. Still-product composition curves calculated by Smoker equation for ideal binary mixture. $\alpha = 1.05$.

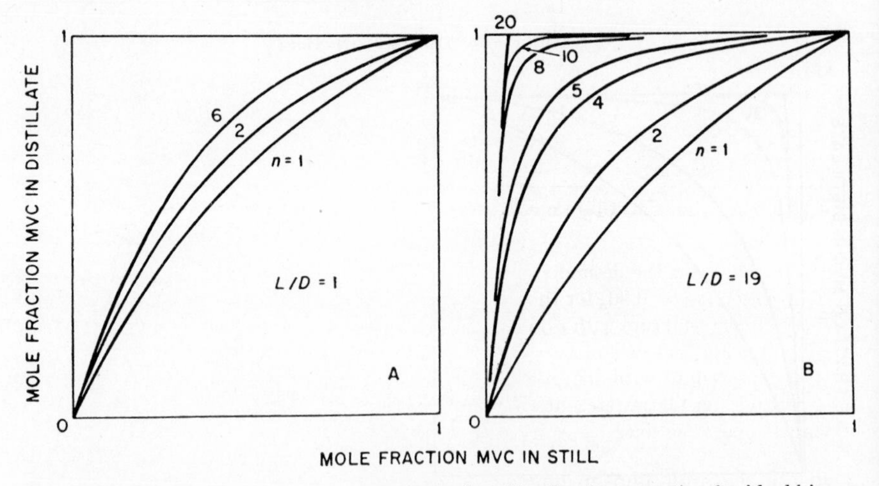

Fig. 18. Still-product composition curves calculated by Smoker equation for ideal binary mixture. $\alpha = 2$.

The method for obtaining the curves of Figures 16 to 18 may be illustrated by the calculation for five plates in Figure 16A. It is first necessary to construct a large-scale graph for the vapor–liquid equilibrium curve for a binary mixture with $\alpha = 1.25$. The points on this curve are obtained by calculatina values of y corresponding to $x = 0.1, 0.2, 0.3$, etc., with the relative–volatility equation

$$\frac{y}{1-y} = \alpha \frac{x}{1-x}$$

A series of operating lines with slope $L/V = 19/20$ are then drawn on this graph. These are so placed that their upper ends cross the 45° diagonal at compositions such as 0.99, 0.96, 0.94, 0.92, 0.90, 0.85, 0.80, 0.70, 0.60, 0.50, 0.30, 0.20, 0.15, 0.10, and 0.05. Additional operating lines may need to be drawn later in order to obtain points for a smooth still–product composition (x_s, x_D) curve such as in Figures 16 to 18.

Figure 19 indicates how points are obtained. The point $x = y = 0.90$ mole fraction of more volatile component represents an arbitrarily chosen product composition (x_D) and the operating line is drawn through this point with slope $L/V = 19/20$. The corresponding still or feed composition (x_s) for a column with an *overall* separation of five theoretical plates, operating on the mixture with $\alpha = 1.25$, reflux ratio $R_D = 19$, is obtained by stepping off five steps along the operating line and equilibrium curve. This gives in succession the following values:

	Composition of	Value
x_1	Liquid from top plate	0.878
y_2	Vapor from second plate (counting from top down)	0.878
x_2	Liquid from second plate	0.854
y_3	Vapor from third plate	0.856
x_3	Liquid from third plate	0.827
y_4	Vapor from fourth plate	0.830
x_4	Liquid from fourth plate	0.797
$y_5 = y_s$	Vapor from fifth plate[a]	0.802
$x_5 = x_s$	Liquid in still in five-plate column (or liquid from fifth plate from top of longer column)	0.765

[a] That is, from the still in a column with overall separation of five theoretical plates.

This last value is the desired still composition (x_s) corresponding to the chosen product composition ($x_D = 0.90$) for the five-plate separation with reflux ratio $R_D = 19$ and the chosen binary mixture with $\alpha = 1.25$. This gives one point on the corresponding x_s, x_D curve (see Fig. 16A, where $x_D = 0.90$, $x = 0.765$ lies on the curve for $n = 5$). Repetition of this procedure with the other operating lines gives additional points. The x_s, x_D curves for ten plates, etc., are obtained by similarly stepping off ten steps along the various operating lines.

The example chosen has a constant relative volatility, but the same procedure could be used for any mixture for which the vapor–liquid equilibrium curve was known. When constant relative volatility may be assumed, the Smoker equation will give results identical with the graphic method described above. The Fenske equation is applicable for total reflux and constant relative volatility. Similar calculations can be made by the Ponchon, Savarit, and like procedures for cases in which the usual simplifying assumptions are not applicable.

The curves indicate the complexity of the effects determining the separation achieved in distillation. They also aid in visualizing the compositions

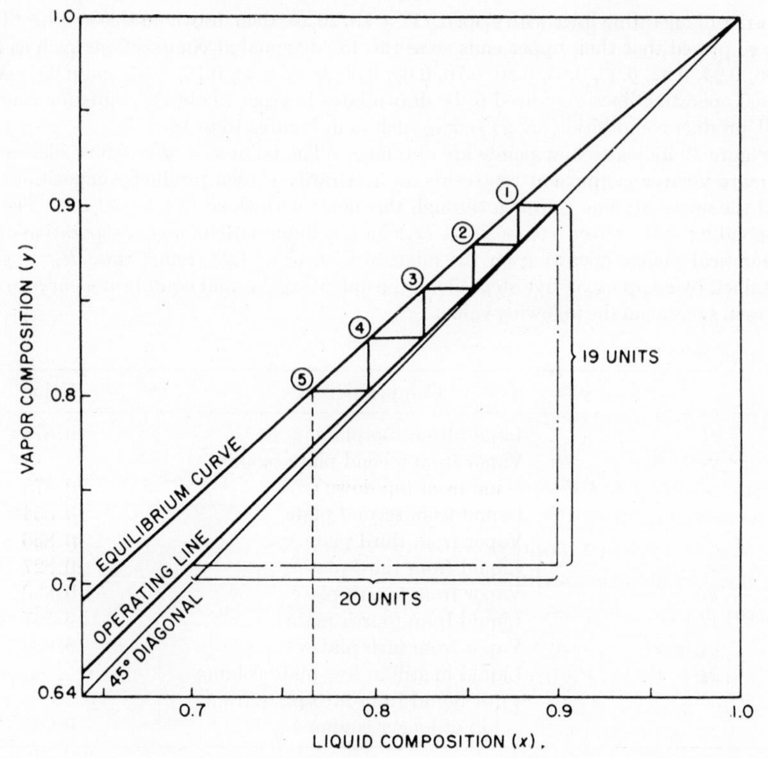

Fig. 19. Calculation by McCabe–Thiele procedure of still or feed composition when distillate composition, reflux ratio, number of theoretical plates, and relative volatility are known and fixed (see Fig. 16).

during actual distillation, and, in cases in which holdup is inappreciable, show how distillate composition changes with the decrease in still composition as a batch distillation is progressing.

In addition to the specific numerical relationships, a comparison of the curves shows the following general relations implicit in McCabe–Thiele diagrams.

(*1*) As the number of plates is increased, less and less improvement in separation results.

(*2*) No matter how large the number of plates, a high-purity distillate cannot be obtained with low still composition and low reflux ratio.

(*3*) At very low reflux ratios almost the same poor separation is obtained regardless of the number of plates or the still composition.

Curves of the type given in this chapter can serve to indicate the general nature of composition relations even for nonideal and azeotropic mixtures. In the latter cases the mixture must be considered to be made up of azeotrope and one of its pure components, rather than the two pure components. The general effect of increase in plates, relative volatility, and reflux ratio will be that indicated by the calculated curves, even though there will be discrepancies for specific cases.

B. UNDER TOTAL REFLUX

Curves under total-reflux conditions, such as those in Figure 20 and 21, which were calculated from the Fenske equation, show the maximum difference in composition that can be achieved with a particular mixture and column. They also serve as a quick means of determining the number of theoretical plates if still and distillate compositions from a test are known. It also appears that in some cases these curves even describe the separation[70] characteristic of batch distillation with appreciable holdup and finite reflux ratio. This arises from the marked shift in the operating lines caused by constantly changing compositions in batch distillation with appreciable holdup.

Under total-reflux conditions a single family of curves may be used to summarize the still-product separations for all different relative volatilities and any number of theoretical plates. The path of any curve is determined by the value of α^n rather than the values of α and n. Thus the curve marked $n = 20$ on Figure 20 is obtained for $\alpha = 1.05$ and $n = 91$ as well as $\alpha = 1.25$ and $n = 20$. The same curve would be obtained for any other

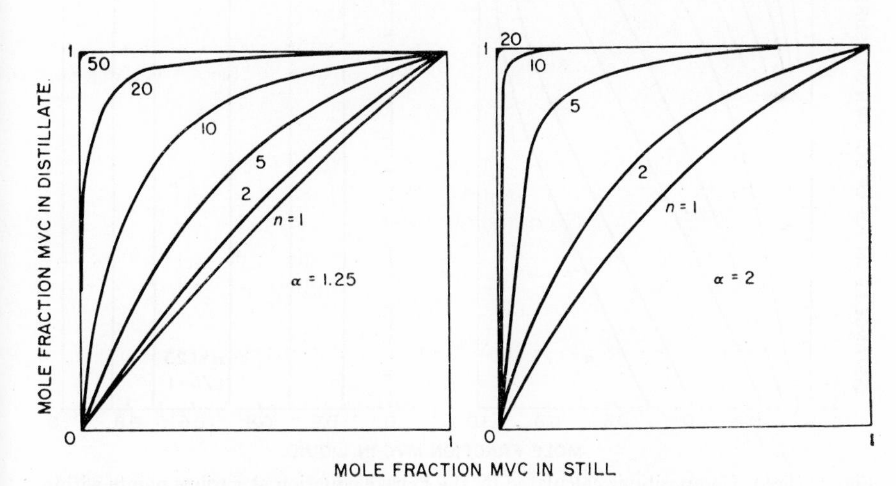

Fig. 20 (left). Still-product composition curves calculated by the Fenske equation for ideal binary mixture. $\alpha = 1.25$. Total reflux.

Fig. 21 (right). Still-product composition curves calculated by Fenske equation for ideal binary mixture. $\alpha = 2$. Total reflux.

combination for which α^n is approximately 86.5. The quantity α^n is known as the *enrichment factor*, or *overall separation factor*, and is a good measure of the maximum sharpness of separation that may be expected in any particular instance.

5. Compositions on Various Plates or at Various Points in a Column

The composition on any plate or at any point in a column may be estimated by the same procedures already discussed for calculating the number of plates and the still-product composition relations. An example was indicated in connection with the x_s, x_D values for Figure 16A. Such calculations are subject to all the limitations and discrepancies already mentioned, and have general interest and utility for the same reasons as the

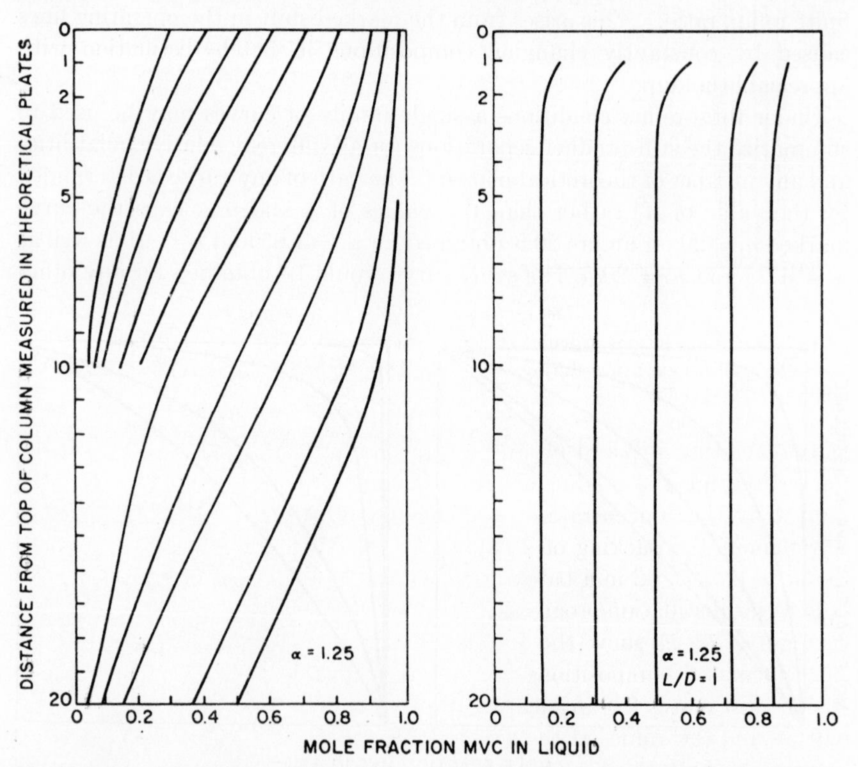

Fig. 22 (left). Compositions calculated by the Fenske equation at various points within a column for an ideal binary mixture; 20 plates; total reflux.

Fig. 23 (right). Compositions calculated by Smoker equation at various points within a column and various times during batch distillations for an ideal binary mixture; 20 plates; partial reflux.

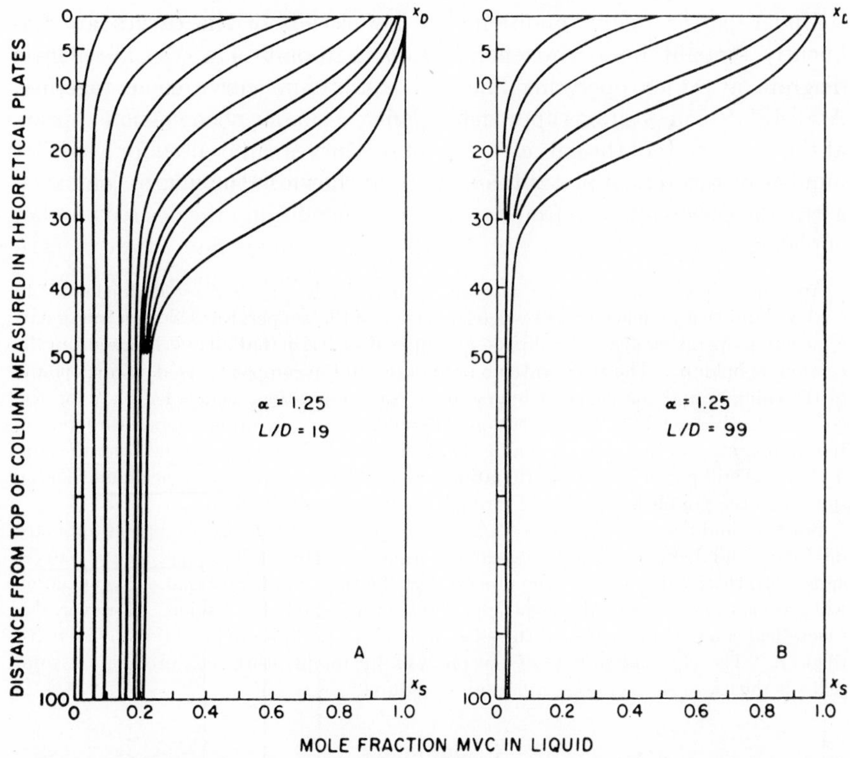

Fig. 24. Compositions calculated by Smoker equation at various points within a column and various times during batch distillation for an ideal binary mixture; 100 plates; partial reflux.

curves relating still and product composition. They are especially useful for estimating the holdup of the individual components. This is determined by the concentration of that component on each of the plates or throughout the packing of a column. This varies from plate to plate or point to point, and in a batch distillation such compositions change gradually as the distillation progresses.

Figures 22–24 show the results of such calculations. Figure 22 gives the calculated compositions under total reflux in a column with twenty theoretical plates for an ideal mixture with $\alpha = 1.25$. The shape of the curves and the values of the compositions are unchanged if the numbering is from the bottom up, or from some intermediate plate, as for the analysis of a shorter column. This is true because all the curves have identical slopes for any particular compositions, and identical average slopes between any two given compositions. This is not true of curves at partial reflux such as those in Figures 23–24.

Under partial-reflux conditions the lower ends of the curves are frequently straight lines, corresponding to that part of a McCabe–Thiele diagram at which operating line and equilibrium curve come together. At distillate compositions approaching unity a similar phenomenon appears at the upper ends of the curves. Any of the curves can be used for a smaller number of theoretical plates than the total shown in the figures. In such a case the curves are read from top down to include only the desired number of plates.

An interesting application of this type of curve is the proposal by Podbielniak[71] to analyze liquids or liquefied gases by determination of the temperatures along a fractionating column operating at total reflux on a sample of such size that all of it is present in the column as holdup. The temperatures are related to the compositions at various points in the column, and the curve of temperature (or composition) versus length along the column closely resembles the conventional distillation curve relating temperature, refractive index, etc., to per cent of charge distilled. It is of course essential that the condenser and still pot of such a fractionating column be designed to have negligible holdup so that all the sample is distributed through the fractionating section.

Bowman and Sastry[72] have also discussed this method of analysis as applied to binary mixtures, and have presented typical experimental data. The experimental curves agree with those calculated for the process, but the theory indicates that a given column will give poorer separation than when operated in the usual batch fashion. However, this theoretical comparison neglected the effect of holdup and finite reflux ratios on batch distillation. The chief advantage of the analysis by temperature measurement at total reflux is the use of simpler apparatus and procedure.

6. Summary

This section has presented the most important methods of determining the number of plates for distillation apparatus. When the number of theoretical plates is known or fixed, all these methods are also useful for estimating the composition differences between still and product or at other points in the column.

A. COMPARISON OF METHODS OF DETERMINING NUMBER OF THEORETICAL PLATES

If the data are collected when the distillation is proceeding under *total reflux*, the number of plates is usually determined by

(*1*) The stepping-off process, using the experimental vapor–liquid equilibrium diagram. This is applicable to both ideal and nonideal mixtures.

(*2*) The Fenske equation, which is the algebraic equivalent of the stepping-off process, but is applicable only when the average value of the relative volatility is within about 5% of the extreme values encountered in the distillation or test.

If the distillation is carried out under steady-state conditions (continuous distillation) at *partial reflux*, the number of theoretical plates may be determined by

(*1*) Sorel's method, which is the basic general procedure for plate-to-plate calculations. It is not used when the following simpler methods are applicable, i.e., when the column is adiabatic, and the thermal properties of the components are similar. Numerous modifications of Sorel's original method have been published (Ponchon and Savarit in particular).

(*2*) Lewis' method, the basis for the most useful modifications of the Sorel method. It applies only when the column is adiabatic and the thermal properties of the components are similar, i.e., under the USA (p. 37). The original Lewis equations are less used than the equivalent.

(*3*) McCabe–Thiele graphic procedure. This is the most frequently used procedure. It is restricted in the same way as the Lewis method, (USA must apply), but like Sorel's and Lewis's methods it is applicable to nonideal as well as ideal mixtures.

(*4*) Smoker equation, which is the algebraic equivalent of the McCabe–Thiele method, but is applicable only under the USA to ideal mixtures in which a constant relative volatility may be assumed.

(*5*) Plate-equivalents procedure. Plate equivalents may be calculated for any case in which still and product compositions and the vapor–liquid equilibrium curve are known. They are of comparative value only, and have no general utility for predicting separation under new circumstances.

The Sorel–Lewis, McCabe–Thiele, and Smoker relations are also at least approximately valid for batch distillation at finite reflux, if holdup is small and reflux ratio is not too small. When holdup is large, all the above methods are inapplicable to batch distillation, and more complex relations apply, as discussed in detail in Secs. III and IV.

B. PRECAUTIONS IN USE OF HEIGHT EQUIVALENT TO THEORETICAL PLATE AND THEORETICAL-PLATE DATA

In general, H.E.T.P. data are not highly reproducible, particularly in packed columns. Even the same test mixture and the same column may give values differing by 10% if the tests are made at different times. Different columns of the same dimensions and packed with the same packing may give different results because of variations in the arrangement of the packing, or because of slight corrosion or the presence of extraneous material. Comparative H.E.T.P. values on several columns with a given test mixture are a reasonably trustworthy basis for choice of the best column packing, reflux ratio, or throughput for a particular separation. Values obtained with standard test mixtures are less dependable when used to predict the height of a column for separation of an entirely different mixture. Table VII (p. 72) indicates some variations found with different types of compounds.[73]

The differences in H.E.T.P. between different test mixtures were about the same with different columns and packings. An empirical equation has been proposed by Murch[74] to correlate such data

$$\text{H.E.T.P. (in.)} = K_1 G^{K_2} d^{K_3} h^{1/3} \left(\frac{\alpha\mu}{\rho} \right)$$

where G is mass velocity of vapor in pounds per hour per square foot of cross-sectional column area, d is column diameter in inches, h is packed height in feet, α is relative volatility, μ is liquid viscosity in centipoises, ρ is liquid density, grams per milliliter, and the K's are empirical constants that vary with the material being tested, size, and configuration of packing. This whole matter will eventually be clarified in terms of the interfacial areas, flow patterns, and the mass transfer characteristics of different packings and substances (Sec. VI).

There is some evidence that relatively high vapor rates in packed columns result in entrainment of liquid which reduces separation efficiency and H.E. T.P. at vapor rates considerably below those that cause flooding. The equation[75]

$$U_E = 0.065 \sqrt{\frac{\rho_L}{\rho_G}}$$

was found to express the vapor velocity, U_E, in feet per second at the top of the column that caused appreciable entrainment, where ρ_L and ρ_G are the densities of liquid and vapor. A 1:1 reflux ratio was used, with seven different liquids in columns 1–6 in. in diameter, and packed with single-turn wire helices or Raschig rings of $^5/_{32}$ to $^9/_{16}$-in. diameters.

Several studies of rectification, some of them in terms of transfer units rather than theoretical plates, show that H.E.T.P. may be expected to vary with reflux ratio and composition.[76]

H.E.T.P. is usually greater in a long column than in a short one of exactly the same kind. Thus a low H.E.T.P. obtained in a test on a short column cannot in general be reproduced in a much longer column.[77] It is even more important to recognize that a low H.E.T.P. in a small-diameter column will not even be approximated with larger diameters, even though packing, test mixture, throughput, and reflux ratio are the same. *Channeling*, i.e., agglomeration of the liquid into relatively large streams, is a partial cause of this behavior, which is sometimes augmented by introduction of the vapor as a high velocity stream concentrated onto a relatively small fraction of the cross-sectional area of packing at the bottom of

a moderate- or large-diameter column.[78] The use of suitable baffles in columns of more than 2-in. diameter is desirable if the vapor stream changes direction just before it enters the packed section.

Channeling is reduced by thorough wetting of the packing by the well-known preflooding procedure. Channeling is also less prevalent with protruded metal or fine screen packing. It has been reported that treatment of stainless steel packing with potassium permanganate solution produces a film of manganese oxide that improves the wetting of the steel by aqueous solutions.[79] If a column with 100 theoretical plates is operating

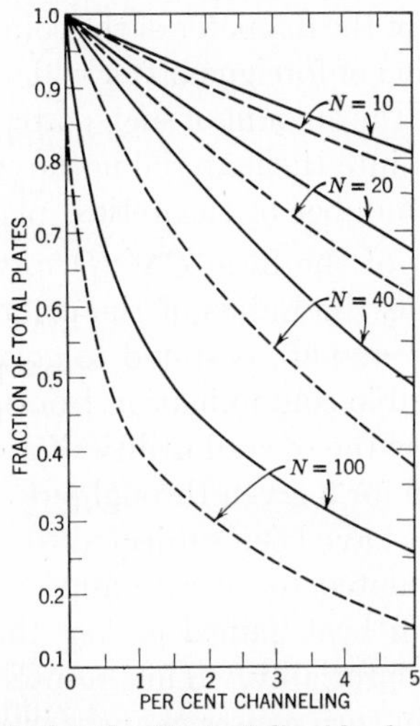

Fig. 25. Calculated effect of liquid channeling for a binary mixture with relative volatility 1.07 in columns with 10, 20, 40, and 100 theoretical plates (N) and for distillate compositions x_D of 0.90 (——) and 0.60 (– – –).[80]

at total reflux on n-heptane–methylcyclohexane with an overhead composition of 90 mole-% n-heptane, and 1% of the reflux stream is caused to channel so as to completely bypass all the packing and the rising vapor, separation will be reduced to 56 theoretical plates. Figure 25 shows other examples of this kind of effect. The use of an interdistributor screen can increase the separation by 10–30% in 6-in. diameter packed columns.[80]

Morris[81] estimated the effect of maldistribution of liquid by assuming the column cross section to be divided into two equal areas with equal vapor flows but with liquid flows divided 75:25 or 70:30. Transfer unit calculations were made and results converted to H.E.T.P. values. The H.E.T.P. calculated for the channeling situation were about 50% greater than those having normal distribution.

The stability of the liquid film on a packing is also related to surface tension changes.[82] If composition changes cause a decrease in surface tensions the film will tend to be unstable and break into rivulets. As a consequence mass transfer rates may be much higher when surface tension is increasing than when composition changes are such as to cause a decrease in surface tension.

Mullin's studies[83] indicate that the most serious effects of poor distribution are at high values of the quantity $m(G_m/L_m)$, in which $m = dy^*/dx$, i.e., the slope of the equilibrium curve, and G_m and L_m are the molar rates of flow of gas and liquid, respectively. Mullin suggests that packing dimensions be less than $^1/_{12}$ of the diameter of the column.

Corrosion or introduction of foreign matter will usually have a deleterious effect out of proportion to the amount of such material. A German patent[84] states that diffusion of air into the material in the condenser of a fractionating column reduced the number of theoretical plates from 100 to 20 in a specific case. A relation of the form $C\sqrt{2D/a}$, where D is the diffusion constant of the vapor, a is the radius of the column, and C is a constant having a value between 1 and 10, is stated to govern the minimum vapor velocity to avoid appreciable contamination from this source.

The H.E.T.P. as well as the overall utility of a column or packing is related to the pressure drop for a given throughput. These relations in both packed and plate columns have been subjected to extensive study.[85]

If a column is not insulated to operate approximately adiabatically at all times, the variation in heat gained or lost through the column walls will change H.E.T.P. appreciably. This results from variation in the amount of reflux, which in turn causes changes in reflux ratio, throughput, and H.E.T.P. (Sec. IV). Small-diameter columns are most affected by such conditions, so that their H.E.T.P. will undergo gross variations with changes in environment if insulation is inadequate.

APPENDIX ON TEST MIXTURES

Test Mixtures for Columns at Atmospheric Pressure

The vapor–liquid equilibrium data in the following tables, and in most papers published, are for a pressure of 760 mm. Little error is involved in using such data for operation at pressures of 700–800 mm., but at lower or higher pressures differences will become appreciable. Some data for pressures below atmospheric are included later.

The mixture *n*-heptane–methylcyclohexane is useful for testing columns with about 10–90 plates. It is particularly suitable for columns distilling close-boiling hydrocarbons. Analysis is by refractive index or density.

TABLE I
Data for n-Heptane—Methylcyclohexane Test Mixture
(All Compositions in Mole Fractions n-Heptane)

Vapor–liquid equilibrium data		Data for analysis of samples		
Vapor comp.	Liquid comp.	n_D^{20}	d_4^{20}	B.p., °C. (760 mm.)
	0.0000	1.4232	0.7693	100.80
0.0350	0.0310			
0.0620	0.0580			
	0.0787	1.4200	0.7613	100.55
0.1030	0.0950			
0.1430	0.1330			
	0.1638	1.4165	0.7535	100.35
0.1920	0.1800			
0.2290	0.2160			
	0.2486	1.4135	0.7454	100.15
0.2890	0.2715			
0.3330	0.3170			
	0.3372	1.4100	0.7377	—
0.3810	0.3630			
0.4200	0.4010			
	0.4126	1.4075	0.7312	99.70
0.4750	0.4560			
0.5210	0.5010			
	0.5186	1.4036	0.7218	99.20
0.5780	0.5590			
0.6180	0.5990			
	0.6056	1.4004	0.7145	99.00
0.6660	0.6470			
	0.6993	1.3970	0.7069	98.85
0.7280	0.7090			
0.7710	0.7560			
	0.7942	1.3942	0.6992	98.60
0.8100	0.7960			
0.8535	0.8430			
0.8900	0.8790			
0.9130	0.9060			
0.9400	0.9310			
	0.9338	1.3899	0.6884	98.50
0.9625	0.9540			
0.9860	0.9800			
	1.0000	1.3878	0.6839	98.40

Griswold[86] recommends refractive index as leading to smaller errors. The data are from Bromiley and Quiggle.[87] The n-heptane and methylcyclohexane used by Bromiley and Quiggle had the following characteristics:

Compound	B.p., °C. (760 mm.)	d_4^{20}	n_D^{20}	F.p., °C.
n-Heptane	98.4	0.6839	1.3878	−40.8
Methylcyclohexane	100.8	0.7693	1.4232	—

The heptane was obtained from a commercial source and was approved by the National Bureau of Standards for determination of knock ratings. The methylcyclohexane was purified by fractional distillation, washed with concd. H_2SO_4, Na_2CO_3 solution, and water, and then dried.

Nerheim and Dinerstein[88] used this mixture for an excellent and exhaustive series of tests on a variety of small laboratory columns. Their mixture contained 10 mole-% *n*-heptane and they used $\alpha = 1.07$ for the relative volatility at atmospheric pressure. Phillips Pure Grade hydrocarbons were percolated through a Hyper-Cal column 25 mm. in diameter and 14 ft. long, to obtain cuts that showed no impurities upon analysis by mass spectrometer.

For columns having a large number of plates (100 or more), Willingham and Rossini[89] suggest the following equations for calculating theoretical plates with this mixture:

(*1*) Refractive index and mole fraction relation at 25°C.:

$$n_D(\text{mixture}) - n_D(n\text{-heptane}) = 0.0306x' + 0.0048(x')^2$$

(where n_D is the refractive index and x' is the mole fraction of methylcyclohexane in the mixture).

(*2*) Theoretical plates and mole fraction relation:

$$n + 1 = [32.15 - 0.34(t - 99)] \log \left[\left(\frac{x}{1-x}\right)_{\text{head}} \Big/ \left(\frac{x}{1-x}\right)_{\text{pot}} \right]$$

over the range 96.5–101.5°C. (where t is mean temperature, in °C., n is number of plates, and x is mole fraction of the more volatile component). The equation is not applicable strictly unless the test liquids used have been purified so that the refractive indices differ by 0.0354 unit.

Benzene–ethylene dichloride is ideal or nearly ideal, with the value of α given as 1.109. It may be used for columns with up to 60 plates, but there is some uncertainty as to the vapor–liquid equilibrium values, and the ethylene dichloride may be hydrolyzed and cause corrosion of metals if water is present. The data given are supplied from Ward[90] and taken originally from Rosanoff and Easley.[91]

The mixture benzene–carbon tetrachloride is suitable for columns with up to about 25 plates. Analysis is almost always by refractive index, but density may be used. The data given are from Mestres,[92] who has

TABLE II
Data for Benzene–Ethylene Dichloride Test Mixture
(All Compositions in Mole Fractions Benzene)

Vapor comp.	Liquid comp.	$n_D^{25.2}$
0.000	0.000	1.44218
0.113	0.100	1.44750
0.222	0.200	1.45287
0.327	0.300	1.45825
0.429	0.400	1.46366
0.527	0.500	1.46914
0.624	0.600	1.47462
0.727	0.700	1.48020
0.818	0.800	1.48596
0.912	0.900	1.49187
1.000	1.000	1.49719

TABLE III
Data for Benzene–Carbon Tetrachloride Test Mixture
(All Compositions in Mole Fractions Carbon Tetrachloride)

Vapor comp.	Liquid comp.
0.06	0.0517
0.10	0.08665
0.15	0.1310
0.20	0.1765
0.25	0.2234
0.30	0.2712
0.35	0.3202
0.40	0.3700
0.45	0.4205
0.50	0.4730
0.55	0.5263
0.60	0.5808
0.65	0.6347
0.70	0.6890
0.75	0.7426
0.80	0.7960
0.82	0.8183

made an extensive study of this system. Initial composition should be such that still composition at the time of taking samples is not much less than 6 mole-% carbon tetrachloride, and the condenser sample should not have more than about 80 mole-% carbon tetrachloride. At these concentrations one theoretical plate corresponds to about 0.0005 change in refractive index. The azeotropic composition of 91.8 mole-% carbon tetrachloride must be entirely avoided. Serious corrosion of alumi-

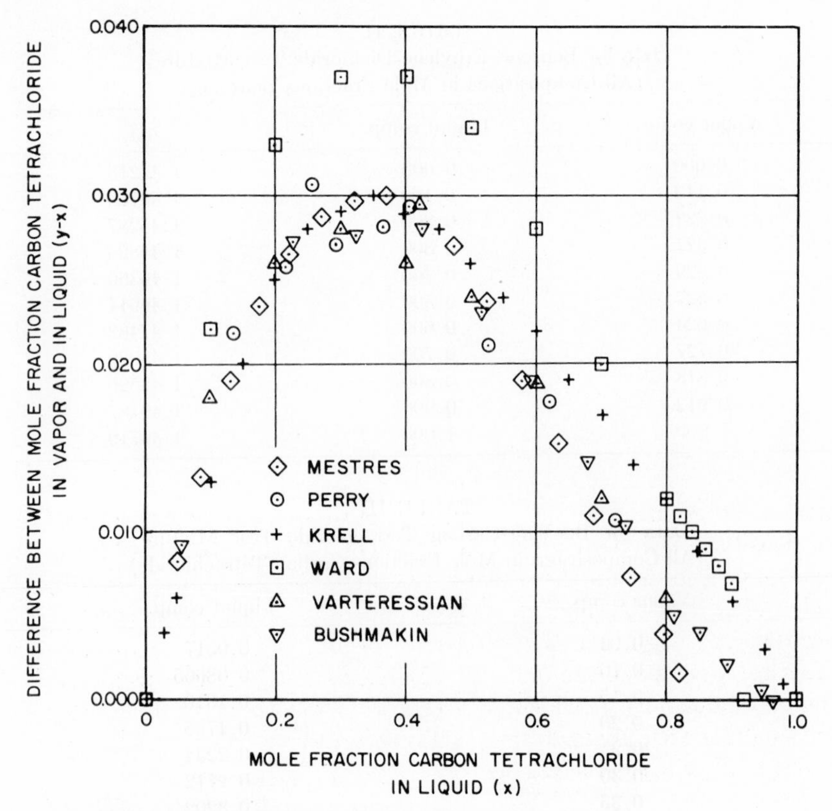

Fig. 26. Plot of x vs. y-x for vapor–liquid equilibrium data for the system CCl_4–C_6H_6 in terms of mole fraction of CCl_4. Sources are Mestres, *Bull. Soc. Chim. France*, **1956**, 876; Perry, *Chemical Engineers' Handbook*, 3rd ed., McGraw-Hill, New York, 1950, p. 573; Krell, *Handbuch der Laboratoriums-Destillation*, 2nd ed., VEB Deutscher Verlag der Wissenschaften, Berlin, 1960, Anhang, Tafel VI/4; Ward, *U. S. Bur. Mines Tech. Papers*, **600** (1939); Varteressian, B.S. Thesis, Pennsylvania State University, 1930; Bushmakin and Voeikova, *J. Gen. Chem. USSR*, **19**, No. 9, a35-48 (1949).

num or iron packings or columns is likely to occur with any concentration of this test mixture.

Although the mixture has been widely used for testing, serious discrepancies exist in the data found in the literature. These may be observed in the plot of x versus y-x (on a scale designed to make the discrepancies visible) in Figure 26. The points are particularly unreliable in the neighborhood of x = 0.8 to 1.0, near the azeotropic composition.

Methylcyclohexane–toluene is useful for testing columns of up to about thirty theoretical plates. Because of the cheapness, ready availability, and ease of purification of the components, it is particularly suitable for

TABLE IV
Data for Methylcyclohexane–Toluene Test Mixture
(All Compositions in Mole Fractions Methylcyclohexane)

Vapor comp.	Liquid comp.	n_D^{20}
0.000	0.000	1.4965
0.143	0.100	1.4871
0.270	0.200	1.4782
0.378	0.300	1.4699
0.470	0.400	1.4620
0.560	0.500	1.4544
0.650	0.600	1.4474
0.737	0.700	1.4408
0.818	0.800	1.4345
0.906	0.900	1.4286
1.000	1.000	1.4235

tests on large-size columns. Analysis may be either by refractive index or density. The data given are those of Quiggle and Fenske.[93] The relations do not follow the relative volatility equation (32) with a constant value of α, i.e., the mixture is not ideal, so that graphic procedures are necessary to determine the number of plates. Composition of the test mixture should be in the range 10–75 mole-% methylcyclohexane to avoid the concentrations in which composition change per theoretical plate is too small for accurate analysis. The materials used by Quiggle and Fenske had the following characteristics:

Compound	B.p., °C. (760 mm.)	d_4^{20}	n_D^{20}
Methylcyclohexane			
Sample I	100.85	0.7695	1.4234
Sample II	100.85	0.7692	1.4235
Toluene			
Sample I	110.6	0.8658	1.4965
Sample II	110.6	0.8663	1.4965

The toluene was nitration grade which had been fractionally distilled through 75 plates with high reflux ratio. The methylcyclohexane was technical grade purified by washing with concd. H_2SO_4, Na_2CO_3 solution, and water.

In addition to the *n*-heptane–methylcyclohexane mixture (Table I) cited as being useful for columns having a large number of plates, i.e., more than a hundred, Willingham and Rossini[94] suggest the use of the two following mixtures for the full-scale testing of such columns and have worked out useful equations for them. The first is 2,2,4-trimethylpentane and methylcyclohexane, whose refractive index–mole fraction relation at 25°C. is

$$n_D(\text{mixture}) - n_D(\text{2,2,4-trimethylpentane}) = 0.0244x' + 0.0072(x')^2$$

where n_D is the refractive index and x' is the mole fraction of methylcyclohexane in the mixture. The number of theoretical plates–mole fraction relation is

TABLE V

Methylcyclohexane–Toluene Refractive Index vs. Plate Number

n_D^{20}	00	01	02	03	04	05	06	07	08	09
1.4270			33.0	32.7	32.3	32.0	31.7	31.3	31.0	30.8
80	30.5	30.3	30.0	29.8	29.5	29.3	29.0	28.7	28.3	28.0
90	27.8	27.6	27.4	27.2	27.0	26.8	26.6	26.4	26.2	26.0
1.4300	25.8	25.7	25.5	25.3	25.2	25.0	25.0	24.8	24.7	24.4
10	24.3	24.1	24.0	23.9	23.8	23.6	23.5	23.4	23.3	23.1
20	23.0	22.9	22.8	22.7	22.6	22.4	22.3	22.2	22.1	22.0
30	21.9	21.8	21.7	21.6	21.5	21.5	21.4	21.3	21.2	21.1
40	21.0	20.9	20.9	20.8	20.7	20.6	20.6	20.5	20.4	20.4
50	20.3	20.2	20.1	20.1	20.0	19.9	19.9	19.8	19.8	19.7
60	19.6	19.6	19.5	19.4	19.4	19.3	19.3	19.2	19.1	19.1
70	19.0	18.9	18.9	18.9	18.8	18.8	18.7	18.7	18.6	18.6
80	18.5	18.5	18.5	18.4	18.4	18.3	18.3	18.2	18.2	18.1
90	18.1	18.0	18.0	18.0	17.9	17.9	17.8	17.8	17.8	17.7
1.4400	17.7	17.6	17.6	17.6	17.5	17.5	17.4	17.4	17.4	17.3
10	17.3	17.2	17.2	17.2	17.1	17.1	17.0	17.0	17.0	16.9
20	16.9	16.9	16.8	16.8	16.8	16.7	16.7	16.7	16.6	16.6
30	16.6	16.5	16.5	16.5	16.4	16.4	16.4	16.3	16.3	16.3
40	16.2	16.2	16.2	16.1	16.1	16.1	16.0	16.0	16.0	16.0
50	15.9	15.9	15.9	15.8	15.8	15.8	15.8	15.7	15.7	15.7
60	15.6	15.6	15.6	15.6	15.5	15.5	15.5	15.4	15.4	15.4
70	15.3	15.3	15.3	15.3	15.2	15.2	15.2	15.1	15.1	15.1
80	15.1	15.0	15.0	15.0	15.0	14.9	14.9	14.9	14.9	14.8
90	14.8	14.8	14.8	14.7	14.7	14.7	14.7	14.6	14.6	14.6
1.4500	14.6	14.5	14.5	14.5	14.5	14.4	14.4	14.4	14.4	14.3
10	14.3	14.3	14.3	14.2	14.2	14.2	14.2	14.1	14.1	14.1
20	14.1	14.0	14.0	14.0	14.0	13.9	13.9	13.9	13.9	13.9
30	13.8	13.8	13.8	13.8	13.7	13.7	13.7	13.7	13.7	13.6
40	13.6	13.6	13.6	13.6	13.5	13.5	13.5	13.5	13.4	13.4
50	13.4	13.4	13.4	13.3	13.3	13.3	13.3	13.2	13.2	13.2
60	13.2	13.2	13.1	13.1	13.1	13.1	13.0	13.0	13.0	13.0
70	13.0	12.9	12.9	12.9	12.9	12.9	12.8	12.8	12.8	12.8
80	12.8	12.8	12.7	12.7	12.7	12.7	12.7	12.6	12.6	12.6
90	12.6	12.6	12.6	12.5	12.5	12.5	12.5	12.5	12.5	12.4

(continued)

TABLE V (*continued*)

n_{20}	00	01	02	03	04	05	06	07	08	09
1.4600	12.4	12.4	12.4	12.4	12.3	12.3	12.3	12.3	12.3	12.3
10	12.2	12.2	12.2	12.2	12.2	12.1	12.1	12.1	12.1	12.1
20	12.1	12.0	12.0	12.0	12.0	12.0	12.0	11.9	11.9	11.9
30	11.9	11.9	11.9	11.8	11.8	11.8	11.8	11.8	11.8	11.7
40	11.7	11.7	11.7	11.7	11.7	11.6	11.6	11.6	11.6	11.6
50	11.6	11.5	11.5	11.5	11.5	11.5	11.5	11.4	11.4	11.4
60	11.4	11.4	11.4	11.3	11.3	11.3	11.3	11.3	11.3	11.2
70	11.2	11.2	11.2	11.2	11.2	11.1	11.1	11.1	11.1	11.1
80	11.1	11.0	11.0	11.0	11.0	11.0	10.9	10.9	10.9	10.9
90	10.9	10.9	10.9	10.8	10.8	10.8	10.8	10.8	10.8	10.7
1.4700	10.7	10.7	10.7	10.7	10.7	10.7	10.6	10.6	10.6	10.6
10	10.6	10.6	10.5	10.5	10.5	10.5	10.5	10.5	10.4	10 4
20	10.4	10.4	10.4	10.4	10.3	10.3	10.3	10.3	10.3	10.3
30	10.3	10.2	10.2	10.2	10.2	10.2	10.2	10.1	10.1	10.1
40	10.1	10.1	10.1	10.0	10.0	10.0	10.0	10.0	10.0	9.9
50	9.9	9.9	9.9	9.9	9.9	9.8	9.8	9.8	9.8	9.8
60	9.7	9.7	9.7	9.7	9.7	9.7	9.6	9.6	9.6	9.6
70	9.6	9.5	9.5	9.5	9.5	9.5	9.5	9.4	9.4	9.4
80	9.4	9.4	9.3	9.3	9.3	9.3	9.3	9.3	9.2	9.2
90	9.2	9.2	9.2	9.1	9.1	9.1	9.1	9.1	9.1	9.0
1.4800	9.0	9.0	9.0	9.0	8.9	8.9	8.9	8.9	8.8	8.8
10	8.8	8.8	8.7	8.7	8.7	8.7	8.6	8.6	8.6	8.6
20	8.5	8.5	8.5	8.5	8.4	8.4	8.4	8.4	8.3	8.3
30	8.3	8.3	8.2	8.2	8.2	8.2	8.1	8.1	8.1	8.1
40	8.0	8.0	8.0	8.0	8.0	7.9	7.9	7.9	7.9	7.8
50	7.8	7.8	7.8	7.7	7.7	7.7	7.7	7.6	7.6	7.6
60	7.6	7.5	7.5	7.5	7.5	7.4	7.4	7.4	7.4	7.3
70	7.3	7.3	7.3	7.2	7.2	7.2	7.2	7.1	7.1	7.1
80	7.1	7.0	7.0	7.0	6.9	6.9	6.8	6.8	6.8	6.7
90	6.7	6.6	6.6	6.6	6.5	6.5	6.4	6.4	6.4	6.3
1.4900	6.3	6.2	6.2	6.2	6.1	6.1	6.0	6.0	5.9	5.9
10	5.8	5.8	5.7	5.7	5.6	5.6	5.5	5.5	5.4	5.4
20	5.3	5.3	5.2	5.2	5.1	5.1	5.0	4.9	4.8	4.8
30	4.7	4.6	4.5	4.4	4.3	4.3	4.2	4.1	4.0	3.9
40	3.8	3.7	3.6	3.4	3.3	3.2	3.1	3.0	2.8	2.7
50	2.5	2.3	2.2	2.0	1.8	1.6	1.4	1.2	1.0	0.5
60	0.0									

TABLE V (*continued*)

$$n + 1 = [48.07 + 0.13(t - 100)] \log \left[\left(\frac{x}{x'} \right)_{\text{head}} \Big/ \left(\frac{x}{x'} \right)_{\text{pot}} \right]$$

(over the range 97–101.5°C.) where n is the number of plates, t is the mean temperature in °C., and x and x' are the mole fractions in the liquid phase of the more volatile and less volatile components, respectively. The preparation of the material for this test mixture is also described by Rossini and coworkers in another publication.[95] The equations given are not applicable unless the test liquids are purified to the degree specified, and in particular the refractive indices must differ by the same 0.0316 units that are involved in the derivation of the equations.

The second mixture is 2,3,4-trimethylpentane (normal b.p. 113.467°C.) and 2,3,3-trimethylpentane (normal b.p. 114.760°C.). The number of theoretical plates–mole fraction relation is

$$n + 1 = [64.95 - 0.36(t - 114)] \log \left[\left(\frac{x}{x'}\right)_{\text{head}} \Big/ \left(\frac{x}{x'}\right)_{\text{pot}} \right]$$

(over the range 111.5–115°C.), where x and x' are the mole fractions in the liquid phase of the 2,3,4- and 2,3,3-isomers, respectively. Analysis must be by infrared spectrometer, and samples are prepared by efficient distillation of commercial mixtures of branched-chain paraffins.

Another appropriate test mixture for columns with more than a hundred plates is *n*-heptane and 2,2,4-trimethylpentane (isooctane). Nerheim and Dinerstein[96] used a mixture containing 12 mole-% *n*-heptane, with $\alpha = 1.023$ as the relative volatility at atmospheric pressure, based on the data of Smith[97] as confirmed by Griswold.[98]

A mixture of 1% thiophene in benzene has been found useful in testing large equipment, and such a mixture also has advantages for ordinary tests.[99,100] The colorimetric method of analysis used by these authors is a disadvantage. The value of $\log \alpha = 0.04313$ and the details of the method of analysis are given by French.[101] Such a dilute solution in which the component in low concentration is the less volatile component has shorter equilibrium times, and errors due to losses at the still head are minimized. High accuracy in the analysis is not essential if the dilute component is determined directly. Relative volatility is very nearly constant over the concentration range involved, even though the mixture is not ideal.

Test Mixtures for Columns at Low Pressures

The *n*-heptane–methylcyclohexane mixture described in Table I and its following paragraphs is also used for testing columns at pressures down to 300 mm.,[96,102] the relative volatilities being

1.068	at 600 mm.
1.062	500
1.055	400
1.050	300

TABLE VI
Data for Ethylbenzene–Chlorobenzene Test Mixtures at Various Pressures
(All Compositions in Mole Fractions Chlorobenzene)

Liquid		Vapor		
n_D^{25}	Mole fraction	n_D^{25}	Mole fraction	Relative volatility
Total pressure of system, 760 mm.				
1.4933	0.000	1.4933	0.000	—
1.4978	0.176	1.4982	0.191	1.106
1.5032	0.378	1.5038	0.399	1.094
1.5080	0.550	1.5087	0.574	1.101
1.5135	0.736	1.5141	0.756	1.111
1.5182	0.895	1.5189	0.904	1.105
1.5215	1.000	1.5215	1.000	—
Total pressure of system, 300 mm.				
1.5020	0.333	1.5027	0.359	1.12
1.5065	0.497	1.5073	0.525	1.11
1.5161	0.824	1.5166	0.840	1.12
Total pressure of system, 20 mm.				
1.4960	0.107	1.4963	0.118	1.117
1.4971	0.150	1.4975	0.165	1.121
1.4987	0.210	1.4991	0.226	1.100
1.5027	0.359	1.5035	0.388	1.130
1.5070	0.514	1.5078	0.543	1.118
1.5090	0.584	1.5098	0.611	1.119
1.5132	0.726	1.5139	0.749	1.125
1.5177	0.877	1.5180	0.888	1.102
1.5190	0.921	1.5193	0.930	1.135

Hawkins and Brent[102] recommend also the mixture ethylbenzene–chlorobenzene for determinations below atmospheric pressure. Table VI gives a condensation of their data.

The mixture *n*-decane–*trans*-decahydronaphthalene (*trans*-Decalin) has been used for determinations below atmospheric pressure for columns of 20–50 theoretical plates.[103,104] The relative volatility values are:

1.30 at	760 mm.
1.28	400
1.25	200
1.22	100
1.19	50
1.14	20
1.11	10

The references given above include discussions of various other mixtures that have been suggested.

For pressures at or below 1 mm. mercury di-*n*-butyl phthalate–di-*n*-butyl azelate[105] and di-2-ethylhexyl phthalate–di-2-ethylhexyl sebacate[106] are used.

TABLE VII

Variation of H.E.T.P. with Different Binary Mixtures

Mixtures	H.E.T.P., in.[107]
Benzene–toluene	10
Acetic acid–water	10
Nitric acid–water	8
Acetone–ethyl alcohol	8
Ethyl alcohol–water	4
Methyl alcohol–water	3
	Beta[108]
Methylcyclohexane–2,2,4-trimethylpentane	0.98
Methanol–acetone	1.00
Methylcyclohexane–*n*-heptane	1.07
Acetic acid–ethyl acetate	1.00
Benzene–ethylene dichloride	1.18
Heptane–benzene	0.76
Butyl acetate–acetic acid	0.80
Acetic acid–water	0.52

Beta = theoretical stages per foot of test mixture/theoretical stages per foot for benzene–carbon tetrachloride.

III. DISTILLATION CURVES IN BATCH DISTILLATION

In Section II the separation achieved in a distillation process was expressed by still-product composition curves. Such curves can be used for relating still and product compositions, relative volatility, number of theoretical plates, and reflux ratio. They are applicable to continuous distillation if certain simplifying assumptions are valid. Their usefulness in batch distillation is limited because the change of composition with time distorts the steady-state relations, unless holdup is comparatively small.

The results of a batch distillation may be most clearly and concisely presented by a curve plotting the quantity of distillate (or the per cent of charge distilled) versus its composition. If desired, the curve for distillate quantity versus still composition may also be included on the same graph and in some cases it is desirable also to include curves for the composition at various points in the column. Such batch-distillation or *collection curves* show the purity of the product at all times during the distillation, and from them the average composition of any fraction of the distillate may be obtained. The sharpness of the breaks and the flatness of the plateaus in the distillation curve are a measure of the effectiveness of the operation. Such curves can also take into consideration the factors of holdup and initial composition.

Boiling-point curves are of this general nature, and have long been used experimentally to follow the progress of a distillation. Refractive index and density are often a more satisfactory means of measuring distillate composition, because boiling points are often inaccurate when obtained directly from the thermometer at the head of a column.

The literature and tradition of batch distillation include much qualitative information regarding the effect of reflux ratio, relative volatility, number of plates, and other process variables on the shape of the distillation curve. There are still only limited direct quantitative data on these relations. In the present section equations are derived and methods described for calculating distillation curves with whatever values of the reflux ratio, number of plates, etc., are of interest. A series of curves may then be worked out to estimate the effect of changes in the process variables. Numerous specific examples of the results of such calculation are given in Sec. IV. The equations and calculations vary in complexity according to the simplifying assumptions used in the derivations. The simplest case is the graphic procedure for *simple* distillation. This assumes only that there is no holdup and that the vapor–liquid equilibrium curve gives the true relation between still and product composition. The algebraic solution for the Rayleigh simple distillation equations includes the additional assumption that the relative volatility equation correctly expresses vapor–liquid equilibrium compositions. The most convenient methods for calculating curves for *fractional* distillation in a column use the Rayleigh procedure but assume that holdup is negligible, the column is adiabatic, heats of mixing are negligible, the thermal properties of the components are similar, and that therefore the procedure of Lewis (p. 37) is applicable in batch as well as continuous distillation, in spite of the gradual change in composition at all points in a batch column (the time effect). These simplifying assumptions can be avoided by use of more complicated calculations. All the methods are illustrated in the following pages. The equations and methods of calculation are considered in approximate historical order, which is also the order of increasing complexity.

1. Curves for Simple Batch Distillation

Equations for the curves relating distillate composition to amount of distillate in simple distillation were first derived by Brown,[109] and improved upon by Young.[110] These included systems of two or more components and apparently dealt only with those mixtures having low relative volatilities. Later Rayleigh[111] derived the general equation for simple distillation, and applied it to the special case of very dilute solutions. At a much later date it was pointed out[112] that the same equations apply to fractional distillation with a column, if holdup is negligible. If the holdup is appreciable, the same reasoning can be extended to derive analogous equations and curves, but complicating factors enter the situation.[113]

A. BASIC RAYLEIGH EQUATION

The fundamental material-balance procedure of Rayleigh is illustrated by the derivations and calculations for the simple distillation of a binary mixture. Consider any instant during the distillation when the mole fraction of the more volatile component in the still is x_s and there are S total moles of material remaining in the still. At this instant assume that the vapor in equilibrium with the mixture in the still will have composition $y = x_D$, and in a perfect simple distillation will give distillate of this same composition. After a very small amount of this distillate (dS moles) is collected, the total moles remaining in the still will be $S - dS$, and the composition in the still will have changed slightly to $x_s - dx_s$. It follows that

$$Sx_s = (S - dS)(x_s - dx_s) + x_D dS \tag{29}$$

or, in words, in terms of the more volatile component:

Moles in still before removal of small quantity of distillate	must equal	Moles in still after removal of small quantity of distillate	plus	Moles in small quantity of distillate

The above equation may be multiplied out and simplified, dropping out the negligible second-order differential $dSdx_s$. After rearranging terms, this becomes

$$Sdx_s = dS(x_D - x_s) \tag{30}$$

or

$$dS/S = dx_s/(x_D - x_s) \tag{31}$$

On integration,

$$\ln S = \int \frac{dx_s}{x_D - x_s} \tag{32}$$

This is the basic form of the Rayleigh equation. In this form, graphic integration is necessary to obtain the numerical values needed to plot a particular distillation curve. An example of such a procedure is given on p. 77.

B. ALGEBRAIC SOLUTION OF RAYLEIGH EQUATION

If x_D and x_s are related by the relative-volatility equation, then,

$$x_s = \frac{x_D}{\alpha - x_D(\alpha - 1)}, \text{ and } x_D - x_s = x_D \left[1 - \frac{1}{\alpha - x_D(\alpha - 1)}\right] \quad (33)$$

and

$$dx_s = \alpha dx_D/[\alpha - x_D(\alpha - 1)]^2 \quad (34)$$

so that

$$\ln S = \int \frac{\alpha dx_D}{[\alpha - x_D(\alpha - 1)]x_D(1 - x_D)(\alpha - 1)} \quad (35)$$

This may be integrated to give

$$\log S = \frac{1}{\alpha - 1}\{\log x_D - \alpha \log (1 - x_D) + (\alpha - 1) \log [\alpha - x_D(\alpha - 1)]\} + \text{Integration const.} \quad (36)$$

or

$$S = k(x_D)^{1/(\alpha-1)}[\alpha - x_D(\alpha - 1)]/(1 - x_D)^{\alpha/(\alpha-1)} \quad (37)$$

Since x_D represents the mole fraction of the more volatile component in the distillate and S represents total moles remaining in the still, the above equations represent the theoretical shape of the batch-distillation curve. If it is desired to plot quantity of distillate, this may be found by the relation

$$D = S_c - S \quad (38)$$

where D is the moles of distillate and S_c the moles of charge.

It is also possible to eliminate x_D instead of x_s from the basic equation and obtain

$$\log S = \frac{1}{\alpha - 1}[\log x_s - \alpha \log (1 - x_s)] + \text{Integration constant} \quad (39)$$

This relates *still* composition to total moles remaining in the still.

The actual use of such equations may be illustrated by calculating the curve for the simple distillation of 100 moles of an equimolar binary mixture with constant relative volatility, $\alpha = 1.25$. It is first necessary to find the value of the integration constant by substituting the initial conditions of the distillation in the equation for log S. The equation for S could be used and would give the same end result, but the computations are more difficult. Any number of moles of starting material may be considered, but for convenience in this example 100 moles are used. Thus $\log S = 2$. Since the initial still composition of the equimolar mixture is $x_s = 0.5$, the composition of the first portion of the distillate is

$$x_D = \frac{\alpha x_s}{1 + x_s(\alpha - 1)} = \frac{(1.25)(0.5)}{1 + (0.5)(1.25 - 1)} = 0.555$$

Using these values of $\log S$ and x_D in eq. (36), the integration constant is 1.2149. This constant is used in all subsequent calculations for this example, so that the equation to be used for finding values of x_D and S during the distillation is

$$\log S = \frac{1}{0.25}\{\log x_D - (1.25)\log(1 - x_D) + (0.25)\log[1.25 - x_D(0.25)]\} + 1.2149$$

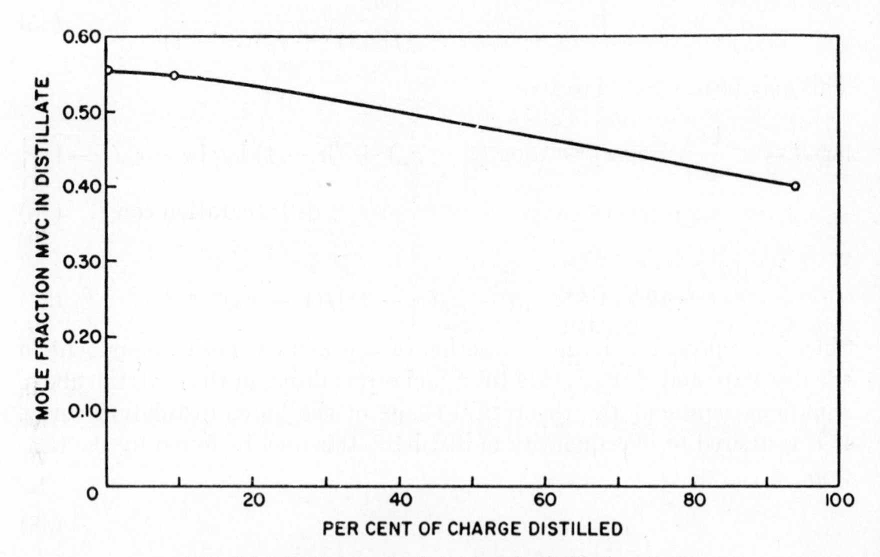

Fig. 27. Points on calculated batch-distillation curve.

Thus if $x_D = 0.550$ (rather than the initial value 0.555), $S = 90.5$, which represents a point on the distillation curve for this instance. Repetition of the calculation for $x_D = 0.40$ gives $S = 6.21$, and it becomes possible to sketch a rough outline of the distillation curve (Fig. 27). It is clear that little separation will be achieved and there is no use in calculating further points in this case.

The values of x_D used in calculations such as the above are chosen at random from the range of possible values. Thus in the above case, no value of x_D can be greater than the initial value of 0.555, because the concentration of the more volatile component in the distillate necessarily *decreases* as the distillation proceeds. The first random choice of x_D should always be somewhat less than the value of x_D corresponding to initial still composition.

It is often less work to use eq. (39) to calculate distillation curves. The calculation for the initial point on the above curve ($x_s = 0.5$) gives 1.6990 as the integration constant. From the vapor–liquid equilibrium relation, when $x_D = 0.55$, x_s will be 0.495. Substituting this last value of x_s and 1.6990 as the integration constant in eq. (39) above gives $S = 90.5$, a value that is identical with that obtained above. The smaller number of terms in this equation makes it simpler to use, particularly when corresponding values of x_s and x_D may be read from a vapor–liquid equilibrium curve.

There are situations such that the relation between distillate composition x_D and still composition x_s is satisfactorily represented by relations other than eq. (33). When the relationship is applicable over the concentration range involved, a derivation similar to that just given will yield other variations of the integrated form of the Rayleigh equation. Thus if

$$x_D = kx_s$$

should happen to be applicable, then

$$\ln S = \frac{1}{k - 1} \ln x_s$$

Johnson, Huang, and Talbot derived useful approximate relations of this type.[114] Various other special equations have been derived.[115]

C. SOLUTIONS OF RAYLEIGH EQUATION BY GRAPHIC INTEGRATION

If the relative-volatility equation does not correctly indicate the relation between x_s and x_D, eqs. (36) and (39) can no longer be used as illustrated above. On the other hand, the fundamental eq. (32) can be used whether or not the relative-volatility relation is valid. In order to make the calculations in such a case, the equation must be expressed with definite limits and signs, and with logarithms to the base 10. The result is

$$\log S_t = \log S_c - \frac{1}{2.303} \int_{x_{st}}^{x_{sc}} \frac{dx_s}{x_D - x_s} \tag{40}$$

Here S_c represents the total moles initially present, x_{sc} the corresponding mole fraction of the more volatile component, and S_t and x_{st} the moles and composition at a particular time during the distillation.

For purposes of illustration the calculations will be repeated, using eq. (40) for the example of Figure 27. The problem was to obtain the curve for the simple distillation of 100 moles of an equimolar binary mixture with α constant and equal to 1.25. In this case $S_c = 100$ and $x_{sc} = 0.5$. Values of x_D and x_s are obtained by solution of the equation

$$\frac{x_D}{1 - x_D} = \alpha \frac{x_s}{1 - x_s} \tag{41}$$

These give the values in the first two columns of Table VIII.

TABLE VIII
Points on Distillation Curve from Rayleigh Equation

x_D	x_{st}	$x_D - x_s$	$1/(x_D - x_s)$	Areas
0.555	0.500	0.055	18.19	
0.550	0.495	0.055	18.19	0.09095
				(x_D = 0.555 to 0.550)
0.500	0.445	0.055	18.19	
0.450	0.395	0.055	18.19	
0.400	0.347	0.053	18.85	2.80
				(x_D = 0.555 to 0.40)

In order to find the value of

$$\int_{x_{st}}^{x_{sc}} dx_s/(x_D - x_s)$$

it is necessary to plot $1/(x_D - x_s)$ versus x_s and determine the areas under the resulting curve and between x_{sc} and x_{st}. Table VIII and Fig. 28 show the values obtained for the desired integral expression over the range of values of x_D (0.555 to 0.40) used in the earlier calculations for eqs. (36) and (39). For the value of S when $x_D = 0.55$,

$$\log S_1 = 2 - (0.09095/2.303) = 1.9605$$

$$S_1 = 91.3$$

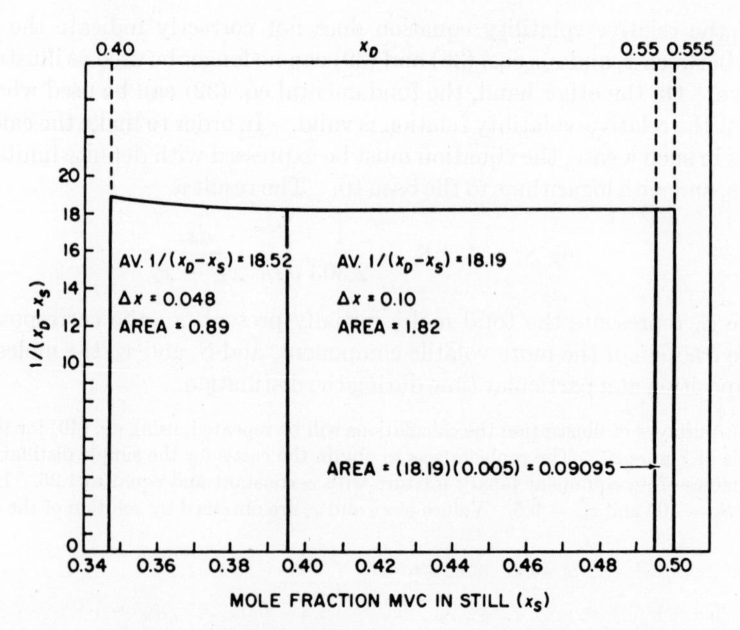

Fig. 28. Graphic integration of $\int[dx_s/(x_D - x_s)]$. Simple distillation.

For the value of S when $x_D = 0.40$,

$$\log S_2 = 2 - (2.80/2.303) = 0.7842$$

$$S_2 = 6.09$$

The use of eq. (40) with values of x_s and x_D from an experimental vapor–liquid equilibrium curve does not depend upon any simplifying assumptions except that there is no appreciable holdup or fractionation between still and receiver, so that still–product composition relations are those of the vapor–liquid equilibrium curve. Although there is undoubtedly some slight holdup on the upper walls of the still and in the condenser during ordinary simple distillation, and slight fractionation may occur, these effects are probably small. Such calculations have been regularly made in connection with the design and operation of simple distillation apparatus.[116] Nomographs have been worked out for the solution of the Rayleigh equation.[117]

2. Curves for Fractional Batch Distillation When Holdup Is Assumed to Be Negligible

A. RAYLEIGH FORM OF EQUATION

The derivation of the equation for the distillation curve for this case is almost identical with that for simple distillation. Consider any instant during the distillation when the mole fraction of the more volatile com-

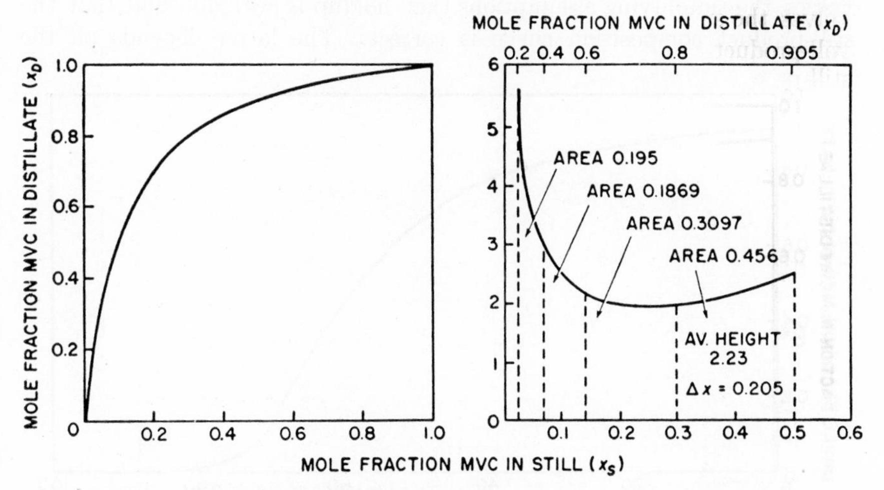

Fig. 29 (left). Still-product composition curve. $\alpha = 1.25$, $n = 10$. Total reflux.

Fig. 30 (right). Graphic integration of $\int[dx_s/(x_D - x_s)]$. Fractional distillation. Ordinate, $1/(x_D - x_s)$.

TABLE IX
Points on Distillation Curve from Rayleigh Equation

x_D	x_{st}	$x_D - x_s$	$1/(x_D - x_s)$	Areas
0.905	0.500	0.405	2.466	
				0.456
0.800	0.295	0.505	1.98	
				0.310
0.600	0.140	0.460	2.174	
				0.187
0.400	0.068	0.332	3.015	
				0.195
0.200	0.023	0.177	5.65	

ponent in the still is x_s and there are S total moles of material in the still. At this instant, assume that the distillate composition is x_D. After dS mole of distillate passes off, the total moles remaining in the still will be $S - dS$, and the composition in the still will be $x_s - dx_s$. As before, eq. (29) is obtained, which on solution and integration gives the fundamental equation (32). This may be expressed in the form suitable for calculation [eq. (40)] and evaluated graphically by use of still–product composition curves (x_s, x_D curves) such as Figures 16–18, 20, and 21. The method is essentially the same as that given above and may be illustrated by calculation of the curve for fractional distillation in the case when $S_c = 100$, $x_{sc} = 0.5$, and the still–product relations are those given in Figure 29. The details of the calculation are given in Table IX and Figure 30. The resulting distillation curve is plotted in Figure 31.

As with the graphic procedure for simple distillation, this method involves the simplifying assumptions that holdup is negligible and that the still-product composition curve is correct. The latter depends on the

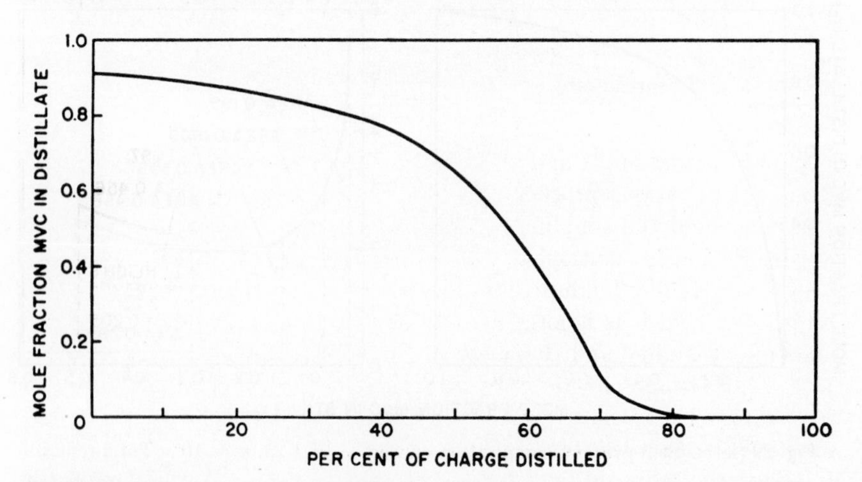

Fig. 31. Distillation curve calculated for $S_c = 100$ and $x_{sc} = 0.5$. Still-product composition as in Figure 29.

validity of the methods given in Section II for calculating distillate composition from still composition (or vice versa) in terms of reflux ratio, number of plates, and vapor–liquid equilibrium data. Experiments with benzene–toluene and benzene–ethylene dichloride mixtures gave good agreement (Fig. 32) between the experimental batch-distillation curves and those calculated by the above graphic method. Since the validity of the methods of calculating distillate compositions from still composition has been well tested in the design and operation of continuous columns, such agreement is not surprising when holdup is but a few per cent of the charge. The important results from calculations of batch-distillation curves of the preceding types are their approximate predictions of behavior

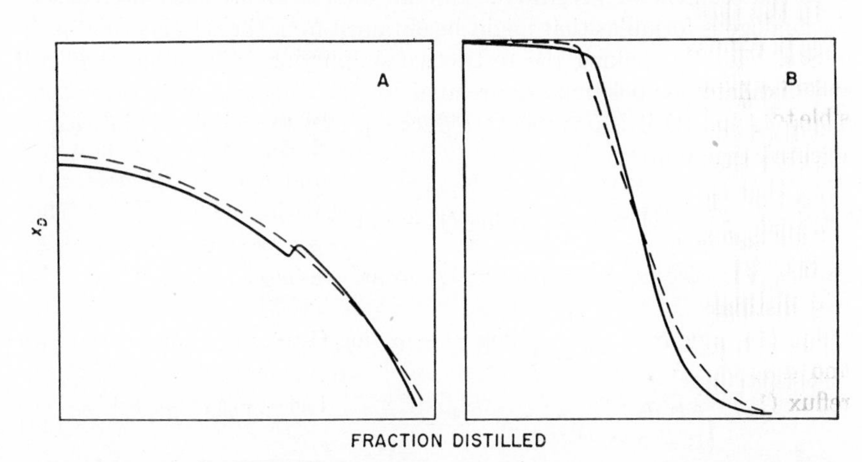

Fig. 32. Calculated (– – –) and experimental (——) curves for batch fractional distillation of benzene–ethylene chloride (A) and benzene–toluene (B).[118a]

in actual distillation,[118] and their general information as to the probable effect of the various process variables.[119] Complete agreement between experiment and the simplified theory cannot be expected for the various reasons previously mentioned. These may be summarized as follows:

(*1*) Even at low holdup there is some effect of the gradual change of composition which is ignored by the simplified theory. (*2*) There is an inherent variability and difficulty in controlling batch-distillation operations. (*3*) The simplified theory assumes finite reflux conditions from the very start, whereas most actual laboratory batch distillations are at total reflux just before the first portion of distillate is withdrawn. (*4*) The simplified theory neglects the effect of reflux ratio on H.E.T.P., and also the similar effect of composition (slope of equilibrium curve). (*5*) The usual simplifying assumptions are always a possible source of discrepancies.

Other types of batch distillation equations can be developed on the basis of empirical or semi-empirical statements for the relation between distillate and still pot compositions, but these have been of limited use.[120]

B. ALGEBRAIC FORMS BASED ON ASSUMPTION OF TOTAL REFLUX

In the theoretical analysis of fractional batch distillation, it is not possible to reduce eq. (32) to a completely integrated algebraic expression as was done for simple distillation. This is due to the fact that the equations relating x_D and x_s at partial reflux, such as the Smoker equation, are so complicated that their use to eliminate x_s from the equation leads to expressions that cannot be integrated. Similar difficulties are encountered with the analogous formulas that might be obtained from the relations discussed in Sec. VI. By making the restrictive simplifying assumption that still and distillate compositions are related by the Fenske equation for total reflux (14, p. 31) it is possible to reduce eq. (32) to completely integrated algebraic equations:

$$\log S = \frac{1}{\alpha^n - 1} \{\log x_D - \alpha^n \log (1 - x_D) + (\alpha^n - 1) \log [\alpha^n - x_D(\alpha^n - 1)]\} + k_D \quad (42)$$

$$\log S = \frac{1}{\alpha^n - 1} [\log x_s - \alpha^n \log (1 - x_s)] + k_s \quad (43)$$

$$S = \frac{k'_s x_s{}^{1/(\alpha^n - 1)}}{(1 - x_s)^{\alpha^n/(\alpha^n - 1)}} = \frac{k'_D x_D{}^{1/(\alpha^n - 1)} [\alpha^n - x_D(\alpha^n - 1)]}{(1 - x_D)^{\alpha^n/(\alpha^n - 1)}} \quad (44)$$

where k_D and k_s are integration constants. The method of deriving these, and also their use for calculating actual curves, are analogous to the corresponding case for simple distillation, since the Fenske equation and the relative-volatility equation are similar in form.

Typical curves represented by the above equations are given in Figure 33. These have been calculated for the fractional distillation of 100 moles of an equimolar mixture under circumstances in which x_D and x_s are related by the Fenske equation with α^n equal to 1.25 and 9.313. The shape of the break in a curve is entirely dependent on the value of α^n and not on particular values of α and n themselves. Thus curve B of Figure 33 is obtained for any values of α and n such that α^n is 9.313. Such combinations as $\alpha = 1.25$ and $n = 10$, $\alpha = 1.28$ and $n = 9$, $\alpha = 1.32$ and $n = 8$, etc., would give the same curve B. It must be strongly emphasized that these relations are based on the simplifying assumptions of negligible holdup and the validity of the Fenske equation. The latter is strictly applicable only under total reflux, and to mixtures in which the variation

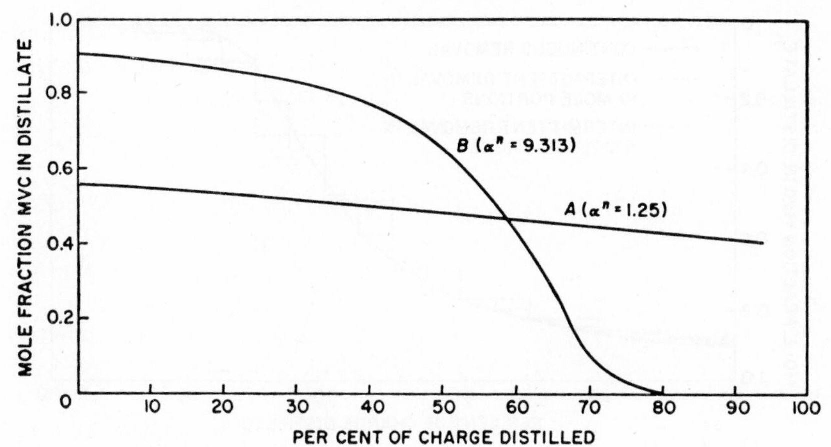

Fig. 33. Distillation curves calculated for $S_c = 100$, $x_{sc} = 0.5$ and (A) $\alpha^n = 1.25$; (B) $\alpha^n = 9.313$.

in relative volatility is not excessive. The curves of Figure 33 and other curves calculated by the equations on which it is based (see p. 149) therefore represent not actual sharpness of separation but only the limiting case of sharpest possible separation, for mixtures in which relative-volatility relations are ideal. This sort of information is useful when a sharp separation is desired, since it leads either to the immediate and definite rejection of the column, or the knowledge that the desired result may be approximated by sufficiently high reflux with the apparatus at hand. The equations and curves are also useful in suggesting the general nature of the relations between relative volatility, maximum sharpness of separation, and minimum number of plates.

The same kind of calculations as those just described may be made by the ratio form of the Rayleigh equation, applicable only when the relative volatility is constant. This equation

$$\log \frac{A_1}{A_2} = \alpha_{AB} \log \frac{B_1}{B_2}$$

is derived on p. 127 as part of the discussion on multicomponent batch distillation. A nomograph has been derived for calculations with the equation.[121] Kuhn[122] has proposed a different method for predicting the course of a distillation when reflux is very large and holdup is negligible.

3. Curves Calculated by Stepwise Method

An approximate batch-distillation curve may also be obtained without use of calculus by employing a stepwise method of calculation.[123] This

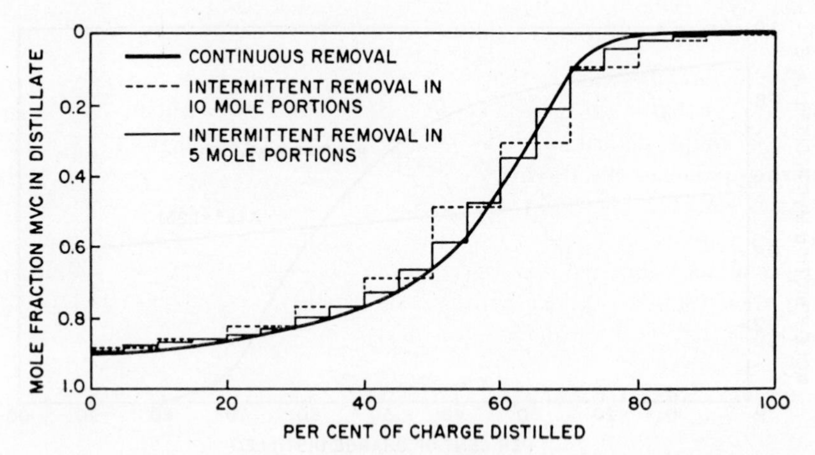

Fig. 34. Calculated batch-distillation curves for continuous and intermittent removal of product.[123]

may be illustrated by carrying out the procedure for fractional distillation of 100 moles of an equimolar mixture with relative volatility, α, constant and equal to 1.25 $n = 10$. These are the same conditions as for the example given on p. 180 and comparison of the methods and resulting curves may be made.

It is assumed at the start that the distillation is to be carried out by allowing distillate to flow through a cup in or just below the condenser, and that the contents of this cup are removed from time to time.[124] If the cup holds 5 moles of material, then at the time of the first removal of distillate, a material balance of the more volatile component gives

$$(100)(0.5) = 95x_1 + 5y_1$$

If the Fenske equation is applicable

$$y_1 = \frac{\alpha^n x_1}{1 + x_1(\alpha^n - 1)}$$

and therefore

$$50 = 95x_1 + 5\,\frac{\alpha^n x_1}{1 + x_1(\alpha^n - 1)}$$

This gives $x_1 = 0.479$ and therefore $y_1 = 0.897$, the latter being the composition of the first portion of distillate removed. This is plotted in Figure 34.

After removal of the first portion of distillate the cup will again fill up, and a second portion of distillate will be removed after the appropriate time interval. A material balance now gives

$$95x_1 = 90x_2 + 5y_2 = 90x_2 + 5\,\frac{\alpha^n x_2}{1 + x_2(\alpha^n - 1)}$$

so that the composition y_2 of the second 5% of distillate may be calculated and plotted. This is repeated step by step to obtain a graph as in Figure 34.

The method is similar to that used in the derivation of the Rayleigh equation, except that in the present case a finite quantity of distillate is removed. If these finite quantities of distillate are made very small, the stepwise curve approaches the Rayleigh curve. The labor of the stepwise calculations is considerable, and errors are cumulative and may become serious after a number of steps. Nevertheless the method is not always at a disadvantage compared with the graphic Rayleigh procedure. Comparative calculations are an excellent way of building up confidence and appreciation of the power of calculus as an analytical tool.

4. Curves Calculated from Minimum Reflux (Infinite Plates) and Henry's Law Equations

When distillation is at finite reflux and with such a large number of plates that the difference between still and distillate composition is independent of the number of plates

$$(x_D - y_s)/(x_D - x_s) = L/V \tag{45}$$

(see p. 43). Colburn and Stearns[125] substituted this relation in eq. (32) and obtained

$$\ln S = \left(1 - \frac{L}{V}\right)\int \frac{dx_s}{y_s - x_s} = \frac{1 - (L/V)}{\alpha - 1}\,[\ln x_s - \alpha \ln (1 - x_s)] + k_I \tag{46}$$

where

$$y_s = \frac{\alpha x_s}{1 + (\alpha - 1)x_s}$$

and k_I is the integration constant. They also derived the corresponding expression for the case of dilute solutions in which $y_s = k_H x_s$ (Henry's law) to obtain

$$\ln S = \frac{1 - L/V}{k_H - 1}\int \frac{dx_s}{x_s} = \frac{1 - L/V}{k_H - 1} \ln x_s + k_I \tag{47}$$

which may be written

$$\frac{S_1}{S_2} = \left(\frac{x_{s1}}{x_{s2}}\right)^{(1 - L/V)/(k_H - 1)} \tag{48}$$

For the case in which Henry's law is applicable but infinite plate conditions are not satisfied:

$$x_D = (k_H)^n x_s \tag{49}$$

and

$$\int \frac{dx_s}{x_D - x_s} = \int \frac{dx_s}{(k_H)^n x_s - x_s} = \frac{1}{(k_H)^n - 1} \int \frac{dx_s}{x_s} = \frac{\ln x_s}{(k_H)^n - 1} \tag{50}$$

or

$$\log S = \frac{\log x_s}{(k_H)^n - 1} + k_I \tag{51}$$

5. Calculation and Determination of Holdup

The preceding derivations and equations have all assumed negligible holdup. The results are of interest in many connections because, in actual distillation, holdup is often so small that it may be neglected. It is however desirable to analyze the batch-distillation process for cases in which holdup must be taken into consideration. The general method of approach is similar to that already discussed, but the basic material-balance equations must be modified to include the quantity of a particular component present in the column as holdup. It is also necessary to know the total holdup.

A. HOLDUP OF MORE VOLATILE COMPONENT[126]

The simplest situation is that in a plate column in which the total holdup per plate, H_i, is the moles of material actually on and over any plate. The holdup in moles of one component h_i, is then given in terms of its mole fraction in the liquid on the plate, x_i:

$$h_i = H_i x_i \tag{52}$$

In many cases the volume of holdup per plate will be constant from plate to plate, and from time to time throughout a batch distillation. The mass of holdup and the total moles of holdup are subject to variations due to density and molecular-weight differences, but it is convenient to ignore these for the present in order to keep this preliminary discussion as simple as possible. On this basis the total moles of the more volatile component of a binary mixture present as holdup in a plate column during a batch distillation would be approximately:

$$h = H_1x_1 + H_2x_2 + H_3x_3 + \ldots H_nx_n = \sum_{i=1}^{i=n} H_i x_i \tag{53}$$

or, if $H_1 = H_2 = H_3, \ldots = H_i$ moles of total holdup per plate:

$$h = H_i \sum_{i=1}^{i=n} x_i \tag{54}$$

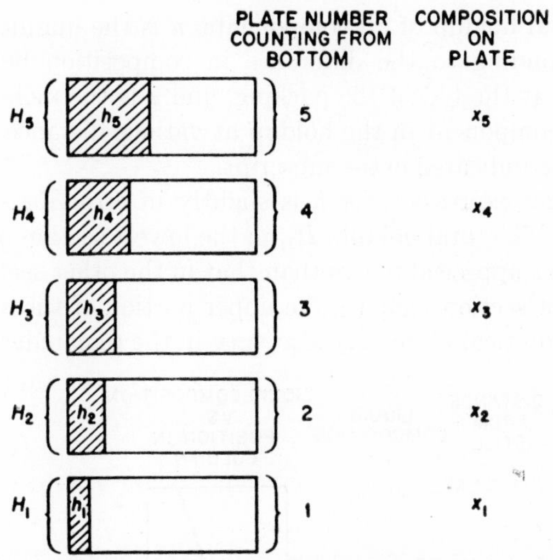

Fig. 35. Holdup of more volatile component in plate column. Total size of block represents total holdup on plate. Shaded portion represents holdup of more volatile component.

If H is the moles of total holdup in the entire column:

$$H_i = H/n \qquad \text{and} \qquad h = \frac{H}{n} \sum_{i=1}^{i=n} x_i \tag{54a}$$

This reasoning is given in diagrammatic form in Figure 35. The compositions of the liquid on the several plates (x_1, x_2, x_3, etc.) will change as the batch distillation progresses, so that the actual values in any case of interest must be obtained by the equations or graphs (p. 56) showing composition from plate to plate.

In the case of a packed column, a somewhat similar situation exists except that the change in composition of the liquid is gradual instead of making sudden jumps from one plate to the next. In this case H_i and h_i refer to the holdup per theoretical plate. The situation is represented graphically in Figure 36, which leads to the approximate equations:

$$h_1 = H_1x_{0.5}, \qquad h_2 = H_2x_{1.5}, \qquad h_3 = H_3x_{2.5}$$

or, in general,

$$h_i = H_ix_{(i-0.5)} \tag{55}$$

where $x_{(i-0.5)}$ signifies the composition one-half theoretical plate below i plates from the still. Then

$$h = \frac{H}{n} \sum_{i=1}^{i=n} x_{(i-0.5)} \tag{56}$$

where H is total holdup of all components, n is the number of theoretical plates corresponding to the difference in composition between the still and the liquid at the top of the packing, and x is the mole fraction of the more volatile component in the holdup at various distances from the base of the column as indicated in the subscript.

The preceding expression for h is slightly in error for several reasons. These are: (*1*) The total holdup, H_1, in the lowest section of the column is probably always appreciably less than that in the other sections higher up, since the lowest section includes the upper portion of the still. The total holdup per theoretical plate may also vary in the remainder of the column.

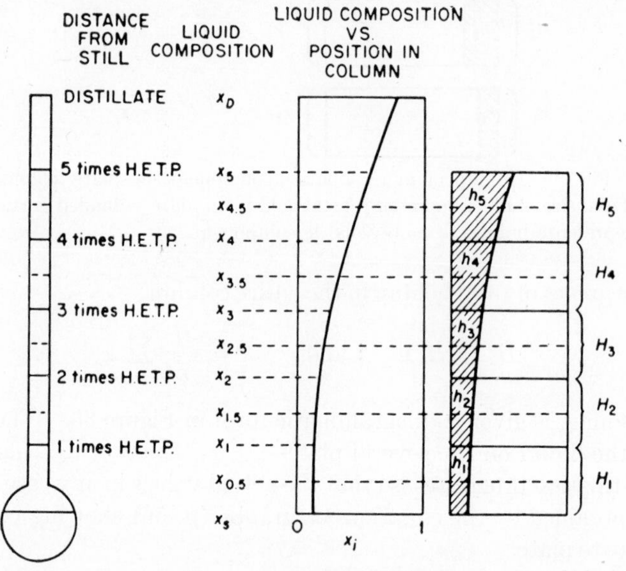

Fig. 36. Holdup of more volatile component in packed column. Total blocks and shading as in Figure 35.

Specific experimental data are required in order to correct these errors. (*2*) The expression assumes that the vapor at any point has the same composition as the liquid. The vapor is a minor proportion of the total holdup, and an expression for it similar to the above may be derived only with considerable increase in complexity. (*3*) The holdup in the condenser is not included. (*4*) The values $x_{(i-0.5)}$ used in the above expression are not the correct average compositions unless the change in composition with distance up the column is a straight-line function. This is generally not true.

The first three of these sources of error are neglected in the subsequent discussion. The fourth is eliminated by deriving an expression in terms of very short units of height. Thus if the sections are made 0.1 of the H.E.-T.P. in height, the expression for h becomes

$$h = h_{0.1} + h_{0.2} + h_{0.3} + \ldots = \sum_{\substack{i=0.1 \\ \text{(by tenths)}}}^{i=n} h_i$$

where H_i and h_i now signify the holdup in 0.1 H.E.T.P. Since

$$h_i = H_i x_{(i-0.05)}$$

$$h = H_{0.1}x_{0.05} + H_{0.2}x_{0.15} + H_{0.3}x_{0.25} + \ldots$$

If, as before, the total holdup is uniformly distributed,

$$H_{0.1} = H_{0.2} = H_{0.3} = (H/n)(1/10)$$

then

$$h = (H/n)(1/10) \sum_{\substack{i=0.1 \\ \text{(by tenths)}}}^{i=n} x_{(i-0.05)}$$

which is nearly equal to

$$(H/n)(1/10) \sum_{\substack{i=0.1 \\ \text{(by tenths)}}}^{i=n} x_i$$

If instead of tenths the sections are made still smaller, the difference between the two forms in the above equation becomes negligible. When the sections are made of a very small height, Δi, where i represents distance up the column in terms of H.E.T.P. units, the last expression becomes

$$h = (H/n)\Delta i \sum_{i=0}^{i=n} x_i = (H/n) \int_{i=0}^{i=n} x_i di \tag{57}$$

In most instances it is necessary to obtain the value of the above expression by graphic means. An algebraic solution is possible in the case of distillation of an ideal binary mixture under total reflux. In such a case the composition x_i of the liquid at any point in the column is related to the still composition by the Fenske equation:

$$\frac{x_i}{1 - x_i} = \alpha^i \frac{x_s}{1 - x_s} \tag{58}$$

or

$$x_i = (\alpha^i x_s)/(1 - x_s + \alpha^i x_s) \tag{58a}$$

If for convenience

$$b = (1 - x_s)/x_s$$

then

$$x_i = \alpha^i/(b + \alpha^i)$$

Equation (57) for the holdup of the more volatile component now becomes

$$h = (H/n)\int_{i=0}^{i=n} \frac{\alpha^i}{b + \alpha^i}\, di = (H/n)\,\frac{\log\,[1 + x_s(\alpha^n - 1)]}{\log \alpha} \qquad (59)$$

or

$$h = (H/n)\log\left(\frac{1 - x_s}{x_s} + \alpha^n\right)\Big/\log \alpha + \text{Integration constant} \qquad (60)$$

The use of both the graphic method and the equations may be illustrated as follows: The graph of Figure 37 represents the composition of the liquid in various parts of a 30-plate column during distillation of a mixture with $\alpha = 1.25$, and at a time when the still composition is $x_s = 0.5$. The values of x_i were calculated by eq. (58a), where i was given the successive values 1, 2, 3, etc., up to 30. By counting squares to the right of the curve in Figure 37, values for the holdup of the more volatile component in that part of the column corresponding to any plate or plates may be determined. For the lowest ten

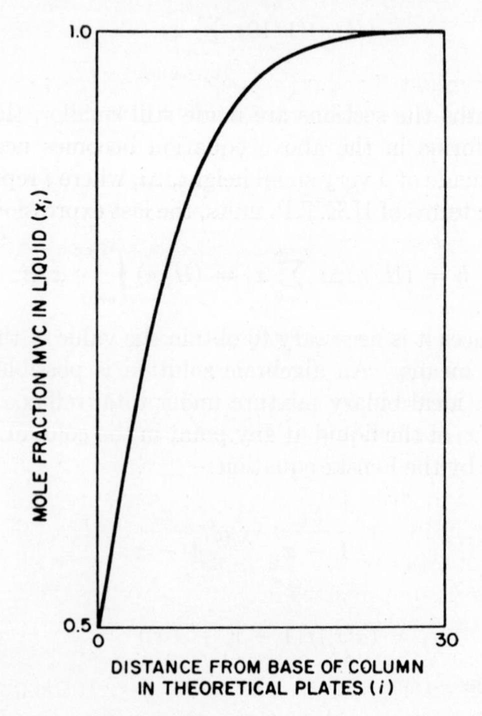

Fig. 37. Composition of liquid holdup at various distances from base of column.

plates the area is 7.348. Thus the holdup of the more volatile component for these ten plates is, from eq. (57), $(H/10)7.348$. If the total holdup for this ten-plate column, H, is 10 moles, $h = 7.348$ moles. If eq. (60) is then solved with the values for the base of the column ($x_s = 0.5$, $n = 0$, $\alpha^n = 1$, and $H/n = 1$), the integration constant is $-\log(1 + 1)/\log 1.25 = -3.11$. When $n = 10$,

$$h = \frac{\log(1 + 1.25^{10})}{\log 1.25} - 3.11 = 7.36 \text{ moles}$$

The graphic information on variation of composition from point to point in a column, as given in Section II, may be used in a similar manner to estimate the holdup of a given component at either total reflux or finite reflux. The algebraic solutions given above are not applicable at finite reflux because of the use of the Fenske equation. By substituting the Smoker equation, it might be possible to derive equations for calculating the holdup of one component at finite reflux. Such equations would be complex and subject to many simplifying assumptions. It is preferable to employ graphic methods for this purpose.

B. TOTAL HOLDUP

Direct Measurement. Factors Influencing Total Holdup. All the preceding discussion has dealt with methods of obtaining the holdup of one component. These methods required the amount of the total holdup as well as the assumption that it was uniformly distributed. *Total holdup* is usually defined as the total liquid on the packing or plates at any time during which the column is operating. The *static holdup* is the liquid remaining in the column after it has been operated and drained, and the *operating holdup* is the difference between the total and static holdups. This approach ignores vapor holdup as negligible and having only a minor effect. In experimental work the various holdups have almost universally been determined and expressed in terms of weight. In theoretical discussions holdup has most frequently been expressed as moles even though the assumption of constancy of moles of holdup during a batch distillation is not often valid, and even though interconversion of weight to moles of holdup adds complications to an already complex relationship. It is probable that constant volume of holdup during batch distillation is a more reasonable assumption than any other simplification. A recently developed computer program for batch distillation uses this approach.[127] However, it appears that for the purpose of experimental determination, the use of weight units is preferable for measuring holdup. Conversion to volume or moles can then be made if advantageous.

Crude measurements of total holdups may be made by several obvious ways that involve collecting the drainage from a column, or the difference between drainage and input of liquid at the top. The best way of measuring total holdup is by direct weighing of the entire column with and without the holdup.[128] The results of such measurements with water and air as the countercurrent materials flowing through various commercial packings showed that there was an initial unsteady state period of several hours or more after normal water flow was started through dry packing. If the operation was started with a very high water rate followed by reduction to the desired rate, the unsteady state period was almost entirely eliminated. There was a half-hour unsteady state period after flow was stopped, before the weight of the column plus static holdup became constant. In all these tests the air flow was continued until after the weighings were made of the static holdup. Packings with rough surfaces showed greater holdup than those with smooth surfaces. The difference is in the static holdup, which is affected by the material of which the packing is made, and by packing shape and size, but is independent of the gas and liquid rates.

At low liquid rates total holdup is almost independent of gas rate up to the flooding point. For higher liquid rates, especially for small packings, and for high gas rates near the point of flooding, the gas rate affects holdup strongly. It is this increase in holdup which causes the more rapid rise in the pressure drop that is usually taken as the beginning of flooding.

The Shulman measurements of operating holdup by direct weighing are not in good agreement with some earlier holdup measurements. This is probably due to differences in materials of construction, methods of packing, and in the drainage times that were allowed. There are also discrepancies because in the earlier work operating holdup was assumed to be independent of gas rate, and because measurements at zero gas rates are not satisfactory.

The Shulman holdup measurement studies provide a good explanation of the beneficial effect of prewetting packings. The wide variations in H.E.-T.P. data in the literature can also be explained as arising from the very long time required for holdup to reach a constant value.

The experiments of Shulman and co-workers[129] also included direct measurements of operating and static holdup for three packings for water solutions of sorbitol, calcium chloride, and a detergent, and for methanol–benzene. The aqueous data were used as the basis for relations to predict holdup for nonaqueous liquids, and the experiments with the latter then served to confirm the predictions. Graphs and empirical equations were used to express the effect of surface tension, viscosity, liquid density, and liquid rate on total holdup. The empirical equations are as follows:

(*1*) Operating holdup for 1.0-in. Raschig rings

For $\mu < 12$ cp.

$$H_o = 0.00039L^{0.57}\mu^{0.13}\left(\frac{1}{\rho}\right)^{0.84}\left(\frac{\sigma}{73}\right)^{0.925\ -\ 0.262 \log L}$$

For $\mu > 12$ cp.

$$H_o = 0.00025L^{0.57}\mu^{0.31}\left(\frac{1}{\rho}\right)^{0.84}\left(\frac{\sigma}{73}\right)^{0.925\ -\ 0.262 \log L}$$

(*2*) Operating holdup for 1.0-in. Berl saddles

For $\mu < 20$ cp.

$$H_o = 0.00043L^{0.57}\mu^{0.13}\left(\frac{1}{\rho}\right)^{0.84}\left(\frac{\sigma}{73}\right)^{1.033\ -\ 0.262 \log L}$$

For $\mu > 20$ cp.

$$H_o = 0.00025L^{0.57}\mu^{0.31}\left(\frac{1}{\rho}\right)^{0.84}\left(\frac{\sigma}{73}\right)^{1.033\ -\ 0.262 \log L}$$

(*3*) Static holdup

$$H_s = c\mu^m\left(\frac{1}{\rho}\right)^{0.37}\sigma^n$$

where c, m, and n have the following values for each packing

Packing	c	m	n
1. 0-in. carbon Raschig rings	0.0185	0.02	0.23
1. 0-in. porcelain Raschig rings	0.00020	0.02	0.99
1. 0-in. Berl saddles	0.00119	0.04	0.55

and L = superficial liquid rate, lb./(hr.)(sq. ft.), μ = liquid viscosity, cp., ρ = liquid density, g./ml., σ = surface tension, dynes/cm.

It was found that any condition that results in foaming causes an increase in holdup.

As stated before, the nature of the packing surface does not influence operating holdup, but static holdup is much larger for a rough surface than for a smooth surface. Although only a limited number of packings were studied, the equations and graphs of the Shulman work can be used to estimate holdup for other packings, by determining water holdup and then multiplying by factors obtained from the equations to correct for the variation in viscosity, surface tension and density. The Shulman results are in general agreement with the earlier measurements of Jesser and Elgin.[130]

Indirect Measurement of Total Holdup. When direct weighing or calculation from related data is not possible, a satisfactory way to determine total holdup is to introduce with the charge a small amount of inert, soluble, nonvolatile material whose concentration can be easily determined.[131] When heat is applied to the charge and the system brought to equilibrium under total reflux, the concentration of the nonvolatile material in the still pot will be increased because some of the volatile material has entered the column as reflux or holdup. The following equations may be set up. The original concentration of the nonvolatile material is

$$w/(C_w + w) = a_1 \quad \text{or} \quad w = a_1(C_w + w) \tag{61}$$

where w is the weight of nonvolatile material introduced into the charge, C_w is the weight of the volatile charge, and a_1 the weight fraction of the nonvolatile material in the charge. The concentration of nonvolatile material after equilibrium is reached at total reflux

$$w/(C_w + w - H_w) = a_2 \quad \text{or} \quad w = a_2(C_w + w - H_w) \tag{62}$$

where a_2 is the concentration of nonvolatile material in the still after equilibrium is reached and H_w the weight of volatile material present as holdup. Since w is the same in both cases:

$$a_1(C_w + w) = a_2(C_w + w - H_w) \tag{63}$$

$$(a_1/a_2)(C_w + w) = (C_w + w) - H_w \tag{64}$$

$$H_w = (C_w + w)\left(1 - \frac{a_1}{a_2}\right) \tag{65}$$

The same type of calculation may be made after a weight, D_w, of distillate is removed, because the new concentration of nonvolatile material in the still is then:

$$w/(C_w + w - H_w - D_w) = a_3 \tag{66}$$

and

$$(C_w + w)(a_1/a_3) = C_w + w - D_w - H_w \tag{67}$$

Thus

$$H_w = (C_w + w)\left(1 - \frac{a_1}{a_3}\right) - D_w \tag{68}$$

By taking samples from the still at intervals during the distillation, the holdup may be followed throughout a distillation. A good choice for an inert, soluble, nonvolatile material for hydrocarbon-distillation studies is stearic acid, which can be easily determined by evaporation of the volatile components or by titration with a base, provided that rust or similar material does not react with part of the stearic acid. A nonvolatile fraction of rosin oil has also been used successfully, analysis in this case being either by means of optical rotation or refractive index. Since the composition of rosin oil varies from batch to batch, it is important that the relation between composition and optical rotation or refractive index be confirmed for each batch.

When optical rotation or refractive index is used for the analysis, it is necessary that the volatile material in the pot consist of a single component, but analysis by titration or evaporation and direct weighing permits the use of a mixture. The latter is the only condition corresponding to actual operation. Whichever procedure is used, a material balance should be made on both the volatile and nonvolatile components, to assure absence of errors from leaks or other losses. Examples of the last are the reaction of stearic acid with rust in an iron pot, and the carbonizing of the nonvolatile material due to overheating a dry section of the still pot.

C. DIRECT DETERMINATION OF HOLDUP OF INDIVIDUAL COMPONENT

This may be determined for a binary mixture by analysis both before and after holdup enters the column, and when nonvolatile additive is absent, but total holdup is known. A material balance of the more volatile component gives

$$C_w x_{wc} = (C_w - H_w)x_{w0} + H_w x_{wh} \tag{69}$$

in which x_{wh} is the average weight fraction of the more volatile component in the holdup. C_w, the weight of the charge, x_{wc}, its composition, and x_{w0}, the composition of the still contents after holdup has entered the column, can be determined experimentally. There are no published applications of this procedure, but it is an excellent tool for checking other calculated values of holdup and the concepts on which they depend. Colburn and Stearns[132] have used a closely related procedure.

6. Curves for Fractional Batch Distillation When Holdup is Appreciable

When holdup is appreciable, the theoretical relations of batch distillation are sufficiently complex so that no simple methods of prediction have been developed. Three different approaches have been used. The first is extension of the Rayleigh equation with inclusion of terms to represent column holdup. The form of the general equation may be obtained as shown later, but numerical solution is very difficult or impossible because there is no method of predicting the still–product composition curves, and a trial and error approach is complex and may not converge to an answer. A second approach involves setting up differential equations for composition of the distillate, still liquid, and liquid on each plate of the column, as functions of the fraction distilled. The algebraic solution of such equations is probably impossible, and even approximate numerical solutions are very laborious. Some progress has been made through use of analog computers. The third approach is by stepwise plate-to-plate calculations. This is also exceedingly laborious, but progress has been made through use of automatic digital computers. Some details of each of these methods are discussed in turn.

A. GENERAL EQUATION BY EXTENSION OF RAYLEIGH EQUATION

The form of a general equation for batch fractional distillation may be derived by extension of the material-balance procedure introduced by Young and by Rayleigh. Since complete experimental data are lacking on the variation of H.E.T.P. values along the length of a column, and also on the distribution of holdup, and in order to take care of all possible variations in these factors, the generalized expression

$$h = f_h(x_s \ldots) \tag{70}$$

can be used to represent the holdup of the more volatile component in the column.[133] This is analogous to eq. (59) used for expressing holdup of the more volatile component in the derivation of eq. (60). Similarly, the relation between product and still composition will also be used in the generalized form

$$x_D = f_n(x_s \ldots) \tag{71}$$

so that the derivation will not be limited by the simplifying assumptions used in calculating distillate and column compositions from still composition. This latter general relation is analogous to the Fenske equation:

$$x_D = \alpha^n x_s/(1 - x_s + \alpha^n x_s) \tag{72}$$

The derivation of the general equation for a batch-fractionation curve involves a material balance just before and after the removal of a very small quantity, $\Delta D = dS$, of distillate, similar to that used in the simpler cases already discussed. This gives

$$Sx_s + f_h(x_s \ldots) + H_c x_D = (x_s - dx_s)(S - dS) + f_h(x_s - dx_s \ldots) + x_D dS + (x_D - dx_D)H_c \tag{73}$$

In this equation Sx_s represents moles of more volatile component present in the still just before removal of the small quantity of distillate, and $(x_s - dx_s)(S - dS)$ represents the moles of the same component just after the removal. The quantities $f_h(x_s. . .)$ represent the moles of the more volatile component present as holdup in the column, while $H_c x_D$ and $H_c(x_D - dx_D)$ are the moles of the more volatile component in the condenser. When terms are transposed and multiplied out, and the second differential $dx_s dS$ is dropped out as being negligible, the equation becomes

$$\frac{f_h(x_s - dx_s. . .) - f_h(x_s. . .)}{dx_s} = x_s \frac{dS}{dx_s} + S - x_D \frac{dS}{dx_s} + H_c \frac{dx_D}{dx_s} \tag{74}$$

The quantity on the left side is by definition equal to $-f'_h(x_s. . .)$ where the prime signifies the derivative of $f_h(x_s. . .)$. Graphically, this is the slope of the curve of eq. (70) at whatever value of x_s is involved in the specific numerical calculations. Also, by definition, the quantity dx_D/dx_s is the derivative of $f_n(x_s. . .)$:

$$dx_D/dx_s = f'_n(x_s. . .) \tag{75}$$

Therefore,

$$x_s(dS/dx_s) + S - x_D(dS/dx_s) + H_c f'_n(x_s. . .) = -f'_h(x_s. . .) \tag{76}$$

and

$$\frac{dS}{dx_s} - \frac{S}{x_D - x_s} = \frac{H_c f'_n(x_s. . .) + f'_h(x_s. . .)}{x_D - x_s} \tag{77}$$

This is a linear differential equation which can be partly solved to give

$$S = k \exp \int \frac{dx_s}{x_D - x_s} + \exp \int \frac{dx_s}{x_D - x_s} \int \frac{[\mathrm{H}_c f'_n(x_s. . .) + f'_h(x_s. . .)]dx_s}{(x_D - x_s) \exp \int dx_s/(x_D - x_s)} \tag{78}$$

The indicated integrations may be performed graphically whenever definite graphs for f'_n and f'_h are available. The equation is essentially a relation of the form

$$S = kf_1(x_D) + f_2(x_D) \tag{79}$$

and is thus the desired relation between product composition and quantity of product distilled, i.e., it represents a distillation curve.

Colburn and Stearns[134] expressed this equation in the form

$$\ln \frac{S_1}{S_2} = \int_{x_{S2}}^{x_{S1}} \frac{dx_s}{x_D - x_s - (Hdx_h/dS)} \tag{80}$$

where Hdx_h/dS is the rate of removal of the more volatile component from the holdup.

The actual use of eq. (78) requires that it be expressed in a form with definite limits, such as[135]

$$S_t = \frac{S_0}{\lambda_{x_{st}}^{x_{s0}}} - \int_{x_{st}}^{x_{s0}} \frac{f_h'(x_s \ldots)dx_s + H_c f_n'(x_s \ldots)dx_s}{(x_D - x_s)\,\lambda_{x_{st}}^{x_s}} \quad (81)$$

in which

$$\lambda_{x_{st}}^{x_{s0}} = \exp \int_{x_{st}}^{x_{s0}} \frac{dx_s}{x_D - x_s} \quad \text{and} \quad \lambda_{x_{st}}^{x_s} = \exp \int_{x_{st}}^{x_s} \frac{dx_s}{x_D - x_s}$$

and x_{s0} is the mole fraction of the more volatile component in the still when product removal is commenced, and x_{st} the mole fraction in the still at time t. By assuming condenser holdup to be negligible so that $H_c = 0$, the equation becomes

$$S_t = \frac{S_0}{\lambda_{x_{st}}^{x_{s0}}} - \int_{x_{st}}^{x_{s0}} \frac{f'_h(x_s \ldots)dx_s}{(x_D - x_s)\lambda_{x_{st}}^{x_s}} \quad (82)$$

In actual calculations with this equation, all the quantities are obtained from the curves of eqs. (70) and (71). Thus the distillation curves calculated with this equation are as correct or as incorrect as the equations for x_D and h. Unfortunately all three of these equations are dependent upon one another, and their form is so complex that combination into a single expression has not been achieved.

The use of the above equations may be illustrated by considering a case for which the Fenske equation may be used to describe the relation between x_D and x_s. This assumption limits applications to systems in which reflux ratios are so large or other circumstances are such that separations approximate those under total reflux. The equation for moles of holdup of the more volatile component then takes the form of eq. (59). This represents the holdup of the more volatile component in the column at every instant during the distillation.

By making a material balance in the same manner as for the preceding cases, and including the terms for holdup,[136] the expression

$$Sx_s + [H/(n \log \alpha)] \log [1 + x_s(\alpha^n - 1)] = (x_s - dx_s)(S - dS) + [H/(n \log \alpha)] \log [1 + (x_s - dx_s)(\alpha^n - 1)] + x_D dS \quad (83)$$

is obtained. This may be solved as follows, using $A = H/(n \log a)$, $b = \alpha^n - 1$, and $q = 1/(\alpha^n - 1) = 1/b$ in order to simplify the writing of the various expressions. The first step is to eliminate x_D by using the Fenske relation, whereupon

$$x_s \frac{dS}{dx_s} + S - \frac{\alpha^n x_s}{1 + bx_s} \cdot \frac{dS}{dx_s} - A \frac{\log [1 + b(x_s - dx_s)] - \log (1 + bx_s)}{dx_s} = 0 \quad (84)$$

Since by the definition of a derivative

$$\frac{\log\,[1 + b(x_s - dx_s)] - \log\,(1 + bx_s)}{dx_s} = \frac{d \log\,(1 + bx_s)}{dx_s} = -\frac{b}{1 + bx_s}$$

then

$$x_s \frac{dS}{dx_s} + S - \frac{\alpha^n x_s}{1 + bx_s} \cdot \frac{dS}{dx_s} + \frac{Ab}{1 + bx_s} = 0 \tag{85}$$

which is a linear differential equation that can be partly solved to give

$$S = K \frac{(x_s)^q}{(1 - x_s)^{q+1}} + \frac{(x_s)^q}{(1 - x_s)^{q+1}} A \int \frac{(1 - x_s)^q}{(x_s)^{q+1}} dx_s \tag{86}$$

The remaining integral may be evaluated as nearly exactly as desired by expanding the numerator by the binomial theorem and then integrating and retaining as many of the terms as is necessary:

$$S = K \frac{(x_s)^q}{(1 - x_s)^{q+1}} + \frac{(x_s)^q}{(1 - x_s)^{q+1}} A \left[-\frac{b}{(x_s)^q} - \frac{1}{b}\left(\frac{1}{1 - q}\right)(x_s)^{1-q} + \frac{1}{2b}\left(\frac{1}{b} \quad 1\right)\left(\frac{1}{2 - q}\right)(x_s)^{2-q} + \ldots \right]$$

The series converges rapidly for all cases of interest and often all terms beyond the first are negligible, so that the equation reduces to

$$S = K \frac{(x_s)^q}{(1 - x_s)^{q+1}} - \frac{Ab}{(1 - x_s)^{q+1}} \tag{87}$$

The Fenske equation may be used to express this relation in terms of distillate composition:

$$S = \frac{K(x_D)^q(\alpha^n - bx_D) - Ab(\alpha^n - bx_D)^{q+1}}{[\alpha^n(1 - x_D)]^{q+1}} \tag{88}$$

For purposes of computation it is usually more convenient to use eq. (87) and the Fenske equation separately.

The integration constant, K, is calculated from the initial conditions of the distillation. The value of x_s used in this calculation is not that of the original mixture. The original value of x_s (hereafter referred to as x_{sc}) decreases somewhat even before any product is removed, due to the passage of some of the charge into the column proper. The value of the still composition x_s (hereafter called x_{s0}) when equilibrium has been reached, but before any product is removed, is given by the solution of the expression

$$S_c x_{sc} = (S_c - H)x_{s0} + H \frac{\log\,(1 + bx_{s0})}{\log\,\alpha^n} \tag{89}$$

Trial and error is the only method available for solving this relation, and the value of x_{s0} so obtained is used in

$$S_c = K(x_{s0})^q/(1 - x_{s0})^{q+1} - Ab/(1 - x_{s0})^{q+1} \tag{90}$$

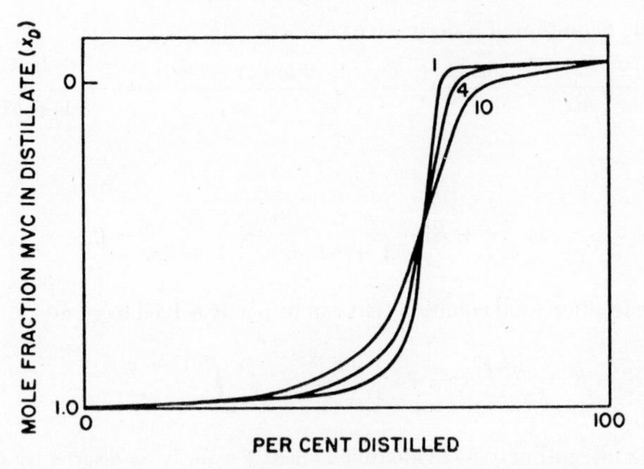

Fig. 38. Calculated distillation curves for 1, 4, and 10% holdup (distillation at total reflux).

or its more complex forms in order to obtain a value of K for use in subsequent calculations. These equations contain the factors, α, n, and H. By assuming suitable values of these and for the initial composition of the mixture, values of S and x_D may be obtained and plotted as in Figure 38.

Huckaba and Danly[137] have proposed a different method of calculating the course of a batch distillation with appreciable holdup, which they recommended for use when a high-speed computer is not available. The method requires as a first step the construction of a trial curve of the desired course of distillate composition versus per cent of charge distilled. A second trial curve is then calculated with the values of the original trial curve as a starting point. The second trial curve is then used to calculate another, and so on until there is no further change. An example is given.

B. DIFFERENTIAL EQUATIONS FOR PLATE COMPOSITIONS

In the case of a five-plate column the following equations[138] describe the rate of change of composition of the liquid on the several plates, if the usual simplifying assumptions are made:

$$dx_5/d\bar{S} = -(S/H_5)[(R_D + 1)y_4 - R_D x_5 - x_D]$$

$$dx_4/d\bar{S} = -(S/H_4)[(R_D + 1)(y_3 - y_4) + R_D(x_5 - x_4)]$$

$$\vdots$$

$$dx_1/d\bar{S} = -(S/H_1)[(R_D + 1)(y_s - y_1) + R_D(x_2 - x_1)]$$

$$dx_s/d\bar{S} = -(1/\bar{S})[R_D x_1 + x_s - (R_D + 1)y_s]$$

In these $\bar{S}$ represents the fraction of the charge remaining in the still and $H_5 = H_4 = H_3$, etc., i.e., the total holdup per plate is uniform. Since such equations describe the composition on the various plates they may be combined to produce the general operating-line equation derived by Colburn and Stearns.[139] The solution of the equation by algebraic means is extremely lengthy if not impossible. Numerical solutions by approximation methods are also lengthy. In the few cases in which such calculations have been completed, the results are in agreement with those of the stepwise plate-to-plate procedure.

Pigford, Tepe, and Garrahan used a differential analyzer to obtain numerical solutions to such differential equations for batch distillation. The results are indicated in Section IV, p. 134.

C. STEPWISE PLATE-TO-PLATE CALCULATIONS

Preliminary Calculation. This procedure[140] necessitates a preliminary calculation for establishment of the compositions of vapor and liquid leaving each plate of the column after initial total- (or finite-) reflux conditions have been established but before any distillate is withdrawn. This preliminary calculation is done by trial and error calculations with the equation

$$S_c x_{sc} = (S_c - H)x_{s0} + Hx_{h0} \tag{92}$$

in which S_c is the total moles charged, x_{sc} is the mole fraction of more volatile component in the charge, x_{s0} is the still composition just before the first distillate is removed, H the total moles of holdup, and x_{h0} the average composition of the material in the column just before the first distillate is obtained. By trial and error it is possible to find the value of x_{s0} that satisfies the preceding equation. Trial values of x_{s0} are chosen to be somewhat less than x_{sc} and values for x_{h0} may then be obtained from graphs of still composition vs. column average composition. An alternative procedure is to choose a trial value of x_{D0} and obtain column compositions (and thus x_{h0} and x_{s0}) by the McCabe–Thiele procedure. Repeated trials lead to a set of values such as in column 0 of Table X. This completes the preliminary calculation of column compositions as they are just before distillate takeoff is commenced.

Example of Stepwise Withdrawal Calculation. When distillate is withdrawn, for example, at the rate of 0.00318 mole per unit time with a reflux ratio $L/D = 4/1$, the following gain and loss of the more volatile component occurs on the top plate during a first interval of time:

$$\text{gain:}\ Vy_4 + Lx_D = 5(0.00318)(0.9736) + 4(0.00318)(0.988)$$

$$\text{loss:}\ Vy_5 + Lx_5 = 5(0.00318)(0.988) + 4(0.00318)(0.9736)$$

The resulting net loss of the more volatile component from the top plate, together with the total holdup on this plate (0.0315 mole) and its original

TABLE X

Distillate, Still, and Column Compositions. Stepwise Plate-to-Plate Calculations for Batch Fractional Distillation

	(0) After total reflux conditions established but prior to removal of first product		(1) After removal of small initial portion of distillate		(2) After removal of second small portion of distillate		(3) After removal of third small portion of distillate	
Moles distillate	none		0.00318		0.00636		0.00954	
Distillate composition	—		0.9873		0.9867		0.9858	
Plate	Liquid	Vapor	Liquid	Vapor	Liquid	Vapor	Liquid	Vapor
No. 5	0.9736	0.9880	0.9722	0.9873	0.9707	0.9867	0.9690	0.9859
No. 4	0.9431	0.9736	0.9400	0.9722	0.9367	0.9706	0.9332	0.9689
No. 3	0.8813	0.9431	0.8751	0.9399	0.8685	0.9365	0.8611	0.9326
No. 2	0.7690	0.8813	0.7578	0.8747	0.7455	0.8672	0.7358	0.8613
No. 1	0.5989	0.7690	0.5819	0.7563	0.5728	0.7494	0.5647	0.7432
Still	0.4010	0.5989	0.3994	0.5973	0.3972	0.5951	0.3945	0.5927
Moles in still	0.3926		0.38942		0.38624		0.38306	
Total moles holdup	0.1590		0.1590		0.1590		0.1590	
Charge	0.5516		—		—		—	
Moles mvc[a] in still	0.15743		0.15553		0.15343		0.15126	
in holdup	0.13248		0.13124		0.13020		0.12923	
in distillate	—		0.00314		0.00628		0.00942	
Total moles mvc.[a]	0.28991		0.28991		0.28991		0.28991	

[a] More volatile component.

composition ($x_5 = 0.9736$), gives a new top plate composition ($x_5 = 0.9722$) for the end of the short time interval. The results of a series of such calculations are given in columns 1, 2, and 3 of Table X and are plotted in Figure 39. For purposes of comparison the values of various plate compositions have been computed by the ordinary McCabe–Thiele procedure for the still composition at the end of the fifth time interval. These are also given on Figure 39.

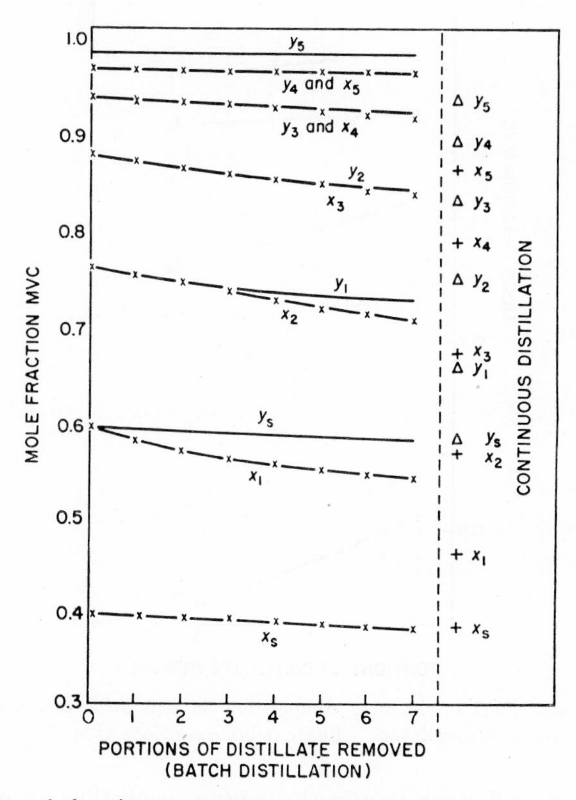

Fig. 39. Effect of changing composition on separation achieved in batch distillation. Total reflux conditions at start.

Solid lines are vapor compositions and dotted lines marked X are liquid compositions, both for batch distillation with total-reflux conditions at start of distillation, as calculated by stepwise plate-to-plate material balances. Points marked Δ are vapor compositions and those marked + are liquid compositions calculated by McCabe–Thiele procedure for continuous distillation conditions, with still composition the same as that at the end of the fifth interval of batch calculations.

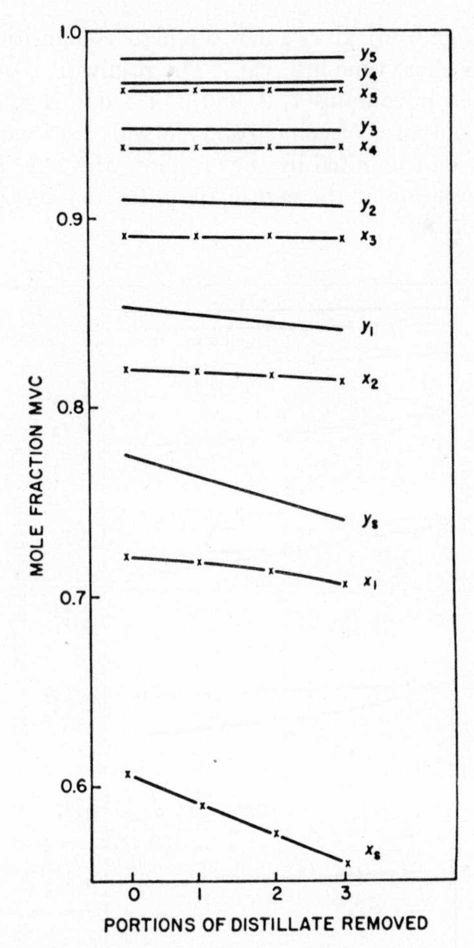

Fig. 40. Effect of changing composition on separation achieved in batch distillation. Finite reflux conditions at start.

The lesser overall separation in the continuous-distillation calculations and the different relationship between the pairs of vapor and liquid compositions are immediately obvious. As the distillation proceeds the composition of the vapor entering the bottom plate rather quickly becomes greater than that of the liquid on the bottom plate, as required by McCabe–Thiele considerations. The effect also begins to appear on the upper plates, one after another, but the relationship continues to be much closer to that for total reflux, than for the finite reflux as predicted by the McCabe–Thiele procedure. The same situation is indicated in a different way in Figure 40. This gives the results of stepwise plate-to-plate calculations showing the effect of shifting to ordinary batch distillation at finite reflux after equilibrium operation at the same reflux with return of distillate to the still. A more extensive series of such calculated curves is in Sec. IV, along with comparable experimental results. It is a comparatively simple matter to perform such computations on an automatic digital computer.

Mathematical Basis. The formal mathematical basis for the calculations described in the preceding paragraphs may be expressed as follows.[141]

The derivation is based on a material balance for the more volatile component around a particular plate n of the column during a short but finite period of time. During this time θ_j the plate receives

$$(Lx_{n+1} + Vy_{n-1})\theta_j$$

moles of the component under consideration and loses

$$(Lx_n + Vy_n)\theta_j$$

moles of this component. At the beginning of this time interval the moles of the component held up on the plate are H_nx_{n0} and at the end H_nx_{n1}. Since any difference between moles in and moles out must appear as accumulation or depletion on the plate, the following equation may be written:

$$(Vy_{n-1} + Lx_{n+1} - Vy_n - Lx_n)\theta_j = H_n(x_{n1} - x_{n0}) \tag{92}$$

Therefore

$$x_{n-1} - x_{n0} = \Delta x_n = \frac{\theta_j}{H_n}[V(y_{n-1} - y_n) + L(x_{n+1} - x_n)] \tag{93}$$

For the simplified case of a column with total condenser, and with negligible condenser and condenser line holdup, so that $y_t = x_D$, the following modified equation is obtained for the top plate, t, if this plate is 100% efficient

$$(Vy_{t-1} + Lx_{t+1} - Vy_t - Lx_t)\theta_j = H_t(x_{t1} - x_{t0})$$

This reduces to

$$x_{t1} - x_{t0} = \Delta x_t = \frac{\theta_j}{H_t}[Vy_{t-1} - Lx_t - Dx_D] \tag{94}$$

Analogous equations may be written for each of the other plates. A material balance around the still pot is expressed by the equation

$$S_1x_{s1} - S_0x_{s0} = \Delta(Sx_s) = (Lx_1 - Vy_s)\theta_j \tag{95}$$

By making the substitution $R = L/D$ and solving for the new composition, x_{n1}, the equations become

$$x_{t1} = x_{t0} + \frac{\theta_j D}{H_t} [(R + 1)y_{(t-1)0} - Rx_{t0} - x_{D0}]$$

$$x_{(t-1)1} = x_{(t-1)0} + \frac{\theta_j D}{H_{t-1}} [(R + 1)(y_{(t-2)0} - y_{(t-1)0}) + R(x_{t0} - x_{(t-1)0})]$$

$$\vdots$$

$$x_{(1)1} = x_{(1)0} + \frac{\theta_j D}{H_1} [(R + 1)(y_{s0} - y_{(1)0}) + R(x_{(2)0} - x_{(1)0})]$$

$$x_{s1} = \frac{S_0 x_{s0} + \theta_j D[Rx_{(1)0} - (R + 1)y_{s0}]}{S_{(1)0}} \tag{96}$$

As already demonstrated in the numerical example on p. 101, as soon as $x_{t1}, x_{(t-1)1} \ldots x_{(1)1}$, and x_{s1} are obtained, they might be used in a set of equations

$$x_{t2} = x_{t1} + \frac{\theta_j D}{H_t}[(\mathrm{R} + 1)y_{(t-1)1} - Rx_{t1} - x_{D1}]$$

to obtain x_{t2}, $x_{(t-2)2} \ldots x_{(1)2}$ and x_{s2}.

Repeated use of these equations allows calculation of all the plate and still compositions during an entire distillation, if a set of starting conditions are available. Examples of several such calculations have been published:

(*1*) Batch distillation when all the usual simplifying assumptions are applicable.[142]
(*2*) Batch distillations when all usual simplifying assumptions are applicable except that plate efficiency is not 100%.[143]
(*3*) Batch distillation when it is not permissible to assume
  (*a*) Constant relative volatility
  (*b*) Equal heats of vaporization
  (*c*) An adiabatic column
  (*d*) 100% plate efficiency[144]

The second of these papers demonstrated that the calculated compositions were in agreement with experimental values. These papers also pointed out the disadvantage of the method; namely, it is very laborious and errors are cumulative. This disadvantage is largely obviated by performance of the calculations on commercially available digital computers. All the following irregular and non-ideal cases can be calculated automatically by this technique.

Only one assumption is inherent in the method. This is that in a short period of time θ_j, referred to as one interval, the compositions of the various streams do not change, or they change in an arbitrarily chosen manner based on general experience or immediate past behavior. This assumption involves an error that may be made as small as desired by decreasing the interval size or determining the rate of change of composition during the interval in a more elaborate manner.

Calculations When Simplifying Assumptions Are Not Applicable. Advantages of the stepwise calculation procedure arise from the freedom of need for simplifying assumptions and restrictions. Thus, if essential, it is possible to make calculations that take into account all the following nonidealities and irregularities, even though they occur simultaneously during a single distillation.

(*1*) Relative volatility is variable.
(*2*) There are unequal heats of vaporization, unequal specific heats, and appreciable heats of mixing of components, resulting in unequal molal overflow.
(*3*) The column is nonadiabatic, also resulting in unequal molal overflow.
(*4*) Plate efficiency is other than 100%.
(*5*) Condenser holdup, or condenser line holdup, is appreciable.
(*6*) Holdup is not uniform on the various plates.
(*7*) Holdup on a given plate changes as the distillation progresses.
(*8*) A partial condenser is used instead of a total condenser.
(*9*) A ternary or multicomponent mixture is distilled.
(*10*) A packed column is used instead of a plate column.
(*11*) Vapor holdup is not negligible.
(*12*) Liquid composition is not uniform across a plate, and not equal to the composition of liquid leaving the plate.
(*13*) A change in the liquid or vapor rate does not affect all plates simultaneously.
(*14*) Reflux ratio is varied during the distillation.

The general approach to these realistic calculations is to modify the relatively simple equations (96) so they take into account the various irregularities. Equation (109) has been derived for the case where irregularities 2, 3, and 6 are taken into account. In general, it is preferable not to derive such complex equations, but to "program" the calculation procedure by listing the order in which the various simpler equations are to be used in obtaining a value of x_{n1} from x_{n0}.

For example, there is little difference in the basic calculation procedure for cases of variable relative volatility compared with constant relative volatility. In each case before the basic equations (96) may be used to calculate new liquid compositions at the end of a new interval, it is necessary to use some means of getting the necessary equilibrium vapor compositions at the beginning of the interval, from the known liquid compositions. Where 100% plate efficiency and constant relative volatility may be assumed, the usual relative volatility expression

$$\frac{y}{1-y} = \alpha \frac{x}{1-x}$$

may be used. When relative volatility is not constant, it is almost always possible to express the vapor–liquid equilibrium relation by some functional relation such as

$$y = ax + bx^2 + cx^3 + \dots$$

In many cases it is convenient to use available equations and constants (activity coefficients or K values) to obtain necessary partial pressures and mole fractions of the equilibrium vapor.[145] In principle it is even possible to use a table of the vapor–liquid equilibrium data, but this greatly extends machine calculation, and so is not advisable. In any case, the calculation procedure involves alternate use of eqs. (96) and some vapor–liquid equilibrium equation or equations, without modification of eqs. (96).

When 100% plate efficiency may not be assumed, the procedure is the same, except that after each equilibrium vapor composition is obtained, an equation such as the Murphree x or y equations must be used to obtain actual vapor composition from the equilibrium value. Thus, the programming is the repetitive use of the sequence (*1*) eqs. (96) (*2*) vapor–liquid equilibrium equation, (*3*) plate-efficiency equation. It is clearly possible to use different plate-efficiency factors for the different plates, and if desired, to go further and take into account the variation of such factors with liquid compositions. This merely introduces into the program sequence a step (*2a*) calculation of plate efficiency from liquid composition according to some predetermined functional relation.

When there is non-adiabatic operation of the column, the values of V and L are different from plate to plate, and may also vary with concentrations in the column. When the latter is not the case, the program of calculation is identical with that previously described, except that the values of V and L will be different for each plate, and the proper values must be known and introduced at the beginning of the calculations. Should it be necessary to take into account a change in the magnitude of the heat leak with concentration, a considerably more complicated, but still straightforward procedure is necessary. Thus, a new step (*4*) would be introduced in which liquid compositions would be used to obtain plate temperature, and this then used (with the temperature of the surroundings and the overall heat-transfer coefficient) to obtain quantity of heat lost, and finally, the new value of V and L.

Inclusion of condenser holdup, condenser line holdup, or use of a partial instead of total condenser requires modification of the program for the top-plate calculation only, in that the simple relation $x_D = y_t$ must be replaced by a more complex relation to obtain the correct value for the compositions of the liquid flowing onto the top plate during any interval. Huckaba and Danly[146] have discussed various specific cases that arise, and carried out related experiments.

If holdup is different on the different plates, but remains constant on any plate throughout the distillation, there is no complication in programming, since it is only necessary to introduce the proper values into the equations for the different plates.

When holdup varies during the distillation, it is probably most frequently because composition changes cause molar volume changes while volumetric holdup remains constant. In this case, a functional relationship $H = f(x)$ must be established and used to calculate the necessary values for H for each plate at the beginning of each new interval. However, there are further complications. This change in H requires a major change in the procedure, because eqs. (96) now have three unknowns (L_n, H_1, and x_n) instead of just one (x_n). Actually L_n and H_1 are related by overall material balances, and x_n and H_1 are also related by $H = f(x)$, but the latter relation will probably seldom be simple enough to permit explicit solution of (96) for x. Although no calculations of this type have been made, the best procedure would probably be a trial-and-error iteration as follows: Use L_0/H_0 as a first trial value of L_1/H_1 and follow the normal procedure to obtain a first trial value of x_{n1}. Use this in $H = f(x)$ to obtain a second trial value of H_1, use this in the overall material-balance equation for the plate to obtain a second trial value of L_n, and use this in eqs. (96) to get a second trial value of x_{n1}, and so on until successive trials give the same answer. The overall procedure for this case then is (*1*) equations (96) iteration as just explained instead of simple use of eqs. (96), followed by step (*2*, *2a*) if variation in plate efficiency is to be taken into account, (*3*) if plate efficiency other than 100% is involved, (*4*) if operation is non-adiabatic and the heat leak is varying with time during the distillation, plus such steps for the top-plate calculation as are required by the condenser holdup and composition relations.

In consequence of this complexity, Huckaba and Tour[147] have pointed out that it is preferable to use weight fractions for all the compositions, and weights to express the flow rates and quantity of holdup. If weight of holdup per plate is constant with time during the distillation, then the complexities can be avoided. It is more likely that it is volume of holdup that is constant, rather than weight. No calculations have been reported on the extent of the differences in end results that exist between cases of constant and variable holdup.

Irregular thermal properties such as unequal heats of vaporization and specific heats, and appreciable heats of mixing, result in complexities of the order of those just described for changing holdup. A simple case where only unequal heats of vaporization need be taken into account may be dealt with simply by using fictitious molecular weights. This merely modifies the vapor–liquid equilibrium equation, and the standard program may be used. A much more complicated case can be dealt with by programming which involves a series of steps. The reasoning in this case requires a heat balance and an overall material balance as well as a material balance on more volatile component. A functional relation between enthalpy and composition is also required. The equations are

$$V_{t-1} + L_R = V_t + L_t \tag{98}$$

$$\theta_j(V_{t-1}y_{t-1} + L_R x_R) + H_t x_{t0} = \theta_j(V_t y_t + L_t x_t) + H_t x_{t1} \tag{99}$$

$$\theta_j(V_{t-1}I_{t-1} + L_R i_R) + H_t i_{t0} = \theta_j(V_t I_t + L_t i_t) + H_t i_{t1} \tag{100}$$

where I and i are the enthalpies of the vapor and liquid, respectively.

An iterative trial-and-error procedure, similar to that described in the preceding paragraph, may be used. Equation (99) is first used in the regular way to obtain a first trial value of x_{t1}. This is used to obtain i_{t1} for eq. (100), from which L_t is also eliminated by use of (98). Solution of (100) is then easily possible to give a first trial value of V_{t-1}, and (98) gives the corresponding value of L_t. These are then used in (99) to get a second trial x_{t1}, etc. Simpler solution is possible at a sacrifice of some of the rigor of the solution. Thus, if the liquid enthalpy terms or their difference is assumed negligible, (100) reduces to

$$V_{t-1}I_{t-1} = V_t I_t \tag{101}$$

When this and (98) are combined with (99), it may be solved explicitly for x_{t1} and the standard program may be used. Equation (109) was derived on this basis, and also nonadiabaticity was accounted for by writing (101) as

$$\theta_j(V_{t-1}I_{t-1}) = \theta_j(V_t I_t) + Q \tag{102}$$

where Q is the heat lost. Defining

$$Q = q'\theta_j(V_{t-1}I_{t-1}) \tag{103}$$

then

$$V_{t-1} = \left(\frac{1}{1 - q'}\right)\frac{I_t}{I_{t-1}}\,V_t = q\,\frac{I_t}{I_{t-1}}\,V_t \tag{104}$$

Assuming that q is constant for each plate; i.e., the per cent of heat in the vapor coming to each plate that is lost is the same for all plates in the column, then

$$V_{t-k} = q^k\,\frac{I_t}{I_{t-k}}\,V_t \tag{105}$$

Writing equations similar to (98) for all plates to $(t - k)$, adding, and substituting (105)

$$L_{t-k} = \left[\frac{q^{k+1}I_t}{I_{t-(k+1)}} - 1\right] V_t + L_R \tag{106}$$

Rewriting (99) for plate $(t - k)$,

$$\Delta x_{t-k} = \frac{\theta_j}{H_{t-k}} \{(V_{t-(k+1)}y_{t-(k+1)} + L_{t-(k-1)}x_{t-(k-1)}) - (V_{t-k}y_{t-k} + L_{t-k}x_{t-k})\} \tag{107}$$

Substituting (105) and (106) in (107),

$$\Delta x_{t-k} = \frac{\theta_j}{H_{t-k}} \left\{\left[\frac{q^{k+1}I_t}{I_{t-(k+1)}} V_t y_{t-(k+1)} - \frac{q^k I_t}{I_{t-k}} V_t y_{t-k}\right] + \left[\left(\frac{q^k I_t}{I_{t-k}} - 1\right) V_t + L_R\right] x_{t-(k-1)} - \left[\left(\frac{q^{k+1}I_t}{I_{t-(k+1)}} - 1\right) V_t + L_R\right] x_{t-k}\right\} \tag{108}$$

$$\Delta x_{t-k} = \frac{\theta_j}{H_{t-k}} \left\{V_t\left[\frac{q^{k+1}I_t}{I_{t-(k+1)}} y_{t-(k+1)} - \frac{q^k I_t}{I_{t-k}} y_{t-k} + \frac{q^k I_t}{I_{t-k}} x_{t-(k-1)} - \frac{q^{k+1}I_t}{I_{t-(k+1)}} x_{t-k}\right] + (L_R - V_t)(x_{t-(k-1)} - x_{t-k})\right\} \tag{109}$$

Multicomponent calculations are relatively simple for cases such as variable relative volatility, plate efficiency, and the simpler cases of holdup and flow variation. In such cases there are as many additional sets of eqs. (96) as there are additional components (beyond the binary pair), and an equal number of vapor–liquid equilibrium equations, plate-efficiency equations, etc. Nothing but the basic information and the computational facilities are necessary. Steps in the calculation of the more complicated multicomponent cases have not been considered in detail, so that unexpected complications may develop for these, even though at first sight the procedures for even these seem clear-cut and straightforward extensions of the binary cases.

Similar statements apply to items *(10)* through *(13)* on p. 107. Item *(14)*, a change in reflux ratio during the distillation, is a simple matter for any combination of the other items.

In those cases where enthalpy composition relations are linear, Huckaba and Danly[148] have devised a much simpler approach that avoids need for a repeated trial and error solution.

7. Equations for Equilibration Time

Coulson[149] has expressed the time for a column to come to equilibrium at total reflux as

$$\theta_e = (h_0 - h_e)/v \tag{110}$$

where h_0 is the moles of the more volatile component in the column at the time a particular boilup rate is commenced, h_e is the corresponding value when equilibrium is reached, and v is the net rate of transfer of the more volatile component into the column. The value of v is easily seen to be approximately

$$v = V(y_s - x_1) \tag{111}$$

where y_s is the composition of vapor entering the base of the column, and x_1 is the composition of material entering the pot from the base of the column. The value of h_e is in general Hx_{h0} where H is the total holdup and x_{h0} is the average composition of the holdup when equilibrium is reached. Methods of obtaining both H and x_{h0} are indicated in connection with the determination of holdup (p. 86). The value of h_0 is also of the form Hx_h. Coulson assumed H to be the same before and after equilibrium was reached, which may or may not be true, but is a reasonable first approximation. For the value of x_h Coulson assumed that the holdup was of the same composition as the vapor initially evolved from the charge ($x_h = x_{hc} = y_{sc}$). On this basis

$$\theta_e = \frac{H}{V}\left(\frac{1}{x_{sc}\left[\dfrac{\alpha}{1 + x_{sc}(\alpha - 1)} - 1\right]}\right) \times \left[\left(\frac{\log\left[\dfrac{1 + (\alpha^n - 1)\alpha x_{sc}}{1 + (\alpha - 1)x_{sc}}\right]}{n \log \alpha}\right) - \frac{\alpha x_{sc}}{1 + (\alpha - 1)x_{sc}}\right]$$

Coulson gives the approximate relation

$$\theta_e \cong \left[\left(\frac{H}{V}\right)\left(1 + \frac{\log x_{sc}}{n \log \alpha}\right)\right] \Big/ [x_{sc}(\alpha - 1)] \tag{112}$$

for cases in which x_{sc} and α are small and n is greater than 50. O'Brien[150] found that in packed columns with 110 and 130 theoretical plates the equilibration time was approximately inversely proportional to vapor velocity as indicated by Coulson's equations.

In the separation of isotopes and in other cases where the separation is extremely difficult, the approach is so very slow toward a total reflux equilibrium or a steady state at even very high reflux ratios, that the prediction of the rate of approach is an important and practical matter to which much attention has been given. Cohen[151] (see also p. 223) gave an early and extensive treatment of this special case.

Berg and James[152] have modified the derivations and equations of Cohen to obtain

$$\left(\frac{x_D}{1 - x_D}\right)\Big/\left(\frac{x_s}{1 - x_s}\right) = (nL/H)(\alpha - 1)(\alpha \ln \alpha)\theta_e + \alpha \quad (113)$$

$$1 - \left(\frac{x_D}{1 - x_D}\right)\Big/\left(\frac{x_s\alpha^{n+1}}{1 - x_s}\right) = \alpha \exp - \frac{nL}{H}\left(\frac{\alpha - 1}{\alpha^n}\right)\theta_e \quad (114)$$

and

$$\frac{1 - \left(\frac{x_D}{1 - x_D}\right)\Big/\left(\frac{x_s\alpha^{n+1}}{1 - x_s}\right)}{1 - (1/\alpha^n)} = \alpha \exp - (\phi_B)\left(\frac{nL}{H}\right)\frac{(\alpha - 1)}{\alpha^n}\theta_e \quad (115)$$

Equations (113) and (114) are simplified versions of eq. (115), which assumes that holdup in the condenser and return system is negligible, that α has the special value $(1 - x_s)/(1 - x_D)$, and that the vapor holdup is negligible. The first equation is applicable when α and n are large so that α^n becomes very large. The second equation assumes $\phi_B = 1$ which is nearly true when α^n approaches 400. ϕ_B is a complex function of $n \log \alpha$, and depends also on the system and the column used. Two experiments gave confirmation of the calculated times predicted by the equations.

Jackson and Pigford[153] have reviewed and evaluated all of the preceding approaches and some others,[154] particularly with respect to the suitability of the simplifying assumptions that are used. They also have made an extensive series of numerical calculations based directly on the underlying equation for approach to steady state

$$V(y_{n-1} - y_n) + L(x_{n+1} - x_n) = H(dx/dt) \quad (116)$$

which for the conventional total reflux approach to initial steady state involves $V = L$, so that if the time required for the liquid stream to fill a single plate is $T = Lt/H$, then

$$y_{n-1} - y_n + x_{n+1} - x_n = dx_n/dT \quad (117)$$

Some of the calculations are for a very large still pot compared with the column (negligible holdup), and others are for a very small still pot relative to the column. The general conclusion is that the equations involving simplifying assumptions are rather likely to be wrong by a factor of two or more in estimating the time required to reach steady state.

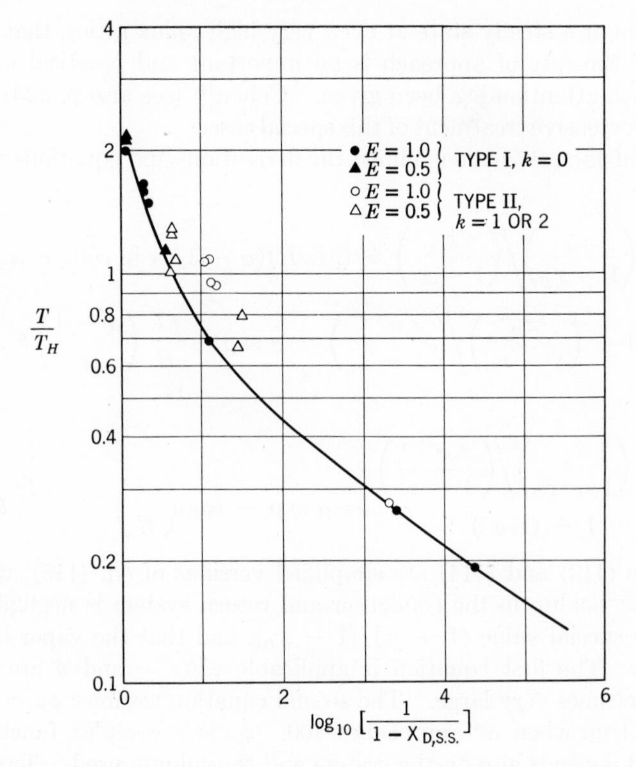

Fig. 41. Generalized plot of time needed to approach steady state—T based on $\epsilon_x = 0.1$; E = Murphree tray efficiency, fractional; k = ratio: moles liquid on one tray to moles liquid in reboiler.[153]

The results of the numerical calculations can be correlated by a graph of T/T_H, the ratio of the time required for the instantaneous distillate composition to reach $\epsilon_x = 0.1$ to the time required to fill the column liquid holdup with its steady-state amount of low boiler, plotted versus $\log_{10}[1/(1 - x_{Dss})]$, the logarithm of the reciprocal of the mole fraction of the high boiler in the distillate at steady state. ϵ_x (the fractional departure of distillate composition from steady-state value, expressed in mole fractions) $= (x_{Dss} - x_D)/(x_{Dss} - \alpha x_s)$; $T_H = N(\bar{x}_{ss} - x_{hi})/(y_s^* - x_s)$, in which N is the total number of plates, $\bar{x}$ is a mean composition of liquid holdup, x_{hi} is the liquid composition in the initial column contents and the subscript ss signifies steady-state compositions. The graph is shown in Figure 41.

The open points correspond to the calculations for large column holdup compared to still pot contents, and in these cases T_H is calculated for only half the column. A numerical example is given of the use of Figure 41 to estimate equilibration time.

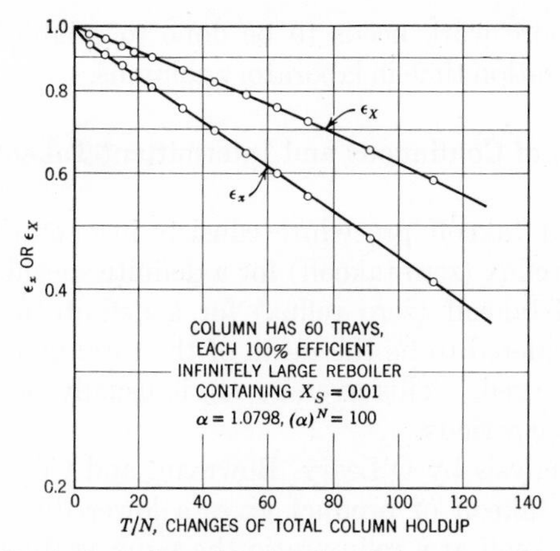

Fig. 42. Typical semilogarithmic plot of departure from steady-state composition of distillate.[153]

The Jackson and Pigford calculations show equilibration time varying as the square of the number of theoretical plates. There are also effects of the separation factor and still composition that are not shown by the analytical equations.

Figure 42 shows the typical straight line relation on a semilog plot of ϵ_x or ϵ_X vs. time expressed as T/N, the changes of total column holdup. (ϵ_X is identical with ϵ_x except that the units are in mole ratios.) This relation permits extrapolation of partially completed calculations, and simple calculation of one T from another for which ϵ_x is known.

Predictions of equilibration time and of the rate of change of composition during the initial approach to steady state of a column at total reflux were made by Biles and Schilk.[155] They used the same unsteady state equations and calculation procedure that had been used for batch distillation with appreciable holdup.[156] Similar equilibration time calculations have been made in connection with studies of distillation column control.[157] The predictions of Biles and Schilk were in reasonable agreement with the corresponding experimental curves obtained in an apparatus that had separating characteristics known with certainty.

A considerable number of experimental determinations of equilibration time in $^1/_2$-in. and 1-in. diameter packed columns with 15 to 160 theoretical plates using binary mixtures of methylcyclohexane–toluene, n-heptane–methylcyclohexane, and isooctane–methylcyclohexane were made by Cottrell, Sanders, and Johnson.[158] The results were not in good agreement with the preceding essentially theoretical predictions. Charge composition and size, throughput, holdup, and theoretical plates, all had an effect on equilibration time, but interrelations were quite complicated.

It appears that more work needs to be done to establish a clear understanding of equilibration time in laboratory columns.

8. Comparison of Continuous and Intermittent Takeoff Procedures

The intermittent takeoff procedure consists in operating a column alternately at total reflux (zero takeoff) for a definite specified period of time and then at total takeoff (zero reflux) for a definite brief period. The reflux ratio is considered to be the mean of the total and zero reflux ratios for the time cycle used. This average R_D is usually nearly equal to the ratio of the two time periods.

A theoretical analysis by O'Leary, Bowman, and Coull[159] indicates that such intermittent takeoff of product gives a lower distillate composition than continuous takeoff at a reflux ratio the same as the mean average reflux ratio for the intermittent process. The indicated difference is small. Experimental measurements in a steady state system confirmed this prediction.

The theoretical analysis assumes exponential decay in time for the composition changes during both the zero and the total reflux periods of intermittent takeoff. The ratio of the growth and decay constants is calculated from the equilibrium distillate composition for continuous takeoff at the average reflux ratio. The average reflux ratio can be expressed as

$$R = \frac{\theta_0 - \theta_1}{\theta_1}$$

where θ_0 is the time for a complete cycle, and θ_1 is the time interval of zero reflux.

During the zero reflux interval

$$y = y_f + (y_1 - y_f)e^{-ra\theta}$$

where y_1 is the distillate composition at the start of the zero reflux interval, y_f is the feed composition, y is the instantaneous distillate composition, r is the ratio of the decay constant to the growth constant, a is the growth constant for approach to equilibrium at total reflux, and θ is the time during the interval 0 to $\theta_0/(R + 1)$, the duration of the zero reflux cycle.

During the total reflux interval

$$y = y_T + (y_2 - y_T) \exp - a\left(\theta - \frac{\theta_0}{R + 1}\right)$$

where y_T is the distillate composition corresponding to total reflux, and y_2 is the distillate composition at the beginning of the total reflux interval.

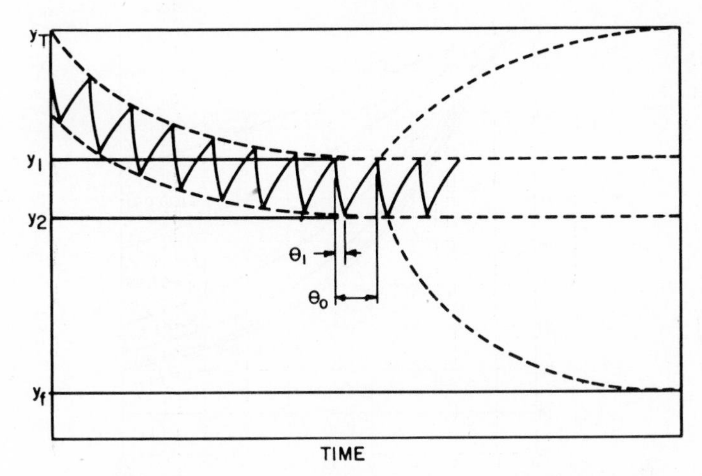

Fig. 43. Plot of y vs. time for intermittent takeoff.[159]

The range of θ would necessarily be between θ_0 and $\theta_0/(R+1)$. Figure 43 describes the process.

Values of y_1 and y_2 at the terminal points of their respective intervals are

$$y_2 = y_f + (y_1 - y_f)\exp - \frac{ra\theta_0}{R+1}$$

$$y_1 = y_T + (y_2 - y_T)\exp - \frac{aR\theta_0}{R+1}$$

These values of y_1 and y_2 are substituted into the two equations for y to obtain expressions for the instantaneous distillate composition as a function of time. A more important quantity is the average composition with intermittent reflux, $\bar{y}$. This comes out as

$$\bar{y} = y_f + \left(\frac{y_T - y_f}{1-\rho}\right)\left[\frac{(1-e^{-\rho\tau})(1-e^{-(1-\rho)\tau})}{\tau(1-e^{-\tau})}\right] \tag{118}$$

$$\tau = \frac{R+r}{R+1}a\theta_0$$

$$\rho = \frac{R}{R+r}$$

The continuous takeoff operation is a special case of intermittent takeoff with $\theta_0 = 0 = \tau$. So

$$\frac{y_c - y_f}{y_T - y_f} = \rho \tag{119}$$

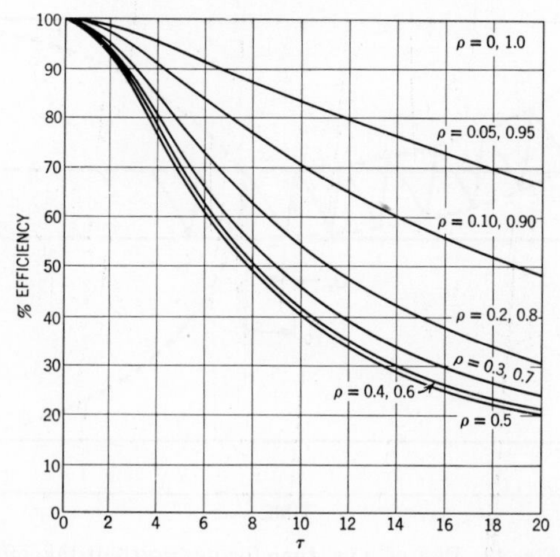

Fig. 44. Percent efficiency vs. τ for intermittent takeoff.[159]

where y_c is distillate composition corresponding to continuous reflux operation. Thus r is dependent only on column equilibrium characteristics and reflux ratio. When eqs. (118) and (119) are combined

$$\frac{\bar{y} - y_f}{y_c - y_f} = \frac{(1 - e^{\rho\tau})(1 - e^{-(1-\rho)\tau})}{\rho\tau(1 - \rho)(1 - e^{-\tau})} = E\ (\rho,\tau) \qquad (120)$$

The function E can be thought of as the efficiency of the refluxing operation. It is plotted in Figure 44. The value of E is unity only at $\theta_0 = 0$, regardless of values of R, r, or a. For all other values of θ_0, E is less than 1. This indicates that intermittent reflux always gives a poorer separation than continuous takeoff. Figure 44 plots E vs. τ and shows that for the values of τ likely to be used the percentage effect is small. The authors' experiments confirmed this prediction. Most earlier experimental work has not agreed with this theoretical analysis.[160]

9. Curves for Changing Reflux Ratio to Maintain Constant Distillate Composition

All the preceding discussions have assumed constant reflux ratio throughout a distillation, and the equations and calculations have dealt with the change in distillate composition as the batch distillation proceeded. It is however, common practice to increase reflux ratio, when the amount of a component in the still becomes depleted, and thereby increase the proportion of the component in the distillate. The equations already obtained can serve to estimate the results of such distillations with more than one reflux ratio.

A. STEPWISE INCREASE IN REFLUX RATIO

For instance, during the distillation of 100 moles of equimolar binary mixture with $\alpha = 1.25$, through fifty theoretical plates with negligible holdup, reflux ratio of 19, calculations by eq. (40) (see also p. 79) show that the distillate composition remains near unity until the still content is reduced to 70 moles (Fig. 45A). When it reaches 65 moles the distillate composition has dropped to 0.98 and after distillation of five more moles would drop to 0.87. At the time still content is 65 moles, the still composition is 0.21. If at this point the reflux ratio is increased to 49, the distillate composition will again rise practically to unity and remain there until still composition drops to approximately 0.1. The distillation curve for the portion of the distillation with reflux ratio 49 can also be calculated by eq. (40) using $S_t = 65$ and values of x_D and x_s from the still-product composition curve for $\alpha = 1.25$, $n = 50$, and $R_D = 49$ (Fig. 45B). The calculations indicate that the increase in reflux ratio will result in nearly pure distillate until about 58 moles remain in the still.

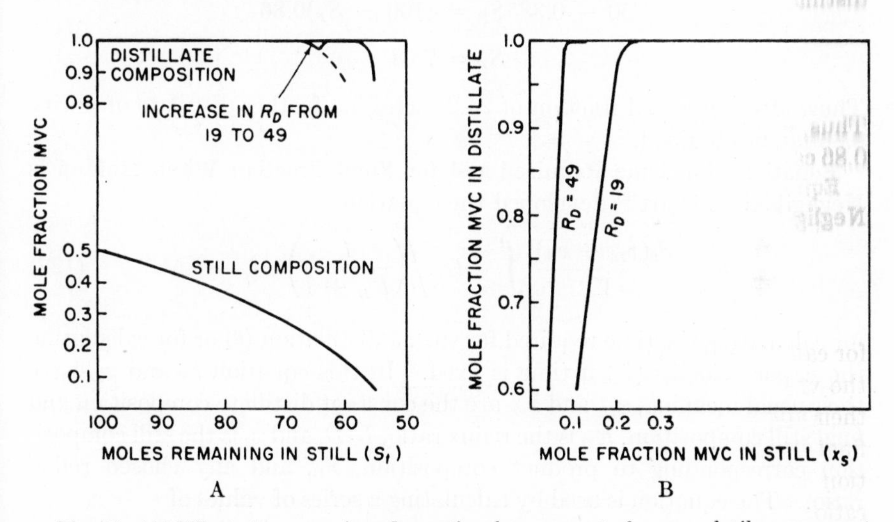

Fig. 45. (A) Effect of increase in reflux ratio when amount of more volatile component in still has been depleted. (B) Still-product composition curves on which A is based. $\alpha = 1.25$, $n = 50$, $R_D = 19$ and 49.

B. GRADUAL INCREASE IN REFLUX RATIO

If the reflux ratio is continually increased at the proper rate from the beginning of a distillation, a limited amount of distillate of constant composition will be obtained. The distillation curve in such a case is merely a straight line that extends to the point where total reflux is required to maintain constant product composition. Any distillate recovered beyond this point will be of lower purity, depending on a new choice of reflux ratio. For instance, if 100 moles of equimolar mixture with $\alpha = 1.25$ is distilled through ten plates with negligible holdup, calculations by the Smoker equation indicate that an initial reflux ratio (R_D) of 19 will be required to produce initial distillate composition of 0.86. This can be maintained during the distillation by gradual increase in reflux ratio. Calculations by the Fenske equation indicate that with $\alpha = 1.25$ and $n = 10$, when still composition reaches 0.385, infinite reflux will be required to maintain distillate composition at 0.86. The moles remaining in the still when this final point is reached, S_F, can be calculated by the material balance

$$S_0 x_{s0} - S_F x_{sF} = (S_0 - S_F)\, x_{Dc} \tag{121}$$

in which $S_c = S_0 = 100$ moles (the charge), $x_{s0} = 0.5$ (the initial composition), $x_{sF} = 0.385$, the still composition at the end of the period of constant distillate composition ($x_{Dc} = 0.86$):

$$50 - 0.385 S_F = (100 - S_F)0.86$$

$$S_F = 75.8$$

Thus, after an initial fraction of 24.2 moles, no further distillate of purity 0.86 can be obtained.

Equations for Time Required and for Yield Fraction When Holdup is Negligible. Bogart[161] developed the equation

$$\theta = \frac{S_0(x_{Dc} - x_{s0})}{V} \int_{x_{sF}}^{x_{s0}} dx_s \Bigg/ \left(\frac{1}{R_D + 1}\right)(x_{Dc} - x_s)^2 \tag{122}$$

for calculating the time required for such a distillation (θ) or for calculating the vapor velocity (V) if time is fixed. In this equation S_0 and x_{s0} have their usual meaning, x_{Dc} and x_{sF} are the constant distillate composition and final still composition, R_D is the reflux ratio, L/D, and x_s is the still composition corresponding to product composition, x_D, and any chosen reflux ratio. The equation is used by calculating a series of values of

$$1 \Bigg/ \left(\frac{1}{R + 1}\right)(x_{Dc} - x_s)^2$$

by choosing random values of R_D, using the McCabe–Thiele procedure to calculate corresponding values of x_s, and then obtaining the value of the integral by graphic means.

Edgeworth-Johnstone[162] has developed formulas for calculating the amount of distillate that can be recovered in such distillations. This is done by means of the yield fraction (ϕ_J), which is the ratio of the distillate actually obtained to the maximum amount that could have been obtained from the charge. When holdup can be neglected,

$$\phi_J = \frac{S_0 - S_F}{S_0 x_{s0}/x_{Dc}} = \frac{S_0 - S_F}{S_0 x_{s0}} x_{Dc} = \frac{Pa_p}{Fa_f} \tag{123}$$

in which S_0 is the total moles of charge, S_F is moles remaining in still when total reflux is reached, x_{s0} is charge composition, and x_{Dc} is distillate composition. P, F, a_p, and a_f are the symbols used by Edgeworth-Johnstone and correspond to $(S_0 - S_F)$, S_0, x_{Dc}, and x_{s0}, respectively. Thus in the preceding example

$$\phi_J = 24.2/(50/0.86) = 0.416$$

Edgeworth-Johnstone uses the material-balance equations (121) and

$$(S_0 - S_F) + S_F = S_0$$

and the Fenske equation to obtain

$$S_0 - S_F = \frac{S_0 x_{s0}}{x_{Dc}} \left[\frac{\alpha^{n+1} - \left(\dfrac{x_{Dc}}{1 - x_{Dc}}\right)\left(\dfrac{1 - x_{s0}}{x_{s0}}\right)}{\alpha^{n+1} - 1} \right]$$

Then with the original equation for ϕ_J

$$\phi_J = \frac{\alpha^{n+1} - \left(\dfrac{x_{Dc}}{1 - x_{Dc}}\right)\left(\dfrac{1 - x_{s0}}{x_{s0}}\right)}{\alpha^{n+1} - 1} \tag{124}$$

This allows calculation of ϕ_J in terms of α, n, x_{s0} and any desired distillate composition. The expression neglects holdup, and assumes distillation is carried out with gradually increasing reflux (so that x_{Dc} is constant) until total reflux is reached.

Since it may not be economical in many cases to continue increasing reflux until total reflux is reached, it is desirable to make the same calculations for specified reflux ratios at which it may be desired to stop the constant distillate composition distillation. As an example, the value of ϕ_J will be calculated for the same initial conditions as on p. 120 but for a final reflux ratio of $R_D = 99$. Calculations by the McCabe–Thiele procedure with $\alpha = 1.25$ and $n = 10$ indicate that, when still composition reaches 0.413, the reflux ratio will be $R_D = 99$. Then, substituting in eq. (121):

$$50 - 0.413 S_F = (100 - S_F)0.86$$

$$S_F = 80.5$$

$$\phi_J = 19.5/(50/0.86) = 0.335$$

Such calculations may be repeated for a series of different choices of final reflux ratio (Table XI), and a graph prepared of reflux ratio versus yield fraction, or against moles of

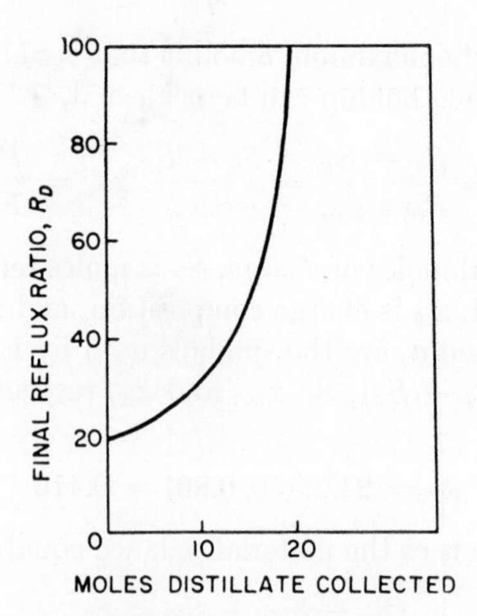

Fig. 46. Final reflux ratio vs. moles distillate in constant distillate composition distillation.[162]

distillate (Fig. 46). From the area under the curve on the graph it is possible to calculate the average reflux ratio for any desired number of moles of distillate collected. Thus for 10 moles distillate collected, $R_{D\,\mathrm{av}}$ can be seen by inspection to be roughly halfway between 20 and 30. Careful graphical integration gives $R_{D\mathrm{av}} = 24$. Other values of $R_{D\,\mathrm{av}}$ are given in Table XI. Each of these average reflux ratios corresponds to a particular final reflux ratio as well as to a certain number of moles of distillate collected. The relative times required for collection of various amounts of distillate are in proportion to the average reflux ratios.

The same general approach has been extended and somewhat simplified by Johnson, Huang, and Talbot.[163] For the situation where the number of plates is so large that pinching at the still pot end of the composition range can be assumed without appreciable error, the equations become

(*1*) For constant reflux ratio

$$\theta = (R+1)\frac{S_0}{V}\left\{1 - \left[\frac{\dfrac{(1-x_{s0})^\alpha}{x_{s0}}}{\dfrac{(1-x_s)^\alpha}{x_s}}\right]^{\frac{1}{(\alpha-1)}\frac{1}{(R+1)}}\right\} \tag{125}$$

(*2*) For variable reflux ratio to produce constant product composition

$$\theta = \frac{S_0(x_D - x_{s0})}{V(\alpha-1)x_D(1-x_D)}\left\{(1-x_D)\ln\frac{x_{s0}}{x_s} + [1+(\alpha-1)x_D]\ln\frac{x_D-x_s}{x_D-x_{s0}} + \alpha x_D\ln\frac{1-x_{s0}}{1-x_s}\right\} \tag{126}$$

TABLE XI
Calculations of Average Reflux Ratio

Final R_D	Final x_s	$x_{Dc} - x_s$	S_F	$100 - S_F$	ϕ_J	Average R_D
∞	0.385	0.475	75.8	24.2	0.416	—
99	0.413	0.477	80.5	19.5	0.335	38
49	0.435	0.425	84.8	15.2	0.261	28
29	0.463	0.397	90.8	9.2	0.158	24
19	0.500	0.360	100	0	0	—

For the situation where the number of plates is too small to justify the preceding assumption, similar but more complicated equations are obtained by a linearization approximation procedure. None of these equations take holdup or variation in relative volatility into account, and they are derived for binary mixtures.

The use of the Bogart equations for estimating heat requirements (roughly proportional to the time required) has been analyzed by Stiehl and Weber.[164] Converse and Gross[165] have shown by mathematical analysis and computer calculation for a batch distillation performed in a specified time with definite known relative volatility, theoretical plates, boilup rate, and specified product purity, that an optimal distillate withdrawal rate policy can give up to 5% greater yield than operation with either constant product composition or constant distillate rate. The work assumed negligible holdup and a binary system.

Equations for Time Required and for Yield Fraction When Holdup Is Appreciable. Holdup is taken into account by modifying the basic equation as follows:

$$\phi_J = \frac{S_c - S_F - H}{S_c x_{sc}/x_{Dc}} \tag{127}$$

in which H is total holdup.

As an illustration, calculations may be made for the same example used above for the case of negligible holdup (100 moles equimolar binary mixture with $\alpha = 1.25$, and ten plates), but with the assumption of a total holdup of 9 moles. The still composition will decrease to $x_{s0} = 0.482$ before any distillate is obtained, due to passage of part of the charge into the column. This value of x_{s0} is found by trial and error solution of the material balance

$$S_c x_{ss} = S_0 x_{s0} + h \tag{128}$$

in which $S_c = 100$, $x_{sc} = 0.5$, $S_0 = S_c - H = 91$, and h is the moles of holdup of the more volatile component when still composition is x_{s0} and distillate composition is the desired value $x_{Dc} = 0.86$. With trial reflux ratios $R_D = 19$ and $R_D = 29$, the McCabe–Thiele operations give the compositions indicated in Table XII. It will be noted that

TABLE XII
Plate Compositions with Various Reflux Ratios

Theoretical plates	Trial reflux ratios (interpolated)			
	$R_D = 19$	$R_D = 29$	$R_D = 24$	$R_D = \infty$
Distillate	0.86	0.86	0.86	0.86
Top plate No. 10	0.83	0.83	—	0.833
Plate No. 9	0.79	0.78	—	0.792
No. 8	0.75	0.74	—	0.753
No. 7	0.715	0.70	—	0.708
No. 6	0.688	0.66	—	0.657
No. 5	0.650	0.62	—	0.610
No. 4	0.610	0.58	—	0.560
No. 3	0.570	0.54	—	0.502
No. 2	0.535	0.50	—	0.445
Still No. 1	0.500	0.465	0.483	0.385
Sum No. 2 to No. 10	6.14	5.92	6.03	5.86

only nine theoretical plates are indicated. This is because the column is assumed to have an overall separating power of ten plates and nine in the column. The values of the compositions are those of the liquid phase.

Since the total holdup is 9 moles, the holdup per plate will be 1 mole (equal distribution being assumed in the absence of any experimental values). The composition values given in Table XII for plates Nos. 2 to 10 are therefore also the actual moles of holdup per plate of the more volatile component, and their sum is the total holdup of this component, i.e., when $R_D = 19$, $h = 6.14$ moles. Substituting in eq. (128):

$$50 \neq (91)(0.5) + 6.138 = 45.5 + 6.138 = 51.638$$

A second trial with $R_D = 29$ gives $h = 5.92$ and

$$50 \neq (91)(0.465) + 5.92 = 42.3 + 5.92 = 48.22$$

A rough interpolation for $R_D = 24$ gives $h = 6.03$ and

$$50 = (91)(0.483) + 6.03 = 43.95 + 6.03 = 49.98$$

This indicates that an initial reflux ratio (R_D) of 24 will be required to obtain the desired distillate composition ($x_{Dc} = 0.86$). It is assumed in this procedure that the distillation is started at this finite reflux ratio, rather than at total reflux, as is more usual.

If distillation is commenced with distillate composition kept constant at 0.86 by gradual increase in reflux ratio, total reflux will eventually be reached and, as before, still composition will be 0.385. The moles remaining in the still are obtained from the material balance

$$S_c x_{sc} - S_F x_{sF} - h = (S_c - H - S_F) x_{Dc} \tag{129}$$

$$50 - S_F(0.385) - 5.86 = (91 - S_F)0.86$$

$$S_F = 71.8$$

Therefore

$$\phi_J = (100 - 71.8 - 9)/58.1 = 19.2/58.1 = 0.330$$

In this instance the holdup has an appreciable effect on the results.

Edgeworth-Johnstone uses the material-balance equations

$$(S_c - S_F - H) + S_F = S_c - H$$

$$(S_c - S_F - H)x_{Dc} + S_F x_{sF} = S_c x_{sc} - h$$

and the Fenske equation to express ϕ_J

$$\phi_J = \left[\frac{S_c x_{sc} - h}{S_c x_{sc}}\right]\left[\frac{\alpha^{n+1} - \left(\frac{x_{Dc}}{1 - x_{Dc}}\right)\left(\frac{S_c - H}{S_c x_{sc} - h}\right) - 1}{\alpha^{n+1} - 1}\right] \quad (130)$$

This is the algebraic equivalent of the operations in the above example, and assumes that the distillation is continued to total reflux. The corresponding equation for a finite reflux ratio is

$$\phi_J = \frac{x_{Dc}[(x_{s0} - x_{sF}) - (h/S_c) + (Hx_{sF}/S_c)]}{x_{s0}(x_{Dc} - x_{sF})} \quad (131)$$

In this case the value of x_{sF} must be obtained from x_{Dc} by a McCabe–Thiele or Smoker calculation, using the desired final reflux ratio. The same procedure also gives the figures for estimating h by graphic means.

As an example of the use of eq. (131) the distillation of mixtures of chloro- and bromobenzene is discussed by Edgeworth-Johnstone. Young's data[166] are used with $\alpha = 1.8896$, $x_{sc} = 0.4$, $n = 10$, $H/S_c = 0.1$, and $x_{Dc} = 0.98$. The resulting values of ϕ_J are given in Table XIII, and in Figure 47. The corresponding values (ϕ_{J0}) when $H = 0$ are also included. The negative values for $R_D = 4$ indicate this reflux ratio is too low to achieve the desired separation. These negative values can however be used in making a graph, and by its means the correct initial reflux ratio can be obtained.

TABLE XIII
Yield Fraction and Reflux Ratio

R_D	x_s	ϕ_J	ϕ_{J0}
4	0.443	−0.365	−0.196
7	0.260	+0.319	+0.476
12	0.157	0.563	0.723
20	0.117	0.659	0.803

Equation 30 is modified by Edgeworth-Johnstone for application to complex mixtures to obtain

$$\phi_J = \left[\frac{S_c x_{sc} - h}{S_c x_{sc}}\right]\left[\frac{\alpha^{n+1} - \left(\frac{x_{Dc}}{1 - x_{Dc}}\right)\left[\frac{S_c(x_{sc} + x_{sB}) - H}{S_c x_{sc} - h}\right] - 1}{\alpha^{n+1} - 1}\right] \quad (132)$$

In this x_{sB} represents the initial mole fraction of the second most volatile component and it is assumed that the distillate and column contain only the two most volatile components.

As an example, 1000 moles of a ternary mixture of A, B, and C, with $x_{sc} = x_{sB} = 0.21$ and $\alpha_{AB} = 1.5$, is to be distilled under constant distillate-composition conditions through ten theoretical plates in a column with holdup of 2 moles per theoretical plate. The product contains 90 mole-% of the most volatile component, A. The holdup, h, was calculated to be 9.94. Substitution in the above equation gave $\phi_J = 0.863$.

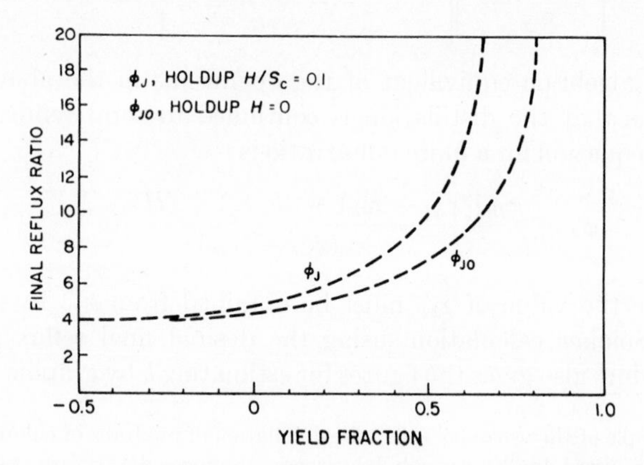

Fig. 47. Yield fraction at finite reflux ratios in distillation of chlorobenzene and bromobenzene.[162]

As another example, it is required to choose between a plate column with ten theoretical plates and holdup of 15 moles per plate, and a packed column with five theoretical plates and holdup of 3 moles per plate. Distillation at atmospheric pressure, with constant distillate composition, is to be used to produce an 80–140°F. fraction in 95% purity from a material containing 4 mole-% of this lowest boiling fraction, and 5 mole-% of the 140–160°F. fraction. These fractions are considered as the two lowest boiling components, and it is assumed no others enter the column during the distillation. Values of the relative volatility were obtained by use of the equation

$$\log \alpha_T = 2.5 \frac{T_B^2 - T_A^2}{T^2}$$

where α_T is the relative volatility at the average absolute temperature, T, of the boiling points T_A and T_B of the two components. The average boiling points of the two fractions, 110 and 150°F., were used, and average temperature at the bottom of column was estimated at 240°F., that at the top as 120°F. The corresponding values of α were 2.24 at top, 1.74 at bottom, resulting in an overall average of 1.99. Using $S_c = 2500$ moles, $x_{sc} = 0.04$, $x_{sB} = 0.05$, and $x_{Dc} = 0.95$, the McCabe–Theile construction gives $h = 9.09$ for the packed column and $h = 58.0$ for the plate column. The corresponding values for ϕ_J are $\phi_J = 0.55$ for the packed column and $\phi_J = 0.415$ for the plate column, so that the use of the packed column is indicated.

The Smoker equation or an equivalent may be combined with eq. (131) or (124), but this is only justified if many calculations are to be made, and if holdup is limited to 5% of the charge.[167]

10. Curves for Fractional Batch Distillation of Multicomponent Mixtures

The best known relation is the ratio form of the Rayleigh equation

$$\log (A_1/A_2) = \alpha_{AB} \log (B_1/B_2) \qquad (133)$$

where A_1 and A_2 are the moles of component A in the still at two different times during the batch distillation, and B_1 and B_2 have a similar meaning for a second component. This applies to any two components A and B in a multicomponent mixture, but is valid only for total reflux, negligible holdup, and constant relative volatility. The equation is derived as follows.

A multicomponent mixture has its compositions expressed, in part, as

$$x_A = A/(A + B + C + \ldots N)$$
$$x_B = B/(A + B + C + \ldots N)$$

where $A, B, C, \ldots N$ refer to the moles of the various components present. If a differential quantity of vapor is formed from the mixture just mentioned, it will contain

$$\partial A + \partial B + \partial C + \ldots \partial N$$

moles of the various components. The composition of this quantity of vapor may be expressed, in part, as

$$\frac{\partial A}{\partial A + \partial B + \partial C + \ldots \partial N} = y_A$$

$$\frac{\partial B}{\partial A + \partial B + \partial C + \ldots \partial N} = y_B$$

The values of x_A, y_A, x_B, y_B may be substituted in the relative volatility equation

$$\alpha = \frac{y_A}{y_B} \Big/ \frac{x_A}{x_B} = \frac{\partial A}{\partial B} \Big/ \frac{A}{B}$$

Thus

$$\frac{\partial A}{A} = \alpha \frac{\partial B}{B}$$

or at times 1 and 2,

$$\log A_2 = \alpha \log B_2 + (\log A_1 - \alpha \log B_1)$$

which becomes eq. (133).

The only useful general method for calculating multicomponent batch distillation curves for realistic situations is the stepwise plate-to-plate method. The procedure is the same as for the binary case except that it is not sufficient to have just one basic material balance equation for each plate in the column. Instead, it is best to set up an equation for each component on each plate and thus get compositions for each component after each interval, using the same method of computation as for the binary case. In general the new plate compositions will not add exactly to unity, so they should be normalized. An appreciable divergence from unity indicates an error in computation. An automatic computer is necessary for such calculations.

Rose and Eckhart have made such calculations for estimating the effect of holdup and reflux ratio in ternary distillation (see p. 201), and have also used the method to study the potential of one form of chromatographic distillation (p. 186). Rose and Stillman have studied amplified distillation through the use of such calculations (see Sec. IV, p. 184).

Bowman[168] devised a composition distribution concept that may be capable of development into a useful tool for multicomponent distillation calculations. The concept is applicable to steady state as well as batch distillation and is therefore described in some detail in Sec. VI.

The composition distribution concept was used by Bowman to predict the progress of a batch distillation involving any number of components. This is carried out for the case of assumed negligible holdup and total reflux by combining the Rayleigh equation in the form

$$(\partial/\partial S)(x_s S) = x_D$$

with the composition–distribution equation relating pot and distillate compositions:

$$x_D = \alpha^n x_s \Big/ \int_0^\infty \alpha^n x_s d\alpha$$

It is assumed that the column has a total of n theoretical plates. This gives

$$(\partial/\partial S)(x_s S) = \alpha^n x_s \Big/ \int_0^\infty \alpha^n x_s d\alpha$$

The variables are separated by the substitutions

$$I_1/S = \int_0^\infty \alpha^n x_s d\alpha$$

to give

$$(\partial/\partial S)(x_s S) = \alpha^n x_s S/I_1$$

or

$$\partial(x_s S)/x_s S = \alpha^n \partial S/I_1$$

and, between the limits $S = 1$ and $S = S$, integration gives

$$\ln (x_s S/x_{s0}) = \alpha^n \int_1^S (dS/I_1)$$

This gives

$$x_s = (x_{s0}/S)e^{-\alpha^n J_1(S)}$$

where

$$J_1(S) = \int_S^1 (dS/I_1)$$

Multiplication by $d\alpha$, and integration with the expression

$$\int_0^\infty x d\alpha = 1$$

gives

$$S = \int_0^\infty x_{s0} e^{-\alpha^n J_1(S)} d\alpha$$

Solution requires trial of various arbitrarily chosen values of $J_1(S)$. These are then plotted against the corresponding values of S from the last equation, and this graph is used to supply values for caculating x_s versus S, according to the relation

$$x_s = (x_{s0}/S)e^{-\alpha^n J_1(S)} \tag{134}$$

The equation

$$x_D = (\alpha^n x_{s0} e^{-\alpha J_1})/I_1 \tag{135}$$

is derived and used in a similar manner to obtain the corresponding distillate compositions. Figure 48 shows plots of distillate composition distribution for various values of S (Bowman's W) during batch distillation of

TABLE XIV
Initial Charge Composition for Hypothetical Batch Distillation of Figures 49 and 50

i	α_i	x_{ci}
1	1.00	0.3
2	1.50	0.3
3	1.75	0.1
4	2.00	0.3

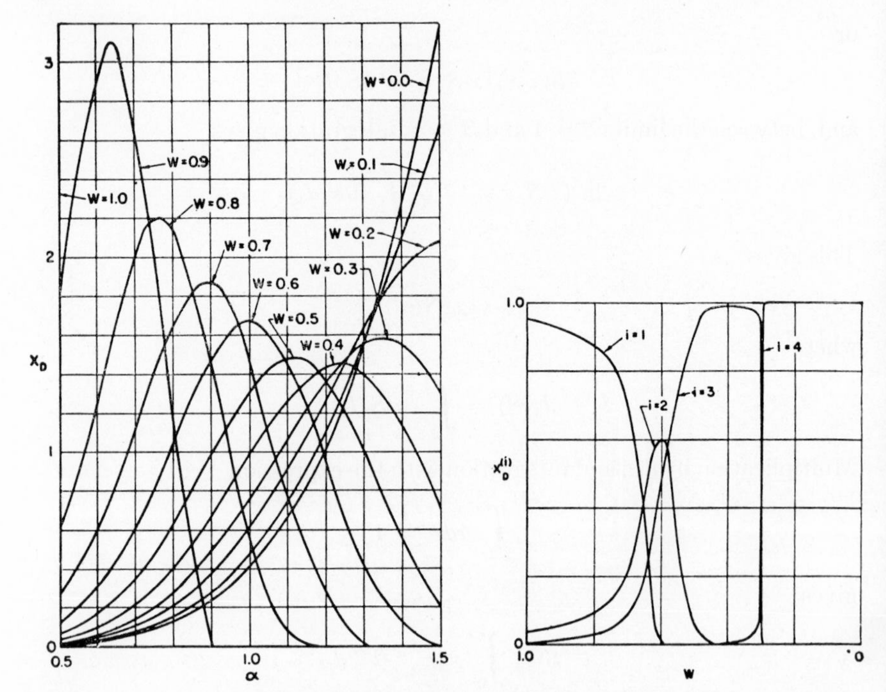

Fig. 48 (left). Distillate-composition distribution during batch distillation of multicomponent mixture.[168] $W = S$ = moles remaining in still.

Fig. 49 (right). Distillation curves for a four-component mixture.[168] $W = S$; i refers to component numbers.

a mixture with initial composition equal to that of curve I of Figure 92 (Sec. VI). Figure 49 shows distillate compositions versus S for a four-component mixture as specified in Table XIV, using a fifteen-plate column. Figure 50 is the corresponding batch-distillation curve in terms of temperature versus per cent of charge distilled. Similar equations have been derived by Bowman for the case of minimum reflux, but the procedures have not been extended to situations involving finite reflux and appreciable holdup. Harbert[169] uses a similar method for calculation of simple distillation curves of mixtures with a very large number of components, such as kerosine or other high-boiling petroleum cuts. Crosley[170] has also presented methods for calculating distillate–collection curves for multicomponent mixtures in simplified cases, but these have not been extended to practical solutions.

Kuhn and Baertschi[171] have also derived equations for the change of distillate composition with time in the distillation of a multicomponent mixture.

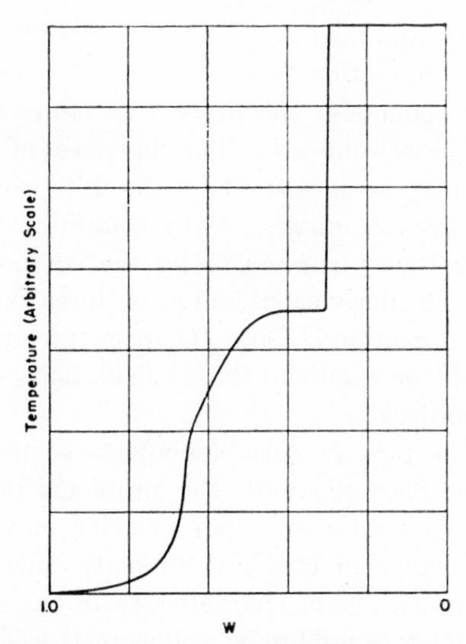

Fig. 50. Distillation curve for four-component mixture, but in terms of boiling point of distillate.[168] $W = S$.

IV. CALCULATED EFFECT OF PROCESS VARIABLES IN BATCH DISTILLATION

1. Process Variables in Batch Distillation

The more important variables of batch distillation are: (*1*) reflux ratio, (*2*) number of theoretical plates, (*3*) ratio of holdup to charge, (*4*) vapor velocity or throughput, (*5*) relative volatility, and (*6*) initial composition. The first four of these are factors dependent upon the apparatus and method of operation. The last two are characteristic of the mixture being distilled. All the variables are subject to some choice and control, but in general they are also dependent upon one another, on the physical properties of the components, and on the nature of the column and its plates or packing. Between them these variables determine the *time* required to complete a batch distillation, and the *sharpness of separation* of the components in the mixture. The minimum time required to complete the takeoff portion of a given distillation is predictable from the actual, operating vapor velocity, the average reflux ratio, and the total quantity to be distilled over. Such calculations of the time involved are straightforward except that they ignore initial equilibration time (p. 112), which is appreciable for the more efficient columns. Such calculations also ignore the fact that many batch distillations are stopped when the desired product or products have been taken overhead and a considerable fraction of the original charge remains in the still pot and does not need to be distilled to achieve the end purpose of the overall operation.

Calculations of the effects of the process variables on the sharpness of separation are much more complex. The sharpness of separation achieved in any specific case may be measured by the difference between still and product compositions (x_s, x_D curves) at any instant, or better, by the shape of distillation curves (S, x_D curves) or by the composition of successive distillate fractions. The derivations and procedures for calculation of these curves are set forth in Sections *II* and *III*, respectively. The present section deals chiefly with the results of these calculations and cites the limited experiments on the subject.

Because each of the process variables affects some of the others, it is difficult to deal *experimentally* with the problems of batch distillation. Thus a change in reflux ratio or vapor velocity may cause a change in holdup, and also a change in H.E.T.P. or plate efficiency. The gradual change in composition with time, characteristic of batch distillation, causes changes in moles or mass of holdup as well as in H.E.T.P. and probably in the rapidity with which equilibrium is established. These in turn affect all the other variables of the process, and the shape of the distillation curve. There has been, and is still, a serious lack of precise experimental data on the above interrelations. A conclusive and rigorous investigation would require a multitude of careful experiments.

Because of lack of experimental data, *calculations* of the effects of the process variables can be most useful as an approximate basis for design and operation. In order to reduce mathematical complexities, theoretical analysis has used simplifying assumptions and has considered the effect of only one variable at a time.

In evaluating and using the methods and conclusions presented, it should be recalled that in ordinary batch-distillation practice it is not usually convenient, in fact probably difficult, to get accurate measurements of reflux ratio, relative volatility, holdup, and equivalent number of theoretical plates. It is therefore of limited value to make precise predictions by calculations. The exact agreement between actual and calculated distillation curves is less important than an approximate general knowledge of how various conditions will affect the results of a particular distillation of practical interest.

The following paragraphs discuss (*1*) calculated effect of holdup; (*2*) calculated effect of reflux ratio, varying the number of plates and relative volatility, but with negligible holdup; (*3*) calculated effect of relative volatility and number of plates, under total reflux and negligible holdup (giving *limiting* conditions); (*4*) calculated effect of initial composition; and (*5*) calculated correlation of the combined effect of relative volatility, reflux ratio, and number of plates, when holdup is negligible. Each of the methods is based on a restrictive assumption, and therefore gives only limiting values or the general nature of certain relations. None of the methods developed so far can be expected to give accurate agreement with experiment. The correlation given last in the above list is the best available procedure for quickly estimating the conditions required for a given separation by batch distillation.

The discussion has been developed with respect to binary systems, which are to be assumed unless otherwise noted.

2. Calculated Effect of Holdup

A large amount of data has been collected on the H.E.T.P. or H.T.U. (described in Sec. VI) of various types of packings and contacting devices. This information is necessarily the starting point in the practical application of distillation theory. While a low H.E.T.P. is certainly desirable, it is only one of the required characteristics of a good column, since production of distillate in adequate quantities is often as important as sharp separation. Low holdup or low holdup per plate is usually mentioned as equally important, and the same may be said of high throughput per unit cross section. The ratio of throughput to holdup per plate (efficiency factor, factor A) has also been cited as a desirable criterion for evaluating packing materials. Yet both the slight experimental evidence and the calculated curves do not justify the assumption that appreciable holdup in a column is always unfavorable.

Holdup has a triple effect in batch distillation, since it limits the proportion of the charge that can be distilled, it affects the sharpness of separation of any two components, and it lengthens the time required to reach an initial degree of enrichment sufficient to warrant the removal of distillate. This has been discussed in the previous section. The disadvantages of a large holdup can sometimes be decreased by use of a larger charge, or by use of chasers (Chap. III), but this is not always possible or advantageous.

A. EFFECT ON PROPORTION OF CHARGE DISTILLED

The effect of large holdup in limiting the proportion of the charge that can be distilled is of major importance when the highest boiling component or components are present in small amount or when the available sample is limited. The magnitude and seriousness of the effect is directly proportional to the ratio between the quantity of holdup and the quantity of the highest boiling components. If the quantity of any of the latter is less than the holdup, their presence may not even be detected. This is more likely with sharp separation than with poor. No precise theoretical or experimental work has been reported on this problem. The effects mentioned are true equally of binary and multicomponent systems. A brief discussion of holdup effects in ternary batch distillation is given on p. 148.

B. EFFECT ON SHARPNESS OF SEPARATION

While the effect of a large holdup in limiting the proportion of the charge that can be distilled may be simply determined, the effect of holdup on sharpness of separation is much more complex. It would seem logical to keep holdup per plate at a minimum in order to avoid concentrating an appreciable portion of the charge within a few theoretical plates, and thus prevent its effective separation. As stated before, the evidence, both experimental and calculated, does not confirm this generally accepted opinion.

Pigford, Tepe, and Garrahan[172] (see pp. 101, 226) have calculated batch-distillation curves for cases involving appreciable holdup. Their calculations were made by using a differential analyzer to solve the basic differential equations previously derived by Marshall and Pigford.[173] The vapor holdup was assumed negligible, and vapor–liquid equilibrium was assumed to be of the form $y = \alpha' x + (\alpha' - 1)x^2$, where $\alpha' = (3\alpha - 1)/(\alpha + 1)$. The usual relative volatility relation was avoided because it reduces the capacity of the differential analyzer. Some discrepancies in material balances also occur when this procedure is used. Calculations were made for eighteen cases, as summarized in Table XV, but five were discarded because material balance errors were more than 3 mole-%. All cases were for a seven-plate column, with initial equilibrium at total reflux. The charge composition was taken as approximately 0.5 mole fraction of the more volatile component, as indicated in Table XV. This also gives the size of the intermediate fractions (I) having composition limits $x_D = 0.95$ and $x_D = 0.05$. The last column of the table gives the mole fraction of the more volatile component that would be obtained if all the distillate and the residue in the column were combined. These values should be identical with charge composition; the discrepancies are apparently due to computation errors of some kind.

Based on these calculations, Pigford, Tepe, and Garrahan concluded that there was a general tendency for the size of the intermediate fraction to increase with increasing holdup. In one case involving high relative volatility the size of the intermediate fraction went through a minimum with increasing holdup, the optimum being for holdup corresponding to 2% of the charge. The authors made a preliminary correlation of the results in terms of $(H_i/S_0)/(\alpha - 1)$ and $1/(\alpha - 1)(R_D)$. They concluded that the presence of holdup in a column results in an inertia effect that makes sharp separations sharper, but fails to affect relatively poor separations. This effect is stated to be more noticeable at the lower reflux

TABLE XV
Effect of Holdup on Size of Intermediate Fraction[172]

α	R_D	H/S_0	I	x_c	x_c (check)
2.23	8	0.024	0.269	0.470	0.451
2.23	8	0.024	0.279	0.470	0.456
2.23	8	0.029	0.294	0.482	0.475
2.23	3.2	0.045	0.490	0.473	0.466
2.23	4	0.045	0.431	0.473	0.468
2.23	8	0.045	0.350	0.473	0.463
2	10	0.02	0.31	0.502	0.478
2	10	0.04	0.38	0.502	0.486
3	10	0.02	0.126	0.510	0.504
3	10	0.04	0.170	0.518	0.495
3	10	0.08	0.310	0.526	0.506
3	3.2	0.04	0.248	0.518	0.515
1.5	10	0.02	0.834	0.535	0.519
1.15	10	0.02	—	0.500	0.484

ratios. Some of the calculations are for cases corresponding approximately to the experiments of Colburn and Stearns,[174] and, while direct comparisons were not made, it was noted that the calculated intermediate fractions approximated those obtained experimentally.

Figures 51 A, B, and C show the results of calculations by Rose, Johnson, and Williams,[175] using the stepwise plate-to-plate method described on p. 101. In Figure 51A the curves were calculated for distillation of a mixture containing 9.6 mole-% ethylene chloride in toluene, through a five-plate column with reflux ratio 4/1 and holdup of 2.88, 7.2, 14.4, 28.8, and 57.6% of the charge. These calculations are for a startup procedure such that the column was at equilibrium at total reflux before the start of the distillation. The curves of Figure 51B were calculated for the same distillation conditions except that holdup was assumed as 28.8 and 57.6% and the column at equilibrium at 4/1 reflux (with return of product to still) before the batch operation commenced. The favorable effect of the total reflux startup is obvious. From the curves of Figure 51A it is clear that the effect of increasing the ratio of holdup to charge is complex. For holdup of 2.88% relatively poor separation is achieved. Holdup-to-charge ratios of 14.4 and 28.8% give the best separation while 57.6% holdup gives poor separation. The calculated separation curves for total reflux–zero holdup, and 4/1 finite reflux–zero holdup are given for comparison. The beneficial effect of holdup involves concentration of the more volatile component in the upper portion of the column by the total reflux startup. There is in addition a damping effect of holdup on maintenance of any favorable composition distribution after takeoff at 4/1 reflux ratio is

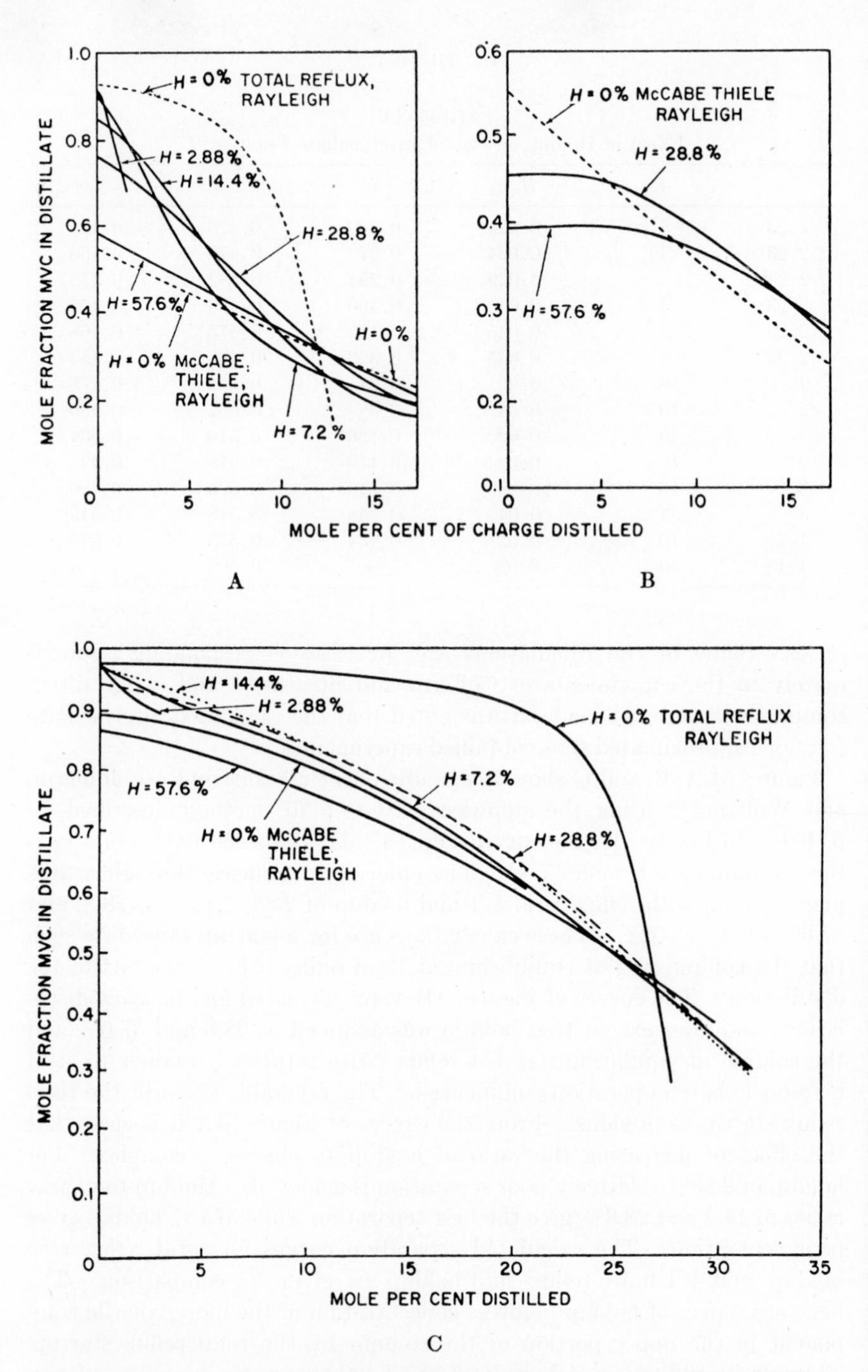

Fig. 51. Curves for batch distillation of ethylene chloride–toluene mixtures with appreciable holdup.[175] (A) Calculated; five theoretical plates and still; 9.6 mole-% ethylene chloride in charge; total reflux startup. (B) Calculated; five theoretical plates and

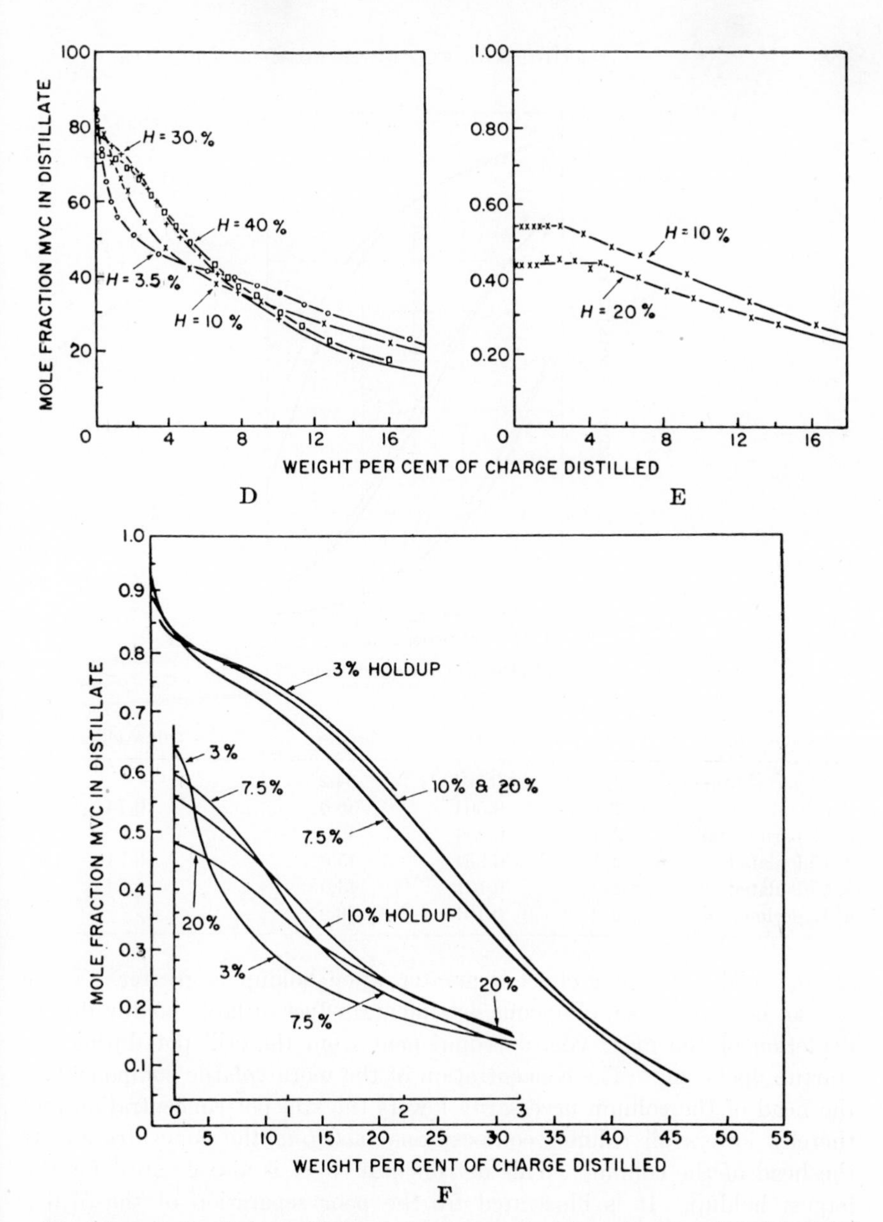

still; 9.6 mole-% ethylene chloride in charge; finite reflux startup. (C) Calculated; five theoretical plates and still; 25 mole-% ethylene chloride in charge; total reflux startup. (D) Experimental; four theoretical plates and still; 9.6% by weight ethylene chloride in charge; total reflux startup. (E) Experimental; four theoretical plates and still; 9.6% by weight ethylene chloride in charge; finite reflux startup. (F) Experimental; four theoretical plates and still; 25% by weight ethylene chloride in charge; total reflux startup. Reflux ratio, R_D, is 4/1 except where otherwise noted. Holdup in A, B, C is mole per cent of charge; in D. E, F it is weight per cent of charge.

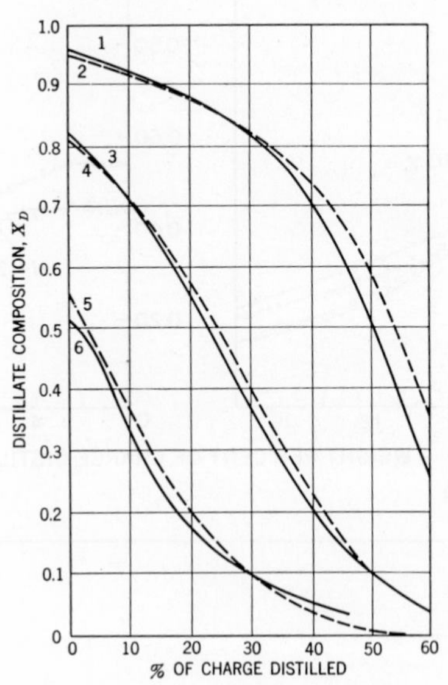

Fig. 52. Results of Calculations.[176]

Curve No.	R_D	x_c	holdup, %	e (plate efficiency)
1. Experimental	2/1	0.504	34.2	
2. Calculated	2/1	0.504	36.0	0.74
3. Experimental	2/1	0.254	40.1	
4. Calculated	2/1	0.254	45.0	0.74
5. Calculated	2/1	0.101	43.0	0.74
6. Experimental	2/1	0.101	36.9	

started. This damping effect is greater when holdup is greater. There is also, however, a simultaneous detrimental effect of large holdup due to depletion of the more volatile component from the still pot during the startup operation. The concentration of the more volatile component at the head of the column necessarily lowers the still pot concentration and thereby lowers all column compositions *including* the concentration at the head of the column. This detrimental effect is also greatest for the largest holdup. It is illustrated by the poor separation of the 57.6% curve. In this case the detrimental effect of high holdup predominates. In the case of the 2.88 and 7.2% holdup curves, the beneficial effect of total reflux predominates, but after takeoff starts, the damping effect is limited and the curves drop rapidly. Curves for holdup even less than 2.88% would start at even greater compositions (near the start of the $H = 0$ total reflux curve) and drop very rapidly nearly to the $H = 0$ McCabe–Thiele 4/1 reflux ratio curve.

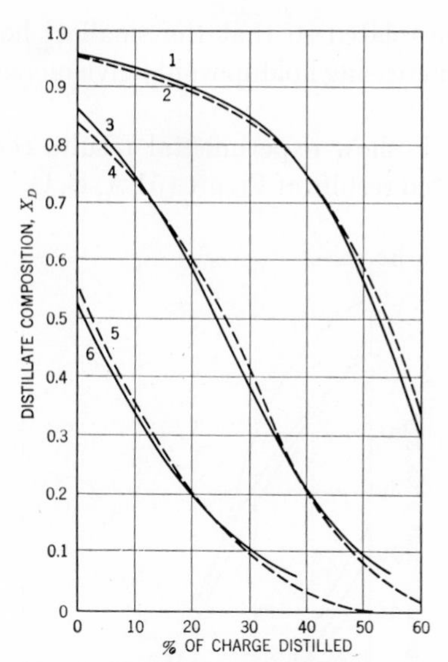

Fig. 53. Results of calculations.[176]

Curve No.	R_D	x_c	holdup, %	e
1. Experimental	4/1	0.504	34.4	
2. Calculated	4/1	0.504	36.0	0.74
3. Experimental	4/1	0.254	30.9	
4. Calculated	4/1	0.254	35.0	0.74
5. Calculated	4/1	0.101	43.0	0.74
6. Experimental	4/1	0.101	36.7	

The same complicated interrelated effects are visible to a lesser extent on Figure 51C, which is for a 25 mole-% charge composition of more volatile component, instead of the 9.6% of Figure 51A. The greater proportion of more volatile material in the charge and the consequent greater proportion of distillate taken off with high purity make all the effects less extreme, and the overall effects of holdup are not so great. The 2.88% holdup curve still shows a relatively rapid initial drop. This is no longer noticeable on the 7.2% curve. The 57.6% holdup curve shows the poorest separation, for the same reasons as mentioned before, and the curves for intermediate holdups are closely similar because the beneficial and detrimental effects of holdup are nearly balanced.

Figure 51B, calculated for a 4/1 finite reflux ratio startup (with return of distillate to the still pot), brings out the importance of the effect of startup procedure. In this case there is no beneficial effect of total reflux startup and as a consequence no beneficial effect of increased holdup is shown. Only two curves are shown but there is no doubt that curves for lesser holdups would all be related so that the smallest holdup would give the best separation and increasing holdup would give increasingly poorer separation.

Figures 51 D, E, F show experimental results corresponding approximately to the calculated results of Figures 51 A, B, C.

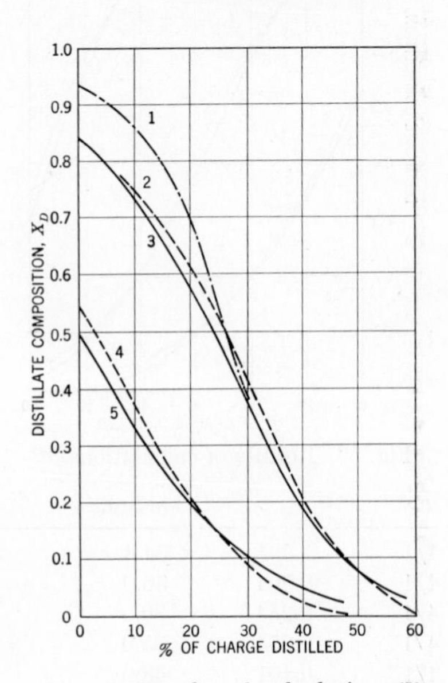

Fig. 54. Results of calculations.[176]

Curve No.	R_D	x_c	holdup, %	e
1. Calculated	9/1	0.250	28.8	1.0
2. Calculated	9/1	0.254	35.0	0.74
3. Experimental	9/1	0.254	30.6	
4. Calculated	9/1	0.101	43.0	0.74
5. Experimental	9/1	0.101	36.6	

The preceding work shows that there are at least two effects of holdup in batch distillation:

(*1*) There is a damping or inertia effect of large holdup that tends to maintain whatever composition has been previously established.

(*2*) There is a depletion effect of large holdup that is always detrimental, but may be overbalanced by the beneficial damping effect.

The general interrelations of the inertia and depletion effects near the beginning of a distillation are evident in the results of the calculations and experiments just described. The same kind of inertia and depletion effects also affect the distillation near the cut point when one component is becoming depleted in the entire system, but the interrelations in this part of the distillation are difficult to clarify.

It is emphasized that throughout the preceding and following discussion there is no reference to the effect of holdup during the startup period prior to removal of any distillate. This is governed by entirely different considerations and is discussed under *equilibration time* in Section III. As is usually the case in laboratory distillation, the discussion here is about total reflux startup except where noted.

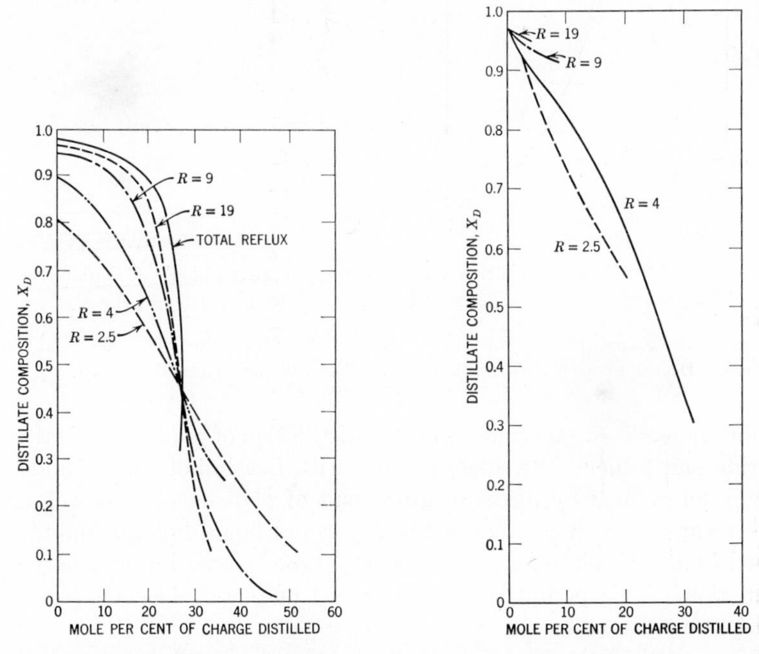

Fig. 55 (left). Distillate composition vs. mole-% of charge distilled. Calculated curves. Holdup = 0, α = 2.23, x_c = 0.250, five plates and still pot, $R = R_D$.[176]

Fig. 56 (right). Distillate composition vs. mole-% of charge distilled. Calculated curves. Holdup = 7.2%, α = 2.23, x_c = 0.250, five plates and still pot, $R = R_D$.[176]

Additional calculations by automatic computer have proved to be a most important tool in confirming the validity of the conclusions just stated. Johnson[176] provided such confirmation by carrying out further calculations and experiments for batch distillation with identical materials, charge compositions, plates, and reflux ratios. In each case there was good agreement. Additional computations were then performed to extend the calculations already presented, all of which were done by the stepwise method (pp. 101 and 135).

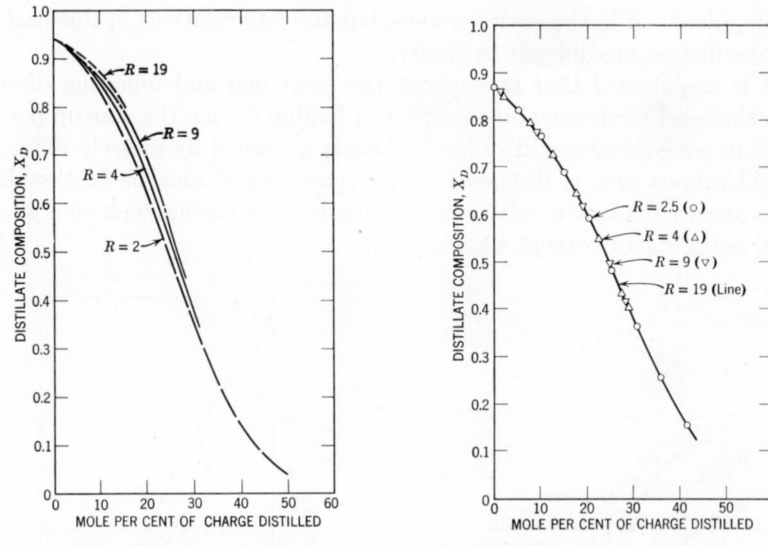

Fig. 57 (left). Distillate composition vs. mole-% of charge distilled. Calculated curves. Holdup = 28.8%, α = 2.23, x_c = 0.250, five plates and still pot, $R = R_D$.[176]

Fig. 58 (right). Distillate composition vs. mole-% of charge distilled. Calculated curves. Holdup = 57.6%, α = 2.23, x_c = 0.250, five plates and still pot, $R = R_{D'}$.[176]

Johnson made 35 experiments on the distillation of a mixture of ethylene chloride and toluene in a small column with five bubble plates and with holdup determined by direct measurement of plate volume as well as by other means. Small samples of the vapor and liquid holdup could be removed from each plate for analysis at any time before, during, or after the distillation. This permitted determination of plate efficiency as well as holdup composition.

The results of the direct comparison of experimental and calculated curves are shown in Figures 52–54.[177] The calculations in this case were made for 74% plate efficiency, corresponding to the results of the plate efficiency measurements based on vapor and liquid samples taken from each plate during actual distillations.

The theoretical, i.e, calculated, curves of distillate composition versus per cent of charge distilled are presented in Figures 55–58. For each individual figure the holdup is constant and the reflux ratio is the parameter. The curves differ most from each other when zero holdup is assumed. As holdup is increased, the reflux ratio has less and less influence on the course of the distillation. At 57.6% holdup (Fig. 58) the curves are practically identical. It should be noted that the curves in each set (for a given holdup) start at the same point, except for the case of zero holdup (Fig. 55).

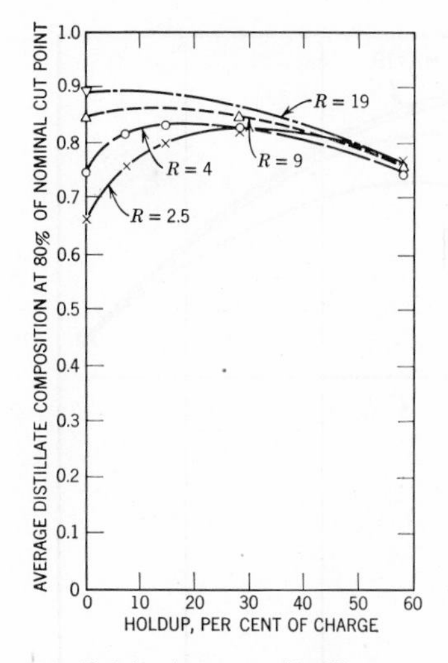

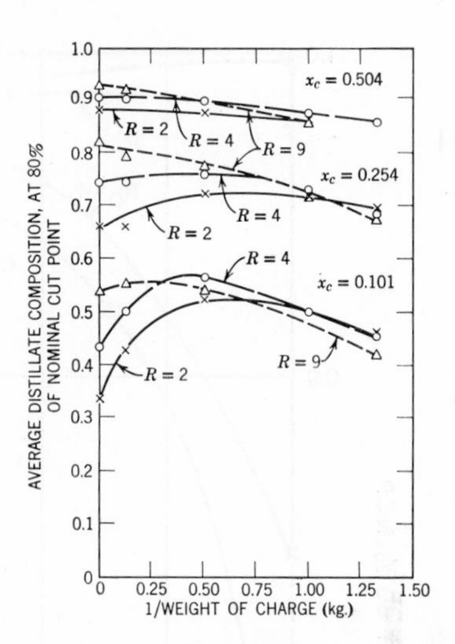

Fig. 59 (left). Average distillate composition at 80% of nominal cut point vs. % holdup—from theoretical calculations. $n = 5$, $R = R_D$.[176]

Fig. 60 (right). Average distillate composition at 80% of nominal cut point vs. reciprocal of weight of charge (equivalent to per cent holdup)—experimental values, $R = R_D$.[176]

This last case is not entirely comparable because zero holdup is an imaginary condition. Curves for a finite but small holdup and finite reflux would start at a common point (the total reflux starting point) and then drop almost vertically so as to appear identical with the curves of Figure 55.

The corresponding series of experimental curves shows exactly these same trends and interrelations.

When the various individual calculated curves were replotted with reflux ratios held constant in any group, and with holdup as the parameter, it was made clear that holdup had the same effect in every case. As holdup decreases the initial composition approaches more closely the initial composition for total reflux-zero holdup. However, in each case, i.e., curve, as the distillation progresses, the curve tends to approach the curve calculated for the McCabe–Thiele zero holdup. The lower the holdup the more closely the main part of the curve tends to follow the latter zero holdup line. The corresponding experimental curves show exactly the same pattern.

It is also possible to express the results of the calculations by plots of distillate composition versus still composition. All the calculated and experimental values follow the pattern shown in Figure 14 (p. 49). Briefly the relationship is this: As the holdup is increased, the x_D vs. x_s curve

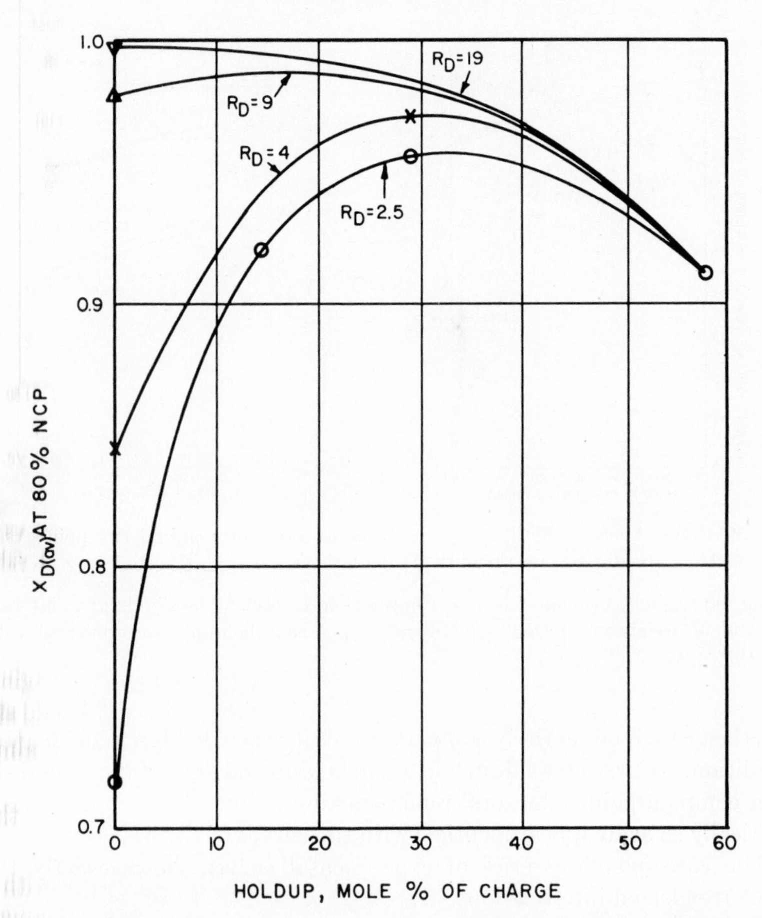

Fig. 61. Average distillate composition at 80% of nominal cut point vs. % holdup—calculated values. Ten plates, $\alpha = 2.23$, $x_c = 0.25$.

approaches the total reflux line; as the holdup is lowered, the x_D vs. x_s curve approaches the McCabe–Thiele line.

In some cases the high holdup curve tends to cross and lie above the total reflux line, thus implying that the operating line may fall below the diagonal. In many cases the low-holdup line falls below the McCabe–Thiele line for a portion of the distillation. This effect is probably caused by total reflux startup.

It is often difficult to compare distillation curves as such. Consequently, various indices have been proposed which make it possible to express a curve as a single number or quantity. In this work the different curves were compared by taking the average product composition at 80% of the

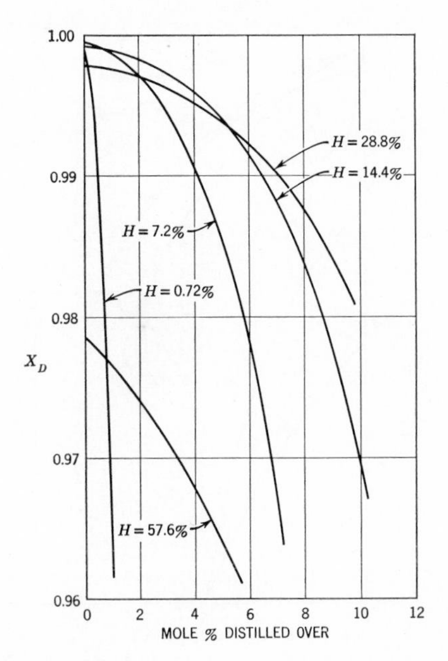

Fig. 62. Initial portions of calculated distillation curves. $R_D = 2.5$, $n = 10$, $x_c = 0.25$. 0% holdup curve not shown, but starts at $x_D = 0.864$.

nominal cut point as a measure of the sharpness of separation. (The nominal cut point is defined as the point in the distillation at which the quantity of distillate removed is equal to the quantity of more volatile component charged.) This allows presentation of all the results of the theoretical calculations on one graph (Fig. 59), and all the results of the experimental distillations on one other graph (Fig. 60). If the terms beneficial and detrimental are interpreted to mean that the average composition at the 80% point is raised or lowered by increased holdup, then the following observations may be made from Figure 59.

At high reflux ratio increased holdup is detrimental. (Not enough points are available on the line for $R = 19$ to show its exact course.) As reflux ratio is decreased the sharpness of separation has more and more of a tendency to start at a relatively low point with low holdup, rise to a maximum, and thereafter decrease as holdup increases. A rather large holdup (15 to 30%) is necessary for the highest degree of separation at the low reflux ratios.

At very high values of holdup the reflux ratio has little influence on the sharpness of separation. Actually, it appears that a low reflux ratio is better, but the difference is small.

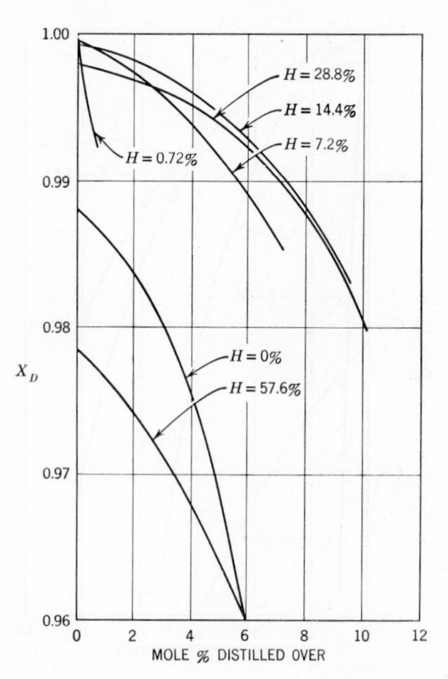

Fig. 63. Initial portions of calculated distillation curves. $R_D = 4.0$, $n = 10$, $x_c = 0.25$.

In addition to verifying the above, the experimental curves (Fig. 60) lead to additional observations:

The effect of reflux ratio is much more pronounced at low values of product composition. In the present work the lower product composition was caused by lower charge composition. This suggests that the chief reason for the beneficial effect of holdup is the total reflux startup that is an integral part of all conventional batch-distillation operations. It is conceivable that the same results would be obtained with a higher charge composition but lower relative volatility or lower separating power of the column.

The results described here confirm those of all earlier work.[178] O'Brien also[179] had observed good agreement between experimental results in 100-plate columns and corresponding calculated results. Results that are apparently contradictory prove not to be so if comparison is made for the same ranges of reflux ratios, holdup, and charge composition.

The results of the inertia and depletion forces during the initial portion of a batch distillation were mentioned previously on p. 140. As the distillation progresses, the inertia force has the effect of improving the separation between the first and second component. The relatively high purity with respect to the first component is caused to persist to a higher per cent of

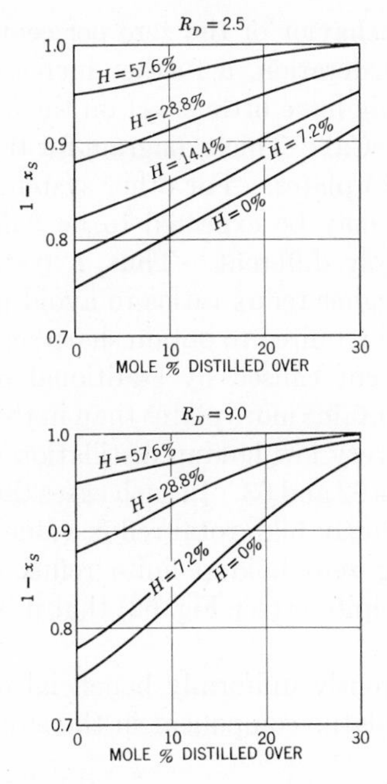

Fig. 64. Still pot composition (less volatile component) vs. % distilled. Calculated curves. $n = 5$, $\alpha = 2.23$, $x_c = 0.25$. Holdup is parameter.

charge distilled for the higher per cents of holdup. The initial effect of depletion is of course carried on into the distillation proper. The actual result of higher holdup in any particular distillation is determined by the relative magnitude of whatever beneficial effects result from the inertia force, as compared with the detrimental effect of the depletion. This will differ greatly for different mixtures, columns, and operating conditions. The situation is further complicated by the fact that *(1)* compositions during the early portion of a batch distillation have an effect on all subsequent compositions, and *(2)* the holdup effects are not independent of one another.

The extension of the work of Johnson to a ten-theoretical-plate column gives the results summarized by Figure 61.[180] The favorable effect of increase in holdup at low reflux ratios is more pronounced with ten plates than with five. An increase in number of plates at any reflux ratio increases the value of average distillate composition at 80% nominal cut point at any value of per cent holdup. For a given reflux ratio, the sharpness of separation increases at any per cent holdup as the number of plates is increased from five to ten. The magnitude of this increase in sharpness of separation increases as the per cent holdup increases.

On the basis of the behavior of the zero per cent holdup curves for the reflux ratios under consideration, a further increase in number of plates above ten would probably have little effect on the sharpness of separation. The pinch point on a McCabe–Thiele diagram for this system occurs in the neighborhood of 10 to 15 plates. For other systems the same qualitative effects of the variables may be expected to be valid. Numerical values may, however, be entirely different. Thus, a system with lower relative volatility will require higher reflux ratios to avoid pinching; at the same time more plates will be required to obtain sharp separations. The diminishing rate of improvement caused by additional plates will not be evident until the column contains more plates than in the case described here.

The true course of a very low holdup distillation that is started at total reflux is shown in Figures 62 and 63. In such cases the distillate composition curve starts at the relatively high total reflux value, but drops rapidly toward the corresponding zero holdup–finite reflux curve. At low reflux ratios the drop is so precipitous (see Fig. 62) that it is difficult or impossible to find it experimentally.

High holdup is apparently uniformly beneficial if the criterion is yield and purity of the *less* volatile component in the still pot. Figure 64 gives typical relations.

Husain and co-workers[180a] have suggested two approximate methods to relate sharpness of separation in batch distillation to holdup and the other operating variables. One of these suggestions was reported to give experimental values on four mixtures (carbon tetrachloride–benzene, *n*-heptane–toluene, benzene–*n*-heptane, and carbon tetrachloride–toluene) that were within ±10% of the predicted yield of the more volatile component in the desired fraction. The method of calculation uses the McCabe–Thiele method to calculate the theoretical plates and reflux ratio required to get from the desired average composition of the total distillate corresponding to a particular per cent distilled to the corresponding bottoms composition. The latter is calculated by material balance based on the charge composition, the desired distillate composition, and empirical corrections for holdup. It has not been reported whether there is any theoretical basis for expecting the empirical corrections to give correct results for mixtures and conditions other than those already studied experimentally.

C. EFFECT IN MULTICOMPONENT DISTILLATION

The effect of holdup in multicomponent batch distillation has been explored experimentally by Rose and O'Brien.[181] Mixtures of *n*-hexane, methylcyclohexane, and toluene were distilled in an 80-plate column with holdup-to-charge ratios ranging from 4.5 to 18 mole-%. Various reflux ratios and two different charge compositions were used. The general effects of holdup were found to be similar to those for binary distillations, except that the effect for any pair of components was related to the ratio of the holdup to the quantity of the same two components in the charge, rather than to the total charge. When two components that came off consecutively constituted a major portion of the charge, then the separation of these two components was similar to their separation when the corresponding binary was distilled under the same conditions. When holdup was 9% or less, the course of the separation of the two most volatile components could be predicted by assuming that they alone were present and calculating the corresponding binary curve for zero holdup. However, the separation of two less volatile components could not be predicted even approximately by this procedure. There was indication that the critical reflux ratio depended mainly on the number of theoretical plates and was numerically equal to roughly one-half of this number. Detailed results were presented for over 20 experimental distillations under different conditions.

The stepwise numerical method for predicting batch distillation curves for cases with appreciable holdup can be applied to multicomponent mixtures. The results of such a calculation are shown in Figure 87 (Sec. V). Figure 88 summarizes the results of a group of such calculations made for ternary mixtures of various compositions and corresponding to various operating conditions.

3. Calculated Effect of Reflux Ratio, Relative Volatility, and Theoretical Plates When Holdup is Negligible

Curves to show the effect of these variables on the sharpness of separation have been calculated[182] by the equation:

$$\log S_t = \log S_c - \frac{1}{2.303} \int_{x_{st}}^{x_{sc}} \frac{dx_s}{x_D - x_s}$$

The details of the derivations and methods of calculation are those described on p. 77. The procedure always depends upon the numerical solution of the log S_t equation. Graphs of per cent distilled vs. distillate composition—$100\ (S_c - S_t)/S_c$ vs. x_D—may be constructed as in Figures 31 and 65. For example, the curve marked 1 in Figure 65A represents the distillation of 100 moles of an equimolar binary mixture with $\alpha = 1.5$, n (number of plates) $= 11$, reflux ratio $(R_D) = 1$, and negligible holdup. The series of values of x_D and x_s used in evaluating the integral in the log S_t equation were obtained from still-product composition curves such as those of Sec. II. These were calculated by using the McCabe–Thiele or Smoker procedures.

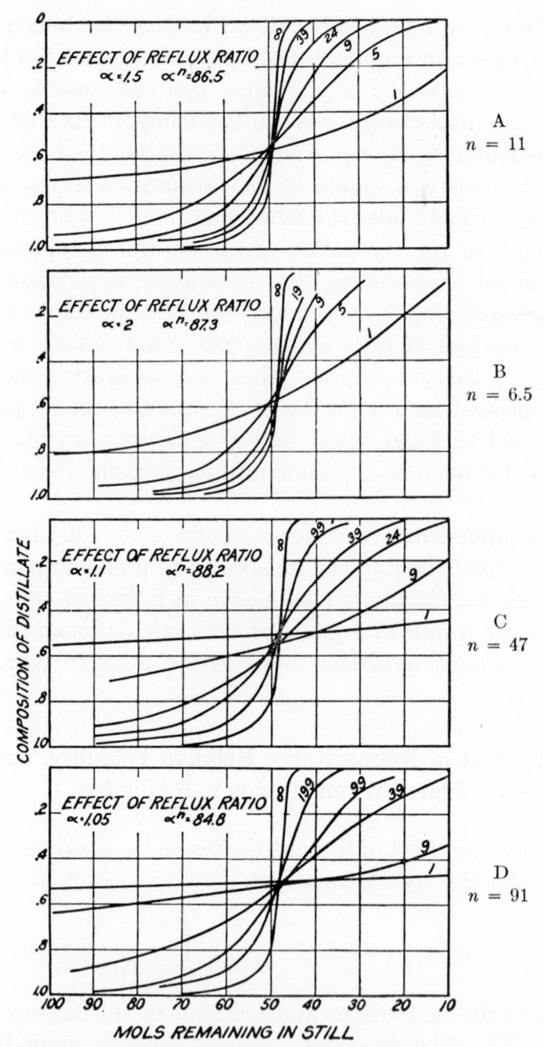

Fig. 65. Calculated effect of reflux ratio when holdup is assumed to be negligible.[182] Ordinary distillation curves. % charge distilled = 100 − moles remaining in still. Numbers on curves indicate reflux ratio, R_D.

The choice of a charge other than 100 moles in the preceding calculation would make no difference in the final curve, if values of S are converted to per cent distilled. The chief effect of an initial composition other than $x_s = 0.5$ would be to displace the curve in a horizontal direction, but there would also be an increase in the sharpness of the break as higher values of S were used. The succeeding curves in this discussion are calculated on the basis of 100 moles and initial composition (x_s) of 0.5. A change in the relative volatility, the number of plates, or the reflux ratio used in this calculation would cause a change in the still–product composition curve, and therefore in the series of values x_s and x_D and finally in values of log S, and thus change the shape of the distillation curve. The McCabe–Thiele procedure or the Smoker equation were used in all the examples of Figure 65, but any other suitable method (Secs. II and VI) could be used if simplifying assumptions are not valid. Thus, if holdup is negligible, the equation above may be used to estimate effect on batch-distillation curves of reflux ratio, relative volatility, theoretical plates, or any other variable that can affect still–product relations. Over the restricted range that has been investigated, curves calculated by use of this equation coincided closely with experimental curves,[183] within the limits of experimental error in reflux ratio and H.E.T.P. determinations.

A. EFFECT OF REFLUX RATIO

Calculations from Log S_t Equation. The calculated curves of Figure 65 give a definite idea of the relative advantage of successive increases in reflux ratio when holdup is negligible. Figure 65A shows the effect when relative volatility is 1.5 and there are eleven plates; Figures 65 B–D give similar sets of curves for mixtures with higher and lower relative volatilities. Each of these sets of curves has distinct characteristics in spite of the fact that the overall fractionating factor, α^n, is approximately equal in all cases. Thus in Figures 65A and B, when $\alpha = 1.5$ and 2, respectively, a reflux ratio of 9 is sufficient for a fair separation, and increase of R_D beyond about 30 results in little further improvement in sharpness of separation. This is emphasized by comparison with the curves for the sharpest possible separation calculated on the assumption of distillation under total reflux ($R_D = \infty$). The curves of Figures 65C and D were calculated for smaller values of α (1.1 and 1.05) but larger n so that α^n is approximately the same as for Figures 65A and B. In these cases a reflux ratio of 9 results in poor separation and high reflux ratios are necessary to achieve sharp separation. Increase of R_D to 99 or 199 results in an appreciable improvement in these examples.

Methods of Summarizing Effect of Reflux Ratio. In order to show clearly the effect of reflux ratio and other process variables under different conditions of distillation, it is desirable to have some method of combining and summarizing all results from studies such as those of Figure 65. This may be done in a variety of ways, some of which are illustrated in Figure 66. Yield fraction (p. 120) could similarly be used, but published curves are lacking.

In Figure 66A the size of the intermediate fraction (I) is plotted against reflux ratio for each of the curves of Figure 65, as well as for some additional similar studies. The intermediate fraction includes all the distillate intermediate in composition between the cut purest in the more volatile

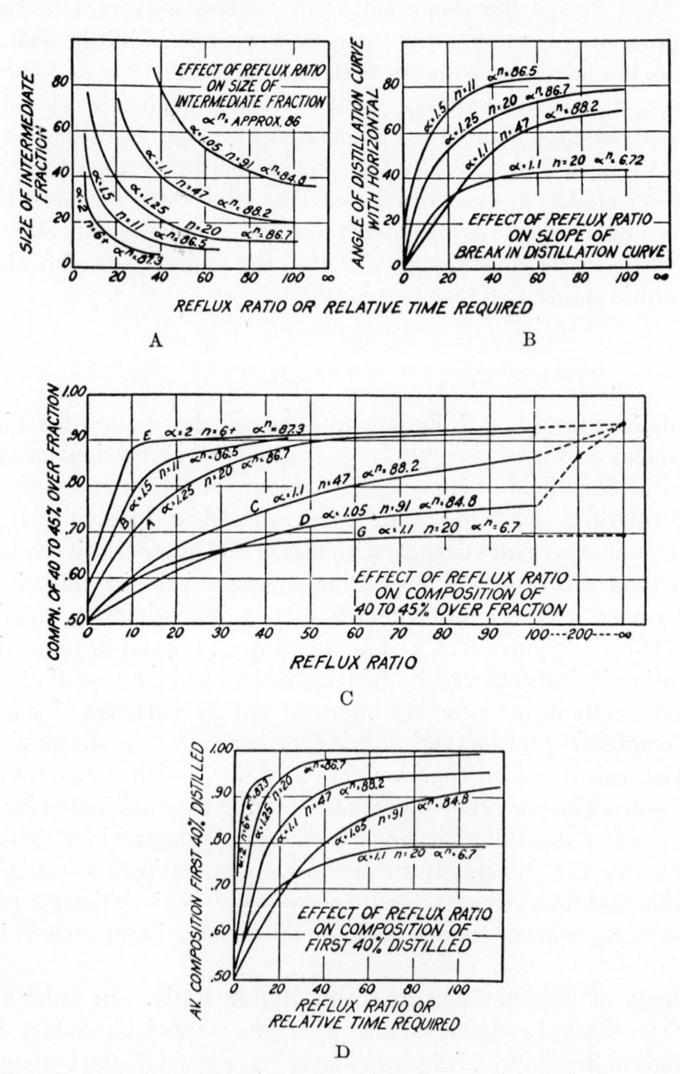

Fig. 66. Calculated effect of reflux ratio when holdup is assumed to be negligible.[182] (A) on size of intermediate fraction. (B) on slope of break in distillation curve; the figure plots the angle of the distillation curve with the horizontal rather than the actual slope. (C) On composition of 40–45% fraction. (D) On composition of first 40% distilled.

component and that purest in the other component. In the present case the limits of purity have been arbitrarily chosen as 0.9 and 0.1 (mole fraction of more volatile component). The numerical value for such an intermediate fraction can be read from Figure 65A as $S_{xD=0.9} - S_{xD=0.1}$. For the $R_D = 9$ curve, this is approximately 33. Such curves are advantageous in that they show the relation between the reflux ratio and the results directly, the lowest possible values of I being the most desirable. The value of I may also be calculated by formulas such as the following. For the simple case in which both total reflux and negligible holdup may be assumed:

$$\begin{aligned} I &= S_{xD=0.9} - S_{xD=0.1} \\ &= k_D'(0.9)^{1/(\alpha^n - 1)}[\alpha^n - (0.9)(\alpha^n - 1)]/(1 - 0.9)^{\alpha^n/(\alpha^n - 1)} \\ &\qquad - k_D'(0.1)^{1/(\alpha^n - 1)}[\alpha^n - (0.1)(\alpha^n - 1)]/(1 - 0.1)^{\alpha^n/(\alpha^n - 1)} \end{aligned}$$

This is a form of the solution of the Rayleigh equation for fractional distillation by means of the Fenske equation (p. 82). The size of the intermediate fraction, that is, the sharpness of separation, depends only on α^n and k_D' in this case. The integration constant k_D' in turn depends upon charge composition and on α^n so that these are the ultimate variables for the case in which total reflux is assumed. The choice of $x_D = 0.9$ and $x_D = 0.1$ as the limits of the intermediate fraction is arbitrary. Other choices may be made as convenience dictates. Similar equations may be derived for cases in which total reflux and negligible holdup cannot be assumed. In such cases the size of the intermediate fraction depends upon the actual reflux ratio and holdup.

A second method of summarizing the effect of reflux ratio is given in Figure 66B in which the slope of the steepest portion of the break in the various curves of Figure 65 is used as a measure of the sharpness of separation and is plotted against the reflux ratio. This method would be useful in cases such as total reflux, in which an algebraic solution exists for the log S_t because the value of the slope at the point of inflection where it is at a maximum can be found directly by mathematical methods and without resort to the plotting of graphs.

Probably the simplest and most useful criterion in batch fractionation is the purity of an arbitrarily chosen fraction collected at a specified point just prior to the break in the distillation curve. In Figure 66C the purity (as to the more volatile component) of the fraction coming over between 40 and 45% distilled ($S = 60$ to 55) is plotted against the reflux ratio. This set of curves probably shows most clearly the effect of reflux ratio and the variation of this effect with α, α^n, and n. The larger values of x_D at 40 to 45% distilled represent sharper fractionation. Curves A, B, and

E show the marked effect of reflux ratio when α and α^n are both large and R_D is small; curves C and D show the relatively slight effect when α is small, even though α^n is just as large as for curves A, B, and E. Comparison of curves G and C shows the effect of increasing n when α is small.

Since the time required for distillation of a specified amount of product is directly proportional to the reflux ratio used, curves such as those of Figure 66 give a relation between the time required and the results of a distillation. In Figure 66D, the average composition of the first 40% distilled is plotted against the reflux ratio for various typical cases of batch distillation. Such relations are of great practical interest since the proportion of the charge that is recovered and the purity of the products obtained in a distillation determine the return on the operation, while the reflux ratio is directly related to the time, heat input, and cooling water consumed. A complete study must of course include the variation of prices with purity, and construction costs per theoretical plate.

B. EFFECT OF REFLUX RATIO ON EFFECT OF NUMBER OF PLATES

Figure 67A gives calculated curves for the distillation of an ideal equimolar binary mixture with $\alpha = 1.25$ and reflux ratio $R_D = 9$ in apparatus

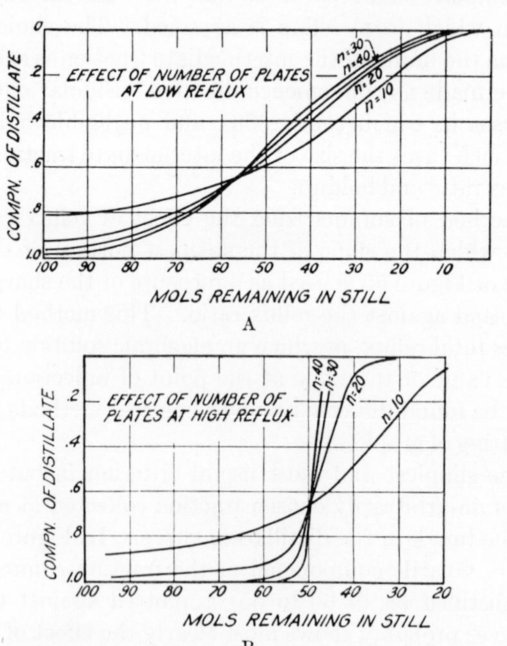

Fig. 67. Calculated effect of number of theoretical plates; $\alpha = 1.25$; (A) at low reflux ratio ($R_D = 9$); (B) at high reflux ratio ($R_D = 49$).[182]

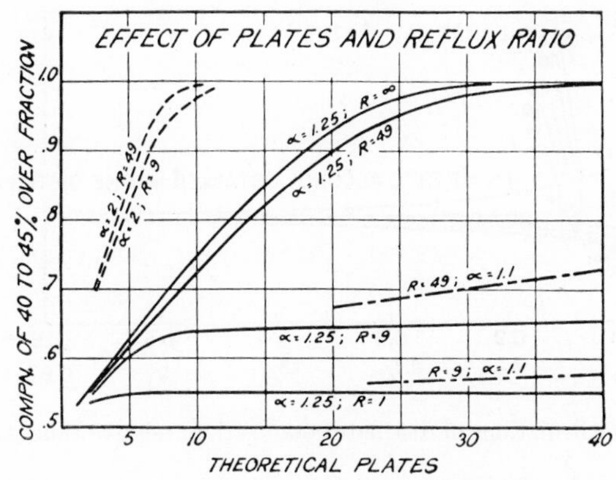

Fig. 68. Summary of calculated effects of theoretical plates and reflux ratio ($R = R_D$).[182]

with the equivalent of 10, 20, 30, and 40 plates. Figure 67B gives similar curves for the identical case when $R_D = 49$. Figure 68 summarizes these and a number of other cases by the method of Figure 66C (40 to 45% fraction). The heavy lines on Figure 68 refer to Figures 67A and B and similar unpublished curves and show the large effect of n when R_D is large and the slight effect when R_D is small. They also show that increase in reflux ratio beyond 49 gives little improvement in separation when $\alpha = 1.25$ and that there is little to be gained by using a large number of plates when R_D has as low a value as 9. The other curves of Figure 68 indicate the changes in these relations when α has smaller or larger values. In each case, as R_D is increased, the sharpness of separation approaches that of distillation under total reflux. When α is large (1.5 or 2.0) the limiting sharpness of separation is nearly reached at low values of R_D, and further increase in R_D can have but little effect. With the smaller values of α (1.1 or 1.05) the limiting sharpness is approached more gradually and regularly as R_D is increased. This approach is often so gradual that it is of considerable value to know the limiting sharpness of separation for a specific case. Thus by making calculations for total reflux it is possible to show definitely that curve D of Figure 66C approaches a value of $x_D = 0.94$ as a limit, while curve G will approach only $x_D = 0.7$ as its limit. The limiting sharpness of separation is determined only by the value of α^n. Thus all the curves of Figure 65 approach almost the same limiting curve as R_D is increased, since α^n is nearly the same for all cases.

C. OTHER EVALUATION METHODS

Stedman[184] suggested that the expression

$$(kn + 1)^{-3/2} V/D$$

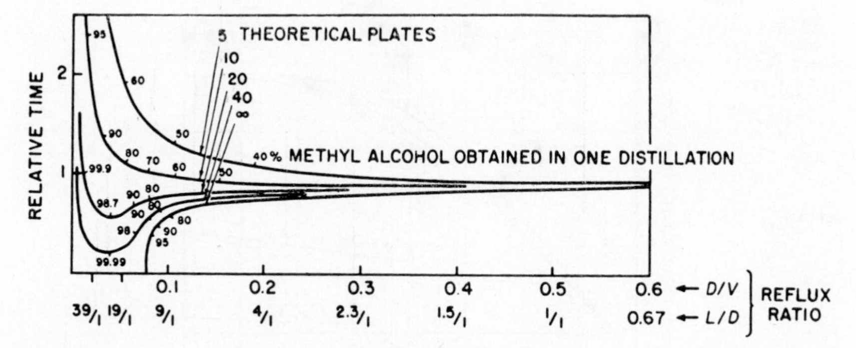

Fig. 69. Stedman calculations of distillate composition, relative time, and reflux ratio.[184]

be used as a meausre of the overall effectiveness of a column and procedure. This formula expresses the relative time required per mole per cent per theoretical plate, in terms of n (theoretical plates) and V/D (the vapor–distillate ratio).

Stedman used this expression to obtain the curves of Figure 69, in which relative times for various separations of ethyl and methyl alcohol are plotted against the distillate–vapor ratio. The graph also shows the more frequently used reflux ratio (L/D), and the purity of the product corresponding to the various reflux ratios and relative times. Consideration is given to columns with 5, 10, 20, 40, and an infinite number of theoretical plates, the last being obtained by a modified method of calculation.

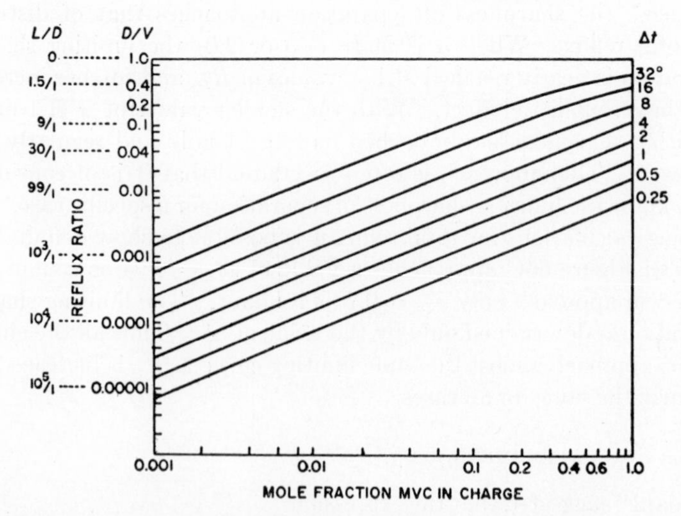

Fig. 70. Stedman calculations of boiling point difference, still composition, and optimum reflux ratio.[184]

It is to be noted that the 40- and 20-plate columns (adequate columns) show a minimum of time required at about $D/V = 0.04$ ($L/D = 24/1$), and that this minimum is about half the D/V value (the critical value) corresponding to zero time on the curve for infinite plates. For smaller numbers of theoretical plates (inadequate columns) the minimum time is displaced to much higher distillate–vapor ratios (lower reflux–distillate ratios). Stedman generalized his recommendations (see Table XVI and Fig. 70) showing the general effect of still composition and relative volatility on the proper choice of reflux ratio.

TABLE XVI
Factor by which Critical Value of D/V for Infinite Column should be Multiplied for Most Economical Work[184]

Charge composition x	Adequate column	Moderately adequate column[a]	Inadequate column
0.2 or higher	0.5 to 1	0.25 to 0.5 or 1 to 1.5	1.5 to 2.5 or more as the column becomes less efficient
0.05 to 0.2	0.5 to 1	0.25 to 0.5 or 1 to 2	2 to 3 or more as above
Less than 0.05	$\sqrt{1/x}$	$\sqrt{1/x}$	$\sqrt{1/x}$

[a] For moderately adequate column take the top figure if the column will just give the desired result in one distillation; if two are needed take the lower figure; if more than two, consider the column inadequate.

Stedman's reasoning involves all the usual simplifying assumptions, i.e., ideal mixtures, normal liquids, and applicability of the McCabe–Thiele type of material balance. The latter necessarily restricts the recommendations to steady-state distillations, or to instantaneous conditions during a batch distillation with inappreciable holdup.

Rietema[185] has discussed means of evaluating the overall performance in distillation in terms of a factor which is the product of actual yield and actual quality increase, divided by the product of yield and quality for an ideal separation. This is the same as the fraction of the actual feed which would need to be used in an ideal separation apparatus, in order to obtain the results achieved by the actual procedure.

4. Calculated Effect of Relative Volatility and Number of Plates (Total Reflux and Negligible Holdup Assumed)

The curves represented by eq. (42) (p. 82) give the relation between distillate composition and per cent distilled on the basis of total reflux and negligible holdup. Curves such as those in Figure 71A are obtained,

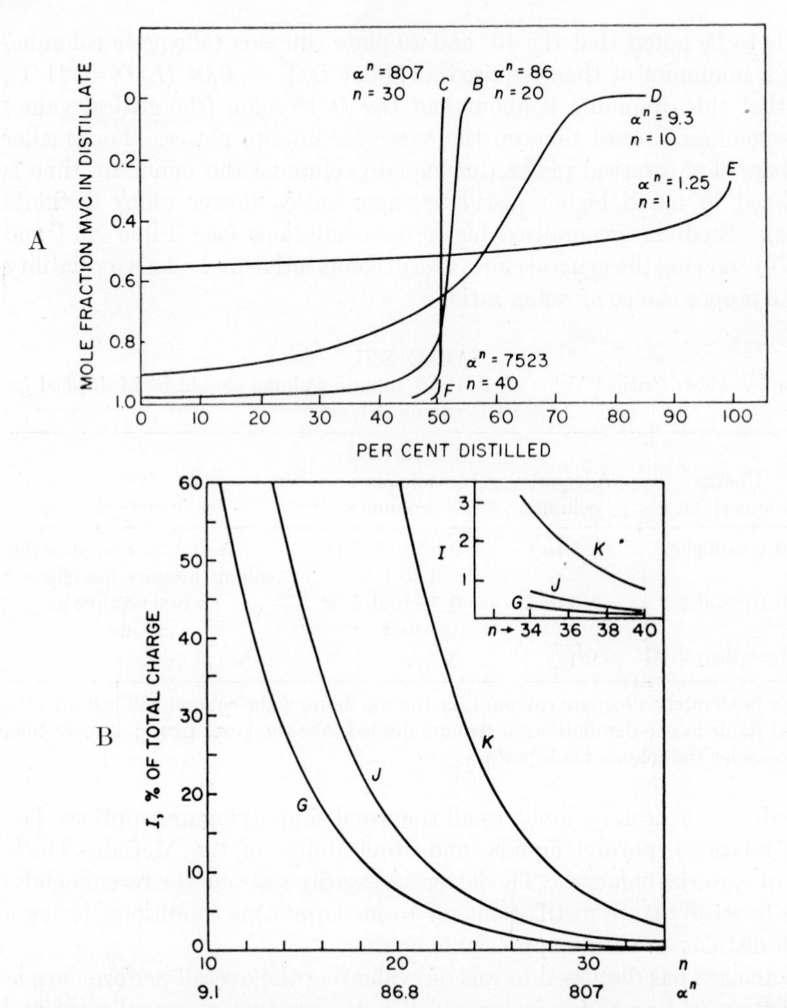

Fig. 71. (A) Calculated effect of relative volatility and number of theoretical plates at total reflux.[186] (B) Calculated relation between size of intermediate fraction and number of theoretical plates. Limits of intermediate fraction: *G*, 10–90%; *J*, 5–95%; *K*, 1–99%.[186]

which vary in shape according to the values of relative volatility (α) and number of plates (n) substituted in the equation. Thus *D* (Fig. 71A) represents the curve calculated for distillation under substantially total reflux of 100 moles of an equimolar mixture with $\alpha = 1.25$ and initial composition (x_s) of 0.5 in a column with the equivalent of ten theoretical plates and no appreciable holdup. Curves *B* and *C* represent the systems with 20 and 30 plates, respectively, with all other circumstances identical.

Curve F is a portion of the corresponding curve for 40 plates. Because of the assumption of total reflux and no holdup, the curves obtained represent only the limiting case of the sharpest possible separation with the specified mixture and column. In this sense they are analogous to product concentrations of a chemical reaction as calculated by means of equilibrium constants—they represent a limiting condition that may not be attained, but probably cannot be exceeded. This sort of information is of great value when a sharp separation is desired. Even casual study of Figure 71A indicates that the increase from 30 to 40 plates has a relatively small effect on the shape of the distillation curve and the maximum sharpness of separation when $\alpha = 1.25$, and that further increases in plates can have even less effect. In order to obtain a definite measure of the sharpness of separation, one may arbitrarily designate as intermediate fraction (I) all that distillate having a composition between 10 and 90% of the more volatile component. In Figure 71B the moles of such intermediate fractions (mole per cent of charge) are plotted against the corresponding values of n. A law of diminishing returns is obviously operating, and there is an optimum number of plates for a given separation. Further increase in plates fails to effect any great improvement in separation.

A. OPTIMUM RANGE OF OVERALL FRACTIONATING FACTOR

The preceding discussions indicate the greater significance of the overall fractionating factor, α^n, as compared with either the relative volatility,

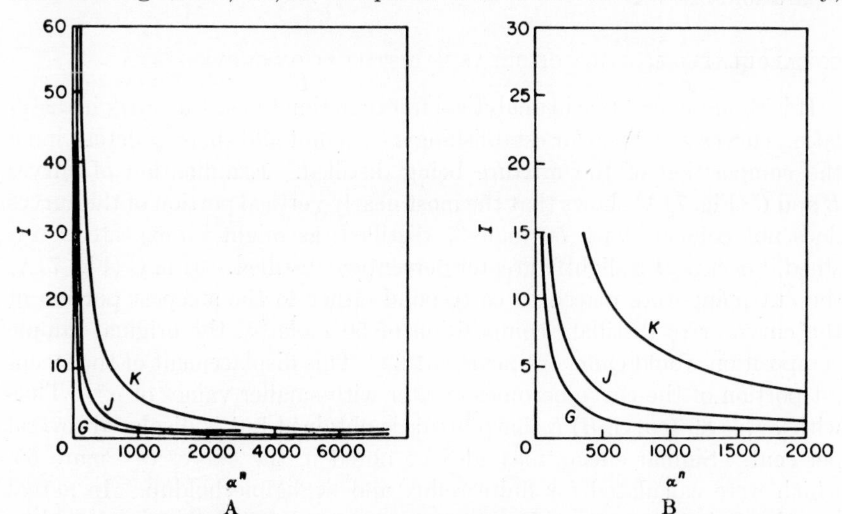

Fig. 72. (A) Calculated relation between size of intermediate fraction and value of overall fractionating factor.[186] (B) Graph of A near origin. G, J, and K have same values as for Figure 71.

α, or the number of theoretical plates by themselves. Examination of Figure 72A shows that only certain relatively narrow ranges of values of α^n (those near the origin) are of practical interest. Decrease of α^n below a minimum value results in poor separation (a large and rapidly increasing intermediate fraction); increase of α^n beyond a certain maximum can result in but little improvement in fractionation but does involve increased cost of construction. In general only intermediate fractions of less than 10 and more than 0.5 mole % and the corresponding values of α^n are of interest. This portion of Figure 72A is plotted on a larger scale in Figure 72B. Figures 72A and B apply only to cases of substantially total reflux and negligible holdup, and show the calculations of the limiting cases of sharpest possible separation and minimum plates.

B. MINIMUM PLATES FOR A GIVEN SEPARATION

By use of Figures 72A and B it is possible to calculate the overall fractionating factor necessary and the minimum plates required for a given separation of a specified mixture. For example, suppose it is desired to make the intermediate fraction containing 90 to 10 mole-% of the more volatile component as low as 5% of the charge. (The remaining 95% would constitute the practically pure fractions of the two components.) In order to achieve this, with $\alpha = 1.25$, n must be about 25. A column of at least this number of plates would be necessary to attain the desired separation.

C. CALCULATED POSITION OF BREAK IN DISTILLATION CURVE

It is common practice in analytical fractionation to use the break in distillation curves as a basis for establishing a cut point and thereby determining the composition of the mixture being distilled. Examination of curves B and C (Fig. 71A) shows that the most nearly vertical portion of the curves does not coincide with 50 mole-% distilled, as might be expected. Instead it occurs at a slightly greater percentage distilled. If in C (Fig. 71A) the cut point were placed to correspond either to the steepest portion of the curve or to distillate composition of 50 mole-%, the original sample composition would come out nearly 51%. This displacement of the steepest portion of the curve becomes greater with smaller values of α^n. Thus with $\alpha^n = 86$ (curve B) a sharp break is obtained but is displaced several per cent. Similar effects may also be noted in the curves of Figure 65, which were calculated for finite reflux and negligible holdup. In actual practice it is often not mole per cent product distilled that is plotted as abscissa, but more probably weight per cent. Furthermore the ordinates are often not composition of product in mole per cent but boiling point or some other property not linearly related to molar composition. These factors lead to distortion of various kinds in actual distillation curves that have not been closely examined.

5. Calculated Effect of Initial Composition on Shape and Position of Distillation Curves

It was stated above (p. 150) that the major effect of a change in initial composition was to displace the calculated distillation curve along the horizontal axis. This statement applies to log S_t curves (p. 77) calculated for cases in which holdup is assumed to be zero. If the initial composition (x_s) is 0.5 in one instance and 0.7 in another case, the corresponding equations are

$$\log S_{t0.5} = \log S_c - \frac{1}{2.3} \int_{x_{st}}^{0.5} \frac{dx_s}{x_D - x_s}$$

and

$$\log S_{t0.7} = \log S_c - \frac{1}{2.3} \int_{x_{st}}^{0.7} \frac{dx_s}{x_D - x_s}$$

in which $S_{t0.5}$ and $S_{t0.7}$ represent values of S corresponding to the same still composition, x_{st}, for each of the two cases. The charge S_c and the x_D versus x_s relations are the same for the two cases, so that subtraction of the first equation from the second gives

$$\log S_{t0.7} - \log S_{t0.5} = \frac{1}{2.3} \int_{0.5}^{0.7} \frac{dx_s}{x_D - x_s} = \text{const.}$$

The distillation curve for initial composition (x_{sc}) of 0.7, i.e., the series of values of log S for this case, can be obtained from the corresponding values for the case $x_{sc} = 0.5$ merely by adding the constant

$$\frac{1}{2.3} \int_{0.5}^{0.7} \frac{dx_s}{x_D - x_s}$$

Thus any value of log $S_{t0.7}$ differs from the corresponding value of log $S_{t0.}$ by a constant factor, as long as S_c is the same and the same series of x_D and x_s values are used. Choice of x_{sc} values other than 0.5 and 0.7 does not alter the reasoning. Because the corresponding logarithms differ by a constant, the values of S themselves differ by an exponentially increasing amount, and so the break in the distillation curve will be *sharper for higher initial* compositions.

6. Calculation of Reflux Ratio and Theoretical Plates by Pole-Height Equations

The pole height, σ, of a binary batch-distillation curve is defined[187] as the product of the slope of the curve at midheight, m_s, and the fraction of the charge not yet taken off as distillate. With appreciable holdup this is the ratio (designated as $\bar{S}_\sigma$) of the still contents plus holdup to the original charge. With negligible holdup this fraction is also the fraction of the charge remaining in the still pot, and is here designated as S_σ, so

$$\sigma = m_s S_\sigma$$

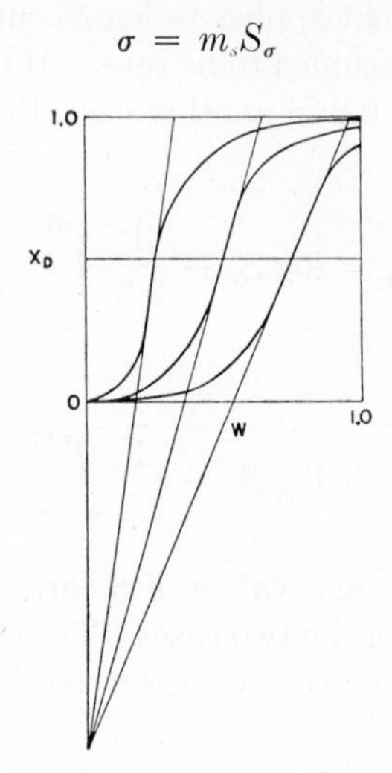

Fig. 73. Uniform pole heights of batch-distillation curves ($W = S$).[187]

When holdup is negligible, the pole height has the property of being independent of charge composition, as exemplified in Figure 73. For usefully sharp separations the fraction of the charge remaining in the pot at the midpoint of the distillation curve is approximately equal to the fraction of the heavy component in the original charge, so that

$$S_\sigma = 1 - x_c$$

This gives

$$\sigma = m_s(1 - x_c) \qquad \text{or} \qquad m_s = \sigma/(1 - x_c)$$

Since σ is identical for a given set of values of α, n, and R_D, it follows that the sharpness of separation is inversely proportional to the concentration of the heavy component in the charge. Better separation is obtained on rich mixtures than on lean ones, as has already been noted in the preceding section on the effect of initial composition. The dependence of the pole height, σ, on α and n at infinite reflux is shown by Bowman and Cichelli to be

$$\sigma = (\alpha^{2n} - 1)/8\alpha^n$$

which reduces to $\sigma = \alpha^n/8$ when separation is sharp so that α^{2n} is large compared with unity. This is derived from the Rayleigh equation in the form

$$S(dx_s/dS) = x_D - x_s$$

by multiplying both sides by dx_D/dx_s

$$S(dx_D/dS) = (dx_D/dx_s)(x_D - x_s)$$

and combining with the derivation of the still product composition relation for total reflux

$$x_s = \frac{x_D}{\alpha^n - (\alpha^n - 1)x_D}$$

$$(dx_D/dx_s) = (1/\alpha^n)[\alpha^n - (\alpha^n - 1)x_D]^2$$

The result is

$$S(dx_D/dS) = (1/\alpha^n)x_D(1 - x_D)(\alpha^n - 1)[\alpha^n - (\alpha^n - 1)x_D]$$

For $x_D = 1/2$ (midheight of distillation curve)

$$S(dx_D/dS) = S_\sigma m_s = \sigma = (\alpha^{2n} - 1)/8\alpha^n$$

The derivation and result are applicable only for total reflux, negligible holdup, constant relative volatility, and the other usual simplifying assumptions.

For these circumstances the corresponding slope of the distillation curve at $x_D = 1/2$ becomes

$$m_s = \alpha^n/8(1 - x_c)$$

if the approximation $S_\sigma = 1 - x_c$ is used. On this basis the number of plates required for a given slope or pole height is

$$n = \log 8(1 - x_c)m_s/\log \alpha = \log 8\sigma/\log \alpha$$

When the number of plates is very large and separation is controlled by reflux ratio, a derivation similar to the above gives

$$\sigma = 1/2[(\alpha - 1)R_D + \alpha]$$

and

$$R_D = \frac{2\sigma - \alpha}{\alpha - 1} = \frac{2(1 - x_c)m_s - \alpha}{\alpha - 1}$$

For very sharp separations these become

$$R_D = \frac{2\sigma}{\alpha - 1} = \frac{2(1 - x_c)m_s}{\alpha - 1}$$

and the quantity $R_D(\alpha - 1)$ is thus a measure of the sharpness of separation for the conditions of the derivation.

Bowman and Cichelli recommend doubling the values of reflux ratio and plates calculated by the above formulas when they are used to estimate the conditions for a particular separation. The formulas are also useful in estimating the lower reflux ratio required for a long column which is to make the same separation as a short one at higher reflux. Laboratory distillations are often run at relatively high reflux ratios, but efficient columns and low reflux are preferable for large-scale operations. Another application is the use of the formula

$$n = \log 8\,\sigma/\log \alpha$$

to estimate the number of plates in a column from a distillation curve obtained at high reflux. The equation

$$S = (1 - x_c)\Big/\left[1 - \frac{1}{(\alpha - 1)R_D}\right]$$

can serve as a means of estimating the proper reflux ratio for cases in which reflux is controlling. The proper value is the minimum that will give substantially pure more volatile component as distillate. Higher reflux will improve purity but little, while a decrease in reflux will decrease purity considerably.

Zuiderweg[188] suggests the semi-empirical pole height formula

$$\frac{1}{\sigma} = \frac{8}{\alpha^{n+1}}\left[1 + \frac{H}{\bar{S}_\sigma}\left(\frac{\alpha^{n+1}}{4.6 \log \alpha^{n+1}} - 1\right)\right] + \frac{2}{R_D(\alpha - 1)[1 + 3(H/\bar{S}_\sigma) \log \alpha^{n+1}]} \tag{136}$$

for the practical operating conditions where holdup is appreciable. When holdup is negligible so that $H/\bar{S}_\sigma = 0$, the preceding equation becomes

$$\frac{1}{\sigma} = \frac{8}{\alpha^{n+1}} + \frac{2}{R_D(\alpha - 1)}$$

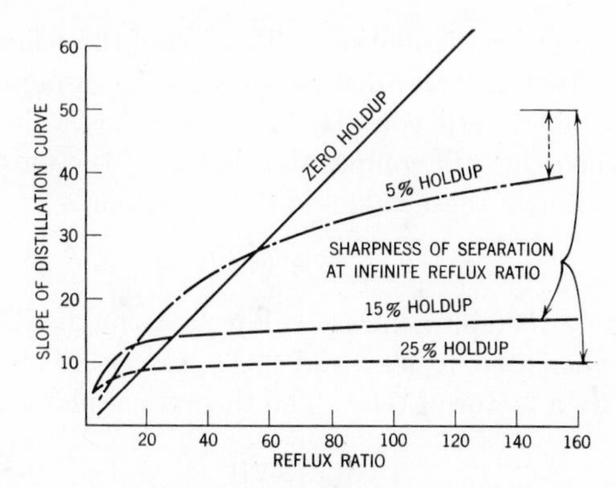

Fig. 74. Effect of holdup and reflux ratio on sharpness of separation according to the Zuiderweg pole height equation.[188]

At total reflux $R_D = \infty$ and the equation becomes

$$\sigma = \frac{\alpha^{n+1}}{8} \frac{1}{1 + (H/\bar{S}_\sigma)\left(\dfrac{\alpha^{n+1}}{4.6 \log \alpha^{n+1}} - 1\right)}$$

These relationships between holdup, reflux ratio, and sharpness of separation are expressed by Figure 74 for a specific mixture and column.

For rough preliminary estimates it is sufficient to ignore the complicated equations and calculate minimum reflux by the equation

$$2\sigma = R_D(\alpha - 1)$$

and minimum plates by

$$8\sigma = \alpha^{n+1} \text{ or } 8\sigma = \frac{\alpha^{n+1}}{1 + (H/\bar{S}_\sigma)\left(\dfrac{\alpha^{n+1}}{4.6 \log \alpha^{n+1}} - 1\right)}$$

Houtman and Husain[188a] extended eq. (136) to obtain some general equations and relations similar to those already described in the preceding sections. Nomographs and other graphs are given to avoid lengthy calculations for new sets of circumstances. This method is useful for predictions where constant relative volatility and sharp separation occur.

7. Calculation of Theoretical Plates from Relative Volatilities and Empirical Fractionating Factors

On the basis of actual experience with a variety of columns Cook[189] has suggested a fractionating factor (α^n) of 1000 for ordinary distillations, and of 10,000 for precision distillation. The first of these figures is obtained on the assumption that ordinary distillation will be satisfactory if the distillate is 99% pure when the still contains 10% of the most volatile component, and 90% pure when the still composition is 1% of the most volatile component. Substitution of these values in the expression

$$x_{DA}/x_{DB} = \alpha^n(x_{sA}/x_{sB})$$

gives approximately 1000 in each case. For precision distillation the distillate purities are increased to 99.9 and 99.0%, respectively, and α^n is accordingly raised by a factor of ten. The theoretical plates needed for various cases may then be obtained from Table XVII. It is of interest to note that these relations are approximately the same as those predicted by use of equations

TABLE XVII

Theoretical Plates from Empirical Fractionating Factors[189]

α	Difference in boiling points, ΔT°C.	Plates needed: Ordinary distillation	Plates needed: Precision distillation
3.00	30	6	9
2.00	20	9	12
1.50	10	17	23
1.30	7	26	35
1.25	6	31	41
1.20	5	38	51
1.15	4	50	66
1.12	3	61	81
	2.5	—	100
1.07	2	104	136

$$n = \frac{2.85}{\log \alpha} = R_D \quad \text{and} \quad n = \frac{T_B + T_A}{3(T_B - T_A)}$$

which are discussed in the succeeding paragraphs.

8. Correlation of Combined Effects of Relative Volatility, Reflux Ratio, and Theoretical Plates[190]

A convenient correlation has been achieved through the concept of a "standard separation." It depends upon calculation of the plates and reflux required for separation of a pair of similar liquids with normal vapor–liquid equilibrium relations, when the usual simplifying assumptions of distillation are justified and holdup is negligible.

In *batch* fractionation it is confusing to use the difference between still and product compositions as a measure of the effectiveness of the process. This is because the compositions and differences in composition are changing continually throughout the distillation. The best procedure is to use the shape of the actual curve of product composition versus per cent distilled as the measure of effectiveness and thus relate the conditions (α, n, R_D, etc.) of the distillation directly to the final results. This has been done by choosing a standard separation, as follows:

Each curve of Figure 2 (p. 11) represents a different separation of two components. Each may be satisfactory for some purpose, and each separation requires different conditions. Thus for an ideal binary equimolar mixture with $\alpha = 1.25$ it can be calculated that 10 plates are necessary to obtain curve A, 20 plates for curve B, and 30 plates for Curve C, provided the proper reflux ratio is used in each case and holdup is negligible. Before attempting to devise any means for calculating the number of plates required for a separation of the two components, it is essential to choose one batch-fractionation curve as a standard of satisfactory separation of the two components.

To make such a choice it has been assumed that for most practical purposes a curve such as B of Figure 2 will be considered a satisfactory separation. The first 40% distilled will have an average purity greater than 95%. This is therefore designated the *standard separation;* the following paragraphs deal with the methods for calculating approximately the number of plates needed to achieve a separation of this standard sharpness. The reasoning assumes charge compositions of 50 mole-%, but is approximately applicable to other charge compositions.

The calculated values of relative volatility, reflux ratio, and equivalent theoretical plates that will result in such a standard distillation curve have been correlated in Figure 3 (p. 12). The individual points for each curve for different values of α were obtained from graphs such as those of Figures 65 and 67. For instance, Figure 67B shows that with $\alpha = 1.25$ and $R_D = 49$, about 20 plates are necessary to obtain a separation as sharp as the standard (B of Fig. 2). This is expressed in Figure 3 by a point A on the curve for $\alpha = 1.25$. A similar set of calculated curves for $\alpha = 1.25$ with reflux ratio $R_D = 29$ and a series of values of n shows that about 25 plates are required in this case to give the desired separation. This is expressed as point B in Figure 3. Other points on the curve for $\alpha = 1.25$ on Figure 3 were obtained by a similar procedure, as were the values needed to obtain the curves shown for $\alpha = 1.05$, 1.1, and 2.

This correlation indicates that it should not be necessary to fix the value of n in order to achieve the desired standard separation, since any value within a considerable range will be adequate. Within this range a lower value of n may be compensated by a corresponding increase in R_D and higher values of n may allow use of a smaller R_D. It is essential for n to remain within the desirable range since values of n that are too low cannot be compensated by increase in reflux and those that are too high do not allow a corresponding decrease in reflux. To achieve the standard separation with the most effective use of the plates in a column (and of the time consumed) the reflux ratio should not be less than $^2/_3$ nor more than $^3/_2$ of the number of plates.

The diagonal straight line

$$R_D = n = 2.85/\log \alpha$$

was arrived at by inspection, and by analogy with the similar equation

$$n = \log \alpha^n/\log \alpha$$

in the following manner: It can be shown (see curve B, Fig. 71A) that the standard separation of a normal mixture could be achieved at total reflux by using a value of n large enough so that the overall fractionating factor, α^n, is about 100. Thus the number of plates could be calculated by the equation

$$n = \log 100/\log \alpha$$

This is of limited usefulness because it applies only for total reflux or its equivalent, but it seems reasonable to assume that the same form of equation might be used for calculation of plates required at finite reflux, i.e., that

$$n = C/\log \alpha$$

The diagonal line in Figure 3 with $C = 2.85$ is the desired relation. The line representing the lower limit of the desirable range of n is given approximately by

$$n = 2.3/\log \alpha$$

and the line representing the upper limit by

$$n = 3.6/\log \alpha$$

The values of the constants were obtained entirely by inspection, that is, it can be seen by examination of Figure 3 that use of a combination of reflux ratios and plates outside these limits involves either the use of too high a reflux ratio or too many plates. Thus for $\alpha = 1.25$, the use of 20 plates and reflux ratio of $R_D = 80$ gives substantially the same separation as 20 plates and $R_D = 40$.

A system for correlating theoretical plates and reflux ratio has also been reported by Kojima and Aoyama.[191]

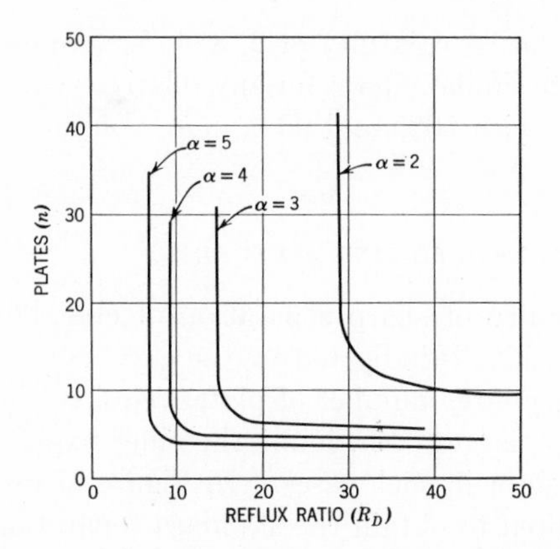

Fig. 75. Calculated operating conditions giving average distillate composition = 0.95 at 85% nominal cut point. Charge composition = 0.10.

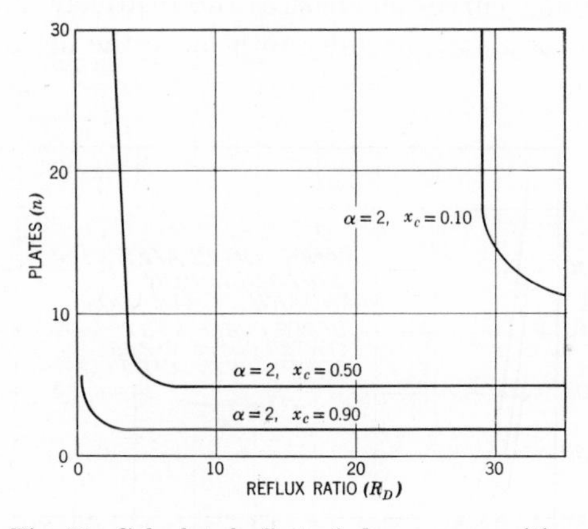

Fig. 76. Calculated effect of charge composition.

Schilk[192] calculated 256 batch distillation curves for a binary with charge composition of 0.10 mole fraction more volatile component and various combinations of relative volatility, number of plates, and reflux ratio. The average distillate composition at 85% nominal cut point (NCP) was selected as a criterion of the sharpness of separation for each of the 256 curves.

The values of $x_{D(\text{av})}$ (85% NCP) were plotted versus n with R_D as a parameter. Calculations and graphs were made for $\alpha = 2, 3, 4, 5$. From these graphs Schilk read the values of n and R_D required to achieve $x_{D(\text{av})} = 0.95$ at 85% NCP. The resulting values of relative volatility, reflux ratio, and theoretical plates that will produce such a standard separation of a charge with 10% more volatile component have been correlated in Figure

75 for values of relative volatility of 2, 3, 4, 5. An empirical method can be used to calculate similar curves for any relative volatility. Similar basic curves for charges with 50% and 90% more volatile component are given in Figure 76.

A. SEPARATION OF CLOSE-BOILING MIXTURES

The great difficulty of sharp separation of close-boiling mixtures with small relative volatility is indicated by the curve for $\alpha = 1.05$ in Figure 3. Not only are a very large number of plates required, but the minimum reflux ratios are also large. No doubt the time required to reach equilibrium becomes a factor in such cases. In Figure 77 are plotted the values of n (or R_D) required to obtain the standard separation with various relative volatilities. This indicates the exponential increase in the plates required as relative volatility approaches unity. The inclusion of the minimum and maximum curves emphasizes the relatively narrow range over which n and R_D may vary in order to achieve the desired separation efficiently, or at all.

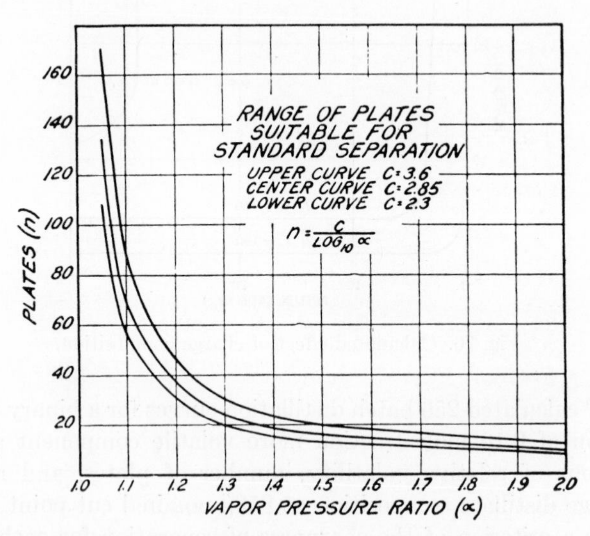

Fig. 77. Calculated ranges of theoretical plates (and reflux ratios) suitable for standard separation at different relative volatilities.[190]

B. CALCULATION OF PLATES REQUIRED FROM DIFFERENCE IN BOILING POINTS

A method for calculating plates required directly from boiling points would obviously be of great use. It must be realized at the start that all such methods are subject to serious limitations and cannot be used indiscriminately. At best they can indicate only the general neighborhood of the value of n, but even this is so important that it seems desirable to point out the basis for such calculations. This basis lies in the combination of the equation $n = C/\log \alpha$ with Trouton's rule and the approximate Clapeyron equation. Thus for a pair of liquids A and B (B is higher boiling), Trouton's rule states

$$20.5(T_B - T_A) = \lambda_B - \lambda_A$$

in which T_B and T_A are the boiling points at absolute temperature, and λ_B and λ_A the corresponding heats of vaporization. The approximate Clapeyron equation for the same two liquids is

$$\lambda_B - \lambda_A = RT \ln p_A - RT \ln p_B$$

in which R is the constant in $pV = NRT$ and p_A and p_B are the vapor pressures of the two liquids at $T = (T_A + T_B)/2$. The last equation may be written as approximately

$$\lambda_B - \lambda_A = 2.3(T_B + T_A) \log \alpha$$

if T_A and T_B are not widely different. Combining this with the Trouton expression gives

$$20.5(T_B - T_A) = 2.3(T_B + T_A) \log \alpha \tag{137}$$

and this with $n = C/\log \alpha$ gives

$$n = 2.3C(T_B + T_A)/20.5(T_B - T_A)$$

which is the form

$$n = (T_B + T_A)/k(T_B - T_A)$$

When the constant C in $n = C/\log \alpha$ has its optimum value 2.85, this becomes

$$n = (T_B + T_A)/3(T_B - T_A)$$

At about room temperature (27°C.) the above equation becomes

$$n = 200/\Delta T$$

and at 77°C.

$$n = 233/\Delta T$$

It is obvious that the same equations and the relation $R_D = n = 2.85/\log \alpha$ may be used for calculating the required *reflux ratio*. (Compare p. 20 for similar relation for α.)

C. USE OF CORRELATIONS IN SPECIFIC PROBLEMS

The preceding relations may be used as the basis for a systematic procedure to aid in the approach to a new and difficult distillation problem.[193] The necessary steps are:

(*1*) Estimate relative volatility.
(*2*) Estimate number of theoretical plates.
(*3*) Estimate reflux ratio.
(*4*) Decide on quantity to be distilled.
(*5*) Choose column diameter, packing, and throughput on basis that holdup must be less than 5% of charge.
(*6*) Note time required and column height.

For a preliminary approach some kind of an average value of the relative volatility is desirable. Chapter II gives numerous approaches. For closely similar liquids the rough relation derived in eq. (137) from Trouton's rule and the approximate Clapeyron equation may be used.

$$\log \alpha = 8.9(T_B - T_A)/(T_B + T_A)$$

For binary mixtures in which the boiling points of the components average about (*a*) 100°C., (*b*) 0°C., the preceding equation reduces to

$$(a)\ \log \alpha = \frac{\Delta T}{85} \qquad (b)\ \log \alpha = \frac{\Delta T}{61}$$

Edgeworth-Johnstone[194] suggested the following equations:

$$\log \alpha = 5(T_B - T_A)/T \text{ or } \log \alpha = 10(T_B - T_A)/(T_B + T_A)$$

in which T is the average of T_A and T_B. Melpolder and Headington[195] proposed

$$\log \alpha = \Delta T(3.99/T + 0.00194)$$

Still other equations have been suggested.[196] In general, discrepancies are to be expected in the use of these equations because of the use of the simplifying assumptions involved in deriving them, and the empirical nature of some of the constants.

For nonideal mixtures, if vapor–liquid equilibrium composition values can be found or estimated, they can be plotted and the resulting curve matched as nearly as possible with known x, y curves for various constant relative volatilities. Another procedure is to step off on the vapor–liquid diagram for the mixture to be separated the number of theoretical plates at total reflux between such arbitrarily chosen limits as 3.6 and 96.4% liquid compositions. The n so found may then be substituted in the Fenske equation [eq. (14) on p. 31], which may be written for these limits as

$$\log \bar{\alpha} = \frac{2 \log 26.8}{\bar{n}} = \frac{2.86}{\bar{n}}$$

Thus if ten plates can be stepped off between 0.964 and 0.036 on the irregular vapor–liquid equilibrium curve, log $\bar{\alpha}$ = 0.286 and $\bar{\alpha}$ = 1.92. If 20 plates are stepped off, $\bar{\alpha}$ = 1.37. A very irregular vapor–liquid equilibrium curve may require use of a more complicated procedure. The choice of n and R_D can be by the equation

$$n = R_D = \frac{2.85}{\log \alpha} = \frac{T_B + T_A}{3(T_B - T_A)}$$

The use of such values of n and R_D in the ideal case of a binary mixture with equimolal composition will produce a so-called standard separation. A somewhat lower value of n may be compensated by increase in R_D, and vice-versa, as explained on pp. 167–8.

If desired, as in the case of an uncertainty regarding the choice of α, a Rayleigh curve may be calculated using the chosen n and R_D and the actual vapor–liquid equilibrium curve, and adjustments made as necessary to get the separation desired.

The quantity of sample to be distilled is affected by many factors. If there are no overriding factors such as availability of sample or of apparatus or need for product, 0.5 liter of sample should be taken as a first trial choice.

The final step is to choose a packing, and the column diameter and throughput with which this is to be used. The column height, holdup, and time of distillation will then be determined, excluding the initial equilibration time. Unless the end result is a column height that is available or can be achieved, a holdup of 5% or less, and a reasonable time for the distillation, all or some of the last steps should be repeated with different choices. Some examples follow.

Examples of Use of Procedure. Suppose that n = 25, then R_D should also be 25. With C (charge) = 500 ml., H must be 25 ml. or less. The time for distillation (in minutes) will be $t = 500 \times R_D/r$ where r is the throughput in ml./min.

For a 1/2-in. diameter column a good median of available data gives an H.E.T.P. of 1.6 cm., a throughput of 5 ml./min., and a holdup of 0.1 ml./plate. Therefore, in this case $t = 500 \times 25/5 = 2500$ min. = 40 + hr.; column height = 25 × 1.6 = 40 cm. or about 18 in. and $H = 25 \times 0.1 = 2.5$ ml. or about 0.5%.

For a 1-in. diameter column median values of the data give an H.E.T.P. of 2.5 cm., a throughput of 20 ml./min., and a holdup of 1.2 ml./plate. t is now 500 × 25/20 = 625 min. = 10 1/2 hr. Column height = 25 × 2.5 = 62.5 cm. or about 25 in., while holdup H is 25 × 1.2 = 30 ml. or about 6%. This latter is higher than the limit of 5% previously mentioned.

For a 2-in. diameter column median values give an H.E.T.P. of 7.5 cm., a throughput of 200 ml./min. and a holdup of 25 ml./plate. In this case t = 500 × 25/200 = 62.5 min. = 1 hr.; column height = 7.5 × 25 = 188 cm. or about 75 in. Holdup H is 25 × 25 = 625 ml. Therefore, the charge is not large enough for the column under study.

In this case the proper choice is obviously the 1/2-in. column. However, serious thought would naturally be given to the possibility of increasing the charge somewhat and using the 1-in. column to achieve the shorter distillation time. It should be emphasized that the data above are median values intended only as an example and, therefore, do not represent any particular type or kind of packing or column.

The attempts to use this procedure will have varying results. There will obviously be errors due to variation of H.E.T.P., throughput, and holdup with the materials to be distilled. In some cases the procedure will break down for lack of basic data. Other cases may produce the conclusion that processes other than distillation should or must be examined because the separations involved are inherently very difficult or impossible by distillation. In many cases significant results are obtained.

9. Evaluation of Distillation in Terms of Thermodynamic Efficiency of Separation

Kuhn[197] defined the thermodynamic efficiency of distillation by a factor η which is the energy necessary to separate components isothermally and reversibly compared with the energy actually expended. The procedure used was to calculate the energy for preparation of one mole of a binary product containing x_e mole fraction of the more volatile component, starting from a very large amount of a binary with mole fraction x_0. Calculations were made for an optimally operated column with and without a heat pump to utilize the heat of condensation. The efficiency is low if heat is not recycled, and becomes lower as the boiling point difference decreases. The efficiency is also small when x_e, the product mole fraction, is near unity, and the feed composition x_0 is low. Kuhn concluded that efficiency could be markedly increased by proceeding in a stepwise manner through the production of intermediate products, indicating that irreversible processes in the column play a minor role. The reduction of material in the process is an important factor in improving the efficiency.

Other approaches to thermodynamic efficiency have been made by Trevissoi, Miller, Freshwater, Denbigh, and Doering.[198] Kahn[199] expressed the thermodynamic efficiency of a distillation as the ratio

$$E = \frac{\Delta F}{\Delta F_0} = \frac{F_c - F_D - F_s}{F_c} \tag{138}$$

where

$$F_D = n_D[x_D RT \ln x_D + (1 - x_D)RT \ln (1 - x_D)] \tag{139}$$

$$F_s = (1 - n_D)[x_s RT \ln x_s + (1 - x_s)RT \ln (1 - x_s)] \tag{140}$$

$$F_c = x_c RT \ln x_c + (1 - x_c)RT \ln (1 - x_c) \tag{141}$$

These expressions depend on the fact that the free energy change per mole of mixing a pure component into a solution, assuming perfect solutions, is $RT \ln x$, where x is the final mole fraction of the specified component in the solution, and R and T are the usual symbols of the perfect gas law. Assuming the pure components have free energy equal to zero, and considering one mole of a charge of a binary mixture, the work required to separate this mixture into two pure components would be the free energy of the solution, which would equal the sum of the free energies of the components, as indicated in eq. (141).

The process of distillation separates this charge into n_D moles of distillate and $1 - n_D$ moles of residue, with compositions x_D and x_s, respectively. The free energies of each of these fractions are given by eqs. (139) and (140). The expression ΔF thus represents the difference between the work required to separate the charge into its pure components, and the work required to separate the products of the distillation, i.e., the distillate and residue, into the original pure components. It is then possible to express E in terms of n_D (the fraction of charge distilled), $x_{D(\text{av})}$, the average distillate composition, and x_c, the charge composition. No systematic evaluation of thermodynamic efficiencies as a means of comparing distillations under different conditions has been reported.

Grunberg[200] proposed development of a general theory of the reversible separation of multicomponent mixtures, and applied this to distillation of ethylene–ethane–propylene mixtures. The most efficient operation is with reflux ratio equal to the equilibrium constant K (see Chap. II, Sec. I) of the least volatile component present at a given point in the enriching section. The generalization of this relation was discussed.

10. Special Methods of Batch Distillation

This part describes and outlines the theoretical basis for special methods of batch distillation and includes:

A. Total reflux distillation
B. Semicontinuous batch distillation
C. Inverted batch distillation
D. Removal of last traces of lighter component by batch rectification
E. Batch distillation of a ternary mixture in which the middle component is predominant
F. Controlled cycling distillation
G. Continuous and batch distillation compared
H. Cascade theory
I. Partial condensation
J. Steam distillation

K. Amplified distillation
L. Chromatographic distillation

A. TOTAL REFLUX DISTILLATION

Total reflux distillation may be done in at least three ways. One of these consists in bringing a distillation system to a condition of total reflux steady state or equilibrium, and then measuring the temperature at numerous points along the length of the column. This temperature profile can be converted to information on the composition of the mixture, in some cases. The theoretical basis and the references for this type of operation are given in Section II, p. 58. A related procedure that brings the system to total reflux steady state and then uses special apparatus to collect separately the material from each plate or section of the column can serve for either analytical or preparative purposes.[201]

A third type of total reflux distillation[202] uses a relatively large collection chamber, in the condenser or between it and the point where reflux enters the top of the column. The system is operated without removal of product, i.e., at total reflux. The prediction of the composition of the material that collects in this receiver after the entire system is at steady state or total reflux equilibrium is a relatively simple matter. An example of the calculation in the case where holdup is negligible is given in Section III, p. 84. If holdup is appreciable, the composition of the material that collects in the receiver at total reflux equilibrium can be calculated by an equation derived in the manner shown in eqs. (59) and (89), with condenser holdup H_c equal to the quantity of material that collects in the distillate receiver already described. The solution gives only the still composition, but the corresponding distillate composition may be easily obtained since at total reflux the Fenske equation is applicable. However, the really important matter in such an operation is the time required to reach a particular distillate composition. This is governed by the relations described in Section III, p. 112.

B. SEMICONTINUOUS BATCH DISTILLATION

Semicontinuous batch distillation with feed to the still pot is a special type of operation in which charge is added to the still pot continuously after distillation has commenced. The rate of addition to the still pot is maintained equal to the rate of removal of distillate. The concentration of less volatile components in the still pot rises more slowly than if there were no addition. The distillate composition will drop slowly unless the reflux ratio is increased. The process is stopped when the desired distillate purity can no longer be maintained or when so much of the heavier components have accumulated in the still pot that no more feed can be added. The basic differential equation for the process is

$$(S - dS)(x_s - dx_s) + x_c dS + H(x_{ca} - dx_{ca}) + dSx_D = 0$$

where x_c is the composition of the charge and x_{ca} is the average composition of the holdup in the column. The literature on this type of operation is very limited[203] and assumes negligible holdup. The most practical method for achieving satisfactory predictions is through stepwise calculations with an automatic computer (Sec. V, p. 198).

C. INVERTED BATCH DISTILLATION

The process has been seldom used, in spite of apparent advantages for separating a less volatile component that is present in minor proportions. Heavy water has been concentrated by the procedure, and apparatus and process have been described. The apparatus is sometimes called a backward feed distillation column, or a stripping column.[204]

The process is not exactly the symmetrical inverse of ordinary batch distillation because in inverted distillation the stream (of liquid) leaving the "still pot" at the head of the column is of the same composition as the content of the "still pot." In ordinary or upward batch distillation the stream (of vapor) leaving the still pot is one equilibrium stage richer in more volatile component than the liquid in the still. The theory of inverted distillation has not been described.

D. REMOVAL OF LAST TRACES OF A LIGHTER COMPONENT BY BATCH RECTIFICATION

Buiten[205] has treated the theory of this in detail and gives the equation

$$\epsilon = (z - 1)e^{-[mz/(z-1)]}$$

(with $m = (\alpha - 1)\Lambda$, Λ = number of transfer units (Sec. VI, p. 210), $z = \dfrac{1}{\alpha x_{s\infty}} = \left[(\alpha - 1)(R + 1) + 1\right]/\alpha$, $\epsilon = \dfrac{X_s}{X_{s\infty}} - 1$, $X_s = \dfrac{x_s}{x_D}$, and $X_{s\infty}$ is X_s for infinite transfer units or minimum reflux) to relate relative volatility, number of transfer units, and reflux ratio with still and distillate composition —all for the case of negligible holdup. For the case of appreciable holdup Buiten shows that the optimum choice of transfer units and reflux corresponds to $dS/dh = 0$, where $S = (d \ln x_D)/(dD/M)$, h is the amount of holdup as a fraction of the total liquid holdup in still pot and column, D is the moles of distillate, and M is the moles of liquid in still pot and column. A graph is given with a family of curves of reflux ratio versus number of transfer units at various values of relative volatility.

E. BATCH DISTILLATION OF A TERNARY MIXTURE IN WHICH THE MIDDLE COMPONENT IS PREDOMINANT

A practical example of such a system is crude naphthalene oil from coal tar. It actually contains more than three components, but naphthalene is the major component and the nearest minor components are somewhat removed in volatility so that the oil behaves approximately like a ternary having components designated as L, N, and H. Since the proportion of N is relatively high and the purpose of the batch distillation is to recover as high a yield of high purity naphthalene as is economically practical, the middle portion of the distillation produces substantially pure N. In consequence the first portion of the distillate is a binary mixture of L and N and the last part is a binary of N and H. Therefore if it is desired to predict the course of the ternary distillation it is possible to treat it as two successive binary distillations, and make the calculations accordingly. If holdup is less than 5% of the charge, the Rayleigh equation can be applied to the first distillation as though only two components were present, because none of the third component H comes overhead. Examples of such practical calculations are given by Rose and Sweeny[206] and Briggs, Waddington, and McNeil.[207] The latter use a modified method of calculation based on empirical relations and symmetry about the midpoint of the distillation, and are thus able to complete the calculations even though the midfractions are not high-purity middle component.

F. CONTROLLED CYCLING DISTILLATION

This can be applied to either plate or packed plate columns, and to either batch or continuous distillation.[208] In this method of operation only one phase flows at a time and the length and ratio of the flow periods are controlled. Thus there is a vapor flow period and a liquid flow period, and continual repetition of such a cycle. There are inherent points of advantage over conventional operation. A greater concentration gradient and larger driving forces are established with controlled cycle operation, and therefore greater separation can be achieved. For the most advantageous ratio of interstage liquid flow or cycle to liquid holdup per plate, the separation per plate can theoretically be double that of the same plate operated in conventional manner, without loss of throughput. This has been experimentally confirmed. Alternatively, with twice the ordinary throughput, an 80% improvement in separation was obtained. The efficiency of a cycling column is little affected by the reflux ratio. It is necessary to have a longer condenser for cyclic operation, since the condenser is only used during part of the overall process, and must condense a higher load during this period. Scaling up from 2- to 6-in. diameter does not reduce efficiency, and up to 30 stages can be cycled.

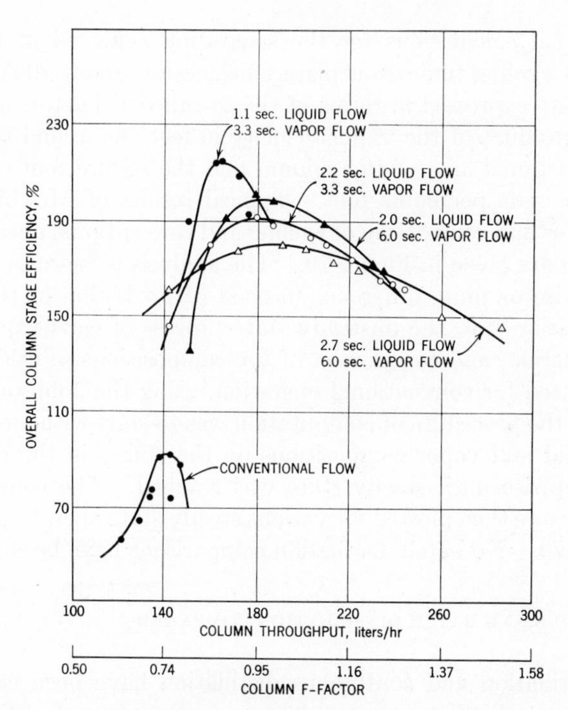

Fig. 78. Comparison of experimental performance of controlled-cycling and conventional-flow packed-plate columns. Distillation of methylcyclohexane–toluene at total reflux with five 3-in. packed plates.[208]

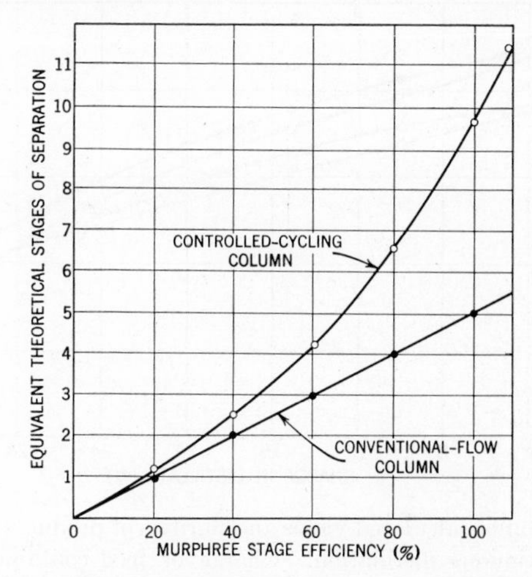

Fig. 79. Comparison of calculated separating ability of controlled-cycling and conventional-flow columns with five plates.[208] Data for total reflux with vapor flow period = 6.5 sec. and liquid flow period = 1.5 sec.

Conventional calculations for the separation achieved at finite reflux in controlled cycling indicate a plate efficiency of about 200% (Fig. 78). The results are expressed in terms of the so-called F-Factor, which equals $V(\rho)^{1/2}$, the product of the vapor velocity in feet per second based on the total cross-sectional area of the column and the square root of the vapor density in pounds per cubic foot. Typical results of Mcwhirter's theoretical analysis and comparison of cycling and conventional operation in the same column are given in Figure 79. The analysis is based on adaptation of the stepwise or finite difference method of prediction of the course of batch distillation[209] to the unsteady state process of each vapor flow and liquid flow period, and comparison of the compositions so calculated with those calculated for conventional operation, using the Johnson equations. In each case the procedure of computation was to start with any arbitrarily selected liquid and vapor compositions on the stages in the column, and calculate stepwise until steady state was reached. The compositions at steady state were then plotted for various steady state operating conditions, as in Figure 79. No batch distillation comparisons have been made.

G. CONTINUOUS AND BATCH DISTILLATION COMPARED

Batch distillation and continuous distillation have been compared by plotting average distillate composition versus the per cent of the charge or feed recovered as distillate.[210] Typical comparisons are shown in Figures

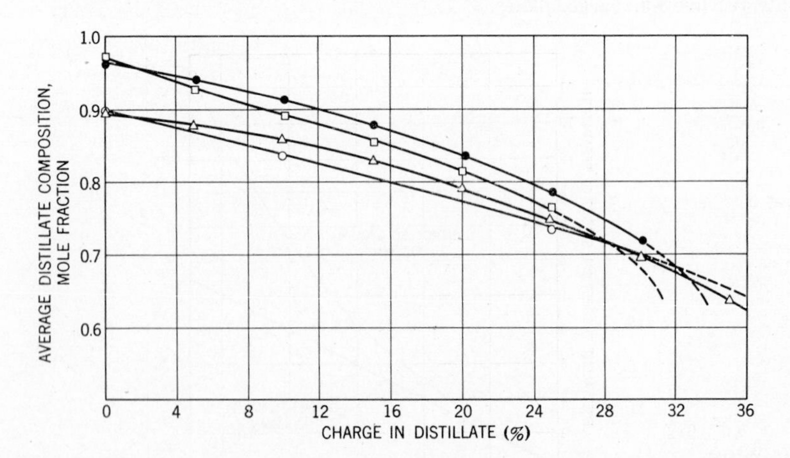

Fig. 80. Comparison of calculated yields and purities of products from ordinary batch and laboratory continuous distillation. Charge or feed containing 25 mole-% more volatile component of mixture with $\alpha = 2.23$. ●, Batch distillation with 15% holdup; □, batch distillation with 7.5% holdup; △, batch distillation with 0% holdup; O. continuous distillation.[210]

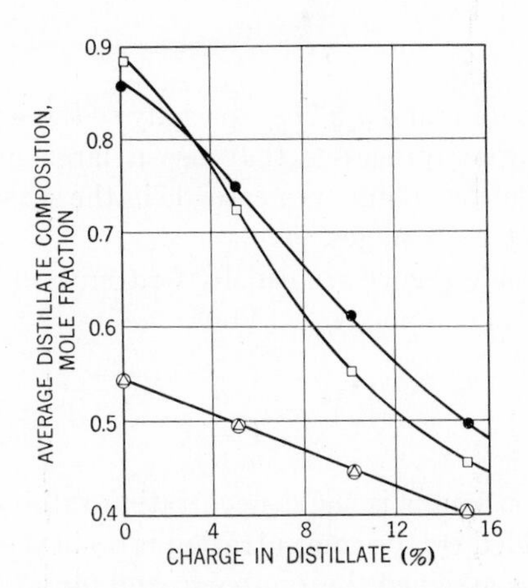

Fig. 81. Comparison of calculated yields and purities of products from ordinary batch and laboratory continuous distillation. Charge or feed containing 9.6 mole-% more volatile component of mixture with $\alpha = 2.23$. ●, Batch distillation with 15% holdup; □, batch distillation with 7.5% holdup; △, batch distillation with 0% holdup; ○, continuous distillation.[210]

80 and 81. In order to specify the conditions of continuous distillation the ratio of distillate to bottoms product must be set. Although only a narrow range of ratios is of practical interest, the choice of this ratio is unrestricted theoretically. Therefore calculations can be made for a complete set of continuous distillations with various ratios of distillate to charge. Such calculations were made to provide the numerical values for the figures.

The values given indicate that batch distillation is advantageous for removing a small proportion of a relatively volatile material, and less advantageous if there is appreciable volatile component. The presence of holdup adds to the relative advantages of batch distillation. Total reflux startup also adds to the advantage of batch distillation, if startup times are neglected in the comparison of the two types. Batch operation also has some advantage because of its complete use of column capacity throughout its entire length. A major advantage occurs to batch distillation when it is not necessary to distill the complete charge of a binary mixture. Inverted batch distillation would have advantages for mixtures with a small proportion of less volatile component.

None of the cited advantages of batch operation are of sufficient weight to overcome the disadvantages of repeated startup when large quantities of material are involved, or when heat-sensitive materials are involved, or design data are to be checked. Multicomponent mixtures are advantageously handled in batch equipment if multiple fractions are to be collected, unless large quantities and operations of long duration are involved.[211]

H. CASCADE THEORY

This was developed for and applies especially to the separation of isotopes by distillation or other processes that use a large number of stages.[212] Any ordinary distillation column is a cascade in the sense that it has a number of theoretical plates or stages.

Equations in cascade theory are usually written[213] in terms of concentration ratios for a pair of components. Thus

$$Y = \frac{y}{1 - y}$$

The stage separation factor is the concentration ratio in the vapor stream leaving a stage, divided by the concentration ratio in the liquid stream leaving a stage. This is assigned the symbol a, and for an equilibrium stage is identical with relative volatility. The symbol b is designated overhead separation factor and is the quotient of the concentration ratios in the distillate and still pot or feed. The Fenske equation is also expressed in terms of concentration ratios

$$X_D/X_W = a^n$$

This corresponds to the maximum possible separation in each stage, with no takeoff of product. A contrasting situation is zero separation at minimum reflux, where $y_{n+1} = y_n$. However, in an ordinary adiabatic column this condition holds true only at the feed plate. In reality every plate, i, has a different minimum reflux ratio, that is, a reflux ratio that causes $y_{i+1} = y_i$ at that plate. These reflux ratios gradually decrease toward zero as the ends of the column are approached. Thus the reflux factor ratio of actual operating reflux ratio to true minimum reflux ratio increases markedly in passing from the feed plate toward the ends of the column. This occurs because in an adiabatic column the reflux ratio is constant from plate to plate. The plates that have very large values of the reflux factor ratios do not contribute much to the separation, yet cost just as much as other trays.[214] In relatively easy separations the burden of the noncontributing trays is inconsequential. When very difficult separations are attempted, it becomes worthwhile to reduce the diameter at the ends of the column as compared with the diameter at the feed plate. This permits lesser flows in plates near the ends and thus lowers the very high reflux factor ratios at these plates. Such an arrangement requires addition of heat at every point below the feed where the diameter changes, and corresponding removal of heat at every point above the feed where diameter changes. This reduces the size and therefore the cost of equipment, reduces the work of moving the flows because quantities are smaller, and also reduces the quantity of material required to fill the system to the point where it can operate. Reduction in quantity of material in the system, i.e., reduction in holdup, also reduces the time to reach a state of productivity, and reduces the time to recover from any accidental upset of this productive state. All these considerations are very important in the separation of isotopes and in other difficult separations. The principles are probably of value for many separations of intermediate difficulty.

An ideal cascade for distillation would be a column which was gradually tapered in its cross-sectional area to provide minimum reflux factor ratios at all points, and which had heat removal or addition at every point as required to achieve the required different flows of vapor and liquid. In practice a series of square or squared-off cascades are used to approximate this in a practical manner. In these the cross-sectional area, i.e., the diameter, is changed by an appreciable amount at a limited number of points, and appropriate heating and cooling is done at these points.

In an ideal cascade the vapor and liquid fed to each stage have the same composition, so that

$$Y_{n+1} = bY_n = b^2X_{n+1} = aX_{n+1}$$

and

$$b = \sqrt{a}$$

The equation for the curved operating line is

$$Y_n = \sqrt{a}X_{n+1}$$

The optimum reflux ratio that minimizes total flow between stages is

$$\frac{L_{n+1}}{D} = \frac{(x_D - y_n)[y_n + b(1 - y_n)]}{y_n(b - 1)(1 - y_n)}$$

The optimum number of plates or stages is

$$n_o = \frac{\ln (X_D/X_W) - 1}{\ln b}$$

Somewhat similar equations apply to square cascades, and permit calculation of design quantities for practical cases.[215]

I. PARTIAL CONDENSATION

A wide range of results is possible as far as separation effects are concerned. Rapid condensation will produce little or no separation, i.e., the condensate will have practically the same composition as the vapor. If condensation is slow and condensate is removed as it is formed, each portion of condensate will be in approximate equilibrium with the vapor from which it forms. This equilibrium partial condensation is analogous to equilibrium simple distillation, and similar mathematical treatment is possible.[216]

Partial condensers of the reflux type are capable of producing substantial fractionation of vapor mixtures.[217] For vapor products having low dew points they may be superior to conventional equipment for adiabatic distillation plus total condensation. Kent and Pigford have studied the condensation of ethylene chloride–toluene. The differential resistance of the liquid phase was found to have a pronounced effect on the fractionation, which does not conform to the Rayleigh theory of equilibrium differential condensation. Partial condensers appear to require more interfacial area than adiabatic distillation equipment in order to produce the same fractionation at the same heat load, i.e., for the same area the partial condenser requires more heat removal. Because of the large influence of liquid phase resistance, the experimental composition points cross the Rayleigh differential distillation line, which therefore should not be used for estimation of fractionation in this type of condenser.

J. STEAM DISTILLATION

Steam batch distillation may occur in numerous ways depending on the solubility and miscibility of the components of the mixture being distilled. The usual elementary treatment of the theory deals with situations where there is only one component other than the steam, and assumes that this component is insoluble in any liquid water that may be present. Many actual practical cases involve two or more components other than steam, and these components may have widely varying solubility in liquid water, and the water may be soluble in the nonaqueous phase that is present. The presence of the steam or liquid water or both often has major effects on the activity coefficients and thus the volatilities and relative volatilities of the nonaqueous components. Practical situations may resemble extractive distillation, azeotropic distillation, amplified distillation, or chromatographic distillation. Some of these special cases have been discussed.[218]

K. AMPLIFIED DISTILLATION

Amplified distillation is a version of ternary or multicomponent distillation in which an inert additive component or mixture is supplied to the still pot to increase the sharpness of separation of difficultly separable components, the increase in separation being independent of any improvement in relative volatility and occurring even when there are no changes in activity and relative volatility. Ordinary amplified distillation makes use of

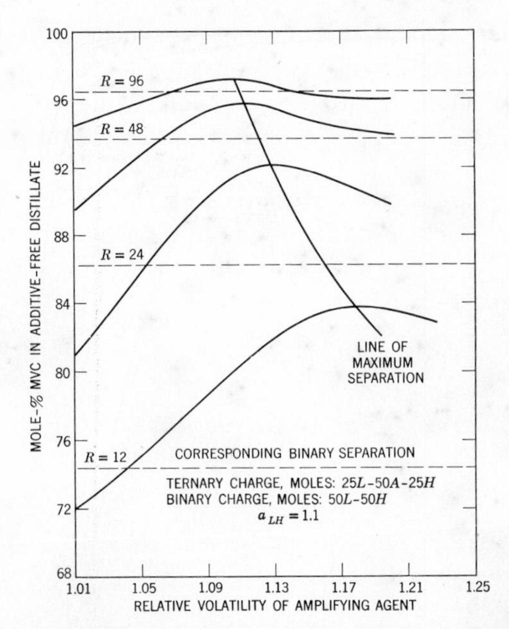

Fig. 82. Calculated effect of relative volatility of amplifying agent in amplified distillation in a 50-plate column with holdup 5% of charge, $R = R_D$.[220]

an amplifying agent (the additive) which has a relative volatility intermediate between those of the components in the mixture to be separated. Ultra-amplified distillation uses an agent with a volatility above those of the components of the original mixture. In any case the amplifying agent must be easily separable from the original components, as is the case with azeotropic entrainers and extractive distillation solvents (Chap. IV).

The term *amplified distillation* was originated by Bratton, Felsing, and Bailey[219] and has been used in a limited number of practical applications. Stillman[220] has made extensive ternary calculations corresponding to various amplified distillation situations, and has performed corresponding experimental distillations. Typical results of the calculations are shown in Figure 82.

L. CHROMATOGRAPHIC DISTILLATION

To be entirely analogous to chromatography, a distillation operation would need to involve a stationary liquid phase, a relatively volatile carrier gas, and would have to be a batch operation. There are no references in the literature to such operations. The stationary liquid phase might be achieved in a plate column with specially designed plates. It is probable that the stationary phase is not an essential feature and that interesting

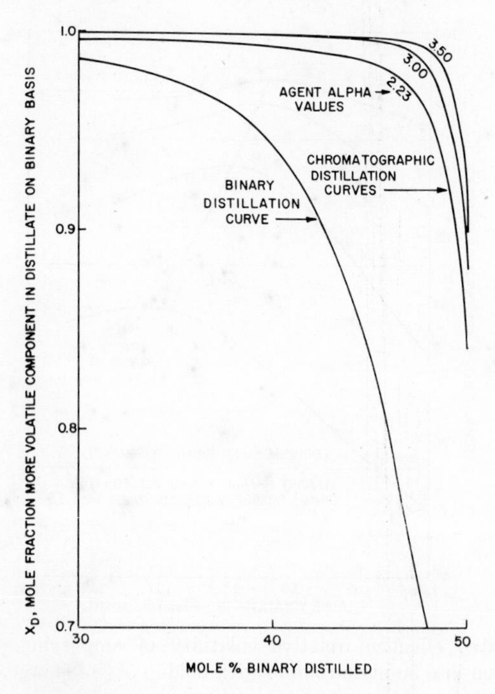

Fig. 83. Typical results of calculations for batch chromatographic distillation. Relative volatility for binary mixture, $\alpha = 2.13$. Relative volativities of additive agent with respect to less volatile compound of binary as shown on graph. Initial charge contained 50 mole-% agent, 25 mole-% each of the binary components. Total column holdup was 25 mole-% of total charge. Agent rate was same as distillate rate. Reflux ratio $R_D = 4$. Column had 10 theoretical plates in addition to reboiler.[222]

results would be obtained if the liquid phase were allowed to move. In this case the operation would be a combination of extractive distillation and carrier distillation, with an extractive distillation solvent added at the head of the column and removed from the bottom of a lower still pot kept free of charge components, a volatile carrier gas introduced at or just above a lower still pot, and an upper still pot into which the batch charge is introduced. Conceivably an ordinary still pot arrangement could be used, and the charge introduced onto a plate near the still pot. The process would be different from gas chromatography in that the liquid and vapor would move in a truly countercurrent fashion, whereas in gas chromatography there is no countercurrent flow but only one-phase flow of the mobile gas phase past the stationary liquid phase.

A less complicated special distillation procedure has been described[221] and investigated in some detail by Eckhart.[222] This has also been referred to as chromatographic distillation. In this work a relatively volatile car-

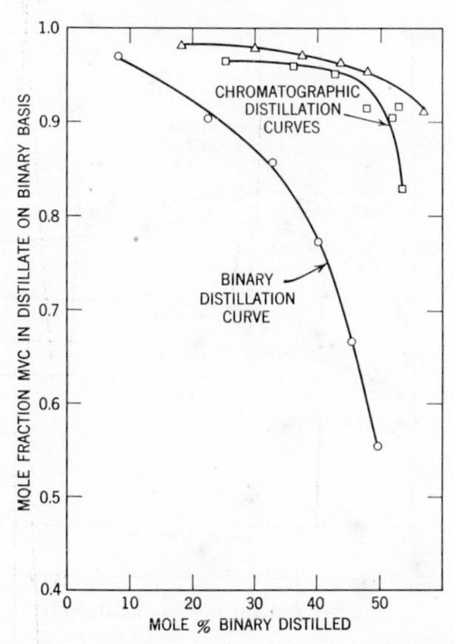

Fig. 84. Typical results of experimental batch chromatographic distillation of toluene–xylene mixture using benzene as agent. Relative volatility of toluene–xylene. α_{TX} = 2.17. Relative volatility of agent, α_{BX} = 4.99. Initial charges were: for binary (O) 50 mole-% each of toluene and xylene; for chromatographic distillation (□) 50 mole-% each of toluene and xylene; for chromatographic distillation (△) 35 mole-% each of toluene and xylene and 30 mole-% benzene. Total column holdup was 12 mole-% of total charge. Agent addition rate was same as distillate takeoff rate. Reflux ratio R_D = 1. Column had 10 actual plates in addition to reboiler.[222]

rier component was added to the still pot continuously during distillation in sufficient amount to maintain a constant quantity in the still pot. The carrier was selected to be such as could be easily removed from the primary components in the distillate. The procedure was applied to both batch and continuous operation. Representative results were as indicated in Figures 83–85.

V. AUTOMATIC COMPUTERS FOR DISTILLATION CALCULATIONS

It has become routine to use automatic digital computers for calculations pertaining to design of large continuous distillation units. There has also been considerable use of both analog and digital computers to obtain a better understanding of the unsteady state behavior necessary to the automatic control of large continuous units. Lastly, the knowledge of batch fractionation has been greatly extended by the calculations made with use of automatic digital computers.

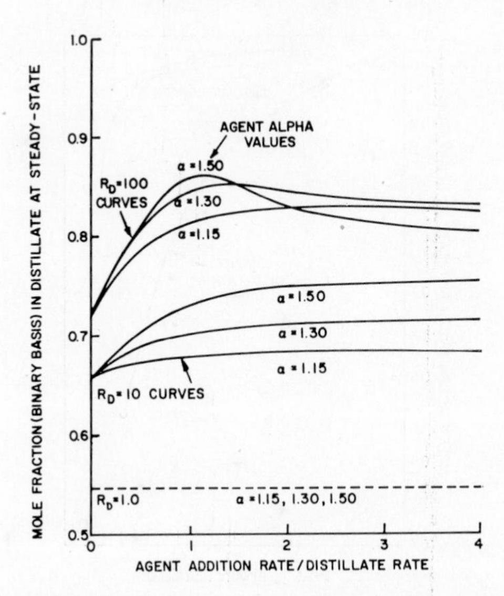

Fig. 85. Typical results of calculations for continuous chromatographic distillation. Relative volatility for binary mixture $\alpha = 1.1$. Relative volatility of additive agent as shown on graphs. Feed contained 50 mole-% of each binary component. Distillate rate one-half of feed rate. Agent addition rate shown as abscissa on graph. Reflux ratio R_D as shown on graph. Curves for $R_D = 50$ very close to those for $R_D = 100$. Column had 20 theoretical plates, plus reboiler.[222]

Early publications on machine calculation were confined to such subjects as interpretation of infrared, mass, and x-ray spectra, and calculations of complex chemical equilibria. Few papers on the use of automatic digital and analog computers for distillation calculations appeared before 1950. The state of the art prior to 1953 is described in the first of the annual review papers on the use of computers in chemistry and chemical engineering.[223] The use of digital computers for calculating batch distillation curves was particularly felicitous, since the solution of the equations for cases of appreciable holdup by desk calculators was so laborious.[224]

During the first years after 1950 there was a much more rapid development of the use of digital computers than of analog computers for distillation calculations. Analog computers are basically fast and inexpensive, but their application to distillation calculations has been slow because of the lack of a single equation or a small number of equations for the overall column process.[225] The inherent iterative nature of the distillation calculations, and the solution through repeated use of the group of equations applicable to a single plate results in a magnification of the errors inherent in the electronic and electrical components of the analog computers. Components with lower inherent error characteristics are relatively more expensive, and sometimes nonexistent. In addition, the cost of even ordinary components is excessive for a sufficient number of replicate sets to produce the analog of a column with 50 or 100 plates. Digital computers, although also highly expensive, are admirably adapted to calculations of a repetitive nature, and while there are problems with respect to retaining accuracy and precision, these can usually be dealt with without undue complication. The disadvantage of analog computers does not apply to distillation control problems, where different kinds of mathematical relations are encountered (Chap. XI).

1. Trial and Error Procedures for Plates and Reflux Ratio in Continuous Distillation

It is not advantageous to try to give working details for the use of automatic computers in this book, but it is desirable to indicate the general approach and method. This will be done first for automatic digital computation of a typical steady state continuous distillation problem—the trial and error calculations to obtain the proper reflux ratio for the continuous distillation of a binary mixture.

A. SIMPLIFIED BINARY CASE

There are a large number of literature references to detailed computer programs for the rather formidable practical version of this problem, and a few of these will be mentioned in a later paragraph. The initial discussion is confined to the simplest possible case.[226]

This example is for the case of a continuous distillation operation which is to be carried out with a binary feed mixture in which the mole fraction of the more volatile component in the feed is $z_f = 0.2000$, the rate at which feed is introduced onto the feed plate is $F = 10.0$ moles per minute, the rate at which distillate is removed is $D = 1.0$ mole per minute, the column has a total $n = 6$ theoretical plates, and the relative volatility of the two components is $\alpha = 2.23$. The problem is to calculate the reflux ratio that must be used to obtain a distillate composition of $x_D = 0.7595$. The feed is supplied as liquid at its boiling point, so that the mole fraction of liquid in the feed is $q = 1$. When this kind of calculation is to be done by hand the steps in the trial and error procedure are as follows.

(*1*) Material balance equations

$$W = F - D \tag{142}$$

and

$$x_W = \frac{Fz_f - Dx_D}{W} \tag{143}$$

are used to calculate W, the moles per minute of bottoms product leaving the bottom of the column, and x_W, the mole fraction of more volatile component in the bottoms stream.

(2) A first trial value is selected for L, the moles per minute of liquid reflux descending through the part of the column above the feed plate.

(3) Material balance equations

$$V = L + D \tag{144}$$

$$L' = L + qF \tag{145}$$

$$V' = V + (q - 1)F \tag{146}$$

are used to calculate first trial values of V, V', and L', the moles per minute, respectively, of vapor ascending in the column above the feed, and the moles per minute of vapor ascending and liquid descending in the part of the column below the feed. Then the applicable vapor–liquid equilibrium relation

$$x_t = \frac{x_D}{\alpha - (\alpha - 1)x_D} \tag{147}$$

and the McCabe–Thiele enriching section material balance equation

$$y_{t-1} = \frac{L}{V}\, x_t + \frac{D}{V}\, x_D \tag{148}$$

are used alternately to calculate compositions at successive plates going from the top down to the feed plate composition. This composition is obtained by the material balance equation

$$x_i = \frac{(L + D)z_f + D(q - 1)x_D}{L + qD} \tag{149}$$

where x_i is the liquid composition at the intersection of the operating lines. From this point on the McCabe–Thiele stripping section material balance

$$y_{m-1} = \frac{L'}{V'}\, x_m - \frac{W}{V'}\, x_w \tag{150}$$

is substituted for the corresponding enriching section equation in calculating successive plate compositions below the feed plate until the bottoms composition is reached.

The McCabe–Thiele graphical procedure can of course be used as an alternate method for the entire procedure of calculating down the column from the distillate composition to the trial bottoms composition.

(*4*) The value of x_W calculated by plate-to-plate calculations is only a first trial value, and as a consequence will almost never be equal to its value calculated by material balance in eq. (143). The latter is of course the correct value, so the plate-to-plate calculations are therefore repeated with different trial values of L, until the x_W obtained by plate-to-plate calculations very nearly matches that obtained by material balance.

(*5*) The last trial value of L, i.e., the one that gives a value of x_W that satisfies the material balance requirements, is used to calculate the reflux ratio whose determination was the object of the work, the necessary equations being

$$R_D = L/D \qquad \text{or} \qquad R_I = L/V$$

for the external and internal reflux ratios, respectively.

The machine calculation involves exactly the same steps, although a slightly different order turns out to be advantageous. This particular presentation is for the use of a comparatively small computer, which avoids some complications encountered on large modern equipment, and gives a better understanding of the interrelation between the calculation procedure and the computer.

The 108 cards required for the computation are punched as indicated in the succeeding paragraphs, which also indicate the corresponding computations performed by the machine. The 108 card deck is introduced into the machine which then proceeds automatically to perform the arithmetic and to print selected intermediate values and the answer.

Cards 1 to 9. The first card clears the machine of numbers present from previous calculations. The second card is punched with numerical values of F, z_f, q, x_D, D, and α, and a first trial value of L. For the example under discussion, this value of L was $L_1 = 9$. As the second and following cards pass through the machine, the various numerical values are transferred to storage units directly associated with the calculating and printing mechanism.

Cards 10 to 32, Inclusive. These cards are punched so as to cause the machine to carry out in proper sequence the calculations corresponding to the following equations.

$$W = F - D = 10 - 1 = 9 \tag{142}$$

$$x_W = \frac{Fz_f - Dx_D}{W} = \frac{(10)(0.2) - (1)(0.7595)}{9} = 0.1378 \tag{143}$$

$$V = L + D = 9 + 1 = 10 \tag{144}$$

$$L' = L + qF = 9 + 10 = 19 \tag{145}$$

$$V' = V + (q - 1)F = 10 + 0 = 10 \tag{146}$$

$$x_i = \frac{(L + D)z_f + D(q - 1)x_D}{L + qD} = \frac{(10)(0.2) + 0}{9 + 1} = 0.2000 \tag{149}$$

$$x_t = \frac{x_D}{\alpha - (\alpha - 1)x_D} = \frac{0.7595}{2.23 - (1.23)(0.7595)} = 0.5861 \qquad (147)$$

$$u = x_t - (x_i + 0.0001) = 0.3860 \qquad (151)$$

(0.0001 has been chosen as the error permitted).

These include the series of material balance calculations referred to in the previous discussion, as well as other values required in subsequent calculation. The resulting numerical values are transferred to storage units where they are held until needed for subsequent calculations.

Cards 33 to 45, Inclusive. These are the first of n (6) identical groups of 13 cards each. Each group of cards supplies the necessary information for the machine to make the plate-to-plate calculations for one plate. The cards are punched with values for both the enriching and stripping section. As long as the value of u [eq. (151)] remains positive, the selector switch causes use of enriching section equations and values. As soon as u becomes negative, the selector shifts and causes stripping section calculations to be made. The results for cards 33 to 45 for the example under discussion are

$$y_{t-1} = \frac{L}{V} x_t + \frac{D}{V} x_D = \frac{9}{10}(0.5861) + \frac{1}{10}(0.7595) = 0.6034 \qquad (148)$$

$$x_{t-1} = \frac{y_{t-1}}{\alpha - (\alpha - 1)y_{t-1}} = \frac{0.6034}{2.23 - (1.23)(0.6034)} = 0.4056$$

$$u = x_{t-1} - (x_i + 0.0001) = +0.2055$$

As u is still positive, the selector switch remains in the position directing use of the enriching operating line for subsequent calculations.

Cards 46 to 58, Inclusive. These function like the previous group of 13, and give values of

$$y_n = y_4 = 0.4410$$

$$x_n = x_4 = 0.2613$$

$$u = +0.0612$$

Cards 59 to 71, Inclusive. These function like the previous group and give

$$y_3 = 0.3111$$

$$x_3 = 0.1684$$

$$u = -0.0317 \text{ (negative)}$$

As u is negative, the selector switch changes position and subsequent calculations for y are made with the stripping line equation.

Cards 72 to 84, Inclusive. These are punched so that the machine calculates

$$y_m = y_2 = \frac{L'}{V'} x_3 - \frac{Wx_W}{V'} = \frac{19}{10}(0.1684) - \frac{9}{10}(0.1378) = 0.1959 \qquad (150)$$

$$x_m = x_2 = \frac{y_2}{\alpha - (\alpha - 1)y_1} = \frac{0.1959}{2.23 - (1.23)(0.1959)} = 0.0985$$

No further tests are made for the value of u, as the selector is wired to remain in the stripping position until the plate calculations are complete.

Cards 85 to 97, Inclusive. These function like the previous groups and give

$$y_1 = 0.0631$$

$$x_1 = x'_W = 0.0293$$

This completes the plate-to-plate calculations.

Card 98. This card merely releases the selector switch.

Cards 99 to 105. These are punched to cause the calculator to obtain a new trial value of L, by means of the equations

$$e_{xW} = x_W - x'_W = 0.1378 - 0.0292 = 0.1085$$

and

$$L_2 = \frac{L_1}{1 + K'(e_{xW})} = \frac{9}{1 + 4(0.1085)} = 6.28 \tag{152}$$

where e_{xW} is the difference in value of x_W calculated by the two different methods, and eq. (360) is semi-empirical, in which $K' = 4$.

Cards 106 to 108. These are unpunched and serve merely to cause the completion of all calculating and printing operations initiated by the immediately preceding cards.

At this point the first 9 cards are removed from the deck and the remainder are reintroduced into the feed hopper of the machine, which then repeats the cycle beginning with the 23 cards (10–32) required for the series of material balance calculations. This deck is passed through the machine time after time. The machine stops after trial 6 through the action of a selector switch that is activated when e_{xW} has a value of less than 0.0005.

The numerical results of a typical calculation are given in Table XVIII.

TABLE XVIII
Typical Trial-and-Error Calculation

Trial	Trial L	x_W Material balance	x_W Plate-to-plate	e_{xW}
1	9.00	0.1378	0.0293	0.1085
2	6.28	0.1378	0.0603	0.0775
3	4.79	0.1378	0.1037	0.0341
4	4.22	0.1378	0.1261	0.0117
5	4.03	0.1378	0.1350	0.0021
6	4.00	0.1378	0.1376	0.0002

B. PRACTICAL TERNARY CASE

A more complicated example calculates the reflux ratio, total plates required, and feed plate location to meet specified requirements for a nonideal ternary continuous distillation of aqueous ethanol–methanol for which the vapor–liquid equilibria are expressed as activity coefficients in terms of three-suffix equations in volume fractions.[227] The steps are as follows:

(*1*) Feed rate, feed composition, and the specified compositions of overhead and bottoms are used to obtain first trial values of the overhead and bottoms take-off rates and the remaining overhead and bottoms compositions.

(*2*) A first-trial reflux ratio is chosen. The equivalent of a relatively high value of L_n/D is chosen to minimize the chance of using a value below minimum reflux; however, no great complication is introduced by a poor choice.

(*3*) A plate-by-plate calculation from the bottom upward is made for the number of plates that will give an overhead ethanol composition that will nearly equal the specified overhead ethanol composition. The plate-by-plate calculation is done by alternate use of material balance and vapor-liquid equilibrium equations. This constitutes the bulk of the numerical computations because the vapor-liquid equilibrium step involves use of Benedict equations and calculation of activities from their logarithms.

(*4*) The discrepancy between the desired overhead ethanol composition and that obtained by the plate-to-plate calculation is used to calculate a new trial value of the distillate product rate and new trial values for the bottoms composition for the ethanol and water.

(*5*) Steps 3 and 4 are repeated until successive repetitions give the same number of plates.

This number of plates with the reflux ratio last used will give the desired separation. Steps (*1*) and (*2*) are performed manually, since they are required only once, but the repetitive steps (*3*) and (*4*) are done automatically by the computer, which prints key values as it proceeds. If the chosen reflux ratio is below minimum, this will be detected on the first cycle of step (*3*), in that a pinch will be reached with little or no change in composition from plate to plate and no normal termination of step (*3*). In such a case the computer is stopped, a new higher L/D reflux ratio is introduced, and calculation is started again. After repeated trials, there are obtained a series of values of reflux ratio and plates that will meet the specifications.

TABLE XIX
Summary of Trials and Results

Calculation	Trial reflux ratio L_m/V_m	Final D	Final reflux ratio L_n/D	Theoretical plates	Feed-plate location	Remarks
1	10					Pinch
2	8					Pinch
3	6					Pinch
4	4					Pinch
5	3					Pinch
6	2.5	1.4004	474.39	87.49	77	
7	2.4	1.4014	507.98	73.25	63	
8	2.3	1.4006	547.45	62.36	52	
9	2.2	1.4013	592.85	55.17	45	
10	2.05	1.4017	677.49	47.00	37	
11	2.0	1.4022	711.17	44.91	35	
12	1.5	1.4050	1,420.49	31.10	22	
13	1.1	1.3985	7,139.52	24.80	16	
14	1.01	1.3823	72,242.20	23.71	15	

Table XIX summarizes the entire sequence of the work and results on the sample problem. As indicated on line 1 of Table XIX, the first choice of a trial reflux ratio was $L_m/V_m = 10$, equivalent to $L_n/D = 96$. This resulted in a pinch, as did the next several choices of reflux ratio shown on succeeding lines. Reduction of the trial choice of L_m/V_m to 2.5 finally resulted in a solution, as shown on line 6. Various other lower values of L_m/V_m led to the other solutions shown on lower lines of Table XIX. In calculations 1 through 5 where a pinch was encountered, the computer proceeded through step (*3*) only once to obtain plate compositions such as are illustrated in Table XX. In calculation 6 and those following, the computer followed the normal sequence of calculations to obtain successive trial values and final values, such as those given in Table XXI.

TABLE XX
Plate Compositions for $R_m = 10$

Plate	Pinch condition		
	x_{n1}	x_{n2}	x_{n3}
1	0.00000346	0.05412713	0.94586941
5	0.00000393	0.06650928	0.93348679
10	0.00000393	0.06656632	0.93342975
99	0.00000393	0.06656638	0.93342969

TABLE XXI
Typical Values for Normal Calculation

Trial	Calculation 12, $R_m = 1.5$	
	1	2
x_{D3}	0.75000	0.70069
D	1.33	1.405
n	31	31.1
$x_{3,1}$	0.00000810	0.00000811
$x_{3,5}$	0.00003294	0.00003299
$x_{3,10}$	0.00009330	0.00009345
$x_{3,20}$	0.00064420	0.00064528
$x_{3,30}$	0.00419687	0.00420421
$x_{3,40}$	0.17687449	0.17719295
$x_{3,42}$	0.37123822	0.37177603
$x_{3,44}$	0.61311601	0.61371439
x_D	0.70069	0.70110

C. GENERAL MULTICOMPONENT CASES

Much more elaborate procedures are of course involved and used for practical problems that involve 20 or more components, various irregularities in heat quantities, vapor and liquid flows, side streams or supplementary feeds and other regularly used arrangements in industrial continuous distillation. The choice is difficult between the many computer programs that have been suggested for solution of the various aspects of the steady state continu-

TABLE XXII

Methods of Calculation for Continuous Multicomponent Distillation Curves

Acrivos, A., and N. R. Amundson, *Chem. Eng. Sci.*, **4**, 29, 68, 141, 159, 206, 249 (1955)
Exhaustive mathematical analysis of the basic material balance equations of multicomponent continuous distillation and application to typical problems

Bachelor, J. B., *Petroleum Refiner*, **36**, No. 6, 161 (1957)
Employs relaxation technique to obtain minimum reflux in multicomponent continuous distillation without assumption of constant α and constant molal overflow

Butler, R. M., *Petroleum Refiner*, **34**, No. 7, 109 (1955)
Method of finding minimum plates in multicomponent continuous distillation by combining Fenske equation with Clausius–Clapeyron equation and Trouton's rule

Edmister, W. C., *A.I.Ch.E. J.*, **3**, 165 (1957)
Absorption and stripping factor method

Eshaya, A. M., *Chem. Eng. Sci.*, **4**, 85 (1955)
Equation for composition on any plate in terms of feed and distillate composition, when α and R are constant

Geddes, R. L., *A.I.Ch.E. J.*, **4**, 389 (1958)
Fractionation index used for correlation purposes and prediction of product composition. Depends upon linear relation between log of ratio of a component in liquid distillate to that in liquid bottoms versus log of ratio of volatility of that component to volatility of a reference component

Hachmuth, K. H., *Chem. Eng. Progr.*, **48**, 570 (1952)
States extension of binary methods to multicomponent mixtures is treacherous because different components in such a mixture have different rates of approach to equilibrium

Happel, J., *Chem. Eng.*, **65**, No. 14, 144 (1958)
Finds optimum plates and reflux in terms of minimum plates and reflux

Hengstebeck, R. J., *Petroleum Engr.*, **29**, No. 12, C6 (1957); *Chem. Eng. Progr.*, **53**, 243 (1957)
Reduces multicomponent system to a binary in terms of key components

Klein, G., and D. N. Hanson, *Chem. Eng. Sci.*, **4**, 229 (1955)
Adapts Underwood equations so that determinants can be used.

Musk, F. I., and E. D. Totman, *J. Appl. Chem. (London)*, **10**, 477 (1960)
Method to be used when feed plate and number of plates are unknown.

Newman, J. S., *Petroleum Refiner*, **42**, No. 4, 141 (1963)
Uses Newton's successive approximation to simplify correction of assumed plate temperatures

Popov, V. V., A. S. Sakhiev, and T. P. Korablina, *Plast. Massy*, **1961**, No. 4, 18
Determines optimum reflux ratio and optimum number of plates from minimum values

Rodriguez, F., and T. J. Walsh, *Ind. Eng. Chem.*, **46**, 2509 (1954)
Nomographs for Lewis-Matheson calculations

Salmon, R., *Petroleum Engr.*, **27**, No. 2, C42 (1955)
Modification of absorption factor method

Surowiec, A. J., *Can. J. Chem. Eng.*, **39**, 130 (1961)
Uses a parameter equal to number of theoretical plates required to do the work of one total reflux tray at bottom of enriching section

Van Wijk, W. R., and Bruijn, P. J., *Chem. Eng. Sci.*, **6**, 79 (1956); **8**, 225 (1958). Van Wijk, W. R., P. J. Bruijn, and H. Goedkoop, *Brit. Chem. Eng.*, **4**, 327 (1959)
Expresses relations in terms of an equivalent binary

Von Halle, E., and G. B. Knight, *AECU-3902*, Aug., 1956, 23 p.
Expresses productivity by an extrapolation procedure

Winn, F. W., *Petroleum Refiner*, **37**, No. 5, 216 (1958)
Gives an analog of the Fenske equation in terms of equilibrium constants

ous distillation problems. It may be true that there is no really good single program that is appropriate for all problems.[228] Various reviews are helpful.[229] Experience is even more helpful.

Many of the proposed computer procedures for multicomponent continuous distillation problems involve plate-to-plate calculations up or down the column, or both ways to or from the feed, with repeated trials to match with overall split and material balance calculations. Almost all of these procedures are for continuous distillation of multicomponent mixtures, with unequal molal overflow and other complicating conditions that are characteristic of practical situations. The basic papers are by Beutler, Bonner, McIntire, and Shelton.[230] Some selected later references are of interest.[231] This approach is merely a more complex version of the examples given in the preceding paragraphs, and at the same time these computations are a mechanized version of long-used hand and desk calculator procedures for binary and multicomponent continuous distillation.[232] See also Table XXII. The advantages of computer use are the ease and quickness with which one or many solutions can be obtained, once a workable computer program is developed. The most important difference between the many programs[233] of this type is in the exact nature of the method used to convert the discrepancy in the result of one cycle of calculations into a new set of trial values for starting the next cycle of calculation. It is of course desirable to have the calculations converge toward the answer with as few trials as possible. It has not been easy to invent computer instructions that were equal to the judgment of an experienced design engineer in obtaining the most advantageous set of trial values for a succeeding cycle of calculations. Unfortunately, the variety of distillation situations is apparently so great that any of the many schemes already devised are likely to be unsatisfactory in a new and different problem because of slow convergence or failure to converge. As a consequence new schemes are regularly suggested. The overall situation is further complicated by the neverending stream of new and different hand and desk calculator methods for solving multicomponent distillation calculation problems. Each of these can be incorporated into one or more computer procedures.

2. New Approach Based on Solution of Simultaneous Equations

The advent of automatic computers has led to the development of several entirely new methods of solving multicomponent continuous distillation problems. One such approach[234] is to write the set of simultaneous equations that describe the material balance that must exist around each plate of a column at steady state. Then the various mathematical procedures for solving sets of simultaneous equations can be applied. Most of these mathematical procedures have already been adapted to computers in connection with other uses. However, the results of this approach have not been uniformly successful with continuous distillation calculations.

3. New Approach Based on Relaxation Procedure

A second approach is to solve the set of simultaneous equations for continuous multicomponent distillation by an unsteady state calculation procedure that loads all plates with feed and then calculates the approach of the system to steady state in a manner similar to the actual behavior of the physical system. This was suggested by Rose, Sweeny, and Schrodt,[235] who named it the *relaxation method*, and has been discussed in detail by Rosenbrock.[236] The approach is probably more general than any of the others, but it is also very much the longest, even with the improvements incorporated by Rosenbrock[236] and Stillman[237] to shorten the procedure. The equations and procedure of this second new approach are identical with those for calculating equilibration time (p. 113) and for the behavior of a continuous distillation apparatus when variations in operating conditions cause upsets of the steady state.[238]

The basic equations used in this second approach are the same as those used by Johnson et al.[239] for the stepwise calculations of batch distillation curves when there was appreciable holdup.

4. Batch Fractional Distillation with Appreciable Holdup

All the kinds of calculations just mentioned (the unsteady state approach to binary or multicomponent distillation, the approach to initial equilibrium, behavior upon upset, and batch operation with holdup) require use of a computer. A typical example is the calculation for a batch distillation with 74% plate efficiency and appreciable holdup.[240] This was carried out on one of the earlier computers, an IBM Card-Programmed Calculator, but is worth detailing here because of its simplicity and usefulness in showing the basic approach. The equations used are as follows.

For change in top plate liquid composition due to removal of a small quantity, D moles, of distillate during one "interval" of time:

$$x_{t(i+1)} = x_{ti} - \left[\left(\frac{V}{H}\right)(y_{ti} - y_{(t-1)i}) - \left(\frac{L}{H}\right)(x_{Ri} - x_{ti})\right] \quad (153)$$

For corresponding change in liquid composition from other plates

$$x_{n(i+1)} = x_{ni} - \left[\left(\frac{V}{H}\right)(y_{ni} - y_{(n-1)i}) - \left(\frac{L}{H}\right)(x_{(n+1)i} - x_{ni})\right] \quad (154)$$

For corresponding change in composition of liquid in still pot

$$x_{s(i+1)} = \frac{S_i x_{si} - [V y_{si} - L x_{1i}]}{S_i - D} \tag{155}$$

For values of vapor composition

$$y_n = e y_n^* + (1 - e) y_{n-1} \tag{156}$$

where $y^* = f_{eq}(x)$ and e is Murphree y-efficiency. In the present work

$$y_n^* = \frac{\alpha x_n}{1 + (\alpha - 1) x_n} \tag{157}$$

For vapor composition from the still pot

$$y_s = y_s^* = \frac{\alpha x_s}{1 + (\alpha - 1) x_s} \tag{158}$$

This method of calculation requires knowledge of the initial liquid and vapor compositions for a batch column operating with a specific mixture, specified number of plates, reflux ratio, holdup, and vapor rate. For a total reflux startup these may be calculated by methods previously described (Sec. III, p. 101), for which a computer may also be used. The first three equations, (153–155) then serve for calculation of new plate and still (liquid) compositions after removal of a small quantity of distillate D. When these new values of x_{t1}, x_{n1}, x_{s1} are obtained, they are used with eqs. (156) and (157) to obtain the corresponding equilibrium y^* values, and then the actual y values corresponding to 74% plate efficiency. Then the first three equations may again be used to obtain new liquid composition values, x_{t2}, x_{n2}, etc., after the removal of a second small quantity of distillate. Additional x values are obtained by repetition of the procedure.

The process of computation is lengthened further by the necessity for making a material balance check after each new set of x and y values is obtained, and by the necessity of averaging or correcting the x values first obtained. The correction is carried out by means of the equation

$$x_{i \text{ corrected}} = \frac{x_{i-1}}{4} + \frac{x_i}{2} + \frac{x_{i+1}}{4} \tag{159}$$

The material balance check is necessary to eliminate arithmetic errors, and the averaging reduces a truncation error to negligible size.

The calculator performs the required calculations automatically by use of a deck of punched cards for the particular conditions used in this study. Each card supplies certain numerical values such as the starting compositions, or it directs the machine to perform a particular arithmetic operation and the related transfers of various numbers from one storage register to another, etc.

The order in which the various calculations are made on the computer is not the same as the order in which the equations are listed in the previous discussion. Rearrangement allows more effective use of the computer. The steps in the actual process of calculation are:

Card 1. Enters the numerical values of starting liquid compositions and the value of efficiency.

Card 2. Causes a transfer of e from one storage position to another, in order to clear the first position for other factors.

TABLE XXIII

Sample Summary of Calculated Composition Values During Batch Distillation[a]

	Time			
	Before removal of distillate[b]	After removal of D moles of distillate	After removal of $2D$ moles of distillate	After removal of $3D$ moles of distillate
$x_D = y_t$	0.8471	0.8438	0.8405	0.8371
$x_t = x_5$	0.7617	0.7572	0.7525	0.7477
x_4	0.6457	0.6397	0.6335	0.6274
x_3	0.5054	0.4983	0.4912	0.4844
x_2	0.3601	0.3527	0.3462	0.3402
x_1	0.2335	0.2276	0.2232	0.2195
x_s	0.1202	0.1196	0.1187	0.1178
% distilled[c]	0	0.35	0.70	1.05

[a] Charge, 284.8318 moles. Holdup, 35.1% of charge. Reflux ratio, 9 to 1. Relative volatility, 2.23. Plate efficiency, 0.74.

[b] But after column is at steady state at total reflux.

[c] Mole % of charge distilled.

Cards 3 to 8. Calculate and store $x_{(0)}/4$ values to be used later in averaging calculations [eq. (159)].

Cards 9 to 14. Calculate $y^*_{1(0)}$ values from eq. (157).

Cards 15 and 16. Clear two counter groups for other uses.

Cards 17 to 33. Calculate $y_{1(0)}$ through $y_{5(0)}$ by eq. (156).

Cards 34 to 63. Calculate preliminary $x_{(1)}$ values at end of interval 1 by eqs. (153)–(155).

Cards 64 to 75. Calculate $x_{(1)}/2$ values which are added to $x_{(0)}/4$ values for later use in eq. (159).

Cards 76 to 129. Repeat the above process of obtaining y^* and y at end of interval 1—i.e., effective during interval 2—and the preliminary values of x at end of interval 2.

Cards 130 to 141. Calculate $x_{(2)}/4$ and add to previously stored factors to obtain averaged values of x at the end of interval 1 using eq. (159).

Cards 142 to 151. Material balance calculation on corrected x values.

Cards 152 to 155. "Cleanup" cards to allow time for storage and transfer of last numbers from previous group of cards.

The result of the passage of the deck of cards through the machine is that the original x_0 composition values are replaced by new $x_{(1)}$ values corresponding to compositions after the removal of D moles of distillate. If desired, these and any intermediate values of interest may be printed as the calculation is proceeding.

The calculation of a set of $x_{(2)}$ (corrected) values is achieved by passing cards 3 through 155 through the process a second time. The first two cards are not necessary after the first passage, as their only function is to introduce original numerical values.

The continuation of the calculation is mere repetition of the passage of cards 3 through 155 through the machine. As the computer operates at the rate of 150 cards per minute, the computation proceeds at the rate of approximately D moles of distillate removed for each minute of computer time. The general sequence of calculation is

(*1*) Preliminary value of x_{i+1}.

(*2*) Preliminary value of x_{i+2}.
(*3*) Averaging of corrected x_i with preliminary x_{i+1} and x_{i+2} to obtain corrected x_{i+1}.
(*4*) Material balance check.
The detailed description of the programming is rather complex, and is summarized by a planning chart, a device now largely superseded, which gives the details for punching the cards that actuate the computer.

Appropriate punching can also direct the computer to print whatever values are desired. Table XXIII gives a sample summary of calculated results. Usually only a few of these results would be printed, possibly the x_D values, or even only every 5th or 20th one of these. In general, printing is one of the quite time-consuming operations in computer operation.

5. Modern Computer Procedures

The preceding discussion relates to use of a computer readily available in the period 1950–1955. Later models of digital computers are improved in the sense that it is almost possible to provide instructions in plain English instead of through a planning chart and cards punched in machine language. One commonly used language for communicating with computers is called Fortran. It is of course necessary to prepare a plan, which is usually done by means of a block diagram which gives the steps in the computation. An expert can often prepare the Fortran program with a block diagram which gives only the general procedure for the calculation, but each and every individual arithmetic step must then be visualized mentally and included in proper order and relationship, in the Fortran program. For computations as complex as the more practical problems in distillation, a novice and most others require a completely detailed block diagram giving every individual arithmetic step in explicit form.

Figure 86 shows such a block diagram of the computer program for the calculation of curves for multicomponent batch distillation with appreciable holdup, for any number of plates and any reflux ratio up to 100. Figures 87 and 88[241] give typical results obtained with this program, showing the effect of charge composition for a ternary distillation where there is appreciable holdup and a minor amount of the intermediate component. Figure 89 gives the Fortran language instructions to execute this calculation. The Fortran printout is prepared by punching individual cards, each line of the Fortran instructions appearing on one or more cards. Modern computers have programs that use the Fortran card deck to prepare a machine language card deck that actually directs the computer operations required to perform the computations.

A more elaborate multicomponent batch distillation computer program has also been prepared.[242] This includes provision for enthalpy balances

1 Read number of components [NOC]; read number of plates [NOP]; read tolerance [TOL].
19 Read reflux ratio R_D [R]; read moles distillate per unit time [D]; read moles distilled at which computation is to stop [FINAL]; read moles distilled between printouts [EVERY]; read time elapsed per interval [THETA].
19A Calculate number of stages [NOS = NOP + 1].
19B, 2 Read relative volatility for each component [ALPH].
2 Read total moles each component in charge [CHG (L)]; read mole fraction each component in charge [X(L, 1].
2A Read total moles in reboiler [H(1)]; 2A, 2B, 7 read total moles holdup each plate [H(2)].

120, 120A, B, 104 Calculate αx for reboiler for each component [ALPH X (L, I)] and sum these.
104B Calculate mole fraction each component in vapor from reboiler [Y(L, I)= (ALPH (L) X (L, I))/SUM].
105 Set mole fraction of each component in liquid from stage above [X(L, I + 1) = Y(L, I)]. Calculate y(L, 2), y(L, 3), etc., repeating 120, 104, 105 until y's for top plate are obtained. Each y gives x for plate above.
106A, B, C, 107 Calculate [HOL (L)], the moles of each component present in reboiler and column, according to x values just calculated.

107A, B, C Calculate difference between CHG(L) for each component and corresponding HOL(L) just calculated.
109, 110 Subtract absolute value of difference from tolerance, a small number.
112, 140, 141 If result of subtraction is zero or plus, calculate value of y for top plate from x for top plate and begin takeoff part of computation (90).
If result of subtraction is negative calculate a new trial reboiler composition (118, 119, 116) including a normalization step, and repeat program beginning with operation 120.

---

90 Set a counter = 0 [DIGIT = 0]; 90A calculate [RPO] = R + 1; 90B calculate [TD] = THETA times D.
90C, D, 9 Calculate total moles all components present in reboiler plus column [AFC].
9A, 3 Printing of operating conditions.
6, 40 Calculate moles of each component present in reboiler [CONT (L)]. CONT(L) = H(1) times X(L, 1).
71, 79, 75, 73 Print total moles distilled [AFD], mole percent distilled [PCTD], moles of each component distilled, moles of each component in reboiler, mole fraction of each component in liquid and in vapor of each stage.

26, 10, 12, 14 Calculate new values of x for reboiler and each plate in column, these being the compositions that exist at the end of a short time interval, [THETA], after takeoff of distillate has started.
33 Calculate new values of HOL(L), the total moles of each component in the reboiler plus column, at end of the time interval THETA.
33B Calculate values [OFX] of the moles of each component distilled off during the time interval THETA [OFX = CHG (L) - HOL (L)].
34 Calculate total moles distilled off for each component [YIELD (L)].
55 Calculate total moles remaining in reboiler and column at end of interval [AFH].
55A Calculate total moles distilled off at end of interval [AFD = AFC - AFH].
55B Calculate mole percent distilled [PCTD].

55C, 37, 93, 8, 4, 5 Replace CHG(L) by HOL(L) and calculate values of y corresponding to values of x last calculated.
26, 10, 12, 14 Calculate new values of x, for each component for each stage, these being for compositions that exist at the end of an additional short time interval.

33, 33B, 34, 55, 55A, 55B Repeat as done for preceding time interval.

55C Check to determine if printing is desired.
If NO, do 37, 93, 8, 4, 5, and 26, 10, 12, 14 and 33, etc. to 55B and 55C. Continue cycling as above.
If YES, do 93, 8, 4, 5, 6, 40, 71, 79, 75, 73 and then 37 and 26, 10, 12, 14 and 33 through 55B to 55C. Continue until desired percent distilled is reached.

Fig. 86. Block diagram for computer program for calculation of batch distillation with appreciable holdup, and up to 9 components, 98 theoretical plates, and reflux ratio up to 99.

and constant volume of holdup on each tray and in the condenser. This is written in Fortran and has been run on an IBM 7070 computer for a four-component mixture. A relationship to vary the size of the increment steps during the course of the program is included. A somewhat similar

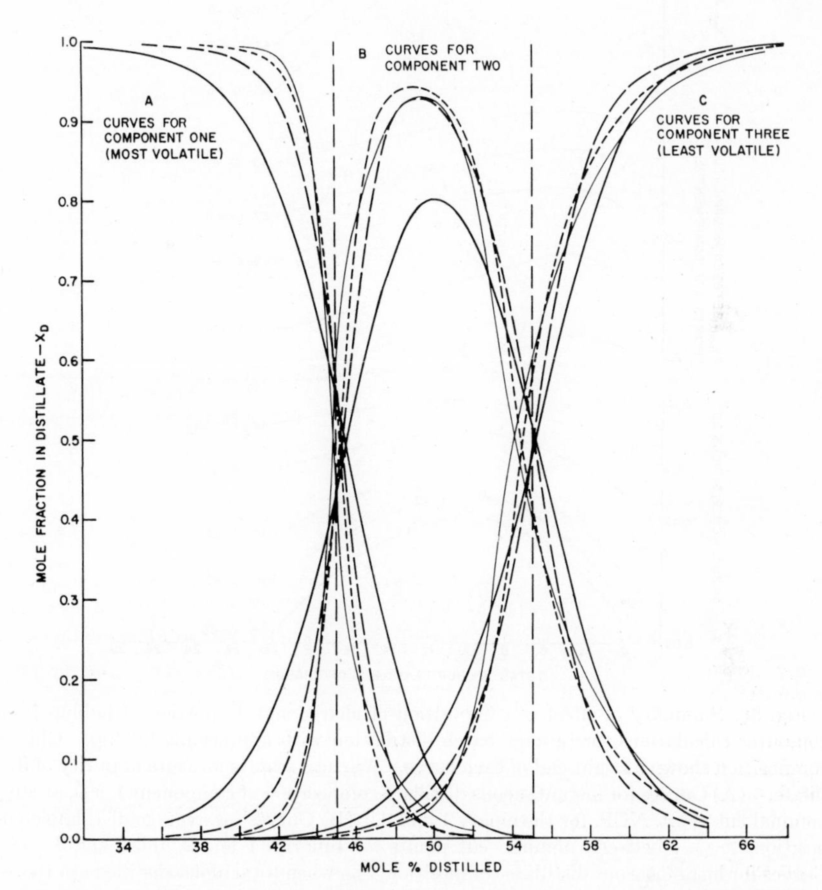

Fig. 87. Curves for computer calculations for ternary batch distillation with appreciable holdup. Charge composition 45 moles component 1, 10 moles component 2, and 45 moles component 3. Relative volatility $\alpha_{1,3} = 4/1$, $\alpha_{2,3} = 2/1$. Reflux ratio $R_D = 10$. Ten theoretical plates and reboiler. Total column holdup: 20 moles (——); 10 moles (— —); 5 moles (- - -); 2 moles (——).

program has also been written for an IBM 650 computer, using Soap II language.[243] This also provides for plate heat balances, and for the preliminary calculations to establish initial compositions in the column. This program provides for 40 theoretical plates.

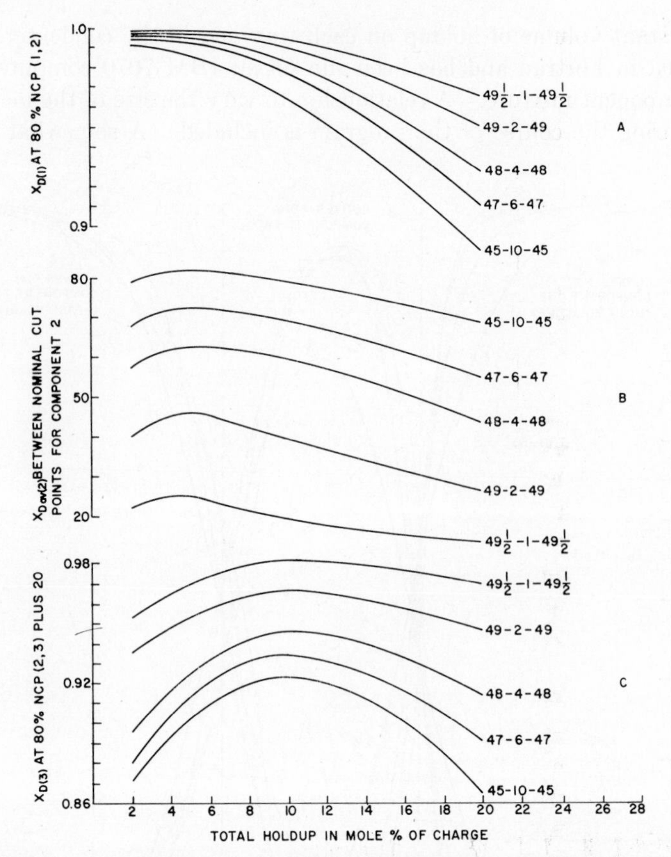

Fig. 88. Summary of effect of composition of charge and proportion of holdup from computer calculations for ternary batch distillation with appreciable holdup. Charge composition shown at right end of each curve. Vertical scale is measure of purity of distillate. (A) Curves for instantaneous distillate composition of component 1, x_{D1}, at 80% nominal cut point, NCP, for the binary 1 and 2. (B) Curves for average distillate composition, $x_{D2(av)}$, between nominal cut points for binaries 1 and 2, and 2 and 3. (C) Curves for instantaneous distillate composition, x_{D3}, when total moles distilled are $100 - 0.80\times(100 - \text{NCP binary } 2,3) = 20 + 0.80\times(\text{NCP binary } 2,3)$. This x_{D3} is a good approximation of the composition of component 3 that could be collected in 80% yield

```
C      PROGRAM RAE 513
C      BATCH DISTILLATION CALCULATION BY THE ROSE METHOD.
C      THIS PROGRAM WILL HANDLE UP TO NINE COMPONENTS AND UP TO NINETY-
C      EIGHT PLATES PLUS REBOILER.  CODED IN THE FORTRAN LANGUAGE FOR THE
C      IBM 7074 DIGITAL COMPUTER.  INPUT IS ON PUNCHED CARDS.  OUTPUT IS
C      ON ON-LINE PRINTER.  OUTPUT IS PROGRAMMED FOR THE PROGRAM CONTROL
C      MODE OF OUTPUT PRINTER. CODED MARCH 17, 1963 RAE, MODIFIED HR JULY, 1963
C      MODIFIED STATEMENT 14    D.J.R.     JULY.1964
       DIMENSION X(9,99),Y(9,99),XN(99),H(99),ALPH(9),CHG(9),HOL(9),
      1YIELD(9),CONT(9),DATE(4)
 1000 FORMAT (2I5,F10.5,4A5)
 1001 FORMAT (5F10.5,I5)
 1002 FORMAT (2F10.5,E14.8)
 1003 FORMAT (2F10.5)
 1999 FORMAT (1H1,2X,18HPROGRAM NUMBER 513)
 2000 FORMAT (1H0,38X,52HBATCH DISTILLATION CALCULATION USING THE ROSE M
     1ETHOD/1H0,41X,15HTHE COLUMN HAS I2,21H PLATES PLUS REBOILER/1H0,39
     2X,34HMOLES OF LIQUID HOLDUP PER PLATE = F9.2/)
 2001 FORMAT (1H ,35X,18HMOLS OF COMPONENT I1,21H IN INITIAL CHARGE = F9
     1.2)
 2002 FORMAT (1H ,10X)
 2003 FORMAT (1H ,37X,33HRELATIVF VOLATILITY OF COMPONENT I1,3H = F8.4)
 2004 FORMAT (1H0,48X,15HREFLUX RATIO = F8.2/1H0,41X,30HDISTILLATE RATE
     1(MOLS/TIME) = F8.2/1H0,47X,15HTHETA (TIME) = F10.8/1H0,25X,69HINIT
     2IAL COMPOSITIONS ARE THOSE OBTAINED AT STEADY-STATE, TOTAL REFLUX/
     31H .41X,37HALL COMPOSITIONS ARE IN MOL FRACTIONS/1H0,46X,7HDATE -
     44A5)
 2005 FORMAT (1H0,2X,17HMOLS DISTILLED = F9.2/1H ,2X,20HPERCENT DISTILLE
     1D = F5.2/1H ,33X,22HDISTILLATE COMPOSITION,10X,18HTOTAL YIELD (MOL
     2S),10X,24HREBOILER CONTENTS (MOLS))
 2006 FORMAT (1H ,7X,10HCOMPONENT I1,E33.8,F28.3,F31.3)
 2007 FORMAT (1H0,57X,6HLIQUID,22X,5HVAPOR)
 2008 FORMAT (1H ,9X,13HPLATE NUMBER I2,E43.8,E28.8)
 2009 FORMAT (1H ,9X,8HREBOILER,F50.8,E28.8/)
 2010 FORMAT (1H ,7X,10HCOMPONENT I1)
 2011 FORMAT (1H0,43X,35HLIQUID MOL FRACTIONS NOT NORMALIZED///)
 2012 FORMAT (1H0,45X,31HLIQUID MOL FRACTIONS NORMALIZED///)
    1 READ 1000,NOC,NOP,TOL,DATE
 2013 FORMAT (1H0,2X,13HFOR CYCLE NO.,I4,11X,9HCOMPONENT,23X,6HHOL(L),14
     1X,24HMOL FRACTION IN REBOILER)
 2014 FORMAT (1H ,32X,I4,15X,E15.8,15X,E15.8)
      IF (NOC) 13,13,19
   19 READ 1001,R,D,FINAL,EVERY,THETA,NORM
      NOS=NOP+1
      DO 2 L=1,NOC
    2 READ 1002,ALPH(L),CHG(L),X(L,1)
      READ 1003,H(1),H(2)
      PRINT 1999
      PRINT 2000,NOP,H(2)
      DO 50 L=1,NOC
   50 PRINT 2001,L,CHG(L)
      PRINT 2002
      DO 51 L=1,NOC
   51 PRINT 2003,L,ALPH(L)
      PRINT 2004,R,D,THETA,DATE(1),DATE(2),DATE(3),DATE(4)
      IF (NORM) 13,80,81
   80 PRINT 2011
      GO TO 300
   81 PRINT 2012
  300 NCY=1
      DO 7 I=3,NOS
    7 H(I)=H(2)
      MORE=0
  120 DO 106 I=1,NOP
      SUM=0.
      DO 104 L=1,NOC
```

Fig. 89. Fortran language printout for the program of Figure 86. (Continued on pages 206 and 207).

```
  104 SUM=SUM+(ALPH(L)*X(L,I))
      DO 105 L=1,NOC
      Y(L,I)=(ALPH(L)*X(L,I))/SUM
  105 X(L,I+1)=Y(L,I)
  106 CONTINUE
      DO 107 L=1,NOC
      HOL(L)=0.
      DO 107 I=1,NOS
  107 HOL(L)=HOL(L)+(H(I)*X(L,I))
      DO 108 L=1,NOC
      DIFF=CHG(L)-HOL(L)
      IF (DIFF) 109,108,110
  109 DIFF=-DIFF
  110 IF (TOL-DIFF) 111,108,108
  111 MORE=1
  108 CONTINUE
      IF (MORE) 117,112,117
  112 SUM=0.
      DO 140 L=1,NOC
  140 SUM=SUM+(ALPH(L)*X(L,NOS))
      DO 141 L=1,NOC
  141 Y(L,NOS)=(ALPH(L)*X(L,NOS))/SUM
      GO TO 90
  117 DO 118 L=1,NOC
  118 X(L,1)=(CHG(L)/HOL(L))*X(L,1)
C     NORMALIZE
      SUM=0.
      DO 119 L=1,NOC
  119 SUM=SUM+X(L,1)
      PRINT 2013,NCY
      DO 116 L=1,NOC
      X(L,1)=X(L,1)/SUM
  116 PRINT 2014,L,HOL(L),X(L,1)
      NCY=NCY+1
      MORE=0
      GO TO 120
   90 DIGIT=0.
      RPO=R+1.0
      TD=THETA*D
      AFC=0.
      DO 9 L=1,NOC
    9 AFC=AFC+CHG(L)
      AFH=AFC
      AFD=0.
      PCTD=0.
      DO 60 L=1,NOC
   60 YIELD(L)=0.
      ALL=0.
    3 IF (AFD) 13,6,93
   93 DO 5 I=1,NOS
    8 SUM=0.
      DO 4 L=1,NOC
    4 SUM=SUM+(ALPH(L)*X(L,I))
      DO 5 L=1,NOC
    5 Y(L,I)=(ALPH(L)*X(L,I))/SUM
      IF (AFD-ALL) 26,6,6
C     COMPUTE NEW X'S
   26 DO 20 L=1,NOC
      DO 15 I=1,NOS
      IF (I-1) 13,10,11
   10 XN(I)=((H(I)/(H(I)-TD))*X(L,I))+((TD/(H(I)-TD))*((R*X(L,I+1))
     1-(RPO*Y(L,I))))
      GO TO 15
   11 IF (I-NOS) 14,12,13
   12 XN(I)=(X(L,I))+((TD/H(I))*((RPO*Y(L,I-1))-(R*X(L,I))-Y(L,I)))
      GO TO 15
   14 XN(I)=(X(L,I))+((TD/H(I))*((R*(X(L,I+1)-X(L,I)))+(RPO*(Y(L,I-1)-Y(
     1L,I)))))
```

Fig. 89 (*continued*).

```
   15 CONTINUE
      DO 16 I=1,NOS
   16 X(L,I)=XN(I)
   20 CONTINUF
      IF (NORM) 13,35,36
C     NORMALIZE
   36 DO 31 I=1,NOS
      SUM=0.
      DO 32 L=1,NOC
   32 SUM=SUM+X(L,I)
      DO 31 L=1,NOC
   31 X(L,I)=X(L,I)/SUM
   35 H(1)=H(1)-TD
      DO 33 L=1,NOC
      HOL(L)=0.
      DO 33 I=1,NOS
   33 HOL(L)=HOL(L)+(X(L,I)*H(I))
      DO 34 L=1,NOC
      OFX=CHG(L)-HOL(L)
   34 YIELD(L)=YIELD(L)+OFX
      AFH=0.
      DO 55 L=1,NOC
   55 AFH=AFH+HOL(L)
      AFD=AFC-AFH
      PCTD=(AFD/AFC)*100.
      IF (AFD-ALL) 70,93,93
    6 DO 40 L=1,NOC
   40 CONT(L)=H(1)*X(L,1)
   71 PRINT 2005,AFD,PCTD
      DO 79 L=1,NOC
   79 PRINT 2006,L,Y(L,NOS),YIELD(L),CONT(L)
      IF (DIGIT-40.0) 68,68,77
   77 IF (DIGIT-68.0) 69,68,13
   68 PRINT 2007
      DO 75 L=1,NOC
      PRINT 2010,L
      I=NOP
   72 PRINT 2008,I,X(L,I+1),Y(L,I+1)
      IF (I-1) 13,75,74
   74 I=I-1
      GO TO 72
   75 PRINT 2009,X(L,1),Y(L,1)
   69 IF (DIGIT-40.) 76,73,73
   76 DIGIT =DIGIT+4.0
   73 DIGIT=DIGIT+1.0
      ALL=EVERY*DIGIT
      IF (AFD) 13,26,70
   70 DO 37 L=1,NOC
   37 CHG(L)=HOL(L)
      IF (FINAL-AFH) 94,1,1
   94 IF (AFD-ALL) 93,26,26
   13 STOP
      END (2,2,2,2,2)
```

Fig. 89 (*concluded*).

VI. DIFFERENTIAL EQUATIONS OF PERFORMANCE

1. Diffusional Processes in Packed Columns

The separation achieved in fractionating columns in terms of theoretical plates was discussed in Sec. II. The Fenske and Smoker equations were treated in detail because they are typical equations of performance that relate the separation achieved to the properties of the mixture being distilled, the length and character of the column, and the operating conditions. It was pointed out that the theoretical-plate concept is useful but essentially unsound for packed columns. Even for plate columns it has been necessary to use the concept of plate efficiency to explain the difference between calculated and experimental results. A number of concepts other than theoretical plates have been used in attempts to gain a clearer picture of the fractionating process, and of these the present section discusses the following:

(*1*) W. K. Lewis equations for differential change in composition from plate to plate or point to point;
(*2*) Chilton and Colburn transfer-unit equations;
(*3*) Westhaver and Kuhn equations;
(*4*) Cohen equations for the rate of approach to equilibrium;
(*5*) Marshall-Pigford equations;
(*6*) Bowman's composition distribution relation for multicomponent mixtures.

All these methods use a differential approach and so are particularly applicable to packed columns.

2. Lewis Equations

An approach toward a differential treatment of the composition change with height in a column was suggested by Lewis.[244] He arrived at an expression for the change in liquid composition from plate to plate by writing the basic material-balance equations as

$$x_{n+1} = \frac{Vy_n - Dx_D}{L}$$

and then with the relation $V = L + D$, subtracted x_n from each side to obtain

$$x_{n+1} - x_n = \frac{dx}{dn} = y_n - x_n - \frac{D}{L}(x_D - y_n)$$

When inverted, this becomes

$$\frac{dn}{dx} = \frac{1}{y_n - x_n - \frac{D}{L}(x_D - y_n)}$$

Integration gives

$$n = \int_{x_s}^{x_D} \frac{dx}{y_n - x_n - \frac{D}{L}(x_D - y_n)} \qquad (160)$$

Graphic integration may always be used to obtain numerical values, but algebraic integration[245] is also possible when the relative-volatility equation is applicable. In this case

$$y_n = \frac{\alpha x_n}{1 + x_n(\alpha - 1)}$$

so that

$$n = \int_{x_s}^{x_D} \frac{dx}{\frac{\alpha x_n}{1 + x_n(x - 1)} - x_n - \frac{D}{L}\left[x_D - \frac{\alpha x_n}{1 + x_n(\alpha - 1)}\right]} \qquad (161)$$

and integration gives

$$n = \frac{[1 + (b/z)]}{\sqrt{b^2 - 4ac}} \ln\left[\left(\frac{x_D + A}{x_s + A}\right)\left(\frac{x_s + B}{x_D + B}\right)\right] - {}^1/_2 \ln\left[\frac{ax_D{}^2 + bx_D + c)}{(ax_s{}^2 + bx_s + c)}\right] \qquad (162)$$

where

$$a = (1 - \alpha),\ b = (\alpha - 1)\left(1 - \frac{D}{L}x_D\right) + \alpha\frac{D}{L}$$

$$c = -\frac{D}{L}x_D,\ A = \frac{b - \sqrt{b^2 - 4ac}}{2a}$$

$$B = \frac{b + \sqrt{b^2 - 4ac}}{2a}$$

It is to be emphasized that this method does not assume the stepwise changes characteristic of plate columns, but provides for a differential change from point to point in a packed column. The equations are also approximately applicable to difficult separations for which a large number of plates are used and the change in composition from plate to plate is small. The Lewis equations are similar to those for theoretical plates in that they do not deal with the fundamental physical mechanism of the mass transfer processes of distillation, but merely provide a means for expressing the separation achieved.

3. Transfer Units

Chilton and Colburn[246] originated a distinctive differential method of design for packed columns which correlates distillation phenomena with other diffusional processes such as absorption. Columns are compared on the basis of their H.T.U., or height of a transfer unit, in correspondence with the H.E.T.P. concept. The number of transfer units is determined by the relation

$$N_{oG} = \int_{y_s}^{y_t = x_D} \frac{dy}{y^* - y} \tag{163}$$

in which y^* is the composition of vapor that would be in equilibrium with liquid at any specified point in the column and y the actual vapor composition at that point. N_{oG} represents transfer units based on overall transfer across both liquid and gas films, referred to vapor (G = gas) concentrations. The limits of the integration y_t and y_s are the vapor compositions at the top of the column and in the still, respectively. Graphic integration is usually necessary, but several short cuts and modifications have been suggested.[247]

The Chilton and Colburn equation for transfer units is derived from consideration of the diffusion and flow phenomena occurring in a packed column. The differential rate of increase of the moles of low-boiling component in the vapor, dw, due to its upward flow may be expressed as

$$dw = d\bar{p}GS/pM \tag{164}$$

where $d\bar{p}$ is the pressure differential of the more volatile component over the small height of the column, dZ, that is under consideration, G is the mass velocity of the vapor, S is the cross-sectional area, p the total pressure, and M the average molecular weight.

The moles transferred by diffusion must balance the above, and may be written as

$$dw = K\Delta\bar{p}SdZ \tag{165}$$

where K is a constant dependent on the stationary vapor film adjacent to the liquid phase, and $\Delta\bar{p}$ is the difference between the actual partial pressure of the more volatile component and the pressure this component would have if in equilibrium with the liquid at the point in the column under consideration.

The above equations may be combined to give

$$d\bar{p}/\Delta\bar{p} = (KpM/G)dZ \tag{166}$$

or

$$\int_{\bar{p}_1}^{\bar{p}_2} d\bar{p}/\Delta\bar{p} = KpMZ/G \tag{167}$$

so that the height of column required for a given separation is

$$Z = (G/KpM) \int_{\bar{p}_1}^{\bar{p}_2} (d\bar{p}/\Delta\bar{p}) \tag{168}$$

The use of this relation has been limited because values of the constant K are difficult to obtain. The transfer-unit concept has been most useful when the equation is expressed in the form

$$N_{oG} = \int_{\bar{p}_1}^{\bar{p}_2} (d\bar{p}/\Delta\bar{p}) \tag{169}$$

or the equivalent

$$N_{oG} = \int_{y_s}^{y_t} (dy/\Delta y) = \int_{y_s}^{y_t} dy/(y^* - y) \tag{170}$$

The transfer unit number can also be expressed in terms of liquid concentrations

$$N_{oL} = \int_{x_S}^{x_D} \frac{dx}{x^* - x} \tag{171}$$

where x^* is the mole fraction of the more volatile component in a liquid that would be in equilibrium with the vapor at a point where the actual liquid composition is x. The values of N_{oL} and N_{oG} for a particular system are usually nearly but not exactly the same.

It is also possible to calculate transfer units for just the gas phase film or liquid phase film.

$$N_G = \int \frac{dy}{y_i - y} \quad \text{and} \quad N_L = \int \frac{dx}{x_i - x} \tag{172}$$

where y_i and x_i are interface compositions, while y and x are bulk concentrations, all at a particular horizontal level in the column. The overall transfer units N_{oG} are related to the film transfer units by a relatively simple equation

$$\frac{1}{N_{oG}} = \frac{1}{N_G} + \frac{mG}{L}\left(\frac{1}{N_L}\right) \tag{173}$$

which is applicable to binary systems, assuming that vapor and liquid are actually in equilibrium at the interface, and that the vapor–liquid equilibrium relationship is linear. In this equation m is the slope of the equilibrium curve and G/L is the molal ratio of vapor and liquid flows in the column. Without the simplifying assumptions, the equations for this relation become so complex that they have not been used.

If equilibrium and operating lines are substantially straight lines, H.T.U. and H.E.T.P. can be related by a simple equation[248]

$$\text{H.E.T.P.} = \text{H.T.U.}\ \frac{(mG/L) - 1}{\ln\,(mG/L)} \tag{174}$$

It should be noted that the transfer unit concept has been of definite practical value in connection with absorption column operations, probably because packed towers are commonly used, rather than plates, and also because the gas–liquid equilibria are often linear, and because multiple components are not often encountered. In distillation calculations the transfer unit concept has been useful in correlating and predicting plate efficiency for single plates, but has not proved to have any special advantages for most column calculations. Part of the reason is human inertia and the labor of changing over from established practices that give satisfactory results. Contributing reasons are the generally small differences between H.T.U. and H.E.T.P. values, the rather considerable uncertainties in both values, and in such matters as vapor–liquid equilibrium and the effect of the usual simplifying assumptions of overall distillation calculations, and finally the uncertainties introduced by the simplifying assumptions inherent in the transfer unit concept itself, particularly for multicomponent systems.

Bowman and Briant[249] derived an extensive series of relations analogous to those described for the transfer units, but based their relations on a driving force for mass transfer proportional to the quantity of material that needs to be transferred to achieve equilibrium. The final relations are little different from those for H.E.T.P. and H.T.U.

A thermodynamic analog of transfer units was obtained by Kafarov and Vigdorov[250] by replacing the concentration driving force Δy by the difference in chemical potential, $-A_h^*$, of the theoretical possible work of separation in an infinitesimal column height. They stated

$$N_{\text{thermodynamic}} = \int_0^{A_H} dA_h/(-A_h^*)$$

where dA_h is the actual work of separation. The values of N based on this approach were not very different from those based on the concentration driving force. The general method has been extended to consideration of plate efficiency in plate columns.

Glaser[251] evaluated various column packing materials in terms of a performance number which is determined by S/L where S is the mass transfer of the low boiler from the liquid to the vapor in weight units per unit of time, and $L = V\Delta P$ is the work needed to move the vapor volume in consistent units per unit of time, and ΔP is the pressure drop.

4. Westhaver's and Kuhn's Equations

The transfer unit, theoretical plate, and other concepts previously discussed are not a truly fundamental expression of the phenomena occurring in distillation, since they are essentially only the means of measuring how much separation has occurred. The concepts to be discussed in the following paragraphs are the beginning of the ultimate basic approach toward understanding and correlation of separation in packed columns, and quite possibly also in other types of distillation operations. This approach consists in merely expressing the composition in a small volume of the column in terms of the quantities of the components entering and leaving this space during one short time period, and then integrating this behavior over the entire column space and over any desired time period. The small volume and small time period have been truly differential in the work done so far, but somewhat larger volumes and time intervals, still small, may turn out to be more useful in examination of situations that are not oversimplified. In derivations for steady-state situations the size of the time unit at steady state is immaterial, but it is probable that the eventual treatment of steady state will be in terms of an approach to steady state through a transient period.

The composition at any particular time in any unit volume in a distillation apparatus that includes a portion of the vapor-liquid interface is determined primarily by

(*a*) The rates of upward flow of the vapor coming into and leaving the unit volume, and the average composition of the vapor in each of the streams;

(*b*) The rate of downward flow of the liquid and the average composition of the liquids entering and leaving;

(*c*) The rate of transfer of material between phases which depends in turn on the interface area, the diffusion coefficients, the composition gradients in each phase in directions normal to the interface, and the mechanism and rate of transfer at the interface;

(*d*) The rate of diffusion or mixing by turbulence or eddy diffusion in the direction of motion of the vapor.

In an ordinary packed column with its tortuous geometry and flow character there certainly will be complexities in executing an approach and analysis along the lines indicated. Some other factors may enter.

For a simple wetted wall distillation column, with liquid present only as a descending film on the wall, and vapor present as a rising column unobstructed by any obstacles, the analysis and derivations are straightforward, as described in succeeding paragraphs.

Westhaver[252] has shown agreement between actual top and bottom composition differences in a column and the same values calculated by a formula based on the diffusion and flow characteristics of the countercurrent streams of liquid and vapor. Kuhn[253] has carried through the same type of reasoning independently and arrived at the same conclusions. Westhaver sets up the equation

$$\underset{(a)}{\frac{D_V}{r} \cdot \frac{d(r\,dy/dr)}{dr}} + \underset{(b)}{D_V \frac{\partial^2 y}{\partial Z^2}} - \underset{(c)}{V \frac{\partial y}{\partial Z}} = 0 \tag{175}$$

to represent the dynamic equilibrium of the convection and diffusion processes that result in constant composition at any point in a column operating under total reflux on a binary mixture. The distillation operation is assumed to be carried out in an unpacked column under adiabatic conditions. The symbol D_V is the molecular vapor diffusion coefficient, r and Z indicate distance from the axis and base of the column, respectively, and V is the vapor velocity. (Some of the original symbols have been changed to conform to those used in this book.) It is assumed that there is laminar or viscous flow of vapor, and also that the descending reflux film evenly wets the entire column walls, is of uniform composition throughout its radial thickness, and has negligible surface-transfer resistance. The last assumption is justified in terms of kinetic-theory calculations which show that the vapor bombarding a liquid surface is of the order of grams per second, most of which is condensed and replaced in the vapor by material evaporating at the same rate. Since this rate of transfer is very great compared with the net transfer due to the distillation operation, it is concluded that there is equilibrium between the liquid surface and the film of vapor adjacent to the liquid.[254] The assumption of uniform radial composition through the liquid film is equivalent to assuming that liquid diffusion is not a transfer-limiting factor.

Term (a) of Westhaver's basic equation describes the change in composition of the vapor at a particular point due to diffusion in a radial direction. This is related to the difference in compositions at the axis and the wall of the column, and the rate of change of composition along a radius. Term (b) describes the change in composition due to diffusion in a vertical direction, and term (c) the change due to the motion of the vapor stream.

At total reflux there is no net flow of either component because the amount of the more volatile component carried upward by the vapor stream is equal to that carried downward by the reflux and vertical vapor diffusion. This may be expressed as

$$\int_0^{r_0} [V(y - x) - D_V(\partial y/\partial Z)]2\pi r dr = 0 \tag{176}$$

This equation involves the previously mentioned assumption that liquid composition is independent of r, and that vertical diffusion in the liquid is negligible. The equation

$$\log\left[\left(\frac{y}{1-y}\right)_{Z=Z_t}\Big/\left(\frac{y}{1-y}\right)_{Z=0}\right] = (Z_t \log \alpha)\Big/\left(\frac{11}{48}\cdot\frac{V_a r_0^2}{D_V} + \frac{D_V}{V_a}\right) \tag{177}$$

is then derived by use of Poiseuille's law for laminar flow, and the further assumptions that downward vapor velocity near the liquid surface is negligible, that change in composition is the same along the axis as along the wall, and that the relative volatility may be expressed as

$$\log \alpha = \frac{(y - x)_{r=r_0}}{y_{r=r_0}(1 - y)_{r=r_0}} \tag{178}$$

In these equations Z_t is the total height of the column, V_a is the radially averaged vapor velocity (flow in cubic centimeters per second divided by πr_0^2). The symbol r_0 is the radius from column axis to the downward-moving liquid surface. Since a column of height equal to the H.E.T.P. has

$$\left(\frac{y}{1-y}\right)_{Z=Z_t}\Big/\left(\frac{y}{1-y}\right)_{Z=0} = \alpha$$

$$l = \text{H.E.T.P.} = (11/48)V_a(r_0^2/D_V) + (D_V/V_a) \tag{179}$$

and for taller columns

$$n = \frac{Z_t}{(11/48)V_a(r_0^2/D_V) + (D_V/V_a)} \tag{180}$$

The minimum value for the H.E.T.P. can be obtained by taking the derivative of eq. (179) and setting it equal to zero, whereupon

$$l_{min} = 0.96r_0 \tag{181}$$

when

$$V_a = 2.1D_V/r_0 \text{ cm./sec.} \tag{182}$$

The latter is of the order of 0.5 cm./sec., which is so low as to be unlikely to be attained experimentally, and is about one-tenth of the values used in practice. The term D_V/F_a arises from the back-diffusion term, $D_V(\partial y/\partial Z)$, in the basic total-reflux equation (176).

At vapor velocities comparable with those in actual use, back diffusion is negligible and the term D_V/V_a may be dropped so that

$$l = 11V_a r_0^2/48D_V \tag{183}$$

Thus smaller values of l or H.E.T.P. should be attainable by using smaller vapor velocities, smaller-bore tubes, and by increasing the diffusion coefficient. Some of the directly comparable experimental data are in reasonable agreement with the Westhaver equations (see Figs. 1 and 2 of Westhaver's original paper), but other experiments showed some discrepancies.[255]

For the case of finite reflux[256] Westhaver assumes a small upward flow of vapor (ΔV_a) beyond that equivalent to the reflux liquid. Equation (176) is replaced by

$$\int_0^{r_0} \left[V(y - x) - D_V \frac{\partial y}{\partial Z} - Z\Delta V_a \frac{r_0^2 - r^2}{r_0^2} \right] 2\pi r dr = 0 \tag{184}$$

and the derivation then gives

$$l' = l\{1 - [(V_a/\Delta V_a)(1 - y)(\log \alpha)]^{-1}\}^{-1} \tag{185}$$

where l' is the H.E.T.P. under finite reflux, $V_a/\Delta V_a = R_D + 1$, and l is the H.E.T.P. under total reflux. This equation indicates that a high reflux ratio at finite reflux is needed to obtain a product approximating the composition of that secured under total reflux. Westhaver gives the illustration that R_D must be at least 200 for a mixture with $\alpha = 1.1$ in order that l' be within 5% of l. The equation for l' may also be used to compute total-reflux H.E.T.P. when a value at finite reflux is known.

Westhaver assumes maximum economy of production occurs when $l'R_D$ is a minimum, and for this condition shows that l' must equal 21. This means operation with a reflux ratio that will halve the number of plates obtained at total reflux. For this R_D must be $2/[(1 - y) \log \alpha]$. He has also derived the similar equations

$$l' = (17/35)(V_a s^2/D_V) + (D_V/V_a) \tag{186}$$

and

$$l = (52/35)(V_a s^2/D_V) + (D_V/V_a) \tag{187}$$

for operation between elongated parallel plates a space of $2s$ apart with, respectively, both sides and one side only wetted by reflux. A derivation for a packed column was not attempted, but the available H.E.T.P. data for packed and empty columns indicate that the turbulence and reduction of dimensions produce at least a tenfold decrease in H.E.T.P. A decrease in pressure should increase the diffusion coefficient and thereby also reduce H.E.T.P., according to these equations.

The expression

$$\frac{\Delta T}{Z_t} = \frac{dT}{dZ} = \left(\frac{R}{\lambda}\right)\left(\frac{T^2}{p}\right)\left(\frac{35\eta D_V l}{r_0^4} + \frac{1.2 \times 10^{-5} M p}{T}\right) \tag{188}$$

is given by Westhaver for the total temperature gradient required to obtain a stable H.E.T.P. equal to l at total reflux. R is the molar gas constant (*not* the reflux ratio here), λ the heat of vaporization, T absolute temperature; p is column pressure, η the viscosity of the vapor, and M the average molecular weight. The instability of l arises from the fact that the velocity of vapor flow in an open-tube column depends on the longitudinal temperature gradient, which is the sum of the flow-producing gradient and that necessary to sustain the weight of the vapor even in the absence of flow. Since the weight-sustaining gradient is usually relatively much larger, a small change in total temperature gradient will cause a large change in the flow-producing gradient, and thereby in the vapor velocity. Thus for a mixture of 95% benzene and 5% ethylene chloride the temperature requirements to hold H.E.T.P. in the range 1 ± 0.1 cm. are shown in Table XXIV.

As a consequence of the apparent severe limitation on temperature gradient, Westhaver suggests the use of a forced stabilization of the temperature gradient by an auxiliary column outside and independent of the

TABLE XXIV

Calculated Temperature-Gradient Requirements[252]

Tube radius, (r_0), cm.	Pressure, atm.	dt/dZ, °C./cm.	Permissible variation of dt/dZ, %
0.95	1.0	9.0×10^{-5}	±0.0017
0.47	1.0	9.0×10^{-5}	0.027
0.47	0.1	8.4×10^{-5}	1.1
0.20	0.1	3.5×10^{-4}	7.9
0.10	0.1	4.5×10^{-3}	9.8

working column. Empirical corroborative evidence along these lines comes from Podbielniak's[257] early discovery of the desirability for a controlled temperature gradient in precise analytical fractionation, and in the observations of Rose[258] that very small but markedly unstable H.E.T.P. values are obtained in a well insulated open-tube column operating at very low vapor velocities.

Westhaver has summarized the assumptions involved in his basic equation (183) as follows:

(*1*) Mixture is close-boiling, i.e., $\alpha = 1.0$ to 1.1. (*2*) Operation at equilibrium under total reflux. (*3*) Vapor-flow laminar. (*4*) Vapor velocity constant and independent of height (uniform vertical pressure gradient and no condensation in column). (*5*) Vapor velocity large compared with liquid velocity. (*6*) Liquid film flows uniformly over entire wall surface and has neither surface-transfer resistance nor radial-diffusion resistance. (*7*) H.E.T.P. is large compared with tube radius. (*8*) The diffusion coefficient is independent of vapor composition. (*9*) Back diffusion is negligible.

A variety of experimental and theoretical contributions have followed the general approach of Westhaver and of Kuhn, and are of interest as relating to confirmation, correction, or extension of this work.[259] Some steps have been taken toward extension of the simple wetted wall approach,[260] including incorporation of resistance to interphase mass transfer in the vapor phase,[261] effect of turbulence and mixing in the vapor phase[262] and wiped films.[263] The further extension of this approach will need to include detailed provision for interface phenomena of the type reported by Cheng and Teller[264] and liquid phase behavior in packed columns as reported by Shulman.[265] Finally, additional provisions will need to be made for the limitation of mass transfer rates due to the thermal effects that must accompany interphase transfer (as noted above). Some studies have been made of the more complex problems of packed towers[266] where the basic approach of Westhaver must eventually be applied to gain complete understanding of these phenomena.

The essence of the large store of information on mass transfer on plate columns must also be indirectly available to aid in understanding of packed column behavior.[267]

5. Theoretical Effects of Pressure, Density, Surface Properties, and Thermal Phenomena

A. EFFECTS OF PRESSURE

Superficial examination of the equations of Westhaver indicates a twofold effect of decreased pressure. Both of these result from the increase

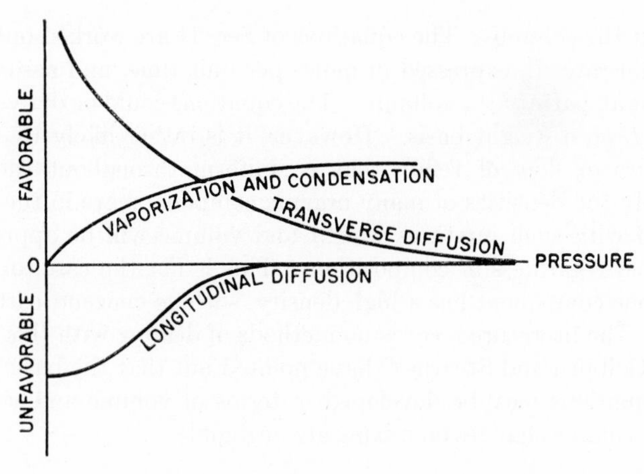

Fig. 90. Relative importance of several factors in determining effect of pressure on separation in fractionation.[268]

in the diffusion coefficient. This increases the rate of mixing in a horizontal direction, which aids diffusion between phases and thus tends to improve separation. At the same time mixing in a vertical direction also becomes more rapid, so that the vapor stream cannot support a vertical concentration gradient. There is also a reduction in the ease of establishment of equilibrium between phases due to reduction in absolute vaporization and condensation rates at low pressures. The practical operating difficulties at low pressure are well known, and include the high vapor velocities and appreciable pressure drops, as well as the effects of hydrostatic head and surface tension on vaporization. Byron, Bowman, and Coull[268] expressed the theoretical relations by the graph of Figure 90. The reduction of the vaporization and condensation rates as the pressure approaches zero more than counterbalances the high transverse diffusion since the latter influences the vapor phase only. At high pressures separation also approaches zero chiefly because of poor transverse diffusion, and at the critical pressure separation must be zero. It is to be recalled that the above discussion applies to contact rectification, and that thermal rectification is influenced by improved longitudinal diffusion as pressure decreases. It is for this reason that thermal rectification is advantageous for vacuum-distillation operations.

B. EFFECTS OF DENSITY

All the derivations and equations described here for calculating the number of theoretical plates or otherwise expressing separating power of a column or packing assume that the moles of reflux liquid flowing are uniform throughout the column. The equations of Sec. II are worked out with the reflux liquid rate, L, expressed in moles per unit time, and assumed to be the same at all parts of the column. The equations could be derived equally well with L on a weight basis. However, it is rather likely that it is the volume rate of flow of reflux that is uniform throughout the column. Fortunately the densities of many organic compounds are in the range 0.8 to 1.0 and with such mixtures weight and volume will be approximately proportional regardless of composition. This is not the case for mixtures in which one component has a high density, such as benzene–carbon tetrachloride. The literature records no methods of dealing with this situation, although Colburn and Stearns[269] have pointed out that the basic material-balance equations may be developed in terms of volume and volume per cent if the volume changes on mixing are negligible.

C. SURFACE AND THERMAL EFFECTS

There is a considerable body of evidence that surface and thermal phenomena exert an important influence on mass transfer in a distillation column. For instance, Westhaver's analysis indicated that a temperature gradient was mandatory for best separation [see eq. (188)]. It may be that interface fine structure and interface microbehavior are much more complicated than conventional mass transfer approaches have assumed.[270] Danckwerts, Sawistowski, and Smith have pointed out that the rising vapor is hotter than the corresponding liquid stream with which interface mass transfer is taking place. Partial condensation of vapor may occur at the interface, and interface liquid may be caused to boil or flash after becoming superheated. Thus thermal rectification may be taking place and cause greater mass transfer than if the transfers were by a simpler mechanism. Liang and Smith have shown that when the rates of heat and mass transfer are not equivalent, either evaporation or condensation will occur, and that as a consequence there should be a composition effect in the performance of distillation columns, and this should show a maximum.

Free and Hutchison interpret their ternary distillation data in a wetted wall column to indicate existence of evaporative condensation at the interface, and also suggest gas film diffusion as a controlling factor. Stern et al. have studied mass transfer in five different systems and expressed results in terms of a heat transfer function and concluded that the ratio of the physical properties of the pure components may be more useful in correlations than the physical properties of the mixtures. Some of the papers on nonadiabatic column operation suggest similar ideas. Zuiderweg, Danckwerts, and Free all point out the dependence of mass transfer on interfacial tension. These and many other studies of plate efficiency

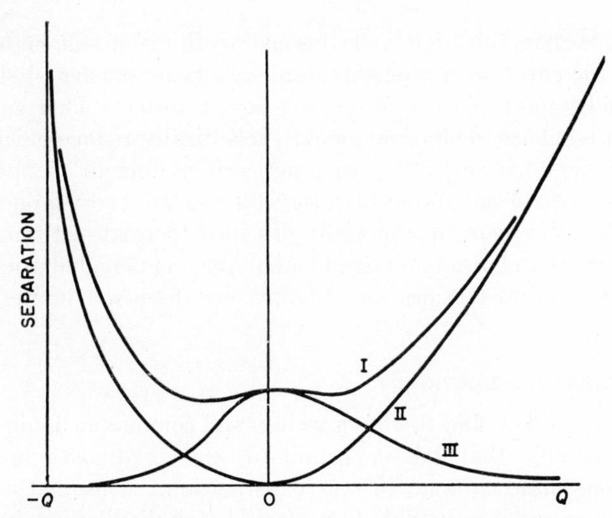

Fig. 91. Qualitative expression of results of nonadiabatic operation.[268] (I) Combination of thermal and contact rectification. (II) Thermal rectification only. (III) Contact rectification only. (Q, $-Q$) Heat added or subtracted.

and bubble plate action are of significance for ultimate clear-cut expression of the separation in packed columns.

A stepwise finite difference type of approach can take all these factors into account, and will probably be the eventual form that the Westhaver approach will merge into.

There is another reservation that should be mentioned regarding the preceding discussions. As higher boiling material rises in the column during the process of batch fractionation, heat must be available to raise the temperature of the packing and column itself as fast as the front of higher boiling material would normally move. The rate of heat transfer is therefore important to the smoothness of the separation process.

Byron, Bowman, and Coull[268] discussed thermal effects in distillation in terms of a graph such as Figure 91, in which the degree of separation or rectification is plotted as ordinate and the quantity of heat added to or lost from the column is plotted as abscissa. If separation due to contact rectification alone is considered, the resulting curve is bell-shaped with a maximum for zero heat transfer to or from the column, and a gradual decrease in separation for either addition (Q) or abstraction ($-Q$) of increasing quantities of heat. However, for any condition of heat addition or removal a composition change occurs due to partial evaporation of liquid or condensation of vapor, i.e., thermal rectification will occur. The curve for the resulting change of composition will be zero for zero heat transfer, but with a parabolic rise as heat transferred is increased. The net effect of the contact rectification and thermal rectification taken together is shown by the curve with a maximum at zero heat transfer, slight minima at either side, and rapid rise for greater heat transfer. Thus small deviations from adiabatic operation should theoretically reduce efficiency, but large ones should improve it. In practice it is difficult to operate with highly nonadiabatic conditions because reflux becomes very large and vapor flow very small, except in a specially designed thermal rectifying column. The advantages and disadvantages of adiabatic and nonadiabatic operation of ordinary contact rectification columns are discussed in the following paragraphs.

D. NONADIABATIC OPERATION

It has been stated, and there is a widespread common belief in the distillation community, that it is important to achieve adiabatic operation to avoid serious disadvantages in batch distillation. This matter deserves discussion, because it is possible to perform batch distillations in a nonadiabatic column and get considerably better separation than when the same column operates in an adiabatic fashion. When this occurs, it is usually because with nonadiabatic operation the vapor and liquid flows and the holdup per plate in the upper part of the column are much less than in the lower part, if heat input to the pot and boilup from the pot are the same for the adiabatic and nonadiabatic operation. The lower vapor and liquid flow rates can result in very much improved separation, i.e., smaller H.E.T.P. and more theoretical plates in the upper part of the column, and therefore a considerable increase in total theoretical plates in the column. This will of course result in a sharper separation. However, with the same reflux ratio for both types of operation, the rate of production of distillate will be greatly reduced with nonadiabatic separation, because of the smaller rate of flow with which vapor reaches the condenser. The longer time required to produce unit quantities of distillate is certainly a serious disadvantage in larger scale batch distillation in which the cost of heat and cooling water and other items proportional to time of use must be restricted. In laboratory distillation where these cost factors are negligible or unimportant, the additional time may still be a disadvantage. The longer time for the nonadiabatic case may be offset by operation with a lower reflux ratio, which will however sacrifice at least part of the improved separation. However, it can also be noted that if operation of the top part of the column with low flow rates is advantageous, in the sense of reducing H.E.T.P., then the same is likely to apply to the lower sections of the column. Thus adiabatic operation at lower vapor rates throughout the length of the column will give smaller H.E.T.P. throughout the column, and thus more theoretical plates, better separation, and just as large a distillate rate and as short a time as the nonadiabatic operation, which therefore has no real advantage, if a longer time period of distillation is acceptable. The low vapor rate adiabatic operation throughout the column would permit a greater lowering of reflux ratio than the nonadiabatic case and thus offset a greater portion of the increased time required by the lower boilup rate. The latter does of course have a practical lower limit, since it becomes more and more difficult to secure smooth operation and good adiabatic control as vapor rate is lowered, and variations in these can have a serious effect on separation at very low vapor rates.

The general conclusion to be reached is that adiabatic operation is almost certain to give better separation and better throughput, and that apparent exceptions should be carefully justified to make certain that the advantage is real.[271]

6. Cohen's Equations

The treatments of Westhaver and Kuhn deal with the interchange between vapor and liquid streams after a column has reached equilibrium at total reflux, and after a steady state is reached in continuous distillation at finite reflux. Cohen[272] used a rather similar approach for the changes occurring during the initial period of operation as the column approaches a steady state. This is important because of the length of such a period when isotopes or other very close boiling mixtures are being separated. Coulson, and Berg and James[273] have also derived expressions for the time required to reach equilibrium; these were discussed in Section III.

Cohen equated the transfer in and out of a small unit length of packed column to obtain the equations

$$H_L \partial x'/\partial t = (-L \partial x'/\partial \bar{Z}) + (H_L \delta x'/\delta t)$$

and

$$H_V \partial y'/\partial t = (V \partial y'/\partial \bar{Z}) - (H_L \delta x'/\delta t)$$

for the liquid and vapor phases, respectively. In these x' is the mole fraction of the less volatile component in the liquid, H_L is the total liquid holdup per unit length, L the liquid reflux flow rate, while y' H_V, and V are the corresponding quantities in the vapor. The length of the column is Z_t, while $\bar{Z}$ is the distance from the top of the column to the unit length under consideration; t is time. Cohen considers only continuous distillation or its equivalent, and for total reflux obtains

$$\left(\frac{y'}{1 - y'}\right)_{\text{top}} = \left(\frac{y'}{1 - y'}\right)_{\text{feed}} e^{2\sigma(1 - \bar{Z}/Z\ )}$$

where

$$\sigma = (kcC/2L)(1 - \alpha)Z_t$$

and

$$\alpha = \frac{[N][m]}{[M][n]} = \left(\frac{x'}{1 - x'}\bigg/\frac{y'}{1 - y'}\right) = \frac{X'}{Y'}$$

$[N]$ and $[n]$ are the concentrations (moles/liter) of the less volatile component in liquid and vapor, respectively; c is $[m] + [n]$, and C is $[M] + [N]$, where $[M]$ and $[m]$ are the concentrations (moles per liter) of the more volatile component in liquid and vapor, respectively. The constant k is defined by the relation, based on analogy with a bimolecular reversible reaction:

$$H_L \delta x'/\delta t = -k([N][m] - \alpha[M][n])$$

The difference in composition between the bottom and top of the column is given by

$$Y'(0)_{\text{top}}/Y'(Z_t)_{\text{bottom}} = e^{2\sigma}$$

where $Y'(0)$ signifies the value of Y' when $\bar{Z} = 0$, and $Y'(Z_t)$ the corresponding value when $\bar{Z} = Z_t$.

Re-examination of the expression for σ shows that for values of α near unity $e^{2\sigma}$ is nearly equal to $(1/\alpha)^{kcCZ_t/L}$. Thus

$$\frac{Y'(0)}{Y'(Z_t)} = \left(\frac{y'}{1 - y'}\right)_{\text{top of column}} \bigg/ \left(\frac{y'}{1 - y'}\right)_{\text{feed}}$$

is nearly equal to $(1/\alpha)^{kcCZ_t/L}$. Recalling that $1 - y'$ refers to the more volatile component, one recognizes the above as the Fenske equation with $kcCZ_t/L$ representing the number of plates.

For the more general case of finite reflux, Cohen obtains

$$\frac{Y'(0)}{Y'(Z_t)} = \frac{\left(1 - \dfrac{D}{L}\right) + \theta}{\left(1 - \dfrac{D}{L}\right)(e^{-2\sigma})^{1+\alpha\theta} + \theta}$$

where D/L is the fraction of flow drawn off (the inverse of ordinary reflux ratio) and

$$\theta = (D/L)/(1 - \alpha)$$

As an example Cohen calculates data for the case $\alpha = 0.98$ and when σ has a series of reasonable values. Even a very small withdrawal of product such as 0.02% ($\theta = 10^{-2}$) effects a marked reduction in the ratio $Y'(0)/Y'(Z)_t$. The above relations are only approximate solutions of the basic differential equations of Cohen. When the quantity $Y'e^{2\sigma}$ is greater than 0.5, it is necessary to use more complex, exact solutions of the equations.

Cohen has also derived the expression

$$Y'(0)_{t=t} = Y'(0)_{t=0}e^{2\sigma} - C_1e^{-|\delta_1|t} - C_2e^{-|\delta_2|t} - \ldots$$

in which t refers to time, C_1, C_2, ... are positive constants, and δ_1, δ_2, ... are parameters. Because of relations among the constants and parameters the time of coming to equilibrium is determined by the parameter δ_1. This is dependent in a complex manner upon α, L, H_L, Z_t, and σ. In an example Cohen obtains

$$\frac{Y'(0)_{t=t}}{Y'(0)_{t=0}} = 6.05 - 4.61e^{-0.0982t} - 18e^{-2.11t} - 0.05e^{-6.06t} - 0.03e^{-12t} - \ldots$$

and a similar equation for the transport of less volatile material from vapor to reflux stream, and finally the value of $X'(\bar{Z})/Y'(\bar{Z})$. Figures 5 and 6 of Cohen's original paper describe the variation of all these with time.

7. Marshall–Pigford Equations

Marshall and Pigford[274] have also derived the basic equations for material transfer in packed and plate distillation columns, as well as other analogous countercurrent diffusional operations. For a packed column the basic relationship is

$$\theta_G\theta_L(\partial^2 y/\partial t^2) + (\theta_L - \theta_G)(\partial^2 y/\partial n \partial y) - (\partial^2 y/\partial n^2) + \left(\theta_L + \frac{aV}{L}\theta_G\right)\frac{\partial y}{\partial t} + \left(\frac{aV}{L} - 1\right)\frac{\partial y}{\partial n} = 0$$

in which θ_G and θ_L are, respectively, the holdup per transfer unit in vapor and liquid phases divided by the corresponding flow rates, V and L, n is the distance up the column (measured in transfer units), t is time, y is the mole fraction of more volatile component in the vapor, and a is a constant defined by the simplified vapor liquid equilibrium relation $y = ax + b$.

For a plate column the corresponding equation is

$$(L/V)\theta_L(\partial x_n/\partial t) + \theta_G(\partial y_n/\partial t) = (y_{n-1} - y_n) + (L/V)(x_{n+1} - x_n)$$

where x_n, y_n, etc., refer to liquid and vapor concentrations from plates indicated by the subscript.

Marshall and Pigford make use of the simplified equilibrium relation $y = ax + b$ and the Laplace transformation in order to obtain solutions to these equations. Thus the first of the two preceding equations is made the basis for estimating the rate of approach to equilibrium of a column operating at total reflux. They assume that the column is initially filled with liquid identical in composition to the vapor entering the column, and the latter is assumed to remain constant during the approach to equilibrium. The reflux returning from the condenser is assumed to have the same composition as the vapor leaving the top of the column. These conditions constitute the boundary conditions required to evaluate the constants introduced in the course of the application of the Laplace transformation and the subsequent solution. The mathematical operations are somewhat extended but the end result is a graph in which the number of transfer units in the column is plotted against the number of times total column holdup must be changed to achieve a particular degree of approach to equilibrium, say 95 or 99%. With log–log scales the relation is nearly a straight line. This relation involves the further approximation that the equilibrium line is parallel to the 45° line. When the relative volatility is near unity the number of times that the column holdup must be replaced is approximately equal to the number of transfer units.

Pigford, Tepe, and Garrahan[275] have used the preceding plate column equation as the basis for predicting the effect of holdup in batch distillation (p. 134).

8. Bowman's Composition Distribution Relation for Multicomponent Mixtures

Bowman[276] devised the scheme of representing composition by a function $x(\alpha)$, in which the mole fraction with relative volatility in the range α to $\alpha + d\alpha$ is $x d\alpha$. This is equivalent to using α as a variable that

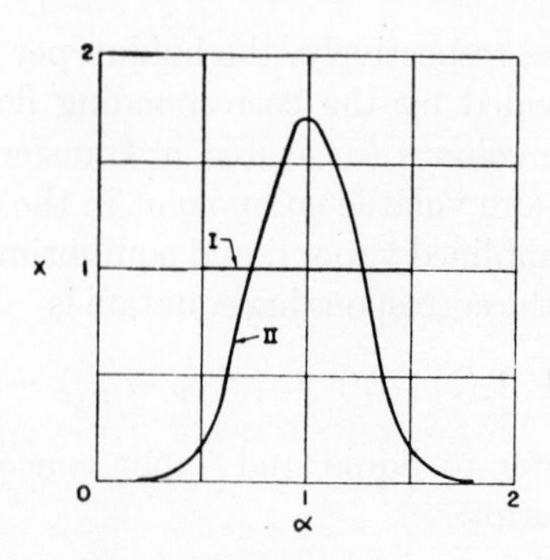

Fig. 92. Composition expressed in terms of relative volatility.[276]

designates the several components. In such a scheme it is most convenient to take the relative volatilities as the ratios of the vapor pressures of the components to the total pressure at some fixed temperature. Figure 92 shows curves expressing the compositions of two typical mixtures. Curve I corresponds to a mixture containing equal amounts of an infinite number of components uniformly distributed with respect to their values of α. Curve II corresponds to a mixture rich in intermediate-boiling material, and with smaller amounts of high- and low-boiling components. These composition–distribution curves are analogous to true boiling-point curves. The area under all composition–distribution curves must be unity, i.e., mathematically

$$\int_0^\infty x d\alpha = 1$$

This is merely equivalent to the requirement that the sum of the quantities of all components must be unity. A simple example of the use of the composition–distribution concept is the derivation of the relation between the compositions on various plates in a column under steady-state conditions with reflux ratio high enough so that separation is determined by the number of theoretical plates. The conventional relation for a multicomponent mixture is

$$y_{n(i)} = \frac{\alpha_i x_{n(i)}}{\sum_i \alpha_i x_{n(i)}}$$

where y_n and x_n are the compositions on the nth plate, and the subscripts i imply the values for ith component. Translated into composition–distribution relations, the above becomes

$$y_n d\alpha = (\alpha x_n d\alpha) \Big/ \left(\int_0^\infty \alpha x_n d\alpha \right)$$

from which the $d\alpha$ factors on the left and in the numerator divide out at once. If the feed plate is assigned the subscript 0, and the plates above are numbered in sequence:

$$y_0 = (\alpha x_0) \Big/ \left(\int_0^\infty \alpha x_0 d\alpha \right) = x_1$$

the latter following because $x_1 = y_0$ for the assumed conditions of high reflux. By substitution of this expression for x_1 in

$$x_2 = y_1 = (\alpha x_1) \Big/ \left(\int_0^\infty \alpha x_1 d\alpha \right)$$

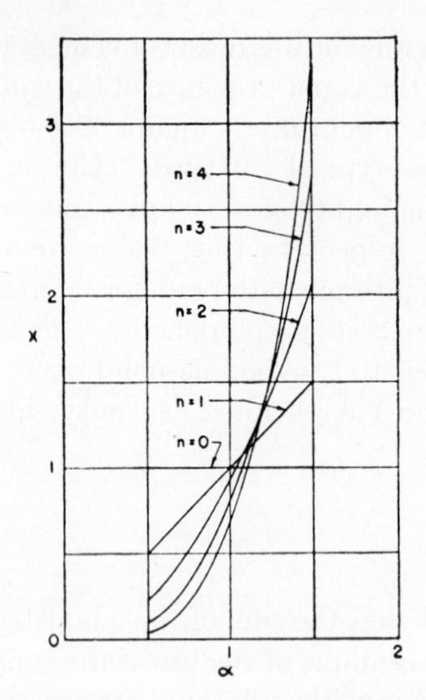

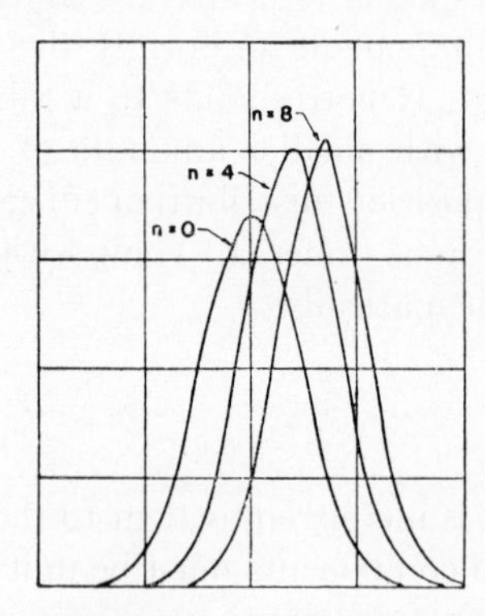

Fig. 93 (Left). Composition distributions on four-plate column at total reflux with feed or charge composition I of Figure 92.[276]
Fig. 94 (Right). Composition distributions on fourth and eight plates at total reflux with charge composition II of Figure 92.[276]

there is obtained

$$x_2 = (\alpha^2 x_0) \Big/ \left(\int_0^\infty \alpha^2 x_0 d\alpha \right)$$

and by continuation of the process

$$x_n = (\alpha^n x_0) \Big/ \left(\int_0^\infty \alpha^n x_0 d\alpha \right)$$

Application of this procedure gives Figures 93 and 94 for the composition distributions on several plates in a column in which the feedplate compositions are those represented by Curves I and II of Figure 92.

The same type of reasoning gives the equation

$$x_D = \left[(R_D + 1) - \left(R_D \alpha^{-1} \Big/ \int_0^\infty y_s \alpha^{-1} d\alpha \right) \right] y_s$$

for steady-state operation in an enriching column in which separation is determined solely by reflux ratio because the number of theoretical plates is high. The equation is applicable only for the special case in which there is a pinch point for all components at the bottom of the column. Equations for more general cases are also possible in principle, but detailed equations have not been derived. Applications to simple cases of batch distillation are presented in Section III. The method should be capable of advantageous application to steady-state multicomponent situations, but no recent references have been noted.

General References

Carney, *Laboratory Fractional Distillation*, Macmillan, New York, 1949.

Coulson and Herington, *Laboratory Distillation Practice*, Interscience, New York, 1958.

Dodg e,*Chemical Engineering Thermodynamics*, McGraw-Hill, New York, 1944, Chap. XIII.

Fenske and Quiggle, in *Science of Petroleum*, Vol. V, Part 3, Oxford University Press, New York, 1955, pp. 232–275.

Forbes, *Short History of the Art of Distillation*, Brill, Leiden, 1948.

Hanson, Duffin, and Somerville, *Computation of Multistage Separation Processes*, Reinhold, New York, 1962.

Hengstebeck, *Distillation: Principles and Design Procedures*, Reinhold, New York, 1961.

Holland, *Multicomponent Distillation*, Prentice-Hall, Englewood Cliffs, N. J., 1963.

Krell, *Handbuch der Laboratoriumsdestillation*, 3rd ed., VEB Deutscher Verlag der Wissenschaften, Berlin, 1963.

Krell, *Handbook of Laboratory Distillation*, translated from 2nd German ed., Elsevier, New York, 1963.

Perry, *Chemical Engineers' Handbook*, 4th ed., McGraw-Hill, New York, 1963, Section 13, Distillation.

Robinson and Gilliland, *Elements of Fractional Distillation*, 4th ed., McGraw-Hill, New York, 1950.

Rose and Rose, *Distillation Literature, Index and Abstracts*, 1941–45, 1946–52, 1953–54, Applied Science Laboratories, State College, Pennsylvania, 1948, 1953, 1955. (Bibliography.)

Smith, *Design of Equilibrium Stage Processes*, McGraw-Hill, New York, 1963.

Zuiderweg, *Laboratory Manual of Batch Distillation*, Interscience, New York, 1957.

Annual or biennial reviews (articles cited will refer to earlier articles in the series):

Leslie and Kuehner, *Anal. Chem.*, **36**, No. 5, 56R (1964).

Fair, *Ind. Eng. Chem.*, 56, 61 (Oct. 1964).

Holdsworth, *Chem. Process Eng.*, **44**, 528 (1963).

References

1. Prologue by Laurence Andrew to *The Vertuose Boke of Distyllacion*, London, 1527 An English translation of Brunswig's *grosse Distillierbuch*.
2. Della Porta, *Magia Naturalis*, Naples, 1589; quoted in Egloff and Lowry, *Ind. Eng. Chem.*, **21**, 920 (1929).
3. Brunswig, *Das kleine Distillierbuch*, Strassburg, 1500; *Das grosse Distillierbuch*, Strassburg, 1512; appeared in several other editions, under several titles and variants of the author's name. See Forbes, *Short History of the Art of Distillation*, Brill, Leiden, 1948; Liebman, *J. Chem. Educ.*, **33**, 166 (1956).
4. Forbes, see ref. 3.
5. See also Underwood, *Trans. Inst. Chem. Engrs. (London)*, **13**, 34 (1935).

6. See Thorpe, *Dictionary of Applied Chemistry*, Vol. I, 4th ed., Longmans, Green, London, 1937, pp. 176–178.
7. Forbes, ref. 3.
8. Young, *Distillation Principles and Processes*, Macmillan, New York, 1922, pp. 98–105.
9. Shepherd and Porter, *Ind. Eng. Chem.*, **15,** 1143 (1923).
10. Kopp, *Beiträge zur Geschichte der Chemie*, Vieweg, Braunschweig, 1869, pp. 217–259.
11. Peters, *Ind. Eng. Chem.*, **14,** 476 (1922).
12. Weeks, *Discovery of the Elements*, 6th ed., Journal of Chemical Education, 1956, Chap. 26.
13. Smyth, *Atomic Energy for Military Purposes*, Princeton University Press, Princeton, N. J., 1945, Chap. 10.
14. Post, Otto, and Craig, *Anal. Chem.*, **35,** 641–647 (1963).
15. Benedict, *Trans. Am. Inst. Chem. Engrs.*, **43,** 41 (1947).
16. Robinson and Gilliland, *Elements of Fractional Distillation*, 4th ed., McGraw-Hill, New York, 1950; Perry, *Chemical Engineers' Handbook*, 4th ed., McGraw-Hill, New York, 1963; Hengstebeck, *Distillation: Principles and Design Procedures*, Reinhold, New York, 1961.
17. Cox, *Ind. Eng. Chem.*, **15,** 592 (1923); Calingaert and Davis, *ibid.*, **17,** 1287 (1925). Wales, *Chem. Eng.*, **53,** No. 10, 124 (1946); nomograph.
18. Othmer, *Ind. Eng. Chem.*, **34,** 1072 (1942).
19. Rose, *Ind. Eng. Chem.*, **33,** 596 (1941).
20. There has been some disagreement over this value. The one chosen is an averaged quantity from the data of Willingham, Taylor, Pignocco, and Rossini, *J. Res. Natl. Bur. Std.*, **35,** 219 (1945).
21. Robinson and Gilliland, *Elements of Fractional Distillation*, 4th ed., McGraw-Hill, 1950, Chap. 4.
22. Murphree, *Ind. Eng. Chem.*, **17,** 747 (1925).
23. See especially the publications of the American Institute of Chemical Engineers: *Bubble-Tray Design Manual*, 1958; *Equipment Testing Procedure: Plate Distillation Columns*, 1962; *Tray Efficiencies in Distillation Columns, Final Reports*, 1958, 1959, 1960. Good review articles are Gerster, *Ind. Eng. Chem.*, **47,** 254 (1955); **52,** 645 (1960); see also ref. 16, Section I.
24. Peters, *Ind. Eng. Chem.*, **14,** 476 (1922).
25. Fenske and Quiggle, in *Science of Petroleum*, Vol. V, Part 3, Oxford University Press, New York, 1955, p. 258.
26. Fenske, in *Science of Petroleum*, Oxford University Press, New York, 1938, p. 1648, Fig. 22.
27. Morton, *Laboratory Technique in Organic Chemistry*, McGraw-Hill, New York 1938, p. 87, Fig. 35.
28. Rose, *Ind. Eng. Chem.*, **28,** 1210 (1936), Fig. 1.
29. Prevost, M.S. Thesis, Pennsylvania State College, 1948.
30. Othmer, *Ind. Eng. Chem.*, **35,** 615 (1943); Stedman, *Can. J Research*, **5,** 458 (1931).
31. Fenske, *Ind. Eng. Chem.*, **24,** 482 (1932).
32. Underwood, *Trans. Inst. Chem. Engrs.* (*London*), **10,** 112 (1932).
33. A graphic solution of the Fenske equation has been published by Melpolder and Headington, *Ind. Eng. Chem.*, **39,** 763 (1947).
34. Rodriguez, *Chem. Eng.*, **62,** No. 2, 182 (1955).
35. McCabe and Thiele, *Ind. Eng. Chem.*, **17,** 605 (1925).
36. Sorel, *Compt. Rend.*, **108,** 1128, 1204, 1317 (1889); **118,** 1213 (1894). These were summarized and expanded in *La Rectification de l'Alcool*, Gauthier-Villars, Paris,

1893, and in *La Distillation et Rectification Industrielles*, Gauthier-Villars, Paris, 1899.
37. Lewis, *J. Ind. Eng. Chem.*, **1**, 522 (1909); *Ind. Eng. Chem.*, **14**, 492 (1922). Walker, Lewis, McAdams, and Gilliland, *Principles of Chemical Engineering*, 3rd ed., McGraw-Hill, New York, 1937, p. 553.
38. Ponchon, *Tech. Moderne*, **13**, 20, 55 (1921).
39. Savarit, *Chim. Ind.* (*Paris*), **9**, Special No., 737 (May 1923).
40. Randall and Longtin, *Ind. Eng. Chem.*, **32**, 125 (1940), and preceding papers of that series.
41. Fisher, *Chem. Eng.*, **63**, No. 8, 234 (1956).
42. Johnson and Huang, *Can. J. Technol.*, **32**, 187 (1954).
43. Randall and Longtin, *Ind. Eng. Chem.*, **31**, 908 (1939).
44. Fowler, *Petrol. Engr.*, **23**, No. 1, C35 (1951); Horvath and Schubert, *Chem. Eng.*, **65**, No. 3, 129 (1958).
45. Lowenstein, *Ind. Eng. Chem.*, **54**, No. 1, 61 (1962).
46. Alleva, *Chem. Eng.*, **69**, No. 16, 111 (1962).
47. Keuffel and Esser Co., No. 47-8062; *Hydrocarbon Process. Petrol. Refiner*, **42**, No. 2, 248 (1963).
48. Smoker, *Ind. Eng. Chem.*, **34**, 509 (1942).
49. Edmister, *Petrol. Engr.*, **19**, No. 11, 66 (1948); Underwood, *J. Inst. Petrol.*, **32**, 614 (1946); *Chem. Eng. Progr.*, **44**, 603 (1948); **45**, 118, 609 (1949); Franklin and Forsyth, *Trans. Inst. Chem. Engrs.* (*London*), **31**, 363 (1953); Robinson and Gilliland, *Elements of Fractional Distillation*, 4th ed., McGraw-Hill, New York, 1950; Hengstebeck, *Distillation: Principles and Design Procedures*, Reinhold, New York, 1961.
50. Ponchon, *Tech. Moderne*, **13**, 20, 55 (1921); Savarit, *Chim. Ind.* (*Paris*), **9**, Special No., 737 (May 1923). These are summarized in Brown, *et al.*, *Unit Operations*, Wiley, New York, 1950; see also Robinson and Gilliland, *op. cit.*; Billet, *Chem. Ingr. Tech.*, **30**, 513 (1958).
51. Cave, *Ind. Chemist*, **36**, 531 (1960).
52. See Section V and also the complete series of articles by Edminister (1947–49) and Underwood (1945–49).
53. Smoker, *Trans. Am. Inst. Chem. Engrs.*, **34**, 165, 583 (1938).
54. Clark, *Trans. Faraday Soc.*, **41**, 718 (1945).
55. Bisesi, *Petrol. Refiner*, **22**, 236 (1943).
56. Ramalho and Tiller, *A.I.Ch.E. J.*, **8**, 559 (1962).
57. Underwood, *Trans. Inst. Chem. Engrs.* (*London*), **10**, 112 (1932); *J. Soc. Chem. Ind.* (*London*), **52**, 223 T (1933).
58. Thomson and Beatty, *Ind. Eng. Chem.*, **34**, 1124 (1942).
59. Clark, *Trans. Faraday Soc.*, **41**, 738 (1945).
60. Underwood, *J. Inst. Petrol.*, **29**, 147 (1943); **30**, 225 (1944).
61. Amundson, *Trans. Am. Inst. Chem. Engrs.*, **42**, 939 (1946); Batuner, *Tr. Leningr. Khim.-Farmatsevt. Inst.*, **1958**, No. 34, 19; Eshaya, *Trans. Am. Inst. Chem. Engrs.*, **43**, 555 (1947); Harbert, *Ind. Eng. Chem.*, **37**, 1162 (1945); Junge, *Chem. Tech.* (*Berlin*), **8**, 642 (1956); Matz, *Angew. Chem.*, **B19**, 131 (1947); Stoppel, *Ind. Eng. Chem.*, **38**, 1271 (1946); Szapiro, *Przemysl Chem.*, **35**, 106 (1956).
62. Faasen, *Ind. Eng. Chem.*, **36**, 248 (1944).
63. Billet, *Chem. Ingr.-Tech.*, **32**, 517 (1960); Dietze and Pilz, *Chem. Tech.* (*Berlin*), **12**, 81 (1960); Ellis, *Ind. Eng. Chem.*, **46**, 279 (1954); Holland, Brinkerhoff, and Carlson, *Chem. Eng.*, **70**, No. 4, 153 (1963); Jaulmes, *Chim. anal.*, **1953**, 57, 82; Kirschbaum, *Z. Ver. Deut. Ingr.*, *Verfahrenstech.*, **1943**, No. 1, 15; Mestres, *J. Chim.*

Phys., **55,** 370 (1958); Miller, O., *Bull. Soc. Chim. Belges*, **53,** 97 (1944) and earlier articles; Nikolaeva, *Neft. Khoz.*, **24,** No. 12, 33 (1946); Pohl, *Chem. Ingr.-Tech.*, **1956,** 562; see also Section VI.

64. Collins and Lantz, *Ind. Eng. Chem., Anal. Ed.*, **18,** 673 (1946).
65. Baker, Barkenbus, and Roswell, *Ind. Eng. Chem., Anal. Ed.*, **12,** 468 (1940).
66. Hawkins and Brent, *Ind. Eng. Chem.*, **43,** 2617 (1951).
67. Colburn and Stearns, *Trans. Am. Inst. Chem. Engrs.*, **37,** 291 (1941).
68. O'Brien, M.S. Thesis, Pennsylvania State College, 1948; Prevost, M.S. Thesis, Pennsylvania State College, 1948; Rose and Pfeiffer, "Effect of Reflux Ratio on the Separation Achieved in a Packed Fractionating Column in Continuous and in Batch Distillation," American Chemical Society Meeting, Atlantic City, N. J., 1947; see also Colburn and Stearns, *Trans. Am. Inst. Chem. Engrs.*, **37,** 291 (1941).
69. Rose, Johnson, and Williams, *Ind. Eng. Chem.*, **42,** 2145 (1950).
70. See, in Figure 14, the lines labeled $H = 57.6\%$ for total reflux startup.
71. Podbielniak, U.S. Patent 2,377,900 (June 12, 1945); Smittenberg, *Rec. Trav. Chim.*, **79,** 635 (1960).
72. Bowman and Sastry, "Analysis by Continuous Rectification," American Chemical Society Meeting, New York, 1947; Legatski, U. S. Patent 2,443,011 (May 25, 1948).
73. Peters, *Ind. Eng. Chem.*, **14,** 476 (1922); Bushmakin, *Zh. Prikl. Khim.*, **32,** 2416 (1959).
74. Murch, *Ind. Eng. Chem.*, **45,** 2616 (1953).
75. Hands and Whitt, *J. Applied Chem. (London)*, **1,** 19 (1951).
76. Duncan, Koffolt, and Withrow, *Trans. Am. Inst. Chem. Engrs.*, **38,** 259 (1942); Schultze and Stage, *Oel u. Kohle*, **40,** 66 (1944); Rose and Pfeiffer, Abstracts of Papers, American Chemical Society, 111th Meeting, Atlantic City, N. J., 1947, p. 121, Storrow, *J. Soc. Chem. Ind. (London)*, **66,** 41 (1947); Hawkins and Brent, *Ind. Eng. Chem.*, **43,** 2617 (1951); Chahvekilian, *Compt. Rend.*, **236,** 1273 (1953); Bushmakin, *Zh. Prikl. Khim.*, **33,** 127, 296 (1960).
77. Kirschbaum, *Angew. Chem.*, **B19,** No. 1, 13 (1947).
78. Gaska, Ph.D. Thesis, Pennsylvania State University, 1959.
79. Normau and Hu, *International Symposium on Distillation*, Brighton, England, 1960, Institution of Chemical Engineers, London, p. 100.
80. Manning and Cannon, *Ind. Eng. Chem.*, **49,** 347 (1957).
81. Morris, *International Symposium on Distillation*, Brighton, England, 1960, Institution of Chemical Engineers, London, p. 108.
82. Zuiderweg and Harmens, *Chem. Eng. Sci.*, **9,** 89 (1958).
83. Mullin, *Ind. Chemist*, **33,** 408 (1957).
84. Kuhn, German Patent 970,432 (Sept. 18, 1958).
85. Eckert, *Chem. Eng. Progr.*, **57,** No. 9, 54 (1961); Hausen, *Chem. Ingr.-Tech.*, **32,** 509 (1960); Hoffing and Lockhart, *Chem. Eng. Progr.*, **50,** 95 (1954); Jacobs, *Petrol. Refiner*, **35,** No. 6, 187 (1956); Leva, *Chem. Eng. Progr. Symp. Ser.*, **50,** No. 10, 51 (1954); Sakiadis and Johnson, *Ind. Eng. Chem.*, **46,** 1229 (1954).
86. Griswold, *Ind. Eng. Chem.*, **35,** 247 (1943).
87. Bromiley and Quiggle, *Ind. Eng. Chem.*, **25,** 1136 (1933).
88. Nerheim and Dinerstein, *Anal. Chem.*, **28,** 1029 (1956).
89. Willingham and Rossini, *J. Res. Natl. Bur. Std.*, **37,** 15 (1946).
90. Ward, *U. S. Bur. Mines Tech. Papers*, **1939,** 600.
91. Rosanoff and Easley, *J. Am. Chem. Soc.*, **31,** 953 (1909).
92. Mestres, *Bull. Soc. Chim. France*, **1956,** 876.
93. Quiggle and Fenske, *J. Am. Chem. Soc.*, **59,** 1829 (1937).

94. Willingham and Rossini, *J. Res. Natl. Bur. Std.*, **37**, 21 (1946).
95. Forziati, Glasgow, Willingham, and Rossini, *J. Res. Natl. Bur. Std.*, **36**, 129 (1946).
96. Nerheim and Dinerstein, *Anal. Chem.*, **28**, 1029 (1956).
97. Smith, E. R., *J. Res. Natl. Bur. Std.*, **24**, 299 (1940).
98. Griswold, *Ind. Eng. Chem.*, **35**, 247 (1943).
99. Zel'venskii and Shalygin, *Neft. Khoz.*, **33**, No. 8, 65 (1955).
100. Herington, *International Symposium on Distillation*, Brighton, England, 1960, Institution of Chemical Engineers, London, p. 83.
101. French, *J. Soc. Chem. Ind. (London)*, **65**, 15 (1946).
102. Hawkins and Brent, *Ind. Eng. Chem.*, **43**, 2613 (1951).
103. Fenske, Myers, and Quiggle, *Ind. Eng. Chem.*, **42**, 649 (1950).
104. Struck and Kinney, *Ind. Eng. Chem.*, **42**, 77 (1950).
105. Williams, *Ind. Eng. Chem.*, **39**, 779 (1947).
106. Perry and Fuguitt, *Ind. Eng. Chem.*, **39**, 782 (1947).
107. Peters, *Ind. Eng. Chem.*, **14**, 476 (1922).
108. Bushmakin, *Zh. Prikl. Khim.*, **32**, 2416 (1959).
109. Brown, *Trans. Chem. Soc.*, **35**, 550 (1879); **37**, 49, 304 (1880); **39**, 317 (1881).
110. Barrell, Thomas, and Young, *Phil. Mag.*, (V) **37**, 8 (1894).
111. Rayleigh, *Phil. Mag.*, (VI) **4**, 521 (1902).
112. Rose and Welshans, *Ind. Eng. Chem.*, **32**, 668 (1940).
113. Colburn and Stearns, *Trans. Am. Inst. Chem. Engrs.*, **37**, 291 (1941).
114. Johnson, Huang, and Talbot, *A.I.Ch.E. J.*, **1**, 111 (1955).
115. Nord, *Chem. Eng.*, **58**, No. 2, 144 (1951); Glotzer, *ibid.*, **69**, No. 10, 202 (1962); Stiehl and Weber, *A.I.Ch.E. J.*, **3**, 391 (1957).
116. Robinson and Gilliland, *Elements of Fractional Distillation*. 4th ed., McGraw-Hill, New York, 1950, pp. 108–110.
117. Nord, *Ind. Eng. Chem.*, **39**, 232 (1947); Stanton, *ibid.*, **39**, 1042 (1947).
118. (a) Smoker and Rose, *Trans. Am. Inst. Chem. Engrs.*, **36**, 285 (1940); (b) O'Brien, M.S. Thesis, Pennsylvania State University, 1948.
119. Rose, *Ind. Eng. Chem.*, **33**, 594 (1941); Rose and Long, *ibid.*, **33**, 684 (1941).
120. Chao, *Chem. Eng.*, **61**, No. 1, 165 (1954).
121. Stanton, *Ind. Eng. Chem.*, **39**, 1042 (1947).
122. Kuhn, *Helv. Chim. Acta*, **29**, 26 (1946).
123. Rose and Welshans, *Ind. Eng. Chem.*, **32**, 671, 672 (1940).
124. Fenske and Quiggle, in *Science of Petroleum*, Vol. V, Part 3, Oxford University Press, New York, 1955, pp. 258–259.
125. Colburn and Stearns, *Trans. Am. Inst. Chem. Engrs.*, **37**, 291 (1941).
126. Rose, Welshans, and Long, *Ind. Eng. Chem.*, **32**, 673 (1940); Edgeworth-Johnstone, *ibid.*, **35**, 407 (1943); **36**, 1068 (1944).
127. Meadows, Program, A.I.Ch.E. Meeting, Baltimore, Md., May 1962, p. 48.
128. Shulman, Ullrich, and Wells. *A.I.Ch.E. J.*, **1**, 247 (1955).
129. Shulman, Ullrich, Wells, and Proulx, *A.I.Ch.E. J.*, **1**, 259 (1955).
130. Jesser and Elgin, *Trans. Am. Inst. Chem. Engrs.*, **39**, 277 (1943).
131. Tongberg, Quiggle, and Fenske, *Ind. Eng. Chem.*, **26**, 1213 (1934).
132. Colburn and Stearns, *Trans. Am. Inst. Chem. Engrs.*, **37**, 291 (1941).
133. Rose, *Ind. Eng. Chem.*, **32**, 675 (1940).
134. Colburn and Stearns, *Trans. Am. Inst. Chem. Engrs.*, **37**, 291 (1941).
135. Rose and Johnson, *Chem. Eng. Progr.*, **49**, 15 (1953).
136. Rose, Welshans, and Long, *Ind. Eng. Chem.*, **32**, 673 (1940).
137. Huckaba and Danly, *A.I.Ch.E. J.*, **6**, 335 (1960).
138. Rose and Johnson, *Chem. Eng. Progr.*, **49**, 15 (1953).

139. Colburn and Stearns, *Trans. Am. Inst. Chem. Engrs.*, **37**, 291 (1941).
140. Rose, Johnson, and Williams, *Ind. Eng. Chem.*, **42**, 2145 (1950); **43**, 2459 (1951).
141. Rose and Johnson, *Chem. Eng. Progr.*, **49**, 15 (1953).
142. Rose, Johnson, and Williams, *Ind. Eng. Chem.*, **42**, 2145 (1950).
143. Rose, Johnson, and Williams, *Ind. Eng. Chem.*, **43**, 2459 (1951).
144. Rose and Williams, *Ind. Eng. Chem.*, **42**, 2494 (1950).
145. Rose, Stillman, Williams, and Carlson, *Chem. Eng. Progr. Symp. Ser.*, **55**, No. 21, 79 (1959).
146. Huckaba and Danly, *A.I.Ch.E. J.*, **6**, 335 (1960).
147. Huckaba and Tour, Preprint 23, A.I.Ch.E. Meeting, St. Louis, Dec. 1953.
148. Huckaba and Danly, *A.I.Ch.E. J.*, **6**, 335 (1960).
149. Coulson, *J. Soc. Chem. Ind. (London)*, **64**, 101 (1945).
150. O'Brien, M.S. Thesis, Pennsylvania State University, 1948.
151. Cohen, *Theory of Isotope Separation as Applied to Large Scale Production of* U^{235}, McGraw-Hill, New York, 1951; *J. Chem. Phys.*, **8**, 588 (1940).
152. Berg and James, *Trans. Am. Inst. Chem. Engrs.*, **44**, 307 (1948).
153. Jackson and Pigford, *Ind. Eng. Chem.*, **48**, 1020 (1956).
154. Bardeen, *Phys. Rev.*, **57**, 35 (1940); Davidson, *Trans. Inst. Chem. Engrs. (London)*, **34**, 44 (1956); Huffman and Urey, *Ind. Eng. Chem.*, **29**, 531 (1937); Marshall and Pigford, *Applications of Differential Equations to Chemical Engineering Problems*, University of Delaware, Newark, Del., 1947; Montroll and Newell, *J. Appl. Phys.*, **23**, 184 (1952); Pigford, Tepe, and Garrahan, *Ind. Eng. Chem.*, **43**, 2592 (1951); see also Devyatykh, Agliulov, and Frolov, *Zh. Fiz. Khim.*, **33**, 161 (1959).
155. Schilk, M.S. Thesis, Pennsylvania State University, 1953; Biles, M.S. Thesis, Pennsylvania State University, 1952.
156. Rose, Johnson, and Williams, *Ind. Eng. Chem.*, **42**, 2145 (1950).
157. Williams, Harnett, and Rose, *Ind. Eng. Chem.*, **48**, 1008 (1956).
158. Cottrell (1950); Sanders (1951); B. Johnson (1952); all M.S. Theses, Pennsylvania State University.
159. O'Leary, Bowman, and Coull, *Ind. Eng. Chem.*, **43**, 541 (1951).
160. O'Brien, M.S. Thesis, Pennsylvania State University, 1948; Oldroyd and Goldblatt, *Ind. Eng. Chem. Anal. Ed.*, **18**, 761 (1946); Podbielniak, *ibid.*, **13**, 639 (1941); Romanet, *Compt. Rend.*, **235**, 1390, 1645 (1952).
161. Bogart, *Trans. Am. Inst. Chem. Engrs.*, **33**, 139 (1937).
162. Edgeworth-Johnstone, *Ind. Eng. Chem.*, **35**, 407 (1943); **36**, 1068 (1944).
163. Johnson, Huang, and Talbot, *A.I.Ch.E. J.*, **1**, 111 (1955); see also Hibino, *Proc. Fujihara Mem. Fac. Eng. Keio Univ. (Tokyo)*, **3**, 84 (1950); Billet, *Chem. Ingr. Tech.*, **30**, 407 (1958).
164. Stiehl and Weber, *A.I.Ch.E. J.*, **3**, 391 (1957).
165. Converse and Gross, private communication, Carnegie Institute of Technology, 1962.
166. Young, *J. Chem. Soc.*, **81**, 768 (1902).
167. Chu, *Chem. Eng. Progr.*, **46**, 215, 635 (1950); Rose, *ibid.*, 635.
168. Bowman, *Ind. Eng. Chem.*, **41**, 2004, 2608 (1949); **43**, 2622 (1951).
169. Harbert, *Ind. Eng. Chem.*, **39**, 1118 (1947).
170. Crosley, "Batch Rectification of Complex Mixtures," American Chemical Society Meeting, Chicago, Illinois, 1956; see also Haase and Lang, *Chem. Ingr. Tech.*, **23**, 313 (1951); Fu, *Hua Kung Hsueh Pao*, **1958**, No. 2, 123, *Chem. Abstr.*, **54**, 17977b (1960).

171. Kuhn and Baertschi, *Helv. Chim. Acta*, **29**, 692 (1946).
172. Pigford, Tepe, and Garrahan, *Ind. Eng. Chem.*, **43**, 2592 (1951).
173. Marshall and Pigford, *Application of Differential Equations to Chemical Engineering Problems*, University of Delaware, Newark, Delaware, 1947.
174. Colburn and Stearns, *Trans. Am. Inst. Chem. Engrs.*, **37**, 291 (1941).
175. Rose, Johnson, and Williams, *Ind. Eng. Chem.*, **42**, 2145 (1950).
176. Rose, Johnson, and Williams, *Ind. Eng. Chem.*, **43**, 2459 (1951); *Chem. Eng. Progr.*, **48**, 549 (1952); see also Huckaba and Danly, *A.I.Ch.E. J.*, **6**, 335 (1952).
177. See also Chahvekilian, *Rev. Inst. Franc. Petrole Ann. Combust. Liquides*, **13**, 997 (1958).
178. Colburn and Stearns, *Trans. Am. Inst. Chem. Engrs.*, **37**, 291 (1941); Podbielniak, *Analytical Distillation and Its Application to the Petroleum Industry*, Podbielniak, Inc., Chicago, p. 7; Rose and Houston, "Experimental Determination of the Effect of Ratio of Charge to Holdup in Batch Distillation," American Chemical Society, Meeting, Chicago, Illinois, 1948; Rose, Williams, and Prevost, *Ind. Eng. Chem.*, **42**, 1876 (1950).
179. O'Brien, M.S. Thesis, Pennsylvania State University, 1948.
180. Rose, Johnson, and Schilk, "Automatic Computer Procedure for Prediction of Batch Fractionation with Appreciable Holdup and Any Number of Theoretical Plates," American Chemical Society Regional Meeting, Philadelphia, Pa., February 1956.
180a. Husain, *Brit. Chem. Eng.*, **13**, 668 (1958); Houtman and Husain, *J. Chem. Ed.*, **32**, 529 (1955).
181. Rose and O'Brien, *Ind. Eng. Chem.*, **44**, 1480 (1952).
182. Rose and Long, *Ind. Eng. Chem.*, **33**, 684 (1941).
183. Smoker and Rose, *Trans. Am. Inst. Chem. Engrs.*, **36**, 285 (1940).
184. Stedman, *Can. J. Research*, **5**, 455 (1931).
185. Rietema, *Chem. Eng. Sci.*, **7**, 89 (1957).
186. Rose and Welshans, *Ind. Eng. Chem.*, **32**, 669 (1940).
187. Bowman and Cichelli, *Ind. Eng. Chem.*, **41**, 1985 (1949); Cichelli, Weatherford, Bowman, and Coull, *Ind. Eng. Chem.*, **42**, 2502 (1950).
188. Zuiderweg, *Laboratory Manual of Batch Distillation*, Interscience, New York, 1957, p. 51.
188a. Houtman and Husain, *Chem. Eng. Sci.*, **5**, 178 (1956).
189. N. C. Cook, personal communication.
190. Rose, *Ind. Eng. Chem.*, **33**, 594 (1941).
191. Kojima and Aoyama, *Kagaku Kogaku*, **23**, 393 (1959).
192. Rose, Johnson and Schilk, "Automatic Computation and Correlation of Rayleigh Batch Fractionation Curves," American Chemical Society Regional Meeting, Philadelphia, Pa., February 1956.
193. Rose, *Anal. Chem.*, **22**, 1369 (1950); see also Verheus, *Anal. Chim. Acta*, **2**, 681 (1948).
194. Edgeworth-Johnstone, *J. Inst. Petrol.*, **25**, 558 (1939); *Ind. Eng. Chem.*, **35**, 826 (1943). The second reference is a comment on the first, and on Griswold.[196]
195. Melpolder and Headington, *Ind. Eng. Chem.*, **39**, 763 (1947); see also Robu, *Inst. Petrol Gaze Bucuresti Studii*, **1955**, No. 1, 41.
196. Griswold, *Ind. Eng. Chem.*, **35**, 247 (1943).
197. Kuhn, Narten, and Peterli, *Helv. Chim. Acta*, **40**, 1066 (1957); *Chimia* (*Aarau*), **12**, 131 (1958).
198. Denbigh, *The Thermodynamics of the Steady State*, Wiley, New York, 1951; Doer-

ing, *Ber. Oberhess. Ges. Natur.-Heilk. Giessen, Naturw. Abt.*, **25**, 108 (1952); Freshwater, *Trans. Inst. Chem. Engrs. (London)*, **29**, 149 (1951); O. Miller, *Bull. Soc. Chim. Belges*, **48**, 447 (1939); Trevissoi, *Ann. Chim. (Rome)*, **47**, 530 (1957).
199. Kahn, Ph.D. Thesis, Pennsylvania State University, 1951.
200. Grunberg, *Proc. Cryog. Eng. Conf., 2nd, Boulder, Colo.*, **1956**, Plenum Press, New York, 1957, p. 27.
201. Legatski, U. S. Patent 2,443,011 (May 25, 1948).
202. Carney, U. S. Patent 2,415,337 (Feb. 4, 1947); Kojima, *Kagaku Kogaku*, **23**, 381 (1959).
203. Fu, *Zh. Prikl. Khim.*, **32**, 543 (1959).
204. Langdon, *Ind. Eng. Chem., Anal. Ed.*, **17**, 590 (1945); *Anal. Chem.*, **20**, 338 (1948); Fenske and Quiggle, in Science of Petroleum, Vol. V, Part 3, Oxford University Press, New York, 1955, p. 263.
205. Buiten, *Chem. Eng. Sci.*, **9**, 104 (1958); *International Symposium on Distillation*, Brighton, England, 1960, p. 173; see also Wohl, *Rev. Chim. (Bucharest)*, **13**, No. 6, 351 (1962).
206. Rose and Sweeny, *Ind. Eng. Chem.*, **50**, 1687 (1958).
207. Briggs, Waddington, and McNeil, *Ind. Eng. Chem.*, **52**, 145 (1960).
208. McWhirter and Lloyd, *Chem. Eng. Progr.*, **59**, No. 6, 58 (1963). McWhirter, Ph.D. Thesis, Pennsylvania State University, 1962.
209. Rose and Johnson, *Chem. Eng. Progr.*, **49**, 15 (1953).
210. Rose, Williams, and Kahn, *Ind. Eng. Chem.*, **43**, 2608 (1951); Biles, M.S. Thesis, Pennsylvania State University, 1952; see also Kirschbaum, *Destillier- und Rektifiziertechnik, 3rd. ed.*, Springer, Berlin, 1960, p. 201.
211. Coates and Pressburg, *Chem. Eng.*, **68**, No. 2, 131; No. 4, 145 (1961); Ellis and Shelton, *Chem. Process Eng.*, **34**, 193, 280 (1953); Klinkenberg, *Chem. Eng. Sci.*, **4**, 39 (1955); Lloyd, *Petrol. Refiner*, **29**, No. 2, 135 (1950).
212. Cohen, *The Theory of Isotope Separation*, McGraw-Hill, New York, 1951; Benedict and Pigford, *Nuclear Chemical Engineering*, McGraw-Hill, New York, 1957, Chap. 10.
213. Maclean, *Chem. Eng.*, **68**, No. 17, 123 (1961).
214. Brown and Martin, *Trans. Am. Inst. Chem. Engrs.*, **35**, 679 (1939); Gilliland, *Ind. Eng. Chem.*, **32**, 1220 (1940).
215. Gupta and Ray, *Ind. Eng. Chem., Process Design Develop.*, **1**, 255 (1962).
216. Robinson and Gilliland, *Elements of Fractional Distillation*, 4th ed., McGraw-Hill, New York, 1950, p. 116; Junge, *Chem. Tech. (Berlin)*, **8**, 708 (1956); Kirschbaum and Lipphardt, *Chem. Ingr. Tech.*, **29**, 393 (1957).
217. Kent and Pigford, *A.I.Ch.E. J.*, **2**, 363 (1956).
218. Holland and Welch, *Petrol. Refiner*, **36**, No. 5, 251 (1957); Holland and Hayes, *ibid.*, No. 4, 203; Coulter, *ibid.*, **31**, No. 11, 156 (1952); Perry, *Chemical Engineers' Handbook*, 3rd ed., McGraw-Hill, New York, 1950, pp. 580–583; Robinson and Gilliland, *Elements of Fractional Distillation*, 4th ed.; McGraw-Hill, New York, 1950, pp. 111–115.
219. Bratton, Felsing, and Bailey, *Ind. Eng. Chem.*, **28**, 424 (1936).
220. Stillman, Ph.D. Thesis, Pennsylvania State University, 1961.
221. Rose, Eckhart, and Wanser, "Chromatographic Distillation," American Chemical Society Meeting, Atlantic City, N. J., September 1962.
222. Eckhart, Ph.D. Thesis, Pennsylvania State University, 1963.
223. Rose, Schilk, and Johnson, *Ind. Eng. Chem.*, **45**, 933 (1953).
224. Rose and Williams, *Ind. Eng. Chem.*, **42**, 2494 (1950); Rose, Johnson, and Williams,

ibid., 2145. The first paper shows the application of digital computer methods to the equations of the second paper.

225. O'Brien and Franks, *Chem. Eng. Progr. Symp. Ser.*, **55**, No. 22, 25 (1959); Bergo et al., *Khim. Prom.*, **7**, 555 (1959); Wojtasik, Rosner, and Badzynski, *Przemy l Chem.*, **38**, 474 (1959); Brown and Rosenberg, *Chem. Eng. Progr.*, **59**, No. 10, 75 (1963).
226. Rose, Williams, and Kahn, *Ind. Eng. Chem.*, **43**, 2502 (1951).
227. Rose, Stillman, Williams, and Carlson, *Chem. Eng. Progr. Symp. Ser.*, **55**, No. 21, 79 (1959).
228. Geddes, *Chem. Eng. Progr. Symp. Ser.*, **55**, No. 25, 87 (1959).
229. Kwauk, *A.I.Ch.E. J.*, **2**, 240 (1956); Gerster, *Ind. Eng. Chem.*, **52**, 645 (1960); *Chem. Eng. Progr.*, **59**, No. 3, 35 (1963); Maddox, *Chem. Eng.*, **68**, No. 25, 127 (1961); Goulcher, *Brit. Chem. Eng.*, **7**, 590, 663 (1962).
230. Beutler, "A Practical Computer Approach to Distillation Column Design Calculations," Program, A.I.Ch.E. Meeting, Pittsburgh, 1956, p. 37; Bonner, *Chem. Eng. Progr. Symp. Ser.*, **55**, No. 21, 87 (1959); McIntire, *ibid.*, p. 59; McIntire and Shelton, *ibid.*, p. 69.
231. Maddox, *Petrol. Eng.*, **30**, C15 (1958); Maddox and Erbar, *Proc. Ann. Conv. Nat. Gasoline Assoc. Am. Tech. Papers*, **38**, 5 (1959); Erbar and Maddox, *Can. J. Chem. Eng.*, **40**, 25 (1962); Graven, *Petrol. Refiner*, **38**, No. 5, 209 (1959); Lyster et al., *Petrol. Refiner*, **38**, No. 6, 221; No. 7, 151; No. 10, 139 (1959); Peiser, *Chem. Eng.*, **67**, No. 14, 129 (1960); Wenske and Gelbin, *Chem. Tech. (Berlin)*, **12**, 127 (1960).
232. Robinson and Gilliland, *Elements of Fractional Distillation*, 4th ed., McGraw-Hill, 1950, Chaps. 9 and 12.
233. Hanson, Duffin, and Somerville, *Computation of Multistage Separation Processes*, Reinhold, New York, 1962; Holland, *Multicomponent Distillation*, Prentice-Hall, Englewood Cliffs, N. J., 1963.
234. Amundson and Pontinen, *Ind. Eng. Chem.*, **50**, 730 (1958); Amundson, Pontinen, and Tierney, *A.I.Ch.E J.*, **5**, 295 (1959); Greenstadt, Bard, and Morse, *Ind. Eng. Chem.*, **50**, 1644 (1958); Eckhart and Rose, "Fast Solution of Simultaneous Equations for Multicomponent Batch Distillation by Linearization and Tridiagonal Elimination Procedure," Abstracts of Papers, American Chemical Society Meeting, Atlantic City, N. J., 1962, p. 4M.
235. Rose, Sweeny, and Schrodt, *Ind. Eng. Chem.*, **50**, 737 (1958).
236. Rosenbrock, *Brit. Chem. Eng.*, **3**, 364, 432, 491 (1958).
237. Stillman, Ph.D. Thesis, Pennsylvania State University, 1961.
238. Williams, Harnett, and Rose, *Ind. Eng. Chem.*, **48**, 1008 (1956); Rose, Johnson, and Williams, *ibid.*, p. 1173.
239. Rose, Johnson, and Williams, *Ind. Eng. Chem.*, **42**, 2145 (1950).
240. Rose, Johnson, and Williams, *Ind. Eng. Chem.*, **43**, 2459 (1951).
241. Eckhart, Ph.D. Thesis, Pennsylvania State University, 1963.
242. Meadows, "Multicomponent Batch Distillation Calculations on a Digital Computer," Program, A.I.Ch.E. Meeting, Baltimore, 1962, p. 48.
243. Danly and Huckaba, in Computer Program Abstracts, *Chem. Eng. Progr.*, **56**, No. 3, 86 (1960).
244. Lewis, *Ind. Eng. Chem.*, **14**, 492 (1922); see also Robinson and Gilliland, *Elements of Fractional Distillation*, 4th ed., McGraw-Hill, New York, 1950, p. 178.
245. Dodge and Huffman, *Ind. Eng. Chem.*, **29**, 1434 (1937); Dodge, *Trans. Am. Inst. Chem. Engrs.*, **34**, 585 (1938).

246. Chilton and Colburn, *Ind. Eng. Chem.*, **27**, 255, 904 (1935).
247. Baker, *Ind. Eng. Chem.*, **27**, 977 (1935); White, *Trans. Am. Inst. Chem. Engrs.*, **36**, 359 (1940); Colburn, *Ind. Eng. Chem.*, **33**, 459 (1941); Scheibel and Othmer, *Trans. Am. Inst. Chem. Engrs.*, **38**, 339 (1942); *Ind. Eng. Chem.*, **34**, 1200 (1942); Underwood, *J. Inst. Petrol.*, **29**, 147 (1943); **30**, 225 (1944).
248. See also Suroviec, *Ind. Eng. Chem.*, **53**, 289, 992 (1961); Standard, *ibid.*, p. 991.
249. Bowman and Briant, *Ind. Eng. Chem.*, **39**, 745 (1947).
250. Kafarov and Vigdorov, *Zh. Prikl. Khim.*, **33**, 1506 (1960).
251. Glaser, *Chem. Ingr.-Tech.*, **32**, 726 (1960).
252. Westhaver, *Ind. Eng. Chem.*, **34**, 126 (1942); see also Docksey and May, *J. Inst. Petrol. Technol.*, **21**, 176 (1935).
253. Kuhn, *Helv. Chim. Acta*, **25**, 252 (1942); Kuhn and Ryffel, *ibid.*, **26**, 1693 (1943).
254. Interface equilibrium has been questioned by Chiang and Toor, *A.I.Ch.E. J.*, **5**, 165 (1959).
255. Donnell and Kennedy, *Ind. Eng. Chem.*, **42**, 2327 (1950).
256. See also Devyatykh and Agliulov, *Zh. Fiz. Khim.*, **34**, 2509 (1960); Ruckenstein, *Comm. Acad. Rep. Populare Romine*, **6**, No. 2, 263, 405 (1956).
257. Podbielniak, *Analytical Distillation and Its Application to the Petroleum Industry*, Podbielniak, Inc., Chicago, n.d., p. 8.
258. Rose, *Ind. Eng. Chem.*, **28**, 1210 (1936).
259. Chahvekilian, *Rev. Inst. Franc. Petrole Ann. Combust. Liquides*, **13**, 782 (1958); Michalski and Serwinski, *Zeszyty Nauk. Politech. Lodz. Chem.*, **No. 9**, 89 (1961); Nikolaev, *Zh. Prikl. Khim.*, **31**, 711 (1958); Stern, Ph.D. Thesis, Georgia Institute of Technology, 1962.
260. Qureshi and Smith, *J. Inst. Petrol.*, **44**, 137 (1958); Ruckenstein, *Comm. Acad. Rep. Populare Romine*, **6**, 263, 405 (1956).
261. Tsyun and Malyusov, *Dokl. Akad. Nauk SSSR*, **120**, 151 (1958).
262. Adolphi and Fleischer, *Chem. Tech. (Berlin)*, **7**, 638 (1955).
263. Billet, *Chem. Ingr.-Tech.*, **29**, 733 (1957).
264. Cheng and Teller, "Effect of Surface Regeneration on Liquid-Phase Mass Transfer," Program, A.I.Ch.E. Meeting, New Orleans, 1963.
265. Shulman, Ullrich, Proulx, and Zimmerman, *A.I.Ch.E. J.*, **1**, 253 (1955).
266. Brauer, *Chem. Ingr.-Tech.*, **29**, 520 (1957); Grein, *Dechema Monograph.*, **32**, 183 (1959); Kohoutek, Dolezalik, and Vermouzek, *Chem. Listy*, **52**, 869 (1958); Shulman and Robinson, *A.I.Ch.E. J.*, **6**, 469 (1960); Tierney, Stutzman, and Daileader, *Ind. Eng. Chem.*, **46**, 1595 (1954); Yoshida, Koyanagi *et al.*, *ibid.*, **46**, 1756 (1954); Yoshida, *Chem. Eng. Progr. Symp. Ser.*, **51**, No. 16 (1955).
267. Gerster, *Ind. Eng. Chem.*, **52**, 645 (1960); *Chem. Eng. Progr.*, **59**, No. 3, 35 (1963)
268. Byron, Bowman, and Coull, *Ind. Eng. Chem.*, **43**, 1002 (1951).
269. Colburn and Stearns, *Trans. Am. Inst. Chem. Engrs.*, **37**, 291 (1941).
270. Danckwerts, Sawistowski, and Smith, *International Symposium on Distillation*, Brighton, England, 1960, p. 1; Free and Hutchison, *ibid.*, p. 166; Liang and Smith, *Chem. Eng. Sci.*, **17**, 11 (1962); Paratella, *Chim. Ind. (Milan)*, **42**, 7 (1960); Sawistowski and Smith, *Ind. Eng. Chem.*, **51**, 915 (1959); Stern, Deshpande, and Murdock, *Trans. Indian Inst. Chem. Engrs.*, **8**, 6 (1955–56); Zuiderweg and Harmens, *Chem. Eng. Sci.*, **9**, 89 (1958).
271. Bergo, *Kislorod*, **1959**, No. 5, 6; Chahvekilian, *Rev. Inst. Franc. Petrole Ann. Combust. Liquides*, **13**, 997 (1958); Donnell and Kennedy, *Ind. Eng. Chem.*, **42**, 2327 (1950); Heiny, M.S. Thesis, Pennsylvania State University, 1951; Kaminskii, *Soobshch. Akad. Nauk Gruz. SSR*, **28**, 529 (1962); Rius, Otero de la Gandara,

and Clement Casado, *Anales Real Soc. Espan. Fis. Quim. (Madrid)*, **B53**, 391 (1957); Romanet, *Compt. Rend.*, **235**, 412 (1952); Simonetta, *Chim. Ind. (Milan)*, **27**, 157 (1945); **28**, 114 (1946); Ulusoy and Cakaloz, *Rev. Fac. Sci. Univ. Istanbul*, **C24**, 239, 280 (1959).

272. Cohen, *J. Chem. Phys.*, **8**, 588 (1940); *Theory of Isotope Separation as Applied to Large Scale Production of* U^{235}, McGraw-Hill, New York, 1951; see also Rozen, *Proc. Acad. Sci. USSR, Chem. Technol. Sect.*, **107**, 27 (1956).
273. Coulson, *J. Soc. Chem. Ind. (London)*, **64**, 101 (1945); Berg and James, *Trans. Am. Inst. Chem. Engrs.*, **44**, 307 (1949).
274. Marshall and Pigford, *Application of Differential Equations to Chemical Engineering Problems*, University of Delaware, Newark, Delaware, 1947, p. 144.
275. Pigford, Tepe and Garrahan, *Ind. Eng. Chem.*, **43**, 2592 (1951).
276. Bowman, *Ind. Eng. Chem.*, **41**, 2004 (1949).

CHAPTER II

VAPOR–LIQUID EQUILIBRIA

CARL H. DEAL, *Shell Development Company*

I. INTRODUCTION

Separations by distillation depend upon differences between the compositions of liquid mixtures and those of the vapors at equilibrium with them. Consequently, in dealing with a distillation problem, one needs to know, first of all, the relation between equilibrium liquid and vapor compositions over the range of liquid compositions, temperatures, and pressures that are of interest. In practical distillation problems such relations need to be known at least to within a few percent, and, as a rule, must be determined experimentally for each system of interest. Nonetheless, some impressions of the ways systems commonly behave are useful—not only in understanding distillations, but in reducing the experimental effort necessary for a given problem.

This chapter deals with liquid–vapor equilibria of simple systems of nonelectrolytes at the moderate temperatures and pressures ordinarily used in distillations. In the first section, equilibria of perfect systems are described as a reference case. In the second, equilibria of real systems are described in terms of deviations from perfect systems. In the third, some of the ways of interpolating between and extrapolating from experimental points are described. Finally, in the fourth section a number of the more useful experimental techniques are mentioned.

For the sake of brevity, there is no attempt to review the extensive literature here, and the above areas are dealt with from a single viewpoint. The problem of describing equilibria is viewed for the most part as one of describing the changes in suitable activity coefficients which occur with changes in the general nature of the liquid, the temperature, and the pressure. Use is made of thermodynamic quantities, but the formal thermodynamics of liquid mixtures are not dealt with directly. A list of general references is given at the end of the chapter.

II. PERFECT MIXTURES

In dealing with solutions of nonelectrolytes, a perfect solution is defined as one which obeys Raoult's Law. For each component i

$$y_ip = \bar{p}_i = x_ip_i \tag{1}$$

where y_i and x_i are the mole fractions in the vapor and liquid phases and p, $\bar{p}_i$, and p_i are the total pressure exerted by the mixture, the partial pressure exerted by the component, and the vapor pressure of the pure component (p when $x_i = 1$), respectively. In a perfect liquid, the components other than the component i thus reduce $\bar{p}_i$ and y_i only through their diluting effect and have no special effect on the tendency of a given molecule of the component i to escape from the liquid phase.

As illustrated in Figure 1 for a nearly perfect binary system, at constant temperature a number of the quantities useful in treating distillations are very simply related to liquid compositon. The partial pressure curves as already indicated by (1) are linear. The distribution ratio of a component (K_i, defined as the ratio of vapor concentration to liquid concentration) is simply the ratio of the vapor pressure of the component to the total pressure

$$K_i = y_i/x_i = p_i/p \tag{2}$$

and depends on composition only through p. The volatility of a component (v_i, defined as the product of the distribution ratio and pressure) is simply the vapor pressure of the component

$$v_i = K_ip = (y_i/x_i)p = p_i \tag{3}$$

and is independent of the composition. The volatility of one component relative to a second ($\alpha_{i,j}$, defined as the ratio of the respective distribution ratios or volatilities) is simply the ratio of the respective vapor pressures

$$\alpha_{i,j} = (y_i/x_i)/(y_j/x_j) = v_i/v_j = p_i/p_j \tag{4}$$

and is independent of composition. Finally, the vapor composition as a function of liquid composition is the simple bowed curve defined by (4) when α is a constant.

It is noteworthy that, since $\alpha_{i,j} = p_i/p_j$ is independent of composition, azeotropes (compositions at which $\alpha_{i,j} = 1$) cannot occur in a perfect system at constant temperature.

The temperatures and pressures at the top and bottom of a distillation column are not ordinarily the same, and variations in both temperature

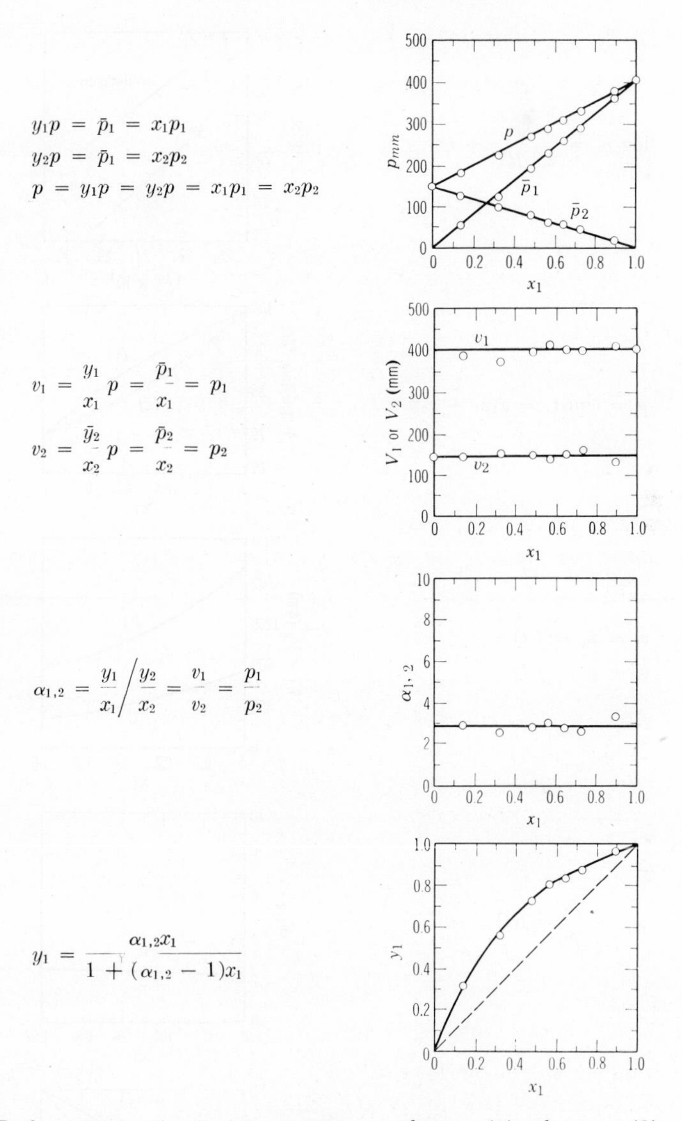

Fig. 1. Perfect system, constant temperature: *n*-hexane (1)–*n*-heptane (2). (Smyth and Engel, *J. Am. Chem. Soc.*, **51,** 2646 (1962).)

and pressure must, in principle, be taken into account in describing equilibria for distillation purposes. As a rule, however, equilibria at constant pressure more closely approximate those applicable to a distillation than do equilibria at constant temperature. As illustrated in Figure 2 for the same

$$\log p_1 = \frac{\lambda_i}{2.3\,RT} + C_i$$

Log p_i: 3.4, 3.2, 3.0, 2.8, 2.6, 2.4
n-Hexane
98.4°
68.7°
n-Heptane
26 27 28 29 30
$1/T \times 10^4$

$$p = \text{const.} = x_1 p_1 + x_2 p_2$$

Temperature, °C.: 100, 90, 80, 70, 60
(y)
(x)
0 0.2 0.4 0.6 0.8 1.0
x_1

$$v_1 = p_1 = f(t)$$
$$v_2 = p_2 = f(t)$$

V_1 or V_2 (mm): 2000, 1600, 1200, 800, 400, 0
p_1
p_2
0 0.2 0.4 0.6 0.8 1.0
x_1

$$\alpha_{1,2} = \frac{p_1}{p_2} = f(t)$$

$\alpha_{1,2}$: 10, 8, 6, 4, 2, 0
0 0.2 0.4 0.6 0.8 1.0
x_1

$$y_1 = \frac{\alpha_{1,2} x_1}{1 + (\alpha_{1,2} - 1)x_1}$$

y_1: 1.0, 0.8, 0.6, 0.4, 0.2, 0
0 0.2 0.4 0.6 0.8 1.0
x_1

nearly perfect system shown in Figure 1, the curves are all somewhat more complicated than the corresponding ones for constant temperature. Both volatilities and relative volatilities depend upon composition through the temperature dependencies of the p_i's. Although they do not depend on composition at any fixed temperature, they do depend critically on temperature; and the temperature at which different mixtures in the system boil at constant pressure varies with the composition. The boiling temperature of any given composition is, of course, that one for which $x_1p_1 + x_2p_2$ equals the fixed pressure and may be obtained by trial and error to give a boiling temperature–composition curve (t vs x) such as that shown. Except in the special case in which the vapor pressure curves of the pure components cross at some temperature between their boiling temperatures at the pressure in question, there is, of course, only one composition which boils at each temperature between the two boiling temperatures of the components. In this special case, a perfect system may form an azeotropic mixture; that is, at the temperature at which the vapor pressures are the same and at the corresponding liquid composition, the components have identical volatilities.

In many real, nearly perfect systems the changes in relative volatilities are not large—either because the temperature range is small and the changes in the volatilities themselves are small or because the heats of vaporization of the components are nearly the same and the changes in the individual volatilities cancel out. If the components of a nearly perfect mixture follow Trouton's Rule, the relative volatility is constant and

$$\log \alpha_{i,j} \simeq 8.9\ (T_j - T_i)/(T_j + T_i)$$

where T_j and T_i are the boiling points of the components in °K.

In nearly perfect systems of more than two components, behavior is, in principle, the same as the above but is, of course, somewhat more complicated in that a larger number of components are involved.

Unfortunately, the laws of perfect mixtures are of little practical use since systems which are within a few per cent of perfect are the exception rather than the rule. A listing of the maximum deviations from perfect behavior in a number of simple systems is shown in Table I and gives some indication of the magnitudes of the deviations from perfect behavior that are commonly encountered in real systems. As a rule, nearly perfect behavior can be counted on in a system only when the components contain

Fig. 2. Perfect system, constant pressure: *n*-hexane (1)–*n*-heptane (2). (Leslie and Carr, *Ind. Eng. Chem.*, **17**, 810 (1925).)

TABLE I
Deviations from Perfect Solution of Some Single Systems

Solute (1)	Solvent (2)	t, °C.	Max. deviation of solute, %	Ref.
n-Hexane	*n*-Heptane	25	<5	13
n-Dotriacontane	*n*-Heptane	25	−50	13
Cyclohexane	*n*-Heptane	25	+13	13
Benzene	*n*-Heptane	25	+55	13
Dodecylbenzene	*n*-Heptane	25	+70	13
Decalin	*n*-Heptane	70	+50	13
Tetralin	*n*-Heptane	25	+240	13
Anthracene	*n*-Heptane	25	+1250	13
Chrysene	*n*-Heptane	25	+5600	13
Carbon tetrachloride	*n*-Heptane	50	*ca.* +20	14
Ethylene dichloride	*n*-Heptane	50	*ca.* +300	15
n-Butyl chloride	*n*-Heptane	50	*ca.* +25	14
n-Butyl bromide	*n*-Heptane	50	*ca.* +45	14
Acetone	*n*-Heptane	25	+740	13
Diisobutyl ketone	*n*-Heptane	25	+240	13
Methanol	*n*-Heptane	25	+9260	13
n-Octanol	*n*-Heptane	25	+3270	13
Ethylene chlorohydrin	Benzene	80	+900	16
Chloroform	Benzene	35	38	17
Carbon tetrachloride	Benzene	40	11	18
Tin tetrachloride	Benzene	10	240	19
Carbon disulfide	Benzene	20	50	20
Aniline	Benzene	70	58	21, 22
Methanol	Benzene	35–55	1000	23
Ethanol	Benzene	50	630	24
n-Propanol	Benzene	40	330	24
Acetic acid	Benzene	50	63	35
Acetone	Ethanol	25	+230	13
Acetaldehyde	Ethanol	60	−45	13
Ethylacetate	Ethanol	25	+320	13
Methyl propionate	Ethanol	73	+210	13
Heptane	Ethanol	25	1,600	13
Eicosone	Ethanol	25	15,200	13
Benzene	Ethanol	25	660	13
Dodecylbenzene	Ethanol	25	8,100	13
Chrysene	Ethanol	25	44,000	13

identical polar or polarizable groupings in their molecules and have about the same size, but occasionally mixtures of components widely different in structure are nearly perfect.

III. IMPERFECT MIXTURES

As indicated, real solutions are imperfect in their behavior to a degree which must usually be taken into account in dealing with distillations. In real mixtures the partial pressure of a solute component is not simply dependent on the solute concentration and its vapor pressure. It depends also on the nature of the liquid environment presented by the mixture to the solute molecules, that is, on the kinds and concentrations of the molecules which make up the liquid environment.

Solutions of nonelectrolytes are usually described in terms of activity coefficients which indicate the deviations from Raoult's Law.

$$y_i p = \bar{p}_i = \gamma_{i(m)} x_i p_i \tag{5}$$

where $\gamma_{i(m)}$ is the activity coefficient which depends upon the nature of the solute and the solvent environment as indicated by the subscripts. It is essentially a thermodynamic activity coefficient for which the pure liquid i under its saturation vapor pressure is the standard reference state.* For imperfect mixtures, the distribution ratios, volatilities, and relative volatilities defined in the previous section became

$$K_i = y_i/x_i = (\gamma_{i(m)} p_i)/p \tag{6}$$

$$v_i = K_i p = (y_i/x_i)p = \gamma_{i(m)} p_i \tag{7}$$

and

$$\alpha_{i,j} = (y_i/x_i)/(y_j/x_j) = v_i/v_j = (\gamma_{i(m)} p_i)/(\gamma_{j(m)} p_j) \tag{8}$$

* Strictly, differences in the pressures on the standard state and the solution as well as mixing effects in the vapor should be taken into account in defining γ by (5). For the systems and conditions far removed from the critical regions of interest here, these effects usually amount to only a few per cent and can frequently be neglected. If no special mixing effects occur in the vapor and the partial molal volume is approximately the same as the molal volume, the pressure effect can be approximated quite well by replacing (5) with $\theta_i y_i p = \gamma_i x_i p_i$, where

$$-\ln \theta_i = (V_i - \beta_i)(p - p_i)/RT$$

In the latter, V_i is the liquid molal volume of (i) and β_i is the vapor compressibility factor of (i). The factor β_i may be usually evaluated from generalized equations of state with sufficient accuracy; however, when the vapors are quite imperfect, e.g., for carboxylic acids whose vapor association is pressure sensitive, direct compressibility measurements may be required.

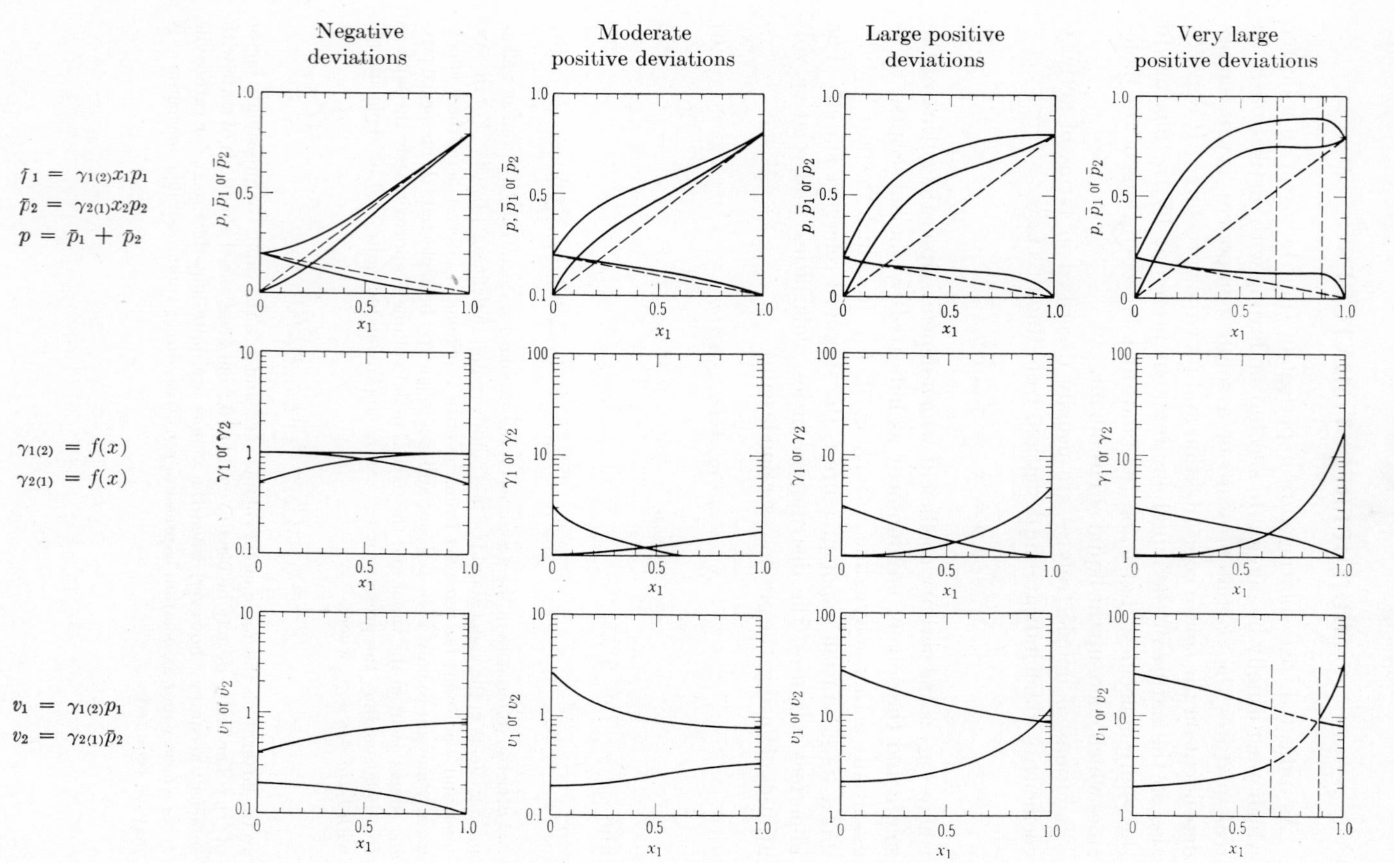

Fig. 3. Imperfect system, constant temperature ($p_1/p_2 = 0.8/0.2$).

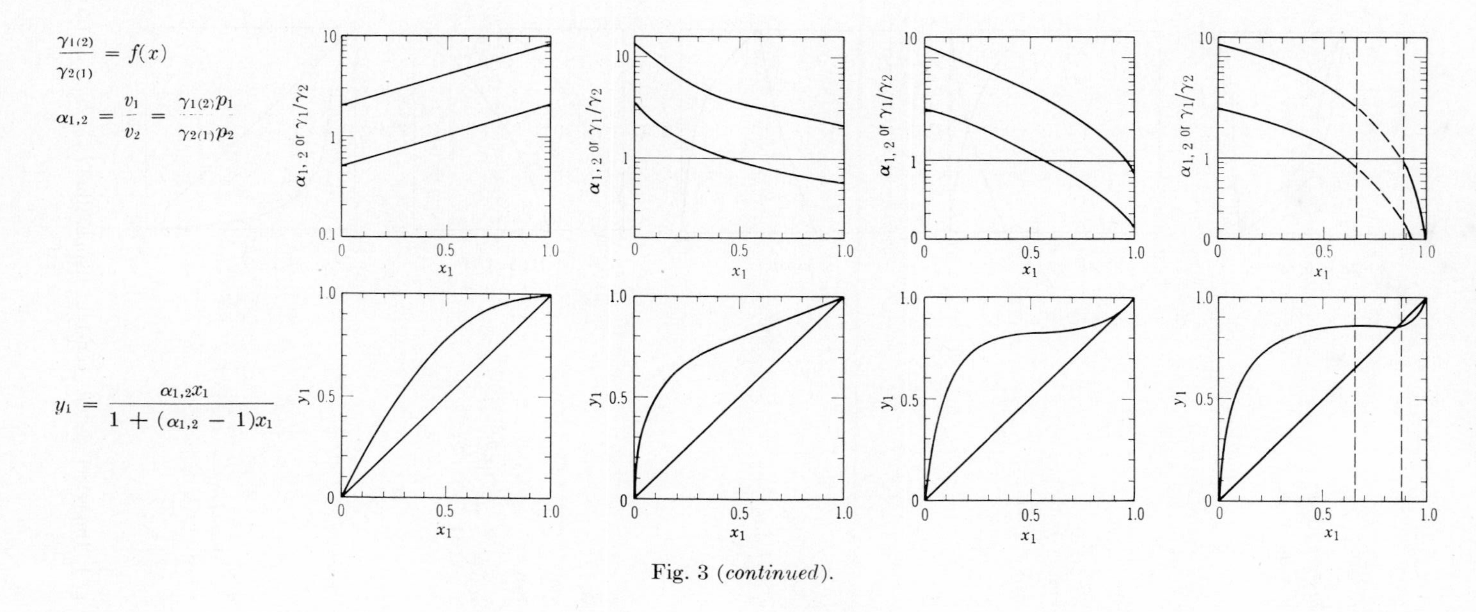

$$\frac{\gamma_{1(2)}}{\gamma_{2(1)}} = f(x)$$

$$\alpha_{1,2} = \frac{v_1}{v_2} = \frac{\gamma_{1(2)}p_1}{\gamma_{2(1)}p_2}$$

$$y_1 = \frac{\alpha_{1,2}x_1}{1 + (\alpha_{1,2} - 1)x_1}$$

Fig. 3 (*continued*).

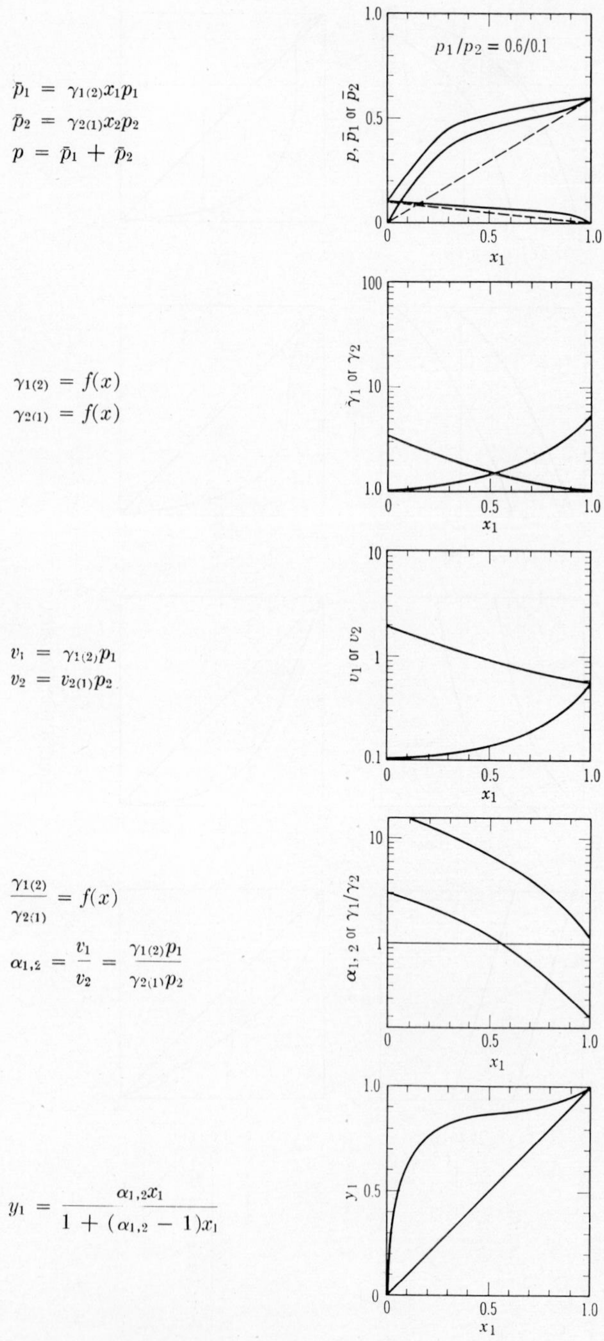

$\bar{p}_1 = \gamma_{1(2)}x_1p_1$
$\bar{p}_2 = \gamma_{2(1)}x_2p_2$
$p = \bar{p}_1 + \bar{p}_2$
$p_1/p_2 = 0.6/0.1$
$p, \bar{p}_1$ or $\bar{p}_2$
$\gamma_{1(2)} = f(x)$
$\gamma_{2(1)} = f(x)$
γ_1 or γ_2
$v_1 = \gamma_{1(2)}p_1$
$v_2 = v_{2(1)}p_2$
v_1 or v_2
$\frac{\gamma_{1(2)}}{\gamma_{2(1)}} = f(x)$
$\alpha_{1,2} = \frac{v_1}{v_2} = \frac{\gamma_{1(2)}p_1}{\gamma_{2(1)}p_2}$
$\alpha_{1,2}$ or γ_1/γ_2
$y_1 = \frac{\alpha_{1,2}x_1}{1 + (\alpha_{1,2} - 1)x_1}$
y_1
x_1

Fig. 4. Imperfect system, constant temperature ($\overset{\circ}{\gamma}_{1(2)}/\overset{\circ}{\gamma}_{1(2)} = 1.5$).

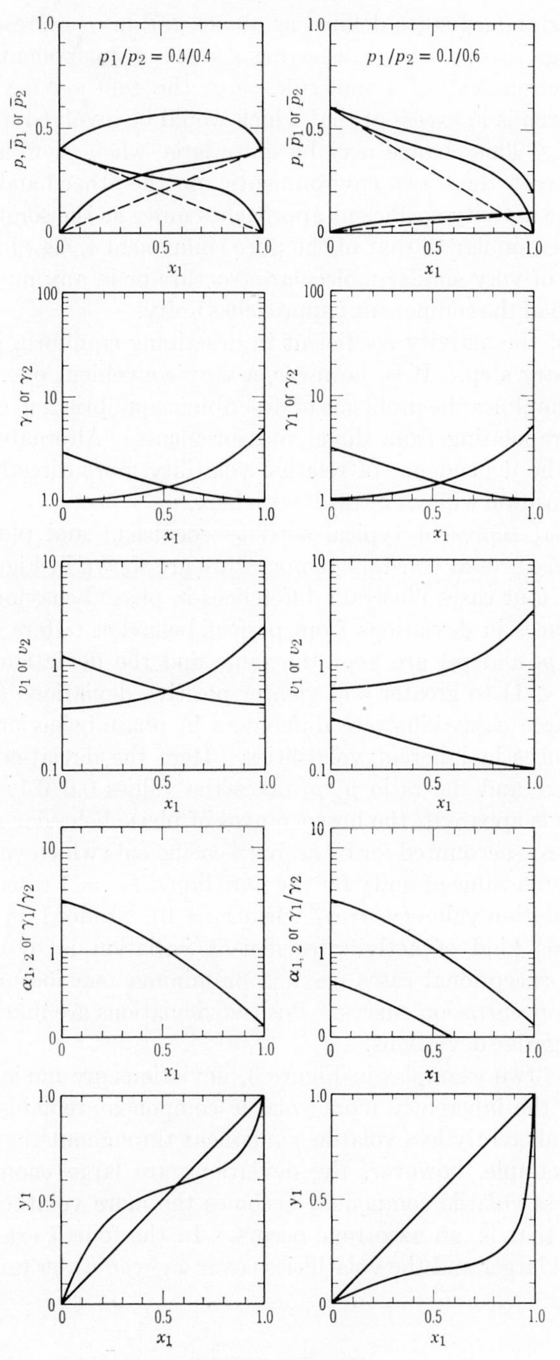

Fig. 4 (*continued*).

With the standard state defined as above, $RT \ln \gamma_i$ represents the free energy change involved in transferring a mole of component i molecules from an environment of i molecules into the solution environment in question, which is in excess of that which would be involved if the solution were perfect. This change may be quite large when there are large differences between these two environments; on the other hand, it becomes small and the activity coefficient approaches unity as the solution environment becomes similar to that of the pure component i, e.g., in mixtures of components of very similar molecular structure or in any mixtures as the mole fraction of the component i approaches unity.

The use of the activity coefficient in describing equilibria is, of course, not a necessary step. It is, however, a very convenient one. As will be evident, it simplifies the problems of describing equilibria and of interpolating and extrapolating from direct measurements. Alternate approaches of treating the dependence of relative volatility more directly as a function of composition will not be dealt with here.[1,2]

Curves that represent typical activity coefficient and phase relations for binary mixtures at constant temperature are shown in Figures 3 and 4. In Figure 3, four cases illustrate differences in phase behavior which arise from differences in deviations from perfect behavior. Here the inherent volatilities (p_1 and p_2) are kept the same and the deviations vary from negative ($\gamma < 1$) to greater and greater positive deviations ($\gamma > 1$). In Figure 4, three cases illustrate differences in phase behavior which arise from differences in inherent volatilities. Here the deviation factors are kept the same and the ratio p_1/p_2 takes the values 0.6/0.1, 0.4/0.4, and 0.1/0.6. As is apparent, the broad ranges of phase behavior illustrated in these figures are accounted for by activity coefficients which vary monotonically between a value of unity for the pure liquid ($\gamma_i = 1$ when $x_i = 1$) and an infinite dilution value ($\gamma_i = \gamma_i^0$ when $x_i = 0$). Indeed, in most simple mixtures, this kind of activity coefficient variation is to be expected; however, in exceptional cases maxima or minima may occur in activity coefficient–concentration curves. Positive deviations are much more common than negative deviations.

In the first two examples in Figure 3, deviations are moderate and the volatility of the inherently more volatile component remains larger than that of the inherently less volatile component throughout the system. In the third example, however, the deviations are large enough that the inherently less volatile component becomes the more volatile at low concentrations, that is, an azeotrope occurs. In the fourth example, deviations are still larger and the volatilities cover an even wider range. In this case, the deviations are so large and are dependent on the liquid composition in such a way that two liquid phases occur between the compositions indicated by the vertical dashed lines; that is, the activity coefficients change with composition in such a way that at these two compositions,

$$(x_1', x_2') \text{ and } (x_1'', x_2''),$$

and

$$\gamma_1' x_1' = \gamma_1'' x_1'' \text{ and } \gamma_2' x_2' = \gamma_2'' x_2'' \quad (9)$$

Since the activity (γx) of each component in both the phases remains the same throughout this range of compositions, the equilibrium partial pressures of the components remain constant throughout the range of composition. As a result, there is a range of overall liquid compositions with constant equilibrium vapor compositions. This may be contrasted to the previous case of an homogeneous azeotrope in which $\alpha = 1$ for a single liquid composition. In connection with heterogeneous azeotropes, it is noteworthy that the occurrence and composition of two liquid phases depend on the way the activities of both components change with composition but that, commonly, two phases occur when the limiting activity coefficient of one of the components exceeds 15 or 20. It is also noteworthy that the two-phase region need not encompass the point at which $\alpha = 1$, since this also depends upon the inherent volatilities of the components.

In the first example of Figure 4, deviations are not great enough to give rise to an azeotrope, but some "pinching" of the x–y curve occurs at high concentrations of the first component. As the vapor pressure ratio becomes smaller, the deviations are sufficiently large that an azeotropic composition occurs at high concentrations of the first component. At still lower vapor pressure ratios, the azeotropic composition moves to lower concentrations as illustrated in the second example. Finally, when the vapor pressure ratio is sufficiently low, the azeotrope disappears and only a "pinching" is apparent at low concentrations of the first component as illustrated in the final example.

Since the limiting values at infinite dilution (γ^0's) usually represent the maximum solution effects, these values alone may usually be used to assess the separability of components in a system of interest and even to assess the ease of separation. Thus, for a binary pair, the relative volatility normally varies monotonically between the limits of

$$\alpha_{1,2} = (\gamma_{1(2)}{}^0) p_1 / (1) p_2 \text{ (at } x_1 = 0, x_2 = 1) \quad (10)$$

and

$$\alpha_{1,2} = (1)p_1/(\gamma_{2(1)}{}^0)p_2 \text{ (at } x_1 = 1,\ x_2 = 0) \tag{11}$$

If both of these limiting α's are greater than unity or less than unity, the components are separable by simple distillation and the magnitudes of the α's give an idea of the ease of separation. If these two values fall on opposite sides of unity, then there is some intermediate concentration at which

$$\alpha_{1,2} = (\gamma_1)p_1{}^\circ/(\gamma_2)p_2{}^\circ = 1 \tag{12}$$

i.e., an azeotrope occurs and the components are not separable by simple distillation. If deviations are negative this composition corresponds to a minimum in the p–x curve at constant temperature or to a *maximum* boiling azeotrope at constant pressure; if deviations are positive, it corresponds to a maximum in the p–x curve and to a *minimum* boiling azeotrope at constant pressure.

Likewise in many practical distillations, the appropriate γ^0's provide an immediate idea of the ease or difficulty of a separation or of the fate of minor components. Thus, whenever one material predominates in setting the liquid environment in a section of a distillation column, the limiting γ^0's of the various other components of the mixture may be enough to indicate which are easily separated and which are difficulty separated. In this connection, it is frequently useful to consider the limiting activity coefficient ratio between two components in a third "solvent" component ($\gamma_{1(3)}{}^0/\gamma_{2(3)}{}^0$) as a measure of the "inherent" selectivity of the "solvent" (extractive or azeotropic distillation).

Curves which qualitatively represent typical temperature dependencies of vapor pressures, limiting activity coefficients (γ^0's), and the corresponding volatilities and relative volatilities are shown in Figure 5. In all cases the abscissa ($1/T$) scale is inverted so that high temperatures appear to the right. The first set of curves represents vapor pressures identical for all three examples; the second set represents the limiting activity coefficients for three cases, one with negative, one with positive, and one with large positive deviations. It is noteworthy that as a rule the slopes of the the activity coefficient curves are such that systems tend toward more ideal behavior with increasing temperature and that as a rule the larger the deviations the more temperature sensitive are the activity coefficients. The third set of curves represent volatilities and are plotted as bands, one

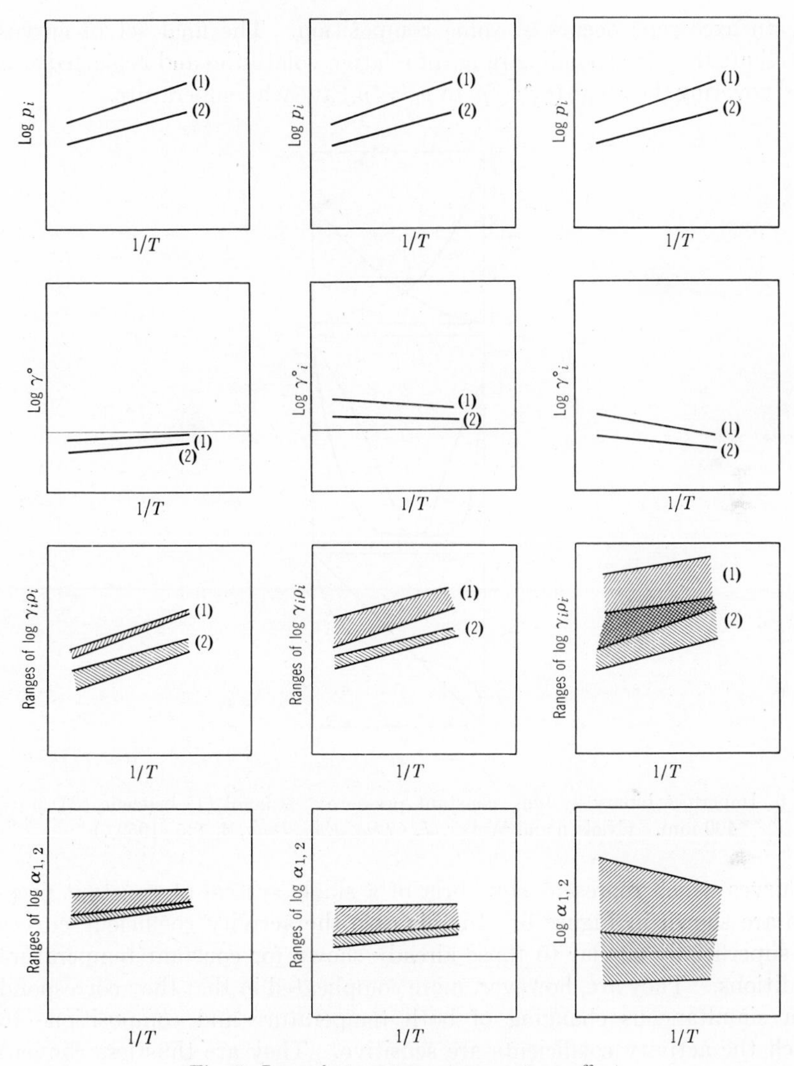

Fig. 5. Imperfect systems, temperature effects.

extreme of which represents the limiting volatility at infinite dilution ($\gamma_i^0 p_i$) and the other extreme of which represents the volatility of the pure material (p_i). With positive deviations, the limiting volatility at infinite dilution is usually less temperature sensitive than the inherent volatility of the pure material. When such bands as those illustrated overlap, an azeotrope occurs at some composition. The final set of curves represents the corresponding range of relative volatilities and is plotted as a band covering the range ($\gamma_1{}^0 p_1/p_2$ to $p_1/\gamma_2{}^0 p_2$) at each temperature.

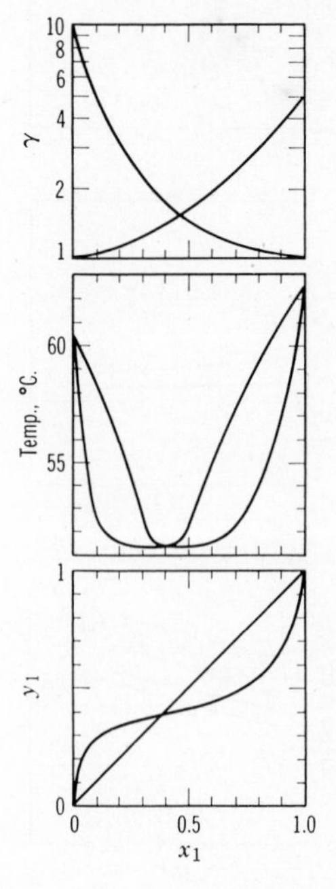

Fig. 6. Imperfect binary system, constant pressure: ethanol (1)–benzene (2), p = 400 mm. (Nielsen and Weber, *J. Chem. Eng. Data*, **4**, 145 (1959).)

Curves which represent equilibria of a single system at constant pressure are shown in Figure 6. In this case the activity coefficient curves are superficially similar to those already shown for constant temperature conditions. They are, however, more complicated in that they correspond to a simultaneous changing of both temperature and composition—to which the activity coefficients are sensitive. They are thus less conveniently interpolated and extrapolated than are constant temperature curves (see below). The minimum boiling azeotrope indicated corresponds to a maximum in the pressure–composition curves for constant temperature which were shown earlier.

In systems of more than two components, volatility behavior at constant temperature is more complicated than in binary systems in that a larger number of components affect the liquid environment. The activity coefficients, however, change regularly between the limits imposed by the binary systems of which the multicomponent system can be composed. Indeed, it is usually useful to consider such more complicated mixtures in terms of the limiting binaries. An illustrative example which corresponds to the usual extractive distillation case is shown in Figure 7. Here, com-

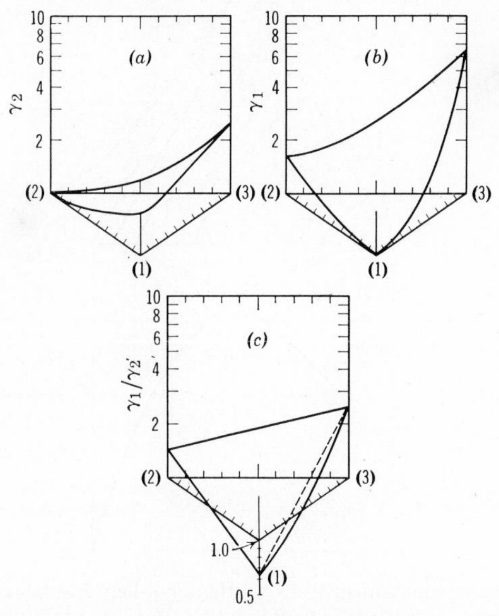

Fig. 7. Activity coefficients in a ternary ($\log \overset{\circ}{\gamma}_{1(3)} > \log \overset{\circ}{\gamma}_{2(3)} > \log \overset{\circ}{\gamma}_{1(2)} = \log \overset{\circ}{\gamma}_{2(1)}$).

ponent (3), the selective solvent, is taken such that the (1)–(3) binary shows greater deviations than the (2)–(3) binary. The surface representing log, γ_1 as a function of composition is a fairly simple surface joining the appropriate binary log γ vs. x curves with no maxima or minima. It is sometimes represented by projecting the contour lines on the base plane. The logarithm of the ratio γ_1/γ_2, which corresponds to the difference in elevation of this surface and the analogous one for log γ_2 as a function of composition is also shown in Figue 1. The latter is also a simple surface connecting the appropriate limiting binaries with no maxima or minima. Usually in such a system at constant x_1/x_2, log (γ_1/γ_2) is approximately linear in x_3.

In systems of more than two components, volatility behavior at constant pressure is more complicated than at constant temperature. The surfaces representing the activity coefficients of the components are smooth

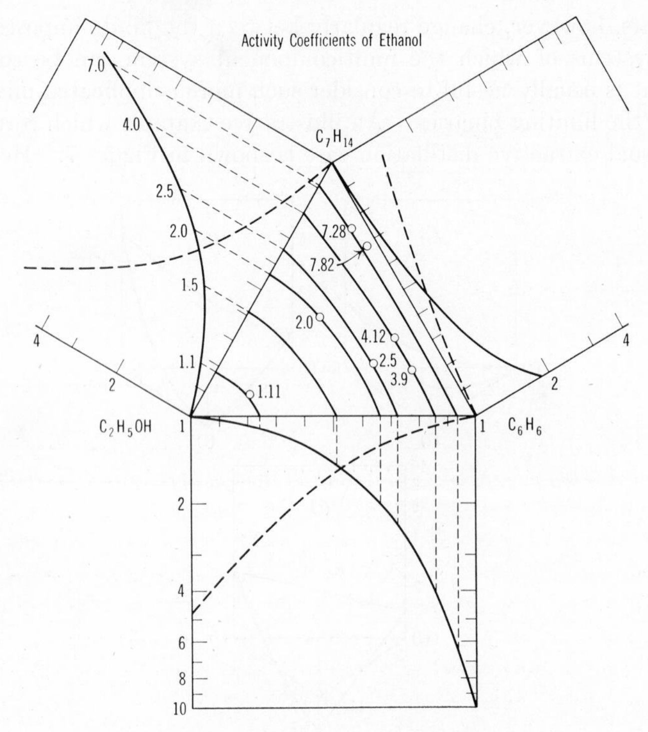

Fig. 8. Ternary system, constant pressure: ethanol–*n*-heptane–benzene, $p = 400$ mm. (Nielsen and Weber, *J. Chem. Eng. Data*, **4**, 145 (1959).)

surfaces between the limiting curves for the binary systems, but are much more complicated as a result of the simultaneous temperature variations with composition. A simple ternary at constant pressure is shown in Figure 8.

IV. INTERPOLATIONS AND EXTRAPOLATIONS

In dealing with vapor–liquid equilibria, ways of putting experimental measurements into some sound framework which will, on the one hand, permit interpolations and extrapolations and, on the other hand, permit some assessment of individual points are virtually a necessity. Unfortunately, there is as yet no adequate theory of solution, but the foregoing description of commonly encountered kinds of equilibria is, in effect, a partial framework of the kind required. In addition, there are a number of largely empirical but sound generalizations which may be put to very good use in interpolating, extrapolating, and assessing data.

They vary from simple graphical procedure to much more sophisticated and detailed procedures which attempt to take maximum advantage of empirical experience. Most frequently, such extrapolations and interpolations are made across compositions and/or temperatures within a given system of components for which direct measurements are available. There are also, however, sound relations between behavior and physical properties or chemical structure which, in effect, permit interpolations and extrapolations from one system of components into a second on the basis of component properties or structures when no direct data are available. The latter are particularly useful in screening separation schemes.

1. Graphical Interpolation and Extrapolations

Direct graphical methods which take into account the necessary limits or the relative sensitivities of the various curves which have been illustrated are, of course, useful. Thus, for instance, the partial pressure of a component must be zero at zero concentration of the component, the activity coefficient usually has its largest value at zero concentration and must have a value of unity at unit mole fraction, etc. Such techniques are, however, so straightforward that they require no further comment here.

In addition to the above, there are thermodynamic criteria which may be applied not only in assessing the thermodynamic consistency of the set of data and thus arriving at some judgement of the validity, but also as an aid in interpolating and extrapolating graphically. The thermodynamic condition which requires that the free energy of a system at equilibrium be a minimum gives rise to the conditions (Gibbs–Duhem) that

$$x_1(\partial \ln \gamma_1)/\partial x_1 + x_2(\partial \ln \gamma_2)/\partial x_1 + x_3(\partial \ln \gamma_3)/\partial x_1 + \ldots = 0 \quad (13a)$$

$$x_1(\partial \ln \gamma_1)/\partial x_2 + x_2(\partial \ln \gamma_2)/\partial x_2 + x_3(\partial \ln \gamma_3)/x_2 + \ldots = 0 \quad (13b)$$

etc. $(T,P \text{ constant})$

It is impractical to apply these criteria directly in a system of many components, but the condition for thermodynamic consistency in a binary system is simply that

$$(\partial \ln \gamma_1/\partial x_1)/(\partial \ln \gamma_2/\partial x_1) = -x_2/x_1 \qquad (T,P \text{ constant}) \quad (14)$$

and can be used in graphical interpolations and extrapolations. Thus, the slopes of log γ_1 and log γ_2 vs. x_1 curves must have opposite signs (a maximum in one curve can occur only with a minimum in the other) and, further, the slopes must be related quantitatively as indicated. Strictly, this condition is applicable only at constant temperature and pressure, but in practice at moderate pressures it is commonly necessary only to hold temperature constant.*

One of the more convenient ways of applying Gibbs–Duhem restriction is by the use of the "area" rule, that is, the equivalent condition that

$$\int_0^1 \log (\gamma_1/\gamma_2)(dx_1) = 0 \tag{15}$$

Thus, the areas above and below zero in a plot of log (γ_1/γ_2) vs. x_1 or x_2 must be equal if a set of data are consistent. In many simple systems with moderate deviations, the log (γ_1/γ_2) curve is essentially a straight line; more commonly, particularly in strongly polar systems or associated systems, the plot is not linear and the intercepts are, of course, not identical (see Figures 3 and 4). Even when the curve is a complex one the area condition is helpful in interpolating and extrapolating and may give tentative bases for identifying systematic errors.

2. Thermodynamically Consistent Analytical Expressions

Frequently it is convenient to interpolate or extrapolate with the use of suitable analytical relations between activity coefficients and concentrations, particularly when computations are to be made by computer. For this purpose there are a number of analytical expressions available which automatically satisfy the conditions for thermodynamic consistency for all values of the adjustable parameters and which experience has shown approximate concentration dependencies rather well.

Even though they are usually derived by differentiating some expression for the excess free energy of solution which is reasonable from a theoretical viewpoint, they may be viewed simply as empirical relations and are in practice usually used in an empirical fashion. Nonetheless, they are most properly applied at constant temperature since only under these conditions are the thermodynamic consistency aspects brought most consistently to bear. In this case it can normally be expected that the same kind of concentration dependency which describes a system at one temperature will be adequate for a second temperature with suitable adjustment in the parameters. In this sense, the concentration and temperature dependencies of activity coefficients are separable and can be treated more or less independently.

* The Gibbs–Duhem restriction has occasionally been applied to constant pressure data without recognition of temperature variations; this is generally not sound and can lead to serious error.

Thermodynamically consistent expressions may include a large number of adjustable parameters in order to fit a very wide range of solution effects, but, usually, the use of only two or perhaps three parameters for a pair of components is warranted by experimental data. Indeed, the use of a large number of parameters in order to provide a more or less exact fit to any but the most accurate data may lead to unrealistic interpolations and extrapolations.

Two of the widely used two-parameter descriptions of binary mixtures are the van Laar,

$$\left\{\begin{aligned} \log \gamma_1 &= \frac{A_{12}}{\left(1 + \dfrac{x_1}{x_2}\dfrac{A_{12}}{A_{21}}\right)^2} \\ \log \gamma_2 &= \frac{A_{21}}{\left(1 + \dfrac{x_2}{x_1}\dfrac{A_{21}}{A_{12}}\right)^2} \end{aligned}\right\} \tag{16}$$

and the Margules (Redlich–Kister),

$$\left\{\begin{aligned} \log \gamma_1 &= (1 - x_1)^2 \, [(B + C\,(-1 + 4\,x_1)]] \\ \log \gamma_2 &= x_1^2 \, [B + C\,(-3 + 4\,x_1)] \end{aligned}\right\} \tag{17}$$

where the parameters characteristic of the particular system are A_{12} and A_{21} or B and C, respectively. The parameters may be thought of as representing, in effect, an interaction free energy characteristic of a pair of dissimilar molecules and an effective molecular size ratio or they may be considered as the logarithms of the two limiting activity coefficients. For the van Laar,

$$A_{12} = \log \left(\lim_{\substack{x_1 \to 0 \\ x_2 \to 1}} \gamma_1 \right) = \log \gamma_{1(2)}{}^0 \tag{18}$$

and

$$A_{21} = \log \left(\lim_{\substack{x_1 \to 1 \\ x_2 \to 0}} \gamma_2 \right) = \log \gamma_{2(1)}{}^0 \tag{19}$$

For the Margules (Redlich–Kister),

$$B - C = \log \left(\lim_{\substack{x_1 \to 0 \\ x_2 \to 1}} \gamma_1 \right) = \log \gamma_{1(2)}{}^0 \tag{20}$$

and

$$B + C = \log \left(\lim_{\substack{x_1 \to 1 \\ x_2 \to 0}} \gamma_2 \right) = \log \gamma_{2(1)}{}^0 \tag{21}$$

Thus, the limiting activity coefficients are usually not only a good measure of maximum effects but they provide directly two convenient parameters for interpolations from infinite dilution to finite concentration.

The two expressions are similar in that they become identical as the $\gamma_{1(2)}{}^0$ approaches $\gamma_{2(1)}{}^0$.

van Laar:

$$\lim_{A_{12} \to A_{21}} \log \gamma_{1(2)} = A_{12}\, x_2{}^2 \tag{22}$$

and Magules (Redlich-Kister):

$$\lim_{B + C \to B - C} \log \gamma_{1(2)} = Bx_2{}^2 \tag{23}$$

They differ quite markedly for unsymmetrical systems ($\gamma_{1(2)}{}^0 \neq \gamma_{2(1)}{}^0$) as is illustrated by the comparison in Figure 9.

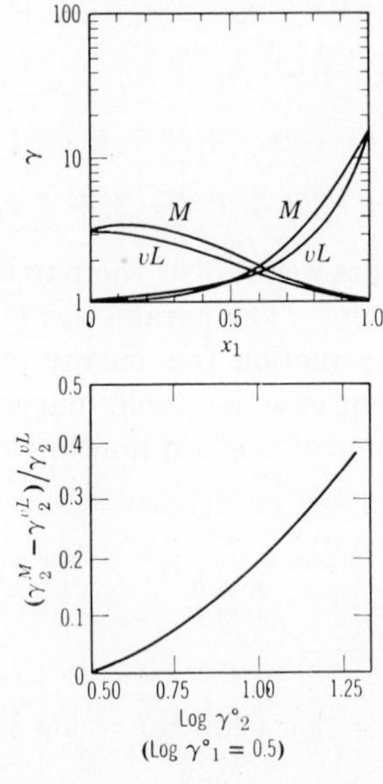

Fig. 9. Comparisons of Margules and van Laar relations.

For the most part, the dependency expressed by the two-coefficient van Laar seems to give a better fit to unsymmetrical systems than does the Margules but is somewhat more difficult to handle. The van Laar is, however, incapable of fitting the occasional system which has a maximum in a log γ vs. x curve or which tends strongly toward such a situation. A comparison of various such correlating expressions has been given by

Wohl.[3] When data warrant a more precise fit than that provided by a simple two-coefficient van Laar or Margules, relations with additional terms are useful, e.g., more complete Redlich–Kister[4] relations or the modified van Laar expressions proposed by Black.[5] With regard to the latter, a plot of $(\log \gamma_1)^{0.5}$ vs. $(\log \gamma_2)^{0.5}$ gives an indication of the need for modifying the simple van Laar. For a simple van Laar, such a plot is strictly linear.

Although such relations as the above are generally sound and provide a very useful means of averaging, interpolating, and extrapolating measurements, they must, of course, be used with some care. Thus, for instance, a fitting to data points in the middle concentration region of a system may give an adequate averaging of and interpolation between the points, but only approximate values for the logarithms of the activity coefficients at infinite dilution and only approximate values for the two correlating coefficients. Such a long extrapolation is sensitive not only to small errors in the data points but to the form of the relation used—a fact which is not fully recognized in some of the literature. Indeed, although the accurate experimental determination of activity coefficients for components at high dilution is usually difficult, there is frequently a real incentive to emphasize accurate measurements in the dilute regions, and thus to tend toward making interpolations rather than extrapolations. This is particularly the case when the separation of interest involves producing high-purity material and impurities are present at high dilutions. Such an emphasis is also particularly important if systematic changes in solution behavior with systematic changes in structure of solute or solvent are to be revealed.

In dealing with systems of many components, use can be made of thermodynamically consistent relations analogous to those shown above. The details of treating such multicomponent systems are beyond the scope of the present chapter and the reader is referred to the original literature or the general references. There are, however, several comments which are pertinent.

In general, the multicomponent expressions use as parameters the parameters for the binary systems of which the multicomponent system can be considered composed (since in the limits they must reduce to the same relations) plus, in some cases, additional "multicomponent" parameters characteristic of the system. Frequently, these multicomponent parameters are not necessary and the practice of interpolating into the multicomponent system on the basis of the binary parameters has developed. Although this practice is probably sound in principle, it may be hazardous, particularly if demands for accuracy are great, because of the sensitivity of many systems to relatively small changes in binary parameters.

On the other hand, if demands for accuracy are not great, quite simple interpolation can frequently be made. Thus a practical case is one in which two components, (1) and (2), have only moderate deviations (symmetrical system), but both form quite imperfect mixtures with, say, an extractive distillation solvent. In this case, the Redlich–Kister relation without ternary terms gives

$$\log(\gamma_1/\gamma_2) = (B_{13} - B_{23})\,x_3 - (C_{13} - C_{23})\,x_3^2 + (2\,x_1\,C_{13} + 2\,x_2\,C_{23})\,x_3 + B_{12}\,(x_1 - x_2) \tag{24}$$

In the first approximation, the predominant term is the first one* and the logarithm of the selectivity of the solvent environment ($\log(\gamma_1/\gamma_2)$) varies linearly with solvent concentration x_3 at constant x_1/x_2. In a second approximation, the $\log(\gamma_1/\gamma_2)$ vs. x_3 curve at constant x_1/x_2 is somewhat concave upwards. At constant x_3 concentration, $\log(\gamma_1/\gamma_2)$ is linear in x_1 or x_2. The resulting $\log(\gamma_1/\gamma_2)$ surface has already been shown in Figure 7 and represents a realistic interpolation in many cases.

3. Physical Properties

From the viewpoint taken earlier, the γ of a solute depends upon the differences in the general nature of the solution liquid environment and the standard state environment (pure liquid solute). Viewed in terms of individual molecules, this becomes a matter of the differences in the molecular interactions of a solute molecule with the molecules of the two environments as well as the interactions of the various solvent molecules with each other. These interactions include not only van der Waals, dipole–induced dipole, and dipole–dipole interactions, but, on occasion, interactions which are definitely chemical in nature (hydrogen bonds, Lewis acid–base bonds). Each of these may contribute substantially to the heat and the entropy of solution in some complicated way which must be expected to depend upon the detailed shapes, sizes, and force fields of the molecules. In practical applications demands for accuracy are actually very severe—it is not simply the heat, entropy, or free energy of solution that is required, or even the partial molal quantities, but the activity coefficients and ratios of activity coefficients that are desired to within a few per cent. It is consequently not surprising that basic molecular theories of solution have not yet been developed to a satisfactory quantita-

* B_{13} and $B_{23} > B_{12}$, $B_{13} - B_{23} \gg C_{13} - C_{23}$, $C_{12} = 0$.

tive point. In spite of this inherent difficulty there are a number of quite simple pictures of a solution which are extremely useful in a qualitative way and, if suitably normalized with direct experimental measurements, are accurate enough for use in practical separation problems.

The Schatchard–Hildebrand relations express the activity coefficient of a solute component of a "regular" solution in terms of the molar volume, volume fraction, and solubility parameter (V_1, ϕ_1 and δ_1) of the solute and the solubility parameter of the solvent (δ_2), i.e., for a binary

$$\log \gamma_1 = V_1(1-\phi_1)^2(\delta_1-\delta_2)^2/RT \tag{25a}$$

and

$$\log \gamma_2 = V_2(1-\phi_2)^2(\delta_1-\delta_2)^2/RT \tag{25b}$$

As is apparent, they are formally similar to the van Laar and Margules relations given earlier in that $\log \gamma_1$ is proportional to a squared concentration term; they differ in that assymmetry is defined by the molar volume ratio $\log (\gamma_{1(2)}{}^0/\gamma_{2(1)}{}^0) = V_1/V_2$, and the mixture parameter $(\delta_1 - \delta_2)^2$ is explicitly taken as a difference in property of the solute and solution environment (δ's).

In practice these relations are useful in several ways which differ in the degree to which they are considered as strictly theoretical. In the strictest use they can be considered to describe "regular" solutions in which the entropy of mixing is the same as in a perfect solution (no significant orientation or chemical effects). In many such cases, the energies of interaction of two unlike molecules are close to a geometric mean of the interactions of like molecules, and the solubility parameter (cohesive energy density) of each component can be reasonably evaluated as the square root of its energy of vaporization per unit volume or by other similar means. In practice, such an evaluation will usually give reasonable estimates for mixtures of simple nonpolar molecules. Its use in such cases provides not only a basis for making estimates, but also a basis for recognizing unreasonable experimental measurements. It should be noted, however, that γ is extremely sensitive to small changes in the δ's. The use of such an evaluation for mixtures containing polar molecules will not usually give a result which is accurate enough for practical purposes. On the other hand, the qualitative ideas that the larger the solute molecular volume and the cohesive energy density difference, the larger will be the activity coefficient, are of themselves useful.

In a less strict use, the solubility parameter may be evaluated directly from experimental activity coefficient data to obtain a more or less direct empirical measure of the internal cohesive energy density. In this case the relations provide reasonable interpolations; indeed, there is abundant evidence that volume fractions are on the average somewhat superior to the mole fractions usually used in practical work. In addition, however, demands on the theoretical base are not so great and somewhat better results or, alternatively, a wider range of applicability with reasonable results, can be expected. The possibility of using a solubility parameter so obtained from one system in a second one is retained, particularly if the two systems are closely related.

4. Molecular Structure

For strongly polar mixtures which do not follow a "regular" solution behavior there are still systematic variations which are very useful. One approach toward finding such regularities which remains quite close to direct experimental observations and which is simple and straightforward has been pursued by Pierotti et al.[6]

As has already been indicated, the limiting activity coefficient of a solute (1) in a solvent environment (2) represents the most useful single activity coefficient point in a solute–solvent system in that it usually represents the maximum effect and is a convenient base point for interpolations. It is also a simple one in that it is not a solution property but rather a property of solute and solvent. One might reasonably suppose that as the structure of a solute is changed within some structurally related family (solvent environment held constant), systematic changes in the limiting solute activity coefficient would occur. Alternatively, one might suppose that as the structures of solvents are changed within some structurally related family (solute held constant), systematic changes in the limiting solute activity coefficient would also occur. In addition, one might hope that various families of a given kind e.g., various methylene homologous series, might fall well enough into a single pattern to provide a framework of extrapolation and interpolation which could be characterized using but a few parameters. Pierotti et al, have shown a number of ways in which the above expectations are indeed borne out. They have, in effect, provided a framework which can be very useful, not only in assessing experimental data, but, if suitable data for related systems are available, in judging whether a separation is difficult in a practical case and whether direct data are indeed required.

A series of plots are shown in Figure 10 to illustrate not only the kinds of systematic behavior of homologous series in various polar–nonpolar combinations, but also the synthesis of what might be called the "Pierotti" model for polar mixtures. They include combinations of polar and nonpolar solute and/or solvent homologous series* taken in a sequence so as to illustrate increasingly complex cases.

Under (*a*), the γ^0's of normal-paraffins in paraffinic solvents show that with mixtures of nonpolar, relatively nonpolarizable, inert molecules deviations are significant but not large and are not very sensitive to solute–solvent molecular size differences. They are quite well described by the Brønstedt–Koefed[7] relation**:

$$\log \gamma_1{}^0 = D\,(n_1 - n_2)^2 \qquad (26)$$

where $D = -0.0005$ at 25°C. and the n's are the numbers of carbon atoms in solute and solvent as indicated.

Under (*b*), the γ^0's of normal-paraffins in ethanol show that with such a polarity difference the deviations are much larger than in (*a*) and are much more sensitive to the size of the solute molecule. Here, they are quite well described, after account is taken of a small Brønstedt–Koefed size effect, by a linear relation between $\log\gamma_1{}^0$ and n_1,

$$\log \gamma_1{}^1 = K + B\,n_1 + D(n_1 - n_2)^2 \qquad (27)$$

and D has the same value as in (*a*).

Under (*c*), the γ^0's of paraffins in a series of methyl ketones as polar solvents show that again deviations are generally fairly large and sensitive to molecular weight, but, further, that both the levels and solute size sensitivity decrease as the number of methylene groups in the solvent molecule becomes larger. Here, they are quite well described by the relation

$$\log \gamma_1{}^0 = \left[K + \frac{F}{n_2{}'}\right] + \left[\frac{B}{n_2}\right] n_1 + D\,(n_1 - n_2)^2 \qquad (28)$$

where $n_2{}'$ is the number of carbon groups in the variable chain including the keto-group; the similarity of the first two bracketed terms to the preceeding case is immediately evident and D takes the same value as before. Not only methyl ketones but other ketones as solvents are quite well described by

$$\log \gamma_1{}^0 = \left[F\left(\frac{1}{n_2{}'} + \frac{1}{n_2{}''}\right)\right] + \left[\frac{B}{n_2}\right] n_1 + D\,(n_1 - n_2)^2 \qquad (29)$$

* Strictly these cases represent straight-chain materials; however, solution effects with moderately branched materials are substantially the same as for straight-chain so long as the branches are several carbon atoms removed along a chain from a polar group.

** Paraffin systems of components of dissimilar size are, of course, not symmetrical, but this relation is adequate for present purposes.

(a). n-Paraffins in n-paraffins

$\log \gamma_1{}^{\circ} = D(n_1 - n_2)^2$

$\text{Log } \gamma^{\circ} = -0.0005\,(n_1 - n_2)^2$

$\gamma_1{}^{\circ}$ (25 °C)

n_1

(b). n-Paraffins in ethanol

$\log \gamma_1{}^{\circ} = K + Bn_1 + D(n_1 - n_2)^2$

$\text{Log } \gamma_1{}^{\circ} = 0.570 + 0.073\,n_1 - 0.0005\,(n_1 - n_2)^2$

$\gamma_1{}^{\circ}$ (50 °C)

n_1

(c). n-Paraffins in methyl ketones

$$\log \gamma_1{}^{\circ} = K + \left[\frac{F}{n_2}\right] + \left[\frac{B}{n_2}\right]n_1 + D(n_1 - n_2)^2$$

$\text{Log } \gamma_1{}^{\circ} = \left[0.201 + \frac{0.402}{n_2'}\right] + \left[\frac{0.182}{n_2}\right] n_1 - 0.0005\,(n_1 - n_2)^2$

$\gamma_1{}^{\circ}$ (25 °C)

n_1

(d). Acetone in n-paraffins

$\log \gamma_1{}^{\circ} = K + D(n_1 - n_2)^2$

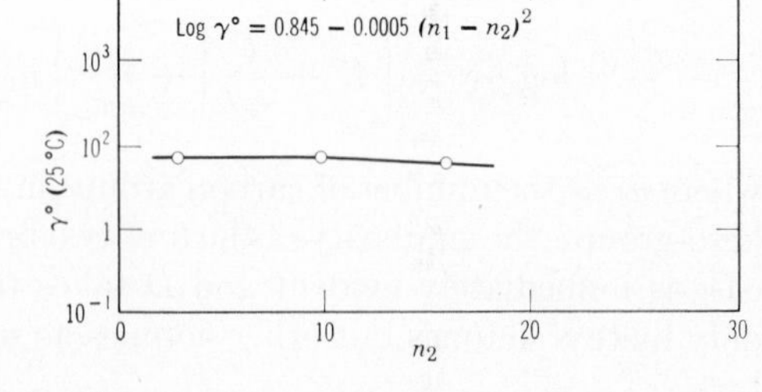

where the primed n_2's are the carbon numbers of the two branches including the keto-carbon in both cases.

Under (d), the γ^0's of acetone in a series of paraffins show that γ^0 levels are still substantial but that as under (a) they are relatively insensitive to molecular weight. The deviations are described by the relation

$$\log \gamma_1{}^0 = K + D\,(n_1 - n_2)^2 \tag{30}$$

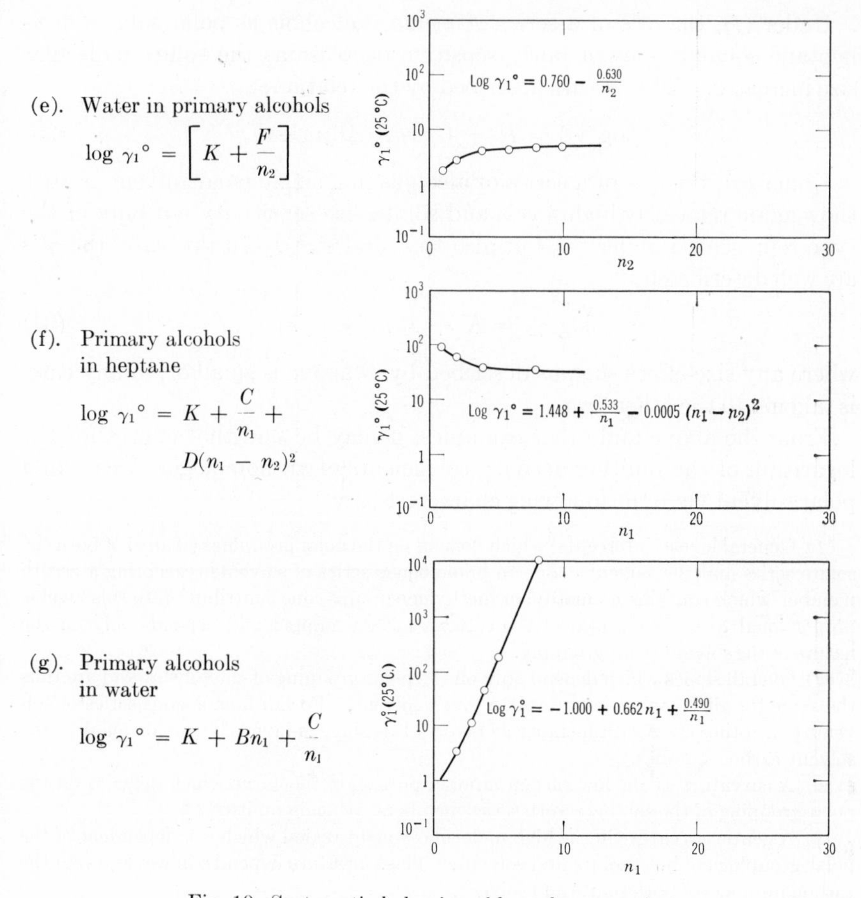

Fig. 10. Systematic behavior of homologous series.

where again D takes the same value as before. The series of ketones as solutes in n-paraffins are well described by the relation

$$\log \gamma_1^0 = K + C\left(\frac{1}{n_1'} + \frac{1}{n_2''}\right) + D\,(n_1 - n_2)^2 \tag{31}$$

where the primed n_2's are counted as under (c) above.

Under (e), the γ_1^0s of water as a polar solute in a series of alcohols as polar solvents show a relation similar to that under (c) with the exception that the solute is unchanging. The γ_1^0s are quite well described by the relation

$$\log \gamma_1^0 = K + F/n_2 \tag{32}$$

Under (*f*), the γ^0's of a series of primary alcohols as polar solutes in *n*-heptane solvent, show a fairly sensitive decrease as the solute molecular size increases. The γ^0's are described by the relation:

$$\log \gamma_1^0 = K + C/n_1 + D(n_1 - n_2)^2 \tag{33}$$

Under (*g*), the γ^0's of a series of alcohols in a single polar solvent, water, show again relatively high levels and solute size sensitivity not only of the type represented under (*f*), but also that under (*b*). In this case, the γ^0's are well described by

$$\log \gamma_1 = K + B\, n_1 + C/n_1 \tag{34}$$

where any size-effect such as described by D above is small or, in any case, is taken into the other terms.

From the above and other examples, it may be said that curves for the logarithm of the limiting activity coefficients of an homologous series in a polar solvent have the following characteristics:

(*1*) General levels (intercepts) which depend on the polar groupings (if any) of both the solute series and the solvent. For an homologous series of solvents (excepting a zeroth member which contains no methyl or methylene groups) one contribution to this level is proportional to the reciprocal of the solvent carbon number and depends only on the nature of the solvent polar grouping.

(*2*) Overall slopes which depend only on the polar grouping of the solvent and are thus the same for all homologous series in a given solvent. For an homologous series of solvents (excepting the zeroth member as before) this slope is inversely proportional to the solvent carbon number.

(*3*) A curvature at the low carbon number portion of the curve which depends on the polar grouping of the solute (zeroth series members are again omitted).*

(*4*) A gentle curvature in the high molecular weight region which is independent of the polar groupings of both solute and solvent. This curvature depends, however, upon the carbon numbers of both solute and solvent.

These observations can be expressed for the special case of homologous series of both solute and solvent [$H(CH_2)_{n_1}X_1$ and $H(CH_2)_{n_2}X_2$ where X is some polar or combination of polar groups] by the following analytical expression:

$$\log \gamma_{1,2}^0 = [A_{12} + F_2/n_2] + [(B_2/n_2)n_1] + [C_1/n_1] + [D_0(n_1 - n_2)^2] \tag{35}$$

in which the successive bracketed terms refer to the respective four statements above. The subscripts on the coefficients indicate the dependencies on the solute or solvent polar groupings. It should be understood that (35) describes other special cases, e.g., water as a solvent only when the

* The dependence of this effect purely on the nature of the solute series may not be strictly adhered to if the solvent nature varies widely, e.g., at 25°C. for primary acohols in heptane $C = 0.533$ whereas for primary alcohols in water $C = 0.558$.

"F" and "D" terms are dropped (no solvent carbon number), paraffins as solutes only when the "C" term is dropped (no solute polar grouping), and paraffins as solvents only when the "F" and "B" terms are dropped (no solvent polar grouping).

Although such a phenomenological approach as the above sacrifices some of the advantages (and complications) of a detailed molecular model, it maintains simplicity and a very close alliance with the direct γ^0 data of interest. The description to within 10–20% in γ^0 of some 350 systems covering carbon number ranges of up to 25 carbon atoms, γ^0 ranges of < 1 to 10^7, and some 40 separate homologous series presented in the original paper attest to its general soundness. In addition, however, the dependencies indicated are intuitively quite straightforward and reasonable. It is, for instance, reasonable to suppose that in a polar solvent environment the attractive interactions between X_2 groups of the solvent are relatively large, that the intrusion of a relatively inert methylene group is opposed with about the same "force" whatever the substituents attached to it, and that the "polar cohesive energy density," which gives rise to this "force," in general, is smaller the lower the overall concentration of the polar groups in the environment; that is, it is reasonable that a contribution to the partial molal excess free energy $(B_2/n_2)n_1$ occurs. A sharp identification of the terms of (35) on a molecular basis is no doubt not possible, but the rough separation of effects indicated below is informative:

Term	Contributing group interactions[a]
A_{12}	$(X_2 - X_2)_S$, $(X_1 - X_2)_S$, $(X_1 - X_1)_{SS}$
$(B_2/n_2)n_1$	$(X_1 - X_2)_S$, $(X_2 - R_1)_S$
C_1/n_1	$(X_1 - X_1)_{SS}$, $(R_1 - X_1)_{SS}$
$D_0(n_1 - {}_2n)^2$	$(R_2 - R_2)_S$, $(R_1 - R_2)_S$, $(R_1 - R_1)_{SS}$
F_2/n_2	$(X_2 - X_2)_S$, $(R_2 - X_2)_S$, $(X_1 - X_2)_S$

[a] S = solution. SS = solute standard state.

It will be immediately evident that the above description of the behavior of polar mixtures is a very efficient means of extending γ^0 data. Thus, if a solute series (X) has been previously characterized in some solvent, C_1 is known and, if a solvent series Y has been previously characterized, B_2 and F_2 are known. In this case, a measurement of γ^0 for a single member of the series X in a single member of the series Y provides A_{12} and a first estimate of the γ^0's of the entire series of solutes in the series of solvents. In practice, the accuracy of such estimates depends not only on the averaging processes that must be implicitly in the pattern itself, but also on the accuracy of any given experimental γ^0 which may be used. Consequently, some care in applying such a pattern is required.

When the Pierotti coefficients have been evaluated in detail for series corresponding to both extremes of a binary of interest, that is, when in effect interpolations between structurally similar systems have already been made, direct estimates of behavior at finite concentrations in simple systems can be made with the van Laar or Margules relations as discussed above. In more complicated systems other data may have to be brought to bear. Thus in the water–methanol system at constant pressure, the γ^0's for the respective components give the quite adequate interpolations shown in Figure 11. In this case both components are strongly associated

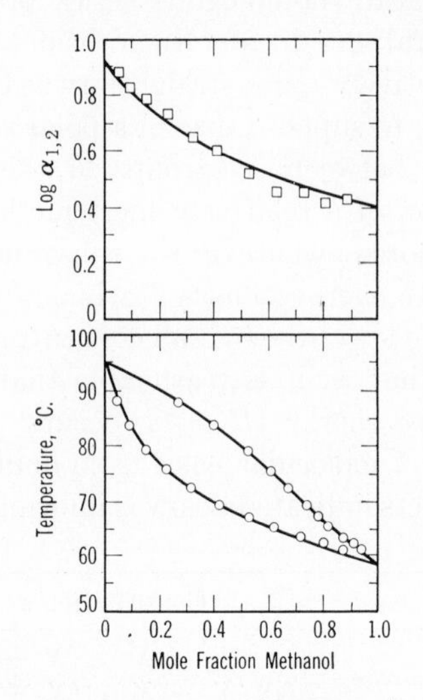

Fig. 11. Methanol (1)–water (2) system, $p = 760$ mm. (——) Estimated curve (Margules), (○) experimental data. (Othmer and Bevenati, *Ind. Eng. Chem.*, **32**, 299 (1945).)

but at each temperature within the boiling points of the components a two-parameter Margules describes the system well enough to give an interpolation which appears to be essentially as accurate as direct measurements. Likewise, in the acetone–methanol system at constant temperature one γ^0 from the Pierotti pattern plus an azeotropic composition gives an adequate interpolation shown in Figure 12. In this case, one of the components is associated and there is no doubt considerable hydrogen bonding between the components, but a two-parameter Margules describes the system adequately. On the other hand, for the isopropyl alcohol–water system shown in Figure 13, a two-parameter Margules based on the two γ^0's gives an unreasonable sharp dip in the log (γ_1/γ_2) vs. x curve. In this case the interpolation is a three-parameter Margules one based on the two γ^0's and the azeotropic composition and boiling point.

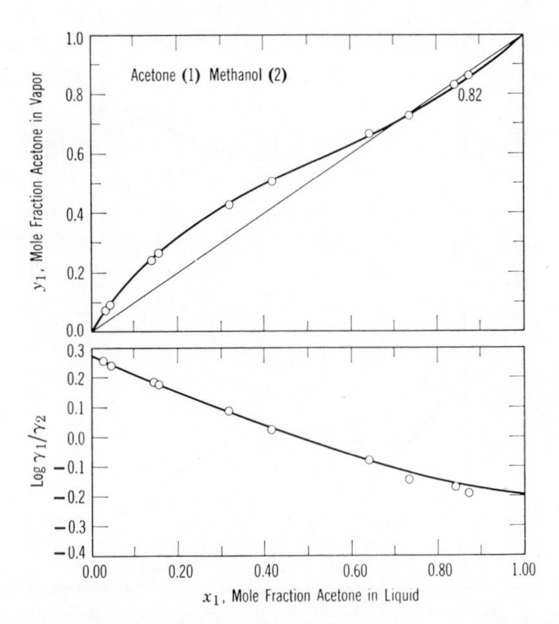

Fig. 12. Acetone (1)–methanol (2) system, $t = 55.7°C$. (——) Estimated curve, (○) experimental data. (E. L. Derr, private communication).

Even when the Pierotti coefficients are not available for a case at hand, the patterns are frequently very useful in making orientive estimates. If, for instance, it is desired to approximate the limiting activity coefficient of *n*-hexanol (HA) in ethylene glycol (EG) from a known value for butanol (BA), the following arguments might be used: The γ^0's of primary alcohols in EG are approximated by the relation,

$$\log \gamma_{A(EG)}^0 = K_{A,EG} + B_{EG}n_A + C_A/n_A + D_0(n_A - n_{EG})^2 \qquad (36)$$

so that

$$\log (\gamma_{HA(EG)}^0/\gamma_{BA(EG)}^0) = B_{EG}(6-4) + C_A(1/6 - 1/4) + D_0[(6-8)^2 - (4-2)^2] \qquad (37)$$

The D effect is negligible for such small differences in carbon numbers. The "C" effect is usually not very large except at the beginning of a series and is at least approximated by means of the C derived from γ^0's of alcohols in water, a solvent of the same general nature as EG, i.e., at 25°C.: $C_1 = 0.56$ and $0.56\,(1/6 - 1/4) = -0.05$. The B_{EG} may be evaluated from the solubilities of two hydrocarbon homologs in EG which supply γ^0's for the expression

$$\log \gamma_{HC(EG)}^0 = K_{HC(EG)} + B_{EG}n_{HC} + D(n_{HC} - n_{EG})^2 \qquad (38)$$

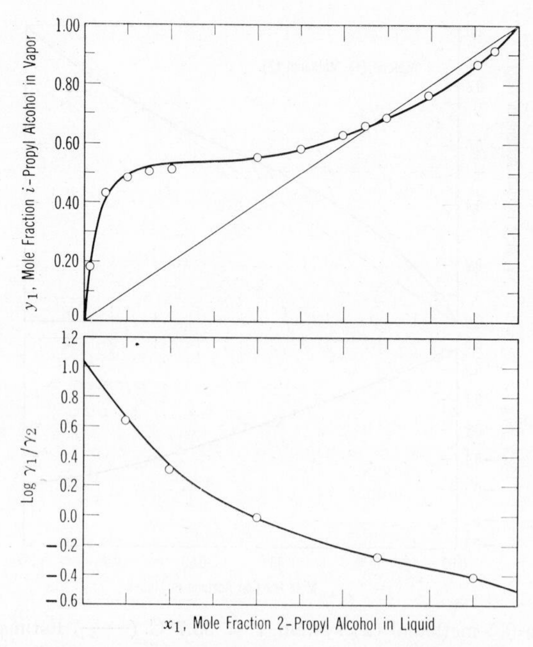

Fig. 13. Isopropyl alcohol (1)–water (2) system. (——) Estimated curve, (O) experimental data. (Pierotti, Deal, and Derr, American Documentation Institute, 1958.)

On this basis, $B_{EG} = 0.225$ at 25°C, (extrapolated from higher temperatures). Thus,

$$\log (\gamma_{HA(EG)}^0/\gamma_{BA(EG)}^0) \cong 0.55 - 0.05 \cong 0.5$$

or

$$(\gamma_{HA(EG)}^0/\gamma_{BA(EG)}^0) \cong 3.1 \tag{39}$$

Neglecting the "C" effect would have given a value only about 10% higher.

It is of interest that the above patterns can be made somewhat simpler by use of an artifice which, in effect, avoids the complication that a change in the nature of the standard state environment occurs from solute to solute in a series.[8] Thus, if a standard solvent environment, for instance n-heptane, is adopted as a reference state,

$$\log K_1 = \log \gamma_{1(S)} - \log \gamma_{1(H)} = (K_{1,S} - K_{1,H}) + (B_S - B_H)\, n_1 \tag{40}$$

in which the terms involving C_1 and D_0 coefficients have largely cancelled out. Thus, plots of $\log K_1$ vs. n_1 for all homologous series in a given polar solvent can be expected to be not only linear but parallel. Likewise, this can be expected to hold true for any fixed environment, whether it be a pure solvent or not.

The usefulness of such an overall framework in considering equilibria and separations broadly will also be evident. Thus, for instance, logarithmic plots of limiting volatilities of various series from a fixed solvent such as that shown in Figure 14 tend to be parallel (solvent characteristic "B" and approximately constant $\partial \log p_1/\partial n_1$) and give an immediate idea not only of the magnitudes of the volatilities from the solvent, but also an idea of which components are separable in an extractive distillation or in a portion of a column in which the environment is essentially that of the one "solvent" component. It may be noted that the "B" of water in the example shown is unusually large and is, in fact, greater than $\partial \log p_1/\partial n_1$. The result is unusual in that volatilities from water actually increase with solute carbon number.

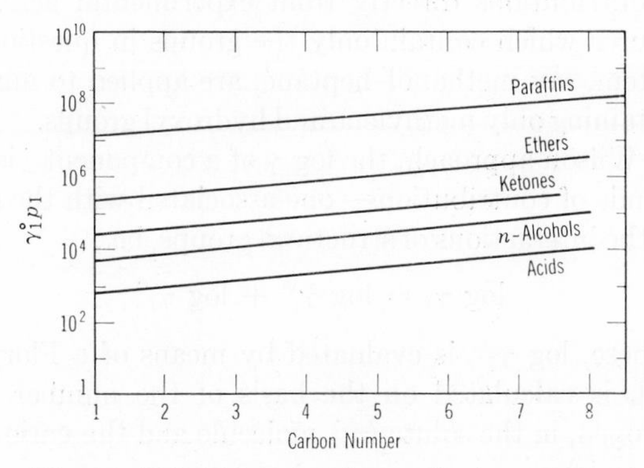

Fig. 14. Volatilities of various series from water.

It is also noteworthy that the Pierotti patterns do not depend critically on the detailed nature of the predominating interaction. The pattern applies quite well where the solute or solvent is a simple polar molecule, e.g., a ketone, where one or both are strongly associated, e.g., alcohols and water, or where a strong chemical interaction occurs, e.g., acetals for which γ^0's are <1. Likewise, the general approach applies to polar solvents in which the polar part of the molecule is a complex one or to such solute series as the alkyl benzenes or the alkyl cyclohexanes, in which the phenyl, cyclohexyl, etc., rings are considered units with special interaction properties. In addition series such as those starting with benzene and naphthalene, or cyclohexane and decalin can be quite successfully handled in the same fashion as the homologous series.

Even though the idea of separating solution effects into contributing structural group effects is an old one[9] and has many practical uses, the possibilities have not yet been fully explored. Two approaches related to the above will be mentioned here. One of these[10,11] treats the energy of interaction (rather than the free energy or log γ^0) in terms of an average energy of interaction of each contact of two groupings (paraffinic CH_2, aromatic CH, olefinic =CH—, etc.) and an interaction probability (cross section) derived from group volumes. Heats of mixing of hydrocarbons have been treated successfully and the approach may be useful also with polar mixtures. Since this approach deals with heats of solution rather than activity coefficients it will not be dealt with further.

A second approach[12] avoids so rigid a model as the above and deals directly with free energies, i.e., activity coefficients. In essence, it considers the log γ of a solute molecule in a molecular mixture as a sum of contributions from its groups which depend, except for a size correction, only upon the number and kinds of groups in the environment. It evaluates these contributions directly from experimental activity coefficient data for mixtures which contain only the groups in question. Thus data from one system, say methanol–heptane, are applied to mixtures of other molecules containing only methylene and hydroxyl groups.

In this, the Wilson approach, the log γ of a component j is treated as the sum of two kinds of contributions—one associated with the molecular sizes and one with the interactions of structural groups, i.e.,

$$\log \gamma_j = \log \gamma_j^{S} + \log \gamma_j^{G} \tag{41}$$

The first of these, log γ_j^{S}, is evaluated by means of a Flory–Huggins expression which is calculated on the basis of the number of atoms, not counting hydrogen, in the solute (n_j) molecule and the various components of the solution (n_i's):

$$\log \gamma_j^{S} \equiv \log (n_j/\textstyle\sum_i x_i n_i) + 0.434(1 - n_j/\textstyle\sum_i x_i n_i) \tag{42}$$

As will be seen, it is only by means of this relation that two solution environments, which are different molecular mixtures but are the same with regard to the concentrations of groups, e.g., an equimolal methanol–hexane mixture and pure heptylalcohol, are distinguished from each other.

The second contribution, log γ_j^{G}, is taken as dependent upon the kinds of groups in the solute molecule, the number of each kind of group (ν), and the environments in the solution and the molecular standard state. If the solution is denoted by S and the molecular standard state by SS,

$$\begin{aligned} \log \gamma_j^{G} &= \nu_1(\log \Gamma_1)_S - \nu_1(\log \Gamma_1)_{SS} \\ &\quad + \nu_2(\log \Gamma_2)_S - \nu_2(\log \Gamma_1)_{SS} \\ &\quad + \cdots \\ &= \textstyle\sum_k \nu_k \left[(\log \Gamma_k)_S - (\log \Gamma_k)_{SS}\right] \end{aligned} \tag{43}$$

where the log Γ_k's characterize the environments with respect to the various solute groups (k) in much the same way as the B's of the Pierotti approach characterize the solvent for methylene groups.

Finally, the log Γ_k's are taken to be dependent on the concentrations and kinds of the various groups which make up the mixture but independent of the way in which they are tied together chemically. Thus, once suitable log Γ_k vs. group fraction relations have been established for a set of structural groups, log γ_j's may be calculated from (41), (42), and (43) for any molecular mixture of interest which contains only groups of the set.

In practice the inverse procedure is used with a set of experimental data to establish a set of values of

$$(\log \Gamma_k)_S - (\log \Gamma_k)_{SS}$$

which correspond to experimental log γ–x data points for use in estimating γ's in other systems containing the same groups. Thus, for instance, γ-data for methanol and hexane in their various mixtures are converted to

$$(\log \Gamma_{-CH_2})_S - (\log \Gamma_{-CH_2})_{C_6H_{14}}$$

and

$$(\log \Gamma_{-OH})_S - (\log \Gamma_{-OH})_{CH_3OH}$$

points corresponding to the γ-data. At this point it is convenient to consider Γ_{-CH_2} and Γ_{-OH} as "group activity coefficients" for which the reference states are pure methylene (methylene–methyl) and hydroxyl groups, respectively, and to construct from the above differences log Γ_{-CH_2} and log Γ_{-OH} vs. group concentration (X_{CH_2} and X_{OH}) curves as illustrated in Figure 15.

The construction of these curves requires some extrapolation and the use of some judgement in making the extrapolation; however, much the same rules of extrapolation can be used as are used in extrapolating log γ vs. x curves. In this connection, it can be shown that if a base set of

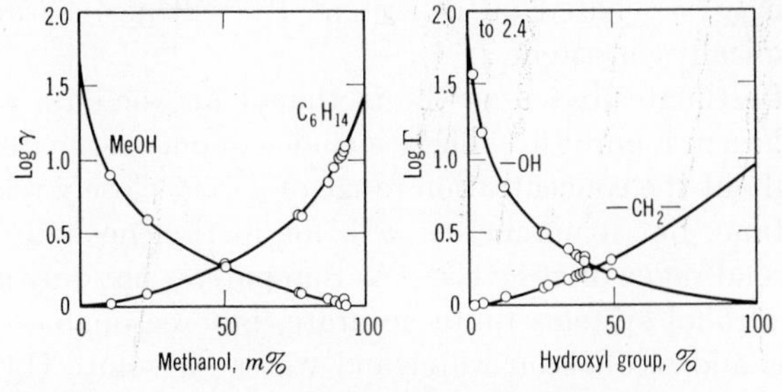

Fig. 15. Molecular and group activity coefficients after Wilson and Deal. Methanol (1)–n-hexane (2), t = 45°C. (Ferguson, Freed, and Morris, *J. Phys. Chem.*, **37**, 87 (1933).)

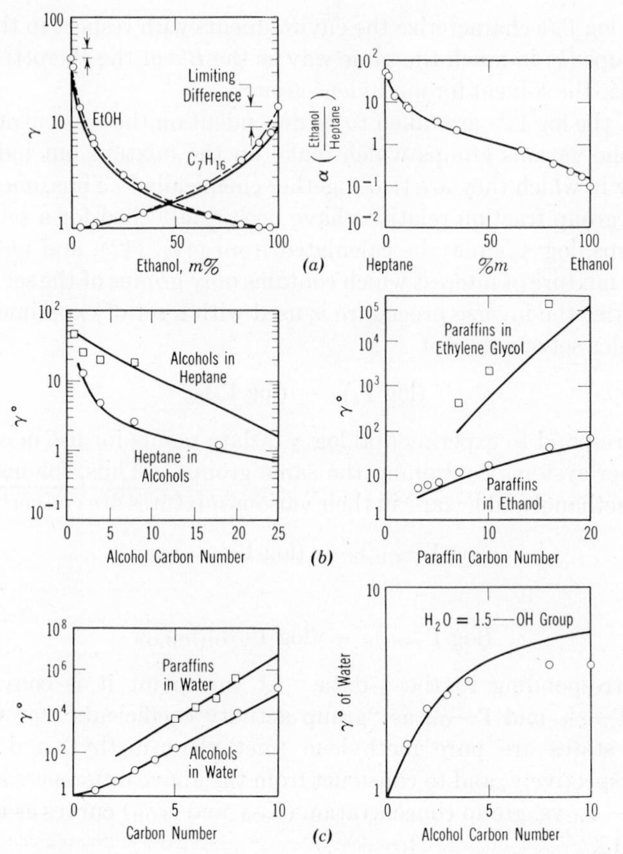

Fig. 16. Estimates based on methanol–hexane system. (——) Estimated curves, (O) experimental data.

γ-data are thermodynamically consistent, the Γ-curves which derive from them follow the same rules associated with thermodynamic consistency. Correspondingly, γ's based on consistent Γ's will also be automatically thermodynamically consistent.

A series of estimates based on the methanol–hexane data are compared with actual data in Figure 16. These include not only estimates for changes in γ's throughout the concentration range of a very closely related system, ethanol–heptane, but a number of γ^0's for methylene–hydroxyl systems covering a broad ragne of γ^0 levels. As is apparent, not only are estimates for paraffin–alcohol systems quite accurate, but reasonable estimates for hydrocarbons and alcohols in water and water (as solute $H_2O \equiv 1.5$ OH groups) in alcohols are obtained. On the other hand, estimates for ethylene–glycol systems are only order of magnitude.

TABLE II
Estimates of Limiting Activity Coefficients for Complicated Molecules[a]

Solute	Solvent	"Groups"	Log γ^0 of "groups" in water	Log γ^0 of solute in wate Est'd.	Exp.
Ethyl acetoacetate	Water	Acetone	0.86	1.79	1.75
		Ethyl formate	1.72		
Butyl Cellosolve	Water	Ethyl alcohol	0.65	1.85	
		Diethyl ether	2.15		1.74
Paraldehyde	Water	Dimethyl ether	1.18	2.17	2.04
Ethyl adipate	Water	Ethyl proprionate	2.46	3.94	3.42
Glycol dimethyl ether	Methanol	Dimethyl ether	0.34	0.37	0.22

[a] Wilson and Deal, *Ind. Eng. Chem., Fundamentals*, **1**, 20 (1962).

In addition to the above very simple groups, the Wilson approach may be applied to more complex groups and to combinations of solute groups if suitable base data are available. Thus, for instance, ethylacetoacetate may be considered as composed of acetone and ethylformate and direct data for acetone and ethylformate in water as solvent may be applied in estimating the γ^0 of ethylacetoacetate from water. A series of such examples are shown in Table II.

It is apparent that the Wilson approach provides a basis for some what more widespread estimates from a given experimental base than do the Pierotti patterns. For just this reason, it may give somewhat less precise estimates. As shown in Figure 16 (*b*), for example, the carbon number dependency of the γ^0's of polar solute in nonpolar solvent is somewhat different from the observed for alcohols in paraffins. The approach, however does not tie itself very strictly to a rigid model and uses direct experimental data for systems very close in nature to those being estimated as a base. The closer the base system is in structure to the one of interest, the more accurate can estimates be expected to be. The approach may be particularly useful in estimating effects in systems for which direct measurements are difficult or impossible to make, e.g., in cases in which the components are chemically unstable.

V. DETERMINATION OF EQUILIBRIA

As already indicated, the exact demands for experimental measurements vary quite widely in accord with the use to which the measurements are to be put and the nature of the system of interest. In any case, a number of interdependent choices are available and affect the experimental problem, e.g.,

(*1*) Whether direct measurements are in fact necessary;

(*2*) Whether simply a single α will suffice or complete phase relations are required for the case in question

(*3*) Whether measurements will be made under constant temperature or constant pressure conditions;

(*4*) Whether the direct measurements are to be interpreted in terms of γ's;

(*5*) Whether measurements will be made with a liquid and vapor directly or with two suitable liquid phases or with liquid and solid phases;

(*6*) At what concentration levels will the measurements be made;

(*7*) By what detailed techniques will the measurements be made.

It will have been apparent from the discussions above that first estimates based on the vapor pressures of pure components are frequently not only inadequate but misleading. On the other hand, vapor pressures in conjunction with some estimate of γ^0-values of structurally related systems may suffice to show that a separation is not at all difficult. In such a case, even a substantial error in the estimate may be of little consequence and the estimate itself may be enough for the purpose in mind. More commonly in practice such estimates will show which components of a mixture to be separated represent the key ones for which more accurate experimental estimates are required to evaluate or design the distillation in question. Similarly, some preliminary estimates will usually already provide an idea of just what measurements are most useful and how precise they need to be.

It will also have been apparent from the foregoing that measurements at constant temperature can, in general, be more easily put into various frameworks, compared with other data, and evaluated than can measurements at constant pressure. Although in some cases it may be experimentally more convenient to measure liquid–vapor equilibria at constant pressure, particularly since the pressure range from top to bottom of a distillation column is not great, such conveniences seldom outweigh the advantages of making measurements at constant temperature.

The question regarding treatment of experimental data is closely allied in that it is normally much simpler and sound to analyze, interpolate, and extrapolate on the basis of γ's and p_i's with a set of constant temperature measurements than with constant pressure measurements. In careful work it is becoming more and more the practice to determine γ's at each of several temperatures so as to cover the range of conditions of interest and to interpolate or extrapolate these measurements so as to cover the specific distillation conditions expected throughout the distillation column. Indeed, some such complete pattern of data is required if full advantage is to be taken of modern computational possibilities. It will, of course, be apparent that such an approach provides a flexibility and a coverage of conditions not normally obtained with measurements at constant pressure.

In many cases, particularly if data are to be treated in terms of γ's, measurements of liquid–liquid or solid–liquid equilibria may provide γ's which may be obtained more easily than direct liquid–vapor measurements. As a matter of fact, the occurrence of two liquid phases in a system usually complicates the experimental problem of determining liquid–vapor equilibrium. Liquid–liquid or solid–liquid measurements may either replace liquid–vapor measurements or augment them and in the latter case provide a check on liquid–vapor measurements which, by virture of the large difference in the mechanics of the measurements, may be considered as independent checks.

The choice of concentrations at which to make measurements also depends upon the specific case at hand. Usually, if an entire system is to be described, well spaced experimental points throughout the concentration range are called for whether the system be a simple binary or one of many components; however, as has been indicated, an emphasis on the maximum effects in the system, i.e., at as low concentration levels as is consistent with the analytical techniques available, is usually worthwhile.

Insofar as specific techniques are concerned, the most direct and widely used ones involve isolating a mixture of materials at a fixed temperature or pressure, establishing equilibrium between the phases which occur under the chosen condition of temperature or pressure, obtaining a sample of the respective phases, and finally determining the compositions of these samples. Thus, the technique is essentially that of locating the ends of tie lines between t–x and t–y curves (constant pressure) or between p–x and p–y curves (constant temperature). In some cases, however, it is convenient to vary temperature or pressure on an homogeneous mixture of known composition and to observe the temperature or pressure at which a second phase occurs, or, alternatively, to vary the composition of a system by the addition of new material at constant temperature or pressure and to observe the composition at which a new phase appears. The latter techniques in principle establish only phase boundaries; but they do supply tie lines between the phase boundaries in two-phase binary mixtures. Whatever the detailed technique, the experimental problems are concerned with assuring that the system is in fact sufficiently close to equilibrium and with assuring that concentrations (samples), temperatures, and pressures are representative.

1. Distillation Techniques

The most commonly used distillation techniques involve continuous, single theoretical plate distillation.* Occasionally the distillation involves

* The alternative of performing a single theoretical plate batch distillation and following the compositions of liquid and vapor is, of course, in principle possible. It has not, however, been very much used because of the difficulty of ensuring a close approach to equilibrium (one theoretical plate) and of analyzing the phases during the distillation.

feeding a mixture of fixed composition at a constant rate to an appropriate still, supplying heat at a constant rate, and continuously withdrawing the resulting liquid and vapor phases. This technique requires not only close control of a number of rates, but usually requires rather large amounts of materials. It will not be dealt with here. More frequently the amounts of material required are minimized and the still operation is somewhat simplified by the use of a recirculating still. In this case, both liquid and vapor phases are recirculated at whatever rate they happen to be generated until a steady state is reached. Samples are then withdrawn for analysis.

The technique may be applied to systems of widely varying behavior, but as a rule is most easily applied to systems which form a single liquid phase not only at the temperature of interest but at somewhat lower temperatures (because of the difficulties of handling a two-phase recycle stream). It may be applied over wide ranges of pressure and temperature, but is ordinarily not used at pressures more than a few atmospheres because of the difficulty in fabricating apparatus to withstand high pressure. It cannot be conveniently applied at pressures lower than about 50 mm. of Hg. Charges to such stills may be fairly moderate in size (50–500 ml.). The time taken to achieve a steady state is normally moderate (*ca.* $^1/_2$ hr. with relatively small condensed vapor hold-up).

A detailed description of the many designs of equilibrium stills which have been used is beyond the scope of the present chapter, but several comments on stills and their use may be helpful. A well-designed still, such as that shown in Figure 17 consists of

(*1*) A boiler for generating vapor at a constant rate (usually also for holding the major portion of the charge);

(*2*) A space for disengaging liquid and vapor;

(*3*) Some means of leading off and condensing the vapor stream which usually has sufficient hold-up to supply a sample for analysis;

(*4*) A means of returning the condensed vapor to the reboiler in a steady flow;

(*5*) A means of measuring the equilibrium temperature;

(*6*) A means of withdrawing a liquid and condensed vapor sample for analysis.

The operation of the still consists of

(*1*) Setting the pressure on the charged still at some constant level by means of an inert gas pressure at the condenser;

(*2*) Boiling the charge at some essentially constant rate until the various hold-ups remain constant, the condensed vapor has been recycled a number of times, and both compositions and temperatures have arrived at a steady state;

(*3*) Withdrawing samples of liquid and condensed vapor with a minimum disruption of the system;

(*4*) Analyzing the samples.

Ordinarily, this technique is most convenient for a series of measurements at constant pressure but it may be used for essentially constant tempera-

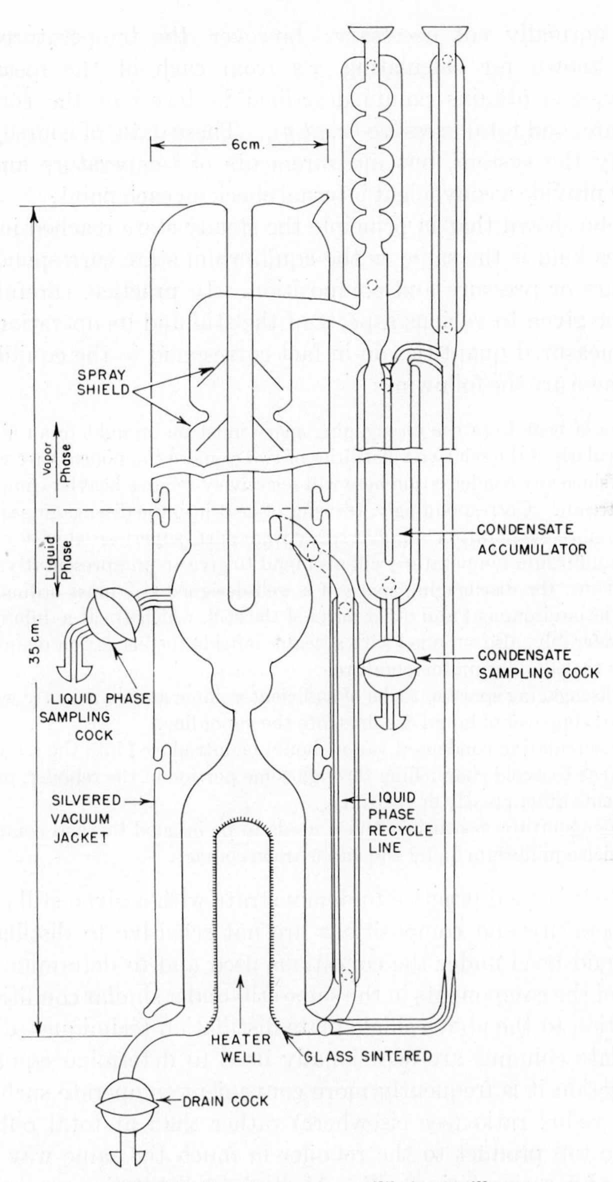

Fig. 17. Liquid–vapor equilibrium still.

ture measurement by adjusting the pressure for each experimental point until the steady temperature is essentially some predetermined value. In as much as α's, y–x curves or γ's are not extremely temperature sensitive, extreme precision of the temperature levels in a series of measurements is normally not necessary; however, the temperatures must be precisely known for calculating γ's from each of the measurements. Ordinarily, one obtains points described in terms of the compositions, temperature, and total pressure (x,y,t,p). These data, of course, in general overspecify the system, but measurements of temperature and pressure ordinarily provide a convenient internal check on each point.

It may be shown that in principle the steady state reached in a distillation of this kind is the same as the equilibrium state corresponding to the temperature or pressure and composition. In practice, careful attention needs to be given to various aspects of the still and its operation to ensure that the measured quantities do in fact correspond to the equilibrium one. Some of these are the following:

(*1*) Losses of heat from the disengaging space must be brought to an absolute minimum, particularly if the relative volatilities of two or more components are very different from unity, since any condensation here will selectively remove heavier components from the vapor stream. Correspondingly, transfer of heat into the disengaging space must be a minimum, since evaporation of liquid spray from parts superheated with respect to the measured equilibrium temperature will also tend to give an unrepresentative vapor composition. Thus, the disengaging space of a well-designed still must ordinarily be insulated from the environment and other parts of the still, which are at a different temperature, and preferably, also supplied with a heater outside the insulation maintained at approximately the equilibrium temperature.

(*2*) The disengaging space must be of sufficient volume and sufficiently well baffled to avoid the carrying over of liquid droplets into the vapor line.

(*3*) The recirculating condensed vapor should be introduced into the reboiler liquid in some way so as to avoid channelling through some portion of the reboiler, particularly if the components differ greatly in volatility.

(*4*) The temperature measuring device needs to be in good thermal contact with the region in which equilibrium liquid and vapor are in contact.

As a rule it is good practice to demonstrate with a given still and system that temperature and compositions are not sensitive to distillation rates and/or liquid level under the conditions used and to determine the vapor pressures of the components in the same still under similar conditions.

In addition to the above single plate distillation techniques, distillations in multiplate columns are occasionally used to determine equilibria. In this connection it is frequently more convenient to operate such a column at a fixed reflux ratio (see elsewhere) rather than at total reflux and to recycle the top product to the reboiler in much the same way as in the operation of a recirculating still. Multiplate distillation methods are for the most part useful only when the relative volatilities in the system of interest are substantially constant. They have the inherent difficulty that the number of theoretical plates in a given column may vary significantly from system to system. They are consequently not very much used in determining equilibria. For the special case of determining a minimum boiling azeotropic composition, however, a multiplate distillation is quite convenient. In this case the distillation is ordinarily a batch distillation at high reflux ratio. The top product comes quite rapidly to the azeotropic composition and temperature which corresponds to the pressure on the system and is not sensitive to the exact number of theoretical plates or the reflux ratio. There is some hazard of confusing a difficult separation and an azeotrope; however, approaching the azeotropic composition from more than one direction will normally eliminate the possible error of misidentifying a difficult separation as an azeotrope.

2. Equilibrium Technique

The equilibrium method involves equilibrating liquid and vapor phases in a thermostated vessel and withdrawing samples of the phases for analysis when equilibrium has been established. It has not, perhaps, been so widely used for ordinary pressures and temperatures as the recirculating still technique because of the difficulty of obtaining a vapor sample of sufficient volume for analysis, but it is commonly used for high pressure measurements. With the advent of analytical methods which require only very small samples (e.g., mass spectrometric and gas–liquid chromatographic analysis), however, its use is likely to become more widespread.

The technique is naturally adapted to constant temperature measurements and the apparatus may be extremely simple in some cases. It may be applied to systems of widely varying behavior and, insofar as vapor sampling is concerned, can be used with no great difficulty in systems in which a second liquid or solid phase occurs. It may be applied over wide temperature and pressure ranges, but must be used with care for measurement of pressures at low pressure levels because of the difficulties of completely degassing the system. Charges may be small in size and the time for a single determination is moderate.

If only measurements of the vapor and liquid compositions are required at a temperature not far from room temperature and at moderate pressures, an extremely simple equilibrium vessel may be used. In this case a bottle closed with a serum cap serves quite well as an equilibrium vessel. In such measurements a bottle of, say, 100-ml. capacity, which has been charged with perhaps 10–20 ml. of liquid and partially evacuated at low temperature to remove most of the air, is placed in a thermostat and occasionally shaken manually until equilibrium is established. Small samples are withdrawn with a syringe, which is at approximately the same temperature as the equilibrium system, and injected directly into a gas–liquid chromatographic column for analysis.

If measurements at temperatures widely different from room temperature or if more complete x,y,p,t data are called for, the equilibrium vessel and its operation cannot generally be so simple. A suitable equilibrium vessel for fairly flexible use at low pressures is shown in Figure 18. The equilibrium vessel in this case is constructed of glass and equipped with a magnetically activated stirrer, small hold-up lines for the removal of vapor samples, and a mercury pressure null leg to isolate the vessel from a pressure measuring system. A liquid sample line could, of course, be included in such a vessel.

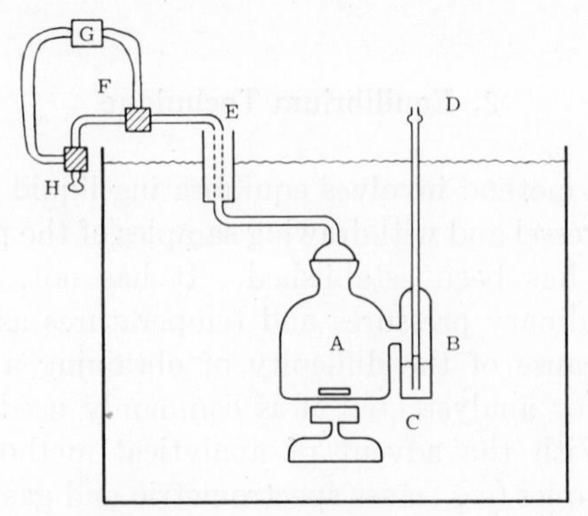

A. 250 ML GLASS VESSEL AND STIRRING MAGNET.
B. MERCURY NULL INDICATOR.
C. AIR MOTOR FOR ACTUATING MAGNET.
D. TO PRECISION MANOMETER.
E. SUPER-HEATED VAPOR TAKE-OFF.
F. SOLENOID VALVES.
G. ALTERNATING SWITCH FOR SOLENOID VALVES.
H. TO EVACUATED SAMPLING VESSEL.

Fig. 18. Liquid–vapor equilibrium vessel.

Operation of an equilibrium vessel is also straightforward; it consists usually of observing the temperature and pressure after equilibrium is assured and then sampling and analyzing the liquid and/or vapor phase. The liquid composition may sometimes be estimated from the initial charge and vapor hold-up; solvent partial pressure at high concentrations ($\gamma \simeq 1$) may sometimes be estimated from composition (x_2p_2); and the partial pressure of the solute may be estimated from the total pressure ($\bar{p}_1 = p - x_2p_2$). Nonetheless, careful attention to a number of aspects is generally called for. The following are worth explicit mention:

(*1*) Inert gases or other very volatile contaminants, if not adequately removed, may make pressure measurements meaningless. Heating and evacuating the vessel prior to charging removes the major part of inert gases from the system. Freezing and pumping the charge removes most of the dissolved gases. If the total pressure is less than about 100 mm. of mercury at the temperature in question, however, these steps may be inadequate, and pressure measurements at a given temperature may not be reproduced if the vessel has been heated to a higher temperature and returned to the original one. A final "flushing" of the vessel by freezing out vapor into an evacuated receiver just prior to a final equilibration and measurement is, consequently, good practice. Such a procedure also tends to remove small quantities of very volatile incidental contaminants or decomposition products whicy do not affect the solution environment, hence γ's, significantly but which may exert significant partial pressures and give rise to error in pressure measurements. Although this practice does make estimates of the liquid composition on the basis of the charged materials more difficult, a running inventory of the vessel contents from the compositions and amounts of the material removed is still possible in many cases.

(*2*) Inappropriate sampling techniques may provide nonrepresentative samples, particularly in the case of the vapor sample. Frequently, the vapor sample must be relatively large in comparison with the vapor space in the vessel and the greatest hazards in sampling probably come from reducing the pressure too much and too rapidly in withdrawing vapor. As a result the liquid surface becomes depleted in the volatile components and a sample too rich in the less volatile components is obtained. If relatively large samples are required, a very slow sampling with a minimum disruption of equilibrium is usually adequate if care is taken that selective condensation outside of the sample receiver is avoided. A convenient technique involves the use of a small decompression lock (*ca.* 10% or less of the vapor volume of the vessel) between the equilibrium vessel and an evacuated, chilled receiver. Two magnetically operated valves activated by an alternating switching sequence and an electric timer permit a controlled sampling rate with no opportunity for large, rapid drops of pressure in the vessel. The lock and lines to the evacuated sample receiver should be superheated slightly to avoid selective condensation.

(*3*) Sampling the liquid phase usually involves withdrawal of volumes of material which are smaller than in the case of the vapor phase and disturbs the equilibrium less. Dead space in lines leading to and from the equilibrium vessel are normally kept to a minimum and are flushed prior to taking samples for analysis. It is frequently convenient to sample in a closed system, i.e., in a cooled, evacuated receiver, in order to avoid loss of vapors from the hot liquid sample as it is withdrawn from the vessel.

(*4*) Hot spots in regions which may come in contact with liquid phase or cold spots in regions which may come in contact with vapors may give rise to important local evaporation or condensation and, thus, to faulty compositions in vapor of liquid samples.

3. Flow Techniques

In some cases, particularly in determining the activity coefficient of a volatile solute in a relatively involatile solvent, equilibrium may be conveniently established by means of a continuous flow of a gas or vapor through a sample of the solvent held at constant temperature. The transfer of material may be in either direction, i.e., from gas phase to liquid or from liquid to gas phase.

In the first case a gas carrying some known parital pressure of solute is passed through the solvent sample until the liquid phase comes to an equilibrium composition. The liquid is then sampled and analyzed. In this case the contacting method is not very critical since the flow of solute gas mixture can be continued more or less indefinitely to achieve equilibrium. On the other hand, the total amount of solute transferred to a given amount of liquid phase may be relatively large and a relatively long time may be necessary to reach equilibrium. In practice a simple gas-scrubbing bottle is usually adequate for establishing equilibrium. It should have a small hold-up so as to minimize both the amount of material which must be transferred to achieve equilibrium and the pressure drop across the vessel. The feed mixture may be generated by saturating the flowing gas in a series of similiar bottles held at such a temperature that the solute vapor pressure is the desired partial pressure. As a rule, this method becomes more difficult to control the closer the gas saturation bottles come to the boiling point of the solute material.

In the second case the stream of gas is brought to equilibrium with a liquid phase of known composition and, after having contacted the solution, is sampled and analyzed. In this case the method of contacting the gas and solution is quite critical, since the time of contact of gas and solution cannot be controlled very easily. In practice several scrubbing bottles in series are usually used. In this case there is only a small difference in the composition of the incoming and outgoing gas in the last bottle and the composition of the final solution changes slowly.

In both of the above cases the gas or liquid can sometimes be conveniently saturated on a very small scale by means of a small tube containing solvent or solution supported on a solid carrier as in gas-liquid chromatography. This technique provides very good contacting of the phases but has the hazard that the equilibrium involved is not purely that between gas and bulk liquid phase desired. In addition, the solvent must be quite involatile so that solvent stripping from the tube is not so large that corrections aimed at taking solvent depletion into account do not become unmanageably large. Conditions (temperature, solute partial pressure, γ^0-level) such that the total quantity of solute material in the liquid phase is large in relation to the sorption capacity of the solid itself will minimize the effect of the solid support. The more heavily the support is charged with solvent the less likely is significant solid sorption to occur, but the total charge of solvent or of solute plus solvent at equilibrium must not, of course, become so high that the liquid tends to plug the tube or to flow out of the tube.

In addition to the above flow techniques, gas–liquid chromatographic methods may be used directly in some cases. Both the breakthrough technique and the more usual pulse technique can be expected to give good measures of limiting solute activity coefficients in appropriate systems and under appropriate experimental conditions, but in some cases a suitable compromise of conditions is difficult to achieve.

In the breakthrough technique, a mixture of solute and gas of known solute concentration is passed continuously into a column of known solvent content until the solute breaks through and builds up in the effluent gas to reach the input concentration. The breakthrough point is usually taken as the point at which the concentration in the effluent reaches one half the input concentration. If the amount of solvent in the column is large enough and the column is long enough so that the end effects are not large, essentially the entire solvent content of the column is saturated at this point with respect to the solute at the composition of the incoming mixture, and the solute concentration can be estimated on the basis of the volume of effluent gas from which the solute has been absorbed. Low gas flow rates not only favor a close approach to equilibrium, but minimize the pressure gradient along the column (hence, solute partial pressure gradient) which is inherent in the method. As in the supported solvent method mentioned above, the solvent must itself be relatively involatile if solvent losses are to be kept within bounds and the effects of incidental sorptions are to be kept to a minimum. It is nonetheless usually convenient to have established as steady a flow as is possible with solute-free gas and to switch to the solute-containing gas at the same inlet pressures.

In the pulse technique a small pulse of solute-containing gas is inserted into a flowing stream of gas at the entry of gas–liquid chromatographic column containing a known charge of solvent. The volume of gas (retention volume) necessary to carry the solute through the column into a detecting device at the column end provides a measure of the limiting solute activity coefficient in the solvent in question.* As a rule, the pulse tech-

* $V_R^0 - V_F^0 = (M_S RT/\gamma^\circ p_1)V_S$ where V_R^0 is the volume of gas passed from the injection of the pulse to its appearance (maximum) in the effluent corrected for volume changes across the pressure gradient, V_F^0 is the volume of the column not occupied by liquid or its solid support, M_S is the moles of solvent per unit volume, and V_S is the volume of the solvent in the column. The corrected retention volume is obtained from the observed volume, V_R, the inlet pressure, p_i, and the outlet pressure, p_0, $V_R^0 = V_R/[2/3[(p_i/p_0)^3 - 1]/[(p_i/p_0)^2 - 1)]]$.

nique requires a somewhat more careful compromise of conditions than the breakthrough technique. Rate effects, end effects, concentration effects in the liquid phase, and extraneous sorptions tend to complicate the interpretation of the experimental results and to restrict the temperature region over which the γ^0 of a given solute may be determined.

A number of effects must be taken into account in arriving at a suitable compromise:

(*1*) Distortions of the pulse in charging the column or in sensing the effluent pulse with some device which has finite volume have small but frequently significant effects upon the retention of the pulse. Their occurrence can sometimes be recognized by pulse assymmetry ("tailing") and their effects can be minimized by use of conditions (temperature, solvent charge) which give rise to retention volumes large with respect to the free volume of the column. "Tailing" may also arise, however, from extraneous sorptions and is frequently compensated for by concentration effects in the liquid.

(*2*) With a column of given characteristics at a given temperature, the equilibrium between vapor and liquid phase may be so much in favor of the vapor that very little material is absorbed by the liquid phase. If this sorption is so low as to be comparable in magnitude to sorption on incidental surfaces such as that of the solid support, the latter strongly influences the retention volume observed and, thus, retention volumes cannot be related to bulk solution effects. This effect is usually more important the more polar the solute in relation to the solvent, but is also generally more important the higher the γ of the solute, since it is the distribution between the liquid and the incidental surfaces which determines their relative importance. The effect can sometimes be recognized by "tailing" of the effluent pulse. It can be minimized by using high solvent loadings on the support, as inert a support as possible, and relatively large, concentrated solute pulses at relatively low temperatures so that the liquid has a high capacity for solute material ($\gamma^0 p^0$ usually falls rapidly with decreasing temperature).

(*3*) On the other hand, with a given column and operating temperature, the distribution of solute may be so in favor of the liquid phase that at least in the beginning of the column (before the pulse has become relatively broad) the solute concentration in the liquid is relatively large. In this case the distribution coefficient* is not constant from the peaks to the edges of the pulse (nonlinear isotherm). The result is not only a distortion of the pulse shape (normally "fronting" instead of "tailing") and some effect on the apparent retention volume, but also an initial rate of pulse movement which is not the same as that finally obtained in a long

* $y_i/x_i = (p_i/p_0)10^{(\log \gamma_i^0)(1-x_i)^2}$

column after the pulse has broadened and the maximum concentration fallen substantially. This effect is minimized when solute charges are small and dilute in the gas which comes to the column and when the column is relatively long so that during the majority of the residence time the concentration in the liquid phase is no more than a per cent or two.

In spite of these factors, quite satisfactory γ^0's can be obtained with the pulse technique. As a rule, satisfactory results can be most easily obtained with relatively nonpolar solutes in more polar solvents, but, with extreme care, even the more difficult case of polar solute in relatively nonpolar solvent has been satisfactorily handled (see Table III). In general,

TABLE III
Activity Coefficients of Polar Solutes in *n*-Hexadecane[a]

Solute	γ^0 By GLC	γ^0 By static methods
Methanol	71.5	75.1
Dimethyl ketone	6.3	6.1
Methylethyl ketone	3.8	3.6

[a] Kwantes and Rijnders, *Gas Chromatography*, D. H. Desty, ed., Butterworths, London, 1958, p. 125.

the relative volatility of two solutes, which are closely related so that the miscellaneous extraneous effects tend to be about the same, can be expected to be more accurate than either the γ's. A series of plots shown in Figure 19 will illustrate the magnitudes which some of the above effects can have even in the more favorable cases.

4. Dew and Bubble Points

The foregoing methods in general determine the composition of two phases at equilibrium under either constant pressure or constant temperature conditions. The alternate approach of determining the pressure at constant temperature or the temperature at constant pressure at which a mixture of known composition just begins to vaporize (bubble point $\equiv t,p,x$) and to condense (dew point $\equiv t,p,y$) may also be used to determine equilibria in binary systems. At constant temperature the technique involves compressing (usually with mercury) a mixture of known composition in a calibrated vessel in order to obtain a curve of V vs. p. The dew point and bubble point pressures are obtained from the curve by noting the pressures at which breaks in the V vs. p curve occur. In some cases the bubble point is more easily determined by direct visual observation.

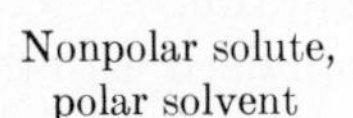

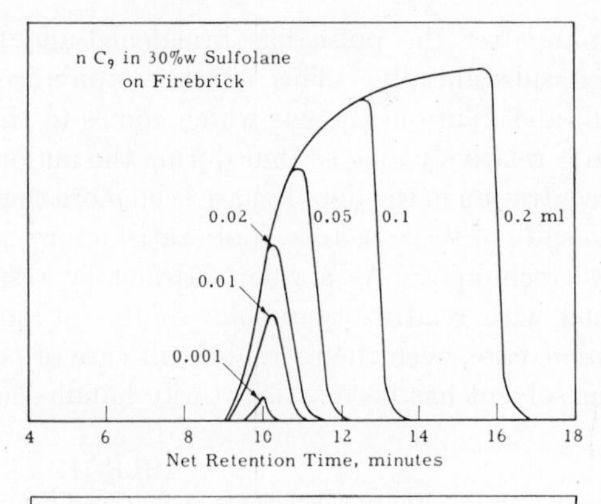

Polar solute,
nonpolar solvent

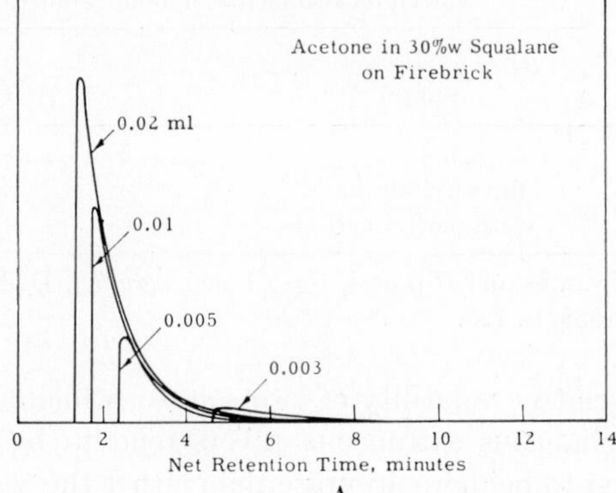

A

Fig. 19. CLC effects: (A) pulse size (ml. liquid) (Deal, C. H. and E. R. Freitas, unpublished data);

The method has the advantage over many others that sampling and analysis of equilibrium liquid and vapor is not required and that, in principle, the equilibrium point can be approached from either side. On the other hand, the volume difference between the completely condensed and the completely vaporized charge is inconveniently large with systems not close to the critical region. It will be clear that measurements are sensitive to dissolved gases and/or incidental relatively volatile or involatile impurities. Gases which usually present the greatest problem can be selectively rejected with but little change in the overall composition of the charge by discarding the last vapors from preliminary compressions.

Dew point and bubble point temperatures can be determined by altering temperature at constant pressure and observing visually the appearance of liquid or disappearance vapor. Quite accurate bubble temperatures can be obtained in a recirculating still in which the liquid–vapor hold-

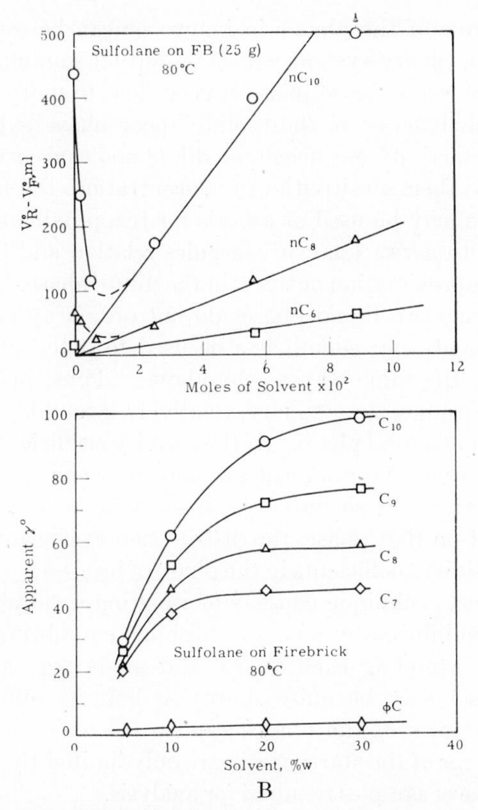

B

Fig. 19 (*continued*). (B) Amount of solvent on support.

ups are arranged so that the equilibrium liquid composition is substantially the same as that of the charge.

5. Liquid–Liquid Equilibria

In many systems two liquid phases occur, either in the temperature ranges of interest or at temperatures not far from those of interest. Since the composition of equilibrium phases is extremely sensitive to the way activity coefficients change with composition, liquid–liquid equilibria frequently provide the most accurate and easily obtained γ's. Indeed, it is normally quite difficult to determine γ–x relations from liquid–vapor measurements with sufficient accuracy to give an accurate specification of the composition of liquid phases which occur. Needless to say, the direct measurement of the composition of two equilibrium phases provides only a relation between the γ's of each component in the respective phases ($\gamma_1 x_1 = \gamma_1' x_1'$). This single relation is particulary useful, however, when the activity in one of the phases in known or can be estimated. Thus, for instance, in a binary system with low mutual solubilities the activity coefficient in the "solute"-rich phase is very close to unity ($x_1' \cong 1$, therefore $\gamma_1' \cong 1$) so that (γ_1) in the "solute"-poor phase is large, and $\gamma_1 \cong 1(x_1')/x_1$. Since activity coefficients in dilute and concentrated phases are quite different in their sensitivities to concentration, the first estimate for the dilute phases may be used as a basis for reapproximating γ_1' (concentrated phase) with a van Laar or Margules relation and this in turn may be used for a reapproximation of the γ_1 in the dilute phase.

In some systems two liquid phases do not ordinarily occur but liquid–liquid measurements can nonetheless be used to determine activity coefficients in much the same way as the above. Thus, in some cases it is convenient to introduce an auxiliary, relatively insoluble material in order to generate a second liquid phase. If the activity coefficients of components of interest in this new environment are known or can be estimated and if the auxiliary material is so insoluble in the original mixture that it has little or no effect on that phase, the distribution coefficients ($K = x/x' = \gamma'/\gamma$) supply activity coefficients in the phase of interest.

The most direct technique consists of isolating a suitable mixture in a thermostated equilibrium vessel, establishing equilibrium, allowing the phase to settle, sampling each phase, and analyzing each phase. The equilibrium vessel may be quite simple so long as sufficient stirring is supplied and samples of the phases can be conveniently withdrawn for analyses. Charges of the starting mix are only limited by the convenience of mixing and size of samples required for analysis.

Although the technique is straightforward, several aspects may be worth explicit note. Particularly when the equilibrium concentrations in the phases are greatly different, quite good temperature control and a clean separation of the phases is required. Even an extremely small amount of a phase concentrated in a component of interest as a contaminant in a phase which is dilute in this component or which separates during sampling and is not recovered as part of the sample usually gives rise to serious errors. In practice, a few minutes settling time usually gives adequate phase separation, but in some cases many hours may be required. As a rule, sampling lines should be flushed with the sample liquid just prior to removing samples for analysis.

A second liquid–liquid technique, analogous to the bubble or dew point technique, is a particularly convenient one. In essence various mixtures of the components are slowly heated or cooled until a second phase disappears or appears and the temperatures are noted. The technique involves no analysis and, in principle, supplies only the phase boundary; however, in binary systems tie lines may be drawn between the phase boundaries.

Other than a suitable heat source whose temperatures can be conveniently controlled and measured, no special apparatus is required. Commonly, small glass ampoules serve quite satisfactorily as a container in which phase changes can be observed.

In practice it is usually best to seal the sample-containing ampoule in order to avoid losses of material and to adjust the amount of charge in order to minimize changes in the overall liquid composition from vaporization within the tube. A fairly rapid cooling (several degrees/minute) of a sample which is initially at a high enough temperature to be homogeneous, usually provides a rough measure of the cloud temperature; however, a slow cooling and heating around this value with a careful observation of the phases and intermittent mixing usually provides a more accurate cloud temperature.

For cases in which the refractive indices of the two phases are close to each other (e.g., close to the critical solution temperature), it is sometimes extremely difficult to see a second phase; however, usually the cloud temperature can be determined within a few tenths of a degree.

6. Solid–Liquid

Although conditions at which solid phases occur are ordinarily avoided in distillations, occasionally it is convenient to exploit solid–liquid equilibria in establishing activity coefficients. The activity of a given component in solution and an equilibrium pure solid phase are, of course, identical and the γ in the liquid phase is simply the ratio of ideal to actual solubility.* For a given temperature the solid solubility gives but a single γ–x point; however, in cases for which the solid activity can be estimated such a point may be useful. If ΔH's and ΔC_p's cannot be obtained or estimated with sufficient accuracy it is sometimes possible to compare solubilities in a set of solvents in at least one case of which the activity coefficient is known.

In practice the classical thermal analysis techniques may be used to determine a t–x curve. Cloud point techniques similar to those mentioned above are, however, also useful. Quite substantial supercooling can, of

* If the solid is a pure solid (no solid solutions), its activity referred to the pure (supercooled) liquid is given by the relation

$$\log a^S = -(\Delta H_m{}^F)(T_m - T)/TT_m/2.3R + \Delta C_p(T_m - T)/T/2.3R - \Delta C_p \log (T_m/T)/R$$

in terms of the molar heat of fusion ($\Delta H_m{}^F$) at the melting point (T_m), the molar heat capacity at constant pressure of the liquid less that of the solid (ΔC_p) and the temperature (T). If the solution is perfect $a^S = x^i$.

course, occur, but a rapid supercooling of a mixture to produce many very small crystals followed by a slower warming with frequent shaking to the temperature at which the crystals disappear usually gives the solubility temperature to within about $^1/_2$ degree. If such a mixture is illuminated with polarized light and viewed through a crossed polaroid screen, even a very small amount of crystalline material can be detected.

The author would like to express his appreciation for the helpful aid and comments of associates in the Physical Chemistry Department, Emeryville Research Center, Shell Development Company, particularly those of E. L. Derr, E. R. Freitas, and M. N. Papadopoulos.

General References

I. Thermodynamics and/or Theory of Solutions

Hildebrand and Scott, *Regular Solutions*, Prentice-Hall, Inc., Englewood Cliffs, New Jersey, 1962.

Hildebrand and Scott, *Solubility of Non-Electrolytes*, Reinhold Publishing Co., New York, 1950.

Rowlinson, *Liquids and Liquid Mixtures*, Butterworths, London, 1959.

Hala, Pick, Fried, and Vilim (translated by G. Standart), *Vapour–Liquid Equilibrium*, Pergamon Press, New York, 1958.

Schatchard, *Chem. Rev. 8*, 321 (1931); *d.*, **44**, 7 (1949).

Prigogine, Bellemans, and Mathot, *The Molecular Theory of Solutions*, Interscience, New York, 1957.

II. Correlation of Experimental Data

Wohl, *Trans. Am. Inst. Chem. Engrs.*, **42**, 215 (1946).

Redlich, Kister, and Turnquist, *Chem. Eng. Progy: Symp. Ser.*, **48**, 49 (1952).

Hala, Pick, Fried, and Vilim (translated by G. Standart), *Vapour–Liquid Equilibrium*, Pergamon Press, New York, 1958.

International Symposium on Distillaton, Brighton, England, 1960, Institution of Chemical Engineers, 16 Belgrave Square, London, S.W.I.

Black, Derr, and Papadopoulos, "Systematic Prediction of Separation Factors," *Ind. Eng. Chem.*, **55,** No. 8, 40 (1963); **55,** No. 9, 38 (1963).

III. Experimental Techniques

Hala, Pick, Fried, and Vilim (translated by G. Standart), *Vapour–Liquid Equilibrium*, Pergamon Press, New York, 1958.

IV. Experimental Data and/or References

Hala, Pick, Fried, and Vilim (translated by G. Standart), *Vapour–Liquid Equilibrium*, Pergamon Press, New York, 1958.

Rose and Rose, *Distillation Literature Index and Abstracts 1946–52, 1953–54*, State College, Pennsylvania, 1953, 1955.

Chu, Wang, Levy, and Paul, *Vapor–Liquid Equilibrium Data*, J. W. Edwards Publisher Inc., Ann Arbor, Michigan, 1956.

Kogan and Fridman, *Handbuch der Dampf-Flussigkeits Gleichgewichten*, Veb Deutscher Verlag Der Wissenschaften, Berlin, 1961.

Timmermans, *The Physico-Chemical Constants of Binary Systems in Concentrated Solutions*, Interscience, New York, 1959.

References

1. Hirata, M., *Chem. Eng.* (*Japan*), **13**, 138 (1949) and *Japan. Sci. Rev., Ser. I*, **2**, 265 (1952).
2. Gilmont, R., Weinman, E. A., Miller,E., Hachmall, F., and Othmer, D. F., *Ind. Eng. Chem.*, **42**, 120 (1950).
3. Wohl, K., *Trans. Am. Inst. Chem. Eng.*, **42**, 215 (1946).
4. Redlich, O., and Kister, A. T., *Ind. Eng. Chem.*, **40**, 341 (1948); **40**, 345 (1948).
5. Black, C., *Ind. Eng. Chem.*, **50**, 391 (1958); **51**, 211 (1959).
6. Pierotti, G. J., Deal, C. H., and Derr, E. L., *Ind. Eng. Chem.*, **51**, 95 (1959).
7. Brønstedt, J. N., and Koefed, *Danski Videnskab, Selskab. Mat. Fys. Medd.*, **22**, No. 17 (1946).
8. Deal, C. H., Derr, E. L., and Papadopoulos, M. N., *Ind. Eng. Chem. Fundamentals*, **1**, 17 (1962).
9. Langmuir, I., *Colloid Symposium Monograph*, **3**, 48 (1945).
10. Redlich, O., Derr, E. L., and Pierotti, G. J., *J. Am. Chem. Soc.*, **81**, 2283 (1959).
11. Papadopoulos, M. N. and Derr, E. L., *J. Am. Chem. Soc.*, **81**, 2285 (1959).
12. Wilson, G. M., and Deal, C. H., *Ind. and Eng. Chem., Fundamentals*, **1**, 20 (1962).
13. Pierotti, G. J., Deal, C. H., and Derr, E. L., *Ind. Eng. Chem.*, **51**, 95 (1959), American Documentation Institute (1958).
14. Smyth, C. P., and Engel, E. W., *J. Am. Chem. Soc.*, **51**, 2660 (1929).
15. Stage, H., and Schultze, G. R., *Oel und Kohl*, **40**, 90 (1944).
16. Snijder, H. B., and Gilbert, E. C., *Ind. Eng. Chem.*, **34**, 1519 (1942).
17. Schulze, A., *Z. Physik. Chem.*, **97**, 388 (1921).
18. Seatchard, G., Mochel, J. M., and Wood, S. E., *J. Am. Chem. Soc.*, **62**, 712 (1940).
19. Schulze, A., and Hoch, H., *Z. Physik. Chem.*, **86**, 445 (1914).
20. Sameshima, J., *J. Am. Chem. Soc.*, **40**, 1503 (1918).
21. Martin, A. R., and Callic, B., *J. Chem. Soc.*. **1932**, 2658.
22. Martin, A. R., and George, C. M., *J. Chem. Soc.*, **1933**, 1414.
23. Seatchard, G., Wood, S. E., and Mochel, J. M., *J. Am. Chem. Soc.*, **68**, 1957 (1946).
24. Lee, S. C., *J. Phys. Chem.*, **35**, 3558 (1931).
25. Zawidzki, J., *Z. Physik. Chem.*, **35**, 129 (1900).

CHAPTER III

ORDINARY FRACTIONAL DISTILLATION

Frederick E. Williams, *Hercules Powder Company*

APPARATUS

I. INTRODUCTION

A batch rectification unit consists of a still pot, rectifying section, and still head as major components. The still pot holds the distilland and transmits the heat required to boil the charge and to supply vapor to the bottom of the fractionating section. In the rectifying section or column, the upflowing vapors and downflowing reflux liquid are intimately contacted to obtain interaction leading to the exchange of heat and material between the phases to produce fractionation. Since the actual separation of the individual components making up the still-pot charge is effected in the rectifying section, it is the most important part of the entire unit. Most of the increased efficiency of modern laboratory rectification equipment has been achieved by improvement of the rectifying section.

The devices used for vapor-reflux contacting are of two general types: the film type and the plate type. The film-type rectifying section can be further subdivided into the simple and complex varieties. In the simple or "wetted-surface" variety of film-type rectifying section the countercurrent vapor and liquid streams follow predetermined simple paths through the column, and diffusional processes are relied upon for interaction of the two phases. A vertical open tube is an elementary example of this form of column. Numerous modifications exist in which devices are inserted in the tube to change the shape and length of the passageway or modify the liquid-film surface, but in all cases the two phases follow prescribed paths. The complex form of film-type rectifying column is generally called a "packed" column and consists of a vertical tube filled with solid material or "packing" to break up the direct path through the tube. The packing material is usually of a regular size and shape and is packed at random in the distilling tube. The vapor and reflux follow a tortuous, unpredictable path through the packed section, and the two phases thoroughly interact by diffusion at the surface of the packing. Since packed columns are easy to construct and have good operating characteristics, they are more widely used in the laboratory than any other type.

A plate rectifying column consists of a tube containing a vertical series of equally spaced horizontal plates which impede the downward flow of the reflux. Liquid gathers on the upper surface of the plate until it reaches a predetermined level maintained by an overflow pipe. This pipe extends into the liquid layer on the next lower plate and furnishes it with reflux. Various methods of plate construction are employed to disperse the ascending vapor to allow it to bubble through and interact with the reflux liquid on the plate.

Other considerations being equal, the rectifying section showing the greatest enrichment per unit length is the most desirable. However, depending upon the particular fractionation problem involved, other factors may have a more important bearing on the choice of the rectifying section. The throughput or capacity of the column is one of the factors which determines the time required to carry out the fractionation. Plate and packed columns generally have much higher throughputs than the simple wetted-surface columns for a given fractionating efficiency. The operating holdup is another important factor in the choice of a rectifying section. Generally, it is desirable to have the holdup as small as possible, particularly when fractionating charges contain some constituents in small amount. Simple wetted-surface columns have low holdup compared with plate or packed columns. Pressure drop across the rectifying section is an important consideration particularly in vacuum fractionations. The pressure drop of plate columns is considerably higher than that of the other types for a given throughput.

The still head which is above the rectifying section serves the dual function of furnishing the column with reflux and of delivering fractionated product to the distillate receiver. As a consequence of these functions, the still head also controls the reflux ratios. The vapors from the column are either partially or totally condensed in the still-head condenser. If a partial condenser is used, all the condensed vapor is returned to the column as reflux and the uncondensed portion passes to an auxiliary condenser. If a total condenser is employed, the still head contains a partitioning device for withdrawing a portion of the condensate as product and returning the remainder to the column as reflux. Partial condensers improve the fractionation by effecting further enrichment of the vapors; however, the enrichment achieved is very slight and since the operation of a partial condenser is difficult to control, most laboratory fractionating units employ total condensers. The proper functioning of the still pot, rectifying section, and still head requires considerable auxiliary equipment. Many well constructed and potentially highly efficient fractionating units give unexpectedly poor results in actual operation due to the inadequacy of the auxiliary control equipment.

As shown in Chapter I, the rectifying section must operate under adiabatic conditions in order to obtain the maximum amount of separation. None of the latent heat of the vapors entering the rectifying section should be used to compensate for heat lost to the surroundings through the column walls. Neither must heat flow through the column walls and vaporize a portion of the reflux. Vacuum jackets or compensating heat jackets are the methods generally used to obtain adiabatic conditions.

Since the column efficiency varies with throughput, it is essential for proper interpretation of the distillation curves that the throughput be maintained constant. To accomplish this, vapors must be generated in the still pot at a steady, uniform, and controllable rate. If the still pot is properly designed and is readily responsive to changes in the heat supplied by the still-pot heater, a back-pressure manometer can be connected between the still pot and condenser section to indicate and control the throughput.

In order to follow the course of the fractionation it is customary to measure the temperature of the reflux. Several types of temperature-measuring devices are used for this purpose. The proper placing of the measuring element in the still head to ensure accurate and reproducible readings is the most important problem connected with the measurement of reflux temperatures. Accurate determination of reflux temperature, particularly in vacuum fractionations, requires a constant pressure at the head of the column. In addition to affecting the reflux temperature, variations in pressure also affect the efficiency of the rectifying section. It is almost imperative that the pressure be controlled automatically; a number of manostat systems have been devised for this purpose. When the column is operating under reduced pressure, it is essential that the fractionating unit be equipped with a distillate receiver to permit withdrawal of fractions without disturbing the operation of the column.

Many precise fractionations require more than a month of continuous operation for completion; therefore, in order to prevent excessive distillation losses, the number of joints must be kept to a minimum. In particular, ground-glass joints in contact with hot vapors are to be avoided. All stopcocks should be precision ground and lubricated with a grease which will not react with or be dissolved by the material being distilled.

A properly constructed fractionating unit combines all the elements mentioned into a good workable unit. Construction should be such that the assembly is mechanically strong, easily cleaned, versatile as to operating temperatures and pressures, and the construction material should be corrosion resistant toward the materials to be fractionated.

In the laboratory, fractionating columns are used for a wide variety of problems involving the purification or analysis of materials. The equipment requirements relative to theoretical plates, throughput, holdup, and similar factors for optimum efficiency in these various applications may not be identical. Furthermore, in cases in which laboratory-scale fractional distillation is used extensively as a primary tool for analysis or sample preparation, expensive intricate equipment is justified; whereas in cases in which fractional distillation has infrequent application, only the simpler and less expensive types of apparatus are justified. For these reasons, no attempt will be made in the ensuing discussion to designate any rectification assembly as the best; instead, the advantages and disadvantages of the various designs in common use will be presented to aid the reader in the selection of equipment for particular rectification problems.

II. COLUMN SECTION

1. Types of Columns

A. WETTED-SURFACE COLUMNS

In the wetted-surface variety of film-type column, the vapor and reflux streams follow prescribed paths through regularly shaped passageways, generally of simple structure, such as an open tube, concentric tube, or spiral tube. The downward flowing reflux covers the surface forming the passageway with a thin film of liquid which interacts with the ascending vapor stream to effect the separation of the constituents. The overall transfer process consists of three parts: mixing across the liquid film, vapor–liquid transfer at the phase interface, and radial mixing of the vapor. Usually the first two processes are quite rapid, and the vapor diffusion process controls the overall rate of transfer. This has been verified by Fastovskii and Petrovskii.[1] In most wetted-surface columns the vapor flow is streamlined, and under these conditions the vapor diffusion process is slow so that the throughput is low when the column is operating with reasonable fractionation efficiency. It is not unusual to operate wetted-surface columns at take-off rates as low as 0.1 ml./hr.; at these rates the rectification efficiency may be very high.

Owing to the open, uncomplicated construction, the holdup and pressure drop of wetted-surface columns is generally very much lower than can be obtained in packed columns or plate columns of equivalent rectification efficiency. In order to obtain the low throughputs required for efficient operation, it is essential that the jacket surrounding the rectification section be extremely efficient.

The combination of high rectification efficiency and low holdup make wetted-surface columns very attractive for analytical fractionations, particularly those involving small quantities of material.

Empty-Tube Columns. The simplest type of rectifying section consists of a straight, vertical empty tube of circular cross section. This design is amenable to mathematical treatment as is shown in Chapter I (Sec. IV). In spite of their simplicity, empty-tube columns have not been extensively studied; however, the literature gives a few references.[1-5] Rose[2] studied 1-ft. sections of empty tubes, 0.3 cm. and 0.6 cm. in diameter; the results are shown in Table I.

TABLE I

Empty-Tube Column (30.3-cm. Long) Rectification Efficiency at Total Reflux

Column diameter							
0.3 cm.				0.6 cm.			
		H.E.T.P., cm.[a]				H.E.T.P., cm.[a]	
Throughput liquid, ml./min.	Vapor velocity, cm./sec. (calc.)	Vacuum jacket	Air jacket	Throughput liquid, ml./min.	Vapor velocity, cm./sec. (calc.)	Vacuum jacket	Vacuum jacket and heater
				8.0	144	—	60.6
3.00	216	30.3	23.3	6.2	112	—	60.6
				5.0	90.0	60.6	30.3
2.00	144	15.1	20.2	2.5	45.0	30.3	30.3
1.60	115	7.6	13.8	1.9	34.2	—	15.1
1.30	93.6	10.1	7.6	1.4	25.2	15.1	—
1.00	72	5.05	4.33	0.9	16.2	6.1	15.1
0.80	57.6	4.33	[b]	0.8	14.4	4.33	7.6
0.56	40.3	3.19	[b]	0.45	8.1	[b]	5.05
				0.22	3.96	[b]	2.33
				0.17	3.06	[b]	1.73

[a] Determined with benzene-carbon tetrachloride test mixture.

[b] No reflux at top of column.

As illustrated in Figure 1, Westhaver[6] showed that calculated values of H.E.T.P. were in good agreement with Rose's[2] experimental results for the 0.6-cm. column insulated with a vacuum jacket and compensating heater. Using only the vacuum jacket, the 0.6-cm. column showed greater efficiency than when the heater was also used. Since throughputs were measured only at the base of the columns, the results can probably be explained on the assumption that the vapor velocities in the upper sections of the unheated vacuum-jacketed column were less than calculated from the throughput at the base. This is borne out by the fact that Rose was unable to obtain reflux in the unheated column at very low throughputs. A comparison of the results obtained in the 0.3- and 0.6-cm. columns does not indicate a greater efficiency for the smaller column as predicted

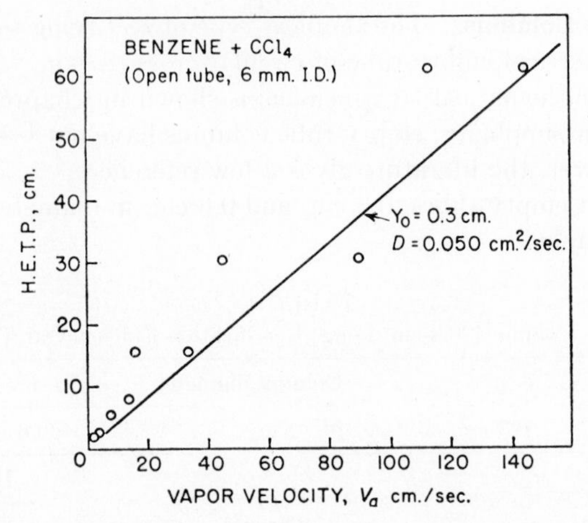

Fig. 1. H.E.T.P. values of an empty-tube column. Experimental vs. theoretical.

by the theory. Here again the explanation probably lies in the insulation. In this regard Rose says:[2]

"Operation of columns becomes more and more difficult as the rate of boiling becomes very low because the slightest variation in the insulation of the column or heat input to the pot destroys the equilibrium in the column. For successful operation at very low rates of boiling the columns should be insulated almost as well as a calorimeter. Under such conditions efficiencies as high as 30 plates per foot seem possible."

Kuhn and Ryffel[7] investigated the rectification efficiency of 11- and 100-cm. open-tube columns 1.0 cm. in diameter. The columns were vacuum jacketed and of similar design to that used by Rose. To further minimize heat losses the columns were operated at 60 mm. of mercury. At this pressure the carbon tetrachloride–benzene test mixture boiled at about 15°C.

TABLE II

Empty-Tube Column (1.0-cm. diameter) Rectification Efficiency at Total Reflux

Column length					
11 cm.			100 cm.		
Vapor velocity, cm./sec.	H.E.T.P., cm. Obs.	H.E.T.P., cm. Theor.[a]	Vapor velocity, cm./sec.	H.E.T.P., cm. Obs.	H.E.T.P., cm. Theor.[a]
4.3	1.1	0.95	101	20	22
2.5	0.92	0.56	31	7.1	6.9
—	—	—	24	5.9	5.3

[a] Calculated from Westhaver's equation using D_v = 0.26 cm.^{2}/sec.

The experimental and calculated H.E.T.P. values given in Table II show good agreement.

Unfortunately, experiments on empty-tube columns have not included studies of the pressure drop and holdup. However, theoretical equations are available which enable both these factors to be estimated with good accuracy. To calculate the pressure drop for an empty-tube column, Westhaver[6] developed the equation

$$\Delta p = \left[\frac{8\eta_v V_a}{r_0^2} + 1.2 \times 10^{-5}\frac{Mp}{T}\right]l \qquad (1)$$

Where Δp is the total pressure drop, p is the average column pressure (dynes/cm.^{2}), η_v is the vapor coefficient of viscosity, V_a is the radially averaged vapor velocity, M is the average molecular weight of vapor in the tube, T is the average column temperature (°K.), and l is H.E.T.P. in centimeters.

The holdup can be calculated from the equation relating throughput to the thickness of the liquid film:[7,8]

$$w = [3Q\eta_l/p_l g]^{1/3} \qquad (2)$$

Where w is the thickness of the film, Q is the throughput, η_l is the viscosity of the liquid, p_l is the density of the liquid, and g is the acceleration due to gravity. For a tube 3 in. in diameter, holdup values calculated by eq. (2) have been found to be in good agreement with holdup values determined experimentally.[9]

TABLE III

Empty-Tube Column (0.6-cm. diameter) Pressure Drop, Holdup, and Efficiency Factor

Throughput liquid, ml./min.	H.E.T.P., cm.	Pressure drop, mm. Hg/plate	Liquid holdup, ml./plate	Efficiency factor plates/hr.
8.0	60.6	1.9	1.05	460
6.2	60.6	1.8	0.96	390
5.0	30.3	0.94	0.45	670
2.5	30.3	0.92	0.36	420
1.9	15.1	0.46	0.16	710
0.9	15.1	0.46	0.13	430
0.8	7.6	0.23	0.061	790
0.45	5.05	0.15	0.031	880
0.22	2.33	0.069	0.012	1090
0.17	1.73	0.052	0.0083[a]	1230

[a] At a low but unmeasured throughput, Podbielniak (Table VI) found the holdup of a 101.6-cm. long, 0.64-cm. diameter empty tube to be 0.374 ml., which compares to a holdup of 0.0064 ml. for a tube 1.73 cm. long. This agreement is close enough to indicate that the calculated values in this table are fairly accurate.

In Table III by means of eqs. (1) and (2), the pressure drop and holdup per plate have been calculated from Rose's data for the column 0.6 cm. in diameter. The calculations are based on a 50:50 benzene–carbon tetrachloride test mixture and estimated values of 1.5×10^{-4} for η_v and 4.4×10^{-3} for η_l. Table III also includes the "efficiency factor" defined by the relation:

$$\text{Efficiency factor} = \frac{\text{throughput (liquid ml./hr.)}}{\text{holdup (ml./theoretical plate)}}$$

In reciprocal form, this factor was first used by Bragg.[10] Podbielniak[11] introduced its use in the present form. Since it is a measure of the number of theoretical plates through which the material passes per unit time, the efficiency factor is a valuable aid for evaluating and comparing columns.

The data presented in Table III show that empty-tube rectifying sections combine high fractionation efficiency with low holdup and low pressure drop, provided the throughput is kept extremely low. Design theory is available so that empty-tube columns can be built to meet specific fractionation problems. The construction is very simple requiring only a straight, smooth, empty tube mounted absolutely vertically so as to obtain uniform wetting.

Chiefly because of their low throughputs, empty-tube rectifying sections require the finest type of insulation, such as an extremely efficient vacuum jacket combined with an auxiliary compensating heater. In addition, columns of this type are unduly sensitive to very slight changes in the still-pot heat input, and consequently are difficult to operate. Best still-pot operation is obtained with a bare-wire immersion heater and vacuum mantle insulation. Owing to their operating difficulties empty-tube columns are not recommended for general use.

Modifications of the straight, open-tube rectifying sections to provide large contacting surface for vapor and liquid without sacrificing reasonable overall physical size have taken several forms. The indentations of the Vigreux Column are well known. Ray,[12] utilizing indentations made normal to the column wall, claims improved efficiency of the conventional Vigreux Column. Warren,[13] Young,[14] and Shepherd[15] wound straight tubes into elongated spirals of uniform pitch; these were suitably insulated.

Despite the number of descriptions of spiral columns in the literature, very few data are available to permit an accurate appraisal of their rectification characteristics for comparison with other types. It seems likely that accumulation of reflux on the lower inner surface of the spiral would tend to reduce the efficiency of vapor–liquid contact.

Another modification of the straight tube column consists in creating a spiral passageway in the annulus formed by two concentric tubes or by a

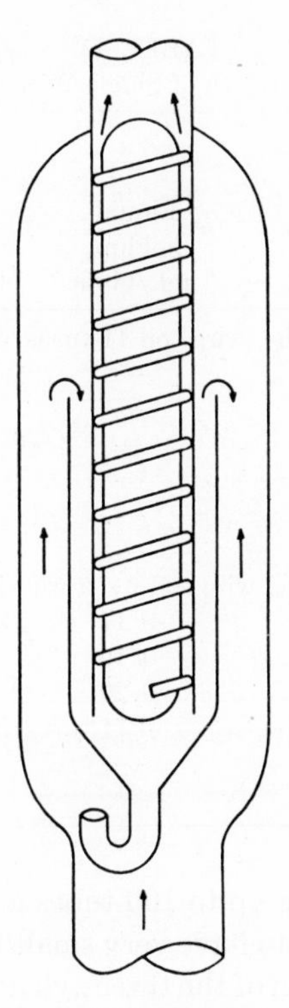

Fig. 2. Widmer column.

tube and solid centerpiece. This construction for the Widmer[16] column is shown in Figure 2. Constructional details for making the glass spiral are given by Fahlandt.[17] Midgley[18] devised an all-metal construction.

A third modification of the straight, open-tube column consists in the insertion of long spiral wire coils which fit snuggly against the column walls. The coils have five to eight turns per inch. Table IV shows the rectification characteristics of several columns of this design.

Aside from the effect of the reduction in cross-sectional area, the wire coil offers little resistance to the flow of vapor. The reflux, however, bridges the interstices between the wire coil and the tube with capillary films which increases the liquid surface exposed to the ascending vapor. The added film surface caused by the wire increases the holdup compared with that of a similar, open-tube column, and at high throughputs, appears to increase the fractionating efficiency.

By utilizing a multiplicity of small diameter tubes in parallel operation, reasonable throughput as well as good separation efficiency can be realized with the principle of the open tube column. Kuhn[19] has described several

TABLE IV
Rectification Characteristics of Single Wire-Coil Packed Columns

Throughput liquid, ml./min.	H.E.T.P., cm.	Liquid holdup, ml./plate	Pressure drop, mm. Hg per theoretical plate	Efficiency factor, plates/hr.
0.3-cm. I.D. tube, wire coil 11 turns/in. No. 26 wire[2]				
0.60	3.6	—	—	—
0.70	5.1	—	—	—
1.00	6.1	—	—	—
1.60	5.1	—	—	—
2.00	5.1	—	—	—
2.00	3.8	—	—	—
0.4-cm. I.D. tube, wire coil 6–7 turns/in. No. 20 wire[20]				
0.80	10.7	0.17	0.02	280
1.6	10.0	0.19	0.05	510
2.7	9.4	0.29	0.10	560
0.6-cm. I.D. tube, wire coil 11 turns/in. No. 26 wire[2]				
1	4.7	—	—	—
5	7.6	—	—	—

units of this kind, employing up to 100 tubes and up to 2 meters in length. Kuhn reports these columns to have very small H.E.T.P.'s. One such unit provided complete separation of the three xylene isomers.

Concentric-Tube Columns. In concentric-tube rectifying sections, vapor–liquid contacting takes place in the annular space formed by two concentric tubes. The formula developed for predicting the ideal performance of parallel-plate columns[21,22] is applicable to the concentric-tube column, and has been discussed in Chapter I (Sec. IV). The formula shows that rectification efficiency of concentric-tube columns is improved by decreasing the vapor velocity, decreasing the thickness of the annular space, or increasing the diffusion coefficient of the vapor. In these respects the concentric-tube column resembles the empty-tube column. However, in an empty-tube column operating at a given vapor velocity, the diameter cannot be changed without affecting the throughput. In a concentric-tube column, on the other hand, the throughput can be varied independently of the vapor velocity and the distance between the tubes by changing the mean circumference of the annular space. In other words, in a concentric-tube column, the number of theoretical plates per unit length depends on the difference in the diameter of the tubes forming the annular space and is independent of their absolute magnitude.

Concentric-tube columns were used as early as 1909 by Rosanoff and coworkers,[23] but their development lagged until 1937 when Craig[3] showed that columns of this construction had excellent rectification characteristics. Since then concentric-tube columns have been the subject of several exhaustive investigations,[24–28] which demonstrated that H.E.T.P. values well below 1 cm. can be achieved with this type of construction.

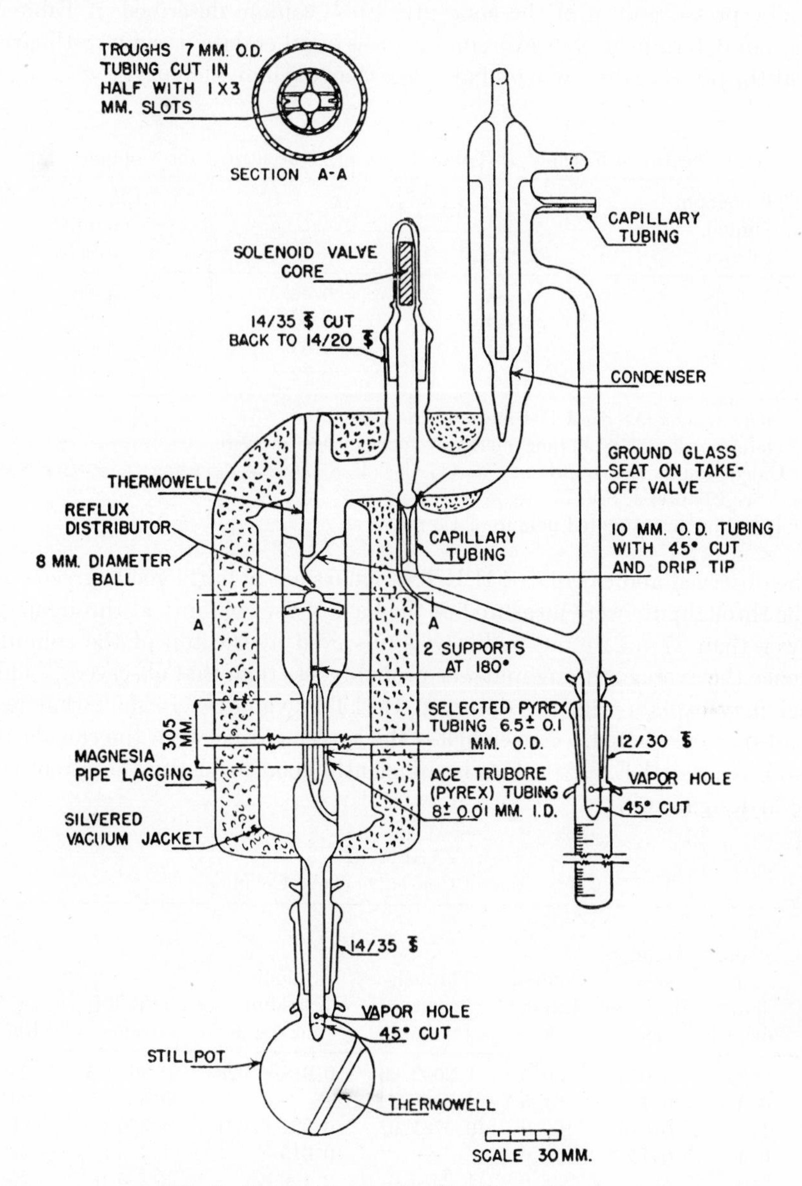

Fig. 3. Concentric-tube fractionating column.

The lowest H.E.T.P. values reported for concentric-tube columns were obtained by Naragon and Lewis.[27] The fractionating section was insulated with a vacuum mantle and pipe lagging. Construction is shown in Figure 3. The results of the efficiency tests are shown in Table V.

The pressure drop of the concentric-tube column described in Table V was not determined; however, on the basis of other data it can be estimated that the pressure drop was probably less than 0.5 mm. mercury.

TABLE V

Rectification Efficiency at Total Reflux of Concentric-Tube Column[a]

Throughput liquid, ml./min.	H.E.T.P., cm.		Efficiency factor,[d] plates/hr.
	Obs.[b]	Theor.[c]	
1.38	0.36	0.46	4300
1.53	0.40	0.55	4600
1.78	0.49	0.63	4500
2.06	0.58	0.72	4300

[a] 30.5-cm. long, 0.8-cm. I.D. tube, 0.64-cm. O.D. tube.

[b] Determined with *n*-heptane–methylcyclohexane test mixture.

[c] Calculated by the equation: $l' = (17/35)(V_aS^2/D_v)(D_vV_a)$ using $D_v = 0.04$ cm.²/sec. See Chapter I, Sec. IV.

[d] Based on an estimated holdup of 1.5 ml.

The observed and calculated H.E.T.P. values are in fairly good agreement. The throughputs were measured at the base of the column; at throughputs lower than 77 ml./hr. no reflux was observed at the top of the column. Hence the average throughput was probably less than that observed. This fact may explain why the observed H.E.T.P. values were somewhat less than those predicted. Nevertheless the agreement between the calculated and observed H.E.T.P. values is sufficiently good to justify the use of eq. (5) in design work.

TABLE VI

Comparison of Concentric-Tube Columns

Outside diam. of inner tube, cm.	Annular, space thickness cm.	Column length, cm.	Through-put, ml./min.	Liquid holdup, ml./plate	H.E.T.P., cm.	Ref.
0.65	0.075	30.5	1.20–2.06	0.018–0.028	0.36–0.58	26
0.3	0.1	31.5	—	—	0.5	24
1.255	0.075	100.0	0.67–1.67	0.022–0.031	0.7–0.9	27
0.4	0.15	10.0	—	0.015	1.3	22
1.0	0.15	238.0	1.25–5.0	0.1–0.4	2.2–5.6	25

The results of other investigations of concentric-tube columns (two-tube type) are summarized in Table VI.

Figure 4 shows the results obtained in the fractionation of a known mixture (boiling-point spread 2.3°C.) in a concentric-tube column. The separation is excellent, and the consistency of the data points shows that the column gives smooth, stable operation. However, the distillation curve represents 90 hr. of still operation during which time only 9.8 ml. of overhead product was obtained.

Jantzen and Wieckhorst[29] have discussed the construction of concentric tube columns for use at atmospheric pressure and at low pressure (0.04 mm.). They investigated three columns, two with 30-cm. rectifying sections with 0.1- (I) and 0.4-cm. (II) spacings, and one column (III) with a

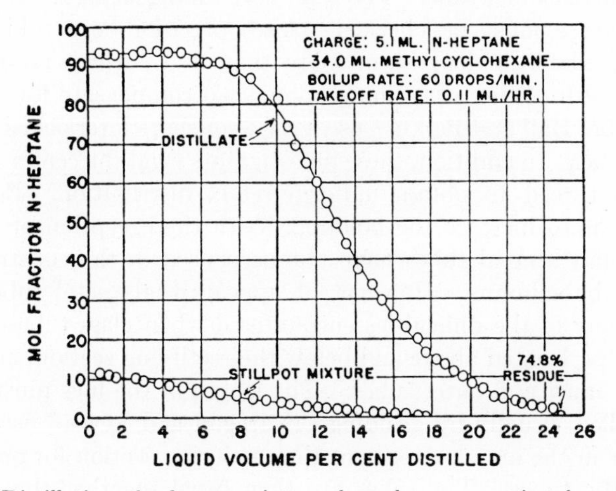

Fig. 4. Distillation of a known mixture through a concentric-tube column.

50-cm. rectifying section with 0.32-cm. spacing. (I) was estimated to have 40–50 theoretical plates; (II) 20 plates, and (III), while not specifically rated for efficiency, was shown to be able to separate completely the methyl esters of oleic and stearic acids having a boiling-point difference of 3.3°C. at 0.2 mm. pot pressure. The distillation time was 78 hr. for a 10-g. charge. At atmospheric pressure, (I) separated a 10-g. sample of methanol and ethanol into the pure components in 4.5 hr. Quite obviously, these columns are suitable only for small charges, and then only if operating conditions can be achieved within the limits of permissible thermal hazard.

Donnell and Kennedy[30] have reported H.E.T.P.'s for concentric tube columns of the order of 5–6 millimeters, if certain constructional features are maintained. This requirement has been recognized by the earliest workers. In general, the construction of a concentric-tube fractionating section of high efficiency is somewhat difficult and requires more precision work than many other types of columns. To meet the requirement of a uniform annular clearance, the tubes used in the construction must be straight and perfectly round, and they must be assembled concentrically and held in that position. In order to have a thin even flow of reflux over the tubes, the surfaces must be smooth and uniform, and the rectifying section mounting must not deviate from the vertical. In addition, concentric-tube columns require a reflux distributor to maintain even distribution of the reflux over both tube surfaces.

Most designers of concentric-tube columns agree that precision-bore tubing is more satisfactory for the outer tube. Ordinary tubing, carefully selected for straightness, roundness, and uniform diameter, is generally acceptable for the inner tube. Precision-bore tubing is not always straight, and this feature must be checked. Also, precision-bore tubing is not ordinarily available in lengths of more than 3 ft., which automatically limits the length of the rectifying section. To compensate for bowing of the outer tube, Hall and Palkin[26] use a series of short interlocked tubes for the center tube. In addition, these investigators wind the center tube with a fine glass thread to obtain uniform reflux distribution. Both these devices appear to increase the holdup. With the exception of a column made by Kuhn[21] metal tubes have not been used in the construction of concentric-tube columns. However, it appears that metal tubes should eliminate many of the difficulties encountered when glass tubes are used.

Spacing lugs, located above and below the rectifying section, are used to separate the inner and outer tubes. The length of the lugs must be carefully controlled, usually by grinding. Naragon and Lewis[27] use a metal-spiral spacer in the annular space of the rectifying section for preliminary spacing of the tubes. The tubes are then fused together through glass spacers above and below the rectifying section, and the metal spiral is dissolved in acid. (Detailed directions for the construction of concentric-tube columns are given by Naragon and Lewis.[27])

Kuhn[21] solves the difficult problem of reflux distribution by forming reflux on both tube surfaces. This is accomplished by extending both tubes into a jacketed space through which the condenser liquid flows. The inner and outer tubes are joined by a dewar seal. Naragon and Lewis[27] direct all the reflux liquid to the top of a sphere. Troughs attached to the sphere at the circumference direct the reflux to the tube surfaces. Since the distribution of reflux will be uniform around the circumference, the width of the trough automatically determines the amount of reflux going to each tube surface.

Like all low-throughput columns, the concentric-tube column requires very efficient insulation. Most investigators have used a vacuum jacket supplemented by lagging or by an auxiliary heater. The still pot should be designed to secure even boiling; heat input must be stable. This can be secured by using constant voltage in the heater and enclosing the still pot in a vacuum jacket.

Packed Columns. (*a*) *Dump Packings.* In packed columns, the rectifying section consists of a tube filled with an inert material or "packing" in the form of small regularly shaped particles, or irregular-shaped pieces turned or chipped from larger masses. Packings consisting of small individual particles are called "dump packings," from the mode of introducing them into a column. The packing may be an integral unit packed at random in the column in the case of chain packing, or may be a preformed close-fitting, rigid structure as in the case of Heli-Grid packing.

The downflowing reflux wets the packing surface to provide a large area of liquid film for contacting the ascending vapor stream. Both packed and wetted-surface columns are film-type columns, and the vapor–liquid processes are similar. In the usual wetted-surface column, however, the laminar flow of the vapor reduces the rate of exchange between vapor and liquid necessitates very low vapor rates to secure good rectification. In packed columns the packing causes frequent splitting of the vapor stream and produces a more turbulent flow. The turbulence increases the vapor diffusion coefficient and consequently permits higher vapor rates or throughputs.

The vapor and liquid streams in packed columns are not confined to a definite path but follow a haphazard course dictated by chance irregularities in the packing. Variations in the size or density of the packing are likely to cause loss of rectification efficiency due to channeling of the vapors or localized flooding. These effects are more pronounced in large-diameter columns and are minimized when the packing is of uniform size, symmetrically shaped, and the ratio of column diameter to the diameter of the individual packing units is greater than 8 to 1. In packed columns reflux collects and is retained at the points of contact between the packing units so that the holdup of packed columns is generally greater than in wetted-surface columns.

A good packing is one that can be packed uniformly and has the proper balance between surface area and free space to ensure efficient vapor–liquid contacting and high throughputs without excessive holdup and pressure drop. The rectification efficiency of most packings is increased if the packing is thoroughly wet by flooding at the start of the distillation. This treatment removes all entrapped air from the packing interstices and causes the reflux to spread uniformly over the packing surface.

Packed columns combine good rectification efficiency with high throughput and usually the holdup and pressure drop are not excessive. These characteristics combined with ease of construction and operation make packed columns ideal for general laboratory use.

(*b*) *Helices.* Of the numerous packings in many different shapes and of many materials of construction that have been used in laboratory fractionating columns, single-turn metal[31] and glass helices[32] have had widest application. Difficult problems of research in the petroleum industry which required separation of complex mixtures of hydrocarbons were largely responsible for development of metal helices for column packing. Glass helices were developed as a substitute for metal helices where the latter had insufficient resistance to corrosion, as in the fractionation of many organic compounds.

Several methods and machines have been devised for constructing glass and metal helices.[33–38] Fundamentally, all methods consist in winding wire or glass fibers on a rotating mandrel, adjacent turns being very nearly in contact. A high-speed rotating knife or stone then cuts, or, in the case of glass, knicks each turn across the fiber to produce a single helix of packing. Commercial production of both types of helices has been so well developed that there is no justification for building a machine to produce helices for a few columns.

Metal helices are available in several sizes to allow both large- and small-diameter columns to be packed with a size having the proper ratio of column diameter to helix diameter. If this ratio is 8 or higher, the packing fits closely to the tube wall and provides maximum efficiency in a given length. Standard metal helices are manufactured, usually of stainless steel, with

TABLE VII

Efficiency of Various Diameter Single-Turn Helices in a Column 5.0-cm. I.D. with Packed Section 259 cm.[a, 40]

Packing	Boil-up rate, ml./min.	Total press. drop range, mm. Hg.	No. of theor. plates	H.E.T.P., cm.
1/4-in. I.D. aluminum[b]	325–355	—	17–17.5	15.2–14.7
3/16-in. I.D. aluminum[c]	18–180	1–6	27–16.5	9.7–15.7
5/32-in. I.D. stainless steel[c]	58–197	– to 22	25.5–19	13.7–10.7
5/32-in. I.D. nickel[d]	168–265	10–22	32.5	7.9
1/8-in. I.D. nickel[c]	168	—	45.0	5.8
3/32-in. I.D. stainless steel[d]	33–125	4–23	68–44	3.8–5.8

[a] Tested with *n*-heptane–methylcyclohexane test mixture at total reflux.

[b] Incipiently flooded just prior to test.

[c] No flooding.

[d] Fully flooded prior to test.

inside diameters of $^3/_{64}$, $^1/_{16}$, $^3/_{32}$, and $^5/_{32}$ in. of No. 40, No. 36, No. 30, and No. 26 gage wire, respectively.[39]

The effect of helix diameter on H.E.T.P. in a column 50 mm. I.D. is shown in Table VII. The data include results on several sizes not commonly used to emphasize the effect of helix diameter on efficiency.[40]

It is apparent from the results of Table VII that decreasing the diameter of the helices leads to a marked reduction of H.E.T.P., particularly between helix diameters of $^1/_4$ in. and $^3/_{32}$ in. Permissible boil-up rate diminishes sharply with smaller diameter packing; the maximum efficiency is attained at lower boil-up rates.

More complete data, including holdup, efficiency factor, and pressure drop, of columns packed with $^1/_{16}$-in. and $^3/_{32}$-in. single-turn metal helices are given in Table VIII.

Metal helices $^1/_{16}$ and $^3/_{64}$ in. in diameter are of chief interest for packing high-efficiency columns of small physical size to minimize holdup and so permit fractionation of small charges. Construction of the rectifying section of an 80-plate analytical column packed with $^3/_{64}$-in. helices is shown in Figure 5.[41] H.E.T.P. of this column is 0.35 cm. Maximum boil-up rate is about 2.5 ml./min.; holdup is 8 ml., which gives an efficiency factor of about 1000.

TABLE VIII

Rectification Characteristics of Metal Helices[40]

Column		Through-put, ml./min.	Theor. plates	H.E.T.P., cm.	Holdup, ml./plate	Effic. factor	Pressure drop, mm. Hg/plate
Length cm.	Diam., cm.						
$^1/_{16}$-In. I.D. stainless steel of No. 34 wire							
71	0.8	0.38	55	1.3	0.16	140	—
105	2.54	8.3	65	1.6	1.2	420	0.02
105	2.54	16.7	62	1.7	1.6	630	0.07
105	2.54	51.0	43	2.5	3.3	925	0.65
$^3/_{32}$-In. I.D. stainless steel of No. 30 wire							
70	0.8	0.54	27	2.6	0.29	110	—
81	1.2	7.5	37	2.2	0.54	820	—
266	2.54	8.5	140	1.9	1.2	425	0.13
266	2.54	16.9	126	2.1	1.6	630	0.05
266	2.54	50.7	88	3.0	3.4	900	0.57
225	5.08	22.0	58	3.9	13.5	98	0.009
225	5.08	44.0	54	4.2	16.3	162	0.048
225	5.08	132.0	44	5.2	31.0	255	0.72

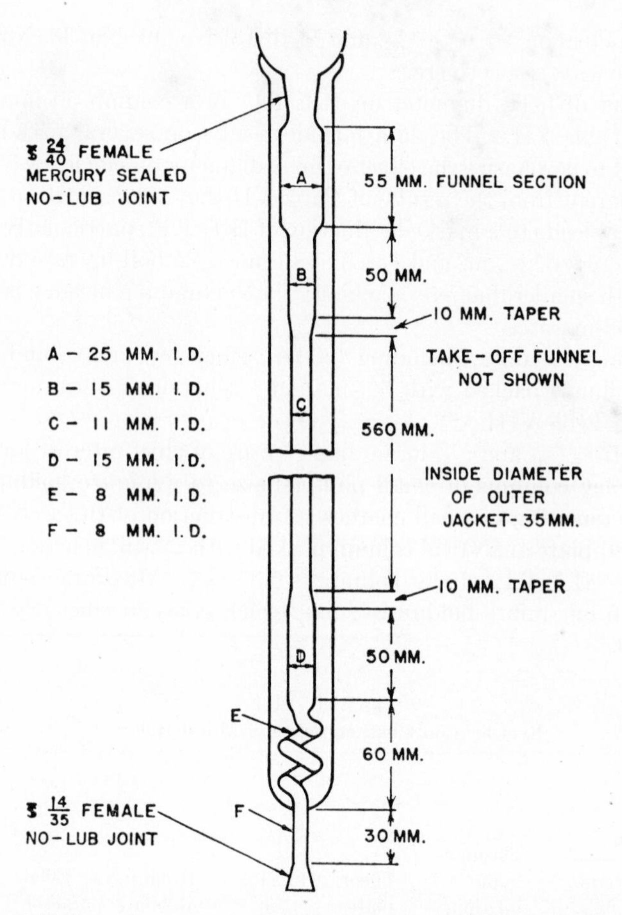

Fig. 5. Design of vacuum-jacketed column for analytical distillations.

Metal helices have achieved eminence as packing for laboratory columns chiefly because they provide high efficiency in reasonable column height at relatively low cost. Construction is easy, and column characteristics are fairly reproducible, particularly if the packing process is carefully and properly performed. Variations of H.E.T.P. in different columns of similar size and packing dimensions among different operators are to some extent a function of test procedure, purity of components of a text mixture, and analytical accuracy in making the tests, rather than vagaries in the behavior of the packing. Pressure drop across helices-packed columns is not excessive if reasonable throughputs are acceptable. Efficiency factor tends to be somewhat low, but except in analytical distillations of very complex mixtures whose components are close boiling, this factor is not serious.

Columns packed with metal helices probably diminish in efficiency as the packing undergoes a certain amount of corrosion inevitable under the most careful operating and cleaning conditions, and as small amounts of insoluble material deposit on the packing. These changes in efficiency will vary widely depending to a very large degree on the material distilled and on the extent of air leakage into the still pot, as well as on the effectiveness of the cleaning process after a distillation has been performed. No data are available on the effect of corrosion and deposits on the efficiency of helices-packed columns; however, a large Stedman column was tested after 3 years of use and found to have lost nearly 50% of its efficiency at high throughputs, but only a few per cent at low throughputs.[42]

Glass helices may be substituted for metal helices as packing for rectifying sections when the metal type is not resistant to chemical action of a distillate. Glass helices are not available in as many diameters as metal helices, they are less uniform in fiber diameter, and their fragile character prevents

TABLE IX
Rectification Characteristics of 1/8-in. Glass Helices at Total Reflux

Column length, cm.	I.D., cm.	Throughput, ml./min.	Theor. plates	H.E.T.P., cm.	Holdup, ml./plate	Effic. factor
43	1.0	2.7	11	3.9	0.70	230
43	1.0	7.8	11	3.9	0.77	610
80	1.2	3.7	21	3.8	—	—
80	1.2	11.3	18	4.3	—	—

TABLE X
Rectifying Efficiencies of 1/8-in. Glass Helices[a]

Column diam., cm.	Packed height, cm.	Theor. plates	H.E.T.P., cm.
1.1	26	9.0	2.8
1.3	38	5.0	7.6
0.8	40	6.7	6.1
1.4	44	8.6	5.1
1.3	44	11.5	3.8
1.4	45	11.0	4.1
0.9	53	14.0	3.8
1.6	60	9.7	6.1
1.3	63	9.0	6.9
1.7	82	12.5	6.6
1.5	87	18.5	4.8
1.4	135	21.3	6.3

[a] Tested with benzene–carbon tetrachloride at maximum throughput and total reflux.

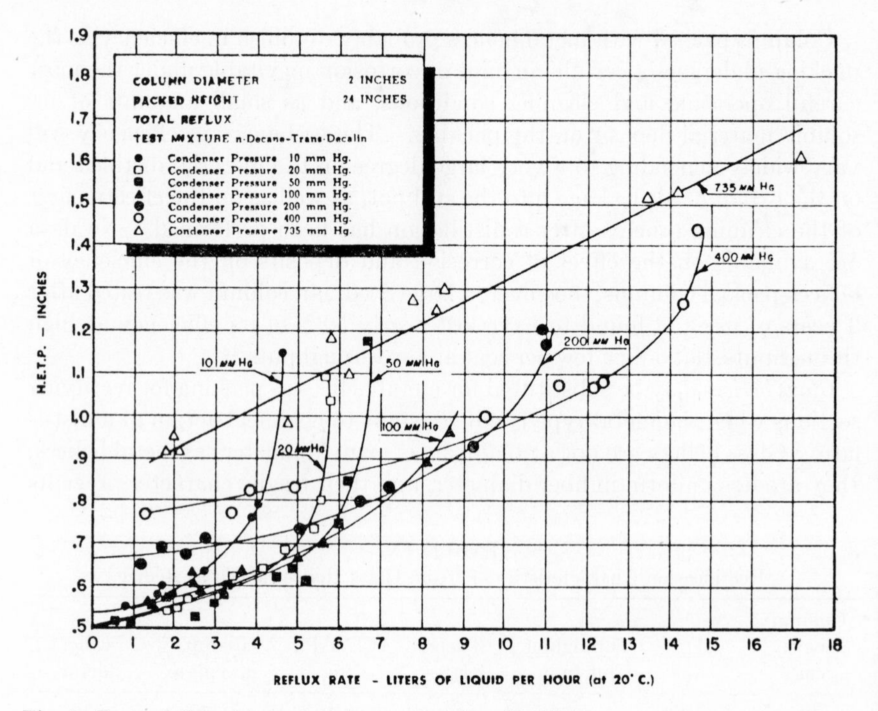

Fig. 6. Protruded packing—0.16 in. × 0.16 in.—H.E.T.P. vs. reflux rate for various reduced pressures.

tamping to provide a uniform packed section; consequently, a column packed with glass helices may have a greater H.E.T.P. than one packed with metal, other factors being equal.

Table IX gives the rectification characteristics of $^1/_8$-in. glass helices.[40] A tabulation by Fenske et al.[43] of a large number of columns built and tested by different workers is given in Table X.

The large variations of H.E.T.P. shown in Table X are not only the result of differences in column diameter, length of packed section, and inevitable differences in testing techniques, but are indicative of variations in packing density which occur when helices may not be tamped. The use of glass helices as packing is justified only when a noncorrosive packing is required, as in the fractionation of acids, organic halides, certain sulfur compounds, and some phenolic products.

(*c*) *McMahon Packing.* Although single-turn stainless-steel helices are one of the most efficient packings for laboratory columns 2 in. in diameter and smaller, they show increasingly poorer results as column diameters are increased. Values of H.E.T.P. increase, and under the most favorable conditions, a column 15.2 cm. (6 in.) in diameter would have an H.E.T.P.

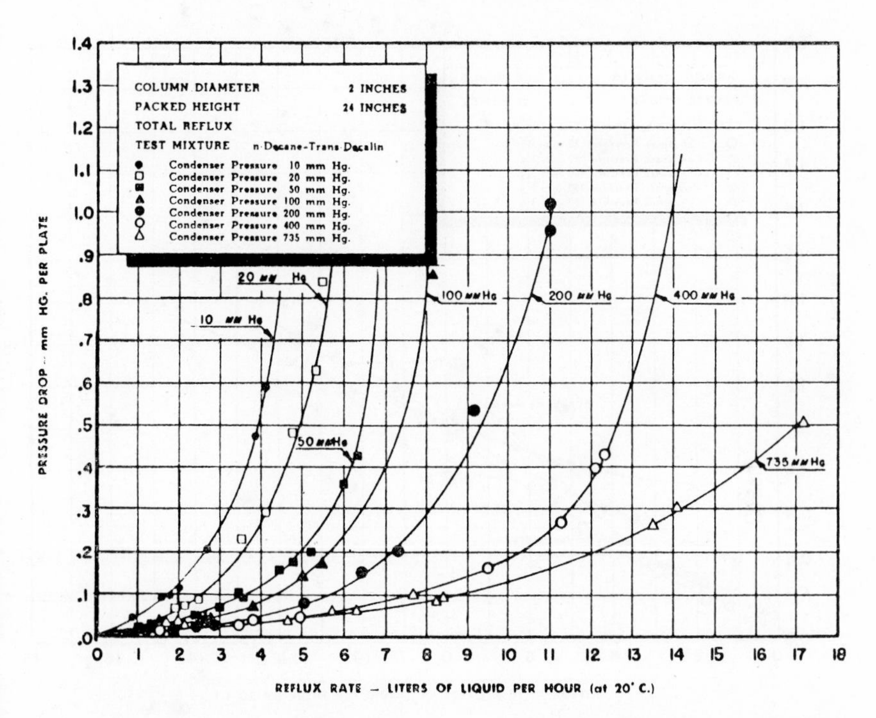

Fig. 7. Protruded packing—0.16 × 0.16 in.—pressure-drop vs. reflux rate for various reduced pressures.

TABLE XI
Rectification Characteristics[a] of McMahon Packing

Length packed section, cm. (in.), and material	Throughput, ml./min. Bottom	Top	Theor. plates	H.E.T.P., cm.	(in.)	Holdup, ml./plate	Effic. factor	Pressure drop, mm. Hg/plate
145 (57)	765	575	27.4	5.1	(2.1)	—	—	0.09
brass	1060	—	23.0	6.3	(2.5)	—	—	0.25
	1400		19.2	7.6	(3.0)	197	425	0.60
266 (105)	755	570	45.5	5.8	(2.3)	—	—	0.09
brass	1040	920	41.9	6.4	(2.5)	—	—	0.23
	1370	1260	30.1	6.4	(3.5)	197	415	0.60
146 (57.5)	810	—	17.3	8.4	(3.3)	—	—	0.13
Monel	1100	—	16.6	8.9	(3.5)	—	—	0.27
	1410	—	14.6	9.9	(3.9)	197	430	0.59

[a] Column diameter 15.2 cm. Benzene–ethylene dichloride test mixture at total reflux. Column was partially preflooded.

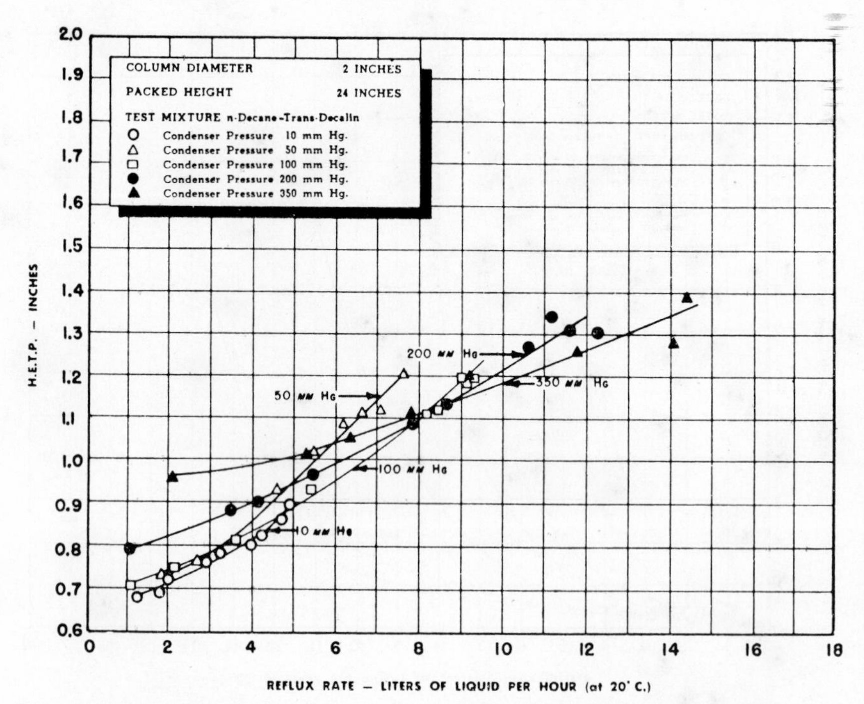

Fig. 8. Protruded packing—0.24 in. × 0.24 in.—H.E.T.P. vs. reflux rate for various reduced pressures.

equal to the column diameter or larger; McMahon packing[44] appears to have more favorable characteristics in this respect. This packing is made[45] by bending $^1/_4$-in. squares of wire cloth into the form of saddles; the cloth is 100 × 100 mesh with a wire diameter of 0.0045 in. The characteristics of the $^1/_4$-in. packing are given in Table XI.[46]

(*d*) *Protruded Packing.* A very satisfactory packing for use in columns 2.5 cm. in diameter and larger is known as "Protruded" packing.[47] It consists of small units made from thin metal which contain more than 1000 holes per square inch of surface and is shaped into a half-cylinder with corners or edges bent in to prevent stacking. The holes are not clean-cut, but a burr or protrusion is formed on one side. These burrs and holes impart an important property to the metal—because of them it is readily wetted by liquids. Preflooding is not necessary with this packing, a fact which greatly lowers the time required for initial equilibrium to be reached.

Protruded packing is available[48] in two nominal sizes of 0.16 × 0.16 and 0.24 × 0.24 in., made of stainless steel or of other metals on special order. Rectification characteristics of the packing in columns of several diameters, and for 2-in. columns at several pressures between 10 mm. and atmospheric

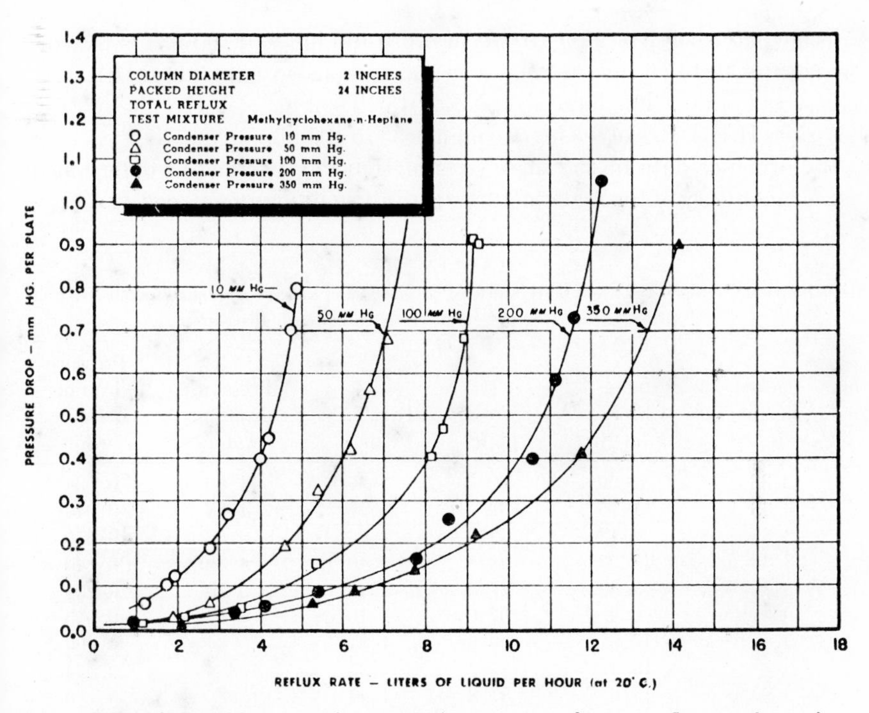

Fig. 9. Protruded packing—0.24 in. × 0.24 in.—pressure drop vs. reflux rate for various reduced pressures.

pressure are given in Tables XII and XIII, and in Figures 6–9.[48] For columns 4 in. and larger in diameter, the manufacturer recommends the use of redistributor plates to produce the most favorable values of H.E.T.P., and consistent operations; tested designs for these are available.[48] Excellent efficiency is obtained with all column diameters under reduced pressure operation with protruded packing.

(*e*) *"Heli-Pak" Packing.* Heli-Pak[49] packing, designed on the principles of the preformed Heli-Grid packing described below, consists of short lengths of rectangular wire coils, precisely spaced to effect capillary reflux liquid formation, lateral redistribution of reflux, and intimate vapor–liquid contacting. This packing has the desirable property of pouring freely without tangling and is easy to introduce into a column. The Heli-Pak packing is reputed to produce low H.E.T.P.'s and can be used to fill columns of all sizes from 8 mm. to 6-in. diameters. It is available in several corrosion resistant metals such as Nichrome, Hastelloy B, and Type 316 stainless steels. Heli-Pak is available in three sizes. The smallest size, No. 2916 (0.035 in. × 0.070 in. × 0.070 in.) is recommended for columns from 5 to 15 mm. in diameter and is capable of H.E.T.P. as low as 0.2 in. The intermediate size, No. 2917 (0.050 in. × 0.100 in. × 0.100 in.) is for columns from 10 to 50 mm. in diameter and is reported to yield an H.E.T.P. as low as 0.3 in. The large size, No. 2918 (0.092 in. × 0.175 in. × 0.175 in.) gives H.E.T.P.'s of 0.5 in. in columns 35 to 100 mm. in diameter.

Performance data of the three sizes of Heli-Pak packing as determined in the laboratory of the manufacturer[49] are given in Figures 10 and 11.

TABLE XII

Rectification Characteristics of 0.16 × 0.16 Protruded Packing as Measured with Normal Heptane–Methylcyclohexane at Atmospheric Pressure

Column diam., in.	Packed height, ft.	Reflux liters of liq./hr.	Total plates	H.E.T.P., in.	Pressure drop, in. water	Pressure drop per plate, in. water
1	3.38	1.50	29.6	1.37	1.00	0.034
	3.38	1.75	32.0	1.26	1.38	0.043
	3.38	2.12	32.0	1.26	2.52	0.079
	3.38	3.00	28.8	1.40	4.30	0.149
	3.38	3.50	27.3	1.48	5.70	0.209
2	9.8	6.4	107.0	1.10	1.6	0.015
	9.8	10.0	90.0	1.31	5.3	0.060
	9.8	13.4	87.2	1.35	10.8	0.124
	9.8	14.6	81.8	1.44	15.2	0.186
	9.8	17.6	85.6	1.38	21.2	0.248
	9.8	18.0	82.0	1.44	53.0	0.647
4	9.5	16.0	61.6	1.85	3.54	0.0575
	9.5	29.0	59.0	1.93	11.90	0.202
	9.5	42.0	63.3	1.80	31.0	0.49
6	6.08	29.5	35.1	2.1	0.8	0.023
	6.08	35.0	41.7	1.8	1.0	0.024
	6.08	41.6	30.3	2.4	1.1	0.036
	6.08	51.8	28.8	2.5	1.6	0.056
	6.08	69.5	31.2	2.3	2.4	0.077
	6.08	80.5	30.0	2.4	3.1	0.103
	6.08	95.8	28.1	2.6	4.4	0.157
	6.08	113.0	27.0	2.7	5.5	0.204

(*f*) *Dixon Packing.* Dixon packing has the familiar shape of Lessing rings but is constructed of fine wire mesh instead of solid metal strip. The packing is available in 1/16- and 1/8-in. diameter, each piece having a length equal to the diameter. It was developed mainly for laboratory columns in which high efficiency in small volume is desired. To attain minimum H.E.T.P. with Dixon packing, careful attention to preflooding is imperative, as has been shown by the inventor.[50] Table XIV gives the rectification characteristics of Dixon packing.[52]

TABLE XIII
Rectification Characteristics of 0.24 × 0.24 Protruded Packing as Measured with Normal Heptane–Methylcyclohexane at Atmospheric Pressure

Column diameter, in.	Packed height, ft.	Reflux liters of liq./hr.	Total plates	H.E.T.P., in.	Pressure drop, in. water	Pressure drop per plate, in. water
2	8.4	3.7	57.2	1.77	1.02	0.018
	8.4	6.1	51.2	1.97	2.38	0.0464
	8.4	11.3	49.5	2.04	7.22	0.146
	8.4	15.6	48.0	2.10	14.3	0.298
4[a]	10.0	16.6	71.0	1.70	1.0	0.01
	10.0	28.2	66.0	1.83	2.2	0.03
	10.0	40.6	57.0	2.10	6.0	0.11
	10.0	48.0	53.0	2.26	9.1	0.17
	10.0	65.1	47.0	2.54	19.0	0.40
	10.0					
6	6.08	26.1	49.3	1.5	0.6	0.0122
	6.08	27.6	47.0	1.6	0.7	0.0149
	6.08	40.9	36.9	2.0	0.9	0.0244
	6.08	43.9	34.7	2.1	0.9	0.0260
	6.08	50.7	29.5	2.5	1.2	0.0407
	6.08	55.5	34.8	2.1	1.3	0.0374
	6.08	71.2	30.6	2.4	1.9	0.0620
	6.08	90.5	27.1	2.7	2.9	0.107
	6.08	104.0	25.9	2.8	3.6	0.139
	6.08	118.0	25.0	2.9	4.5	0.180
12						
	3.0	254.0	18.3	1.97	0.71	0.0388
	3.0	340.0	16.0	2.25	1.13	0.0713
	3.0	405.0	15.9	2.27	1.58	0.0993
	3.0	503.0	14.9	2.41	2.99	0.200
	3.0	560.0	15.1	2.39	3.31	0.220
	3.0	607.0	14.4	2.50	4.18	0.290
	5.4[b]	282.0	32.1	2.01	1.57	0.049
	5.4[b]	383.0	29.4	2.20	2.68	0.091
	5.4[b]	444.0	25.1	2.57	3.66	0.146
	5.4[b]	503.0	22.0	2.93	4.69	0.213
	5.4[b]	585.0	20.6	3.13	6.36	0.309
	5.4[b]	630.0	18.9	3.41	7.28	0.385

[a] New interdistributors used every 3 feet.
[b] Interdistributor plate at 2.8 ft. level. Design of distributor plate furnished upon request.

(*g*) *Miscellaneous Packings.* Many particle shapes have been used for column packings. These have been reviewed by Fenske, Lawroski, and Tonberg.[40] Generally, they show no superiority to currently available packings and are not readily available in suitable materials of construction.

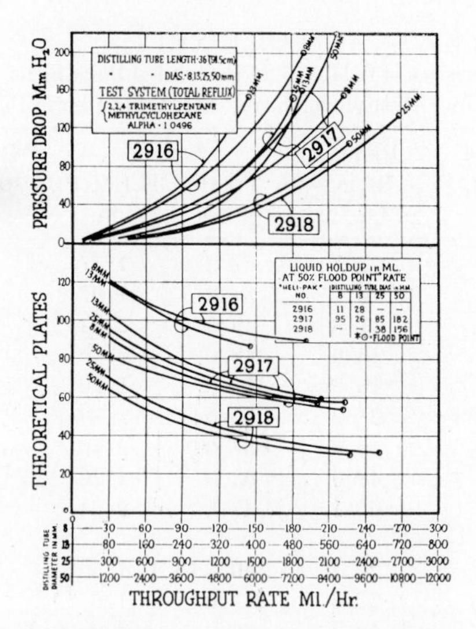

Fig. 10. Heli-Pak test data (760 torr.) Nichrome packing; particle size: No. 2916, 0.035 in. × 0.070 in. × 0.070 in.; No. 2917, 0.050 in. × 0.100 in. × 0.100 in.; No. 2918, 0.090 in. × 0.175 in. × 0.175 in.

(*h*) *Preformed Packings.* A. Stedman Packing. A number of wire-gauze packings for laboratory and industrial rectification columns have been developed by Stedman.[53,54] Figure 12 shows the conical type which has been found most suitable for laboratory columns. It consists of a series of wire-gauze disks stamped into flat, truncated cones and welded together alternately, base to base and edge to edge, to form a regular series of cells. Each cone has a semicircular opening which extends about two-thirds of the

TABLE XIV
Performance of "Dixon" Gauze Packing

Vapor velocity, ft./sec.	H.E.T.P., in.			
	A[a]	B[b]	C[c]	D[d]
1.4	1.08	1.21	1.25	1.76
1.2	1.03	1.15	1.20	1.63
1.0	0.95	1.06	1.16	1.56
0.8	0.86	0.96	1.09	1.54
0.6	0.74	0.83	0.97	1.51
0.5	0.67	0.75	0.86	1.50

[a] A, values for $^3/_{32}$-in. packing in $^3/_4$-in. I.D. column.[50]
[b] B, Data corrected for $1^1/_4$-in. I.D. column.[51]
[c] C, Values for $^1/_8$-in. packings in $1^1/_4$in. I.D. column.[52]
[d] D, Values for $^1/_8$-in. single-turn glass helices, $1^1/_2$-in. I.D. column.[52]

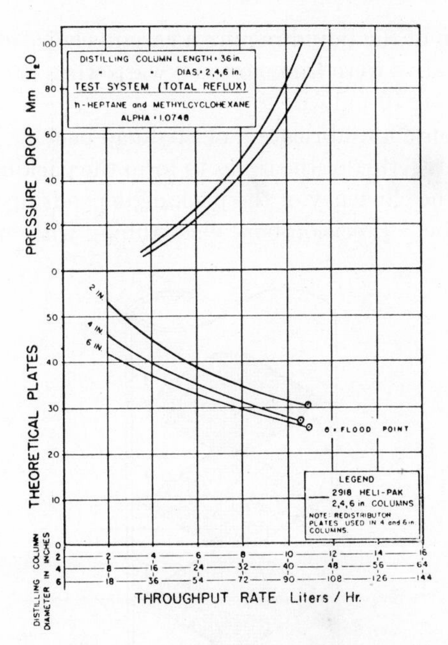

Fig. 11. Heli-Pak test data (760 torr) Nichrome packing; particle size: No. 2918, 0.090 in. × 0.175 in. × 0.175 in.

distance from the edge of the cone to the flat disk in the center. The cones are assembled so that the perforations, which serve as vapor passageways, are located alternately on opposite sides of the cells. Sections of packing are inserted into a close-fitting vertical tube to form the rectification section.

In operation, the ascending vapor enters the vapor hole in the lowest cell, flows practically horizontally through the cell, and leaves through the vapor perforation in the upper cone of the cell. The vapor stream then divides and passes between the containing tube and the gauze to the side of the column where it entered the first cell. The vapor stream then enters the second lowest cell. This flow pattern is repeated until the vapor has passed through all the cells.

The reflux liquid flows along the gauze as a thin film which seals the openings of the mesh and makes the vapor follow its prescribed course. The reflux also provides a liquid seal at the points of contact between the packing and the containing tube, and this prevents bypassing the vapor as the reflux descends the column it flows out toward the tube wall on the upper cone of each cell and then back toward the axis of the column as it flows along the lower cone of the cell.

To provide the proper mechanical strength, to furnish a surface of suitable roughness, and to give a mesh opening of a size that can be sealed by the surface tension of the liquid require a careful choice of gauze; the most satisfactory mesh sizes were from 36 to 60 warp wires per inch and from 36 to 40 weft wires using 10-mil wire.[53]

Stamping the cones for fabrication of Stedman packing requires precision dies; the welding together of the cones to form the packing requires the use of special jigs. The efficiency of the packing depends upon a close fit with the containing tube. Precision-bore glass tubing with an inside-diameter

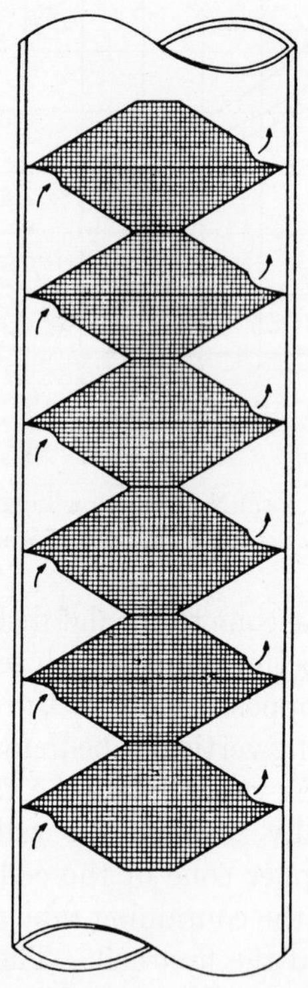

Fig. 12. Conical type Stedman packing.

tolerance of 0.001 in. is generally used for the containing tube. Furthermore, the insertion of the packing in the tube is rather difficult, and if not done properly the column efficiency is greatly decreased. For these reasons it is much easier and cheaper to purchase the assembled tube and packing than to construct it.[55]

A modification offered by Koch and van Raay[56] in which the cells are given a more spherical shape makes them flexible so that they can be readily inserted into the glass columns and are reported to function satisfactorily even when used in nonprecision bore columns.

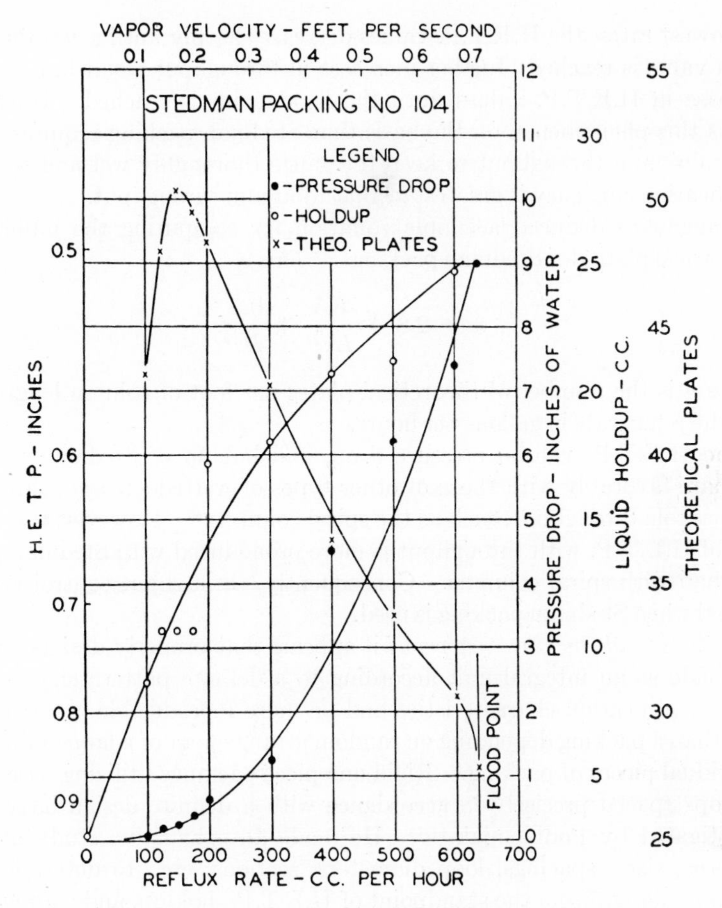

Fig. 13. Performance of conical-type Stedman packing.

The rectification characteristics of Stedman packings have been carefully studied.[9,57,58] In order to obtain the full efficiency of the packing it was necessary to preflood the packing before running the efficiency test. The enhanced efficiency caused by preflooding packings was first noted by Nickels.[59] In the case of Stedman packing, the preflooding operation appears to free thoroughly the gauze surfaces of entrapped air so that a strong, uniform liquid film forms, which completely prevents channeling with resultant loss of rectification efficiency.

Inspection of Figure 13, a plot of the data for the 1.9-cm. diameter packing, shows that, in contrast to other types of wetted-surface columns, the H.E.T.P. values of Stedman packing are not lowest at the lowest throughput. Instead, as the throughput of the Stedman packing is increased from the lowest rates, the H.E.T.P. values decrease sharply until a certain minimum value is reached; further increases in throughput result in a gradual increase in H.E.T.P. values until the flood point is reached. Bragg explains this phenomenon on the basis that Stedman packing requires a certain minimum throughput to keep the gauze thoroughly wet and that the rectification efficiency is greatest at this minimum throughput.

Bragg[57] has deduced a simple equation for computing the number of theoretical plates for Stedman packings. This is

$$n = 2.8 + \frac{6.5}{L^{0.27}} + \frac{0.5}{L^{0.9}}$$

where n is the number of theoretical plates per foot of column length and L is the reflux rate in gallons per hours.

The H.E.T.P. values, pressure drop, and holdup of Stedman packing compare favorably with those of other types of wetted-surface columns of comparable throughput, such as the spiral columns.[60] However, the variation of H.E.T.P. with throughput is more pronounced with Stedman packing than with spiral columns. Consequently, throughput control is more critical when Stedman packing is used.

B. Heli-Grid Packing. *A priori* it appears that properly designed packing made as an integral unit according to a definite pattern should have better rectification characteristics and be more reproducible constructionwise than a packing depending on random arrangement of a large number of individual pieces of packing. Rigid one-piece packings utilizing wire turns or loops spaced precisely in accordance with a definite design have been investigated by Podbielniak.[11,49] He made an exhaustive study of wire patterns, sizes, spacings, loop diameters, sections, etc., to determine the optimum design from the standpoint of H.E.T.P., holdup, and throughput.

Two forms of close-clearance wire packings which Podbielniak[49] found to have exceptionally good rectification characteristics are shown in Figure 14 and described as follows:

> "The packing in Fig. 14A consists of coils of sectorlike section, wound around each and around a very small core wire, to yield a number of uniform nonflooding vapor passageways, lined perfectly with capillary liquid reflux films extending between vertically adjacent wire loops. Another form of packing (Fig. 14B) consists of wire cage staircases, wound around a central solid core and around each other in concentric telescoping layers, if necessary to obtain larger diameters and capacities."

These packings, which have been called Heli-Grid, have been made in diameters ranging from 0.57 to 2.5 cm. and in length up to 6 ft. Wire sizes and spacings vary with the design, but usually the wire is about 0.010-in. diameter with spacings between wires about equal to wire diameter. The packing is made from corrosion-resistant Nichrome or Inconel.

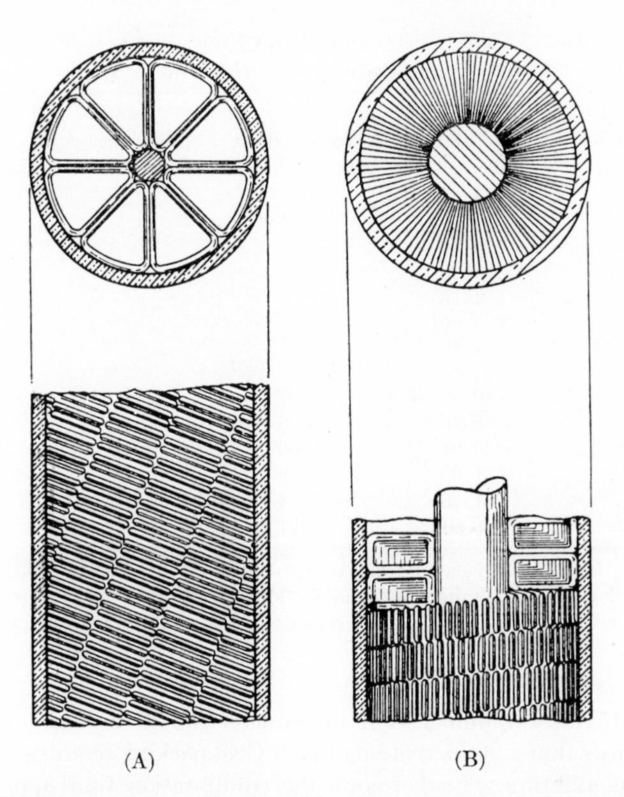

Fig. 14. Heli-grid packings: (A) Assembly of sector-section coils twisted around central core; (B) Staircase assembly of rectangular section coils around central core.

The results of fractionating-efficiency tests on Heli-Grid rectifying sections of various diameters are given in Table XV. The data show that the Heli-Grid packings combine low H.E.T.P., low holdup, and low pressure drop with a fairly high throughput resulting in an excellent efficiency factor. Over most of the useful operating range, the H.E.T.P. shows a rather marked variation with throughput so that the packing requires an extremely efficient adiabatic jacket and exact control of the heat input to the still pot in order to secure stable operation and full utilization of the fractionating efficiency of the Heli-Grid packing. A remarkably efficient vacuum jacket and auxiliary accessories have been developed to attain this end.[49]

The time required for a rectifying section to reach equilibrium is an important criterion for comparing column designs. Unfortunately, the literature does not contain much information on this subject. In the case of the Heli-Grid packing, however, such data are available[61] and are plotted

TABLE XV

Rectification Characteristics of Heli-Grid Packing[a]

Throughput, ml./min.	H.E.T.P.,[b] cm.	Pressure drop, mm. Hg/plate	Liquid holdup, ml./plate	Efficiency factor plates/hr.
		0.57-cm. diameter		
0.83	0.76	—	—	—
1.25	1.20	—	0.02	3750
1.67	1.76	—	—	—
2.50	2.29	—	—	—
		0.80-cm. diameter		
1.25	0.59	0.02	—	—
1.67	0.73	0.04	—	—
2.08	0.91	0.06	0.04	3120
2.50	1.09	0.09	—	—
3.33	1.36	0.14	—	—
4.17[a]	1.60	0.19	—	—

[a] 91.5-cm. length interpolated from curves published by Podbielniak.[49] Data at H.E.T.P. below 0.9 cm. obtained in 35-cm. section.

[b] Determined with *n*-heptane–methylcyclohexane test mixture, packing preflooded, at total reflux.

in Figure 15, for a column 2.5 cm. in diameter and 36 in. long. Inspection of data shows that a 36-in. section of Heli-Grid packing requires about 8 hr. to reach equilibrium; furthermore, the equilibration time appears to be independent of throughput.

Like many types of column packing, the Heli-Grid exhibits improvement of fractionation efficiency upon preflooding. The effect of preflood is illustrated in Figure 16, for a column 2.5 cm. in diameter and 30 in. long. The data show that the number of theoretical plates in the Heli-Grid packed column is increased about one-third as a result of preflooding. Of interest is the fact that the preflooded and unpreflooded columns both require the same equilibration time.

To secure the best results from a fractional distillation, the usual practice is to use a still-pot charge which is large with respect to column holdup. Podbielniak,[49] however, obtained some remarkable fractionation results when he used a still-pot charge which was roughly equivalent to the total column holdup, and used a column containing more plates than theoretically necessary for the separation. The distillation curve shown in Figure 17 shows an analytical separation of *n*-heptane and methylcyclohexane (boiling-point difference 2.5°C.) in a 2.2-cm. diameter, 6-ft.-long Heli-Grid packed column. The total distillation time was only 10 hr. and a reflux ratio of only 12:1 was used. The sample size of 75 ml. was approximately

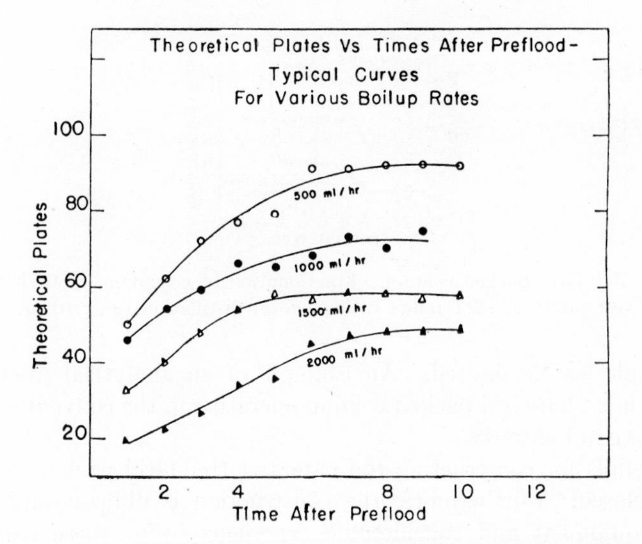

Fig. 15. Heli-Grid packed rectifying column, 2.5-cm. diameter, 36-in. long.

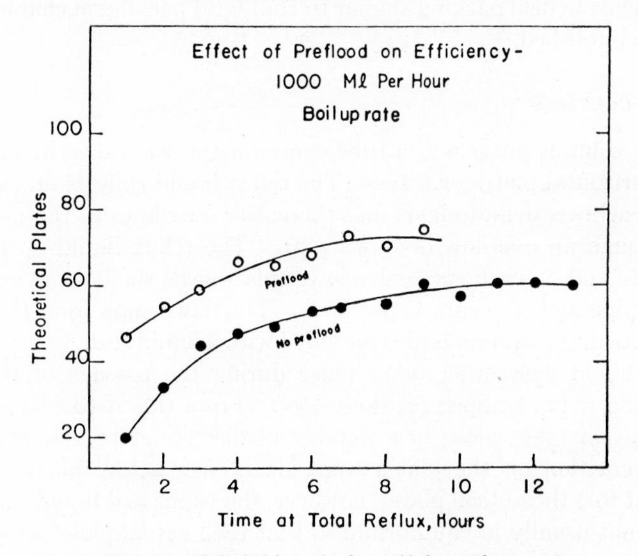

Fig. 16. Heli-Grid packed rectifying column.

equal to the column holdup. Toluene was used as a chaser to "push" the sample up the column. Podbielniak's procedure should be applicable to other types of rectifying sections.

The rectification characteristics of the Heli-Grid packing make it especially useful for analytical fractionations, particularly when the avail-

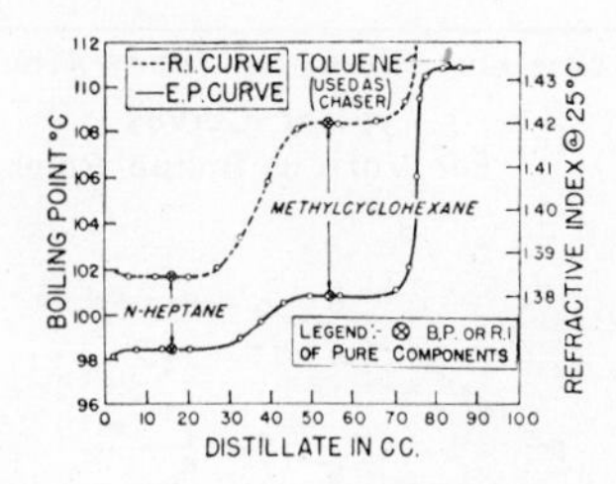

Fig. 17. A Heli-Grid packed column. Fractionation of *n*-heptane–methylcyclohexane test mixture, 12:1 reflux ration; total distillation time, 10 hr.

able sample size is limited. An example of an analytical fractionation obtained in a Heli-Grid packed column operating in the conventional manner is shown in Figure 48.

Full details for constructing the patented Heli-Grid packings have not been disclosed. Furthermore, the construction is difficult and requires precise equipment and considerable experience. For these reasons the purchase of the assembled columns is recommended.[49] Constructional details of a glass helical packing similar to Heli-Grid packing in characteristics have been published.[62]

B. PLATE COLUMNS

A plate column consists of a tube containing a vertical series of equally spaced horizontal plates or trays. The reflux liquid collects on each plate until it reaches a definite level and thereafter overflows to the next lower plate through an overflow or down pipe. The reflux liquid on this next lower plate and on each successive lower plate seals the bottom end of the overflow pipe and prevents vapor flow. The down pipe from the first or lowest plate in the column is also provided with a liquid seal.

Vapor–liquid contacting takes place during the passage of the vapor through the reflux trapped on the plates. From this it can be seen that the separation takes place in a number of discrete steps. If the vapor–liquid interaction on the plates were ideal, each actual plate would be equivalent to 1 theoretical plate; however, the vapor and liquid leaving the plate are not usually in equilibrium so that each actual plate is equivalent to only about 0.50 to 0.75 of a theoretical plate, or each actual plate has an efficiency of 50 to 75%.

Two methods of plate construction are commonly used for dispersing the vapor in the liquid: bubble-cap plates and perforated plates. Each plate of a bubble-cap column contains one or more vapor-riser tubes which extend above the liquid level on the plate. A circular cup or bubble cap of larger diameter than the riser is inverted over each vapor riser and deflects the

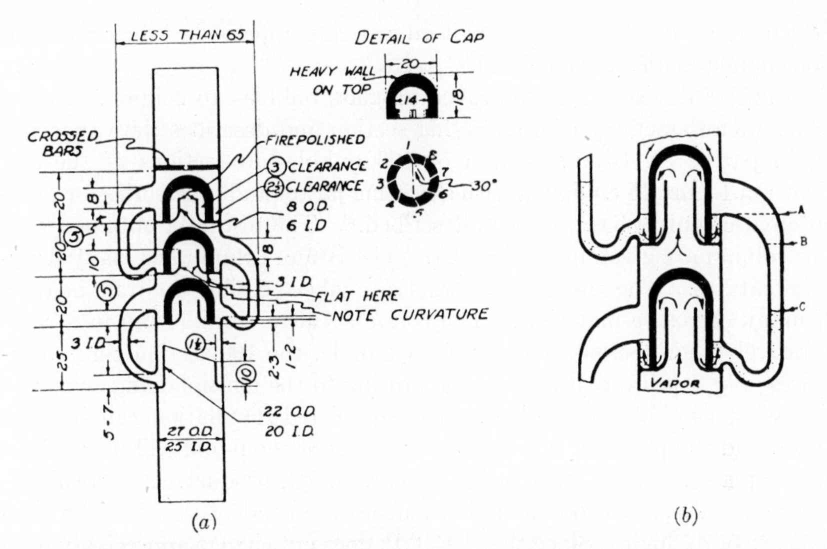

Fig. 18. Brunn bubble-cap rectifying section. (*a*) Bubble-cap column design: Slots in bubble cap about 0.5 to 1 mm. deep, at 30° angle. All dimensions in millimeters, exact dimensions circled. (*b*) Operation of bubble cap: (*A*) flood point; (*B*) maximum operating rate; (C) normal operating rate.

vapor beneath the surface of the liquid. The vapor passes through the slots in the periphery of the cap and enters the liquid as a stream of small bubbles. In perforated-plate columns vapor rises through perforations in the plate. The pressure and velocity of the vapors passing through the perforations must be sufficient to hold up the liquid on the plate. If the pressure and velocity are too low, the liquid descends through the perforations, and if too high the liquid is pushed off the plate and the contacting efficiency decreases.

Plate columns have much higher throughputs than film-type columns, and the rectifying efficiency is nearly independent of boil-up rate so that operation is simple and uniform. Owing to the necessity of maintaining a liquid layer on the plates, the holdup and pressure drop are comparatively high. The rectifying efficiency of plate columns as measured by the H.E.-T.P. is usually lower than in film-type columns. Generally speaking, the construction of laboratory-size plate columns is more difficult than that of an average laboratory film-type column.

The characteristics of plate columns make them extremely useful for the purification or analysis of large samples.

Bubble-Cap Columns. Laboratory bubble-cap columns were first employed by LeBel and Henninger.[14] Their column and several other early types[63,64] are described by Young;[14] unfortunately, the test data presented are insufficient to permit an accurate appraisal of their rectification characteristics and efficiencies.

Bruun[66,67] developed an improved all-glass bubble-cap column. Figure 18 shows an assembly of a rectifying section and describes the vapor and liquid paths. A Bruun column of 100 bubble-cap sections of the size shown in Figure 18 equipped with a heating jacket and accessories for semiautomatic control has also been described.[68] The test data obtained with this column are given in Table XVI. The Bruun column has many desirable features. The all-glass construction makes possible the fractionation of many corrosive materials. The column reaches equilibrium in a comparatively short period of time; for example, the 100-section column requires only 2–6 hr., and furthermore, owing to the nonsiphoning construction of the bubble-cap section, an uncompleted distillation can be shut down, and the partially fractionated portions of the liquid will be retained on the plates. When the distillation is resumed, product withdrawal can commence almost as soon as reflux reaches the condenser. The throughputs are fairly high. Since the H.E.T.P. does not change appreciably with throughput, the Bruun column is easy to operate.

TABLE XVI

Rectification Characteristics of Bruun Bubble-Cap Column[a]

Throughput, liquid, ml./min.	Total No. theor, plates[b]	H.E.T.P., cm.	Liquid Holdup, ml./theor. plate[c]	Efficiency factor, plates/hr.
5	70.6	2.8	—	320
8	84.2	2.4	0.93	450
10	72.6	2.8	—	650
30	Flood Pt.			

[a] 2.5-cm. diameter, 100 bubble-cap section, 2-cm. spacing between plates.

[b] Determined with *n*-heptane–methylcyclohexane test mixture.

[c] Dynamic holdup determined at an undisclosed but normal throughput. Static holdup is much larger.

The Bruun column is also useful for the distillation of materials containing dissolved water. Frequently during the early stages of a distillation, the presence of water will be detected in a supposedly "dry" still-pot charge. The water distills as an azeotrope, and usually the azeotrope is heterogeneous and is the lowest boiling constituent. Thus when the column is being brought to equilibrium, water condenses in the fractionating section. The presence of two liquid phases in the fractionating section usually makes column operation very difficult. The Bruun column is an exception in this respect. The main disadvantage of this column is the exceptionally high pressure drop. Tests in the author's laboratory of a 50-section column of

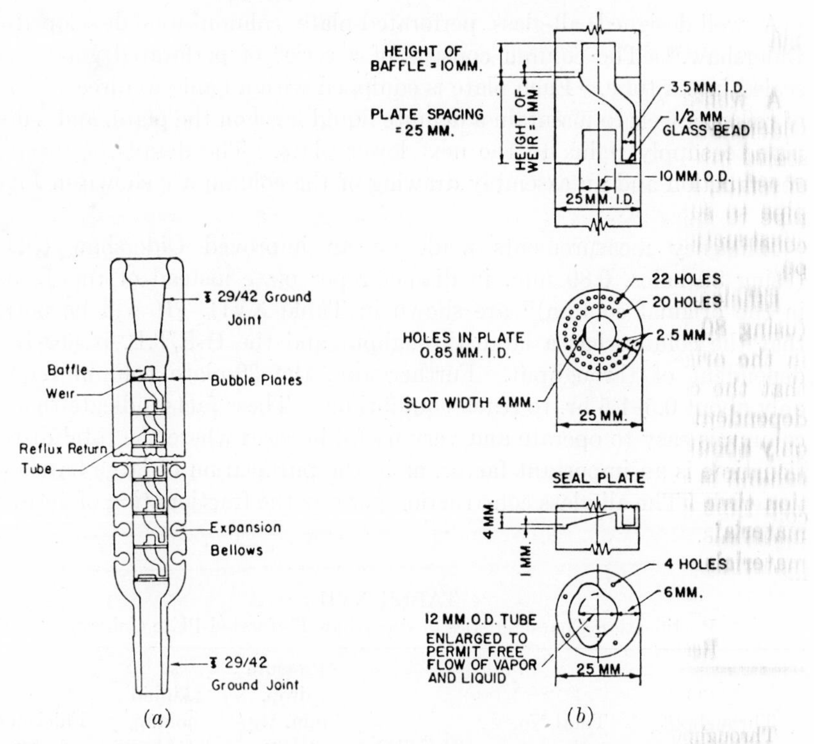

Fig. 19. Oldershaw perforated-plate column: (*a*) column; (*b*) plate construction.

the type described in Figure 18 indicate a pressure drop of 0.7–2.0 mm. mercury per theoretical plate at the minimum and maximum throughputs, respectively. The high pressure drop makes the column unsuitable for many vacuum fractionations.

The Bruun column is difficult to construct but is available from several glass fabricators, who manufacture this column as a stock item.[69] Despite its appearance of fragility, a properly manufactured, installed, and operated Bruun column is as rugged as most types of glass equipment and has a long life. Vacuum-jacketed columns of the same type are also available.[70]

Perforated-Plate Columns. Perforated-plate columns have been used for laboratory distillations since 1871.[71] The early columns generally employed metal gauze or screen for the plates and glass for the retaining tube and down pipes. The published data on these older columns do not permit a reliable evaluation of their rectification characteristics, but the designs indicate H.E.T.P. values in the order of several centimeters and large holdups. Readers interested in the earlier designs are referred to the original articles.[72–75] Several of the designs are discussed by Young.[14]

A well-designed all-glass perforated-plate column was developed by Oldershaw.[76] The column consists of a series of perforated glass plates sealed into a tube. Each plate is equipped with a baffle to direct the flow of reflux, a weir to maintain a definite liquid level on the plate, and a down pipe to supply reflux to the next lower plate. The details of the plate construction and an assembly drawing of the column are shown in Figure 19.

Efficiency measurements made on an improved Oldershaw column (using 80 holes, 0.89 mm. in diameter per plate instead of the 42 used in the original column)[77] are shown in Table XVII. It will be noticed that the column has a large throughput and the H.E.T.P. is nearly independent of throughput. Furthermore, the 30-plate column requires only about 0.5–1.5 hr. to reach equilibrium. These facts indicate that the column is easy to operate and very useful in cases where the total distillation time is an important factor, as in the purification of large batches of material. The all-glass construction permits the fractionation of corrosive materials.

TABLE XVII
Rectification Characteristics of Oldershaw Perforated-Plate Column[a]

Throughput liquid, ml./min.	Total No. theor. plates[b]	H.E.T.P., cm.	Pressure drop, mm. Hg/ theor. plate	Liquid holdup, ml./theor. plate	Efficiency, factor, plates/hr.
25	17.2	4.4	—	2.7	550
42	18.8	4.0	0.98	2.7	930
50	19.4	3.9	0.98	2.7	1100
58	18.2	4.1	1.11	3.0	1150
67	16.7	4.5	1.29	3.5	1140
80–85	Flood Pt.				

[a] 2.6 to 2.8-cm. diameter; 30 actual plates; 80 0.89-mm. diameter holes per plate; 2.5-cm. spacing between plates.
[b] Determined with *n*-heptane–methylcyclohexane test mixture.

The Oldershaw column has a plate efficiency of 60–65%, which is slightly lower than that of the Bruun column and uses a 2.5-cm. spacing between plates compared with 3.0 cm. for the Bruun column. As a consequence, the H.E.T.P. of the Oldershaw column is somewhat higher than that of the Bruun column. However, the Oldershaw column was designed for ease of operation and flexibility rather than low H.E.T.P. The plate efficiency of the Oldershaw column is increased by decreasing the size of the perforations;[76] when fritted-glass plates are used, extremely high plate efficiencies

TABLE XVIII

Oldershaw Perforated-Plate Column Pressure Drop with Liquids of Various Surface Tensions

Throughput liquid, ml./hr.	Pressure drop per actual plate, mm. Hg			
	n-Heptane	Methylcyclo-hexane	Benzene	Formic acid
200	—	—	—	0.88
400	—	—	—	0.95
600	—	—	—	1.02
800	—	—	—	1.09
1000	—	—	0.76	1.18
1125	—	—	—	1.23[a]
1500	0.50	0.62	0.82	—
2000	0.53	0.63	0.84	—
2500	0.55	0.65	0.87	—
3000	0.57	0.67	0.91	—
3500	0.60	0.71	1.00	—
4000	0.64	0.77	1.11	—
4280	—	—	1.17[a]	—
4500	0.70	0.85	—	—
5000	0.77	0.93	—	—
5230	0.80[a]	0.97[a]	—	—
				—
Physical Constants				
Boiling pt., °C.	98.4	100.8	80.1	100.8
Density, g./ml.				
at 20°C.	0.6837	0.7601	0.8790	1.220
at b.p.	0.6180	0.6989	0.8153	1.170
Surface tension, dynes/cm.				
at 20°C.	20.26	23.73	29.02	37.6
at b.p.	12.5	15.7	21.3	29.0

[a] Flood point with given liquid.

can be obtained;[78] increasing the weir height also increases the plate efficiency.[79] It should be possible to reduce the plate spacing of the Oldershaw column to give a lower H.E.T.P., but this change would cause increased operating difficulties, lower throughput, and higher holdup and pressure drop.

Using a 1-in. sieve plate column, Umholtz and VanWinkle[80] showed that best performance was obtained with holes of 1.9 mm./diameter and that performance fell off rapidly as the pressure on the column was reduced from atmospheric.

Owing to the capillarity of the holes in the plate, the throughput and pressure drop of the Oldershaw column are dependent upon the surface tension of the material being distilled. This has been illustrated (Table XVIII) by pressure-drop measurements of the column at various throughputs using several compounds of different surface tension as the distilland. The data of Table XVIII indicate the column is not suitable for the fractionation of materials of high surface tension; small amounts of undissolved water in the reflux are very troublesome and may cause the column to become inoperable. Additional work on the interaction of the plate and the physical properties of the distilling liquid have been reported.[81] In this respect the Bruun column is decidedly superior to the Oldershaw column. The high pressure drop of the Oldershaw column makes it unsuitable for many types of reduced-pressure operations. The 30-section column is not recommended for head pressures much below 250 mm.[77] The Oldershaw column has a high dynamic holdup (Table XVII). However, insofar as sharpness of separation is concerned, the extremely high throughput tends to offset the holdup and enables fairly sharp separations to be made. This same effect also results in a good efficiency-factor rating for the column. As a consequence, the Oldershaw column is satisfactory for analytical fractionations provided the available quantity of still-pot charge is not limited. The column is self-draining and tests with *n*-heptane indicate a static holdup of about 0.02 ml. per actual plate.[77]

Instructions for the construction of the Oldershaw column are available;[76] however, the construction is quite difficult and requires the services of a skilled glass blower and special tools. The columns are available commercially.[82] A simplified version of the Oldershaw column has been described in which the plates are supported by spacers rather than sealed into the column tube.[79] However, the difficult construction of the perforated plate remains.

In many laboratory distillations the presence of metal in the Oldershaw type of column is not harmful. In such cases an all-metal perforated plate offers distinct advantages from the standpoint of construction; the perforated plates, for example, can be stamped from metal screen. Furthermore, a metal perforated-plate column can be designed with rectification characteristics closely approaching those of the all-glass Oldershaw column. Such a column along with complete constructional details has been described.[83]

C. RECTIFYING SECTIONS EMPLOYING MOVING PARTS

Several investigators have advocated the use of mechanical agitation in the rectifying section of wetted-surface columns with the object of increasing diffusion effects to attain more rapid equilibrium than occurs naturally in such columns, and thereby permit high throughputs and constant efficiency to be attained.

One of the most elegant and unusual columns of this type was devised by Podbielniak.[84] A $^1/_8$-in. spiral passageway 4 in. wide and 160 ft. long provides the vapor–liquid contacting area. The spiral is rotated at 1200 r.p.m. to move reflux by centrifugal action from the center of the spiral to the still pot. The efficiency of the contactor is about 80 theoretical plates at 12 l./hr. boil-up. Pressure drop at that rate is 10–20 mm. mercury at atmospheric pressure.

Huffman and Urey[85] and Mair and Willingham[86] replaced packing or plates by a series of inverted and truncated widely interleaved fixed and rotating cones; each of the latter discharges a spray of reflux onto the upper side of the fixed cone immediately below it. Vapor flows in the spaces between the fixed and rotary cones. Although the efficiency factor (100–300) is much lower than in other wetted-surface columns, the permissible throughput is fairly high and the H.E.T.P. is surprisingly uniform and is independent of the speed of rotation of the cones between 250 and 1500 r.p.m.

The low efficiency factor of the rotating cone column contrasts with the spectacularly high efficiency factor of 10,600 attained by the rotating concentric-tube column developed by Willingham, Sedlak, Westhaver, and Rossini.[9] This column combines the low holdup, low pressure drop, and high rectification efficiency characteristic of film-type columns with the high throughput characteristics of plate or packed columns. In this type of rectifying section, vapor–liquid contacting takes place in the annular space formed by a stationary outer tube and a rotating concentric inner tube. At sufficient speeds of rotation the vapor phase is thrown into turbulence. This increases the diffusion coefficient in accordance with theory and allows vapor velocity or throughput to be increased without decreasing rectification efficiency.

The column studied by Rossini et al. at the National Bureau of Standards used a stationary tube 7.658 cm. I.D. and a rotor 7.440 cm. O.D. The annular space was 0.109 cm. thick. The rectifying section was 58.4 cm. long.

Characteristics of this column are interesting. Pressure drop, although quite low for a given throughput, increases with both throughput and speed of rotation of the rotor (up to 4000 r.p.m.) H.E.T.P. decreases with throughput, but for a given throughput increases with rotor speed up to the maximum studied (4000 r.p.m.). At about 2300–2500 r.p.m., the rectification efficiency increases markedly as a result of vapor flow becoming turbulent. At a throughput of 1500 ml. of liquid per hour, for example, and 4000 r.p.m., the H.E.T.P. is about 1 cm.

The major objection to the three foregoing fractionating devices is the numerous mechanical problems of construction, balance, and lubrication associated with the necessary support of high-speed rotating parts. No simple solution for some of these problems is apparent.

A simpler design of column with moving parts is the spinning-band column. These have been investigated by a number of workers.[87–100] The interest has usually been to attain low holdup, but in the instance of Birch, Gripp, and Nathan,[91] the aim was to use the low impedance of this construction to attain low-pressure drop in vacuum fractionation where low-pressure drop is important, in fact, imperative. In its simplest construction, a spinning-band column may be similar to that of a packed column with the packing and its support replaced by a thin metal band, the width of which is very nearly equal to the inside diameter of the column. The latter is preferably of Tru-bore quality. The band is twisted lengthwise through several revolutions to produce a highly stable rotator, and to provide a modicum of lift to the vapor to help overcome pressure drop. The spinning band is light enough in weight to be supported only at its upper end on a light thrust bearing located in an area free of vapor and liquid. Column diameters investigated have ranged from 6 to 40 mm. Bands for the small diameter columns are of the simplest construction.

Murray[92] studied in some detail various band designs and found some that were better for vacuum operation while others functioned best at atmospheric pressure. One type consisting of flat blades of stainless steel interspaced with bearings at regular intervals, to center the band in the column, gave an H.E.T.P. of 2.07 cm. at atmospheric pressure. At a pressure of 0.5 mm. Hg the effectiveness of the blade rotor was substantially decreased. A more suitable rotor was therefore developed consisting of stainless steel gauze attached to the blades. The gauze wiped the walls of the column and provided an even film of reflux. Sharp separations of fatty acids, methyl esters, and fatty alcohols were achieved with the gauze rotor at pressures of 0.5–2.0 mm. Hg. The author claims that it should be possible to fractionate compounds with 30 or 32 carbon atoms without decomposition.

Another study of rotor design was made by Nerheim[96] using Teflon material. Several rotors were made having a different number of blades. The author credits the high efficiency of the Teflon rotors to the specific design features such as: more blades, larger band core, and more points of contact with the reflux on the column wall. These features achieve better mixing, shorter vapor diffusion paths, and smoother band rotation. In addition higher optimum band speeds are obtained because of less frictional heat developed due to the low coefficient of friction of the Teflon.

Winters and Dinerstein[98] and Nerheim and Dinerstein[99] have tabulated in one instance some comparative information on three types of small columns suitable for precise distillation work, and in another instance the

TABLE XIX
Typical Column Data[98]

	Spinning band	Hyper-Cal[a]	Concentric tube
Inside diameter, mm.	5	8	8
Length, cm.	90	60–90	60
Sample size, ml.	10–50	20–100	10–50
Fraction size, ml.	0.5	0.5–1.0	0.5
Throughput, w./hr.	10–30	20–30	20–30
Take-off rate, ml./hr.	0.5–1.5	0.5–1.5	0.2–0.5
Reflux ratio	40:1	40:1	100:1
H.E.T.P., cm.[b]	1.1	0.7	0.9
Holdup per 90 cm., in ml.[a]	1.9	4.8	3.2[c]

[a] Contains Heli-Grid packing.[49]
[b] At 20 ml./hr. throughput and total reflux.
[c] Determined on 60-cm. column.

physical characteristics, operational conditions, and performance for the same kind of stills. The columns compared include the spinning band, the Hyper-Cal, and the concentric tube. The data are presented in Tables XIX and XX.

TABLE XX
Comparable Still Data[99]

	Diam., mm.	Length, cm.	Band speed, r.p.m.	Through-put, ml./hr.	H.E.T.P.
Spinning band column					
Podbielniak[49]	5	60	2500	60	1.0
Lesene, Lochte[89]	6	37.5	1000	—	2.5
Zuiderweg[93]	6	60	3600	40	1.3
Murray[92]	6	75	—	—	1.2
Cruthirds et al.[94]	6.5	60	4000	100	3.8
Crozier et al.[95]	8	110	2300	20	3.2
Hyper-Cal column					
Podbielniak[49]		30		26	0.49
Concentric-tube column					
Naragon, Lewis[27]	8[a]	30		77	0.35
Podbielniak[49]	8[a]	60		20	0.67
Donnell and Kennedy[30]	14[a]	70		30	0.53

[a] Annular space 0.75 mm.

Most of these units have H.E.T.P.'s close to 1 cm. for throughputs in the range of 20 ml./hr. and for total reflux operation. The spinning band columm has a low pressure drop and low holdup which makes it especially useful for distilling small samples under reduced pressures. The Hyper-Cal[49] column gives best performance at atmospheric pressure and should be most useful when efficiency rather than holdup is important. The all-glass concentric tube still offers primarily inertness to corrosive distillands; its low H.E.T.P. is achieved at the expense of very low boil-up rate.

A column similar to that designed by Birch, Gripp, and Nathan[91] was tested in the author's laboratory at atmospheric pressure with a methylcyclohexane–heptane test mixture, and at 1.0-mm. pressure with a *n*-butyl azelate–*n*-butyl phthalate test mixture.[97] The H.E.T.P. at atmospheric pressure was about 2 in. and, at 1 mm. about 8 in. Pressure drop at the lower operating pressure was only about 0.05 mm. for a boil-up rate of 300 g./hr. A spinning band twisted through a greater number of revolutions, and fitting the column tube more closely to obviate rivulation of the reflux on the column wall, should improve the low-pressure efficiency significantly.

A fairly recent design of a column with moving parts is the brush column developed by Perry.[102] This column is primarily for low-pressure operation. Evaporation occurs initially from the reboiler; when these vapors reach a centrally located rotating condenser, condensation occurs. This condensate is spun off the condenser onto the heated wall where re-evaporation takes place. In the annular space and attached to and rotating with the condenser is a spiral stainless steel brush extending along the length of the rotating condenser. This brush agitates the vapor and stirs reflux on the column wall. The combination of multiple evaporation and condensation, plus the agitation, produces the rather remarkably low H.E.T.P. of about 1–1$^1/_2$ in. with a phthalate–sebacate test mixture at an operating pressure of less than 1 mm. The pressure drop is only a fraction of a millimeter.

The various rectifying devices discussed in the preceding text largely represent the developments of only about two decades, 1930–1950, yet these developments appear likely to be definitive. In the last dozen years nothing of consequence has been added to the arsenal of currently available equipment. The advent and rapid development of gas–liquid chromatography has completely dissipated the urgency to develop distillation as an analytical tool, leaving to distillation only the role for which it is best suited, the isolation of substantially pure volatile compounds in reasonable quantities.

2. Construction of Columns

A. COLUMN TUBES

Packed columns are usually constructed of a straight tube of uniform bore. The length and diameter are chosen to give a prescribed efficiency and boil-up rate with a given type of packing. A packed section of uniform diameter and packing is most suitable for narrow-range distillands; if the latter are of wide boiling range, 2–6 in. of the lower end of the column may be packed with somewhat coarser packing than that to be used in the major length of the packed section. For example, $^3/_{16}$-in. helices may be used in the lower section and $^3/_{32}$-in. in the main section. To avoid using two sizes of packing, the lower end of the tube for a distance of 2–6 in. may be enlarged to have a cross-sectional area approximately twice that of the main section. (A 2.1-cm. I.D. tube has nearly twice the cross-sectional area of a 1.5-cm. tube, for example.) Vapor of wide boiling range entering the bottom of the column is rapidly fractionated into a higher boiling reflux and a narrow-boiling vapor, which proceeds to the upper rectifying zone. The higher boiling reflux would tend to overload and flood the lower end of the column if the packing and cross-sectional area were uniform, whereas with the coarser packing on the enlarged section at the bottom, the vapor and liquid capacity is greater and flooding is prevented. Figure 5 shows a design incorporating an enlarged section at the bottom and in addition two vapor disengaging zones at the top of the column to prevent flooding at the top.

B. PACKING SUPPORTS

Proper support for the packing is of utmost importance to ensure that the supporting mechanism will not be a limiting factor in the column capacity, and will not allow the packing to drop into the still pot. For metal packing, a corrosion-resistant cone of screen provides a satisfactory support. The mesh of the cone should be such that the greatest dimension of any mesh is slightly less than the diameter of a particle of packing. Another type of support consists of a cylinder of wire screen, closed at one end by a cone or spherical section of the same wire screen. Either the cone or cylindrical type provides an area for liquid and vapor flow that is greater in area than the cross-sectional area of the column, providing the column is enlarged in the region where the cone or cylinder is to be located. A slight but sharp constriction in the column wall will provide adequate support without offering significant impedance to vapor flow. If a section of coarse packing is used at the bottom of the column, a second cone may be set on top of the coarse packing to act as a secondary support for the finer packing of the main part of the rectifying section.

Noncorrosive packing (glass helices, etc.) may be supported on a cone of platinum screen (poisoned with hydrogen sulfide or otherwise to eliminate catalytic activity) in the same way as metal packing. The relatively expensive platinum cone may be eliminated by using an enlarged section at the bottom of the column in which a glass cross is sealed. A shallow layer of coarse glass spirals rests on the cross. Progressively smaller diameter spirals are then dropped into the column until a layer deep enough to hold the finer main packing has been formed. The coarser spirals tend to break up on heating and cooling which may eventually necessitate repacking of the column.

In the usual preflooding operation, column packing is subjected to forces which tend to loosen the packing, particularly small particles near the top of the packed section. To minimize this action of preflooding and prevent packing particles from being carried into the condenser section, a tight roll of wire screen may be constructed from a strip 1 in. wide and of sufficient length to make the resulting roll fit fairly tightly in the top of the column against the packing. Another method consists in placing a circular disk of wire screen, having a diameter equal to the inside diameter of the column, on top of the packing and forcing several broken circles of wire down against the screen. The diameter and circumference of the broken circles should be such as to allow them to make a spring fit against the inner walls of the column. Glass spirals and other inert packing may be held in place by a layer of progressively coarser spirals placed in an enlarged section of the column above the packed section.

C. PACKING PROCEDURE

Packings, such as balls, Raschig rings, and Berl saddles, which have no tendency to form clusters or groups by intertwining, will pack properly if the individual particles are dropped into the column singly or a few at a time. Single- and multiple-turn helices, on the other hand, form large clusters by intertwining, and must accordingly be separated and dropped into a column singly, or in clusters of only a few rings, if the packing is to be efficient and the column easy to operate.

Metal helices of the sizes used in laboratory columns attain their maximum efficiency only when they are properly introduced into the column and tamped to eliminate loose clusters and voids in the finished packed section. A method which works well has been described.[103] A 6-in. glass funnel is placed in the top of the column to be packed; then a piece of wire screen having a mesh which will pass the helices is bent into a rough cup shape and set into the top of the funnel. Small clusters of helices are dropped into the mesh cup and, by properly vibrating the screen, the cluster gradually breaks up into single helices or clumps of only a few particles, and drops into the column. When enough helices have been put in the column to cover the top of the supporting cone, tamping should begin. For short columns up to 3 ft. in length, a $^1/_8$-in. welding rod may have a metal cross attached at the lower end; the arms of the cross should be slightly shorter than the column diameter to prevent jamming of the tamper by the helices. The tamper rod passes up through the stem of the funnel and the screen cup.

For longer columns, the tamper may consist of a brass block cut in the shape of a 4- or 6-sided pyramid. The major dimension of the base should be somewhat less than the column diameter. A small hole drilled through the apex of the tamper provides an attachment point for a piece of No. 26 Nichrome wire to operate the tamper. The upper end of the wire may be attached to a spool on which to wind the wire as the required wire length diminishes during the packing operation. Occasional examination of the tamper should be made during the packing operation so that any helices which may have collected on the wire may be removed.

The fragile nature of glass helices prohibits tamping. Dust and broken helices should be removed by screening. This is most easily accomplished by construction of an all-metal sieve, the bottom of which is made of a metal plate slightly thicker than the diameter of the helices to be screened. A large number of holes slightly smaller in diameter than the outside diameter of the helices should be drilled in the bottom. This type of sieve[104] will remove dust and broken helices, but will not allow a complete helix to hook through a hole as might occur with ordinary wire sieves of suitable mesh. Small clusters of glass helices break up into smaller clusters or single units during the sifting, and may then be dropped into the packed zone.

D. COLUMN INSULATION

Because of their large ratio of surface area to volume, laboratory fractionating columns require adequate insulation to minimize heat loss, reduce internal reflux, and increase column efficiency and vapor capacity. Internal reflux resulting from excessive heat loss may under some conditions bring about a slight increase in fractionating efficiency, but such results are probably fortuitous to a large extent. Poorly insulated columns are generally less reliable in operation and lower in fractionating efficiency over a wide temperature range than are columns properly designed to minimize heat losses.

Two general methods are available for preventing heat loss from fractionating columns. The first and simplest of these consists in covering the column with a layer of material of low heat conductivity, such as 85% magnesia, glass wool, asbestos, or mineral wool. For very large commercial columns, this method is commonly used and is entirely satisfactory; for small columns of laboratory size, simple insulation is not effective if the temperature difference between the inside of the column and its surroundings is large. Increasing the thickness of the insulation does not reduce the heat losses indefinitely after a certain depth of insulating material has been used. On very small diameter columns of the order of a quarter of an inch, increasing the thickness of the insulation beyond a certain value will lead to an increase of heat loss because of the large surface area of the insulation available for radiation.

Table XXI gives a summary of heat losses (neglecting end effects) to be expected for a column 1 in. in diameter and 1 ft. long when insulated with 85% magnesia of the thickness shown.

TABLE XXI

Heat Losses Through 85% Magnesia, and Equivalent Condensation

	Insulation thickness			
	1 in.		2 in.	
ΔT[a]	Heat loss, cal./hr.	Ml. condensed/hr.	Heat loss, cal./hr.	Ml. condensed/hr.
55°, Benzene	4,800	54	3450	42
85°, Toluene	7,600	101	5400	73
151°, *p*-Cymene	13,800	238	9800	170

[a] ΔT^* = normal boiling point minus room temperature (25°C.). All calculations based on heat-loss data from Johns-Manville bulletins.

In striking contrast to the insulating efficiency of low-conductivity lagging materials mentioned above is the extraordinarily high insulating efficiency of vacuum jackets. These consist of two concentric glass tubes of suitable relative diameters sealed one to the other with a glass-to-glass seal at each end. Through a small tube sealed near one end of the outer tube, air is removed from the annulus down to a pressure of 10^{-5}–10^{-6} mm. of mercury. During the evacuation, the whole jacket is baked at a high temperature (300–400°C.) to remove occluded gases and moisture to ensure a permanent vacuum. Although a jacket of the above construction has good insulating qualities, its efficiency in this respect can be greatly improved by silvering the inner walls of the jacket or by placing a highly reflecting radiation shield in the annular space during the fabrication of the jacket. In either case, the annular space is highly evacuated. In order to observe the packing through the jacket, a strip may be left unsilvered or in the case of jackets with an inner radiation shield, small holes about $^1/_4$ in. in diameter are punched near the top and bottom of the shield. Vacuum

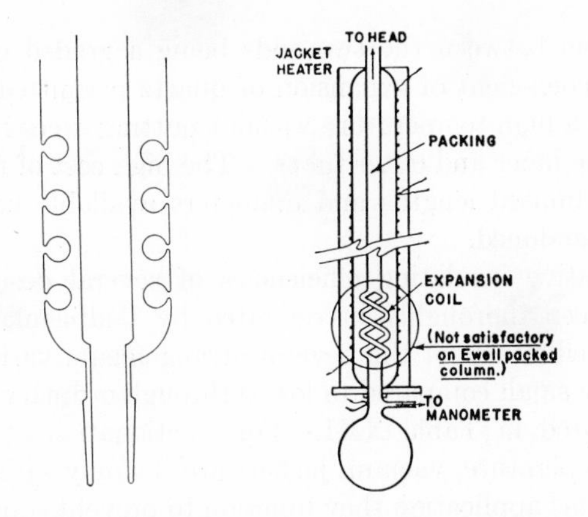

Fig. 20 (left). External expansion section for vacuum-jacketed column.

Fig. 21 (right). Internal expansion section for vacuum-jacketed column.

jackets of this construction have been used as separable insulation for a fractionating column by slipping the column into the jacket and closing the small annular spaces between the column and each end of the jacket with solid insulation, but the more common practice consists in making the inner tube of the jacket serve as the column proper. Extensions of the inner member are used to attach the still head and still pot by suitable joints.

A column of the above construction would be usable, but the permissible temperature differential between the inner and outer tube would be small, at least for a column of significant length, if intolerable strain and breakage were to be avoided. To allow for the differential expansion between the inner and outer members of a vacuum-jacketed column, an expansion member is made part of either the inner or outer tube. When the expansion element is part of the outer tube, one or more short sections of this member are made into the form of a glass bellows; the number of such bellows depends on the length of the jacket, a larger number being required with a long jacket. When the expansion member is part of the inner tube, it consists usually of two or three small-diameter glass tubes in the form of coils attached to the inner tube at the lower end to form parallel vapor lines feeding the larger tube. The flexibility of the coils allows the necessary expansion of the inner tube to take place without placing undue strain on any part of the column. Difficulties in producing satisfactory expansion elements have limited vacuum-jacketed columns to diameters of about 1 in. and to lengths of about 12 ft. The two types of construction are shown in Figures 20 and 21.

In an earlier design,[105] expansion elements were avoided by constructing the inner member of the jacket of fused quartz and the outer jacket of

Pyrex, the union between the two ends being a graded glass seal. The extremely low coefficient of expansion of quartz permitted the inner tube to be heated to a high temperature without putting excessive strain on the seal between the inner and outer tubes. The high cost of the quartz inner tubes and the limited lengths and diameters available have caused this design to be abandoned.

The comparative insulating efficiencies of several designs of vacuum jackets have been thoroughly investigated by Podbielniak.[105] Although the insulating efficiency of the several arrangements varied widely, heat losses were very small compared to losses through ordinary insulation such as those indicated in Table XXI. For fractionation of liquids boiling below room temperature, vacuum jackets are the only satisfactory type of insulation; in this application they function to prevent superheating of the column. In columns operating above room temperature, vacuum jackets minimize heat losses. The most efficient vacuum jackets lose some heat (largely by radiation) when liquids of boiling points far removed from ambient temperatures are distilled; to minimize these losses still further, a small heater is inserted into the evacuated space between the column proper and the radiation shield.[49] The energy dissipated in the heater (if properly adjusted) just compensates for the residual radiation losses of the column.

Willingham and Rossini[106] enclose long vacuum-jacket columns with a metal tube on which are wound electric heaters. A layer of 85% magnesia and finally a layer of aluminum foil cover the heaters. Not only does this method reduce heat losses to an extremely small value, but it serves to bring the outer surface of the vacuum jacket to a temperature close to that of the inner tube, and consequently greatly reduces the strain on the expansion members of the columns.

For larger laboratory columns made of either metal or glass the second of the general methods is used for preventing heat loss. This method consists in maintaining the region immediately adjacent to the column at the vapor–liquid temperature in the column by circulation of suitably preheated air, vapor, or liquid in a jacket surrounding the column, or by dissipating energy in an insulating medium around the column. To be completely effective, either of these methods should establish theoretically a temperature gradient throughout the length of the column on the outside exactly equal to the temperature gradient caused by fractionation and to some extent pressure drop prevailing inside the column; practical limitations will permit this condition only to be approximated.

Several arrangements have been used to provide a region of suitable temperature adjacent to the column. Kistiakowski[107] enclosed the packed section with a jacket of somewhat greater diameter through which a liquid, heated to the proper temperature, was circulated. For short columns, this design is probably satisfactory at temperatures not too far removed from the ambient temperature; at high temperatures heat losses from the jacket would be excessive, and insulation would be necessary. Some temperature gradient would exist as a result of natural cooling of the liquid as it moves up the jacket; on tall columns, this type of construction would probably not supply the proper temperature gradient. The chief objection to this design is the necessity for circulating a hot liquid. This not only poses a mechanical problem, but introduces a certain amount of hazard in the event of fracture of the glass jacket.

Widmer[108] achieved the same result automatically by surrounding the column with a jacket so arranged that the vapors of the material being distilled were forced to pass to the top of the jacket, reverse their direction down the inside of the jacket, and thence up through the fractionating column proper (see Fig. 3). This design requires considerably greater heat input to the still pot to attain a given throughput in the column proper than would be required for a vacuum-jacketed column, or for other designs in which heat losses are compensated independently. The Widmer column has greater dynamic holdup for the same reason, and hence would not separate components of a charge as sharply as other designs. The jacket section of the column has little fractionating efficiency compared to the packed rectifying section; consequently, the temperature gradient in the column would be upset to some extent. For short columns of moderate efficiency, the Widmer column should be satisfactory.

The most widely used system, and one of widest applicability, for minimizing heat losses from fractionating columns consists of electric heaters appropriately placed around the column. Fenske et al.[109] used this method in a column 52 ft. high and 1 in. in diameter in which were separated the two isomers of diisobutylene. Borns, Coffey, and Garrard[110] used it on a Stedman column 3 in. in diameter and 12 ft. long, and it is being used on Stedman columns 6 in. in diameter and 18 ft. long.[111] Electric heaters are particularly suitable for those who build their own columns and lack the facilities for building vacuum-jacketed columns of glass; their use is the only feasible method of heat-loss compensation for large or small columns of metal.

In order to attain the best external temperature gradient throughout the length of the column, the electric heaters are put on in sections, each independently controlled by a variable transformer. Short columns up to about 3 ft. long operate satisfactorily with a single heater; longer columns should have heater sections not exceeding 3 ft. in length.

When all-glass construction is to be used, the column is placed concentrically in a second glass tube of an inside diameter $^3/_4$ in. larger than the outside diameter of the column, and slightly longer than the proposed packed section. Four to six lengths of asbestos cord are then fastened longitudinally on the jacket at equal angular spacing to prevent contact on the heater wires and jacket, and to minimize slippage of the heater element. Sufficient resistance wire or tape of the proper current-carrying capacity and resistivity should then be wound on the jacket to carry the full load of the variable transformer to be used with the jacket (see Table XXII). Adjacent turns should be $^1/_2$ to $^3/_4$ in. apart. The variable

TABLE XXII
Power Dissipated in 22-ohm Resistor at Various Voltages

V	I	$P = RI^2$, w.	cal./hr.
0	0	0	0
10	0.455	4.5	3,870
20	0.910	18.2	15,300
30	1.365	30.0	25,800
40	1.820	74.3	63,800
50	2.275	117.7	100,000
60	2.730	164.0	141,000
70	3.185	235.4	202,000
80	3.640	290.4	250,000
90	4.095	367.4	316,000
100	4.550	453.2	390,000
110	5.000	550.0	474,000

transformer used for this purpose usually has a maximum rating of 5 amp. at 110 v.; the resistance should be accordingly about 22 ohms. The full heater dissipation may not be required, but by using 22 ohms there is no danger of exceeding the rating of the transformer in the event the full voltage is thrown on the winding. A second glass tube of suitable diameter for a snug fit is then slipped over the jacket for protection if full visibility of the packing is desired; otherwise, a layer of 85% magnesia may be put over the winding to reduce power requirements, and to minimize the effect of drafts on the regulation of the jacket temperatures (see Figs. 22 and 23). When several jacket sections of the above construction are used on a column, a Transite plate drilled to slip onto the column with snug fit should be placed between adjacent sections to prevent circulation of heated air between the sections.

To indicate the proper power input to a given heater section, thermocouples hooked up in opposition offer the most convenient method. If glass jackets are being used, one thermocouple is silver-soldered to a circular band of Nichrome ribbon about $^3/_8$ to $^1/_2$ in. wide, and slipped into the jacket to a point equidistant from the ends. Spring action of the ribbon will usually

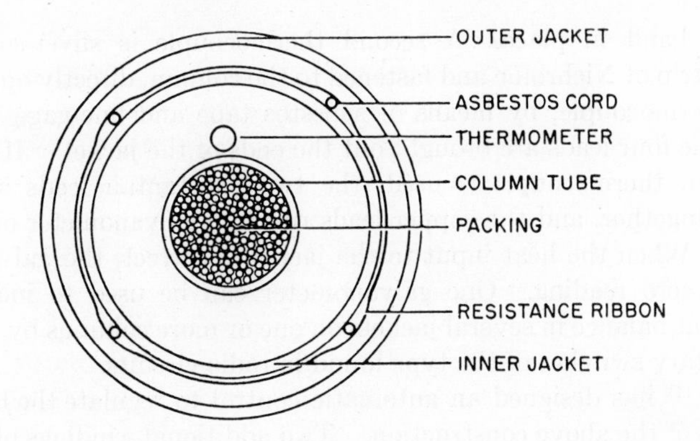

Fig. 22. Cross section of column with compensating jacket.

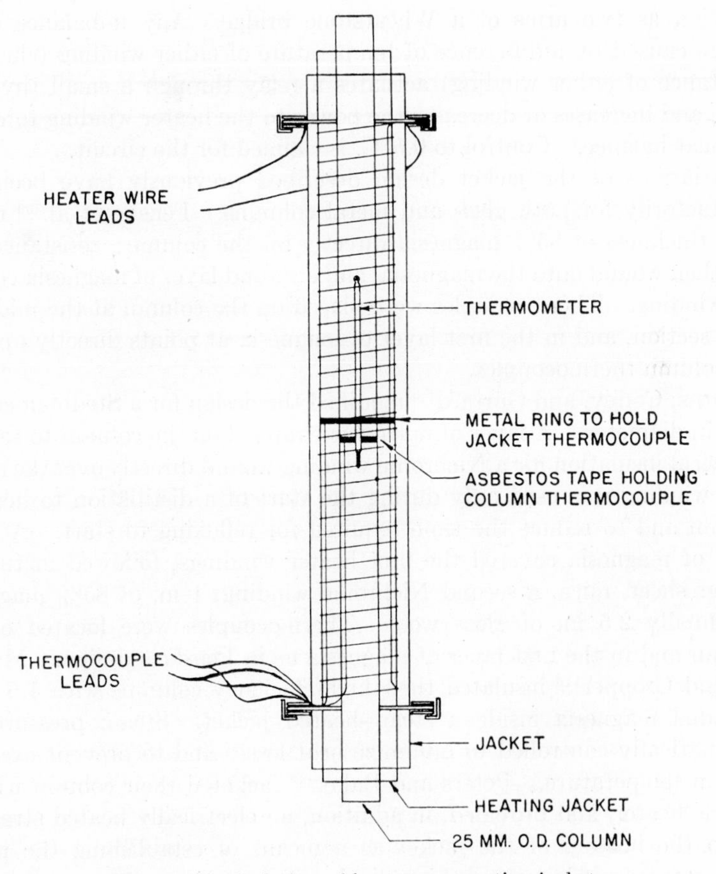

Fig. 23. Vertical view of heat-compensating jacket.

hold the band in place. A second thermocouple is silver-soldered to another strip of Nichrome and fastened to the column, directly opposite the jacket thermocouple, by means of asbestos tape and fine-gage Nichrome wire. The four leads are brought out the ends of the jacket. If a copper-constantan thermocouple is used, the two constantan leads are silver-soldered together, and the copper leads run to a galvanometer of fair sensitivity. When the heat input to the jacket is correct, the galvanometer will give zero reading. One galvanometer can be used to indicate the proper heat balance in several jackets on one or more columns by the use of simple rotary switches of the type found in radio circuits.

Prevost[112] has designed an automatic control to regulate the heat input to jackets of the above construction. Two additional windings of fine wire having a high coefficient of resistance are wound, one directly on the column and the other located on the inside surface of the jacket; they function as two arms of a Wheatstone bridge. Any unbalance of the bridge caused by a difference of temperature of either winding (change of resistance of either winding) actuates a relay through a small thyratron tube, and increases or decreases the power to the heater winding to restore the heat balance. Control to 0.5°C. is claimed for the circuit.

Variations of the jacket design described previously have been used satisfactorily for both glass and metal columns. Fenske et al.[109] used a 2-in. thickness of 85% magnesia directly on the column; resistance tape was then wound onto the magnesia, and a second layer of magnesia covered the winding. Thermocouples were placed on the column at the middle of each section, and in the first layer of magnesia at points directly opposite the column thermocouples.

Borns, Coffey, and Garrard[110] modified the design for a Stedman column 3 in. in diameter. A layer of mica was wrapped on the column to serve as electrical insulation for a Nichrome winding wound directly over the media. This winding was used only during the start of a distillation to heat the column and to reduce the time required for refluxing to start. A $^5/_8$-in. layer of magnesia covered the first heater windings, followed in turn by copper sheet, mica, a second Nichrome winding, 1 in. of 85% magnesia, and finally 2.5 in. of glass wool. Thermocouples were located on the column and in the first layer of magnesia as in Fenske's design. Marschner and Cropper[113] insulated their high-efficiency columns with 1.5 in. of shredded magnesia inside a steam-heated jacket. Steam pressure was automatically controlled to minimize heat losses and to prevent excessive column temperature. Peters and Baker[114] jacketed their column with an electric heater, and provided, in addition, an electrically heated stream of air to the bottom of the jacket as a means of establishing the proper temperature gradient along the packed section.

Either vacuum jacketing or heat-loss compensation provides satisfactory column insulation. For small-diameter columns not exceeding a length of about 10 ft., vacuum jacketing may be preferable. Actual experience has shown that somewhat lower boil-up rates can be maintained in a vacuum-jacketed column. On larger diameter columns (>1 in. in diameter) and for all-metal columns, heat-loss compensation is the only satisfactory design. All-metal vacuum-jacketed columns have been built[115] and the jacket given a long period of evacuation to degas the metal. When further degassing of the metal under operation raises the jacket pressure to 10^{-4} mm., the evacuation is repeated. This procedure introduces complexities scarcely justified for the little additional efficiency and operating smoothness achieved.

III. CONDENSER SECTION

1. General

Vapors from the still pot pass up through the column proper, or rectifying section, where they are enriched in the more volatile components, and emerge into the condenser section at the top of the column to be totally or partially condensed to a liquid. If the vapors are partially condensed, condensate automatically returns to the top of the rectifying section as reflux, and the remaining vapor passes into an auxiliary condenser in which the vapor is liquified and withdrawn as product. If all the vapors emerging from the rectifying sections are liquified in the condenser section, the system operates as a total condenser, and a portion of the condensate is withdrawn as product. Both types of condensers are operated as total condensers while the column is being preflooded and brought to equilibrium before product collection begins.

Historically, there has been some controversy on the relative merits of partial versus total condensers. Peters and Baker[114] and later Podbielniak[116] favored the partial condenser because the unavoidable holdup in the total condenser works against the sharpest separation. Podbielniak's Hyper-Cal column uses a total condenser.[116] Young[117] contends that no plant column can be thoroughly efficient without some form of partial condenser (dephlegmator). Robinson[118] argues that the usual type of condenser is peculiarly unadapted for good fractionation. Birch et al.[91] published the design of a low-pressure column using a partial condenser to which was ascribed a part of the fractionating efficiency. Leslie[119] has shown mathematically that fractional distillation is superior to fractional condensation.

Regardless of the theoretical merits of partial condensers (and these are not imposing), their use on modern laboratory columns for high-temperature distillations is very limited. A partial condenser must be supplied with a carefully metered quantity of coolant, or with a suitable quantity of coolant at a closely controlled temperature, in order to maintain the proper reflux ratio while a product of constant boiling point is being collected. During breaks, the rate of circulation of the coolant or its temperature must be closely watched and changed as necessary to maintain flow of product to the receiver.

Total condensers, on the other hand, need only be supplied with enough coolant to condense all vapors entering the condenser section; excess coolant does no harm, and is of no significance for laboratory columns. If the heat picked up by the coolant is to be used for calculating the boil-up rate, the rate of flow of the coolant must be closely controlled during the time measurement is being made. This applies to the partial condenser system also; here, two rates will have to be determined, one of which is by temperature difference; and product rate directly. A portion of the condensate can be withdrawn continuously, or all the condensate for a fraction of unit time can be withdrawn to establish the proper reflux ratio; all the vapor can be withdrawn for a fraction of unit time as product and thus establish the reflux ratio. The simplicity of control of condensation and product collection with a total condenser has made it the preferred system. When several columns are attended by a single operator, as frequently occurs in large laboratories, the impracticability of partial condensers is immediately obvious.

The condenser systems of a fractionating column should be constructed with sufficient cooling surface to condense all vapors entering the condenser. It is assumed that the coolant circulating through the condenser is significantly colder than the lowest boiling material to be condensed. Inasmuch as many types of laboratory columns have to be preflooded to achieve their maximum efficiency, the condenser system must be capable of condensing the abnormal supply of vapor during the preflooding operations; if it does this, the condenser will be more than adequate for the normal vapor load. In addition to condensing the vapors entering it, the condenser system of laboratory columns is provided with a partitioning device by which a regulated fraction of the condensate or vapor is withdrawn as product, and the very important "reflux ratio" is established.

2. Total Condensers

For ease of construction, ruggedness, low holdup, large vapor capacity with no tendency to flood, and low pressure drop, a form of the modified Liebig condenser is frequently used. Somewhat greater condensing surface for a given length of condenser can be obtained by introducing a "cold-finger" into the center tube. This design has a smaller liquid capacity than the simpler form, and may more readily discharge reflux overhead into the fraction receiver during the preflooding operation. Another design consists of a plain glass jacket with a "cold-finger" in the center. This may consist of a plain glass tube through which the coolant is circulated, or may be a glass or metal coil or small-diameter tubing. The turns of the coil must be separated far enough to prevent the formation of a bridge of condensate between adjacent turns of the coil if condenser holdup is to be minimized. The simple Liebig type of condenser in a vertical position probably has the lowest holdup of all the designs; this supposition has not been verified, however.

Physical dimensions of condensers are not critical; 150 sq. cm. of condensing surfaces (30 cm. long by 1.6 cm. I.D. standard Pyrex tubing) for high-efficiency columns having a maximum boil-up rate of 1560 ml./hr. of hydrocarbon is satisfactory.[106] If there is a small differential between vapor and coolant temperature, or if the vapors have high latent heat somewhat greater condensing area may be required.

As mentioned above, a portion of the vapors entering the condenser section is withdrawn as product, either as liquid or as vapor which is subsequently liquefied. Some form of partitioning device regulates this process. How well this is done determines to a marked extent the success of a fractionation.

Two general methods are used to control the product rate. One consists of a flow-regulating device, which allows a steady stream of condensate to flow from the reflux condenser to the product receiver, excess condensate flowing back to the rectifying section as reflux; the other consists of a mechanism by which all the condensate can be diverted either to the product receiver or to the rectifying section of the column. This mechanism is operated by a timing device. If the timing device, for example, holds the column on total reflux for 59 sec., and then on total takeoff for 1 sec., out of every 60 sec., the time ratio is 59:1 and theoretically the reflux ratio is 59:1. (The boil-up rate is assumed to be constant during the full 60 sec.) This system should give the same reflux ratio regardless of boil-up rate; however, holdup in the diverting mechanism, time lag in the operation, and condensation in parts of the column other than the condenser tend to give a higher reflux ratio than the time ratio indicates. A modification of this system uses a magnetically controlled valve to close the entrance to the condenser and open an exit valve and thus direct the vapor into an auxiliary condenser where it is liquefied.

Historically, the ubiquitous stopcock was the first device used to control product rate from a column. It served this purpose admirably, particularly in that its vagaries led to decidedly better methods of control. The

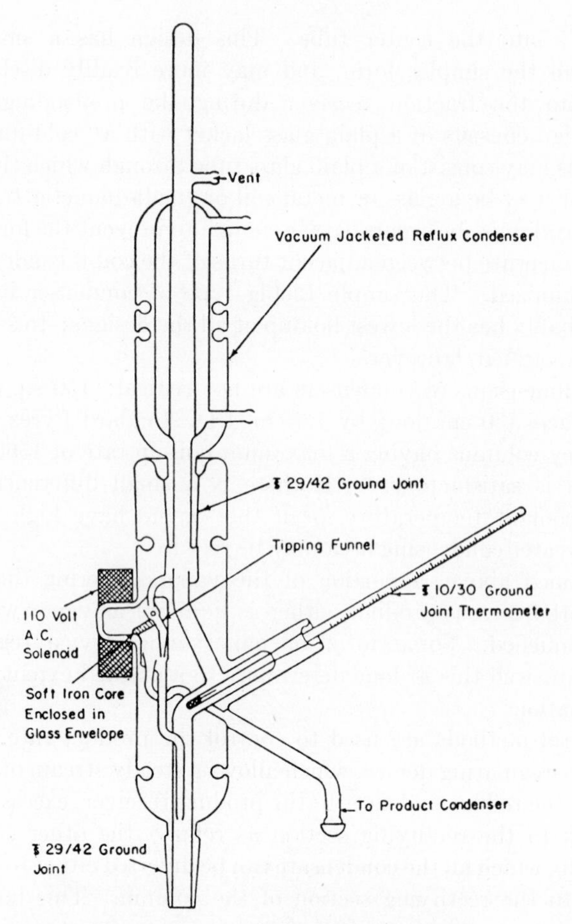

Fig. 24. Automatic liquid-dividing head.

necessity for using a lubricant which sooner or later dissolved in the product, air leakage during reduced-pressure distillations, difficulties of precise adjustment, and intermittent and irregular flow when two-phase condensates appear make the stopcock a generally unsatisfactory device for control of product rate. Some improvement, so far as adjustment of the rate was concerned, was made by the development of the variable-flow stopcock, but this did not overcome the disadvantages mentioned above.

A design which eliminated in one step all the difficulties encountered with stopcocks except irregular flow of two phase condensates was developed by Willingham and Rossini.[106] Flow of product is controlled by withdrawing a small tapered glass plug from its matching seat by means of a micrometer screw arrangement. A vertically oriented condenser delivers

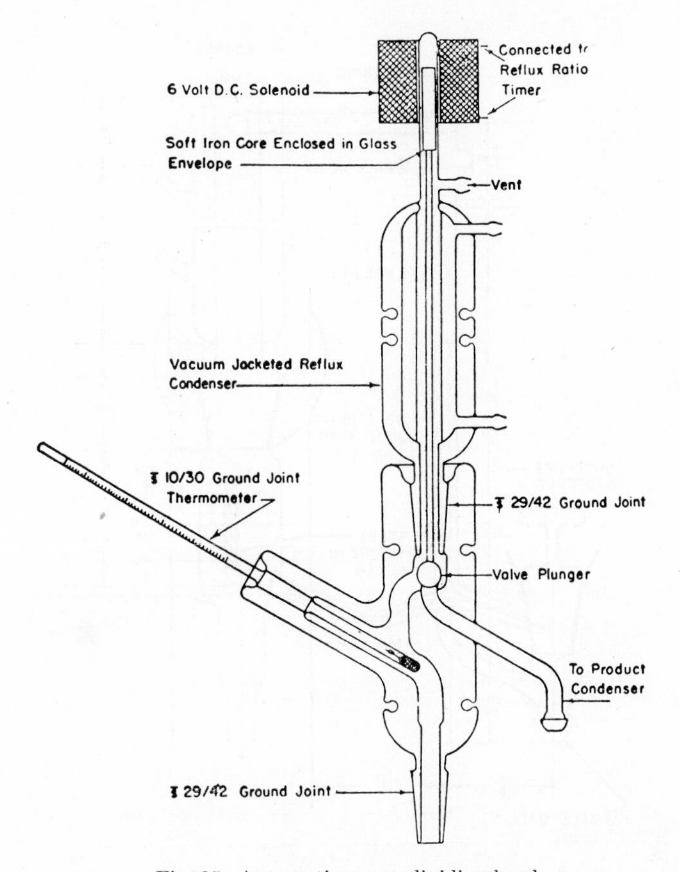

Fig. 25. Automatic vapor-dividing head.

reflux to the plug and keeps the orifice covered with reflux at all times to maintain a very small but adequate supply of product. No lubricant is needed since the product acts as its own lubricant. When the valve parts are properly constructed and ground as recommended, the valve does not leak with the column on total reflux. Product rate is very constant so long as the surface tension and viscosity of the reflux do not change. In the distillation of pure hydrocarbons, tests have shown the rate to remain constant within 2% or less for periods of 16 hr. or more. The design is satisfactory for both atmospheric and lower pressure distillations because the valve has substantially the same pressure on both sides. Holdup is minimum and is almost entirely the normal holdup of the condenser and associated surfaces.

The generally unsatisfactory regulation of product rate by means of stopcocks, the difficulties of determining reflux ratios with the best systems

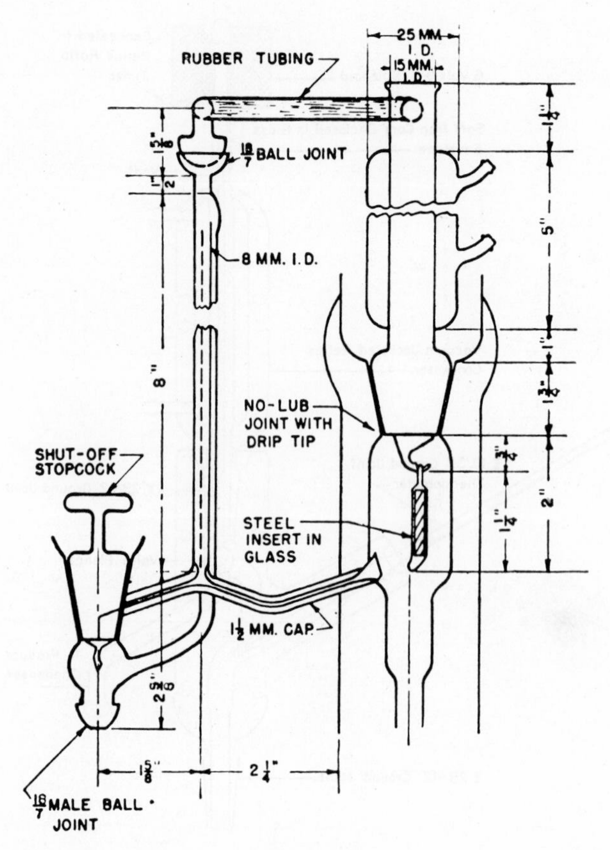

Fig. 26. Liquid-dividing head and condenser section for analytical distillation column of Figure 5.

of continuous product collection, and demonstration of equality or slight superiority of intermittent take-off compared to continuous take-off[120] have led to wide use of intermittent take-off systems. Figures 24 and 25 show two designs for liquid and vapor take-off, respectively.[121] In the case of liquid take-off (Fig. 24), a timer energizes the solenoid which moves the tipping funnel over the opening of the product line to discharge the reflux to the product cooler and receiver; interruption of the current to the solenoid by the timer then diverts the reflux back to the column. For vapor take-off (Fig. 25), the solenoid when energized closes the opening of the condenser and allows the vapor to flow into the product condenser for a given interval of time. The ratio of time on total reflux to time on total take-off is the reflux ratio, theoretically. Studies by Collins and Lantz[121] of these two designs show that the time ratio is smaller than the actual

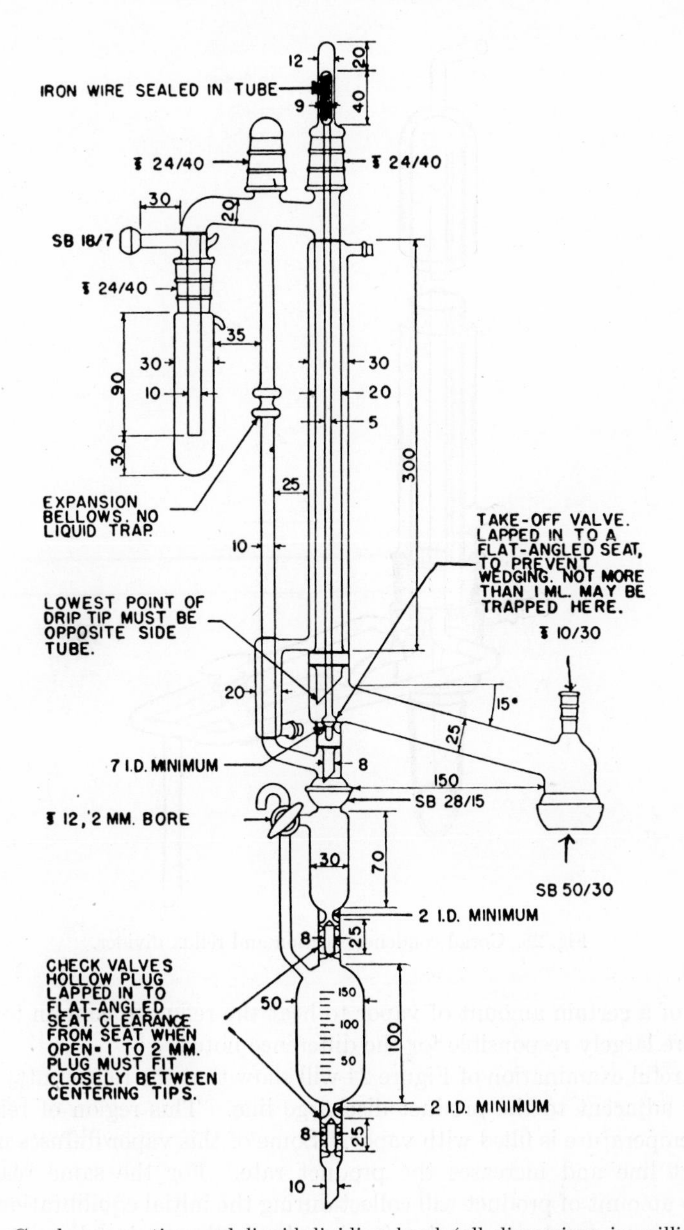

Fig. 27. Condenser section and liquid-dividing head (all dimensions in millimeters).

reflux ratio, that the actual reflux ratio varies with boil-up rate, and that the vapor take-off system gives a smaller reflux ratio than the liquid take-off system. Imperfect insulation and cold reflux, requiring the conden-

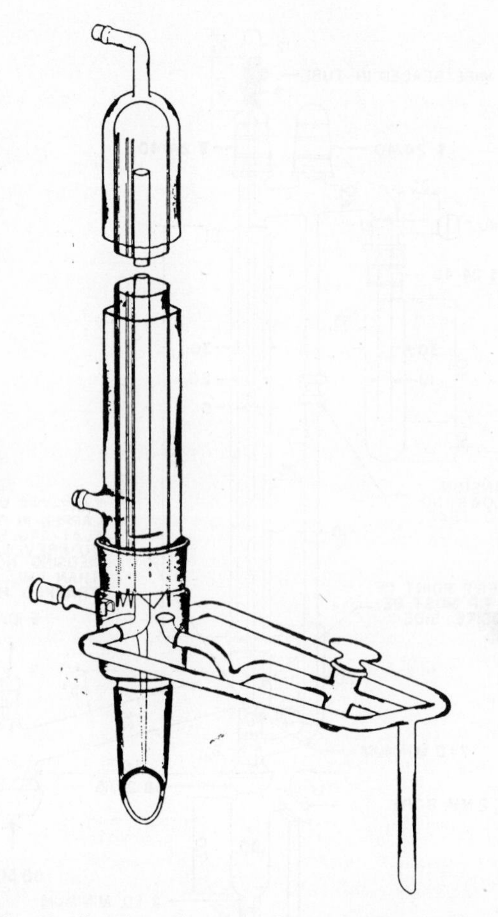

Fig. 28. Corad condenser section and reflux divider.

sation of a certain amount of vapor to heat the reflux to column temperature, are largely responsible for the difference noted.

A careful examination of Figure 24 will show that the reflux entry port is closely adjacent to the product discharge line. This region of relatively high temperature is filled with vapor. Some of this vapor diffuses into the product line and increases the product rate. For the same reason, a certain amount of product will collect during the initial equilibration of the column under total reflux. A suitable valve in the product line as close as possible to the product port will hold this flow to a minimum during the period of total reflux (see Fig. 26). Figure 26[122] is another design of liquid-dividing heat, similar in principle to Figure 24. A somewhat different design of liquid-dividing head is shown in Figure 27.[123] Drainage of the condensate from the condenser to the valve is positively directed by the drip tip; the short extension in the bottom of the valve plug produces a "pouring rod" effect by virtue of the surface tension of the condensate to aid in carrying all condensate into the receiver during the time the valve is open. Excessive boil-up rates will probably overload the product valve unless the valve size is increased considerably. Leakage of condensate can be kept to a very low value if the valve is properly ground, and given a final lapping with jeweler's rouge.

To avoid inadvertent heat losses the product valve and condenser are located in an enlarged section of the vacuum-jacketed Hyper-Cal fractionating column just above the top of the packing.[49] Some holdup prevails around the valve plug. At high boil-up rates, the amount of holdup is not significant, but at very low boil-up rates as used at reduced pressures (if the pressure drop is to be kept low), the holdup requires the ratio of time on total reflux to time on total take-off to be much larger than the desired reflux ratio.

For controlling reflux ratios of 30:1 and below, the design shown in Figure 28 was developed and designated the Corad head, COnstant RAtio heaD.[124] Several condensation strips of different areas are provided on the condenser surface to vary the fraction of the total condensate dropping off any one tip. The condenser surface can be rotated to bring any drainage tip over the product discharge port; drainage from the other tips returns to the column as reflux. During the construction of the condenser, the area and number of strips are set, and hence the several possible reflux ratios are pre-established. A reasonably good estimate of the amount of vapor reaching the condenser can be made by maintaining the boil-up rate constant by appropriate means, collecting the condensate from each drainage tip in turn for a measured time interval, and dividing the total weight or volume of material collected by the total time required. This will give the rate of boil-up at the condenser. Tests have shown that the reflux ratio established by any one drainage tip will vary somewhat with the amount of vapor reaching the condenser. Product rate is also increased by vapor diffusion into the product line; this is probably more pronounced at the higher reflux ratios. The Corad head has the advantage of simplicity in that an auxiliary timer and solenoid are not required for its operation. At reduced pressures, the ground-glass joint has a tendency to bind when rotated; this condition may lead to breakage if the force applied is too great.

3. Partial Condensers

Partial condensers have been almost entirely superseded by total condensers on laboratory columns. Doran,[125] Kistiakowsky,[107] and Laughlin,

Nash, and Whitmore[126] have described columns using partial condensers. Birch et al.[91] used a partial condenser in a low-pressure spinning-band column. An extension of the column proper is surrounded with a short jacket through which air is blown to condense the vapors partially, and to regulate the product rate. Inasmuch as the reflux must flow down the column walls in a thin uniform film, the partial condenser offers an advantage in this type of column. For low-temperature columns, partial condensers offer simpler control of product take-off rate than total condensers, chiefly because the distillate is collected as a gas, not as a liquid.

The best systems so far devised for establishing reflux ratios give only approximate values. Unavoidable condensation of vapor in inaccessible parts of the condenser system–product collecting system and internal reflux caused by imperfect insulation tend to make the actual reflux ratio greater than the measured value. For example, one group of six vacuum-jacketed perforated-plate columns had internal condensation rates varying from 170 to 260 ml. *n*-heptane/hr.; the internal reflux was independent of the boil-up rate, as would be expected.[121] Less efficient insulation would allow greater internal reflux. As a practical matter, uncertainty regarding the reflux ratio is not too important. If a given column will produce a product of satisfactory purity at some reasonable reflux ratio, its absolute value is not generally of major importance.

IV. STILL POTS

The still pot of a batch distillation column is the part of the column into which the distilland is charged. It is attached to the lower end of the fractionating section. Heat is applied to the still pot from a suitable source; the still pot transmits the heat to the distilland and brings about evaporation at a more or less uniform rate. The vapors so generated pass up through the column where they are rectified or fractionated, a portion is withdrawn as product, and the remainder flows down the column as liquid reflux, finally returning to the still pot. At the end of a distillation the still pot will contain the undistilled part of the distilland and the drainage from the rectifying section.

The most commonly used still pot for laboratory fractionating columns is a round-bottom or balloon flask of suitable size. These are available in several standard sizes, equipped with either standard-taper joints or spherical joints, for easy attachment to a companion joint on the lower end of the column. The same types are also available with sealed-in thermometer wells for distillations requiring a knowledge of still pot temperature. When the pressure drop across the column is to be deter-

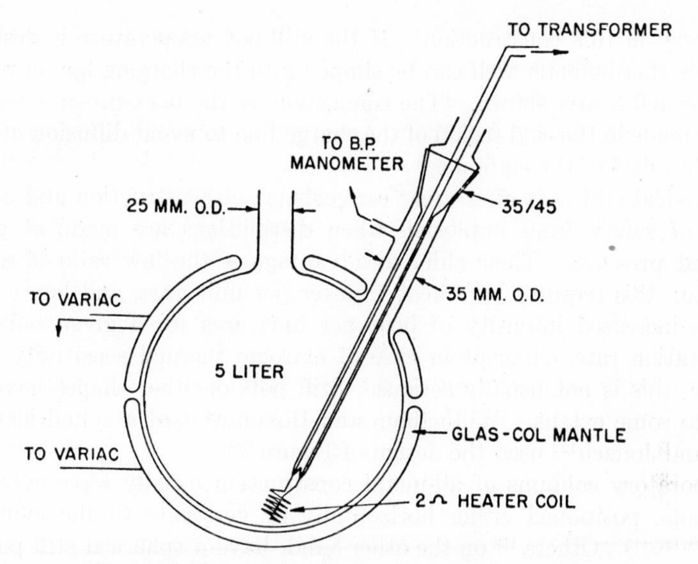

Fig. 29. Stillpot for permanent attachment to column.

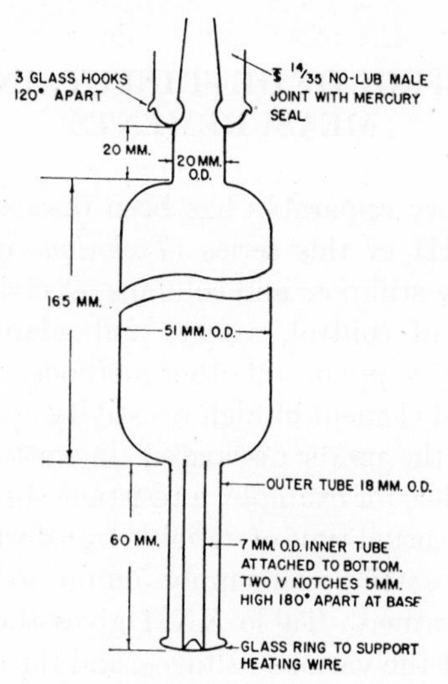

Fig. 30. Still pot for analytical distillation column of Figure 5.

mined, or when it is used to control boil-up rate, a tubulation in the neck of the flask is provided for connecting the back-pressure manometer.

Permanently attached still pots of the same general type are frequently used. A satisfactory design[127] is shown in Figure 29. The sealed-in thermometer well has been eliminated to avoid the use of a fragile ring seal necessary in this construction. If the still-pot temperature is desired, a suitable thermometer well can be slipped into the charging line in place of the internal heater shown. The connection to the back-pressure manometer is made in the cold region of the charge line to avoid diffusion of vapor into that part of the equipment.

Spherical still pots offer great convenience of construction and a maximum of safety from implosion when distillations are made at greatly reduced pressure. Their chief disadvantage is the low ratio of area to volume; this requires high heat transfer per unit area, and hence necessitates increased intensity of heat per unit area for a given boil-up or evaporation rate. Except in case of extreme thermal sensitivity of the charge, this is not usually serious. Still pots of other shapes have been used to some extent. Willingham and Rossini[106] used a cylindrical type; Hall and Jonach[122] used the design of Figure 30.

Laboratory columns of all-metal construction usually have cylindrical still pots, positioned either horizontally or vertically to the cylindrical axis.[109,110,113] Others,[130] on the other hand, have a spherical still pot constructed from a large-volume stainless steel float.

V. HEATING, CONTROL OF HEAT INPUT, AND TEMPERATURE MEASUREMENTS

Heating of laboratory apparatus has been discussed rather completely by Egly in Volume III of this series (*Technique of Organic Chemistry*). For heating laboratory still pots and columns, electric power is almost universally used. Ease of control, safety, and adaptability to automatic operation have made it supplant all other methods. Heat is generated by dissipating power in an element of high resistivity according to the formula $P = RI^2$, where P is the power dissipated (in watts) and I is the current (in amperes). Consider, for example, a resistance of 22 ohms and a supply voltage of 110 v. The usual type of variable transformer used in laboratory work at its maximum setting will supply 5 amp. to this element, the safe output for the transformer. Table XXII gives the power (watts) dissipated in the resistor at the various voltages, and the equivalent calories per hour dissipated (1 watt hour = 860 cal.). If we assume 10 to be the lowest and 110 the highest voltage used, there is a voltage variation of 11:1 available on the adjustable transformer; the power ratio, however, will be $11^2:1^2$ or 121.

Energy supplied to a still pot is used in part to overcome the heat losses arising from imperfect insulation and thereby hold the charge at its boiling point; the remainder provides the heat of vaporization. Heat losses are greater, the higher the operating temperature of the still pot. When distilling benzene, for example, at a rate of 1000 ml./hr., the energy supplied for evaporation would be 95 w./hr.; the same volume of *p*-cymene (b.p. 175°C.) would require 67 w./hr.; yet the much higher heat losses from the still pot at 175°C. would make the total energy requirements considerably higher than when distilling benzene at 80°C.

Little information is available in the literature on the power requirements for laboratory still pots. Goldsbarry and Askevold[128] using Glas-Col heating mantles as their heat source showed that a mixture of *n*-heptane and methylcyclohexane could be distilled at a rate of 1000 and 2000 ml./hr. with heat inputs of 125 and 215 w., respectively. In this case, heat losses were apparently 35 w./hr.

Two general methods are used to heat still pots. The more common method consists in surrounding more or less of the still pot surface with the electric heating element, a thin layer of insulating material being used to prevent direct contact of the element with the still-pot surface. A less frequently used method of heating consists in submerging a heating element directly in the material being distilled. Sometimes in the interest of close control of the evaporation rate, the two methods are combined.

1. External Heating

Heated-oil baths, sandbaths, molten-salt baths, and lead-shot baths, heated either by gas or electric power, have been used to some extent for supplying heat to still pots, but the general inconvenience of several of these and their slow response to control have nearly eliminated them as a source of heat. Cylindrical-shaped still pots can be readily equipped with an electrical heating element of suitable resistance wire or tape. The insulating wire may be wound directly on a glass still pot and covered with a thick layer of 85% magnesia to minimize heat losses. If bare wire or tape is used, a thin layer of asbestos paper should be applied to the surface of the glass to support and hold the wire or tape in position. Additional heavy insulation is then put over the resistance element. If the heater element is to be controlled by a variable transformer, the current-carrying capacity of the wire or tape should be of a size to carry safely the total current available from the transformer, and the total resistance of the element should be great enough to ensure that the current will not exceed the transformer rating at the highest voltage setting. For example, a variable transformer supplying 5 amp. at 110 v. should be used with a resistance of at least 22 ohms.

Table XXIII gives data to guide the designer in choice of the proper resistance wire or tape to use as heating elements for still pots and column

TABLE XXIII
Temperature, Current, and Resistance of Nichrome V Wire and Tape[a]

Wire size	Resistance, ohms/ft.	Current, amp.	Temp., °C.
1/16-in. × 0.0089-in. tape	0.97	5.7	565
20 gage	0.63	5.07	315
22 gage	1.02	5.0	575
24 gage	1.61	5.06	650
26 gage	2.57	5.25	871

[a] Data from Catalog R-46, Driver-Harris Company, Harrison, New Jersey.

jackets. Temperatures given are for straight wires of the indicated sizes in open air. Enclosed wires will reach considerably higher temperatures. Maximum safe operating temperature for Nichrome V wire is 1175°C.

Electrical heaters for cylindrical metal still pots can be similar to those described above. A sufficient thickness of asbestos paper should be applied to the surface for adequate electrical insulation before the resistance wire is put in place. Fenske et al.[109] used this method, and provided additional heat on the bottom by means of a ring heater. To aid heat transfer to the liquid, copper fins were brazed onto the inside surface of the still pot. Strip heaters offer a convenient means of heating metal still pots having horizontal axes. These heaters are available shaped to fit the contour of surface, the heater being placed parallel to the axis of the cylinder. Adequate insulation over the whole still pot reduces heat losses.

Electric heaters for spherical still pots are difficult to construct. Fortunately, the standardization of round-bottom flasks has led to the development of woven-glass heating mantles well suited for heating spherical still pots.[129] These mantles are available in several sizes ranging from 500 ml. to 22 liters. The smaller sizes up to and including 3 liters have one pair of input terminals; larger sizes have two or three sets of elements to be controlled by a corresponding number of variable transformers. On the smaller mantles a part of the heating element is in the upper half of the mantle to minimize condensation at the top of the still pot. Heat losses are kept at a reasonably low value by the use of a thick layer of glass-wool insulation. The mantles may be easily removed from detachable still pots; when used on permanent still pots, years of service may be expected from the mantle, provided the manufacturers' recommendations are not exceeded.

A somewhat unusual design of external heater suitable for very small still pots has been used.[130] This consists of a 30-w. heater, 3/8 in. in diameter and 1.5 in. long. It slips into the heater well of the still pot shown in

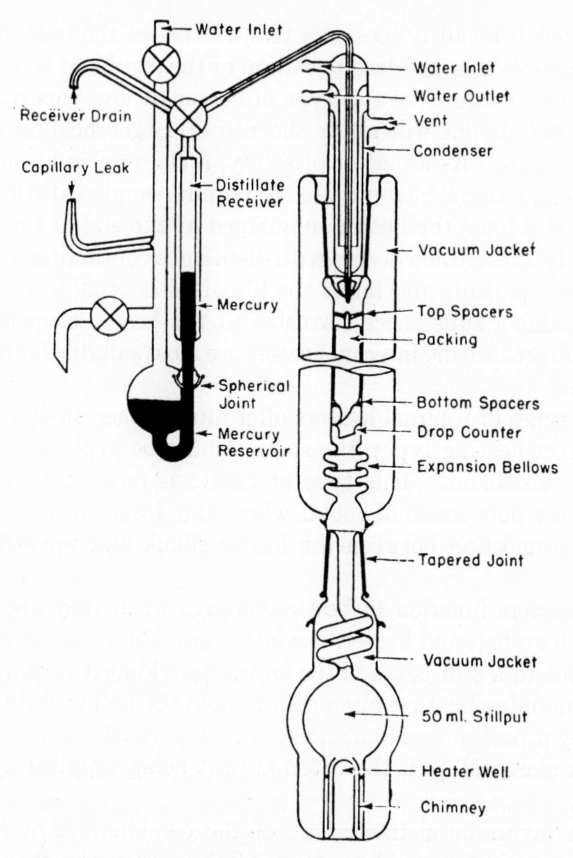

Fig. 31. Vacuum-jacketed still pot for small charges.

Figure 31. Birch, Gripp, and Nathan[91] surrounded the spherical still pot of their spinning-band column with an insulated steel box to provide an air bath; a 1000-w. electric resistance element placed in the bottom of the box supplied heat.

2. Internal Heaters

Internal heaters are of two types: those in which the resistance element is submerged in the distilland, heat transfer being by direct contact of the liquid on the heating element; in the other type the resistance element transfers its heat to a surrounding sheath which in turn heats the liquid in which the sheath is submerged. Direct-heating internal heaters when used in conventional types of glass still pots are of necessity small in order that they may be inserted and properly located. Consequently the amount of heat dissipated is small if excessive temperature of the resistance element leading to possible thermal decomposition of the distilland is to be avoided. This limits the usefulness of this type of heater to low vaporization rates. Special still-pot design will allow the use of larger heaters and greater vaporization rates. As a matter of safety, a chaser should be added to a charge when an internal heater is used to permit complete distillation of the charge, and still have the heater submerged at the end of the distillation. Some electrolytic corrosion occurs with distillands containing water or other conducting components and limits the life of an internal heater. Still-pot charges containing substances corrosive to the heater element should be avoided. Direct-heating internal heaters are most suitable for hydrocarbon fractionations.

Sheathed types of internal heaters offer much larger dissipating surfaces than the direct-heating type; the surface must be kept submerged at all times in the distilland. This type of heater is most suitable for use in cylindrical still pots made of metal where the design will allow a liquid-tight screw connection between the heater shank and the still pot to be made.

Internal heaters function to best advantage when they operate in conjunction with an external heater, the latter providing the major portion of the heat input to a still pot, and the former providing a varying amount of the small remaining heat requirements to hold the boil-up rate constant as controlled by a back-pressure manometer. Figure 29 shows this principle applied to a glass still pot, the external heat being supplied by a mantle-type heater.

The most favorable characteristic of the combination of internal and external heaters is the rapid response of the system to changes in back pressure when a back-pressure manometer is used to control vaporization rate from the still pot. Of the energy supplied to a still pot, a portion is used to hold the distilland at its boiling point, and the remainder supplies the heat of vaporization. If the external heater supplies all the former and 90% of the latter, the internal heater will supply 10% of the heat of vaporization to maintain a constant evaporization or boil-up rate. The mass of the internal heating element can be kept small to reduce heat lag because the total heat dissipated is smaller; response of the internal heater to changes of power input as controlled by the back-pressure manometer is accordingly quite rapid. As an example, consider a heating system designed for evaporating 1000 ml. benzene/hr., or 880 g. Heat of vaporization is 93 cal./g.; total heat of vaporization will be $880 \times 93 = 81{,}840$ cal./hr., or $81{,}840/860 = 94$ w. The external heating mantle therefore will be required to supply the heat losses plus 90% of 94 w., or 85 w. The internal heater will, accordingly, supply 9 w. If its resistance is 2 ohms, the current will be, from $P = RI^2$, $I = \sqrt{P/R} = \sqrt{9/2} = 2.06$ amp. This will be the average current; to allow the necessary control by the back-pressure manometer, a resistance of 1.4 ohms will be hooked in series with the heater, and 5.16 v. will be impressed across the pair in series; during this period the internal heater will dissipate 4.5 w. As the boil-up rate drops, the back-pressure manometer will short out the series resistor, and increase the dissipation of the internal heater to 13.5 w. to restore the boil-up rate of the benzene. A small transformer with a 110-v. primary, and 10-v., 5-amp. secondary, powered from a variable transformer will allow a wide range of adjustment of the power dissipation in the internal heater; direct operation of the low-voltage internal heater from the variable transformer is neither safe nor convenient.

The internal heater of Figure 29 is made by winding 38 in. of No. 20 Nichrome wire on a steel mandrel 1 in. in diameter; spacing between turns is one wire diameter. After the winding is completed, the wire is heated to redness in an air gas flame to "set" the turns so that the coil will hold its shape and size when it is removed from the mandrel. The ends of the wire are then bent to meet the two tungsten leads of the glass closure tube of the still-pot charge line; connection to the tungsten leads is by silver-soldering.

3. Control of Heat Input

Heat input to the still pot of a fractionating column is one of the important operating variables in a distillation. Too little or too much heat leads, respectively, to interruption of reflux or to flooding; between these extremes the proper choice of heat input will determine the column efficiency to some extent, the reflux ratio in columns having constant take-off, and the optimum productivity of the column. It has been shown[61] that the efficiency of a Hyper-Cal fractionating column varies from 92 theoretical plates at a boil-up rate of 500 ml./hr. to 48 plates at 2000 ml./hr. These results were confirmed, in a general way, in another column of the same type.[128] The same investigators showed, however, that a perforated-plate column and a helix-packed column of the same packed length and diameter lost efficiency quite slowly with increasing boil-up rate. Collins and Lantz[121] confirmed the work on perforated-plate columns. Reed's[131] work on a Ewell column indicated some decrease in efficiency with increasing boil-up rate. High-efficiency helix-packed columns (of 100 theoretical plates) have been found to lose efficiency as boil-up rates increases. If it is assumed that these results as measured under total reflux are indicative of column behavior with finite reflux ratios, the importance of control of boil-up rate with many types of columns is apparent, particularly in those instances requiring the highest efficiency from a given column for a critical separation.

Columns using constant take-off devices are more sensitive to changes in boil-up rate than are those using the intermittent type of take-off. With the former, an increase of boil-up rate will change the reflux ratio in a favorable direction, and a decrease in boil-up rate will lower the reflux ratio for an adverse effect. A certain amount of compensation may take place if column efficiency increases or decreases, respectively, with decreases or increases in boil-up rate. With intermittent take-off, where the partitioning mechanism gives reasonably good approximations of the true reflux ratio, changes of boil-up rate are less serious except insofar as such changes adversely affect column efficiency. As a practical procedure, operation of a column should be confined to conditions in which efficiency is not unduly sensitive to boil-up rate.

Control of heat input[132] to the still pot can be either manual or automatic; both require some means of measuring boil-up rate, either in arbitrary terms or in absolute terms by precalibration, and of detecting changes in boil-up rate in order that appropriate changes of controlling elements may be made. The most commonly used device for measuring boil-up rate is a back-pressure manometer, one leg of which is connected to the still pot and the other leg to the top of the condenser section. Either mercury or other liquid of low volatility is used as the manometer fluid. Columns operating with small pressure drop require low-density liquids to show significant changes for small variations in boil-up rate.

A back-pressure manometer simply measures the difference in pressure arising from the flow of vapor through the constrictions of the column packing between the still pot and the top of the reflux condenser, as so many units of length of the manometer fluid. To be a measure of boil-up rate, the relationship between back pressure and the grams or milliliters of liquid condensed in the head, per unit of time, or evaporated from the still pot must be established by independent means. A calibration of this kind applies strictly only to the calibrating liquid in a particular column at a single temperature level. Two or more liquids similar in structure and boiling point should give closely related calibration curves in a given column. During fractionation of such mixtures, the boil-up rate should remain constant for a given back pressure. On the other hand, a mixture of structurally different components whose molal heats of vaporization differed widely, and whose individual calibration curves of boil-up rate versus back pressure showed wide differences, would probably exhibit a variety of boil-up rates for a given back pressure during a fractionation of the mixture. The initial boil-up rate of the mixture would be some average of the curves of the individual components; as the fractionation proceeded, the composition of the distilland would change, and hence the boil-up rate would change. It would be necessary under these circumstance to deter-

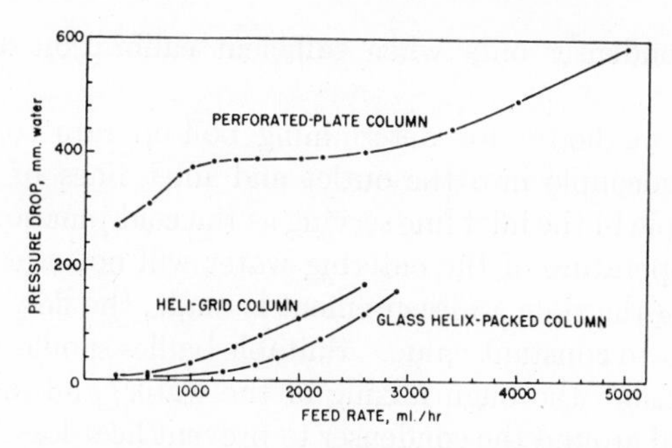

Fig. 32. Pressure-drop vs. feed-rate for three types of columns.

mine the boil-up rate during the distillation by an absolute method in order to maintain a constant flow of vapor at the head of the column. With a properly constructed condenser system operating on the principle of intermittent take-off, changes in the boil-up rate are indicated by an increase or decrease in the time required to collect a given amount of product, provided the apparent reflux ratio is kept constant. Necessary adjustment of the back pressure may then be made to restore the desired boil-up rate.

Available information on pressure drop versus boil-up rate is meager. Hall and Jonach[122] report pressure drop in one column in mm. of mercury at a boil-up rate of 150 ml./hr. as follows: C_8 alkylate 2.5, C_{12} alkylate 3.5, benzene 3.6, toluene 3.9, and xylene 5.0. Goldsbarry and Askevold[128] made measurements on methylcyclohexane–heptane mixtures in three columns. Their results are shown in Figure 32. ("Feed rate" is the total vapor leaving the still pot and represents the vapor condensed at the head plus internal condensation in the column arising from imperfect insulation or heat-loss compensation.) It is apparent that back-pressure readings give substantially no measure of true boil-up rate over the range 1000–3000 ml./hr. in the perforated-plate column. In the Heli-Grid packed column, the back pressure is very nearly a linear function of feed rate between 800 and 2600 ml., while in a helix-packed column the back pressure changes slowly and nonlinearly with feed rate up to about 1800 ml./hr., and linearly to about 3000 ml./hr. The helix-packed column was maintained adiabatic by heated jackets which allowed internal reflux of 620 ml./hr., whereas the Heli-Grid column was vacuum-jacketed and had internal reflux of 305 ml./hr. These differences in internal reflux may have contributed to the differences in the character of the back-pressure curve.

It is apparent that the back pressure or pressure drop through a column may be kept constant, either by manual or automatic control, but the absolute value of back pressure will indicate the true amount of vapor reaching the condenser only when sufficient calibration data have been established.

An effective method[109] for determining boil-up rate consists of introducing a thermocouple into the outlet and inlet lines of the head condenser, the couple in the inlet line serving as the cold junction. In this way changes in temperature of the entering water will not affect the measurements. During the time a measurement is made, the flow of water has to be held at a known constant value. Suitable baffles should be placed in the condenser to ensure thorough mixing of the water, and proper insulation should be placed around the condenser to prevent heat losses. Calculation of the boil-up rate is simple:

$$V_B = tw/\lambda$$

where V_B is boil-up rate grams per hour, w is grams of water flowing through the condenser per hour, λ is latent heat of vapor in calories per gram, and t is temperature of the water (t is not the true temperature of the water, but the increase in its temperature resulting from heat picked up; the arrangement of the thermocouples, however, gives the apparent temperature of the water). Boil-up rate determined by this method is accurate to about 5%, if the water rate is held sufficiently constant during the time a temperature measurement is being made, and if the temperature is great enough to permit an accurate measurement to be made. This method is excellent for determining boil-up rate versus back pressure for a series of pure compounds whose mixtures are to be fractionated. Its usefulness is limited to those compounds whose heat of vaporization is known or may be calculated from vapor-pressure data. By suitable construction of the condenser system, this method can be used to check the boil-up rate during a distillation and indicate appropriate changes in the setting of a controlling back-pressure manometer to maintain a prescribed boil-up rate.

The usual back-pressure manometer consists of a simple U-tube partly filled with a fluid of low volatility. One leg of the tube is connected to the top of the reflux condenser, and the other leg to the still pot at a point not exposed to the hot vapor from the distilland. Safety traps are usually attached to each leg to catch the liquid contents of the U-tube in the event the back pressure exceeds the range of the manometer, either as a result of excessive heat input to the still pot or by violent bumping of the charge as sometimes occurs, particularly when water is present in the charge. Figure 33 is an example of a satisfactory back-pressure manometer. Mercury, dibutyl phthalate, propylene glycol, diethylene glycol, or lubricating oil of light grade may be used as the manostatic fluid; mercury offers the greatest possible range of pressure in a given instrument, but low sensitivity; lower density liquids reduce the pressure range but offer the advantage of

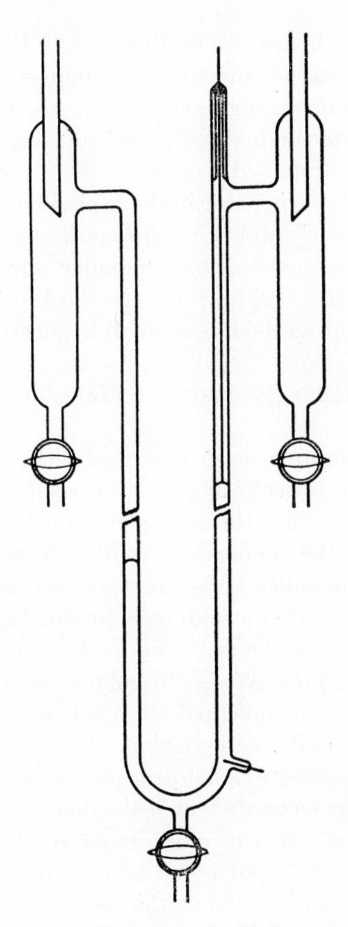

Fig. 33. Back-pressure manometer with electrodes for controlling heat input.

increased sensitivity, greater by a factor of 10 to 15. Mercury or the glycols containing a small amount of dissolved sodium nitrite may be used when conductivity of the manostatic fluid actuates an electronic switch for control purposes. Nonconducting liquids may be used as manostatic fluids in controlling manometers if a photoelectric control is used.[133]

Certain precautions should be observed in working with back-pressure manometers. During the preflooding operation, the high-pressure side of a low-range manometer should be closed by a valve just before the operation is started, and the valve opened when normal boil-up is resumed. Introduction of a very slow stream of carbon dioxide or nitrogen gas into the still pot through the back-pressure line will stop any diffusion of vapor into the line during the preflooding period. 1 or 2 ft. or 2-mm. capillary tubing used as a section of the high-pressure line next to the still pot will help to minimize diffusion of vapor toward the manometer. Variations in the temperature of the gas in the high-pressure line to, and in the body of, the back-pressure manometer undoubtedly lead to variations of boil-up rate if the back pressure is maintained constant. Diffusion of the gas into the still-pot vapor is an unknown factor in the behavior of the manometer. Its simplicity and general adaptability to automatic control of boil-up rate has made the back-pressure manometer a popular auxiliary of many distillation columns, but unless boil-up rates are checked frequently by a more reliable and independent method, considerable uncertainty attends its use.

4. Reflux-Temperature Measurement

Fractionating columns are usually equipped with a thermometer or other temperature-measuring device[134] located at a position immediately outside the fractionating section where the issuing vapor impinges on the measuring element on its way to the condenser section. In a properly constructed column, the temperature indicated is the vapor–liquid equilibrium temperature, or very nearly so. If the column is producing a substantially pure compound, the indicated temperature will be the boiling point of the compound at the prevailing pressure; if the column is producing a mixture of two or more compounds, the indicated temperature will be the boiling point of the mixture of a specific composition. (Azeotropic mixtures, either binary or ternary in composition, act as a pure compound at a given pressure.) The above statements are true if the quantity of vapor is sufficient to supply all heat losses, either of radiation or conduction, of the thermometric element, and if the vapor is not superheated. Unavoidable small heat losses from the element provide a thin layer of condensate to establish the desired liquid–vapor equilibrium condition for correct temperature reading.

Proper displacement of the thermometric element in the vapor stream is of primary importance to ensure the closest approach to true vapor–liquid equilibrium-temperature readings. In low-temperature columns, this condition is most easily established by the use of an efficient vacuum jacket to conduct the vapors from the rectifying section to the thermometric elements; in addition, means should be provided to keep the thermometer wetted, either by refrigeration or by directing a part of the reflux onto the thermometer. In high-temperature columns, the possibility of superheating is unlikely under proper operating conditions, and hence insulation is used to prevent excessive heat losses. At very low pressures (1–10 mm.), polished-metal radiation shields and external heaters may be necessary to minimize heat losses to ensure correct temperature readings.

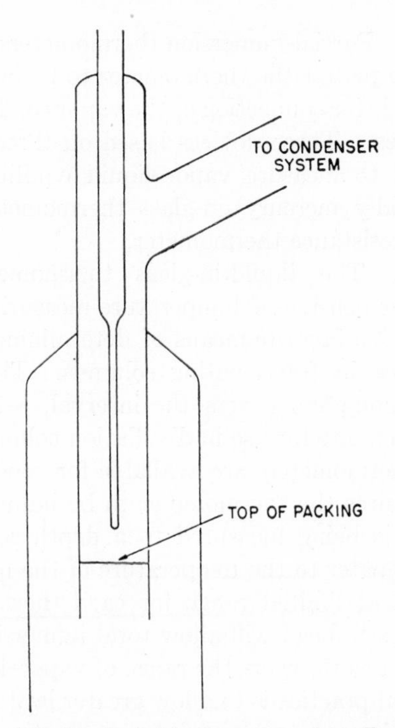

Fig. 34. Sealed-in thermocouple well.

In many column designs, the thermometric element is part of the condenser system, as is indicated in Figures 28–37. Fenske et al.,[109] on the other hand, using thermocouples for temperature measurements, buried them several inches in the packing of the rectifying section to ensure true vapor–liquid equilibrium. This system requires that the measuring element be far enough below the top of the packing to allow the cold reflux to reach equilibrium temperature before contact is made with the thermometric element. The vapor–liquid equilibrium temperature so indicated may be higher than the temperature measured just above the top of the packing because of the fractionation occurring in the packed section above the thermocouple. Willingham and Rossini[106] used a design in which a resistance thermometer was located in an unpacked section of a column immediately above the top of the packing. The vacuum jacket extended very nearly to the terminal block of the thermometer and hence provided excellent insulation against heat losses and consequent errors in temperature readings. The vapor conduit to the total condenser was sealed to the column just above the vacuum jacket. This design is probably ideal for proper placement of the thermometric element, but is usable only with resistance thermometers of suitable length, or with thermocouples, as shown in Figure 34. Partial-immersion thermometers do not have enough immersible length to permit the thermometer to be inserted to the correct depth and still provide for connection of the vapor conduit to the condenser.

Measuring Devices. Three devices based on three different principles are commonly used to measure vapor–liquid equilibrium temperatures: (*a*) the liquid (usually mercury)-in-glass thermometer, (*b*) the thermocouple, and (*c*) the resistance thermometer.

(*a*) *Thermometers.* The liquid-in-glass thermometer is the oldest, simplest, and least expensive of temperature-measuring instruments; for these reasons it is still a favorite means of determining vapor–liquid equilibrium temperatures in fractionating columns. The working range of liquid-in-glass thermometers covers the interval, −190° to 500°C., and hence, is entirely adequate for use in distillation columns.[135]

Two designs of thermometers are available for general use. The total-immersion type requires the thermometer to be immersed in the medium whose temperature is being measured to a depth sufficient to bring all liquid in the thermometer to the temperature of the medium; this type is generally small and of limited range for each thermometer of a series. Suitable design of a still head will allow total immersion thermometers to be used in distillation work where the range of vapor–liquid temperature is small, but the general practice is to allow greater latitude by using partial-immersion types of thermometers.

Partial-immersion thermometers are constructed to give the correct or nearly correct reading of a temperature when they are immersed to a specified depth in the vapor whose temperature is being measured. This commendable effort on the part of the manufacturers cannot overcome the variations of indicated temperature arising from the variable temperature of the emergent stem of the thermometer; nor is it generally possible to create a still-head design which allows adequate circulation of vapor around the section of the thermometer specified for immersion. Generally, a pocket exists where the thermometer enters the still head and poor vapor circulation prevails. These two factors introduce errors in the indicated readings that are not easily corrected.

TABLE XXIV

Couple	e.m.f., mv.	
	100°C.	200°C.
Copper-constantan	4.28	9.29
Iron-constantan	5.28	10.78
Chromel-constantan	6.30	13.30
Chromel-Alumel	4.1	8.13

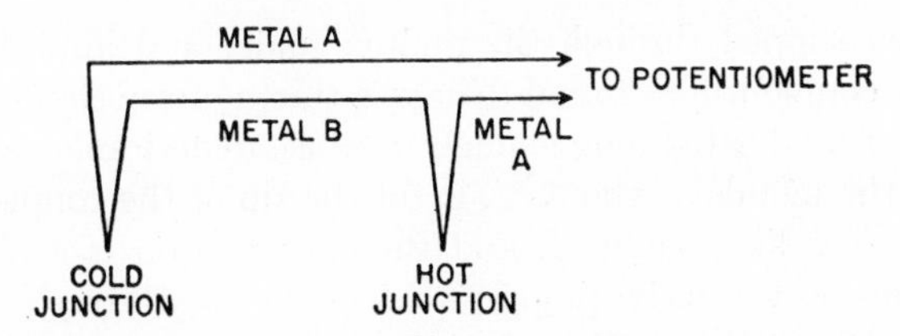

Fig. 35. Thermoelectric circuit for temperature measurement.

Thermometers must of necessity be located in the vapor stream leaving the fractionating section; this position offers no problem in reading with short fractionating columns operated from floor level; but taller columns require the use of a ladder or superstructure to make the thermometer accessible for reading. When a battery of columns is under the care of one operator, this expedient is entirely too burdensome and time consuming. The objectionable features of liquid-in-glass thermometers can be largely overcome by one of the electrical methods of temperature measurement.

(b) *Thermocouples.* In the practical application of thermoelectric thermometry only a few pairs of metals have received wide application. These are shown in Table XXIV. Any of the four couples, commonly called base–metal types, of the above list are satisfactory for measuring vapor–liquid equilibrium temperatures in distillation columns where the temperature will not exceed about 300°C. Iron-constantan and Chromel-constantan have somewhat greater thermal electromotive force (e.m.f.) for a given temperature compared to the other two, but the difference is not marked. Copper-constantan thermocouples offer certain distinct advantages. This pair is usable over the range −200–350°C.; since one element of the couple is copper, a relatively short length of constantan can be used to form one couple for the high-temperature position and the other couple for the reference junction located nearby; long leads of low-resistance copper wire can then be used to connect to the measuring instrument at a convenient position for operation. Number 28 or 30 gage copper and constantan wire, insulated with enamel and silk, are satisfactory for most purposes, the smaller wire being preferred from the point of view of low conductivity of heat from the junction.

Construction of a junction is simple; insulation is removed from about $^1/_2$ in. of the ends of the two wires forming the couple; enamel insulation can be removed by use of fine emery paper. The two bared ends are then twisted together, and given a very light coat of a flux suitable for silver-soldering. A loop about $^1/_8$ to $^3/_{16}$ in. in diameter is formed at the end of a 6-in. length of No. 18 Nichrom wire, and filled with silver solder in a small air-gas flame. After the solder in the loop is molten, it can be kept in this condition by holding the flame slightly above the loop. The prepared couple is then slipped through the molten solder and immediately withdrawn. The couple will be found to have a thin uniform coat of solder, and will not have been heated long enough to cause undesirable changes in the character of the metals. About $^3/_8$ in. of the tip of the couple is then cut off, any adhering flux removed, and the construction is complete. The other junction is similarly prepared. The finished couples are shown diagrammatically in Figure 35.

A thermocouple should be protected by a suitable well to prevent corrosion of the couple by chemical reaction with components of the vapor stream. The small physical dimensions of a couple constructed from the recommended size of wire permits the use of small-diameter wells. For greater mechanical strength, only the lower end of the well, for a length of 10 to 15 diameters, need be made small diameter. A suitable design for sealed-in construction is shown in Figure 34. About $^1/_2$ in. of high-boiling liquid such as dibutyl phthalate should be introduced into the test-tube end with a capillary pipet before the couple is placed in position. This will ensure excellent heat transfer to the junction. As soon as the column is in operation with a liquid whose boiling point is near the highest temperature at which the column is to be operated, a cork should be inserted firmly in the top of the thermometer well, and completely covered with Apiezon W wax to provide a vacuum-tight seal. This will prevent "breathing" of the well and prevent hydrolysis of the dibutyl phthalate and subsequent corrosion of the couple.

Multiple-junction thermocouples, in series, may be used to give greater thermal e.m.f. for a given temperature level to provide greater sensitivity. Space limitations in laboratory columns limit the number of junctions to two or possible three. Installation is more difficult than with single junctions since each junction must be well insulated from its companion to avoid short circuits; this is most easily accomplished by installing multiple-tip wells to isolate each element, or by use of the construction shown in Figure 36. The U-tube should have enough high-boiling liquid in the bottom to provide heat transfer to the two couples. (It may be mentioned that, by removal of the thermocouples and the high-boiling liquid, the U-tube may be used as a condenser for measuring boil-up rates by the method outlined in Sec. V-3.)

Thermocouples for determining vapor–liquid equilibrium temperatures can be most readily calibrated *in situ*. A suitable amount of a pure compound of known boiling point may be charged to the still pot, the column put into operation, and kept under total reflux. Traces of water may be removed from the system by withdrawing a few grams of the distillate. The thermal e.m.f. developed at several boil-up rates should be identical for a given charge of pure material. If significant variations of e.m.f. develop

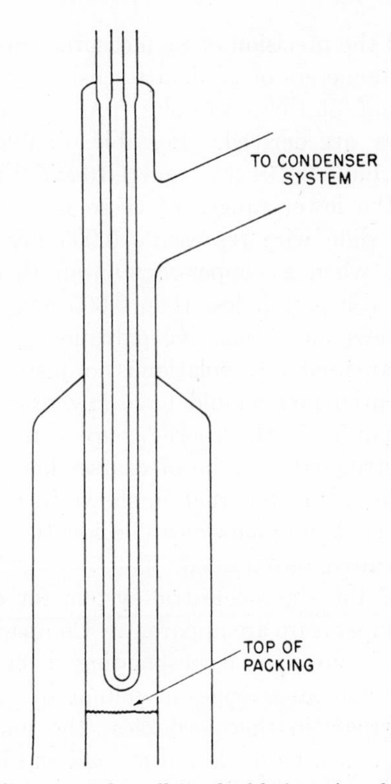

Fig. 36. Thermocouple well for double-junction thermocouple.

under different boil-up rates, improper placement of the thermocouple is indicated. Three or four check points in the proposed working range of the thermocouple will suffice to establish the necessary corrections to be applied to measured e.m.f. to give true temperature readings on conversion from standard tables.

The reference junction for thermoelectric systems on laboratory columns is most easily maintained constant by the use of a bath of ice and distilled water; one-quart wide-mouth Thermos bottles are suitable containers for this purpose. A well similar to that shown in Figure 34 should be provided for shielding the junction. The reproducibility of the ice point is excellent, variations being 0.0002°C. or less.[136] This is smaller by a factor of 50 than the variation expected in the most precise column operation. Automatic cold-junction compensators used in some industrial instruments are not satisfactory substitutes for an ice-bath reference junction if temperatures are to be measured to 0.1°C., or less.

Precise measurement of the e.m.f. of a thermocouple is possible only with a potentiometer. The principle of this instrument, the history of its development, and the precision of its measurements are fully discussed by White.[137] Potentiometers of moderate sensitivity are usually suitable for measuring the e.m.f. of thermocouples from which vapor–liquid equilibrium temperatures are derived. Portable, double-range instruments having scales of 0–10.1 and 0–101 mv., and 0–16 and 0–80 mv. are available commercially. On the lower ranges of these instruments, the smallest dial division of the slide wire represents 0.005 mv.: the temperature equivalent is 0.1 °C. when a copper-constantan thermocouple is being used. Interpolation will permit less than 0.005 mv. to be read on these instruments, but unless more sensitive galvanometers than those built into the instruments are used, interpolation is not justified.

Leads to the potentiometer should have low resistance to permit accurate readings of e.m.f. If the thermocouples are made of fine wire, long leads to the instrument may be of coarser low-resistance wire (No. 16 or 18 gage) by use of the construction shown in Figure 37. The temperature of the two cold junctions must be identical and known if true temperature readings are to be obtained.

The advantages of the thermoelectric system for determining vapor–liquid equilibrium temperature are apparent. Compared to liquid-in-glass thermometers, there is no error corresponding to emergent stem error; the temporary or permanent changes in volume of the bulb of thermometers have no counterpart in thermocouples; the mass of the sensitive part of a thermocouple can be made quite small and hence it responds to changes in temperature more rapidly than a thermometer. The indicating instrument can be located at a convenient position reasonably remote from the column; when a number of columns are under the care of one operator, a central operating position can be permanently set up at which complete thermal data on all the columns can be obtained.

(*c*) *Metal Resistance Thermometers.* The operating principles and methods of using resistance thermometers have been discussed in detail elsewhere.[134–139] As a means of measuring vapor–liquid equilibrium temperatures in distillation columns, they have not had wide use. At the National Bureau of Standards, however, they are used in preference to thermocouples.[106]

For measuring vapor–liquid equilibrium temperatures in distillation columns, the resistance thermometer offers the highest accuracy and maximum reliability and reproducibility. It is less convenient to use than thermoelectric systems because each temperature reading is derived from two instrument readings, compared to one instrument reading for thermoelectric systems; the latter, on the other hand, requires proper maintenance of the cold junction. The large physical size of resistance thermometers compared to thermocouples makes their use less convenient on most columns and impossible on very small columns. Their large heat capacity compared to that of thermocouples reduces their speed of response to temperature changes to a value far below that of thermocouples. Initial cost of instruments for resistance thermometry is much greater than a suitable potentiometer and associated equipment for measuring temperatures thermoelectrically. The latter system is an excellent compromise between the high cost and reliability of resistance thermometry, and the low cost and poor reliability of liquid-in-glass thermometers.

(*d*) *Thermistor Resistance Thermometers.* Thermistors[140] are devices which make use of the very large negative temperature coefficient of resistivity of solid-state semiconductor materials. Values of temperature coefficient for semiconductors are reported in the range of 5–8%/°C. This property of thermistors makes them obviously applicable to temperature measurement and control. Because of the magnitude of the temperature coefficient, the thermometer derived from the thermistor is capable of a sensitivity of 0.0005°C. This makes it at least one order of magnitude more sensitive than the metal resistance thermometer. The maximum permissible operating temperature of the thermistor is limited by the stability of the semiconductor material used; it is generally less than 300°C. for long term stability. Some transistors are claimed to operate satisfactorily at temperatures as high as 1000°C. with moderate stability.

Since the thermistor thermometer is a resistance thermometer it is used as one element of a four-element Wheatstone bridge circuit as is done with metallic resistors. The thermistor element of the bridge circuit must have a low current flow through it to minimize heat generation which would impair its sensing capability. The thermistor thermometer devised by Becker, Green, and Pearson[141] and as described by Sturtevant[134] has the following temperature-resistance characteristics:

Temp., °C.	Resistance, ohms
−25	580,000
0	145,000
25	46,000
50	16,000
100	3200
200	305

The lag, $1/K$, is 70 sec. in still air compared to 200 sec. for an ordinary laboratory thermometer in still air. Its calibration was found to be constant to within 0.01°C. for two months when used below 100°C.

Besides the high degree of sensitivity, the thermistor thermometer has other favorable advantages: (*1*) The resistance of the lead wires is

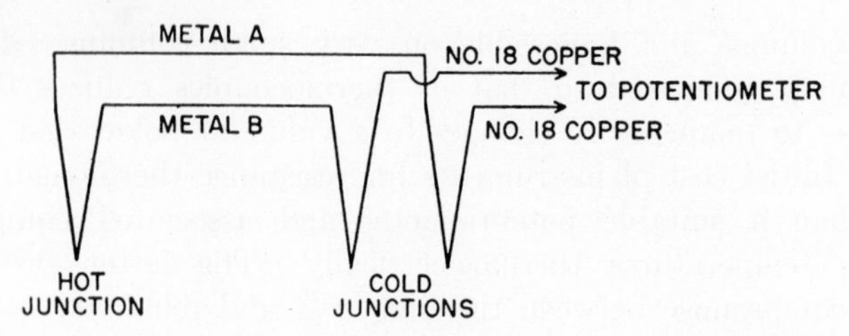

Fig. 37. Circuit to provide low-resistance leads to potentiometer.

insignificant compared to the resistance of the thermistor permitting long distances between the thermistor and the read-out instrument. (*2*) No cold junctions are necessary. (*3*) The thermistor element can be made in almost any shape and in tiny size; beads as small as 0.015 cm. diam., sheathed in glass or noble metals, and having platinum leads of 0.0025 cm. diam. have been described.[140a]

It is obvious that the thermistor thermometer with its inherent high sensitivity, low heat capacity, and low thermal lag should be useful for measuring temperatures in special situations such as in thin liquid films, small liquid streams, vapors, and vapors at subatmospheric pressures.

Thermistor thermometers are commercially available in a variety of probe shapes and sizes with either simple indicator readout, recording readout, and in combination with controlling units.[142]

VI. PRESSURE CONTROL

1. General

Precise measurement of vapor–liquid equilibrium temperature has a definite meaning only when the pressure at which the temperature is measured is closely controlled. If a pure compound is being distilled, for example, the vapor–liquid equilibrium temperature is the temperature at which the compound has a vapor pressure equal to the operating pressure at the head of the column; if the operating pressure is lowered or raised, vapor–equilibrium temperature will decrease and increase, respectively. A generalized picture of the manner in which vapor pressure changes with temperature is shown in Figure 38.

Consider T the temperature at which the vapor pressure of a compound is 1 atm., or 760 mm. mercury. Small change in temperature makes large changes in vapor pressure in this region. At T' an equal change in temperature will make a much smaller change in the vapor pressure. In distillation columns the pressure should be kept constant; changes in

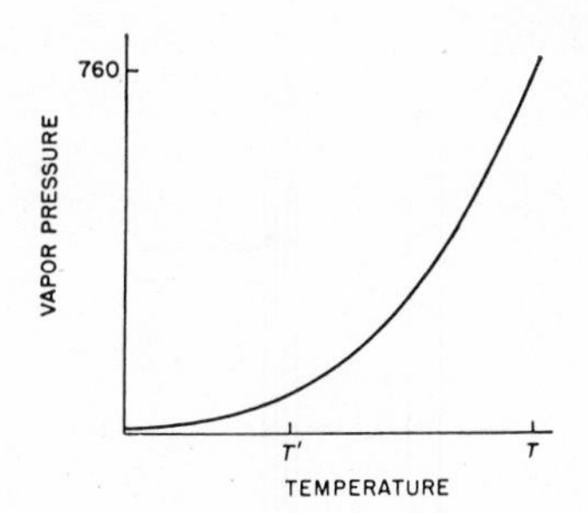

Fig. 38. Temperature-vapor pressure curve.

vapor–liquid equilibrium temperature then indicate a change in the composition of a distillate. If the pressure is not constant, vapor–liquid temperature will change without necessarily indicating a change in the composition of the distillate.

Inspection of Figure 38 will show the importance of precise pressure control in column operation, and why the pressure must be more closely controlled at greatly reduced pressure than at atmospheric pressure if the vapor–liquid equilibrium temperature is to have equal validity at both operating pressures.

Many devices have been designed to control the operating pressure of distillation columns. One investigator[143] found about 30 publications on pressure control covering the period 1840–1933; in the last 25 years the number has nearly doubled. Leck[144] has summarized methods of pressure measurements in some detail. Many of these designs were related to specific problems and were entirely satisfactory for the purpose. On the other hand, the developments in high-precision thermometry require greater precision in pressure control to utilize profitably the high precision possible in temperature measurements.

2. Manostats

The majority of pressure-controlling devices operate on the principle of the manometer and are called manostats. A simple design[145] is shown in Figure 39. As the pressure is lowered, the mercury in the right leg of the manostat approaches the adjustable contact rod, and finally, when contact is made, an electric circuit through a relay is completed to stop the pump motor or open a gas leak which slightly exceeds the capacity of the pump; this permits a slight increase in pressure, the electric contact is broken, and the pump starts, or the leak closes, and the cycle is repeated. The pressure so established is an average value varying slightly above and below an absolute value determined by the adjustment of the manostat; the extent of

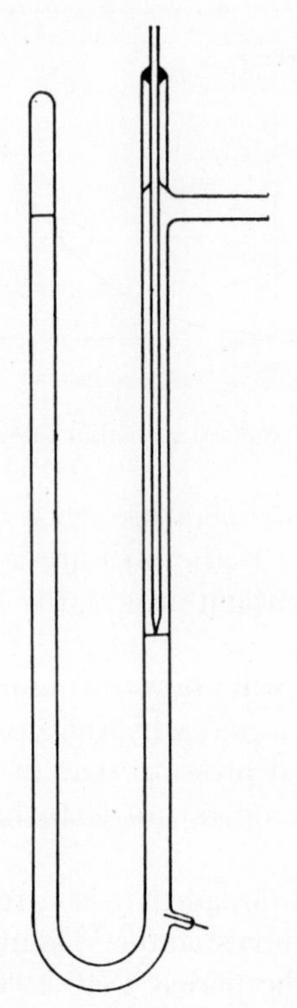

Fig. 39. Simple mercury manostat.

the variation, assuming a constant temperature, is dependent upon the inertia of the system as a whole.

The continuously adjustable manostat of Figure 39 has been modified to operate at a number of fixed pressures by sealing in tungsten contacts at different positions in the open leg of the manostat.[146,147] To change the operating pressures, one electrical connection is shifted to the appropriate contact.

Greater precision of control is possible with a cascade system in which a closely controlled operating system exhausts into a roughly controlled system at somewhat lower pressure.[148] The pressure differential of the two systems ensures an exhaust rate from the closely controlled system low enough to permit the manostat to follow the pressure without significant overshoot. The system, as outlined, requires intermittent operation of the evacuating pump.

To obviate the use of an electric circuit and associated relays, a mercury balance manostat was developed by Schierholtz and modified by Bailey.[149–152] Flow of mercury from one leg to the other in the manostat

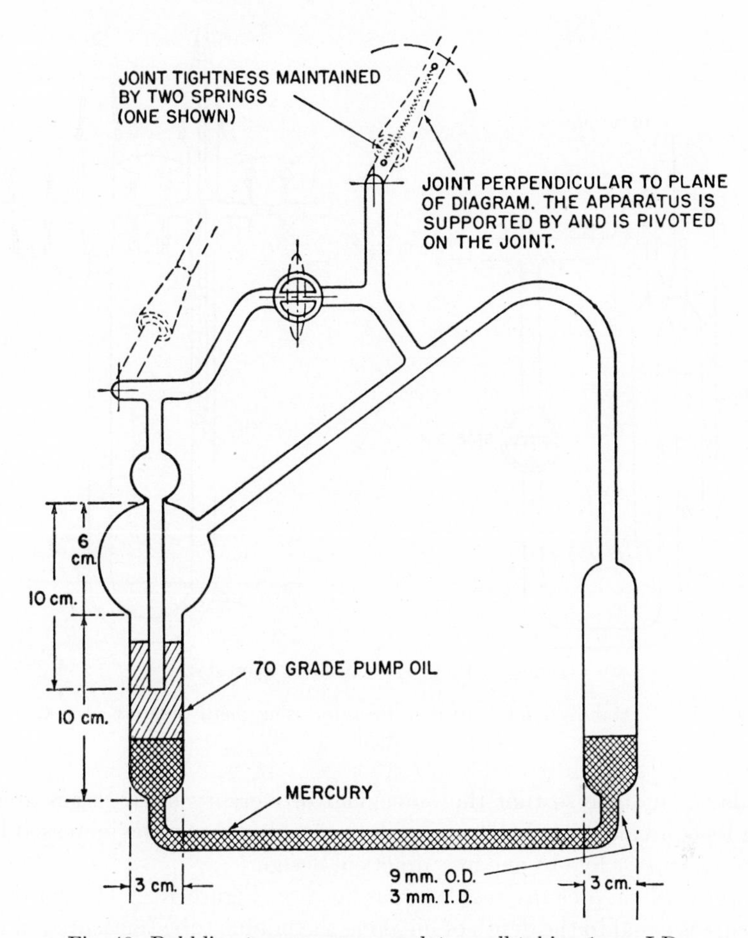

Fig. 40. Bubbling-type pressure regulator; all tubing 1 cm. I.D.

shifts the balance point of a lever arrangement to open or close a bleed valve and thereby restore the pressure to its equilibrium value. Consistent behavior in this design is difficult to attain.

The high density of mercury makes it undesirable as a manostatic fluid from the standpoint of sensitivity. To achieve greater sensitivity than is possible with mercury, sulfuric acid of density 1.71 has been used to give a sensitivity of 7.9 compared to mercury.[153] The maximum sensitivity with the acid is probably not attained because surface tension maintains the contact beyond the time when the general level of the liquid in the contact leg is below the electrode.

To retain the advantages of mercury as a manostatic fluid yet provide improved sensitivity. Ferry[154] designed a manostat in which one leg

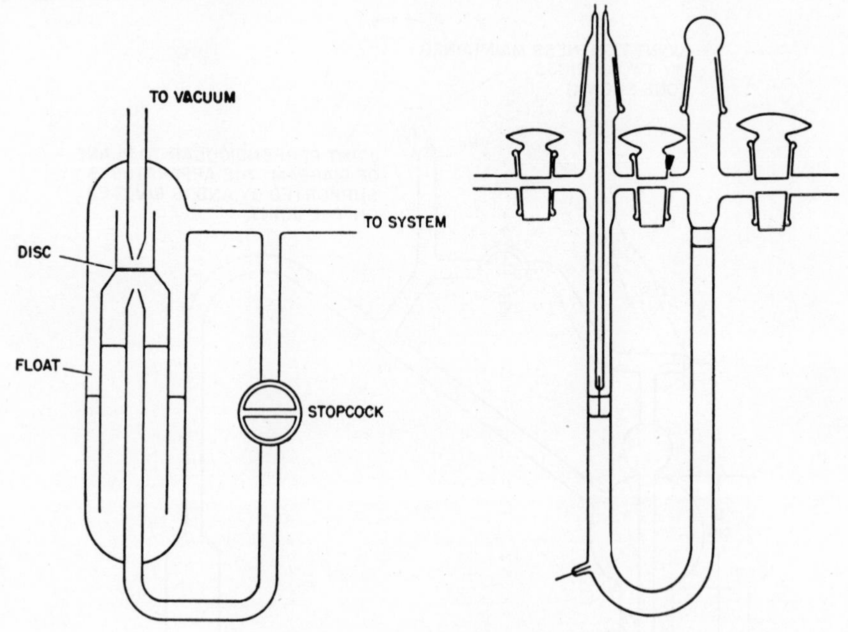

Fig. 41 (left). Cartesian-diver manostat.

Fig. 42 (right). Manostat for 1–10 mm. pressure using diethylene glycol as manostat fluid.

stands at an angle so that the movement of mercury in the leg is greater than its equivalent vertical movement. Sensitivity may be increased by a factor of four or five to one in a practical design.

A very simple pressure regulator is shown in Figure 40. The controlled pressure is equal to the depth of oil along the bubble tube (measured in mm. mercury), plus the pressure in the pump side of the manostat.[91,155]

The Cartesian diver pressure control, based on the principles of a baroscope,[156] is diagrammed in Figure 41. The operating principle of this instrument and the mathematics of its behavior have also been described.[157] Operation is as follows: With the stopcocks open, the system is evacuated to very nearly the desired pressure, and the stopcock is closed; an evacuation continues, the pressure in the inner chamber increases relative to the pressure in the outer chamber and raises the floating bell until the disk closes the exhaust port to stop further reduction of the pressure in the system.

Precise pressure control at 10 mm. and below is somewhat difficult. Mercury manostats become sluggish; manostatic liquids which wet the glass walls overcome this if allowance is made for the viscosity of the usual high-boiling liquids suitable for this purpose. A simple design of manostat

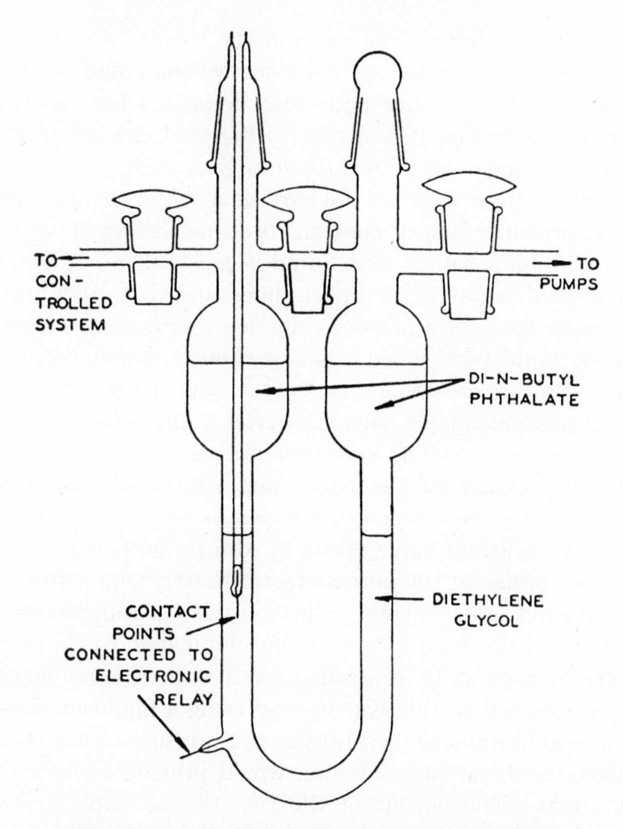

Fig. 43. Two-liquid manostat for 1-mm. operation.

for 10-mm. operation and giving fair control at 1 mm. is shown in Figure 42. Diethylene glycol containing about 0.5% sodium nitrite in solution provides sufficient conductivity to operate an electron relay for controlling the pump. A thin layer of diamyl phthalate on the surface of the glycol in each leg minimizes evaporation. A reference vacuum is provided on one side of the manostat by a small mercury-vapor pump. Dry-ice traps are provided between the manostat and the mercury-vapor pump and the system under control to condense moisture and vapors which would dissolve in the glycol and change its density.

Pressure control at 1 mm. is possible with fair precision (±0.01 mm.) with the two-liquid manostat[158] of Figure 43. The upper layers are dibutyl phthalate saturated with diethylene glycol, and the lower layer, diethylene glycol saturated with dibutyl phthalate. A trace of sodium nitrite in the glycol layer provides sufficient conductivity to operate a controlling electron relay. The sensitivity of the manostat is related to the ratio of cross-sectional areas of the large chambers and the U-tube, and to the relative densities of the two liquids. A reference vacuum and cold traps are provided as described in the preceding design. Close control of the temperature of the manostat is necessary to avoid changes in the mutual solubility of the liquids and to obviate density changes.

An entirely different type of pressure control for 1-mm. operation is based on the principle that at constant pressure the vapor–liquid equilibrium temperature of a boiling pure liquid is constant.[159] A suitable boiler containing a small amount of diphenylmethane (b.p. 80°C. at 1 mm.) provides a vapor bath for a multiple-junction thermocouple system. The thermoelectric voltage developed is balanced out in a potentiometer circuit with the aid of a mirror-type galvanometer. At the null point, the light beam from the galvanometer circuit actuates a photoelectric relay circuit, which in turn closes a solenoid valve connecting the boiler to the vacuum pump. If the pressure in the boiler and controlled system increases, vapor–liquid equilibrium temperature increases slightly, the galvanometer deflects, and the solenoid valve opens to restore the balance. Inevitable changes in the voltage of the potentiometer battery and shifts in the zero setting of the galvanometer cause a drift in the controlled pressure. The potentiometer circuit could probably be eliminated by having another pressure system accurately controlled by a conventional manostat. A second boiler attached to this system, and using a liquid having the same vapor–liquid equilibrium temperature at the pressure of the second boiler as the diphenylmethane has at 1 mm. would provide a thermal e.m.f. of equal magnitude. The output of the two thermocouple systems when delivered to the galvanometer in opposition would give no deflection until the pressure in the 1-mm. system increased when the photoelectric relay would function as described previously.

A. EFFECT OF TEMPERATURE CHANGES IN MANOSTATS

Temperature changes of a manostat affect the absolute value of a pressure being controlled. A manostat of the type shown in Figure 39 is subject to three effects by temperature: (*a*) the total volume of mercury increases; (*b*) the glass expands to increase its volume and to a slight extent compensates for *a*; and (*c*) the adjustable contact arm increases in length with increases in temperature.

If in Figure 39 a horizontal line is drawn from the contact point to intersect the left, or measuring, leg of the manostat, any expansion of the mercury above this line will not affect the pressure because the product of density, d, and height, h, will remain constant. The mercury in the U-tube section below the horizontal line will also expand to force mercury above the line and hence increase the numerical value hd. The adjustable contact arm will likewise increase in length and have the effect of forcing still more mercury above the line and increase *hd* still more. The net effect of the increase in temperature is an increase in the controlled pressure. Expansion of the contact arm can be completely eliminated by the construction shown in Figure 42; the outer tube will increase in length with temperature and tend to raise the contact point, but the inner tube will similarly increase in length to hold the tungsten contact point in a fixed position. Substitution of this contact point for the metal contact arm of Figure 39 will eliminate a part of the temperature effect. A manostat, modified as indicated, to control pressures over the range 50–760 mm. of mercury will give fair control at the higher pressure and poor control at the lower pressure. For example, if the manostat, when set at 760 mm., has 21% of the total volume of mercury in the U-tube section, an increase of 10°C. in temperature (from 25–35°C.) will increase the controlled pressure to 760.4 mm.; when adjusted to control at 50 mm., the U-tube would contain 95% of the total mercury, and an increase of 10°C. in the temperature would increase the controlled pressure to 51.65 mm. of mercury. It is apparent from these results that the mercury in the U-tube section below the measuring arm is chiefly responsible for the changes in controlled pressure resulting from increased temperature.

A manostat constructed as shown in Figure 44 will be compensated to changes in temperature (excluding the slight effect of expansion of the glass), as the following analysis will demonstrate:

Let V equal total volume of mercury at some standard temperature T_s; (a) is volume of mercury in height h; (b) is volume of mercury below height h; then V is $a + b$; A is area of upper bulb, $\pi D^2/4$; α is coefficient of expansion of mercury; d_s is density of mercury at T_s; $p_s = h_s$ is pressure at T_s; p_t is pressure at another temperature $(T_s + \Delta t) = h_t$; d_t is density of mercury at $(T_s + \Delta t)$:

$$p_s = d_s h_s \text{ and } p_t = d_t h_t = (h_s + \Delta h)(d_s + \Delta d)$$

When the manostat is completely compensated

$$p_s - p_t = 0$$

and

$$d_s h_s - (h_s + \Delta h)(d_s + \Delta d) = 0$$

Simplifying

$$h_s \Delta d = -\Delta h d_s \tag{1}$$

Now $d_s = M/V_s$ and $d_t = M/V_t$, where M is the mass of mercury in the manostat.

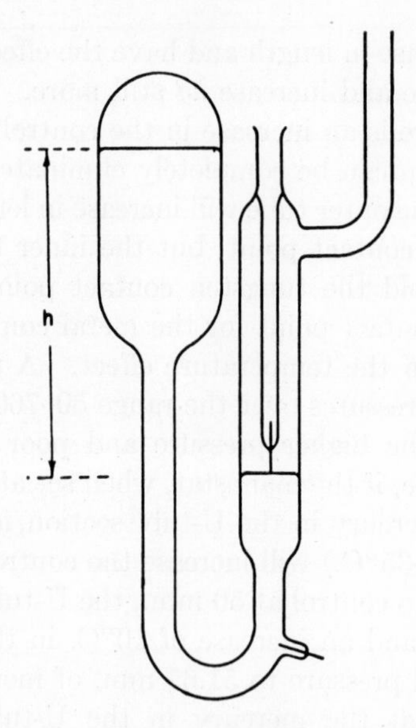

Fig. 44. Fixed-pressure, temperature-compensated mercury manostat.

Then

$$d_s V_s = d_t V_t$$

But

$$d_t V_t = (d_s + \Delta d)(V_s + \Delta V)$$

$$\Delta d = -d_s(\Delta V)/V \qquad \text{(a)}$$

By definition

$$\alpha = (\Delta V)/\Delta t V$$

Therefore

$$\Delta V = \alpha \Delta t V \qquad \text{(b)}$$

(a) and (b) may be combined and simplified to

$$\Delta d = -d_s \alpha \Delta t V/V = -d_s \alpha \Delta t \qquad (2)$$

Since point P is fixed

$$\Delta h = \Delta V/A = \alpha \Delta t V/A \qquad (3)$$

Substituting (2) and (3) in (1), $V = h_s A$, which is the equation for expansion of mercury only.

Equations (1) and (2) are independent of expansion of glass. To allow for the latter, eq. (3) must be modified as follows: Let β = coefficient of cubical expansion of glass. Subscripts Hg and gl refer, respectively, to mercury and glass.

$$\Delta h_{\mathrm{Hg}} = \frac{\Delta V_{\mathrm{Hg}} - \Delta V_{\mathrm{gl}}}{A_{\mathrm{gl}} - \Delta A_{\mathrm{gl}}} + \Delta h_{\mathrm{gl}} \tag{4}$$

$$\left.\begin{aligned} \Delta V_{\mathrm{Hg}} &= d\Delta t V \\ \Delta V_{\mathrm{gl}} &= \beta \Delta t V \\ \Delta A_{\mathrm{gl}} &= {}^2/_3 \Delta t \beta A \\ \Delta h_{\mathrm{gl}} &= {}^1/_3 \Delta t \beta h_s \end{aligned}\right] \text{by definition}$$

Substituting these definitions in eq. (4)

$$\Delta h_{\mathrm{Hg}} = \frac{\Delta t V(\alpha - \beta)}{A(1 + {}^2/_3 \Delta t \beta)} + {}^1/_3 \Delta t \beta h \tag{5}$$

Substituting (2) and (5) in (1)

$$h(-d_s \alpha \Delta t) = -d_s \left[\frac{\Delta t V(\alpha - \beta)}{(1 + {}^2/_3 \Delta t \beta)} + {}^1/_3 \Delta t \beta h \right]$$

$$h_s d = \frac{V(\alpha - \beta)}{A(1 + {}^2/_3 \Delta t \beta)} + {}^1/_3 \beta h_s$$

$$h_s(d - {}^1/_3 \beta) = \frac{(V)}{(A)} \frac{\alpha - \beta}{(1 + {}^2/_3 \Delta t \beta)}$$

$$V = \frac{h_s A(\alpha - {}^1/_3 \beta)(1 + {}^2/_3 \Delta t \beta)}{\alpha - \beta}$$

The term $(1 = {}^2/_3 \Delta t \beta)$ is very nearly unity:

$$V = \frac{h_s A(d - {}^1/_3 \beta)}{\alpha - \beta}$$

For Pyrex:

$$\beta = (3.6 \times 10^{-6})3 = 1.08 \times 10^{-5}$$

For mercury:

$$\alpha = 18.186 \times 10^{-5}$$

$$V' = \frac{h_s A(17.826 \times 10^{-5})}{17.106 \times 10^{-5}} = 1.042 h_s A$$

The compensated manostat of Figure 44 maintains its compensation if tilted in or out of the plane of the paper. This permits a fine adjustment of the absolute pressure at which the instrument controls. To avoid capillarity effects, the open leg of the manostat should be constructed of tubing 15- to 20-mm. I.D., and the closed side of 40-mm. I.D. tubing for manostats controlling at 50–200 mm.; for controlling at 725 mm., for example, the manostat may be constructed entirely of 15-mm. tubing. If the controlling contact is placed in the closed arm of the manostat instead of the open arm, the instrument fails to compensate for temperature change. Manostats of the above design have been constructed to operate at 50 mm. and above. At lower pressures, the volume V' becomes too small to permit satisfactory glass-working operations.

Manostats which embody a volume of trapped gas at a pressure near a prescribed pressure of operation[151,153,154] are seriously affected by temperature changes; the trapped gas expands or contracts in accordance with the gas laws. Consequently, the controlled pressure will change about 0.3%/°C. Unless these types of manostats are thermostated, they are not reliable for extended periods of operation.

B. MISCELLANEOUS FACTORS IN PRESSURE CONTROL

Elimination of temperature effects on manostats either by temperature control or compensation, ensures precise control of pressure only when the inertia of the whole pressure system permits a manostat to follow pressure changes very closely. If leakage into a pressure-control system is rapid, the exhaust pump will of necessity function frequently to maintain the desired pressure as controlled by the manostat. If the frequency of pump operation is of the same order of magnitude as the natural frequency of oscillation of the controlling manostat, the latter will be kept in a state of oscillation. As a result, the absolute value of the controlled pressure will vary above and below the nominal value at which the manostat should control. Inasmuch as the frequency of oscillation of a column of liquid is an inverse function of the square root of its length, a manostat designed to control at 725 mm., for example, will be thrown into a condition of oscillation more readily than will a manostat designed for 50-mm. control. (This assumes that the length of liquid column in each instance is roughly proportional to the pressure being controlled.) Precise control of pressure requires, therefore, that the leakage be small, so as to necessitate infrequent operation of the pump. By increasing the total volume of the controlled system, a given amount of leakage will change the pressure more slowly and require less frequent operation of the exhaust pump; by the same token, the pump will reduce the pressure more slowly to nominal value.

Large surge tanks[106] of 30- to 60-gal. capacity, insulated and properly located where ambient temperature changes are slow, are necessary if control is to be precise. Smaller surge tanks may be used if the exhaust rate is sufficiently reduced by insertion and proper adjustment of a throttling valve between the pump and surge tank. A slight amount of leakage, preferably of carbon dioxide or nitrogen deliberately introduced into otherwise tight systems in order to activate the exhaust pump for 1 or 2 sec. of each minute, will obviate the possibility of subnormal pressures, should the surge tanks drop in temperature; increases in the temperature of the tanks will be taken care of automatically.

Motor-driven pumps coast for a few revolutions after the power is cut off by action of the manostat. The effect of this after-pumping may be eliminated by placing a solenoid valve between the pump and surge tank and connecting the solenoid in parallel with the motor circuit so that the valve opens when the motor is energized and closes immediately when power is cut off. At pressures near atmospheric, the exhaust rate of conventional oil pumps is too great for precise control; reduction of the pump speed to $^1/_6$ to $^1/_{10}$ of its normal value by means of a speed-reducing system, and use of a solenoid valve mentioned previously permits satisfactory control.

Convenient location of surge tanks usually requires long lines to bring the controlled pressure to a fractionating column. For permanent installation 1.5-in. copper tubing should be used. This should be soft-soldered to suitable copper or bronze T's; diaphragm values[160] may be used at each T to provide a vacuum outlet near each column.

VII. MISCELLANEOUS ACCESSORIES

1. Joints and Stopcocks

The most unsatisfactory parts of a laboratory distillation column are the joints and stopcocks. Standard interchangeable joints and stopcock plugs, although they are within the allowable manufacturing tolerances, permit unavoidable losses of distilland or oxidation by air leakage, especially at reduced pressures. Sometimes a lubricant can be used to prevent the losses or leakage when certain types of compounds are being distilled, but these instances are exceptional, especially at higher temperatures and low pressures. The simplest solution to the problem of joints is to connect the still pot and condenser section to the column by fused glass seals. The design shown in Figure 29 is satisfactory because the one lubricated joint can be kept sufficiently cool to be out of contact with significant concentrations of vapor or liquid. In other parts of the column and auxiliary equipment where the concentration of vapor is low, or where contact of the distillate with the lubricated surfaces is minimized, joints and stopcocks are usually satisfactory, provided a lubricant insoluble in the distillate is used for lubrication.

Joints are either of tapered construction or spherical. They consist of male and female sections and are available in a variety of standard sizes. Spherical joints offer certain advantages in use; the two sections need not be so precisely lined up when equipment is being assembled and clamped,

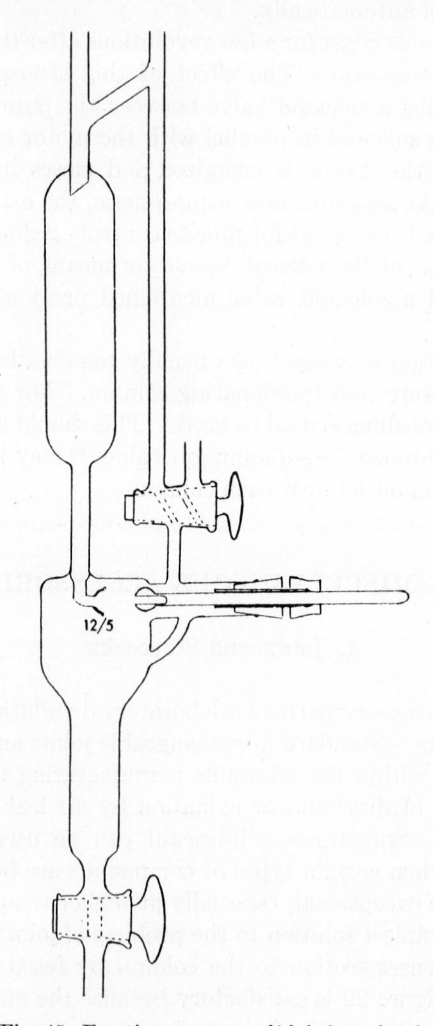

Fig. 45. Fraction cutter—self-lubricated valve.

strains are less likely to develop, and the sections are more easily separated than are tapered joints.

2. Fraction Cutter

A device in which to receive distillate as it is withdrawn from a column, and one which will permit removal of the distillate as fractions without disturbing column operation, is an important auxiliary for a distillation column, particularly when the column is operated at reduced pressure. The fraction cutter shown in Figure 45 was developed by the author to handle liquids, and normally solid or highly viscous materials which must be heated to produce mobile liquids. The small spherical joint which takes the place of a stopcock is lubricated by the distillate and will not leak air even with the upper chamber at greatly reduced pressure and the lower chamber at atmospheric pressure. To attain this behavior, the spherical joint (after the unit is constructed) is polished first with optical emery, and finally, with a suspension of jeweler's rouge, until leakage of gas is eliminated.

The glass rod to which the male section of the spherical joint is sealed is chosen enough larger than the bore of the $^1/_4$-in. pressure tubing (which produces a vacuum seal), to give a snug, not a tight, fit. A trace of lubricant on the inside of the rubber tubing will ensure easy manipulation of the rod.

Major advantages of this design over one having a stopcock between the chambers are elimination of air leakage and contamination which will occur with a stopcock, and elimination of any tendency to seize (necessitating column shutdown), which can occur with a heated stopcock. The fraction cutter shown in Figure 45 has given entirely satisfactory service at temperatures to 200°C.

3. Lubricants

Glycerol–starch has been found suitable as a stopcock lubricant when nonpolar compounds are being handled.[161] Sucrose or mannitol in glycerol containing 1–3% of medium-viscosity polyvinyl alcohol has been recommended for the same purpose.[162] A partially esterified and polymerized mixture of tetraethylene glycol and citric acid[163] or the same mixture modified by the addition of cellulose acetate[164] has been used as a lubricant when working with aliphatic and aromatic hydrocarbons. Alcohols, ketones, and water attack this mixture. The resinous mixture formed by reaction of sebacic acid and ethylene glycol is insoluble in aliphatic hydrocarbons, alcohols, and diethyl ether, but is soluble in benzene, pyridine, and alkyl halides.[165] Polymerized phthalate esters of di- and triethylene glycol are effective lubricants in contact with aliphatic hydrocarbons.[165] Proprietary mixtures available from many suppliers of laboratory equipment are generally of limited usefulness as stopcock lubricants.

4. General Suggestions for Mounting Equipment

When one or more columns are to be set up permanently, a suitable framework should be installed to hold and protect the column. One satisfactory design is shown in Figure 46.

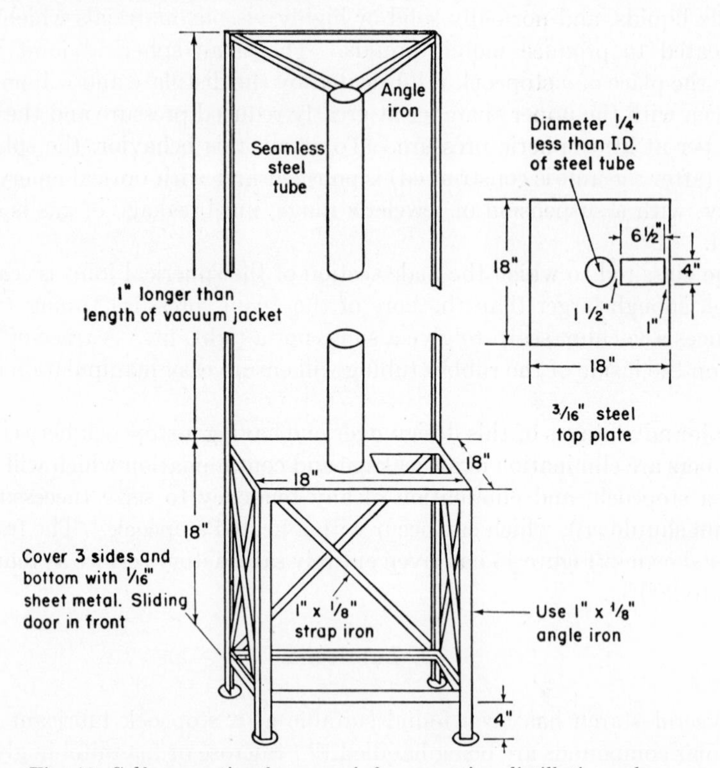

Fig. 46. Self-supporting framework for mounting distillation column.

Variable transformers* for controlling the power input to the column may be attached to the column panels or set on top of the base. If several columns are located together, the variable transformers may be more conveniently mounted in standard steel cabinets.

* Available from General Radio Company, Cambridge, Massachusetts, and Superior Electric Company, Bristol, Connecticut.

The receiver may be attached to steel bars bolted to the column frame. A single-turn glass spiral about 3 in. in diameter made of 6-mm. tubing should be used to connect the product line to the receiver. This provides enough flexibility to prevent breakage when the column expands at elevated temperatures. For the same reason, the reflux condenser should be lightly clamped.

PROCEDURE

I. INTRODUCTION

A batch distillation of the simplest possible mixture, that of two volatile components, is not strictly amenable to theoretical treatment, as is shown in the chapter on theory. The complex interrelations of column efficiency, reflux ratio, column holdup, and ideality or nonideality of the mixture become still more complicated as the number of components in the distilland (or charge) increases. Fortunately, so far as the practical application of batch fractional distillation is concerned, the shortcomings of theory do not greatly reduce the value of distillation as a laboratory technique of great power and usefulness. Some theory, an adequate column, and the proper operating procedure are sufficient to resolve all but the most complicated mixtures of volatile compounds and azeotropes.

This section discusses the procedure to be followed in making a fractional distillation. The choice of column, method of sampling and charging, the preliminary operations of preflooding and establishment of initial equilibrium, choice of reflux ratio, collection of product, and interpretation of data will be the chief points of discussion. Certain miscellaneous items found helpful in many distillations will also be included.

II. PURPOSE OF FRACTIONAL DISTILLATION

Batch fractional distillations on a laboratory scale usually have one of two purposes: to determine quantitatively the composition of the distilland, or to isolate one or more of the components from a mixture for further examination.

An analytical distillation is not of itself sufficient to establish the quantitative analysis of a mixture in many instances, particularly those involving complex mixtures such as hydrocarbons or any mixtures which form azeotropes. In such cases, an analytical distillation serves to isolate and remove interfering components, or to concentrate components present in small amounts, and to permit other analytical means such as infrared, ultraviolet, or mass-spectral analysis to establish the final analysis with certainty and precision. Sometimes, this procedure is followed of necessity because columns having fractionating efficiency adequate to separate every component are not available; in other instances, a combination of distillation and other analytical means requires much less time than would a complete analytical fractionation when a column having adequate efficiency is available.

It is obvious that an analytical distillation can accomplish both purposes if a charge of sufficient size is used for the fractionation. Normally, analytical fractionations are made on quantities of a few milliliters to several hundred milliliters; considerably larger volumes are employed when significant quantities of a component are to be isolated.

Depending on the purpose of the distillation, the column efficiency required may differ when a given mixture is being fractionated. If the fractionation is for analytical purposes, the column efficiency required will be governed by the relative volatility of the most closely boiling components whose separation is desired; if from the same mixture only one component, for example, is to be separated in high purity, and the volatility of this component is large compared to all other components in the mixture, a column of lower efficiency and greater productivity will be satisfactory.

III. CHOICE OF COLUMNS

Gas–liquid chromatography can be profitably used at this time to determine quickly an approximate analysis of a feed to serve as a guide for choosing the characteristics of a column to be used in the fractional distillation, and to provide information from which required reflux ratios can be estimated. Distillation time can be significantly reduced as a result, particularly if a mixture is to be fractionated to recover only one component in high purity, rather than to resolve the entire mixture.

When small still charges are to be fractionated, columns with low holdup are desirable, and for analytical distillations, they are a necessity in the interest of sharp separations. In the majority of columns, particularly packed columns, low holdup implies small size, which limits throughput and, consequently, product rate for a given reflux ratio. If small quantities (20–200 ml.) of material are to be fractionated, small concentric-tube columns provide the best solution for the problem. (See Fig. 3.) Packed columns of low holdup such as Hyper-Cal or the column of Figure 5 are suitable for charges of 200 ml. or somewhat larger. Larger still charges can be satisfactorily fractionated in columns of considerably greater holdup; boil-up rate can be increased greatly and product rate likewise increased for a given reflux ratio. Total distillation time will not be significantly different in the two cases if the ratio of charge to holdup is about the same. Certain advantages accrue in the use of larger columns and proportionately larger charges when sufficient material is available. Components present in the charge in small proportion relative to the holdup will not usually be isolable with either the large or small column. Evidence of their presence may be indicated by the character of the distillation or the refractive-index curve. Fractions from a large charge suspected of having such components will frequently be of sufficient amount, when combined, to be refractionated through an adequate column of low holdup to determine their composition. This procedure was used in studying 5% fractions derived from gallon charges of heptane alkylate containing 11 components.[113] In working with large charges, handling losses will be a smaller fraction of the charge, and the material balance will be better than in the case of small charges.

Although small holdup is necessary for sharp separations, adequate fractionating efficiency is required to ensure a prescribed degree of separation. Unknown mixtures can be most profitably examined analytically in a column having an efficiency of the order of 100 theoretical plates; results of this investigation may then indicate use of a less efficient, more productive column for further work. More commonly, some knowledge exists of the qualitative composition of a mixture to be separated. This may be deduced from the source of the material, the chemical reaction by which the mixture was produced, or by a qualitative chemical examination to establish the key components. The actual efficiency chosen for a given fractionation is determined by the relative volatility of the components of the mixture to be separated. Frequently, relative volatilities are not known, although differences in boiling points are known. In either case, Table XVIII of Chapter I will be a helpful guide in choosing an adequate column.

It should be borne in mind, when considering differences in boiling points, that relative volatilities may shift markedly in a way not indicated by differences in boiling points. For example, in a mixture of toluene and methylcyclohexane, the components of which boil 10°C. apart, the x, y diagram shows a sharp "pinch" in the vapor composition curve for those mixtures containing large mole fractions of methylcyclohexane. Separation of these components would accordingly require greater column efficiency than would be expected for components of more normal behavior boiling 10°C. apart.

When choosing a column for a particular fractionation, it is well to remember that its normal efficiency is a measure of its separating power at total reflux, not at finite reflux, the condition required for productivity. This is discussed in Chapter I, 3,A. In this same connection, significant variations in column efficiency occur with large variations in boil-up rate, as has been noted under *Packings*. In practical work, this means that the column could make an excellent separation on a close-boiling mixture at a low liquid-return rate, while at a much higher liquid-return rate, the same column would make only a fair separation. Vacuum-jacketed columns packed with metal helices have shown similar behavior in the author's laboratory.

Reliable data on column efficiency and the effect of boil-up rate on the efficiency can be obtained only if the utmost care is used in the purification of the components of the binary pair used in the test mixture. For the test mixture of *n*-heptane and methylcyclohexane, the heptane should be obtained from a source other than petroleum to avoid possible presence of isomeric hydrocarbons. The *n*-heptane should be fractionated through a column of at least 100 theoretical plates at a high reflux ratio; only those cuts having the correct refractive index and correct freezing point should be used for the test mixture. Methylcyclohexane prepared by hydrogenation of pure toluene is preferred to that isolated from petroleum. This material, before use, should be washed with several small portions of concentrated sulfuric acid until the acid layer is no longer colored. Following this, the hydrocarbon should be washed with water, dilute sodium hydroxide, and finally again with water, and then dried. The final step is to fractionate the washed product through a column of at least 100 plates at a high reflux ratio. Only those fractions having the proper refractive index and freezing point should be used in the test mixture. Unless these precautions are taken, efficiency tests, particularly of columns of high efficiency may prove erroneous.

Choice of packing material is determined by the characteristics of the material to be distilled. If this is not corrosive, metal packing may be satisfactory. Organic halides, acids, anhydrides, sulfur compounds, and certain phenols corrode metal packing to a greater or lesser degree and permanently reduce its efficiency; glass or other inert packing is essential when working with these types of compounds. Alcohols are dangerously corrosive to aluminum packing. If the material being fractionated has a tendency to polymerize and form an insoluble coating on the packing, glass or other inert packing is advisable inasmuch as it can be cleaned by use of drastic reagents.

If a distillation is to be successful, the thermal and chemical stability of the materials in a charge require careful consideration. Polymerization, cleavage, dehydration of materials containing hydroxy compounds, chemical reaction between components of the distilland, and oxidation through leakage of air into the still may change the composition of a distilland and vitiate results. Reduction of the operating pressure to lower the distillation temperature will usually reduce or eliminate several of these effects; air leakage into the still may increase at reduced pressure, but this can easily be remedied by eliminating the joint between still pot and column.

To diminish still-pot temperatures significantly, operating pressures should be reduced from atmospheric to 100 or 50 mm. Materials boiling at 150°C. at 760 mm., for example will boil at about 90 and 70°C., respectively, at the above reduced pressures; even lower pressures may be necessary in some instances. Pressure drop across the column will increase as the operating pressure is lowered if a given boil-up rate is maintained. Generally, however, the permissible boil-up rate is much less at greatly reduced pressures than at atmospheric pressure. A rough guide for predicting permissible boil-up rate when the boil-up rate at atmospheric pressure is known is to multiply the boil-up rate at atmospheric pressure by the square root of the pressure ratio. For example, if a given mixture in a given column can be evaporated at a rate of 1000 ml./hr. at atmospheric pressure, the rate at 76 mm. will be $1000\sqrt{0.10} = 310$ ml./hr. Permissible boil-up rate is likely to be somewhat less than this as a result of increased pressure drop across the column; with tall columns, the square root rule is more adversely affected than with short columns. With some mixtures, low-pressure operation may introduce a problem in condensation; circulation of ice water or acetone cooled by dry ice, through the reflux condenser, will usually ensure satisfactory condensation.

Some mixtures may give distillates which solidify in the condenser section. If their melting points are substantially below their boiling points at the operating pressure, proper control of the temperature of the condenser will allow the distillation to proceed normally. If the solid components boil below their melting point (sublime), the distillation will have to be conducted azeotropically to remove such materials as liquid azeotropes.

IV. THE DISTILLAND

1. Pretreatment

Hydroperoxides and peroxides may be present in large or small amounts in many mixtures, particularly hydrocarbons, aldehydes, and ethers. To avoid the possibility of an explosion during the distillation, large amounts of hydroperoxides should be removed by suitable pretreatment; and small amounts should be eliminated to prevent peroxide-initiated polymerization of other components of a distilland.

Hydroperoxides may be detected by shaking the suspected material with potassium iodide solution acidified with acetic acid. (Some materials having very low solubility in water may require glacial acetic acid solution to respond to the iodide test.) If the material releases iodine, the hydroperoxide may be decomposed by shaking the material with several batches of ferrous sulfate, alkaline sodium sulfide, or sodium bisulfite solution until the test with acidified iodide is negative. Raney nickel may also be used to decompose hydroperoxides and peroxides. Judicious heating of water-soluble materials containing peroxides with sodium hydroxide solution is also effective in destroying these compounds. Possible undesirable effects of any reagent on the other components of a charge should be considered before the reagent is used to remove hydroperoxides and peroxides.

In general, peroxides are present to some extent whenever hydroperoxides are detected; since the former are not so readily decomposed as hydroperoxides, they are likely to reach a dangerous state of concentration in the still pot as the distillation progresses. By the addition of a large quantity of high-boiling chaser to the still pot, the concentration of the peroxide is kept low, and hence it cannot attain an explosive concentration. The progressively higher temperature of the contents of the still pot as the distillation proceeds gradually decomposes the peroxide into harmless products. Any pretreatment to remove hydroperoxides from a still charge will produce alcohols or ketones in the distilland. These may distill as such, or they may form azeotropes with other components present. This possibility should be recognized when interpreting the distillation data.

When working with easily dehydrated hydroxy compounds, such as tertiary alcohols, slight traces of acidic material may be present in the still pot or column; if present, these may catalyze dehydration and change the composition of the charge. A dilute solution of sodium methoxide in methanol poured through the column, followed by removal of the methanol by a stream of dry nitrogen, will frequently condition the column to obviate dehydration. However, in such cases, due consideration must be given to the possibility of initiating condensation reactions by any sodium methoxide adhering to the packing. Excess sodium methoxide solution should be removed from the still pot before introducing the charge.

Occasionally a fractionation has to be performed on a mixture which contains components with a pronounced tendency to polymerize either slowly or rapidly. Suitable inhibitors may be added to the distilland at the beginning of the distillation to prevent or minimize polymerization. The proper inhibitor to use will depend on the chemical character of the compound or compounds in the distilland, and hence will be a specific problem in each instance.

It should be pointed out that an inhibitor will ordinarily be effective only in the still pot and, possible, to a slight extent in the lowest part of the column, depending on the volatility of the inhibitor, which is usually low.

To circumvent this limitation, a solution of a suitable inhibitor in a part of the distillate may be added dropwise through the reflux condenser into the reflux stream to provide inhibitor throughout the length of the column. Inasmuch as many polymerizations are initiated by small traces of peroxide, the importance of rigidity excluding all leakage of air into the lower part of column through a still-pot joint is apparent.

All charges to a fractionating column should be single phase with respect to physical state except for two-phase systems, which become single phase by the time the charge reaches boiling temperature. A system which remains two phase at its boiling point will probably bump severely when boiled and prevent satisfactory adjustment of the boil-up rate. Even if the two-phase system becomes single phase at its boiling temperature as sometimes occurs in azeotropic distillations, two phases may form in the reflux condenser, making it difficult to maintain a uniform product rate; if the product is taken off intermittently by the use of special heads, such as the tilting-funnel type, a fairly uniform product will be collected, even through two phase.

In work with hydrocarbons, water is usually present to some extent; a water layer can be mechanically separated, and suspended and dissolved water removed with a small amount of desiccant. Anhydrous potassium carbonate, calcium chloride, magnesium sulfate, calcium sulfate, and copper sulfate are suitable for drying hydrocarbons. If alcohols are present, calcium chloride should not be used because the alcohols form addition products with it. If ketones are present, potassium carbonate may cause condensation reactions. In doubtful cases, anhydrous calcium sulfate is least likely to cause undesirable reactions in a mixture. In instances in which none of the hydrocarbons present form azeotropes with isopropyl alcohol, this compound may be added to remove the water as an azeotrope. This procedure has the advantage that at any given pressure the azeotrope is of definite composition and boiling point and can be withdrawn as a definite product of normal behavior. When isopropyl alcohol is not or may not be used, a water–hydrocarbon azeotrope may condense in the reflux condenser. In such a case, the water adheres in droplets and is slowly eliminated with the product, meanwhile causing wide fluctuations in vapor temperature and difficulies in regulating the product rate. When water does collect in the condenser, it may be eliminated by shutting off the coolant for a short time to allow the condenser temperature to rise. This procedure may have to be repeated several times to eliminate all the water. The two-phase hydrocarbon mixture in the receiver is then separated mechanically, and the hydrocarbon layer is dried with a suitable reagent and returned to the still. A small chamber connected to the top of the reflux condenser through a valve, or a separatory funnel attached to the charge tube of the still, can serve for this purpose, and for other purposes mentioned in Section V-2.

Mixtures of water-soluble and -insoluble compounds, such as reaction products which contain considerable amounts of dissolved water, may be difficult to distill, particularly if the water-soluble material is considerably lower boiling then water. When the low-boiling material has been eliminated, a two-phase system remains in the still pot and will bump; frequently, an azeotrope of water and other material will distill. Use of isopropyl alcohol, as explained above, will eliminate trouble during the distillation. Due consideration must be given to possible formation of a ternary azeotrope of water, alcohol, and a third component, and of a binary azeotrope of alcohol and another component. A compilation of binary and ternary azeotropes[166] will be found useful in this connection.

2. Size of Batches. Chasers. Charging

As was discussed in Chapter I, the proper size of a charge in comparsion to column holdup is still an unsettled question. Until the problem has been more completely investigated, the standard practice of maintaining the ratio of charge to dynamic holdup at 10 or above should be followed for satisfactory results in high-temperature distillations. If the volume of sample is only a few milliliters, a special column of low holdup will be needed (see Apparatus). A series of columns of a given diameter, type, and size of packing will have efficiencies and holdups roughly proportional to the height of the packings; accordingly, a distillation requiring the highest efficiency will require the largest sample, and one requiring the lowest efficiency will require the smallest sample if the above rule for sample size is followed.

In any batch fractionating, assuming that the charge is completely distillable, all the charge can never be collected as distillate. The uncollectable material is equal to the dynamic holdup of the column if the still pot is taken to dryness; but this is a practice not to be recommended with any type of still, especially if an internal electric heater is used in the still pot. The column holdup plus any volatile material remaining in the still pot may be distilled out if a chaser is added to the charge to drive them into the receiver. Any chaser used should be nonreactive with the material being distilled, should not form azeotropes with it, and should not attack the column or packing. Its boiling point should be considerably higher than the boiling point of the highest component of the charge in order that any of the vaporized chaser may be easily fractionated out of the vapor stream entering the bottom of the column. For laboratory distillations, a compound devoid of impurities boiling at or near any component of the charge is highly desirable as a chaser so that complete removal of the charge from the column may be shown by determination of the boiling point or refractive index of the chaser. Toluene, tetralin, and diphenyl ether are often satisfactory chasers.

When the still pot contents have become free of the charge (the condition prevailing when the still would become dry were no chaser present), chaser vapor gradually fills the column to an increasing degree until it appears in essentially pure condition at the head of the column. In the meantime, the column continues to fractionate the last components of the charge insofar as the decreasing effective length of the column will permit. If the holdup is a single component from the original charge, and the chaser is considerably higher boiling, the separation will be quite satisfactorily sharp. When the column holdup consists of two or more components, the separation achieved becomes increasingly poorer as the column becomes less efficient so far as those components are concerned. If a nonvolatile residue is known to be present in a charge, a chaser may be used to push all volatile material in the charge to the head of the column, the conditions being as noted above. The nonvolatile residue then remains as a solution in the chaser if it is soluble in the chaser. If a residue of this sort is to be studied, the use of a chaser is inadvisable unless the two can be satisfactorily separated.

When a chaser is not used, the column holdup and still residue may be recovered by refluxing a low-boiling solvent in the column; and the resulting solution may then be fractionated in a small column of low holdup and adequate efficiency. This slightly complex procedure will allow nearly 100% of a large charge to be fractionated without the necessity of using a low-capacity, low-holdup column for the entire fractionation.

Charging a column consists of pouring the material to be fractionated into the still pot and adding a volume of chaser equal to about twice the holdup of the column. Still pots using bare-wire internal electric heaters may need an amount of chaser greater than twice the column holdup in order to ensure that the heater is completely submerged in liquid when the end of the distillation is reached.

The charge may be introduced either on a weight basis, or a volume basis referred to some standard temperature. For general laboratory fractionations, charging on a weight basis is probably more satisfactory. Similarly, fractions can be collected on a weight basis. If final results are desired on a volume basis, a simple mathematical conversion suffices to give this. For operating on a weight basis, no equipment to maintain a constant receiver temperature is required. Much greater precision can be expected by weighing than can normally be attained in measuring volume. Still residues can be weighed directly if a detachable still pot is used, whereas if the volume is measured, considerable drainage error may occur, particularly if the residue is viscous. In case of permanently attached still pots, one error is introduced by incomplete removal of residue from the still pots by suction, and a second error is made through incomplete drainage of the suction flask if the volume is measured. A torsion balance of 120-g. capacity, weighing directly to 0.01 g., offers a rapid means of weighing fractions taken from a column. Larger fractions may be weighed on an ordinary trip balance.

V. OPERATION

1. Beginning of Operation

After the still pot has been charged and attached to the column, coolant is started through the condenser and the system is brought to the desired operating pressure. Preferred practice is to have one exit from the column, usually at the top of the reflux condenser, connected to a cold trap, to condense small amounts of low-boiling products not liquefied by the condenser, and thence to the pressure-control system. A cold trap is especially important in low-pressure operation to keep condensable vapors out of the surge tanks, manostats, and pumps. The use of powdered dry ice around the cold trap without liquid is entirely adequate, and obviates loss of liquid by foaming that frequently occurs when dry ice is added to a liquid in a Dewar flask surrounding the trap.[41]

When starting a distillation, time can be saved if the total available heat is applied to the still pot to bring the distilland to boiling as rapidly as possible. With low-boiling distillands, the back pressure should be carefully watched to detect the start of boiling; otherwise, the column may flood and force large amounts of distillate into the receiver and cold trap. Once boiling has started, the heat should be reduced to approximately the value required for the desired back pressure and boil-up rate. When the column uses heated jacket sections to eliminate heat loss, proper adjustment of the power input to the jackets should be made. This adjustment can be guided only by experience. Except when the reflux has high solubility for water, drops of water will usually appear in the condenser. If the amount appears significant, it should be eliminated as described in Section IV-1. Once the water is eliminated, the column may be preflooded.

2. Preflooding

Preflooding consists in increasing the boil-up rate to such a degree that the reflux cannot return to the still pot, but fills or nearly fills the column with liquid; in so doing, the packing is thoroughly wetted with the liquid being distilled, and hence is in the condition of maximum efficiency. Only packed columns need to be flooded; the efficiency of bubble-cap and perforated plate columns is not improved by preflooding.

Several details are of great importance in the flooding operation if the column is to be conditioned to a state of maximum efficiency. No attempt should be made to flood the column rapidly; if excessive heat is applied to the still pot to cause rapid flooding, the insulation around the still pot reaches a high temperature. This stored heat will cause excessive flooding and force condensate into the receiver and cold trap. If the flood is brought on gradually by increasing the heat over a period of 15 min. to 2 hr. or more, depending on the size of the charge, the heater and still-pot insulation reach the temperature necessary to give a vaporization rate satisfactory for a controllable flood. At this point reduction of the heat input may commence and the flood will slowly subside. As the liquid in the column slowly returns to the still pot, it thoroughly wets the packing.

The flood stage should be maintained until liquid fills the column and the still head a short distance up the condenser tube. If the column is equipped with a back-pressure manometer, the flooding may be continued until the back pressure equals the static pressure that would be produced if the columns were filled with the liquid (at the prevailing column temperature). As soon as the flooding has stopped and refluxing is normal, the column should be flooded a second time, and if necessary a third time, or until the back pressure reaches a maximum during the flooding operation. In general, the second and third flooding will not require quite as much heat on the still pot because the first flooding causes a reduction of column capacity. Under no circumstance should refluxing stop entirely. If it does, the favorable effect of preflooding will be partially or totally lost. Sometimes significant amounts of product will be forced through the reflux condenser into the receiver during the flooding operation. This material can be returned to the still as outlined in Section IV-1. After preflooding, the jackets are balanced and the boil-up rate adjusted by reference to back-pressure reading, or by other suitable means.

Back-pressure readings are not absolute criteria of boil-up rate. In a given column, under one set of operating conditions, a particular back pressure will indicate a certain boil-up rate for one mixture and another boil-up rate for another mixture. For example, back pressures in millimeters mercury for one type of column at 150 ml./hr. boil-up are as follows:[41] C_8 alkylate, 2.5; C_{12} alkylate, 3.5; benzene, 3.6; toluene, 3.9; and xylene, 5.

Back pressure in a perforated-plate column was constant in the region of 1100–2200 ml./hr. boil-up, but below and above this range showed variation with boil-up.[128]

3. Establishing Primary Equilibrium

In normal operation the column is kept at total reflux for a time to allow a primary equilibrium to be established. Time on total reflux is generally greater for columns of large dynamic holdup than for columns of low dynamic holdup. No exhaustive study of the factor has been made. High-efficiency columns (100 or more theoretical plates) are kept at total reflux for a period of 24–36 hr.;[106] 3–4 hr. has been found satisfactory on small 80-plate analytical columns;[41] 7 hr. at total reflux is required to reach equilibrium in a Hyper-Cal column of 65 theoretical plates.[61] A practical guide is to hold the column at total reflux until the head temperature reaches a minimum after the column has been flooded and is operating smoothly. Precise control of operating pressure and means of detecting small changes in head temperature are necessary if this method is to be used. Small amounts of material in the distilland boiling much lower than the next higher boiling component may falsely indicate equilibrium before true equilibrium is established in the column.

4. Product Collection

Once the column has been brought to its primary equilibrium, collection of product is started. Mechanically this consists of putting into operation whatever device is used to permit withdrawal of a part of the distillate from the column at a uniform rate, the balance being condensed and returned to the column as reflux. The ratio of these two quantities is the reflux ratio; the larger numerical value conventionally being in the numerator. The reflux ratio must be fixed at a value as high as necessary to give the desired purity in the distillate; any higher value wastes time. The actual reflux ratio to be used can only be approximated. For columns with low boil-up rate, the number of drops falling off the cold finger of the reflux condenser per unit time can be counted and the product rate adjusted to a fraction of this number to give a prescribed reflux ratio. Vapor and liquid dividing heads, actuated by a timing mechanism, may be used to collect all the distillate for a fraction of the time, and thus establish the reflux ratio. None of these methods is precise because side-wall condensation, existing to some degree in all columns, is not included in the estimate of the reflux ratio.

A fairly sound empirical method for setting the reflux ratio consists in establishing a product rate that will give a product of the desired purity as measured by boiling point, refractive index, or other suitable means. If boiling point is to be used as a criterion of purity, the temperature-measuring element must be protected from extraneous effects, such as drafts and splashing of cold reflux, that would cause changes in temperature readings unconnected with real variations in vapor temperature. Significant variations in operating pressure should also be excluded when vapor temperature is used as a measure of product purity. Elimination of these factors ensures that a temperature reading has real meaning; how precisely a temperature can be read is the limiting factor in the use of vapor temperature as a measure of product purity. Several temperature-measuring elements are discussed in the Apparatus section. It suffices here to state that vapor temperatures should be readable to at least 0.1°C. and preferably to 0.05°C., or less.

Refractive index is frequently a much more accurate indicator of product purity than is boiling point. When sufficient difference exists in refractive indices of two successively distilling components of a mixture, this measurement is more reliable than vapor temperature in that it is not subject to the variations associated with vapor-temperature readings.

In establishing a suitable reflux ratio, no effort should be made to establish the bare-minimum value because the minimum value suffices only for a short interval when the still composition has a certain value. Removal of product changes the still composition, and hence requires a new and higher reflux ratio. Accordingly, the more practical procedure is to set the reflux ratio higher than is actually required at the beginning of a distillation, and then modify the reflux ratio as required by subsequent changes in the composition of the material in the still. If time permits, the simplest procedure is to set the reflux ratio at a value equivalent to or somewhat above the value equivalent to the number of theoretical plates in the column (as measured under total reflux). See Chapter I, Section VI.

Some operators reduce the reflux ratio when a plateau in the distillation curve has been reached. This practice is permissible if the reflux ratio used just prior to the advent of the plateau has been deliberately increased to sharpen the break between the two components under immediate consideration, and if the reflux ratio used during the break is higher than is necessary to give the desired separation of the next higher boiling component from the material in the plateau region. That is, the plateau exists solely because the reflux ratio is adequate, and any significant reduction of the reflux ratio may reduce the separating power of the column for the particular mixture being distilled. Mixtures with which an operator is familiar may allow marked changes in reflux ratio to be made as the several components come into product range; but with unknown mixtures, the permissible variation of reflux ratio is much narrower unless there is no objection to a certain amount of redistillation. Without prior knowledge, there is certainly no justification for reducing a reflux ratio simply because a plateau appears in a distillation curve.

5. Size of Fractions

In analytical distillations when a detailed picture of the composition of a mixture is to be obtained, small fractions of the order of 1% of the charge are satisfactory. Smaller cuts during the transition from one component to the next may be desirable under some circumstances. When a distillation is being performed to isolate one or more components in sizable quantities and prior knowledge of composition justifies it, much larger fractions may be taken if larger receivers are used. A certain amount of caution should be used under this procedure to avoid contaminating a pure distillate with the next higher boiling component should a transition occur unexpectedly.

During a fractionation, a definite schedule for securing the distillation data is desirable to give reliable results; if several columns are attended by one operator, a schedule is imperative. When operating high-efficiency columns where the percentage of product removed per unit time is normally small, readings should be taken hourly if the charge is complex or of unknown complexity. These readings include vapor temperature, still temperature, condition of heat balance in the jacketed sections of the column, back pressure, if this is used as a measure of boil-up rate, or determination of the number of drops of condensate falling from the reflux condenser per minute. Appropriate adjustment of variable transformers controlling the several heaters are made at this time. All temperature readings and voltage readings of the variable transformers are recorded primarily for check purposes and also as a guide for future work on the column. The vapor temperature should also be determined at the time a fraction is taken. A check on product rate should be made occasionally either by counting drops or by noting the volume of product collected in a given time. With simpler mixtures, less frequent checking of column behavior is required, particularly if the composition is known approximately, and only certain major components are of interest.

Less efficient columns are normally operated with greater product rate, and will accordingly require more frequent attention if fractions of the same relative size are being collected; however, the essentials are as outlined above.

When the distillation is nearing completion, the boil-up rate will drop rather rapidly if no chaser is used. If a chaser is used, the approaching end of the distillation will be indicated first by a rapid increase in still-pot temperature, and a large increase in the heat required by the column jackets. When the vapor temperature rises to the boiling point of the chaser, the distillation is finished. At this point the still is disconnected from the pressure-control system, the electric power turned off, and the column immediately brought to atmospheric pressure with oxygen-free nitrogen or carbon dioxide. A positive pressure of one to two pounds of the inert gas will prevent oxidation of liquid adhering to the packing during drainage and cooling. After cooling to a suitable lower temperature, the still pot may be disconnected, weighed, cleaned, and reweighed to determine the residue. If the still pot is permanently sealed to the column, the residue may be withdrawn by suction into a tared flask and weighed. The total weight of material recovered as distillate and residue will be less than the charge weight. The difference represents the static holdup of the column and material adhering to the still pot. This material may be recovered by refluxing an appropriate low-boiling solvent in the column, withdrawing the solution, and distilling off the solvent in a suitable column of low holdup. By this procedure recoveries of 98–100% are easily possible if no leakage has occurred during the distillation and efficient cold traps are used to trap vapors passing through the reflux condenser.

After the static holdup of the column has been removed, methyl or ethyl Cellosolve or other solvent having a high solvent power should be refluxed in the column to remove traces of tarry and polymeric material which may have formed in the packing. Following this, acetone refluxed in the column will remove the higher boiling cleaning agent and simplify drying of the packing with a stream of carbon dioxide. A little heat applied to the jackets will hasten the drying process except in vacuum-jacketed columns. The column should then be sealed to prevent access of air until the next distillation is to be made. This method of cleaning a column will ensure years of satisfactory service.

6. Interpretation of Results

A normal fractionation can provide (*1*) a set of boiling points, or vapor temperatures, for the fractions collected during the distillation, (*2*) the volume or weight percentage of the charge distilled, and (*3*) a group of fractions of greater or lesser purity depending upon the working efficiency of the column, the reflux ratio, and the complexity of the distilland.

The first step in the interpretation of these data consists in plotting vapor temperatures as ordinates and per cent distilled as abscissa on rectangular coordinate paper. Provided that the column was of adequate efficiency and was so operated as to separate each component in substantially pure condition from all other components in the charge, and provided the holdup was small in comparison to the amount of any component present, the resulting curve of boiling points versus per cent distilled will consist of a series of horizontal lines or plateaus parallel to the abscissas joined by sigmoid lines, as shown in Figure 47. Each plateau may repre-

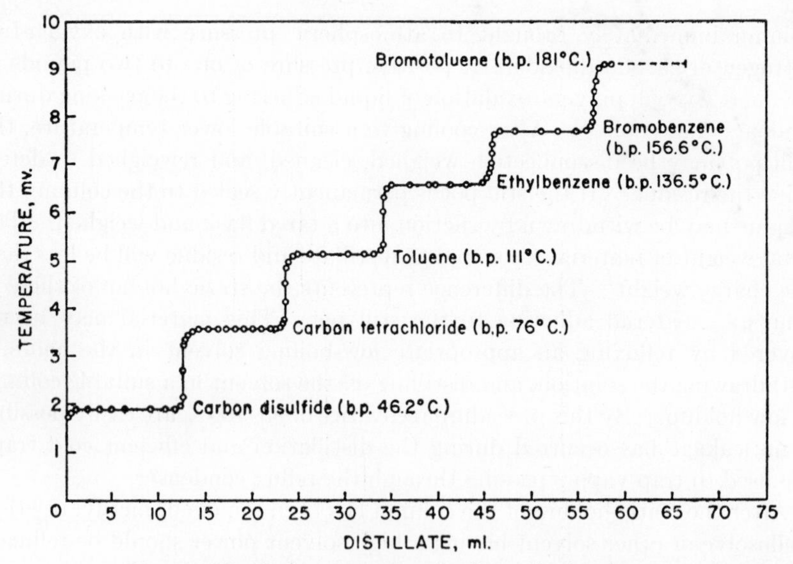

Fig. 47. Distillation curve of a simple synthetic mixture.

sent a pure component, and the amount of the pure component separated by the column can be determined by inspection. The total amount of any component in a mixture will include the material in the breaks indicated on the curve by the sigmoids at each end of a plateau. As a first approximation, the amount of a component in a break can be estimated by drawing a line vertical to the abscissas at a point halfway between the beginning of one plateau and the end of the adjacent plateau representing the next lower and next higher boiling components. For many practical purposes analytical results obtained by this method are of sufficient accuracy. If the analytical requirements are more stringent, other means are advisable for determining the composition of the breaks. These methods will be discussed later.

Although Figure 47 represents a conceivable distillation, it is by no means typical of the majority of cases. An extreme case of complexity is shown in Figure 48, which represents an analytical distillation of C_4 alkylate (H_2SO_4) as carried out in a column of approximately 200 theoretical plates at the National Bureau of Standards.[106]

Inspection of Figure 48 reveals seven plateaus in the boiling-point curve, only one of which is sufficiently inclined to arouse suspicion of inhomogeneity. Within this region of 87% distilled, only six components are indicated, while the rising trend in the region of 54 to 83% distilled indicates two or more components. Actually, a more comprehensive analysis by infrared techniques showed the presence of 19 components in

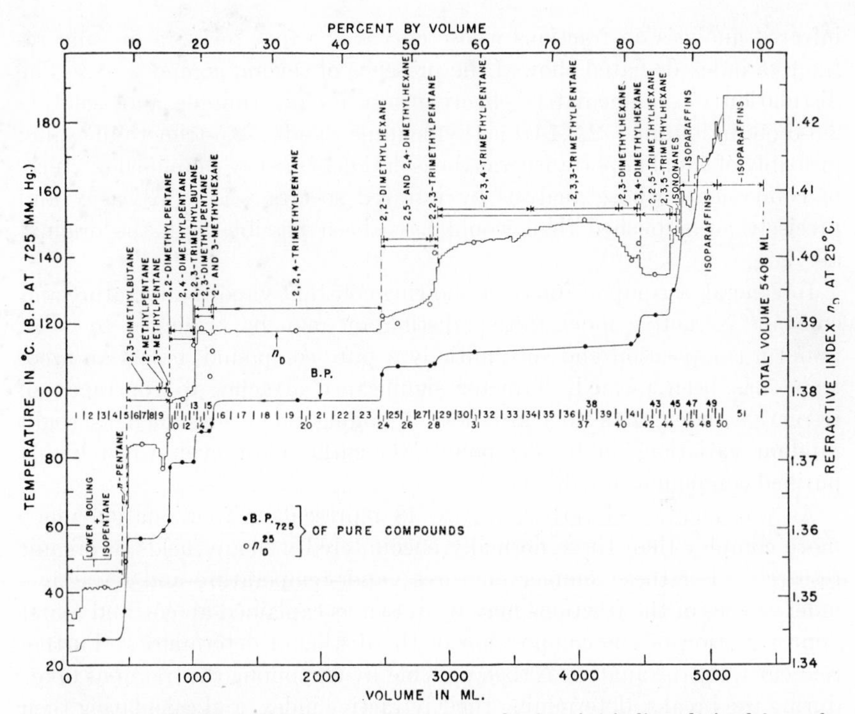

Fig. 48. Vapor–liquid equilibrium temperatures and refractive indices derived from the fractionation of C_4 alkylate (H_2SO_4) through a 200-plate column.

the first 87% distilled; one of the plateaus cited above included three of the 19 components.

Rarely, if ever, is a distillation interpreted on the basis of vapor temperature only. The common practice of determining the refractive index of the fractions as they are collected from a column permits an independent and usually more precise measure of product purity to be made quickly with only a very small amount of sample. Once the refractive indices of the fractions have been measured, a curve of refractive index versus per cent distilled can be drawn, preferably on the same sheet of co-ordinate paper containing the vapor-temperature curve, as shown in Figure 48 by the broken-line curve. The combination of vapor-temperature and refractive-index data provides a sounder basis for interpretation of the fractionation. In the particular case depicted in Figure 48, only three of the seven plateaus of the vapor-temperature curve show corresponding plateaus in the refractive-index curve; all other sections of the refractive-index curve showed wide deviation from flatness. Examination by infrared analysis of those fractions whose vapor-temperature curves and refractive-index curves were parallel confirmed the homogeneity of the samples; on the other hand, infrared analysis on fractions whose curves of vapor temperature and refractive index deviated showed the presence of several components. The distillation was immediately effective only for determining and isolating 2,3-dimethylbutane, 2,2,4-trimethylpentane, and 2,2,5-trimethylhexane; probably of equal importance was the isolation of greatly simplified mixtures of components whose analysis by infrared spectra was more easily and precisely accomplished than would have been possible with the original alkylate.

In general, a group of fractions showing constant vapor temperature and constant refractive index during distillation may be presumed to be of uniform composition and substantially a pure compound, unless an azeotrope has been formed. Greater significance attaches to constancy of refractive index than to constancy of boiling point inasmuch as slight random variations in boiling point frequently occur even when highly purified compounds are distilled.

As was mentioned earlier, Figure 48 represents a fractionation much more complex than those normally encountered in many fields of organic research. For these simpler mixtures vapor-temperature and refractive-index curves of the fractions may be drawn as explained above, and a first approximation of the composition of the distilland determined. Further refinement of the analysis is then possible by combining the fractions taken during the breaks, determining their refractive index, and calculating their composition from the known refractive index of the two components between which the breaks are collected. Whether this procedure is permissible depends in general on the character of the refractive-index curve in the region of the breaks. If the curve shows a smooth transition from the refractive index of one plateau to the next plateau without dips or peaks, the break cuts can be considered to be a simple binary mixture of the two adjacent components. In calculating the composition of the combined break cuts, a linear relationship between refractive index and composition is assumed. If there are no pronounced volume changes or temperature changes when the pure components are mixed, departures from linearity are small; inasmuch as the total break fractions represent a relatively small proportion of the total fractions between which the break occurs, small departures of the refractive index of the mixture from strict linearity will not greatly affect the composition so established. Qualitative information about the composition of the distilland may disclose the presence of small amounts of materials distilling in the region of the break between key components. If this situation exists, other means of analyzing the break fractions will be necessary. If the difference in refractive index of two components in the break fractions is small, the use of refractive index for analyzing these fractions may not be as effective as an estimate made by inspection of the vapor-temperature curve mentioned on p. 412.

The problem of interpreting distillation results has been greatly facilitated in recent years by the use of gas–liquid chromatography (G.L.C.). Its remarkable sensitivity, excellent precision, and speed has relegated the slower techniques of mass spectrometry, infrared and ultraviolet analyses to secondary positions among instrumental analytical methods.

The minute sample size required in G.L.C. make it a highly effective method for checking break cuts for composition, for detecting azeotropes (there is no equivalent of these mixtures in G.L.C.), and for detecting small concentrations of materials which could very readily be missed by any less sensitive analytical methods. It has, in most instances, made strictly analytical distillations superfluous.

Although 20°C. is the temperature commonly used for measuring refractive indices, there is some trend toward 25°C. and a temperature of 30°C. would be more satisfactory in many laboratories. Frequently during hot days of summer, when the relative humidity is high, refractometer prisms held at 20°C. will condense sufficient moisture to make them unusable. At 30°C. no trouble will be encountered. There is the further advantage that, whereas a constant-temperature bath for a refractometer may require refrigerated water for 20°C. operation, ordinary tap water may be satisfactory when the bath is held at 30°C.

There is the objection that much of the literature reports refractive indices at 20°C. For a given laboratory, where the variety of compounds is probably not large, this objection can be overcome by measuring the refractive index of the most commonly used compounds at both 20 and 30°C. to establish the temperature coefficient of the series, and then adopting the higher temperature for practical use.

In addition to vapor temperature and refractive index commonly used in following the course of a distillation and as a means of interpreting a distillation, other physical properties are used to gain a more complete picture of the mixture being investigated. These include determination of density, viscosity, optical rotation, and melting point. Generally these methods are used only when refractive index or boiling point, or both, give an ambiguous answer. Optical rotation is used with such naturally occurring products as the terpene hydrocarbons and their derivatives. Melting and freezing points may have wider application, particularly as a criterion of purity. Use of freezing points has been greatly extended by recent investigations of low-melting hydrocarbons.[167] Procedures for making these physical measurements may be found in books on physicochemical methods[168] or in the original literature. Ultraviolet, infrared, Raman, and mass spectral analyses are widely used both for qualitative and quantitative analyses, although the latter is being rapidly replaced by gas chromatography.

A number of chemical methods are available to help in analyzing and interpreting distillation data. These include determination of bromine number, acid number, saponification number, iodine number, and carbonyl value, used, respectively, in studying unsaturation of hydrocarbons, identification of acids, identification of esters, unsaturation of fatty acids and esters, and determination of ketones and aldehydes.

Specific problems of interpretation may require the use of catalytic hydrogenation to determine unsaturation, the Zerewitinoff method for determining active hydrogen, the acetyl method for hydroxyl groups, and the direct determination of oxygen.[169,170] In addition to these, the methods for determining carbon, hydrogen, methoxyl, halogens, nitrogen, phosphorus, sulfur, and metals in volatile metallo-organic compounds contribute information beyond the limit of fractional distillation and simple physical measurements.

Certain unavoidable losses occur in nearly every distillation with the result that the total weight or volume of distillate, residue, and static holdup does not equal the weight or volume of the distilland. When the equipment is properly constructed and operated, total losses should not exceed 3% of the charge, and may be reported as "loss," or may be distributed over the several fractions in the ratio of the weights or volumes of the fraction to the weight or volume of the charge. This refinement is scarcely justified in ordinary fractionations yielding a great many fractions. When the residue is essentially nonvolatile compared to the distillate, the loss should be distributed among the fractions of distillate.

Larger losses ranging up to 15–20% of a charge may be incurred through leakage at the still-pot joint, or through inadequate traps at the condenser exit, particularly when distilling material containing low-boiling components. Operation of a column at a pressure slightly below atmospheric so that the still-pot pressure is less than the prevailing atmospheric pressure will prevent loss of vapor from a still-pot joint. If leakage at the joint should occur, a drop in vapor–liquid equilibrium temperature will take place; the column may then be shut down and the leak eliminated. At greatly reduced pressures, the same conditions prevail to a greater extent. The air drawn through the still pot and column becomes saturated with vapor, and any vapor not removed from the gas stream becomes a part of the total losses.

When distillation losses are large, as they may be through failure of the equipment as described above, proper distribution of the losses among the different fractions can be only a poor estimate; in fact there is no solution to the problem except to build the equipment and conduct the distillation to avoid all but nominal losses; in other words, the still pot should be sealed to the column with a glass-to-glass seal, and the charge line closed with a lubricated plug which is in a region of low vapor and liquid concentration.

LOW-TEMPERATURE FRACTIONATION

Laboratory fractional distillation as applied to materials boiling below ambient temperature is a subject of little more than historical interest. As a preparative method, it is scarcely used on a laboratory scale since most of the low-boiling hydrocarbons, ethers, alkyl halides, etc., are readily available from commercial sources in high purity (99 + %) in convenient quantities for laboratory use. As an analytical procedure, low-temperature fractional distillation has been almost completely supplanted by gas–liquid chromatography (G.L.C.), as a result of the spectacular development of this technique during the decade 1952–1962. At its best, low-temperature fractionation requires auxiliary use of mass spectrometric and other aids for a complete analysis of complex mixtures, whereas G.L.C. can complete in minutes and frequently without secondary analyses, an accurate analysis of a complex mixture which requires hours by the distillation-auxiliaries methods.

In principle, low-temperature and high-temperature fractional distillations are identical; in practice, complications arise from the low-boiling points (−160 to +35°C.) of mixtures usually encountered, and the low critical temperatures of their components. These characteristics have in very large measure dictated the type and design of equipment and restricted the operating procedures suitable for low-temperature fractional distillation.

Relatively few workers[171–174] have done research in this specialized field, yet a highly satisfactory combination of equipment and operating procedures resulted from their efforts. Podbielniak's work undoubtedly dominated the period of maximum and outstanding developments. His publications, which include a general review of the subject, should be consulted by anyone who needs the special knowledge required for conducting low-temperature fractional distillation.

References

1. Fastovskii and Petrovskii, *Khim. Prom.*, **1956**, 23034.
2. Rose, *Ind. Eng. Chem.*, **28**, 1210 (1936).
3. Craig, *Ind. Eng. Chem. Anal. Ed.*, **9**, 441 (1937).
4. Bragg, *Ind. Eng. Chem. Anal. Ed.*, **11**, 283 (1939).
5. Kuhn and Ryffel, *Helv. Chim. Acta*, **26**, 1693 (1943).
6. Westhaver, *Ind. Eng. Chem.*, **34**, 126 (1942).
7. Kuhn and Ryffel, *Helv. Chim. Acta*, **26**, 1693 (1943).
8. Friedman and Miller, *Ind. Eng. Chem.*, **33**, 885 (1941).
9. Willingham, Sedlak, Westhaver, and Rossini, *Ind. Eng. Chem.*, **39**, 706 (1947).
10. Bragg, *Trans. Am. Inst. Chem. Engrs.*, **37**, 19 (1941).
11. Podbielniak, *Ind. Eng. Chem. Anal. Ed.*, **13**, 639 (1941).

12. Ray, *Rev. Sci. Instr.*, **28,** 200 (1957).
13. Warren, *Mem. Am. Acad. Natural Sciences,* **9,** 121 (1864); *Ann., Suppl.,* **4,** 51 (1865).
14. Young, *Distillation Principles and Processes,* MacMillan, London, 1922, p. 1.
15. Shepherd, *J. Res. Natl. Bur. Std.,* **26,** 227 (1941).
16. Widmer, *Helv. Chim. Acta,* **7,** 59 (1924).
17. Fahlandt, *Chemist Analyst,* **25,** 28 (1936).
18. Midgley, *Ind. Eng. Chem. Anal. Ed.,* **1,** 86 (1929).
19. Kuhn, et al., *Chimia (Switz.),* **8,** 109 (1954).
20. Whitmore et al., *J. Am. Chem. Soc.,* **62,** 795 (1940).
21. Kuhn, *Helv. Chim. Acta,* **25,** 252 (1942).
22. Westhaver, *Ind. Eng. Chem.,* **34,** 126 (1942).
23. Rosanoff, Lamb, and Breithut, *J. Am. Chem. Soc.,* **31,** 448 (1909).
24. Selker, Burk, and Lankelma, *Ind. Eng. Chem. Anal. Ed.,* **12,** 352 (1940).
25. Naragon, Burk, and Lankelma, *Ind. Eng. Chem.,* **34,** 355 (1942).
26. Hall and Palkin, *Ind. Eng. Chem. Anal. Ed.,* **14,** 807 (1942).
27. Naragon and Lewis, *Ind. Eng. Chem. Anal. Ed.,* **18,** 448 (1946).
28. Donnell and Kennedy, *Proc. Am. Petrol. Inst.,* **III 26,** 23 (1946).
29. Jantzen and Wieckhorst, *Chem.-Ing. Tech.,* **26,** 392 (1954).
30. Donnell and Kennedy, *Ind. Eng. Chem.,* **42,** 2327 (1950).
31. Fenske, Tonberg, and Quiggle, *Ind. Eng. Chem.,* **26,** 1161 (1934).
32. Laughlin, Nash, and Whitmore, *J. Am. Chem. Soc.,* **56,** 1396 (1934).
33. Young and Jansaitis, *J. Am. Chem. Soc.,* **58,** 377 (1936).
34. Dostrovsky and Jacobs, *Chem. Ind. (London),* **23,** 204 (1945).
35. Still, *Chem. Ind. (London),* **23,** 130 (1945).
36. Stewart, *Ind. Eng. Chem. Anal. Ed.,* **8,** 451 (1936).
37. Price, and McDermott, *Ind. Eng. Chem. Anal. Ed.,* **11,** 289 (1939).
38. Roper, Wright, Ruhoff, and Smith, *J. Am. Chem. Soc.,* **57,** 954 (1935).
39. Fenske, Petroleum Refining Laboratory, State College, Pennsylvania; Ace Glass Co., Inc., Vineland, New Jersey; American Instrument Co., Silver Springs, Maryland.
40. Fenske, Lawroski, and Tonberg, *Ind. Eng. Chem.,* **30,** 297 (1938).
41. Hall and Jonach, Symposium on High-Temperature Analytical Distillation, American Petroleum Institute Meeting at Chicago, Illinois, Nov. 11, 1946, p. 4.
42. Borns, Coffey, and Garrard, Symposium on High Temperature Analytical Distillation, American Petroleum Institute, Meeting at Chicago, Illinois, Nov. 11, 1946, p. 26.
43. Fenske, Tonberg, and Quiggle, *Ind. Eng. Chem.,* **26,** 1169 (1934).
44. McMahon, *Ind. Eng. Chem.,* **39,** 712 (1947).
45. Wire Cloth Products, Bellwood, Illinois.
46. Forsythe, Stack, Wolf, and Conn, *Ind. Eng. Chem.,* **39,** 714 (1947).
47. Cannon, *Ind. Eng. Chem.,* **41,** 1953 (1949); Heinlein, Manning, and Cannon, *Chem. Eng. Progr.,* **47,** 344 (1951); Peters and Cannon, Paper presented at the 12th International Congress of Pure and Applied Chemistry, Sept. 13, 1951.
48. Scientific Development Co., State College, Pennsylvania, Bulletin 12A.
49. Laboratory Fractional Distillation Apparatus, Catalog No. 2-163, Podbielniak, Inc., Franklin Park, Illinois.
50. Dixon, *J. Soc. Chem. Ind. (London),* **68,** 88, 119, 229 (1949); British Patent 578,309.
51. Griffith and Tatlock Ltd., London, Leaflet G.T.D. 1369, 7.12.48.
52. Highet, *Chem. Ind. (London),* **68,** 783 (1954).

53. Stedman, *Can. J. Research,* **B5,** 383 (1937).
54. Stedman, *Trans. Am. Inst. Chem. Engrs.,* **33,** 153 (1937).
55. Scientific Glass Apparatus Co., Bloomfield, New Jersey.
56. Koch and Van Raay, *Chem. Ing. Tech.,* **8,** 172 (1950).
57. Bragg, *Ind. Eng. Chem.,* **45,** 1676 (1953).
58. Bragg, *Ind. Eng. Chem. Anal. Ed.,* **11,** 283 (1939).
59. Nickels, Thesis, Pennsylvania State University, 1936.
60. Lecky and Ewell, *Ind. Eng. Chem. Anal. Ed.,* **12,** 544 (1940).
61. Brandt, Perkins, and Halverson, *Oil Gas J.*, Dec. 1946; Symposium in High Temperature Analytical Distillation, American Petroleum Institute, Meeting in Chicago, Illinois, Nov. 11, 1946, p. 51.
62. Mitchell and O'Gorman, *Anal. Chem.,* **20,** 315 (1948).
63. LaBel and Henninger, *Ber.,* **7,** 1084 (1874).
64. Brown, *J. Chem. Soc.,* **37,** 59 (1880); **39,** 517 (1881).
65. Clark and Rahrs, *Ind. Eng. Chem.,* **18,** 1092 (1926).
66. Bruun, *Ind. Eng. Chem. Anal. Ed.,* **1,** 212 (1929); Bruun and Schicktanz, *J. Res. Natl. Bur. Std.,* **7,** 851 (1931).
67. Bruun, *Ind. Eng. Chem. Anal. Ed.,* **8,** 224 (1936).
68. Bruun and Faulconer, *Ind. Eng. Chem. Anal. Ed.,* **9,** 192 (1937).
69. Ace Glass Co., Vineland, New Jersey, Otto R. Greimer Co., Newark, New Jersey, Scientific Glass Apparatus Co., Bloomfield, New Jersey.
70. Bruun and West, *Ind. Eng. Chem. Anal. Ed.,* **9,** 247 (1937).
71. Linnenmann, *Ann.,* **160,** 195 (1871).
72. Young and Thomas, *Chem. News,* **71,** 177 (1895).
73. Glinsky, *Ann.,* **175,** 381 (1875).
74. Du Pont, *Chim. Ind. (Paris),* **8,** 549 (1922).
75. Palkin, *Ind. Eng. Chem. Anal. Ed.,* **3,** 377 (1931).
76. Oldershaw, *Ind. Eng. Chem. Anal. Ed..* **13,** 265 (1941).
77. Collins and Lantz, *Ind. Eng. Chem. Anal. Ed.,* **18,** 673 (1946).
78. Schicktanz, *J. Res. Natl. Bur. Std.,* **12,** 259 (1934).
79. Langdon and Tobin, *Ind. Eng. Chem. Anal. Ed.,* **17,** 801 (1945).
80. Umholtz and Van Winkle, *Petrol. Refiner,* **34,** 114 (1955).
81. Jones and Van Winkle, *Ind. Eng. Chem.,* **49,** 232 (1957).
82. Glass Engineering Laboratory, Belmont, California.
83. Griswold, Morris, and VanBerg, *Ind. Eng. Chem.,* **36,** 119 (1944).
84. Podbielniak, American Chemical Society Meeting, New York, April 1935.
85. Huffman and Urey, *Ind. Eng. Chem.,* **29,** 531 (1937); Pegram, Urey, and Huffman, *Phys. Rev.,* **49,** 883 (1936); *J. Chem. Phys.,* **4,** 623 (1936).
86. Mair and Willingham, *J. Res. Natl. Bur. Std.,* **22,** 519 (1939).
87. Bjorkman and Olavi, *Svensk Kem. Tidskr.,* **6,** 145 (1946).
88. Kock, Hilberath, and Weinratter, *Chem. Fabrik,* **14,** 387 (1941).
89. Lesene and Lochte, *Ind. Eng. Chem. Anal. Ed.,* **10,** 450 (1938).
90. Baker, Barkenbus, and Roswell, *Ind. Eng. Chem. Anal. Ed.,* **12,** 468 (1940).
91. Birch, Gripp, and Nathan, *J. Soc. Chem. Ind. (London),* **66,** 33 (1947).
92. Murray, *J. Am. Oil Chemists' Soc.,* **28,** 235 (1951).
93. Zuiderweg, *J. Chem. Eng. Sci.,* **1,** 174 (1952).
94. Cruthirds, Jones, and Seyfried, *Oil Gas J.,* **48,** No. 41, 117 (1950).
95. Crozier, Robert, and Rousseau, *Rev. Sci. Inst.,* Franz. Petrole et Ann. Combustibles Liquides, **8,** 79 (1953).
96. Nerheim, *Anal. Chem.,* **29,** 1546 (1957).

97. Williams, *Ind. Eng. Chem.*, **39**, 779 (1947).
98. Winters and Dinerstein, *Anal. Chem.*, **27**, 546 (1955).
99. Nerheim and Dinerstein, *Anal. Chem.*, **28**, 1029 (1956).
100. Nestor, *Anal. Chem.*, **28**, 278 (1956).
101. Perry and Fuguitt, *Ind. Eng. Chem.*, **39**, 782 (1947).
102. Perry and Cox, *Ind. Eng. Chem.*, **48**, 1473 (1956).
103. Hall and Jonach, Symposium on High-Temperature Analytical Distillation, American Petroleum Institute, Meeting at Chicago, Illinois, Nov. 11, 1946, p. 42.
104. Cook, private communication.
105. Podbielniak, *Ind. Eng. Chem. Anal. Ed.*, **5**, 121 (1933).
106. Willingham and Rossini, *J. Res. Natl. Bur. Std.*, **37**, 15 (1946).
107. Kistiakowski, Ruhoff, Smith, and Vaughan, *J. Am. Chem. Soc.*, **57**, 878 (1935).
108. Widmer, *Helv. Chim. Acta*, **7**, 59 (1924).
109. Fenske, Quiggle, and Tonberg, *Ind. Eng. Chem.*, **24**, 408 (1932).
110. Borns, Coffey, and Garrard, Symposium on High-Temperature Analytical Distillation, American Petroleum Institute, Meeting at Chicago, Illinois, Nov. 11, 1946, p. 26.
111. Foster Wheeler Corp., New York City.
112. Prevost, Thesis, Pennsylvania State College, 1948.
113. Marschner and Cropper, Symposium on High-Temperature Analytical Distillation, American Petroleum Institute, Meeting at Chicago, Illinois, Nov. 11, 1946, p. 35.
114. Peters and Baker, *Ind. Eng. Chem.*, **18**, 69 (1926).
115. Smith, Glasebrook, Begeman, and Lovell, *Ind. Eng. Chem. Anal. Chem.*, **17**, 47 (1945).
116. Podbielniak, *Ind. Eng. Chem. Anal. Ed.*, **5**, 127 (1933).
117. Young, *Distillation Principles and Processes*, MacMillan, London, 1922.
118. Robinson and Gilliland, *Elements of Fractional Distillation*, McGraw-Hill, New York, 1950.
119. Leslie, Motor Fuels, New York, 1923.
120. Oldroyd and Goldblatt, *Ind. Eng. Chem. Anal. Ed.*, **18**, 761 (1946).
121. Collins and Lantz, *Ind. Eng. Chem. Anal. Ed.*, **18**, 673 (1946).
122. Hall and Jonach, Symposium on High-Temperature Analytical Distillation, American Petroleum Institute, Meeting at Chicago, Illinois, Nov. 11, 1946, p. 42.
123. Kieselbach, *Anal. Chem.*, **19**, 815 (1947).
124. Lloyd and Hornbacher, *Anal. Chem.*, **19**, 120 (1947).
125. Doran, *Anal. Chem.*, **5**, 101 (1933).
126. Laughlin, Nash, and Whitmore, *J. Am. Chem. Soc.*, **56**, 1396 (1934).
127. Hercules Powder Company, design.
128. Goldsbarry and Askevold, Symposium on High-Temperature Analytical Distilla-can Petroleum Institute, Meeting at Chicago, Illinois, Nov. 11, 1946, p. 12.
129. Glas-Col Apparatus Co., Terre Haute, Indiana; Scientific Glass Apparatus Co., Bloomfield, New Jersey.
130. Donnell and Kennedy, Symposium on High-Temperature Analytical Distillation, American Petroleum Institute, Meeting at Chicago, Illinois, Nov. 11, 1946, p. 17.
131. Reed, Symposium on High-Temperature Analytical Distillation, American Petroleum Institute, Meeting at Chicago, Illinois, Nov. 11, 1946, p. 4.
132. Sturtevant, in *Physical Methods of Organic Chemistry*, Vol. I, Part I, 3rd ed. in Technique of Organic Chemistry Series, Weissberger, ed., Interscience, New York, 1959, Chap. I.
133. Hall and Palkin, *Ind. Eng. Chem. Anal. Ed.*, **14**, 652 (1942).

134. Sturtevant, Ref. 132, Chap. VI.
135. Busse, "Temperature, Its Measurement and Control" in *Science and Industry*, Reinhold, New York, 1941, p. 228.
136. Thomas, "Temperature, Its Measurement and Control" in *Science and Industry*, Reinhold, New York, 1941, p. 159.
137. White, "Temperature, Its Measurement and Control" in *Science and Industry*, Reinhold, New York, 1941, p. 265.
138. Leeds and Northrup Co., Philadelphia, Pennsylvania; Rubicon Co., Philadelphia, Pennsylvania.
139. Mueller, "Temperature, Its Measurement and Control" in *Science and Industry*, Reinhold, New York, 1941, p. 162.
140. (a) The Properties, Physics and Design of Semi-Conductor Devices, J. H. Shive, D. VanNostrand Co., Inc., Princeton, New Jersey, 1959. (b) Methods of Experimental Physics, Vol. 2, L. Marton, ed., Academic Press, New York, 1964.
141. Becker, Green, and Pearson, *Bell System Tech. J.*, **26**, 170 (1947).
142. Process Instruments and Control Handbook, Considine, D. M., Editor-in-Chief, McGraw-Hill, New York (1957). Fenwal, Inc., Ashland, Mass., Portable Temperature Indicator Cat. No. MC-192; Thermistor Probes, Cat. No. MC-193A; Indicating Electronic Temp. Controllers, Cat. Nos. MC-185A, MC-190 and MC-196, Yellow Springs Instrument Co., Yellow Springs, Ohio, Commercial Catalogs in Series 400, 500, and 600, "Thermistemp" Thermistor Probes, Controllers and Recorders.
143. Huntress and Hershberg, *Ind. Eng. Chem. Anal. Ed.*, **5**, 144 (1933).
144. Leck, *Pressure Measurements in Vacuum Systems*, Chapman and Hall, London, 1957.
145. Cox, *Ind. Eng. Chem. Anal. Ed.*, **1**, 7 (1929).
146. Sunier and White, *Ind. Eng. Chem. Anal. Ed.*, **3**, 259 (1931).
147. Willingham, Taylor, Pignocco, and Rossini, *J. Res. Natl. Bur. Std.*, **35**, 219 (1945).
148. Palkin, *Ind. Eng. Chem. Anal. Ed.*, **7**, 436 (1935).
149. Schierholtz, *Ind. Eng. Chem. Anal. Ed.*, **7**, 284 (1935).
150. Thelin, *Ind. Eng. Chem. Anal. Ed.*, **13**, 908 (1941).
151. Bailey, *Ind. Eng. Chem. Anal. Ed.*, **15**, 283 (1943).
152. Dalin, *Ind. Eng. Chem. Anal. Ed.*, **15**, 731 (1943).
153. Hershberg and Huntress, *Ind. Eng. Chem. Anal. Ed.*, **5**, 344 (1933).
154. Ferry, *Ind. Eng. Chem. Anal. Ed.*, **10**, 647 (1938).
155. Todd, *Ind. Eng. Chem. Anal. Ed.*, **20**, 1248 (1948).
156. Caswell, *Phil. Trans.*, **24**, 1597 (1704).
157. Gilmont, *Ind. Eng. Chem. Anal. Ed.*, **18**, 633 (1946).
158. Williams, F. E., *Ind. Eng. Chem.*, **39**, 779 (1947).
159. Fenske, U. S. Patent, 2,037,125 April 14, 1936.
160. Kerotest Mfg. Company, Pittsburgh, Pennsylvania.
161. Herrington and Starr, *Ind. Eng. Chem. Anal. Ed.* **14**, 62 (1942).
162. Puddington, *Ind. Eng. Chem. Anal. Ed.*, **16**, 415 (1944).
163. Sager, *Ind. Eng. Chem. Anal. Ed.*, **4**, 388 (1932).
164. Pearlson, *Ind. Eng. Chem. Anal. Ed.*, **16**, 415 (1944).
165. Bruun and Schicktang, *J. Res. Natl. Bur. Std.*, **7**, 851 (1931).
166. Horsley, *Anal. Chem.*, **19**, 508 (1947).
167. Glasgow, Streiff, and Rossini, Paper for Division of Petroleum Chemistry, American Chemical Society Meeting, September 1945.
168. Physical Methods of Organic Chemistry, Vol. I, 3rd ed., Technique of Organic Chemistry Series, Weissberger, ed., Interscience, New York, 1959.

169. Marks, *Ind. Eng. Chem. Anal. Ed.*, **7**, 102 (1935).
170. Aluise, Hall, Staats, and Becker, *Ind. Eng. Chem. Anal. Ed.*, **19**, 347 (1947).
171. Podbielniak, *Ind. Eng. Chem. Anal. Ed.*, **3**, 177–88 (1931).
172. Podbielniak, *Ind. Eng. Chem. Anal. Ed.*, **13**, 639–45 (1941).
173. McMillan, *J. Inst. Petroleum Technol.*, **22**, 616–645 (1936).
174. Catalog C-160, Podbielniak, Inc., Chicago, Illinois.

General References

American Institute of Physics, *Temperature—Its Measurement and Control in Science and Industry*, Reinhold, New York, 1941.

American Petroleum Institute, *Symposium on High Temperature Analytical Distillation*, Meeting at Chicago, Illinois, November 11, 1946.

Carney, *Laboratory Fractional Distillation*, MacMillan, New York, 1949.

Coulson and Herington, *Laboratory Distillation Practice*, George Newnes, London, 1958.

Kirschbaum, *Distillation and Rectification*, Chemical Publishing Company, New York, 1948.

Krell, *Handbook of Laboratory Distillation*, (trans. from the 2nd German ed. by C. G. Verver) Elsevier Publishing Company, New York, 1963.

Laboratory Fractional Distillation Apparatus, Catalog No. 2-163, Podbielniak, Inc., Franklin Park, Illinois.

McMillan, *J. Inst. Petrol. Technol.*, **22**, 616–645 (1936).

Morton, *Laboratory Techniques in Organic Chemistry*, 1st ed., McGraw-Hill, New York, 1938.

Perry, Chelton, and Kirkpatrick, eds., *Chemical Engineers' Handbook*, 4th ed., McGraw-Hill, New York, 1963.

Podbielniak, *Ind. Eng. Chem. Anal. Ed.*, **3**, 177–88 (1931).

Podbielniak, *Ind. Eng. Chem. Anal. Ed.*, **13**, 639–45 (1941).

Robinson and Gilliland, *Elements of Fractional Distillation*, McGraw-Hill, New York, 1950.

Rose and Rose, *Distillation Literature Index and Abstracts*, 1941–1945, 1946–1952, Applied Science Laboratories, State College, Pennsylvania, 1953.

Ward, *Review of the Literature on the Construction, Testing and Operation of Laboratory Fractionating Columns*, U. S. Bureau of Mines Tech. Paper 600, 1939.

Weber, *Temperature Measurement and Control*, Blakiston, Philadelphia, 1941.

Willingham and Rossini, Assembly, Testing and Operation of Laboratory Distilling Columns of High Efficiency, *J. Res. Natl. Bur. Std.*, **37**, 15–29 (1946). Research Paper No. 1724.

Young, *Distillation Principles and Practice*, MacMillan, London, 1922.

Zuiderweg, *Manual of Batch Distillation*, Interscience, New York, 1957.

CHAPTER IV

EXTRACTIVE AND AZEOTROPIC DISTILLATION

CARL S. CARLSON and JOSEPH STEWART, *Esso Research and Engineering Company, Linden, New Jersey*

I. INTRODUCTION AND DEFINITIONS

It is evident from the earlier chapters of this volume that fractional distillation is a powerful tool for the separation of mixtures of volatile components. It is used in both laboratory and industrial operations to isolate one or more components of a mixture and, in many cases, suffices to isolate the component in the requisite degree of purity. Frequently, however, separation by fractional distillation alone is either impossible or impractical. In such cases, it may be necessary to resort to azeotropic or extractive distillation to solve the separation problem. This is particularly true where the separation of large quantities is entailed, since chromatographic methods are usually limited by the capacity of the adsorbent to the isolation of relatively small quantities of material.

As discussed in Chapter I, the separation of mixtures by fractional distillation depends on differences in volatility of the materials to be separated. In general, the volatility of a compound is proportional to its vapor pressure and inversely proportional to its molecular weight and boiling point. As the molecular weight of members of an organic series increases, the number of possible compounds of similar volatility increases exponentially, and the complete separation of the liquid mixture becomes increasingly difficult, if not impossible, by fractional distillation. Added to this is the complication that compounds of different molecular types may have nearly the same volatility or boiling point. For example, the six-carbon hydrocarbons, benzene and cyclohexane, boil at 80.10 and 80.74°C., respectively.[1] Such difficult resolutions require highly efficient fractionating columns. Laboratory columns with a separating power of 100 theoretical plates are not uncommon,[2–4] while columns of several hundred theoretical plates have been built[5] for special applications. Even with columns of this separating power, some difference in the volatilities of the materials to be separated must exist for any separation to be achieved.

Another approach to this problem is the modification of the volatilities of the components of the mixture to be separated. In extractive distillation and in azeotropic distillation, this is accomplished by the addition of certain solvents. A condensed summary of these techniques and the physical principles involved has been presented by Gerster.[6] Before discussing extractive and azeotropic distillation, a few terms will be defined and explained.

Volatility, v, is a measure of the tendency of a compound to enter the vapor phase. For a pure compound, the vapor pressure at a given temperature or the boiling point at atmospheric pressure is indicative of its volatility. In a solution the tendency of the compound to vaporize is usually altered by the other compounds present. Since we are interested in the recovery of the compound from solution, the volatility, having varying numerical values in different solutions, must be defined for the material in solution:

$$v = y/x \tag{1}$$

where v is the volatility, y is the mole fraction in the vapor phase at equilibrium, and x is the mole fraction of the same compound in the liquid phase at equilibrium.

Relative Volatility, α. The ease of separation by fractional distillation depends upon the volatility of one compound relative to that of the others present in the system. For simplicity, consider a binary system of A and B. The relative volatility, α_{AB}, is defined as

$$\alpha_{AB} = (v_A/v_B) = (y_A/y_B)/(x_A/x_B) \tag{2}$$

Again, for an ideal solution, α is equal to the ratio of the vapor pressures of the compounds. In general, in the absence of specific experimental data, the vapor pressure ratio is used as a rough index of ease of separation. In multicomponent systems, the relative volatilities are usually referred to the least volatile compound and when written, for example, in a four-component system, they are designated as α_{A-D}, or α_{B-D}, etc., where A is the most volatile and D is the least volatile component.

Modified Relative Volatility, α_S. As indicated above, the normal volatility relationships of a mixture can be modified by the addition of a solvent. In the presence of a solvent, this modified relative volatility will be designated as α_S:

$$\alpha_S = (y_{AS}/y_{BS})/(x_{AS}/x_{BS}) \tag{3}$$

where y_{AS}, x_{AS}, y_{BS}, and x_{BS} are the mole fractions of A and B in the vapor phase (y) and in the liquid phase (x), respectively, all in the presence of a solvent at equilibrium. The above concentrations may be expressed on a multicomponent basis or on a binary basis, as long as the basis is consistent.

Extractive Distillation. Vapor–liquid extraction, or extractive distillation, involves distillation in the presence of a substance which is relatively nonvolatile compared to the components to be separated and which is selected to enhance the relative volatility of the components to be separated. It is added continuously near the top of the distilling column so that an appreciable concentration is maintained in the liquid phase throughout the column.[7,8] In the proportions used, the solvent is miscible with the mixture to be separated at the temperature of the distillation.

Azeotropism. The property by virtue of which certain liquid mixtures distill at a constant temperature under a constant pressure without change in composition is called azeotropism.[9]

Azeotropic Mixture or Azeotrope. An azeotropic mixture or azeotrope boils or distills without change in composition, and in general, it has a boiling point higher or lower than that of any of its pure constituents.[10] A constant-boiling mixture (C.B.M.) is an azeotropic mixture.

Azeotropic Distillation. A distillation in which one of the products is obtained as an azeotropic mixture is known as azeotropic distillation in its broad sense. In the present discussion, however, azeotropic distillation is defined as distillation in the presence of a volatile component added to facilitate separation by distillation when one or more of the components of the original mixture is obtained in a fixed ratio to the added component. Referring to a binary mixture for convenience, the addition to the feed of a third component, S, capable of forming a minimum-boiling azeotrope with all of one component, A, will yield a distillate containing A and S, in a fixed ratio. This will be true as long as sufficient A and S are present.

Homogeneous Azeotrope. A single liquid-phase mixture which has the same composition as the vapor in equilibrium with it is called a homogeneous azeotrope or constant-boiling mixture (C.B.M.). For binary mixtures, vapor and liquid compositions are the same and the binary azeotropes have boiling points different from those of either of the pure materials making up the mixture.

Heterogeneous Azeotrope. The term azeotropic mixture has also been applied to the distillate obtained by the distillation of a binary mixture having two liquid phases. As long as two liquid phases exist, the vapor will be of constant composition. A common example is steam distillation with a water phase present.

Solvent. The separating aid used in extractive distillation is usually referred to as a solvent. It is usually much higher boiling, by 50–100°C., than the mixture to be separated.

Entrainer. Since most azeotropes have minimum boiling points, the agent added to form the azeotrope usually appears in the distillate. Hence, it is commonly called an entrainer. Its boiling point is generally close to that of the mixture to be separated.

In extractive distillation, a solvent is added continuously near the top of the distillation column to maintain a high solvent concentration in the liquid phase. In azeotropic distillation, a solvent is added with the charge to be distilled to produce an azeotropic mixture with one or more of the components of the mixture.

II. EXTRACTIVE DISTILLATION

1. Scope

Extractive distillation is frequently helpful even when a difference in volatilities exists in the absence of a solvent, since an appreciable reduction in the theoretical-plate requirements or the reflux ratio can be obtained. The relationship between relative volatility, α, and the number of theoretical plates required for a given separation is illustrated in Table I.

TABLE I
Relation between Relative Volatility and Number of Perfect Plates

Boiling point difference, °C.	Relative volatility[a]	Number of theoretical plates needed
7.0	1.3	22
6.0	1.25	26
5.0	1.20	32
4.0	1.15	41
2.75	1.10	60
1.5	1.05	110
0	1.00	Infinite

[a] Assuming an ideal solution and the perfect gas laws.

This table[11] is based on the separation of a binary hydrocarbon mixture into a distillate containing 95 mole-% of the more volatile or lower boiling material and a residue containing only 5 mole-% of the same component, the separation being made in a batch fractional-distillation column operating under conditions of total reflux.

Extractive distillation may be used in the laboratory to facilitate separations of three main types:

Virtually Ideal Solutions of Close-Boiling Components. An example of this type is the binary mixture *n*-heptane (b.p. 98.5°C.) and methylcyclohexane (b.p. 100.8°C.). This mixture, which has a relative volatility of 1.07 at atmospheric pressure, is difficult to separate by conventional fractional distillation. When it is extractively distilled with 70 wt.-% aniline as a solvent, the relative volatility is increased to 1.3 and the theoretical-plate requirement for a given separation is reduced by 75%.[12]

Nonideal Mixtures. An example of this type is the binary mixture methylcyclohexane (b.p. 100.8°C.) and toluene (b.p. 110.8°C.). The relative volatility of this mixture decreases with increasing methylcyclohexane concentration; it is only 1.07 at 90 mole-% methylcyclohexane. Therefore it is very difficult to free methylcyclohexane of toluene. The separation is greatly enhanced by an extractive distillation in the presence of a polar solvent such as aniline.[12]

Azeotropes. Constant-boiling mixtures or azeotropes are a special form of nonideal solution. Since they usually consist of dissimilar molecular types, many of them can be separated readily by extractive distillation. For example, cyclohexane–benzene, which at atmospheric pressure forms an azeotrope containing 46.3 mole-% cyclohexane, was extractively distilled with aniline as a solvent. Virtually pure cyclohexane was obtained as overhead with the hydrocarbon portion of the bottoms containing 22.4 mole-% cyclohexane[13] (compositions expressed on a solvent-free basis). The composition of the hydrocarbon mixture in the column obviously passed through what would normally be the azeotropic composition.

Complex fractions that boil over a range of 20°C. or less and which contain compounds of different molecular types can be separated. For example, a narrow boiling range fraction of petroleum naphtha can be extractively distilled in continuous units to separate toluene from nonaromatic substances.[14] Other similar applications are obviously possible.

2. Theory

In extractive distillation, a nonideal system is deliberately created by the addition of a solvent. In the resulting solution, the partial-pressure relationships, and consequently the relative volatilities of the components to be separated will be different. These effects and their magnitudes can best be understood by reference to the following equations and discussion:

In an ideal solution of two components A and S, the vapor pressure of each can be expressed by Raoult's law:

$$\bar{p}_A = p_A x_A \tag{4}$$

$$\bar{p}_S = p_S x_S \tag{5}$$

where p is the vapor pressure of the pure compound, $\bar{p}$ the partial pressure, x the mole fraction, and A and S denote solute and solvent, respectively. The total pressure p above the solution is given by Dalton's law

$$p = \bar{p}_A - \bar{p}_S \tag{6}$$

The relative volatility, α_{AS}, of a compound in an ideal binary solution is obtained as follows: From Avogadro's law:

$$y_A = \bar{p}_A/p \tag{7}$$

$$y_S = \bar{p}_S/p \tag{8}$$

where y_A and y_S are the mole fractions of A and S, respectively, in the vapor. Combining these equations with (4) and (5) we obtain

$$y_A = p_A x_A/p \tag{9}$$

$$y_S = p_S x_S/p \tag{10}$$

Dividing (9) by (10) we obtain

$$\frac{y_A}{y_S} = \frac{p_A x_A}{p_S x_S} \tag{11}$$

Since

$$\alpha_{AS} = \frac{p_A}{p_S}$$

$$\frac{y_A}{y_S} = \alpha_{AS} \frac{x_A}{x_S} \tag{12}$$

and

$$\alpha_{AS} = \left(\frac{y_A}{y_S}\right) \bigg/ \left(\frac{x_A}{x_S}\right) \tag{13}$$

In a nonideal solution the partial pressures and total pressure over a solution at a given temperature differ from those predicted by Raoult's law. The deviations may be positive or negative. Since the vast majority are positive, our discussion will be limited to this case, although the principles hold equally well for negative deviations from Raoult's law. To allow for deviations from Raoult's law, the activity coefficient, γ, must be taken into consideration. With this factor equations for nonideal solutions may be written as follows:

$$\bar{p}_A = \gamma_A p_A x_A \tag{14}$$

$$\bar{p}_S = \gamma_S p_S x_S \tag{15}$$

$$p = \bar{p}_A + \bar{p}_S \tag{16}$$

The coefficient γ is not a constant. Its numerical value is a function of all the components in the solution and of their concentrations. Referring to component A, in a binary system, $\gamma_A = 1$ when $x_A = 1$, since pure liquids

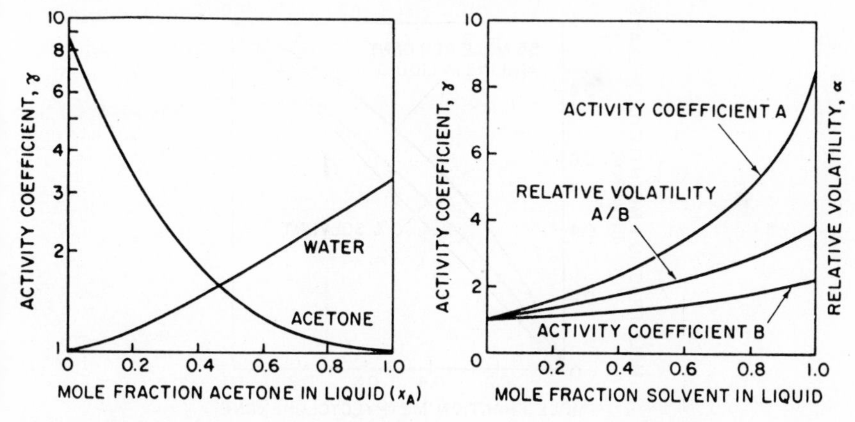

Fig. 1 (left). Activity coefficients for binary system acetone–water at 1 atm.[15]
Fig. 2 (right). Effect of solvent concentration on activity coefficients and relative volatilities of a binary mixture with equimolar proportions of A to B.

are defined as ideal solutions. As the concentration of x_A decreases, γ_A increases and reaches a maximum at $x_A = 0$. The same relations hold for the other component, S. These relationships are illustrated in Figure 1 for acetone and water.[15]

An equation for relative volatility similar to eq. (13) may be written for nonideal solutions:

$$\alpha = \frac{y_A \gamma_S x_S}{y_S \gamma_A x_A} \tag{17}$$

The effect of a solvent and its concentration on the activity coefficients of the two components of a binary system in equimolar ratio is shown in Figure 2. The activity coefficient of each component increases as the solvent concentration increases from 0 to 100%. The activity coefficient of component A increases much more rapidly than that of component B. This is reflected in the variation in the relative volatility with solvent concentration, which is also shown in Figure 2. To realize a relative volatility of 2 or higher, at least 60 mole-% solvent must be present in the liquid.

The effect of solvent concentration is also illustrated in Figure 3, where the x–y diagram for methylcyclohexane–toluene is shown on a solvent-free basis for two solvent concentrations.[12] For this system the effect of solvent is most marked in the high-methylcyclohexane region since the binary system (zero solvent concentration) vapor–liquid equilibrium curve pinches, approaching the $x = y$ line, as the mole fraction of methylcyclohexane approaches 1.

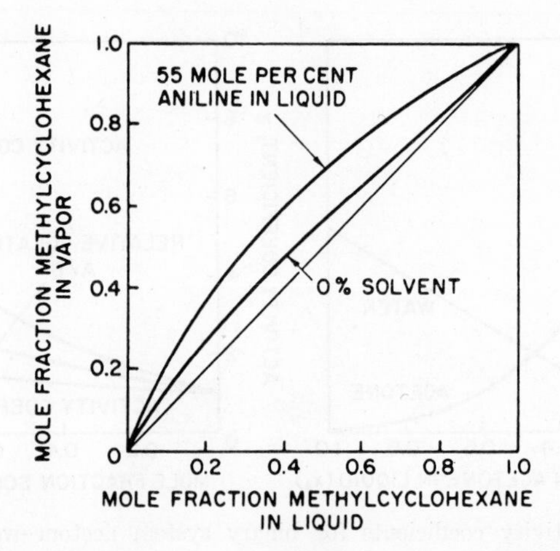

Fig. 3. Methylcyclohexane–toluene vapor–liquid equilibria at 1 atm. expressed on a solvent-free basis.

The foregoing discussion illustrates the effect of solvents on the relative volatilities of binary mixtures. High solvent concentrations are necessary for a maximum effect on the relative volatility. Colburn and Schoenborn[16] have shown by a study of a number of nonideal solutions that this is a general requirement for extractive distillation.

The molecular basis for the effects of solvents has been discussed by Anderson, Cambio and Prausnitz[17] and the thermodynamics of solvent selectivity by Prausnitz and Anderson.[18]

3. Selection of Solvent

A. GENERAL CONSIDERATIONS

The suitability of a solvent for extractive distillation depends on its effect on the volatility of the components to be separated and on certain other factors mentioned below. It is usually advantageous to select a solvent which augments the normal vapor-pressure relationships and which forms a highly nonideal system. In addition, the solvent should be sufficiently high boiling so that the components obtained in the solvent phase can be easily recovered by fractional distillation. It should also be a good solvent and be soluble itself so that excessively high solvent:mixture ratios are not necessary and solvent-phase separation will not occur during the distillation. Should phase separation occur, much of the relative-volatility enhancement will be lost. The solvent should be thermally stable so that no decomposition occurs during extractive distillation or subsequent fractional distillation for removal of dissolved components from the solvent. For ease of handling, the solvent should be nontoxic. It should not react with the components of the mixture, since formation of either stable chemical compounds or of azeotropes with the solvent during extractive distillation may prevent the desired separation. If the solvent boils more than 50°C. above the mixture, the danger of azeotrope formation is negligible (see Sec. III). A broad range of application is desirable, but not essential, in a solvent for laboratory use.

Where the laboratory separation could be the basis for industrial separation, a few additional factors should be considered. The solvent should be inexpensive and readily available. While a high-boiling solvent is necessary for proper operation of the extractive distillation, it should not be so high boiling as to require excessively high temperature levels for regeneration. The corrosivity of the solvent toward commonly used materials of construction should also be kept in mind in making a selection.

B. VAPOR–LIQUID EQUILIBRIA AND EQUILIBRIUM STILLS

The selection of a solvent for use in extractive distillation is best made on the basis of vapor–liquid equilibria data obtained in the presence of a solvent. This is particularly true if much work is planned with the solvent selected. Such data are normally obtained in an equilibrium still so constructed and operated that equilibrium between vapor phase and liquid phase exactly equivalent to one theoretical plate is attained. Analysis of each phase establishes the equilibrium vapor and liquid compositions.

When ternary systems are investigated, particularly those in which one component has a marked influence upon the relative volatility of the other two components of the mixture, it is essential that a standardized procedure be used. A preliminary evaluation of possible solvents is made by investigating a mixture containing the two components to be separated at a 1:1 ratio (mole, weight, or volume) and a constant proportion of solvent (usually one to three times the binary mixture on a mole basis). One or more determinations may be made on a given solvent in initial scanning. An example is given below. In making a solvent survey, difficult analytical problems are frequently encountered because of the presence of the solvent. In such cases, short-cut evaluation methods such as those described later may be used. Any solvent selected by these methods should be checked in an equilibrium still.

Several types of vapor–liquid equilibrium stills have been described in the literature. Many of these are modifications of the Othmer still.[19] One such modification has been described by Jones.[20] It is shown in Figure 4. The still is constructed of borosilicate glass and includes a boiler of about 200 ml. capacity heated by oil circulating in an electrically

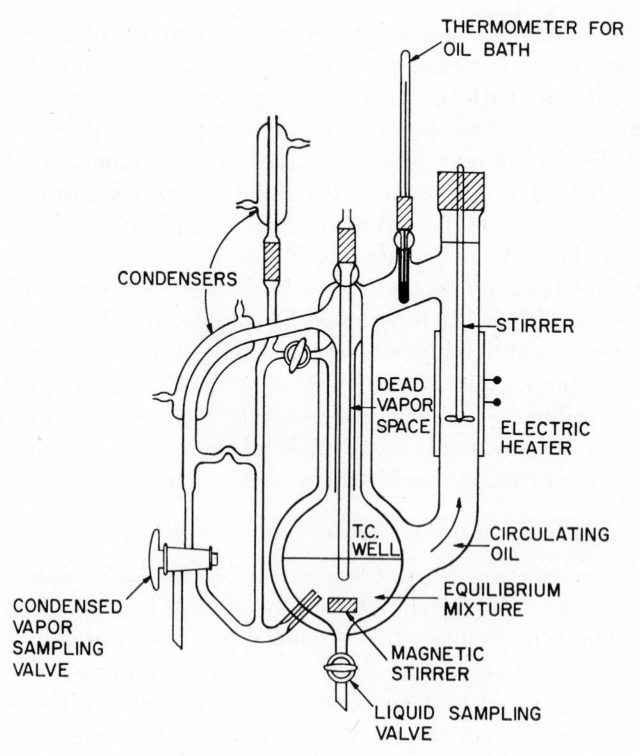

Fig. 4. Othmer-type equilibrium still.

heated jacket. The oil-filled jacket extends along the entire height of the 10-in. disengaging column to prevent condensation and subsequent fractionation. A dead vapor space between the rising vapor stream and the jacket further helps achieve adiabatic operation in the column. The still is provided with a thermometer well so that the temperature of the boiling liquid can be measured. A magnetic stirrer in the pot provides agitation to prevent bumping and superheating and to mix the returning condensate. The vapors on leaving the column pass through a downward sloping tube to the condenser. In this still there is virtually no hold-up of condensate. In operation, the condensate returns immediately to the reboiler through the three-way stopcock. The distillate sample is taken by turning the stopcock 180° and collecting the sample running down from the condenser. A liquid phase sample is taken simultaneously. This still is useful for mixtures where only a few drops of sample are required for analysis and is also useful for the study of immiscible systems. It has so little hold-up in the return line that equilibrium can be reached after only a few minutes of boiling. It is desirable, however, to equilibrate for several hours before

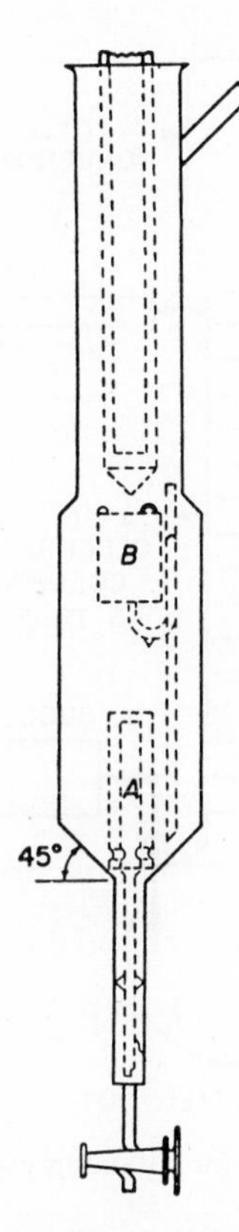

Fig. 5. Penn-State equilibrium still.[21]

sampling. Although only a few drops of sample are removed for analysis, this is sufficient for the commonly used analytical techniques of vapor-phase chromatography, mass spectroscopy, or refractive index measurement.

Another type of circulating equilibrium still, which was developed for use with mixtures having critical solution temperature below the boiling temperature, has been described.[21] The novel features of this equilibrium still, shown in Figure 5, are the internal distillate receiver, *B*, bathed in the ascending vapors and a Cottrell pump, *A*, for the boiling tube permitting simultaneous boiling-point and vapor–liquid equilibrium determinations. It was found that equilibrium was attained in less than three hours when a solvent boiling approximately 80°C. above the binary mixture was used and 12% of the charge was held up as distillate.

Both these stills have a tendency to give difficulty when the distillate returned to the still boils appreciably, i.e., 50°C., below the mixture in the

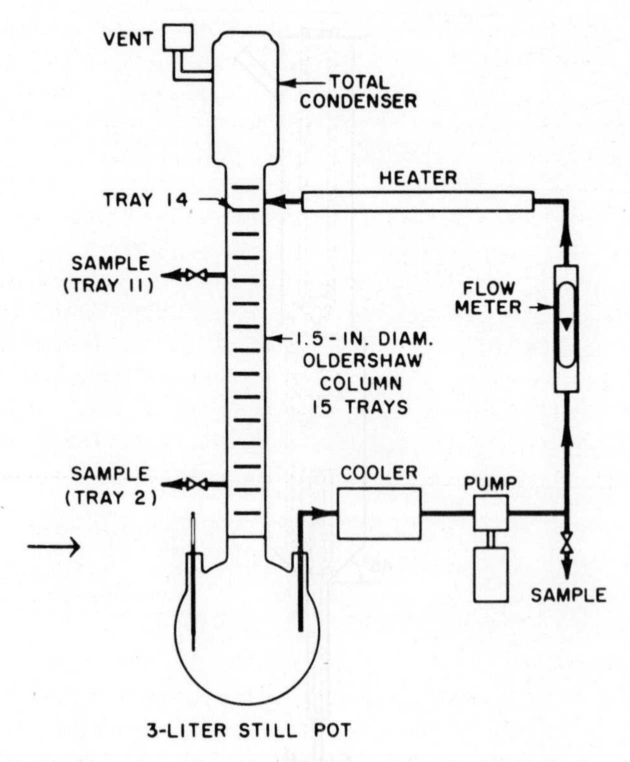

Fig. 6. Fractionation column for obtaining vapor–liquid equilibrium data.

still. In such cases the returning distillate tends to flash into the vapor, thus upsetting true equilibrium. This is sometimes encountered in testing high-boiling extractive-distillation solvents. An equilibrium still which obviates this difficulty has been described.[22] This is a flow-type equilibrium still which usually requires relatively large quantities of test mixtures. It has the advantage that it may be used for mixtures having two liquid phases in either the boiling liquid or the distillate, or both.

After a preliminary exploration of possible solvents has been made, more complete data on the solvent selection may be desired. In this case, the ratio of the two components in the mixture under study is varied, and the vapor–liquid equilibrium is determined with the same mole-% of solvent. This procedure may then be repeated at one or more solvent-mixture ratios. The data can be expressed in terms of modified relative volatilities, α_S, or as x–y data on a solvent-free basis.

In order to avoid the analytical difficulties inherent in the vapor–liquid equilibrium still technique where the compositions of the vapor and of the liquid are similar in value, Swanson and Gurster[23] have suggested the use of a pilot column in which samples may be taken several plates apart and thus have larger composition differences. In this technique a 1.5-in. diam. glass Oldershaw column containing 15 trays was used. The column was designed to permit sampling on two of these trays while the unit was in operation (Fig. 6).

Solvent-rich liquid from the still pot is recycled to Tray 14 by means of a pump. The overhead vapor is condensed totally and returned as reflux. After establishment of steady-state conditions, samples of 2–4 ml. are withdrawn from the recycle liquid line and the two sampling trays.

One system studied was the separation of isoprene from 2-methyl-2-butene using dimethyl formamide as the solvent. With this apparatus they were able to operate at solvent concentrations in the liquid ranging from 54–93 mole-% and at olefin concentrations of 42–72 mole-% on a solvent-free basis. By keeping the liquid to vapor flow rates at high values of the order of 2, it was possible to cause the tray composition to "pinch" and at these conditions the relative volatility calculation is not appreciably affected by the value used for tray efficiency. The data were correlated by a simplification of the ternary Margules equation. Care must be taken in applying this technique to allow for the effect of solvent concentration and temperature on relative volatility.

As the authors point out, the use of an experimental technique of this type can be less time-consuming than the use of conventional methods. It has the additional advantage that predicted tray efficiencies can be checked by carrying out some of the tests in regions where the α values are not dependent upon tray efficiencies. Furthermore, the operability of the system is demonstrated in an actual column, and preliminary information can be obtained on heat loads, flow rates, and the degree of foaming on the trays.

As an example of the evaluation of extractive-distillation solvents, we may cite the effect of a series of solvents upon the separation of the binary mixture methylcyclohexane–toluene by extractive distillation as determined in the internal-receiver equilibrium still described above. In each case the still was charged with the same total number of moles of solution containing 75 mole-% solvent and 25 mole-% hydrocarbon. The latter consisted of methylcyclohexane and toluene in a 1:1 mole ratio. Distillate and residue were freed of solvent by washing with acid, alkali, or water as required, and the resulting binary hydrocarbon mixtures were analyzed by refractive index using the data of Quiggle and Fenske.[24] From the analyses of the hydrocarbon portion of distillate and residue, relative volatilities were calculated and expressed as α_S [see eq. (3)]. In order to avoid misleading conclusions, two additional determinations were made with each solvent, keeping the total number of moles charged to the still and the hydrocarbon:solvent mole ratio the same, but changing the hydrocarbon so that it contained 25 and 75 mole-% of methylcyclohexane, respectively.

Of the solvents investigated,[21] aniline gave the highest values of α_S. For an extended study with this solvent, an analytical procedure was developed permitting the determination of the composition of the ternary system.[25] A series of five samples was made up. All contained the same total number of moles with aniline and hydrocarbon in a 1:1 mole ratio. The hydrocarbon portion of the samples contained 0, 25, 50, 75, and 100 mole-% methylcyclohexane. Each sample was charged to the equilibrium still and distilled for at least three hours to establish equilibrium. At the end of that time heating was stopped and, after distillation ceased, the still was completely drained of distillate and residue for analysis. Typical data for one run, with all analyses expressed in weight per cent, are listed below.

Component	Charge	Distillate	Residue
Methylcyclohexane	26.1	60.0	21.4
Toluene	24.4	31.0	24.2
Aniline	49.5	9.0	54.5

From the results for the hydrocarbon portion, α_S can be calculated by eq. (3):

$$\alpha_S = (60.0/31.0)/(21.4/24.2) = 2.19$$

The data obtained for the five samples served to establish the relative volatility–composition curve. The x–y diagram shown in Figure 3 was calculated by means of eq. (3) arranged for a binary system in the form:

$$y = \frac{\alpha_S x}{1 + (\alpha_S - 1)x} \tag{18}$$

where y and x are the mole fractions of the more volatile component in vapor and liquid, and α_S is the relative volatility of the more volatile hydrocarbon with respect to the other hydrocarbon in the presence of the solvent, aniline. Calculation of the equilibrium vapor compositions for various liquid compositions defines the x–y curve. (Obviously the experimental points expressed on a binary basis as mole fractions will also define the curve.) For $x = 0.20$ and using $\alpha_S = 2.19$, as read from the relative volatility–composition curve just established:

$$y = \frac{(2.19)(0.20)}{1 + (1.19)(0.20)} = 0.353$$

Since the analyses were obtained on a ternary basis, the solvent concentration in the liquid phase at equilibrium is known as well as the solvent concentration in the vapor phase. This is important for design purposes as well as for the operation of a laboratory column employing extractive distillation. Sets of five samples each were made up at solvent concentrations of 40, 60, 70, and 75 mole-% aniline in each charge. The experimental procedure was then repeated.

TABLE II
n-Heptane–Methylcyclohexane Relative Volatility in Presence of Various Solvents

Solvent	Mole-% in liquid phase	*T*, °C. (av.)	Av. rel. volatility, α_S	Improvement factor, α_S/α	Ref.
Aniline	92	139	1.52	1.42	26
	78	121	1.40	1.31	26
	70	110	1.27	1.19	27
	58	113	1.26	1.18	26
Furfural	79	—	1.35	1.26	26
Phenol	81	—	1.31	1.24	26
Nitrobenzene	82	—	1.31	1.24	26
Dichlorodiethyl ether	81	—	1.28	1.20	26
Aminocyclohexane	76	—	1.16	1.08	26
Pyridine	70	—	1.4	1.31	27
Ethanol	70	—	1.3	1.21	27
n-Butanol	70	—	1.3	1.21	27
tert-Butanol	70	—	1.25	1.17	27
Acetic acid	70	—	1.27	1.19	27
None	—	—	1.07	1.00	27

Very few data on the vapor–liquid equilibria of binary mixtures in the presence of a solvent were published prior to 1945. Data for some of the systems investigated are summarized in Tables II–VI. When the data are known, both the liquid and the vapor compositions on a solvent-free basis are given, as well as modified relative volatilities, α_S, and enrichment ratio, i.e., the ratio $\alpha_S:\alpha$ which indicates the effectiveness of the solvent. It should be remembered that α_S depends on the solvent concentration. Studies of the *n*-octane–ethyl cyclohexane–butyl cellosolve and the *n*-octane–ethyl cyclohexane–2-propanol systems have been carried out by Prabhu and Van Winkle,[31] and for ethylbenzene–ethylcyclohexane–xylene glycol by Qozati and Van Winkle.[32] Updike, Langdon, and Keyes have examined the effects of a large number of extractive distillation solvents on the toluene–methylcyclohexane and benzene–cyclohexane systems.[28]

TABLE III
Methylcyclohexane–Toluene Relative Volatility in Presence of Various Solvents

Solvent	Mole-% in charge	T, °C. (av.)	Av. rel. volatility, α_S	Improvement factor, α_S/α	Ref.
Acetic acid	67.9	95	2.2	1.6	28
	70[a]	—	2.1	1.6	27
Methanol	67.3	61	1.72	1.3	28
Ethanol	66.9	70	1.76	1.3	28
Ethanol	70[a]	—	1.9	1.4	27
n-Propanol	67.5	87	1.8	1.3	28
Isopropanol	62.5	73	1.75	1.3	28
n-Butanol	70[a]	—	1.55	1.1	27
tert-Butanol	70[a]	—	1.6	1.2	27
Acetone	36.1	70	2.1	1.6	28
	49.4	66	2.4	1.8	28
	58.3	62	3.15	2.3	28
	61.0	62	2.9	2.1	28
	65.6	61	2.6	1.9	28
	68.1	59	3.3	2.4	28
Methyl ethyl ketone	66.2	80	2.3	1.7	28
Piperidine	65.8	97	1.7	1.3	28
Pyridine	33	102	1.9	1.4	28
	49	101	2.2	1.6	28
	57.5	101	2.3	1.7	28
	70[a]	—	2.4	1.8	27
	66.7	100	2.5	1.9	28
Aniline	32.9	115	2.05	1.5	28
	50.0	115	2.4	1.8	28
	59.8	120	2.6	1.9	28
	60.2	125	2.7	2.0	28
	65.8	121	2.6	1.9	28
	43.2[a]	113.6	1.96	1.45	27
	54.4[a]	117.5	2.19	1.62	27
	66.7[a]	123.0	2.37	1.76	27
	77.7[a]	132.5	2.54	1.88	27
	83.4[a]	139.8	2.59	1.92	27
Nitromethane	32.4	88	2.3	1.71	28
	58.8	87	4.24	3.14	28
Acetonitrile	68.3	73	3.0	3	28
Phenol	34.7	110	2.0	1.5	28
	52.1	113	2.3	1.7	28
	59.8	118	2.2	1.6	28
	65.8	119	2.7	2.0	28
Triethyl borate	65.5	112	1.24	0.9	28
Diethylene glycol mono-ethyl ether	70[a]	—	2.0	1.5	27

TABLE III (*continued*)

Solvent	Mole-% in charge	T, °C. (av.)	Av. rel. volatility, α_S	Improvement factor, α_S/α	Ref.
Diethylene glycol monobutyl ether	70[a]	—	1.3	1.0	27
Ethyl acetate	70[a]	—	1.8	1.3	27
Ethylene glycol monomethyl ether	70[a]	—	2.2	1.6	27
Ethylene glycol monoethyl ether	70[a]	—	1.9	1.4	27
Ethylene glycol monobutyl ether	70[a]	—	1.4	1.1	27
None	—	—	1.1–1.6 (av. 1.35)	1.0	27

[a] Mole-% aniline in liquid phase.

TABLE IV
Cyclohexane–Benzene Relative Volatility in Presence of Various Solvents[28]

Solvent	Mole-% in charge	T, °C.	Relative volatility, α_S	Improvement factor, α_S/α
Acetic acid	69.0	84	1.75	1.78
Methanol	67.3	53	1.58	1.61
Ethanol	67.3	65	1.36	1.38
n-Propanol	70.5	79	1.26	1.28
Isopropanol	67.9	70	1.22	1.24
Dioxane	67.4	86	1.75	1.78
Chlorex (dichlorodiethyl ether)	67.5	105	2.31	2.36
Methyl Cellosolve	66.7	85	1.84	1.61
Carbitol	66.8	87	1.99	2.03
Acetone	66.3	55	2.03	2.07
Methyl ethyl ketone	65.1	72	1.78	1.81
Diacetone	67.3	89	1.82	1.85
Pyridine	66.9	93	1.83	1.86
Aniline	66.8	93	2.11	2.16
Nitromethane	67.8	74	3.00	3.06
Nitrobenzene	68.2	102	2.25	2.30
Acetonitrile	67.3	65	2.85	2.92
Furfural	67.1	79	3.10	3.16
Phenol	66.8	92	2.01	2.05

TABLE V
Nontoluene–Toluene[a] Volatility Ratios in Presence of Various Solvents

Solvent	B.p., °C.	Wt.-% solvent[b]	Volatility ratio, α_S	Improvement factor, α_S/α	Ref.
Antimony trichloride	277	50	3.20	2.4	29
Sulfolane	287	75	5.60	4.2	29
Dimethylsulfolane	281	75	3.23	2.4	29
	281	50	2.75	2.1	29
Dimethylsulfolane–cumene (85–15, wt.-%)	202	50	2.41	1.8	29
Furfural	163	50	2.30	1.7	30
Acetonyl acetone	188	50	2.20	1.7	30
Nitrobenzene	211	50	2.16	1.6	30
Nitrotoluene	222	50	2.16	1.6	30
Phenol	182	75	2.78	2.1	29
Phenol	182	50	2.10	1.6	30
Aniline	183	75	2.75	2.1	29
	183	70	2.08	1.6	30
Chlorex (dichlorodiethyl ether)	178	50	2.09	1.6	30
Phenyl cellosolve	240	50	2.01	1.5	30
Phenol–cresol (60–40)	192	50	1.98	1.5	30
(40–60)	195	50	1.95	1.5	30
Acetophenone	202	50	1.95	1.5	30
1-Methoxy-2-hydroxy-3-phenoxypropane	278	50	1.92	1.5	30
Ethyl carbitol	202	50	1.85	1.4	30
m- or *p*-Cresol	202	50	1.85	1.4	30
1-Ethoxy-2,3-dihydroxy-propane	222	50	1.80	1.4	30
1-Isopropoxy-2,3-dihydroxypropane	226	50	1.70	1.3	30
Diacetone alcohol	190	50	1.64	1.2	30
1-Methoxy-2,3-dihydroxy-propane (2 phases)	220	50	1.46	1.1	30
None	—	—	1.32	1.0	29

[a] Nontoluene fraction was a dearomatized straight-run petroleum fraction boiling between 210 and 235°F. (true boiling point 5 and 95% points, respectively).

[b] Weight-% solvent in charge to equilibrium still. The hydrocarbon mixture was a 50–50 mixture of aromatic and nonaromatic hydrocarbons.

Another technique for determining vapor–liquid equilibrium data has been proposed by Ramalho et al.[34] In this technique a complete equilibrium curve is determined in a single experiment. Starting with a known composition, a simple distillation is performed with continuous determi-

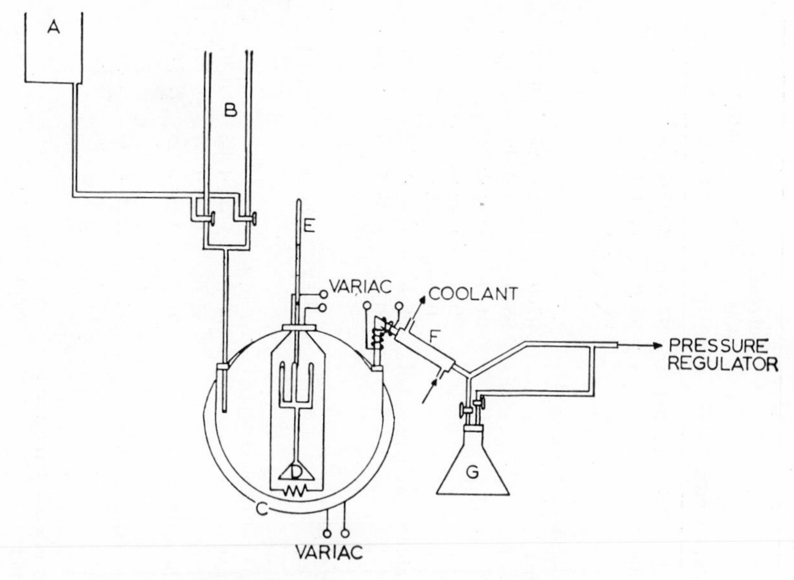

Fig. 7. Ramulho vapor–liquid equilibrium.

nation of the composition of either the liquid or the vapor and the composition of the other stream is determined by material balance. Two techniques are used, either direct analysis or boiling point measurement. The latter depends upon the construction of a boiling point composition curve prior to determination of the vapor–liquid equilibrium curve.

The experimental apparatus is shown in Figure 7 and consists of a 3-liter round bottom flask with the necks removed to reduce fractionation. It is heated with an electric mantle at the bottom and heating tape at the top, using variable transformers to control the heating elements. The heating tape or coil is also placed around the vapor outlet tube to prevent condensation. Most of the heat is put into an internal heater located within the funnel of the Cottrell pump. The vapor formed rises and carries liquid in jets onto the thermometric element. The vapor line is kept as short as possible, and a short 2 to 3-in. long stainless steel condenser was used. The condensate is removed in sample bottle *G* connected to the pressure control system. The thermometric element may be a Beckman thermometer or a platinum resistance thermometer or some other accurate temperature measuring device. The self-zeroing burettes, *b*, are used for continuous feed addition.

To use the boiling point technique, the horizontal condenser is replaced by a vertical reflux condenser which is also connected to a Cartesian manostat pressure regulating system. A weighed charge of the most volatile

TABLE VI

Relative Volatilities of Oxygenated Compounds in Presence of Water[33]

Components, A/B	Solvent, mole-% H_2O	Relative volatility, A/B Exptl.	Relative volatility, A/B Normal[a]	Components, A/B	Solvent, mole-% H_2O	Relative volatility, A/B Exptl.	Relative volatility, A/B Normal[a]
Methanol–ethyl alcohol	95.6	0.62–0.66	1.68	Isobutyl alcohol–*n*-propyl alcohol	97.3	2.07–1.71	0.67
	83.7	0.73–0.79			95.0	1.74–1.53	
	75.9	0.94–0.91			91.0	1.27–1.15	
	66.1	1.00–1.08					
				sec-Butyl alcohol–*n*-propyl alcohol	97.0	1.74–1.67	0.91[b]
Isopropyl alcohol–ethyl alcohol	96.5	1.64–1.54	0.865		95.0	1.86–1.46	
	92.0	1.53–1.44			91.0	1.52–1.34	
	83.8	1.42–1.39			90.0	1.56–1.29	
	60.6	1.09–1.03			0.0	0.91	
n-Propyl alcohol–ethyl alcohol	95.2	1.31–1.22	0.455	1-Pentanol–*n*-propyl alcohol	96.6	1.37–1.32	0.218
	91.6	1.14–1.04			96.0	1.38–1.25	
	77.0	0.83–0.68					
	66.5	0.72					
	52.2	0.51		Isopropyl alcohol–*n*-butyl alcohol	97.5	1.08–1.06	3.61
	11.5	0.47					
sec-Butyl alcohol–ethyl alcohol	95.7	2.06–2.03	0.415	*tert*-Butyl alcohol–isopropyl alcohol	95.8	1.55–1.65	0.97
	85.6	1.32–0.96			85.6	1.28–1.34	
	76.0	0.91–0.73		Acetone–methanol	91.5	2.93–3.59	7.0–1.0[b]
	65.8	0.82–0.65					
				Acetone–ethyl alcohol	95.0	3.23–2.36	2.02
Isobutyl alcohol–ethyl alcohol	95.6	2.17–1.89	0.297		81.5	3.41–3.18	
	92.7	1.83–1.36					
	89.6	1.44–0.98					
	85.7	1.15–0.78		Methyl ethyl ketone–ethyl alcohol	92.0	3.50	0.954
	75.6	0.78–0.60					
	65.6	0.62–0.48		Methyl *n*-propyl ketone–ethyl alcohol	95.0	6.89–5.03	0.48

tert-Butyl alcohol–ethyl alcohol	95.1	2.56–2.48	0.825
n-Butyl alcohol–ethyl alcohol	97.9	1.98–1.79	0.20
	96.2	1.64–1.37	
	93.4	1.30–0.90	
	86.2	0.75–0.57	
	75.9	0.48–0.41	
	66.0	0.36–0.31	
1-Pentanol–ethyl alcohol	95.7	1.91–1.58	0.088
	91.0	1.04–0.74	
	66.9	0.32–0.24	
2-Pentanol–ethyl alcohol	95.9	2.75–2.21	0.18
	85.8	1.10–0.75	
	76.0	0.60–0.51	
	65.8	0.53–0.42	
Isopropyl alcohol–*n*-propyl alcohol	91.0	1.45–1.32	1.76
n-Butyl alcohol–*n*-propyl alcohol	97.3	1.15–1.09	0.416[b]
	91.0	0.81–0.66	0.455
	70.2	0.56	
	59.5	0.49	
	0.0	0.416–0.453[b]	

Methyl isobutyl ketone–ethyl alcohol	65.7	1.29–0.70	0.32
Acetone–isopropyl alcohol	95.7	1.66–1.60	3.4–1.6[b]
Methyl ethyl ketone–isopropyl alcohol	92.0	2.30–2.54	1.09
Methyl ethyl ketone–*tert*-butyl alcohol	91.0	1.71–1.76	1.09
n-Butyraldehyde–methanol	96.0	8.5	0.70
n-Butyraldehyde–ethyl alcohol	96.0	5.1	1.1
Isobutyraldehyde–ethyl alcohol	96.0	4.5 –3.4	1.56
n-Valeraldehyde–ethyl alcohol	85.7	5.9 –4.8	0.47
	75.9	3.8 –2.8	
	65.7	2.48–2.16	
Propionaldehyde–acetone	96.0	2.03–3.07	1.34
Isopropyl ether–ethyl alcohol	90.0	6.0 –5.7	0.96
Isopropyl ether–isopropyl alcohol	90.0	4.9	1.53

[a] Calculated from vapor pressure data at boiling point of reference alcohol, assuming ideal solutions.

[b] Determined experimentally by Othmer still in this laboratory.

component is introduced into the still, and a boiling point curve determined by successively adding weighed quantities of the least volatile component. The procedure is continued until the final still composition is essentially pure high boiling component. This may require occasional withdrawal of part of the still contents.

The equilibrium data are determined in a second stage. After the desired amount of least volatile component is added, distillation is begun. Initial weights range from 1000–3000 g. with vapor samples varying from 10–30 g. The use of an internal heating coil appears to be the most satisfactory method for avoiding small temperature fluctuations due to superheating and bumping.

This method is somewhat limited by the need for precise temperature determination and distillate analysis is more widely applicable than boiling point measurement, particularly in the case of multicomponent systems. In this technique a weighed quantity of the more volatile component is placed in the still and the system is adjusted to the operating pressure. Heat is supplied to the still, and the solution is agitated with a magnetic stirrer. When the first drop of condensate appears in the receiver, addition of the less volatile component is begun. The feed is metered through the 250 ml. self-zeroing burettes which are used alternately in order to permit taking readings while the burettes are being refilled without interruption of feed addition. When the proper amount of distillate has been collected, the feed is stopped from the first burette and started from the second. The stopcocks on the distillate and pressure equalizing lines are closed, the receiver removed, and the temperature recorded. An empty receiver is inserted and the stopcocks opened. The weight of the distillate and volume of feed are determined and recorded. The procedure is continued until the temperature approaches the boiling point of the less volatile component. Vapor–liquid compositions are then determined by analysis of the distillate samples.

In the boiling point techniques, the first few points are discarded in order to be assured of equilibrium operation. From the first stage of the experiment, a graph of liquid composition versus resistance of a platinum resistance thermometer is obtained. The weight of the residue is plotted against the reading on the platinum resistance thermometer from the second phase of the run, and from these two curves it is possible to plot the desired curve of residue versus liquid composition. The slopes obtained by numerical differentiation give the values for vapor concentration. The technique appears to be simple and quite rapid. It has yielded good agreement with the literature for the systems methanol–water, acetone–methanol, and normal propyl alcohol–water. The technique has been applied to the ternary system acetone–methanol–water with good results.[35]

Once a series of measurements have been made, it is desirable to check the data for thermodynamic consistency. As pointed out in Chapter I, various investigators have proposed equations which are useful for expressing the relationship between vapor pressure and concentrate. Among the most useful relationships are the Van Laar equations

$$\log \gamma_1 = \frac{A}{\left(1 + \frac{A}{B}\frac{X_1}{X_2}\right)^2} \tag{19}$$

$$\log \gamma_2 = \frac{B}{\left(1 + \frac{B}{A}\frac{X_2}{X_1}\right)^2} \tag{20}$$

where A and B are empirical constants. Another set of equations developed by Margules can be written

$$\log \gamma_1 = X_2^2[A + 2X_1(\mathrm{B} - \mathrm{A})] \tag{21}$$

$$\log \gamma_2 = X_1^2[B + 2X_2(\mathrm{A} - \mathrm{B})] \tag{22}$$

Another commonly used set of correlating equations are the Scatchard–Hamer equations

$$\log \gamma_1 = Z_2^2\left[A + 2Z_1\left(B\frac{\bar{V}_1}{\bar{V}_2} - \mathrm{A}\right)\right] \tag{23}$$

$$\log \gamma_2 = Z_1^2\left[B + 2Z_2\left(A\frac{\bar{V}_2}{\bar{V}_1} - \mathrm{B}\right)\right] \tag{24}$$

The $\bar{V}$'s in these equations represent the molar volumes of the pure components and the Z's are obtained from

$$Z_1 = \frac{\bar{V}_1X_1}{\bar{V}X_1 + \bar{V}_2X_2} \tag{25}$$

$$Z_2 = \frac{\bar{V}_2X_2}{\bar{V}_1X_1 + V_2X_2} \tag{26}$$

In order to correlate vapor–liquid equilibrium data, the constants for either the Van Laar, Margules, or Scatchard–Hamer equations are determined from the data, and equilibrium ratios are calculated and compared with the observed values. The equation which represents the observed data best is selected as a final correlation. Obtaining a good fit by this procedure is a necessary but not sufficient condition for thermodynamic consistency. An independent check of the correlation may be made by the procedure of Rose et al.[36] where the pressures predicted by the final correlation are compared with the observed pressures. If the pressures check well, it is likely that the data are good and that the correlation is satisfactory. Techniques for data correlation and the estimation of multicomponent phase equilibria have been obtained by Black et al.[37]

When a good fit cannot be obtained by the use of these equations, the data are not necessarily incorrect, since the vapor may not conform to the perfect gas laws, and these isothermal equations may not apply to the system. Both assumptions are inherent in the derivation of these semi-empirical equations. A general system for testing the consistency of data which can be used either isobaric or isothermal data has been developed by Tao.[38]

As pointed out earlier, increasing the number of components in the solution increases the complexity of the equations. The equations are complicated even for ternary systems, and a substantial amount of data is necessary to establish the relationships in any nonideal system containing three or more components. More general equations have been developed, including ternary forms of the Margules, Van Laar, and Scatchard–Hamer equations. These equations may be obtained by reference to Halla et al.[39]

C. ESTIMATION OF EFFECTIVENESS OF SOLVENT

If the necessary data on the respective vapor–liquid equilibria are not known and lack of time or experimental equipment do not permit an investigation of these equilibria, an estimate of the potential applicability of a solvent is desirable. Several methods for such an estimate are available.

Wilson and Deal[40] have proposed a technique for estimating activity coefficients from molecular structure. They assume that the activity coefficient (v_j) is the sum of two contributions, one associated with differences in molecular size ($v_j{}^S$) and the other with the interactions of the structural "groups" ($v_j{}^G$). For any molecular solute in any solution

$$\log \gamma_j{}^S = \log \frac{n_j}{\sum_{i=1}^{n} x_i n_i} + 0.4343 \left[1 - \frac{n_j}{\sum_{i=1}^{n} x_i n_i} \right] \tag{27}$$

where n_i equals the number of atoms (other than hydrogen) in molecular component i and x_i equals the molecular mole fraction of component i.

The contribution from the interactions of the molecular "groups" is assumed to be the sum of the individual contributions of each solute "group" in the solution less the sum of the individual contributions in the conventional standard state environment. For solute j containing groups K:

$$\log \gamma_j{}^G = \sum \nu_{Kj}(\log \Gamma_K - \log \Gamma_K{}^*) \tag{28}$$

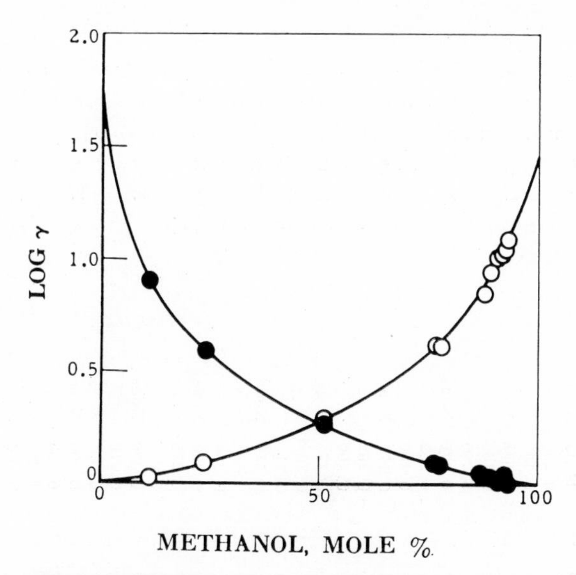

Fig. 8. Activity coefficient for methanol in *n*-hexane.

where ν_{Kj} equals the number of groups of type K in solute component j. Γ_K equals the activity coefficient of group K in the solution environment referred as an arbitrary standard state and Γ_K^* equals the activity coefficient of group K in the standard state environment. This activity coefficient is referred to the same state as Γ_K. Starting with the data for the activity coefficients in methanol-*n*-hexane at 45°C., shown in Figure 8[41] where $\nu_{Kj} = 1$, the hydroxyl group, $n_j = 2$, and $n_i = 6$, one can calculate a set of log Γ_K–log Γ_K^* points for the methylene group and for the hydroxyl groups. A set of Γ_K curves for each group can be constructed and extrapolated over the entire range of group concentrations. These are normalized so that $\Gamma_K = 1$ when the mole fraction of the group equals 1. These are plotted in Figure 9.

With these data, it is possible to estimate the activity coefficient for any system containing hydroxyl and methylene groups only (methyl is considered equivalent to methylene). Extrapolation can be carried over a fairly wide range by this technique. Since in Figure 9 there is a point for 100% hydroxyl group concentration, one can estimate activity coefficients of alcohols and paraffins in water. If it is assumed that one water molecule is equivalent to 1.5 hydroxyl groups, then the activity coefficients of water in alcohols or in paraffins can be estimated. The accuracy of the technique is fair, with agreement between calculated and measured activity coefficients generally being within 10% of log Γ_K. The method has been extended to nitrile groups, ester groups, and ether groups. It has also been

TABLE VII

Correlation Constants for Activity Coefficients (Infinite Dilution of Various Combinations of Homologous Series of Solutes and Solvents[a])

Solute Series	Solvent Series	°C.	*A* Constant	*B* Term	*B* Constant	*C* Term	*C* Constant	*D* Term	*D* Constant	*F* Term	*F* Constant
n-Acids	Water	25	−1.00	Bn_1	0.622	$C(1/n_1)$	0.490	None		None	
		50	−0.80	Bn_1	0.590		0.290				
		100	−0.620	Bn_1	+0.517		0.140				
n-Primary alcohols	Water	25	−0.995	Bn_1	0.622	$C(1/n_1)$	0.558	None		None	
		60	−0.755	Bn_1	0.583		0.460				
		100	−0.420	Bn_1	0.517		0.230				
n-*sec*-Alcohols	Water	25	−1.220	Bn_1	0.622	$C[1/n_1' + 1/n_1'']$	0.170	None		None	
		60	−1.023	Bn_1	0.583		0.252				
		100	−0.870	Bn_1	0.517		0.400				
n-*tert*-Alcohols	Water	25	−1.740	Bn_1	0.622	$C\begin{bmatrix}1/n_1' + \\ 1/n_1'' + \\ 1/n_1''\end{bmatrix}$	0.170	None		None	
		60	−1.477	Bn_1	0.583		0.252				
		100	−1.291	Bn_1	0.517		0.400				
Alcohols, general	Water	25	−0.525	Bn_1	0.622	$C\begin{bmatrix}(1/n_1' - 1) + \\ (1/n_1'' - 1) + \\ (1/n_1''' - 1)\end{bmatrix}$	0.475	None		None	
		60	−0.33	Bn_1	0.583		0.39				
		100	−0.15	Bn_1	0.517		0.34				
n-Allyl alcohols	Water	25	−1.180	Bn_1	0.622	$C(1/n_1)$	0.558	None		None	
		60	−0.929	Bn_1	0.583		0.460				
		100	−0.650	Bn_1	0.517		0.230				
n-Aldehydes	Water	25	−0.780	Bn_1	0.622	$C(1/n_1)$	0.320	None		None	
		60	−0.400	Bn_1	0.583		0.210				
		100	−0.03	Bn_1	0.517		0.0				
n-Alkene aldehydes	Water	25	−0.720	Bn_1	0.622	$C(1/n_1)$	0.320	None		None	
		60	−0.540	Bn_1	0.583		0.210				
		100	−0.298	Bn_1	0.517		0.0				
n-Ketones	Water	25	−1.475	Bn_1	0.622		0.500	None		None	
		60	−1.040	Bn_1	0.583	$C[1/n_1' + 1/n_1'']$	0.330				
		100	−0.621	Bn_1	0.517		0.200				
n-Acetals	Water	25	−2.556	Bn_1	0.622	$C\begin{bmatrix}1/n_1' + \\ 1/n'' + \\ 2/n_1'''\end{bmatrix}$	0.486	None		None	
		60	−2.184	Bn_1	0.583		0.451				
		100	−1.780	Bn_1	0.517		0.426				
n-Ethers	Water	20	−0.770	Bn_1	0.640	$C[1/n_1' + 1/n_1'']$	0.195	None		None	
n-Nitriles	Water	25	−0.587	Bn_1	0.622	$C(1/n_1)$	0.760	None		None	
		60	−0.368	Bn_1	0.583		0.143				
		100	−0.095	Bn_1	0.517		0.00				

n-Alkene nitriles	Water	25	−0.520	Bn_1	0.622	$C(1/n_1)$	0.760	None		None	
		60	−0.323	Bn_1	0.583		0.413				
		100	−0.074	Bn_1	0.517		0.00				
n-Esters	Water	20	−0.930	Bn_1	0.640	$C(1/n_1' + 1/n_1'')$	0.260	None		None	
n-Formates	Water	20	−0.585	Bn_1	0.640	$C(1/n_1)$	0.260	None		None	
n-Monoalkyl chlorides	Water	20	1.265	Bn_1	0.640	$C(1/n_1)$	0.073	None		None	
n-Paraffins	Water	16	0.688	Bn_1	0.642	None		None		None	
n-Alkyl benzenes	Water	25	3.554	Bn_1	0.622	$C(1/n_1 - 4)]$	−0.466	None		None	
n-Alcohols	Paraffins	25	1.960	None		$C\left[\begin{matrix}(1/n' - 1) + \\ (1/n'' - 1) + \\ (1/n''' - 1) + \end{matrix}\right]$	0.475	$D(n_1 - n_2)^2$	−0.00049	None	
		60	1.460	None			0.390		−0.00057		
		100	1.070	None			0.340		−0.00061		
n-Ketones	Paraffins	25	0.0877	None			0.757		−0.00049	None	
		60	0.016	None		$C[1/n_1' + 1/n_1'']$	0.680	$D(n_1 - n_2)^2$	−0.00057		
		100	−0.067	None			0.605		−0.00061		
Water	n-Alcohols	25	0.760	None		None		None		$F(1/n_2)$	−0.630
		60	0.680								−0.440
		100	0.617								−0.280
	sec-Alcohols	80	1.208	None		None		None		$F(1/n_2' + 1/n_2'')$	−0.690
	n-Ketones	25	1.857							$F(1/n_2' + 1/n_2'')$	−1.019
		60	1.493	None		None		None			−0.73
		100	1.231								−0.557
Ketones	n-Alcohols	25	−0.088	$B(n_1/n_2)$	0.176		0.50		−0.00049	$F(1/n_2)$	−0.630
		60	−0.035	$B(n_1/n_2)$	0.138	$C[1/n_1' + 1/n_1'']$	0.33	$D(n_1 - n_2)^2$	−0.00057		−0.440
		100	−0.035	$B(n_1/n_2)$	0.112		0.20		−0.00061		−0.280
Aldehydes	n-Alcohols	25	−0.701	$B(n_1/n_2)$	0.176		0.320		−0.00049	$F(1/n_2)$	−0.630
		60	−0.239	$B(n_1/n_2)$	0.138	$C(1/n_1)$	0.210		−0.00057		−0.440
Esters	n-Alcohols	25	0.212	$B(n_1/n_2)$	0.176		0.260		−0.00049	$F(1/n_2)$	−0.630
		60	0.055	$B(n_1/n_2)$	0.138	$C[1/n_1' + 1/n_1'']$	0.240	$D(n_1 - n_2)^2$	−0.00057		−0.440
		100	0.0	$B(n_1/n_2)$	0.112		0.220		−0.00061		−0.280
Acetals	n-Alcohols	60	−1.10	$B(n_1/n_2)$	0.138	$C(1/n_1' + 1/n_1'' + 2/n_1''')$	0.451		−0.00057		−0.440
Paraffins	Ketones	25	None	$B(n_1/n_2)$	0.1821	None			−0.00049	$F(1/n_2' + 1/n_2'')$	0.402
		60		$B(n_1/n_2)$	0.1145			$D(n_1 - n_2)^2$	−0.00057		0.402
		90		$B(n_1/n_2)$	0.0746				−0.00061		0.401

[a] General expression, $\log \gamma^o = A_{1,2} + B_2(n_1/n_2) + C_1(1/n_1) + D(n_1 - n_2)^2 + F_2(1/n_2)$.

TABLE VIII

Correlation[a] Constants for Activity Coefficients (Various Homologous Series of Hydrocarbons in Specific Solvents)

Temp., °C.	Solute series	Solute dependent C's $\left(\text{Term} = \frac{C}{n_p + 2}\right)$	Solvents							
			Heptane	Methyl ethyl ketone	Furfural	Phenol	Ethyl alcohol	Triethylene glycol	Diethylene glycol	Ethylene glycol
			Solvent-dependent B's (Term $= B_p n_p$)							
25			0.0	0.0455	0.0937	0.0625	0.088	—	0.191	(0.275)
50			0.0	0.033	0.0878	0.0590	0.073	0.161	0.179	0.249
70			0.0	0.025	0.0810	0.0586	0.065	—	0.173	0.236
90			0.0	0.019	0.0686	0.0581	0.059	0.134	0.158	0.226
			Solute–solvent dependent K's (Term $= K$)							
25	Paraffins	0.0	0.0	0.335	0.916	0.870	0.580	—	0.875	—
50		0.0	0.0	0.332	0.756	0.755	0.570	0.72	0.815	1.208
70		0.0	0.0	0.331	0.737	0.690	0.590	—	0.725	1.154
90		0.0	0.0	0.330	0.771	0.620	0.610	0.68	0.72	1.089
25	Alkyl cyclohexanes	−0.260	0.18	0.70	1.26	1.20	1.06	—	1.675	—
50		−0.220	—	0.650	1.120	1.040	1.01	1.46	1.61	2.36
70		−0.195	0.131	0.581	1.020	0.935	0.972	—	1.550	2.22
90		−0.180	0.09	0.480	0.930	0.843	0.925	1.25	1.505	2.08

25	Alkyl benzenes	−0.466	0.328	0.277	0.67	0.694	1.011	—	1.08	—
50		−0.390	0.243	—	0.55	0.580	0.938	0.80	1.00	1.595
70		−0.362	0.225	0.240	0.45	0.500	0.900	—	0.96	1.51
90		−0.350	0.202	0.239	0.44	0.420	0.862	0.74	0.935	1.43
25	Alkyl naphthalenes	−0.10	0.53	0.169	0.46	0.595	1.06	—	1.00	—
50		−0.14	0.53	0.141	0.40	0.54	1.03	0.75	1.00	1.92
70		−0.173	0.53	0.215	0.39	0.497	1.02	—	0.991	1.82
90		−0.204	0.53	0.232	—	0.445	—	0.83	1.01	1.765
25	Alkyl tetralins	+0.28	0.244	0.179	0.652	0.378	—	—	1.43	—
50		+0.24	—	—	0.528	0.364	—	1.00	1.38	—
70		+0.21	0.220	0.217	0.447	0.371	—	—	1.33	—
90		+0.19	—	—	0.373	0.348	—	0.893	1.28	—
25	Alkyl decalins	−0.43	—	0.871	1.54	1.411	—	—	2.46	—
50		−0.368	—	—	1.367	1.285	—	1.906	2.25	—
70		−0.355	0.356	0.80	1.253	1.161	—	—	2.07	—
90		−0.320	—	—	1.166	1.078	—	1.68	2.06	—

[a] Expression, $\log \gamma^\circ = K + B_p n_p + \dfrac{C}{n_p + 2} + D(n_1 - n_2)^2$ where for all systems: $D = -49 \times 10^{-5}$, -55×10^{-5}, -58×10^{-5}, and -61×10^{-5}, where t is 25, 50, 70, and 90°C., respectively.

TABLE IX

Correlation[a] Constants for Activity Coefficients [Unalkylated Cyclic (Aromatic and/or naphthenic) Hydrocarbons in Specific Solvents]

Temp., °C.	Solutes	Solute dependent C's $\left[\text{Term} = Cr\left(\frac{1}{r}\right)\right]$ Condensed	Tandem	Solvents Heptane	Methyl ethyl ketone	Furfural	Phenol	Ethyl alcohol	Triethylene glycol	Diethylene glycol	Ethylene glycol
				Solvent-dependent B's (B_a)[b]							
25				0.2105	0.1435	0.1152	0.1421	0.2125	0.181	0.2022	0.275
70				0.1668	0.1142	0.0836	0.1054	0.1575	0.129	0.1472	0.2195
130				0.1212	0.0875	0.0531	0.0734	0.1035	0.0767	0.0996	0.1492
				Solvent-dependent B's(B_n)[b]							
25				0.1874	0.2079	0.2178	0.2406	0.2425	0.3124	0.3180	0.4147
70				0.1478	0.1754	0.1675	0.1810	0.1753	0.2406	0.2545	0.3516
130				0.1051	0.1427	0.1185	0.1480	0.1169	0.1569	0.1919	0.2772
				Solute–Solvent dependent K's (Term = K)							
25	Cyclics[c]	1.176	1.845	−1.072	−0.7305	−0.230	−0.383	−0.485	−0.406	−0.377	−0.154
70		0.846	1.362	−0.886	−0.625	−0.080	−0.226	−0.212	−0.186	−0.0775	−0.0174
130		0.544	0.846	−0.6305	−0.504	+0.020	−0.197	+0.47	+0.095	+0.181	+0.229

[a] Expression, $\log \gamma^\circ = K + B_a n_a + B_n n_n + Cr(1/r - 1)$.
[b] Term $= B_a n_a + B_p n_p$.
[c] Naphthenes, aromatics, naphthen-aromatics.

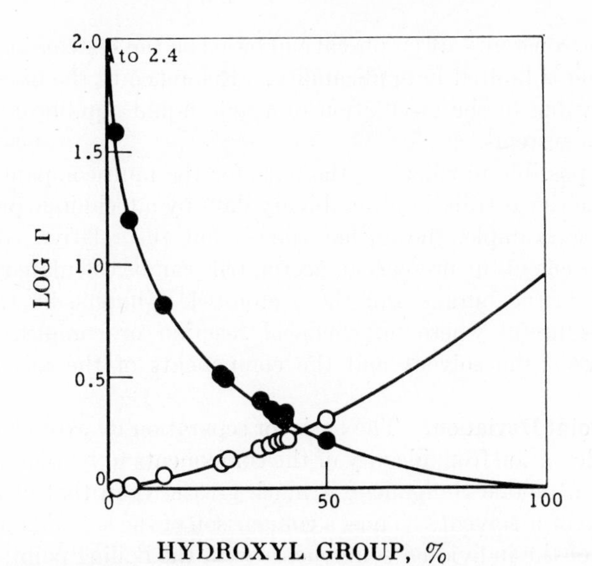

Fig. 9. Activity coefficients for hydroxyl—● and methylene—o groups.

used in systems containing more than two components. It is a useful technique for estimating activity coefficients for limited experimental data.

Another technique for relating activity coefficients to molecular structure has been developed by Pierotti and his co-workers.[42] The activity coefficient at infinite dilution can be estimated by these correlations, and in conjunction with the vapor pressures of the components and the use of the Van Laar or similar equations, can be used to determine the volatilities of the components throughout the concentration range. In view of the large number of systems covered and the utility of this technique for obtaining a first approximation to the activity coefficient of many systems, the correlation constants are reproduced in Tables VII–IX.

In a subsequent paper, Deal et al.[43] have shown that instead of using the five-solvent parameters required in the Pierotti correlation, it is possible in many cases to use only three. It seems that the three-solvent parameter system, when used with some additional rules defined by the authors, is useful for obtaining screening estimates of limiting activity coefficient ratios and limiting activity coefficients in polar solvent–hydrocarbon solute systems. The estimates, however, can be off as much as 20% in some cases, and the original five-parameter equations are somewhat more accurate.

A method which does not depend, as these do, on the assumption of isothermal conditions has been proposed by Tamura and Nagata.[44] As yet, the method has been demonstrated only for hydrocarbon systems. Since several of the constants are empirical and based on the systems investigated, the technique is limited in applicability. Reference to the original paper may be of value in the calculation of vapor–liquid equilibrium data for hydrocarbon systems.

It is also possible to calculate the data for the multicomponent system used in extractive distillation from binary data by a technique proposed by Black.[45] For example, the author shows that the relative volatility of butane/1-butene in the presence of acetonitrile can be calculated from data on the acetonitrile–butane and the acetonitrile–1-butene binaries. This technique is useful where no chemical reaction or complex formation occurs between the solvent and the components of the mixture to be separated.

Boiling-Point Deviation. The basis for separation by extractive distillation is the deviation from ideality of the components to be separated when the deviation of one component is much greater than that of another in the presence of a solvent. Thus, a comparison of the actual boiling points of solutions of the individual components with the boiling points predicted for ideal solutions will give a rough index of the separating efficacy of the solvent. This test can be carried out by mixing equal volumes of one component and of the solvent and determining the boiling point of the mixture. This is repeated with the next component. The difference in the observed boiling points is noted. The theoretical boiling point of each mixture is calculated from its composition and the boiling points of the pure compounds, assuming a linear variation of boiling point with composition. The difference between the calculated boiling points is compared with the experimentally determined difference. If the latter is appreciably greater than the calculated value, the solvent should give improved separation when used in extractive distillation. The exact magnitude of the improvement, however, requires experimental verification in an equilibrium still.

Another method using boiling-point determinations has been applied to the separation of diolefin, olefin, and paraffin hydrocarbons with similar boiling points and, in particular, to solutions of butadiene, butenes, and butanes.[46] The test consists of determining the boiling points of mixtures of 10 g. of proposed solvent, such as 1,4-dioxane or ethylene dichloride, with 1 g. of *n*-butane (b.p. −5.5°C.) and of 10 g. of proposed solvent with 1 g. of butadiene-1,3 (b.p. −4.5°C.). If the boiling point of the latter mixture is 10° higher than that of the former mixture, the solvent is considered sufficiently selective to be used. A difference of 20° or more is preferred.

Critical Solution Temperature. Many solvents useful in extractive distillation are not completely miscible at room temperature with one or both of the components to be separated. The maximum temperature at which any mixture of component and solvent, for example, a hydrocarbon in nitrobenzene, can exist as two liquid phases is defined as the critical solution temperature (C.S.T.) of the mixture. These values have been reported for many binary mixtures. It appears that the greater the difference in C.S.T. of the components to be separated in the solvent, the better the solvent is suited as a separating aid in extractive distillation. For example, *n*-heptane and methylcyclohexane, with critical solution temperatures in aniline of 70 and 41°C., respectively,[47] have been separated by extractive distillation using aniline as a solvent. With a 2:1 aniline to hydrocarbon weight ratio, the separation was more than threefold that attainable by fractional distillation in the same column.[48]

Critical solution temperatures of seven selected nonaromatic hydrocarbons and three nonaromatic oil fractions in a number of solvents have been compiled by Francis.[47] A similar study of 38 cyclic hydrocarbons in a number of solvents has been reported by the same investigator.[49]

In general, aromatic hydrocarbons have been found to be much more soluble than nonaromatic, as indicated by lower critical solution temperature. The latter are frequently completely immiscible with a solvent in

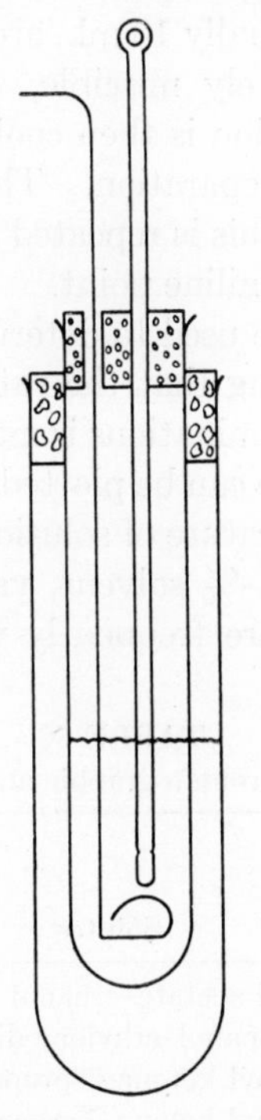

Fig. 10. Aniline-point apparatus.

which aromatic hydrocarbons have fairly low critical solution temperatures and aromatics are often completely soluble in solvents in which the nonaromatic hydrocarbons have low critical solution temperature. In either case such a solvent should facilitate separation by extractive distillation. An example of the latter type is the use of aniline to facilitate the separation of methylcyclohexane (C.S.T. 41°C.) from toluene (miscible down to the freezing point of aniline). By extractive distillation using 40 wt.-% of aniline, toluene-free methylcyclohexane can be obtained as distillate with only 1.6 mole-% of methylcyclohexane in the still. In the same column under fractional-distillation operation at total reflux with 5.5 mole-% methylcyclohexane in the still, the overhead product contained only 82 mole-% methylcyclohexane.[48]

Another form of C.S.T. frequently reported is the aniline point. The aniline point is the highest temperature at which a 1:1 volume mixture of aniline and a given hydrocarbon exists as two liquid phases. The aniline point is widely used in the petroleum industry where a standard apparatus and test procedure have been proposed.[50] A modification of this A.S.T.M. test apparatus is shown in Figure 10. It consists of a jacketed test tube containing a looped wire for agitation and a thermometer. Equal volumes of component and solvent, usually 10 ml., are introduced and heated slowly with agitation until completely miscible, when the temperature of the solution is noted. The solution is then cooled slowly with agitation until cloudiness indicates phase separation. The temperature at which the cloud first forms is noted. This is repeated several times, and the average temperature is taken as the aniline point.

The same apparatus can be used to determine critical solution temperatures, the only variation being that the ratio of solvent to component is varied, and a number of determinations is made so that a solution temperature–liquid composition curve can be plotted. The maximum of this curve is taken as the critical temperature of solution Since this curve is usually flat in the range of 40–60 vol.-% solvent, values for critical solution temperature and aniline point are frequently very close. Aniline points are

TABLE X
Correlation between Chromatographic and Equilibrium Still Data

Solvent	Solutes	Partition coefficient ratio	Modified relative volatility
Diethylene glycol	Ethyl acetate–ethanol	6.0	2.0
Didecyl phthalate	2-Propanol–ethylene dichloride	3.5	1.3
Dibutyl phthalate	Diethyl ketone–1-propanol	2.0	1.5
Dimethyl phthalate	Diethyl ketone–1-propanol	1.9	1.7

sometimes incorrectly reported in the literature as critical solution temperatures. In no case can the aniline point exceed the critical solution temperature. Discrepancies in literature values stem from four sources, which are listed in order of decreasing probable magnitude: (*1*) impurities in sample or solvent. (*2*) too rapid heating and cooling during the determination; (*3*) error in calibration of thermometer; (*4*) heat pickup from unshielded lights near apparatus. Hygroscopic solvents such as aniline must be carefully dried just before use, and a nonaqueous heating and cooling medium must be provided. An extensive survey of aniline points and critical solution temperatures of hydrocarbons in aniline has been made by Ball.[51]

Gas Chromatography. Gas chromatography, like extractive distillation, depends on the effect of the solvent on the components to be reported. As expected, there is a good correlation between partition coefficient ratios determined in a gas chromatograph and relative volatilities found in an equilibrium still. Data presented by Warren et al.[52] suggest that the widely available gas chromatographic technique can be used to screen solvents for extractive distillation. Typical data are shown in Table X.

The technique has been applied to hydrocarbon systems by Sheets and Marchello.[53]

Liquid-Extraction Data. Prior to the development of extractive distillation, separation of narrow boiling-range fractions according to chemical type was effected chiefly by liquid–liquid extraction. Phase-equilibrium studies of a number of systems with partial miscibility have been reported in the literature. Solvents suitable for liquid–liquid extractions can frequently be used in extractive distillation provided that they meet the other qualifications mentioned above, in particular that of having relatively high boiling points. As an aid in selecting a solvent based on such information, a summary of ternary extraction systems prepared by Smith[54] is reproduced in Tables XI and XII. Note that the ternary system aniline–*n*-heptane–methylcyclohexane is listed which can be separated by liquid–liquid extraction with aniline.[55] This system has also been separated by extractive distillation[48] using aniline as a solvent.

Chemical Nature of Solvent. It was mentioned above that solvents which form highly nonideal solutions are usually advantageous. Inasmuch as deviation from ideality is caused by interaction between solute and solvent, the solvent should be selected with reference to the nature of the mixture to be separated. The interaction between solute and solvent may vary from very loose solvation, e.g., by dipole interaction, to fairly stable complexes involving hydrogen bonds and other coordinative linkages. The interaction should take place with the less-volatile component of the distill and in order to enhance the normal volatility relationships.

TABLE XI
Ternary Systems with Water as One Component[54]

Components	Temp., °C.
Acetic acid	
Benzene	25
Benzene	25, 35
Benzene	20, 25
Chloroform	18
Chloroform	20, 25
Epichlorohydrin	10
Toluene	25
Acetone	
Bromobenzene	0
Chloroform	25
Chloroform	0
Furfural	25
Phenol	56.5
Potassium hydroxide	0
Sodium hydroxide	0
Aniline	
Formic acid	0.20
Propionic acid	0.20
Benzene	
Acetic acid	25
Acetic acid	25, 35
Acetic acid	20, 25
Ethanol	25
Ethanol	25, 50
Ethanol	20
Ethanol	20, 25
Ethanol	25
Ethanol	25
Pyridine	25
Isobutanol	
Hydrobromic acid	25
Hydrochloric acid	25
Hydriodic acid	25
n-Butanol–methanol	0, 15, 30
tert-Butanol–ethyl acetate	0, 20
Ethyl ether	25
Ethyl ether	0, 25
Ethyl ether	25
CS_2–acetic anhydride	0, 18
Carbon tetrachloride	
Ethanol	0
Methanol	0
n-Propanol	0
Chloroform	
Acetic acid	20, 25
Acetic acid	18
Acetone	25
Acetone	0
Ethanol	0
Methanol	0
Ethanol	
Isoamyl alcohol	15.5, 28
Isoamyl bromide	0
Isoamyl ether	0
Benzaldehyde	0
Benzene	25
Benzene	25, 50
Benzene	20
Benzene	25
Benzene	25
Benzyl acetate	0
Benzyl alcohol	0
Benzyl ethyl ether	0
Bromobenzene	0
Bromotoluene	0
Isobutanol	0
Isobutyl bromide	0
Carbon tetrachloride	0
Chloroform	0
Cyclohexane	25
Cyclohexane	20, 25
Cyclohexane	25
Cyclohexene	25
Ethyl acetate	0, 20
Ethyl acetate	0
Ethyl butyrate	0
Hydrobromic acid	
Isoamyl alcohol	25
Isobutanol	25

TABLE XI (*continued*)

Components	Temp., °C.	Components	Temp., °C.
Ethyl ether	0, 25		
Ethyl propionate	0	Hydrochloric acid	
Ethyl chloride	0	Isoamyl alcohol	25
Ethylidene chloride	0	Isobutanol	25
Hexane	0	Cyclohexanone	25
Hexane	25	Phenol	12
Mesitylene	0	Hydriodic acid	
Methylaniline	0	Isoamyl alcohol	25
Nitrobenzene	0	Isobutanol	25
p-Nitrotoluene	0		
Phenetole	0	Methanol	
Pinene	0	Isoamyl alcohol	28
Propyl bromide	0	Bromobenzene	0
Toluene	20	*n*-Butanol	0, 15, 30
Toluene	20, 25	Carbon tetrachloride	0
Toluene	25	Chloroform	0
m-Xylene	0, 50	Cyclohexane	25
o-Xylene	0	Cyclohexene	25
p-Xylene	0	Ethyl acetate	0, 20
Ethyl acetate		Ethyl bromide	0
tert-Butanol	0, 20	Toluene	25
Ethanol	0, 20	Nitrobenzene	
Furfural	25	Ethanol	0
Methanol	0, 20	Sulfuric acid	22
Isopropanol	0, 20		
n-Propanol	0, 20	Phenol	
Ethyl ether		Acetone	56.5
Ethanol	25	Hydrochloric acid	12
Ethanol	0, 25	Sodium hydroxide	
Ethanol	25	Potassium hydroxide	
Ethanol	0, 25	Triethylamine	−2, 7, 10
Triethylamine	0, 12.4	Isopropanol	
	30.5	Cyclohexane	15, 35
		Ethyl acetate	0, 20
Furfural			
Acetone	25	Toluene	25
Isoamyl acetate	25		
Ethyl acetate	25		
n-Propanol		Toluene	
Isoamyl alcohol	25	Acetic acid	25
Bromotoluene	0	Ethanol	20
Carbon tetrachloride	0	Ethanol	20, 25
Ethyl acetate	0, 20	Ethanol	25
		Methanol	25
Propionic acid			
Aniline	0, 30	Isopropanol	25
o-Toluidine	0, 20		

TABLE XII
Nonaqueous Ternary Systems[54]

Component	Temp., °C.
Acetone–glycol	
Benzene	27
Bromobenzene	25
Chlorobenzene	23
Nitrobenzene	22
Toluene	27
Xylene	25
Aniline–*n*-heptane–methylcyclohexane	25
Ethanol–benzene–glycerol	25

The relative polarity of a compound has been used in the past to explain its ideal or nonideal behavior in solution. Liquids of similar polarity when mixed are expected to form nearly ideal solutions, while those of different polarity are expected to deviate from ideality in proportion to their difference. Ewell et al.,[56] among others, disagree with this concept in connection with azeotropic distillation, and point out certain exceptions to the above generalization. Hildebrand[57] introduced a modification of the polarity concept to make allowance for steric hindrance existing in some molecules having high dipole moment, which, in effect, tends to neutralize the polarity of the compound. Bearing in mind that there are exceptions, we shall use the concept of polarity as the basis for discussion.

The types of mixtures to be separated by extractive distillation can be classified as follows: (*a*) highly polar; (*b*) nonpolar; (*c*) one component polar, the other nonpolar; and (*d*) both components of intermediate polarity.

For a highly polar mixture such as acetic acid and water, a nonpolar solvent such as a high-boiling oil fraction should be helpful[58] by increasing the relative volatility of the water. If the mixture is nonpolar like cyclohexane–benzene, a polar solvent such as aniline will facilitate the separation[48] by rendering the cyclohexane more volatile.

For the case in which one constituent is nonpolar and the other polar, one might expect either a polar or a nonpolar solvent to be satisfactory. In practice, the solvent which augments the normal relative volatilities is preferred. For example, if the polar component is less volatile, a polar solvent will augment the normal volatilities while a nonpolar solvent will reverse them. Other things being equal, however, a polar solvent will be preferable since a more highly nonideal solution will usually be obtained.

For a mixture of intermediate polarity, one would expect either a highly polar or a nonpolar solvent to be satisfactory. The effect of the solvent on

TABLE XIII
Polarities Expressed as Dipole Moments

	Compound	$\mu \times 10^{18}$ e.s.u. at 20°C.
H_2O	Water	1.85
CS_2	Carbon disulfide	0
SO_2	Sulfur dioxide	1.61
CCI_4	Carbon tetrachloride	0
n-C_6H_{14}	Hexane	0
n-C_7H_{16}	Heptane	0
n-C_8H_{18}	Octane	0
C_6H_{12}	Cyclohexane	0
C_6H_6	Benzene	0
C_6H_5CH	Toluene	0.4
p-$C_6H_4(CH_3)_2$	*p*-Xylene	0
$C_{10}H_8$	Naphthalene	0
$CHCl_3$	Chloroform	1.05
$CHBr_3$	Bromoform	1.0
C_2H_5Br	Ethyl bromide	1.83
C_2H_5I	Ethyl Iodide	1.66
C_6H_5Cl	Chlorobenzene	1.56
C_6H_5Br	Bromobenzene	1.49
C_6H_5I	Iodobenzene	1.30
o-$C_6H_4Cl_2$	*o*-Dichlorobenzene	2.24
m-$C_6H_4Cl_2$	*m*-Dichlorobenzene	1.48
p-$C_6H_4Cl_2$	*p*-Dichlorobenzene	0
CH_3OH	Methyl alcohol	1.68
C_2H_5OH	Ethyl alcohol	1.70
$C_8H_{17}OH$	Octyl alcohol	1.68
C_6H_5OH	Phenol	1.70
$(CH_3)_2O$	Dimethyl ether	1.32
$(C_6H_5)_2O$	Diphenyl ether	1.14
$(CH_3)_2CO$	Acetone	2.8
$CH_3COOC_2H_5$	Ethyl acetate	1.86
CH_3CHO	Acetaldehyde	2.46
CH_3CN	Acetonitrile	3.2
CH_3NO_2	Nitromethane	3.42
$C_6H_5NO_2$	Nitrobenzene	4.19
$C_2H_5NH_2$	Ethylamine	1.3
$C_6H_5NH_2$	Aniline	1.51

normal volatilities is not easy to predict in this case but a polar solvent would be recommended for an initial trial.

The points to be considered in selecting a solvent for enhancing relative volatilities in extractive distillation are:

(*a*) Binary mixture, highly polar: Select a polar solvent or a nonpolar solvent more soluble with the higher boiling component.

(*b*) Binary mixture, nonpolar: Select a polar solvent more soluble with the higher boiling component.

(*c*) Binary mixture, the more volatile component polar, the other nonpolar: Select a nonpolar solvent or a polar solvent. The latter may reverse relative volatilities.

(*d*) Binary mixture, the more volatile component nonpolar, the other polar: Select a polar solvent.

(*e*) Binary mixture, moderately polar: Follow (*a*).

In Table XIII are listed the polarities of a few typical organic compounds reported by Hildebrand,[57] expressed as dipole moments.[59]

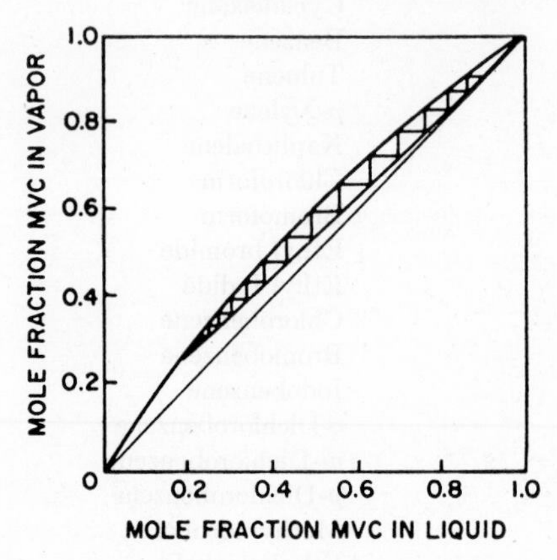

Fig. 11. Theoretical-plate requirements for batch distillation at 10:1 reflux ratio with 1.5 relative volatility.

It was shown in Figure 2 that for a given solvent the enhancement in relative volatility depends upon the solvent concentration, the maximum value of relative volatility being realized for the limiting case of 100% solvent. In practice, a maximum enhancement in relative volatility is not necessary, and a value of 1.5 to 2.0 is in general adequate for good separation by batch distillation in a moderately efficient column. For example, a mixture with a relative volatility of 1.5 at 10:1 reflux ratio in a 15 theoretical plate column will give an overhead product containing 90 mole-% of the more volatile component, with only 20 mole-% in the still. This is very close to the maximum separation at 10:1 reflux ratio, as can be seen in Figure 11.

4. Laboratory Apparatus and Procedures

The apparatus and procedure for laboratory extractive distillation can be very simple or quite elaborate, depending upon the frequency of such distillations and the number of independent operations the operator is willing to make.

A. BATCH EXTRACTIVE DISTILLATION WITHOUT SOLVENT RECYCLE

The simplest laboratory application of extractive distillation involves merely a modification of the operation of a conventional batch laboratory fractional-distillation column. During distillation, solvent is added continuously at the head of the column through the thermometer or thermocouple well or at the condenser. The product withdrawn at the top of the column contains solvent, which can be removed by a separate operation, and solvent builds up in the still pot which should be of adequate size to handle the quantity of solvent added. Bottoms product and solvent can

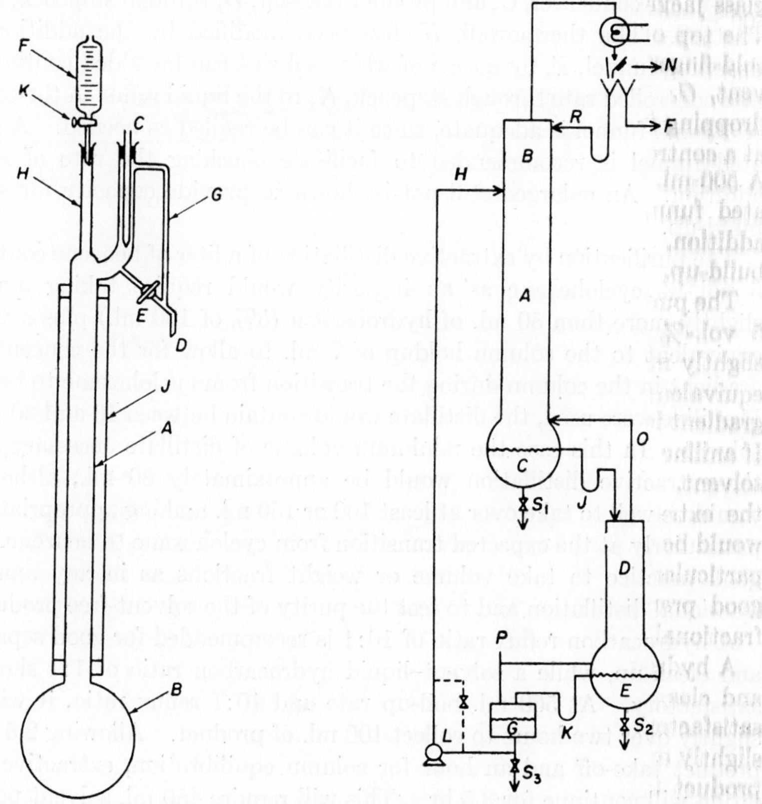

Fig. 12 (left). Modification of laboratory fractional-distillation apparatus for extractive distillation.

Fig. 13 (right). Laboratory extractive-distillation apparatus with solvent recycle, single control point.

be separated after the extractive distillation. This type of operation is particularly suitable for the purification of volatile compounds used in other physical or chemical studies, particularly when the impurities are present in low concentrations (5% or less).

An illustration of such a laboratory setup is shown in Figure 12. A typical packed laboratory column has been selected, which for purposes of discussion has a column section, *A*, 12 mm. I.D. packed for 50 cm. with $^1/_8$-in. stainless-steel helices which will give 30–40 theoretical plates. When operated under adiabatic conditions of total reflux with a thoroughly wetted packing, this column will have a toluene boil-up rate of at least 500 ml./hr. The column is rendered adiabatic by an electrically wound glass jacket, *J*, which is surrounded by a second glass jacket not shown. The top of the column consists of a conventional head which provides a cold-finger condenser, *C*, and product take-off, *D*, through stopcock, *E*, and vent, *G*. The thermowell, *H*, has been modified by the addition of a dropping funnel, *F*, by means of which solvent can be added continuously at a controlled rate through stopcock, *K*, to the liquid reflux in the column. A 500-ml. funnel is adequate, since it can be refilled as needed. A graduated funnel is recommended to facilitate checking the rate of solvent addition. An enlarged still pot is shown to provide capacity for solvent build-up.

The purification by extractive distillation of a liter of benzene containing 5 vol.-% cyclohexane as an impurity would require taking overhead slightly more than 50 ml. of hydrocarbon (5% of 100 ml.) plus a volume equivalent to the column holdup of 7 ml. to allow for the concentration gradient in the column during the transition from cyclohexane to benzene. If aniline were used, the distillate would contain between 10 and 20 vol.-% solvent. In this case the minimum volume of distillate necessary during the extractive distillation would be approximately 80 ml., although it would be well to take over at least 100 or 150 ml. making appropriate cuts, particularly at the expected transition from cyclohexane to benzene. It is good practice to take volume or weight fractions as in any analytical fractional distillation and to test the purity of the solvent-free products.

A hydrocarbon reflux ratio of 10:1 is recommended for good separation and clean-up, while a solvent–liquid hydrocarbon ratio of 1:1 should be satisfactory. At 500 ml. boil-up rate and 10:1 reflux ratio, it will take slightly over two hours to collect 100 ml. of product. Allowing 2.5 hr. for product take-off and an hour for column equilibration, extractive distillation will continue for 3.5 hr. This will require 450 ml. solvent per hour or 1575 ml. total. With an initial still charge of 1000 ml., a 5-liter flask will be required for *B* in Figure 12.

In general, the data on the system to be separated are not as complete as in the above illustration. In such cases a hydrocarbon reflux ratio of 10:1 and a solvent–hydrocarbon ratio of 1:1 are selected and the equivalent of an analytical distillation is carried out. When apparatus such as that shown in Figure 12 is used, the extractive distillation can be carried out in several successive steps, if necessary. First, solvent is added during extractive distillation to the limit of the still capacity; next, solvent addition is discontinued and the unknown mixture is stripped from the solvent by conventional distillation; then the unknown is recharged to the still after removal of regenerated solvent, which is added at the head of the column for continued extractive distillation. A procedure such as that just described would have been necessary in the above example if the mixture had contained 5% benzene and 95% cyclohexane, since it would have been necessary to take all the cyclohexane overhead as distillate.

It should be noted here that if the solvent is not preheated but is at room temperature, as will generally be the case in apparatus such as Figure 12, it will tend to condense some vapors so that the hydrocarbon reflux ratio will be higher than that observed at the condenser. It is usually necessary to warm the solvent to ensure that vapors reach the condenser.

B. BATCH EXTRACTIVE DISTILLATION WITH SOLVENT RECYCLE

Where extractive distillations are carried out with any frequency, a batch laboratory unit designed for solvent recycle will be desirable. The essentials of such an apparatus are shown in Figure 13. It consists of two fractional distillation columns. One contains the extractive-distillation section, *A*, the enriching section, *B*, for solvent removal from the distillate which is recovered at *F*, and an accumulator, *C*, for solvent and mixture. The second column contains a solvent-stripping section, *D*, for solvent regeneration and to provide vapors for the extractive-distillation section, *A*. It has a heated still pot, *E*. If no heat losses were incurred, this would be the sole source of heat in the unit. In laboratory equipment, where heat losses can be a relatively large portion of the total heat, it is usually necessary to heat accumulator, *C*, to ensure adequate vapor for the extractive-distillation zone. Regenerated solvent from *E* is pumped continuously to the extractive-distillation column. For smoothness of control, intermediate storage of solvent at *G*, ahead of the pump, is recommended. A mechanical pump, *L*, is shown, but a thermal pump (total vaporizer) with a condenser at point *H* would be equally satisfactory for heat-stable solvents. There are several points of control in such a unit in addition to the common ones of reflux ratio and boil-up rate in fractional distillation. The liquid level in accumulator, *C*, is held constant by overflow, *J*. Solvent withdrawal from *E* is controlled by a similar overflow, *K*. A swinging-bucket type of column head, *N*, is used with automatic reflux ratio control at a predetermined rate. The heat input at E and C can be set at a safe value, based on a little operating experience, and readjusted gradually as the system is depleted in volatile components during the extractive distillation. The boil-up rates at C and particularly at E become the control points. To be sure the solvent in still pot E is completely stripped of volatiles, the temperature in E should be that of boiling solvent. This can be checked by thermometer or thermocouple in a thermowell in still pot E. Stopcocks S_1, S_2, S_3 permit complete draining of the apparatus. The intermediate solvent storage vessel, G, is vented to the atmosphere at P, which may also serve as a solvent charge line. A large flask or breaker open to the atmosphere makes a good solvent storage vessel. It will usually be necessary to cool the overflow from E and to preheat the solvent at H for satisfactory operation.

Suitable dimensions for the component parts of the apparatus shown in Figure 13 are as follows:

Rectifying section, B, 15–25 mm. O.D. × 25 cm. long.
Extractive distillation section, A, 15–25 mm. O.D. × 60 cm. long.
Accumulator, C, 1–3 liters.
Overflow, J, 8–10 mm. O.D. and 10–20 cm. long with at least 3 cm. difference in vertical length of arms.
Vapor line, O, 8–12 mm. O.D.
Stripping column, D, 25–35 mm. O.D.
Still pot, E, 2–3 liters.
Overflow, K, 8–10 mm. O.D. and 10–20 cm. long with at least 3 cm. difference in vertical length of arms.
Vent line, Q, 2-mm. capillary.
Solvent reservoir, G, 500–1000 ml.
Stopcocks, S_1, S_2, S_3, 2 mm. oblique bore, lubricated with high-temperature stopcock grease.
Solvent feed line, H, 8–10 mm. O.D. A small rotameter in this line to indicate flow rates would be very desirable.
Pump, L, can be a small centrifugal pump such as those available from Eastern Engineering Company provided with a bypass, shown dotted, for flow control.
Other laboratory variable rate pumps which may be used, but which are less desirable because of their pulsating flow, are the positive-displacement pumps, such as those available from Hills-McCanna and Proportioneers, Inc., or pumps such as those available from Wilson Pulsafeeders, Inc.

Equipment not shown in Figure 13:

Heater for still pot, E, 450–550 watts.
Heater for accumulator, C, 450–550 watts.
Heater control: for alternating current, auto transformers such as Variac (General Radio Company) or Varitran (United Transformer Company); for direct current, slide-wire rheostats, 90–180 ohms.
Insulation, various alternatives: (*a*) electrical windings, 10 watts per centimeter length of column to be wound, maximum; (*b*) vacuum jackets; (*c*) vapor bath in jackets.

Timer and solenoid for swinging-funnel reflux divider such as those available from Eagle Signal Company, Scientific Glass Apparatus Company, Ace Glass Company, General Electric Company, or Glass Engineering Laboratories.

Internal construction of columns, various alternatives: (*a*) Packed columns. Single-turn wire helices, Berl Saddles, Raschig rings, or similar small laboratory packing. Nominal diameter of packing should be less than one-fifth inside diameter of column. For example, in a 25-mm. I.D. column, single-turn wire helices should be less than 5 mm. (approximately $^3/_{16}$ in.) in diameter, in this case $^3/_{16}$-in. helices or smaller would be recommended. (*b*) Perforated plates with overflows such as the Oldershaw columns.[60] (*c*) Bubble-cap columns. (*d*) Any suitable vapor–liquid contacting arrangement used in fractional-distillation laboratory columns.

The practicability of a batch laboratory apparatus with solvent recirculation has been demonstrated.[48] The apparatus, shown schematically in Figure 14, was designed for the specific purpose of determining the effectiveness of extractive distillation in a packed laboratory column as compared with fractional distillation. It can be used as shown for extractive distillation or with minor modifications to produce a solvent-free distillate.

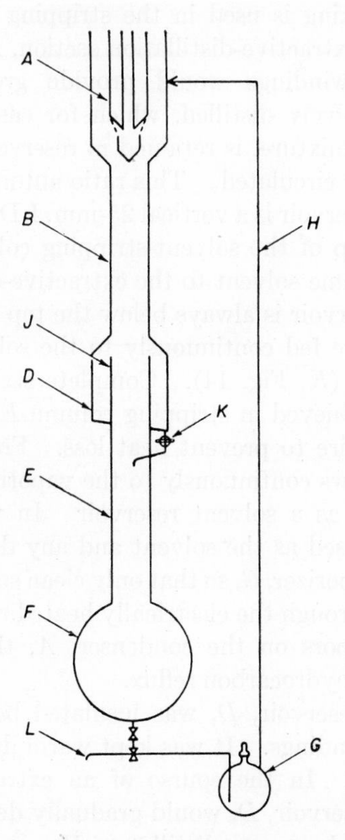

Fig. 14. Batch laboratory extractive-distillation apparatus with solvent recycle.

It contains several unique features: (*1*) A thermal pump to circulate solvent. (*2*) The solvent–stripping column and the extractive-distillation column as one vertical unit. (*3*) Solvent and hydrocarbon reflux mix as vapors at the condenser. The apparatus consists of the following main parts:

A vapor–liquid extractive-distillation contacting section, *B;* a stripping column, *E,* for purifying high-boiling solvent; a means, *G, H,* for recycling solvent to the top of the extractive-distillation section; a condenser, *A*; a means, *E, J,* for introducing hydrocarbon and solvent vapors to the bottom of the extractive-distillation section; and a reservoir or accumulator, *D,* for the mixture being extractively distilled.

Detailed dimensions of the apparatus shown in Figure 14 are given in the original publication.[48] Below the condenser is suspended a positive-displacement distillate receiver. The condenser is of the cold-finger type but hollow in the center to permit distillate withdrawal through a siphon tube, 3 mm. O.D. The extractive distillation section, *B,* is packed with $^3/_{10}$-in. single-turn wire helices made from No. 26 B&S gage stainless-steel wire. The same packing is used in the stripping column, *E.* A vapor jacket surrounds the extractive-distillation section, *B,* for heat control but electrical resistance windings would provide greater flexibility. The mixture to be extractively distilled, which for ease of reference will be called a hydrocarbon mixture, is retained in reservoir *D* and contains solvent in the ratio being circulated. This ratio automatically adjusts itself. In the center of the reservoir is a vertical 25-mm. I.D. tube, open at the top, which is really the top of the solvent-stripping column returning hydrocarbon vapors with some solvent to the extractive-distillation zone. The liquid level in the reservoir is always below the top of this tube. Hydrocarbon and solvent are fed continuously to the solvent-stripping column through the stopcock (*K,* Fig. 14). Complete stripping of hydrocarbon from the solvent is achieved in stripping column *E.* This is wound with electrical resistance wire to prevent heat loss. From the bottom of the reboiler, *F,* solvent flows continuously to the vaporizer, *G,* which serves as a thermal pump and as a solvent reservoir. In working with this apparatus, aniline was used as the solvent and any decomposition products accumulated in the vaporizer, *G,* so that only clean solvent was recirculated. Solvent vapors rose through the electrically heated riser, *H,* and condensed with hydrocarbon vapors on the condenser, *A,* thus ensuring excellent mixing of solvent and hydrocarbon reflux.

The hydrocarbon reservoir, *D,* was insulated both with asbestos and electrical resistance windings. It was kept warm during operation but no boiling occurred here. In the course of an extractive distillation, the volume of liquid in reservoir, *D,* would gradually decrease as hydrocarbon and solvent was withdrawn as distillate. If a solvent-free distillate is withdrawn, the volume of solvent in the reboiler, *F*, and vaporizer, *G*, will increase if a constant solvent:hydrocarbon ratio is maintained in accumulator *D*. Should the solvent volume in *F* and *G* become too great, it can be withdrawn through a drain *L*.

Three obvious modifications of this apparatus for routine extractive distillation are: (*a*) Addition of a rectifying section, 40 cm. long, above the extractive-distillation zone to give a solvent-free distillate. (*b*) Condensation of solvent prior to its addition to the extractive-distillation zone if modification *a* is made. This is also a desirable change without modification (*a*) in order to avoid dilution of hydrocarbon distillate with recycled solvent. (*c*) an increase to 40 mm. of the diameter of the stripping column, which now limits the distillation rates.

When employing solvent recycle, the solvent must be completely stripped of hydrocarbon or the desired separation will be defeated by introducing material of still-pot composition at the condenser.

C. CONTINUOUS EXTRACTIVE DISTILLATION WITHOUT SOLVENT RECYCLE

A more elaborate device for laboratory extractive distillation is shown in Figure 15, where solvent and feed are added continuously to the extractive distillation column, a distillate product, *D*, being withdrawn continuously at the top of the column. A still is provided at the bottom of the column to furnish vapors to the extractive-distillation column. Less volatile components and solvent which accumulate in the still are continuously drawn off and sent to storage. Solvent and less volatile components are recovered in a separate step.

The feed, *F*, is introduced at a point intermediate between solvent feed, *S*, and the reboiler to ensure complete stripping of more volatile material from the solvent–hydrocarbon mixture withdrawn to storage. The solvent is shown entering below the reflux return to give a solvent-free distillate, *D*, as overhead product.

Griswold et al.[61] described a laboratory apparatus operating in a manner similar to that shown in Figure 15. It was designed to operate on hydrocarbon fractions boiling in the C_6–C_8 range with aniline as a solvent. The column consisted of a 1-in. standard iron pipe packed for 48 in. with $^1/_8$-in. metal helices. Feed was pumped directly to a hydrocarbon vaporizer, at the bottom of the column, while solvent and hydrocarbon were withdrawn as a liquid just above the feed vaporizer and sent to storage. Solvent was pumped to the top of the column, mixed with hydrocarbon reflux, and heated to ensure complete miscibility. The extractive-distillation column was lagged with 80% magnesia and wound with resistance wire in four sections of 150 watts each. The hydrocarbon vaporizer and the solvent-reflux preheater each contained a 600-watt cartridge heater.

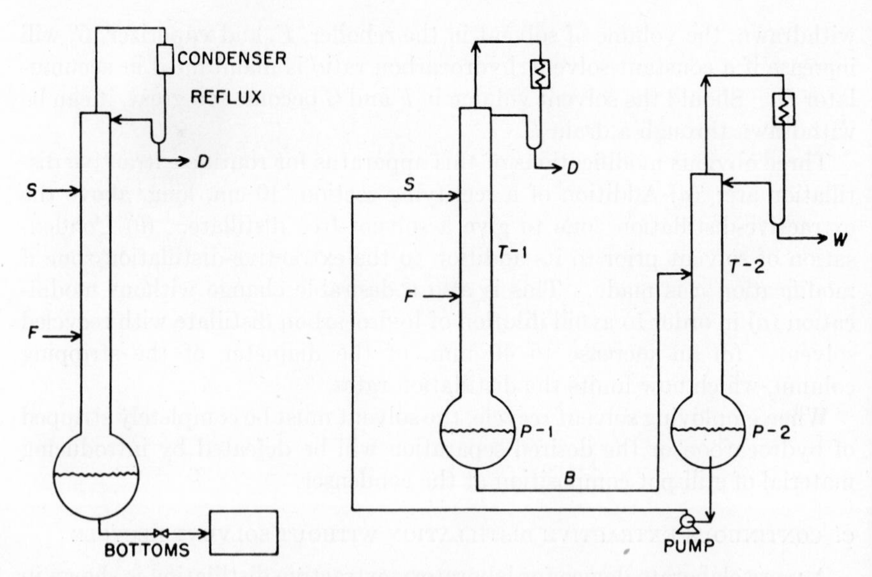

Fig. 15 (left). Continuous extractive-distillation column without solvent recovery and recycle.

Fig. 16 (right). Continuous extractive-distillation apparatus with solvent recycle.

D. CONTINUOUS EXTRACTIVE DISTILLATION WITH SOLVENT RECYCLE

The arrangement of equipment for continuous extractive distillation with solvent recycle is shown in Figure 16. It consists of two complete fractionating columns. The extractive distillation column, *T*-1, is a replica of that shown in Figure 15. Column *T*-2 is the solvent-stripping column, which produces stripped solvent as a bottoms product and an overhead product, *W*, which is the less volatile material in the feed, *F*. In ordinary fractional distillation it would have been the bottoms product (assuming it is the high-boiling material in the absence of solvent).

To carry out this operation in the laboratory, the incorporation of various arrangements such as those discussed for Figure 13 to decrease the number of control points is essential. The schematic arrangement shown in Figure 16 requires eight points of control:

Reflux ratio for each column (2)
Still-pot boil-up rate for each column (2)
Liquid levels in *P*-1 and *P*-2 (2)
Solvent rate
Feed rate

By mounting column *T*-1 at a higher level than *T*-2, a gravity overflow system from still pot *P*-1 can be used for column *T*-1, as well as for *T*-2.

Reflux ratios can be controlled automatically by the use of a swinging-funnel still head. Heat input to P-1 and P-2 needs little adjustment after some experience has been gained in operating such apparatus. Boil-up rate can be controlled automatically if desired by means of a manometer measuring pressure drop across the packing of the column, since pressure drop increases with distillation rate. This leaves two critical points of control, feed and solvent rates. These can be controlled manually or automatically by means of flow control devices, depending upon the elaborateness of the laboratory setup. In any case, a means of indicating flow rates of these streams to T-1 is essential. Such devices as rotameters, orifices, or capillary constrictions are suitable.

Griswold and Van Berg[62] have described an apparatus similar to that sketched in Figure 16. The extractive-distillation column was made from 2-in. standard iron pipe, and had 150 screen plates $1^5/_8$ in. apart. It was wound with six sections of electrical resistance wire, 200 watts each, controlled by individual Variacs. The hydrocarbon vaporizer and solvent-reflux preheater were heated with steam.

The solvent-stripping column was also made from 2-in. standard pipe but packed for 4 ft. with $^1/_8$-in. carding teeth. It was wound with a 300-watt heater element to render it adiabatic. A 2-liter capacity reboiler was provided with a 660-watt heater. Gear pumps were used to control the flow rate of all the liquid streams. A liquid-level controller was used for the bottom of the extractive-distillate column, while the level in the reboiler of the stripping column was manually controlled.

E. CONTROL OF OPERATION IN EXTRACTIVE DISTILLATION

The major factors of control have already been discussed in connection with specific apparatus. One point is so important that it will be repeated for emphasis: The separation realized in extractive distillations results from the presence of a high concentration of solvent in the liquid phase. This must be provided. In those cases in which solvent is recirculated, it must be completely stripped of feed components or the desired separation will not be realized. Solvent preheating is also very important since it will influence markedly the vapor load at the condenser. The solvent should be preheated to the proper temperature and held at this temperature during any distillation.

Since, in general, the solvent used boils 50 to 100°C. above the temperature of the mixture being separated, the most satisfactory way of following the extractive distillation and solvent stripping is by temperature readings. Whenever possible, thermometers or thermocouples should be installed in the apparatus to permit temperature readings at the following points:

Overhead vapor
Solvent just before entering column
Just below solvent feed point
At bottom of extractive-distillation section A (see Fig. 13)
In accumulator, C
At top, middle, and bottom of stripping column, D
In still pot, E

The temperature at the bottom of the packed section of the stripping column, D, should be that of pure boiling solvent.

Heat losses should be minimized by adequate use of lagging and heating elements in order to avoid excess condensation of vapor at various points in the apparatus.

5. Calculation of Extractive-Distillation Separations

Since it has been the practice to express vapor–liquid equilibria, in the presence of a solvent, as a modified relative volatility α_S, indicating the separation realized in a one-plate still, these values can be used directly for extractive distillation calculations in the same manner that α has been used. This is illustrated in the following example:

(*1*) *Data.*

Mixture to be separated: n-heptane–methylcyclohexane.
Solvent: aniline.
Charge: 50 mole-% n-heptane in methylcyclohexane.
Overhead product: 90 mole-% n-heptane on a solvent-free basis.
Aniline, molecular weight 93, d_4^{20} 1.02.
n-Heptane, molecular weight 100, d_4^{20} 0.684, latent heat 76.1 cal./g.
Methylcyclohexane, molecular weight 98, d_4^{20} 0.769, latent heat 76. 9 cal./g.
Column (see Fig. 9):
Section A, 2.5 cm. I.D. $\times$ 150 cm.
Section B, 2.5 cm. I.D. $\times$ 35 cm.
Section D, 3.5 cm. I.D. $\times$ 50 cm.
All sections packed with $^3/_{16}$-in. single-turn helices.
H.E.T.P. 7.1 cm.[48]
Packing throughput, 2800 ml. liquid per hour.[48]

(*2*) *Solvent–hydrocarbon ratio.* From the equilibrium data for this system in the presence of aniline[61] given in Table II, it can be seen that this system is difficult to separate. In order to realize a relative volatility of 1.4 to 1.5, a solvent concentration between 80 and 90 mole-% in the liquid is necessary. As an initial assumption, consider that this corresponds to a 3:1 liquid volume ratio of aniline to n-heptane (initial overhead product):

Basis 100-ml. liquid mixture:

Aniline (75) (1.02)/93 = 0.8222 mole (82.8 mole-%).
n-Heptane (25) (0.684)/100 = 0.171 mole (17.2 mole-%).

Thus a 3:1 solvent: hydrocarbon liquid volume ratio corresponds to approximately 83 mole-% aniline in the liquid phase. This should give a relative volatility of 1.44.

(3) *Reflux ratio at condenser.* The minimum reflux ratio for a binary mixture can be readily calculated using the Fenske equation.[63]

$$R_{min} = \frac{1}{\alpha - 1}\left(\frac{X_{Dh}}{X_{nh}} - \alpha\,\frac{X_{Dm}}{X_{nm}}\right) \tag{29}$$

where R_{min} is minimum ratio of reflux to distillate; α is 1.44 for *n*-heptane to methylcyclohexane in the presence of three volumes aniline per volume hydrocarbon; X_{Dh} is mole fraction *n*-heptane in distillate, 0.90; X_{Dm} is mole fraction methylcyclohexane in distillate, 0.10; and X_n is mole fraction at pinch, in this case considered equal to hydrocarbon composition in still pot, *C*, which will change as the mixture is depleted in *n*-heptane. At the start of the distillation:

$$R_{mim} = \frac{1}{1.44 - 1}\left[\frac{0.9}{0.5} - 1.44\left(\frac{0.5}{0.5}\right)\right] = 3.4 \tag{30}$$

During the extractive distillation the minimum reflux requirements increase as follows, expressing composition on a solvent-free basis:

Mole fraction *n*-heptane in still	R_{min}	R_{actual}
0.50	3.4	5.1
0.40	4.1	6.1
0.30	5.7	8.6
0.20	8.8	13.2
0.15	13.2	20
0.10	20	30

A useful rule of thumb is to operate at 1.5 times the minimum reflux ratio for the desired separation. During a batch distillation the reflux ratio can be increased gradually, but it is usually easier to operate at one setting. At 20:1 reflux ratio, the *n*-heptane in the still can be reduced to a mole fraction of 0.15 (solvent-free basis).

While this technique is satisfactory for determination of the reflux ratio for most laboratory operations, care should be taken to correct the solvent concentration for the effect of reflux ratio since high reflux ratios increase the concentration of the more volatile component in the solvent. An increased reflux lowers the concentration of the solvent in the downflowing liquid and thus lowers the effective relative volatility. As a result, increasing the reflux rate improves the separation efficiency up to a point, after which increases in the reflux rate may actually impair the degree of separation achieved at a given solvent flow rate to the column. This effect may readily be avoided by setting the desired reflux rate and then setting the solvent rate, calculating the instantaneous concentration of solvent at the point where recycle solvent is introduced. This reflux ratio is more than adequate for virtually complete removal of solvent aniline from the overhead distillate since the relative volatility of hydrocarbons to aniline is approximately 8.5.

(4) *Theoretical plates in extractive distillation section.* The final separation desired corresponds to an enrichment ratio[64] of 51. With a relative volatility of 1.44, a minimum of 10 theoretical plates will be necessary. With an H.E.T.P. (height equivalent to a

theoretical plate; see definition, Chap. I) of 7.1 cm. for this packing, a packed length actually provided should be adequate. If this is not the case, the hydrocarbon reflux ratio and the solvent: hydrocarbon ratio need only be increased slightly. It should be noted that the reflux ratio and solvent rate are related if a constant solvent concentration in the liquid is to be maintained. Another useful rule of thumb is that at 1.5 times the minimum reflux ratio 1.5 times the minimum number of theoretical plates necessary should give the desired separation. This holds only over the common operating ranges, 5 mole-% more volatile component in the still to 95 mole-% more volatile component in the distillate, and for mixtures with regular x–y diagrams showing no pinches.

It should be noted that, in the extractive-distillation section, the algebraic calculations for theoretical plates are made using relative volatilities in the presence of solvent. The same calculations could be made graphically using a McCabe and Thiele diagram drawn on a solvent-free basis.

(5) *Theoretical plates in enriching section B and stripping section D.* Taking α as 8.5 for hydrocarbons with respect to aniline, the minimum number of theoretical plates will be less than 3; thus the 35-cm. enriching section, *B*, should be adequate.

For complete removal of hydrocarbon from solvent, a minimum of approximately three theoretical plates will be necessary. At 1.5 times this or 4.5 theoretical plates, a packed length of 32 cm. will be needed in the stripping column, *D*. The 50 cm. provided should be more than adequate.

(6) *Vapor rate in extractive-distillation column.* The column, 2.5 cm. I.D., packed with $^3/_{16}$-in. single-turn helices, will have a distillation rate without solvent of at least 2800 ml. liquid per hour. The addition of solvent will materially decrease this. In the absence of concrete data, it will be assumed the distillation rate will be decreased 50% to 1400 ml. liquid per hour.

(7) *Solvent rate.* Since 1400 ml. hydrocarbon is liquefied per hour at the condenser and a reflux ratio of 20:1 will be used:

$$(1400)(1/21) = 67 \text{ ml. hydrocarbon distillate per hour}$$
$$1400 - 67 = 1333 \text{ ml. hydrocarbon reflux per hour}$$

At a 3:1 volume ratio of solvent to hydrocarbon in the reflux, 3 (1333), or 3999, ml. solvent per hour must be circulated. The hydrocarbon vapors leaving the extractive distillation section will contain 10% aniline.[65] Since this will be refluxed back, an equivalent reduction in solvent requirements of 133 ml. can be made if desired. Thus solvent circulation rate of 3999, −133, or 3866, ml./hr. may be used.

(8) *Heat requirements.* Assuming no heat losses, it will be necessary to vaporize only 1400 ml. per hour of hydrocarbon:

$$n\text{-Heptane: } (1400)(0.684)(76.1) = 73{,}000 \text{ cal./hr.}$$
$$\text{Methylcyclohexane: } (1400)(0.769)(76.9) = 82{,}500 \text{ cal./hr.}$$
$$(73{,}000)/860 = 85 \text{ w.}$$

This will require a minimum of 85 w. input. Experience has shown that at least five times this amount should be provided if an external heater is used.

During the course of the distillation under discussion, the hydrocarbon mixture will gradually be impoverished in n-heptane as it is removed as distillate.

(9) *Summary of example.*

Equipment requirements:

Theoretical plates	Minimum	At finite reflux	Available in column
Section A	10	15	21
Section B	<3	<4.5	5
Section D	3	4.5	7.0

Reflux ratio at condenser:	
Minimum	13.2
At operating conditions	20
Solvent:hydrocarbon volume ratio	3:1
Distillate rate, ml. per hour	67
Solvent rate, ml. per hour	3866
Solvent concentration in liquid, mole-%	83
Relative volatility, *n*-heptane to methylcyclohexane	1.44
Relative volatility, hydrocarbon to aniline	8.5
Heat input to still pot:	
Minimum	85 watts
Recommended	425 watts

6. Equipment Performance

A. PACKED LABORATORY COLUMNS

Few data are available on the effect of a high-boiling solvent on the H.E.T.P. of a column packing or on the efficiency of industrial plate columns. Detailed data on the operation of a packed column during extractive distillation of *n*-heptane and methylcyclohexane with aniline as a solvent have been reported.[48] Similar data were reported for operation in the absence of a solvent. From this information and the vapor–liquid equilibria data of Griswold et al.,[61] it has been possible to calculate packing efficiencies; they averaged 88%. A correlation of plate efficiencies as a function of liquid viscosity, based on commercial towers,[66] would have predicted about 70% efficiency.

B. COMMERCIAL BUBBLE-PLATE TOWERS

Test data on a commercial toluene extractive-distillation unit using phenol as a solvent have been reported by Drickamer and Hummel.[67] An overall average plate efficiency of 50% was found above the solvent-feed tray when 5 mole-% phenol was present. An average plate efficiency of 56% was found below the solvent-feed tray when 55 mole-% phenol was present. If the solvent had any effect, it was the reverse of what one would expect, since the viscosity-plate efficiency correlation[66] predicts 60 and 40% for these two tower sections, respectively.

Test data have also been reported for several towers of another commercial extractive-distillation unit[68] using furfural containing 4–6% water (by weight) as a mixed solvent for the separation of butanes, butenes, and butadiene. In the *n*-butane tower, *n*-butane is separated from butene-2. In the isobutane tower, isobutane is removed from butene-1 and butadiene. In the butadiene tower, separation is made between butene-1 and butadiene. In each tower, the first-named component is rejected as overhead product using aqueous furfural as an extractive-distillation solvent. The plate efficiencies of the individual towers, based on liquid-tray analyses were:

Tower	Murphree plate efficiency, %
n-Butane	23
Isobutane	28
Butadiene	20

Based on additional data not given, an average tray efficiency of 25% is recommended for these towers. The tray efficiency predicted by the correlation of Drickamer and Bradford[66] is also approximately this figure.

In the absence of other data, one is forced to conclude that the effect of the solvent on the efficiency of a packing in a laboratory column is slight. In commercial equipment the effect of the solvent is either slight or in the direction of the viscosity-plate efficiency correlation,[66] where decreasing plate efficiency is predicted for increasing viscosity of the liquid on the plate. Additional data on this score would be desirable.

7. Typical Industrial Applications of Extractive Distillation

Extractive distillation is used in several industrial applications for the purification of mixed feed streams. Approximately two-thirds of all of the butadiene produced in the United States in 1957 was recovered by extractive distillation using furfural as a solvent. A flow diagram of the process developed by the Phillips Petroleum Company is shown in Figure 17.[69]

The material from which butadiene is to be recovered is prefractionated to remove the propane and lighter components before extraction. The depropanized feed stream containing all seven C_4 isomers enters the butene splitter column where butadiene is concentrated in the overhead product to a feed concentration of 26.2 mole-% of butadiene. The bottoms product contains most of the 2-butene and C_4 acetylenes. The overhead product from the butene splitter is charged to the extractive distillation column where it is extractively distilled with furfural as a solvent. The butadiene-rich furfural leaving the bottom of the extractive-distillation column is pumped to a stripping column where the hydrocarbons are stripped from the furfural and sent to a final separation step in the butadiene column. In this column 2-butene and C_4 acetylenes are removed as a bottoms product, and butadiene with a purity of 98.5% is produced. Essentially all of the butadiene is recovered, as the overhead from the furfural extractive distillation column contains only 0.4 mole-% butadiene.

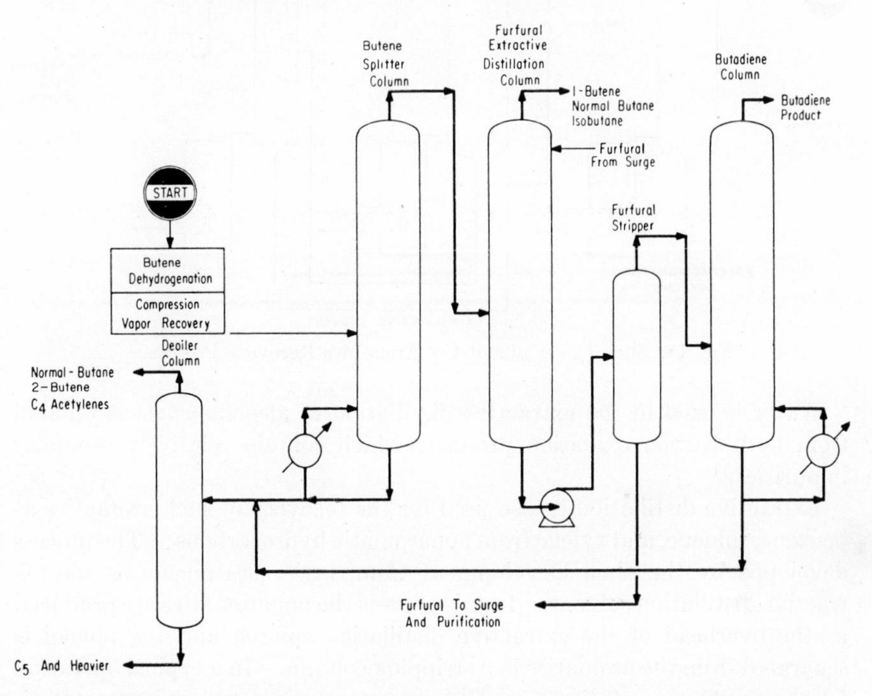

Fig. 17. Phillips Petroleum Co. process for butadiene recovery by furfural extractive distillation.

A similar purification using acetonitrile as the selective solvent has been developed by the Shell Development Company.[70] It is claimed that acetonitrile, when used as an extractive distillation solvent, produces relative volatility ratios which are superior for saturate-olefin separations and somewhat greater for olefin–diolefin separations than those obtained with other solvents such as acetone or furfural. In addition to being non-corrosive and having a small decomposition rate, its low molecular weight, relatively low density, and boiling point give it certain process advantages of economic significance.

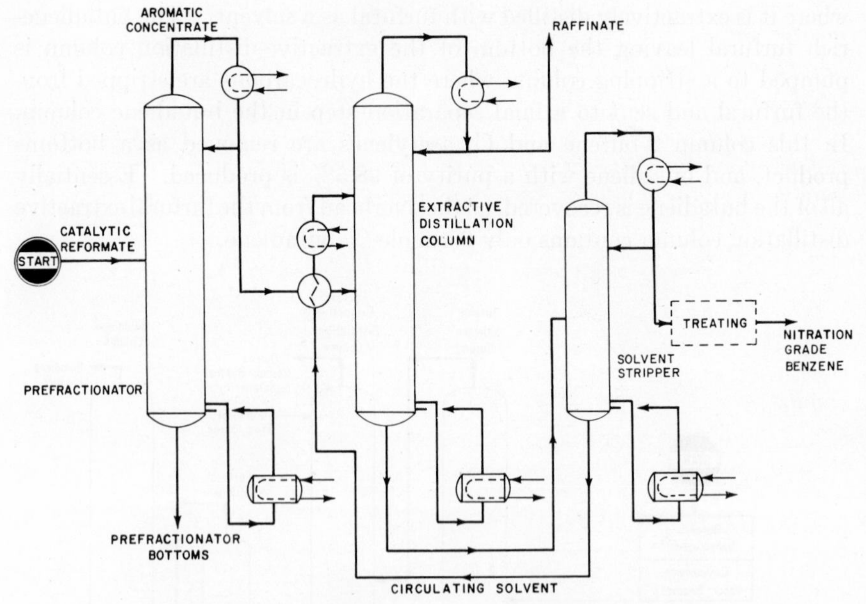

Fig. 18. Shell Development Co. Aromatics Recovery Process.[72]

Water is used in the extractive distillation of alcohols such as ethanol from hydrocarbon oxidation products which contain relatively nonpolar impurities.[71]

Extractive distillation is also used for the recovery of such aromatics as benzene, toluene, and xylene from nonaromatic hydrocarbons. The process developed by the Shell Development Company[72] uses phenol as the extractive distillation solvent. In this process the nonaromatics are produced as the overhead of the extractive distillation column and the phenol is separated from the aromatics in a stripping column. In a typical operation for the production of nitration-grade benzene from depentanized catalytically reformed naphtha containing 45.9 vol.-% benzene according to the process shown in Figure 18, the overhead product from the prefractionator contains 50.5 vol.-% benzene, the overhead from the extractive distillation column contains only 1.0 vol.-% benzene, and the overhead from the solvent stripping tower contains 99.2 vol.-% benzene. At least 12 commercial plants have been reported using this process.

III. AZEOTROPIC DISTILLATION

In azeotropic distillation a solvent is selected which forms a constant-boiling mixture, or azeotrope, with one or more of the components in the feed. The solvent is generally added with the feed to the column. Either minimum-boiling or maximum-boiling azeotropes may be obtained, but Lecat in his first compilation of several thousand azeotropes found less than 10% formed maximum constant-boiling mixtures.[73] For this reason, discussion in the following pages will be in terms of minimum constant-boiling mixtures which are obtained as distillates.

1. Scope

The application of azeotropic distillation, like that of extractive distillation, is usually limited to close-boiling mixtures not readily separable by conventional efficient fractional distillation. A concentrate prepared by efficient fractional distillation often can be further separated by an azeotropic distillation in the presence of a component which forms a minimum or maximum constant-boiling mixture with one of the materials to be separated. In general, the mixture to be separated will boil over a temperature range of less than 20°C. and may even itself be an azeotrope.

2. Theory

Azeotropes exist in the solution because of molecular dissimilarity of the components of the mixture. In binary mixtures exhibiting minimum-boiling azeotropes, a lack of compatibility is evident in view of the large positive deviation from Raoult's law. The ultimate in incompatibility is shown by completely immiscible liquids. When present in the same

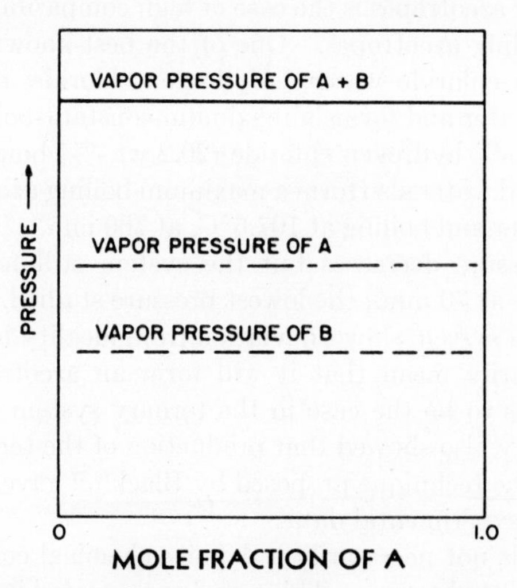

Fig. 19. Vapor pressure–composition relationships for completely immiscible binary mixture.

vessel and boiled, each exhibits its own vapor pressure and a vapor of constant composition is obtained. The distillate from a system such as this has been defined as a heterogeneous azeotrope. Figure 19 shows the vapor-pressure relationships in a binary mixture of this type. The vapor pressures of pure A and pure B are shown as dotted horizontal lines. The vapor pressure above the solution, as long as two liquid phases are present, is the sum of the two vapor pressures as shown by the solid horizontal line. The composition ratio of the vapor equals the ratio of the vapor pressures. The boiling temperature of this system at any pressure is constant. This can be seen from the phase rule relationship:

$$P + V = C + 2 \tag{31}$$

where $P = 3$ phases (2 liquid, 1 vapor), $C = 2$ components, A and B, and $V = 1$ degree of freedom, which in this case is pressure, fixed at one atmosphere. Hydrocarbons and water are good illustrations of mutually incompatible components. Azeotropic distillation of this type is frequently used both in the laboratory and in industry, and has been given the special name of "steam distillation."

An intermediate case of incompatibility is the system *n*-butanol–water. Two liquid phases exist at the boiling point when the overall composition of the liquid is between 65 and 97 mole-% water. Under these conditions one layer is rich in *n*-butanol while the other layer is rich in water. The vapors evolved when two phases are present are of a constant composition.

In contrast with the lack of mutual compatibility which results in minimum-boiling azeotropes is the case of high compatibility, which results in maximum-boiling azeotropes. One of the best-known examples is the system hydrogen chloride–water. Hydrogen chloride, normally a gas, is very soluble in water and forms a maximum constant-boiling mixture containing 11.1 mole-% hydrogen chloride (20.2 wt.-%) boiling at 110°C.

Formic acid and water also form a maximum boiling azeotrope containing 42.4 mole-% water and boiling at 107.6°C. at 760 mm. The water content increases as pressure decreases but the system still forms a maximum boiling azeotrope at 70 mm., the lowest pressure studied.[74]

The fact that a system shows deviation from ideality in the liquid phase does not necessarily mean that it will form an azeotrope. Waldo and Weber found this to be the case in the ternary system benzene–ethanol–*n*-hexane.[75] They also showed that production of the ternary system from binary data by the technique proposed by Black[76,77] gave reasonable agreement with their experimental data.

An azeotrope is not necessarily a definite chemical compound although it is frequently treated as one. This was demonstrated in 1861 by Roscoe,[78] who showed that the composition of the azeotrope varied with the pressure

TABLE XIV
Composition of Ethanol–Water Azeotropes at Different Pressures

Pressure, abs., mm. Hg,	Water in azeotrope, mole-%	Boiling point for azeotropic mixture, °C.
760.0	4.4	78.15
404.6	3.75	63.04
198.4	2.7	47.63
129.7	1.3	39.20
94.9	0.5	33.35
70.0	0.0	—

at which the distillation was carried out, was further verified by the work of Merriman[79] on the system ethanol–water, data from which are reproduced in Table XIV. It will be noted that no azeotrope exists at distillation pressure below 70 mm. of mercury. The manner in which azeotropic composition is influenced by pressure will vary, depending upon the slopes of the vapor-pressure curves of the individual components of the mixture.

The effect of pressure on azeotropic systems can be approximated graphically by a technique developed by Nutting and Horsley.[80] In this method, the vapor pressure of the azeotrope and that of each component is plotted on a Cox chart in which the log of the vapor pressure is plotted versus a function of temperature (°C. + 230) to give a straight line over a wide range of pressures. In a positive azeotrope, the vapor pressure of the azeotrope must lie above that of either component, and in a negative azeotrope it must lie below that of either component. If the vapor pressure curve for the azeotrope crosses the vapor pressure curve for either com-

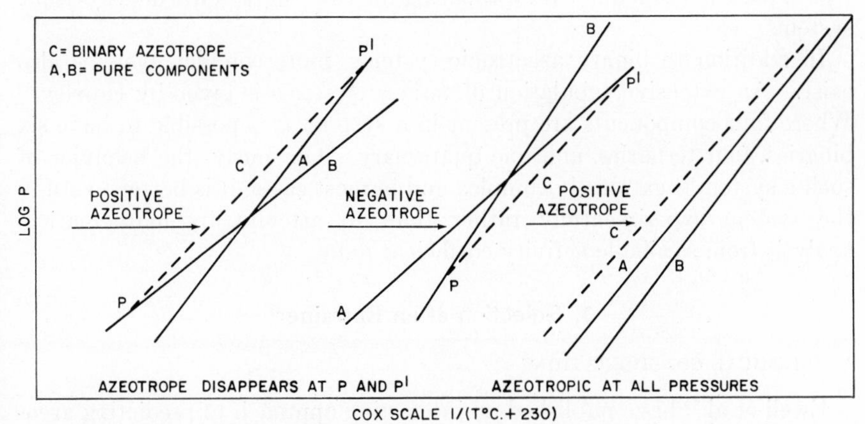

Fig. 20. Schematic diagram of vapor pressure curves of binary azeotropes.

ponent, then its vapor pressure is no longer greater or less than that of the component, and the azeotrope does not exist (see Fig. 20). The azeotrope methanol–methyl ethyl ketone, for example, is not azeotropic at 3000 mm. This technique predicts that the point of intersection would be between 2000 and 4000 mm. The azeotrope methanol–acetone was studied in some detail after it had been predicted that the azeotrope would disappear at both low and high pressures. It is not azeotropic below 200 mm. and above 15,000 mm. Predicted limits are 200–500 mm. and 10,000–20,000 mm. The authors claim that this phenomenon of nonazeotropism at both low and high pressures occurs in several other systems. These charts are relatively simple to construct where the vapor pressure of the azeotrope is known at two temperatures, since only two points are needed to draw the vapor pressure curve on the Cox chart. Where only the azeotropic boiling point is known, the effect of pressure on the system can be estimated by drawing the azeotrope curve through the normal boiling point with a slope equal to the average slopes of the component vapor pressure curves.

Another graphical technique which enables the prediction of the effect of pressure on azeotropic compositions has been presented by Horsley.[81] From the vapor pressure curves of the components of the system, the difference in boiling point can be obtained at any pressure. From a generalized plot of composition versus boiling point difference, it is possible to read the azeotropic composition at the pressure. Also, from a series of plots of the difference in boiling point of the azeotrope and that of the lower boiling component, it is possible to determine the azeotropic boiling point at any pressure. Generalized plots of this type for 45 systems are presented in the original publication. As the authors indicate, the agreement between predicted and experimental values is far from perfect, but the technique is a useful guide for estimating the effect of pressure on azeotropic systems.

In addition to binary azeotropic systems, more complex systems also exist. An extensive tabulation of ternary systems is given by Horsley.[82] Where four components are present in a system, it is possible to have six binaries, four ternaries, and one quaternary. Obviously, the behavior of such a system is extremely complex and in most cases, it is better to study the system experimentally rather than to attempt its mathematical analysis from available activity coefficient data.

3. Selection of an Entrainer

A. CHEMICAL CONSIDERATIONS

Ewell et al.[83] have published an interesting approach to predicting azeotrope formation based on the concept of hydrogen bonds. The deviation from ideality which results in azeotropes is attributed to hydrogen bonds or internal pressure, the former being the more important. The hydrogen-bond concept is stated as follows: "Hydrogen can coordinate between two molecules of oxygen, nitrogen, or fluorine. It can also coordinate between one of these donor atoms (oxygen, nitrogen, fluorine) and a carbon atom, provided a sufficient number of negative atoms or groups are attached to the carbon atom. Hydrogen cannot coordinate between two carbon atoms." Depending upon the atoms between which hydrogen is coordinating, the hydrogen bonds have been classified as follows:

Strong		Weak
	N →	HN
O → HO	O →, N →	$HCCl_2$
N → HO		$HCCl^2$—CCl
O → HN		$HCNO_2$
		$HCCN^2$

Using this classification, organic liquids have been arranged into the five groups given below:

"Class I—Liquids capable of forming three-dimensional networks of strong hydrogen bonds.

"Class II—Other liquids composed of molecules containing both active hydrogen atoms and donor atoms (oxygen, nitrogen, fluorine).

"Class III—Liquids composed of molecules containing donor atoms but no active hydrogen atoms.

"Class IV—Liquids composed of molecules containing active hydrogen atoms but no donor atoms. These are molecules having two or three chlorine atoms on the same carbon as a hydrogen atom, or one chlorine on the same carbon atom and one or more chlorine atoms on adjacent carbon atoms.

"Class V—All other liquids, i.e., liquids having no hydrogen bond forming capabilities."

Typical examples of liquids falling into the above classification are given in Table XV.

From the above five classifications, the authors have predicted deviations from Raoult's law for mixtures of members of the various classes. For positive deviations the vapor pressure above the solution is greater than predicted from Raoult's law, and if it reaches a maximum, a minimum-boiling azeotrope exists (see Figs. 28 and 30). This information is summarized in Table XVI. In the last grouping of classes in this table, the quasi-ideal systems may form azeotropes if the boiling points of the components are very close to each other. Maximum azeotropes have been classified by Horsley:[82]

"1. Water with strong acids—e.g., water with HCl, HBr, HI, HNO_3.

"2. Water with certain associated liquids—e.g., water with formic acid, hydrazine, ethylenediamine.

TABLE XV
Examples of Liquids of Various Classifications

Class I	Class II	Class III	Class IV	Class V
Water	Alcohols	Ethers	$CHCl_3$	Hydrocarbons
Glycol	Acids	Ketones	CH_2Cl_2	Carbon disulfide
Glycerol	Phenols	Aldehydes	CH_3CHCl_2	Mercaptans
Amine alcohols	Primary amines	Esters	CH_2ClCH_2Cl	Iodine
Hydroxylamine	Secondary amines	Tertiary amines	$CH_2ClCHClCH_2Cl$	Phosphorus
			$CH_2ClCHCl_2$	Sulfur
Hydroxy acids	Oximes	Nitro compounds no α H atoms		Halohydrocarbons not in Class IV
	Hydrazine			
Polyphenols	Hydrogen fluoride	Nitriles with no α H atoms		
Amides				
	Hydrogen cyanide			
	Nitro compounds with α H atoms			
	Nitriles with α H atoms			

"3. Donor liquids (Class III) with nonassociated liquids, e.g., acetone + chloroform; cyclohexanone + bromoform; butyl acetate + 1,2,2-trichloropropane.

"4. Organic acids with amines—e.g., acetic acid + triethylamine, propionic acid + pyridine.

"5. Phenols with amines—e.g., phenol + aniline, *o*-cresol + dimethylaniline.

"6. Organic acids with donor liquids containing oxygen—e.g., formic acid + diethyl ketone; butyric acid + cyclohexanone.

"7. Phenols with donor liquids containing oxygen—e.g., phenol + methylhexylketone, *o*-cresol + ethyloxalate.

"8. Phenols with alcohols—e.g., phenol + *n*-octanol; *o*-cresol + glycol."

For ease of discussion, the separation of a binary mixture will be considered although the principles involved apply equally to multicomponent mixtures. An important factor in the selection of an auxiliary agent is that it must have a boiling point relatively close to that of the material to be separated, if a reasonable difference in boiling point between the azeotrope and the other constituents of the mixture is to be realized. (There are notable exceptions to this rule, such as hydrogen chloride, b.p. −83.7°C., and water, which form an azeotrope boiling at 110°C.) This is illustrated in Figure 21 by data for binary azeotropes of paraffin hydrocarbons with methanol and ethanol. The difference between the boiling points of the hydrocarbon and alcohol is given on the abscissa while the difference between the boiling points of the minimum boiling azeotrope and the

TABLE XVI

Summary of Deviations from Raoult's Law

Classes	Deviations	Hydrogen bonding	Example
I + V	Always positive; frequently limited solubility	H bonds broken only	Ethylene glycol–naphthalene, min. azeotrope
II + V	Always positive	H bonds broken only	Ethanol–benzene, min. azeotrope
III + IV	Always negative	H bonds formed only	Chloroform–acetone, max. azeotrope
I + IV	Always positive; frequently limited solubility	H bonds both broken and formed, but dissociation of Class I or II liquid is more important effect	Propylene chloride–water, min. azeotrope
II + IV	Always positive		Methanol–carbon tetrachloride, min. azeotrope
I + I I + II I + III II + II II + III	Usually positive, very complicated groups; some negative give maximum azeotropes	H bonds both broken and formed	Ethanol–water, min. azeotrope 1,4-dioxane–water, min. azeotrope
III + III III + V IV + IV I + V V + V	Quasi-ideal systems, always positive or ideal; azeotropes, if any will be minimum	No H bonds involved	Acetone–*n*-hexane, min. azeotrope Benzene–cyclohexane, min. azeotrope

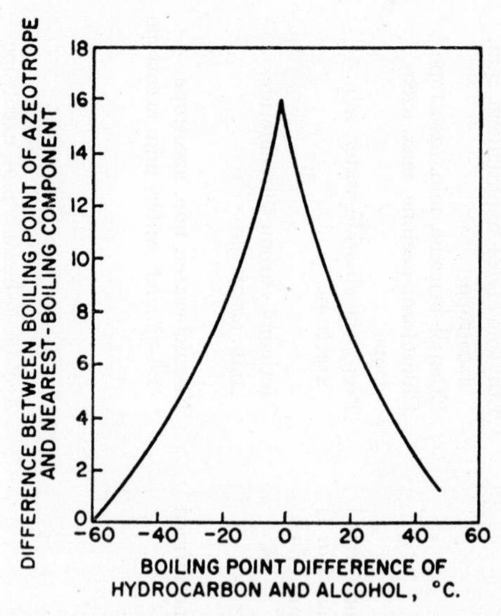

Fig. 21. Relation between boiling-point differences of components of binary mixture and the azeotrope based on paraffin hydrocarbons with methanol and ethanol.

nearest boiling constituent of the mixture is shown as the ordinate. It will be noted that a maximum boiling-point depression of 16°C. is obtained when there is no difference between the boiling points of alcohol and hydrocarbon. The depression decreases rapidly as the difference between the boiling points of alcohol and hydrocarbon increases.

As a rule, auxiliary agents are used which boil within 0 to 30°C. of the material to be separated. For paraffin hydrocarbons, with methanol or ethanol boiling 30°C. from the hydrocarbon, a 5° lowering of boiling point for the azeotrope should be realized. Different mixtures vary in the boiling-point depression realized with various entrainers.

B. SELECTIVE AND NONSELECTIVE ENTRAINING AGENTS

In the separation of a binary mixture an auxiliary agent is desirable which forms an azeotrope with only one of the constituents. Such an auxiliary agent is called a "selective" azeotrope former or entrainer. Entrainers of this type are commonly used in processes in which heterogeneous azeotropes are formed, e.g., in the dehydration of aqueous acetic acid with diethyl ether[84] as the entrainer. Water and entrainer "steam distill" as overhead product, forming two phases on condensing, and the entrainer is recycled as reflux.

In homogeneous azeotropes, nonselective entrainers are more common. For example, methanol and ethanol form azeotropes with successive mem-

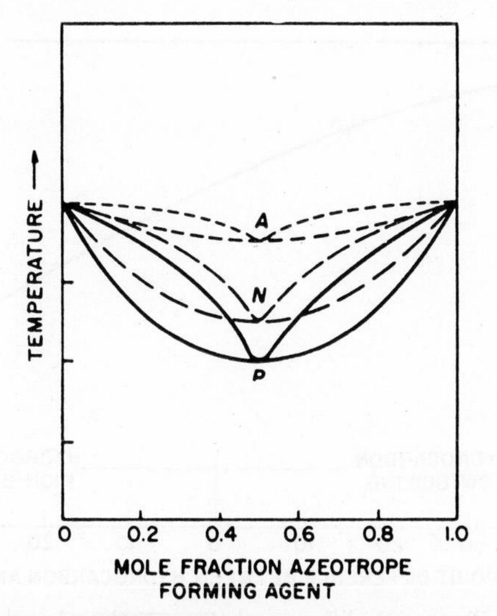

Fig. 22. Relation between boiling points of azeotropes of various types of hydrocarbons having the same boiling point in the pure state, with the same entrainer.[85] *A*, aromatic hydrocarbon; *N*, naphthene hydrocarbon; *P*, paraffin hydrocarbon. Pressure, 1 atm.

bers of the homologous series of paraffin hydrocarbons illustrated in Figure 21. They act in a similar manner with olefins, naphthenes, and aromatic hydrocarbons. The difference in boiling point of the azeotrope and the hydrocarbons of the same boiling point depends on the chemical type of the latter. Mair et al.[85] used this fact to isolate pure hydrocarbons from a straight-run (uncracked) petroleum naphtha, as illustrated by Figure 22, taken from their work. Both vapor and liquid composition curves are shown with the constant-boiling mixture at 50 mole-% entrainer. A petroleum fraction boiling at 110.0 to 110.5°C. and containing paraffins and naphthenes was mixed with toluene, which boils at 110.6°C. Using acetonitrile as an entrainer, an almost quantitative separation of toluene from naphthenes and paraffins was obtained, and likewise a considerable, though not quantitative, separation between the latter.

C. DESIRABLE CHARACTERISTICS OF AZEOTROPIC FORMERS

The difference in boiling point caused by the addition of the entrainer should not be the sole criterion for its selection since the separation is frequently much more complete than can be expected solely from that difference. This means that the spread between the compositions of vapor and liquid is much greater than that of an ideal solution with the same differences in the boiling points of the components. Since we are dealing with highly nonideal systems, this is not surprising.

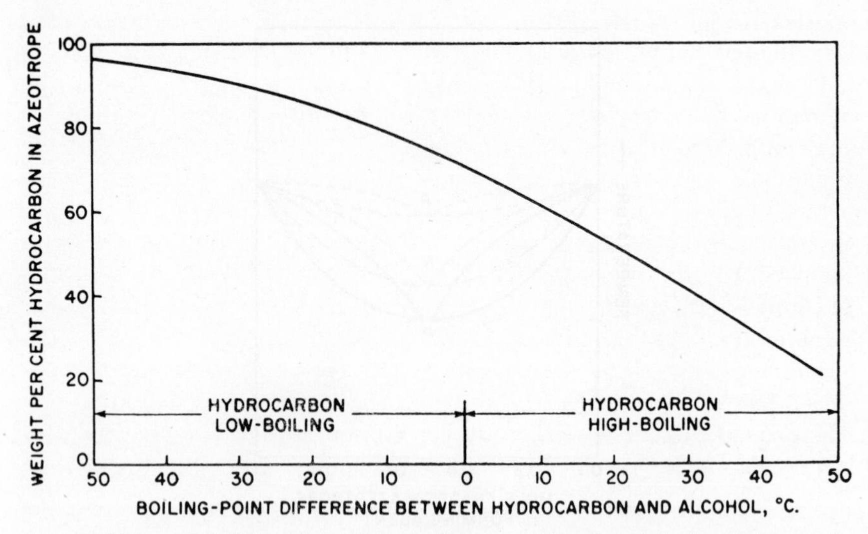

Fig. 23. Effect of boiling-point difference between ethanol and hydrocarbon on the concentration of hydrocarbon in the azeotrope.

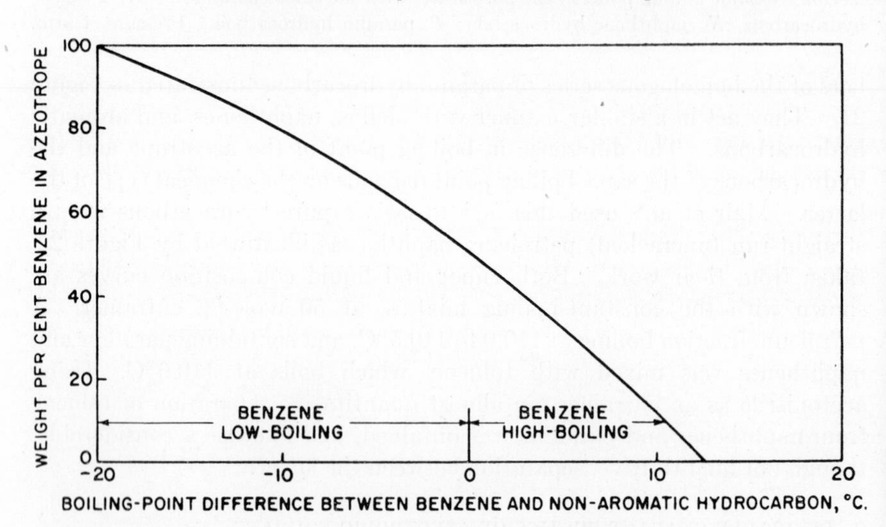

Fig. 24. Effect of boiling-point difference between benzene and non-aromatic hydrocarbon on the concentration of benzene in the azeotrope.

For minimum-boiling azeotropes, the ratio of desired component and entrainer in the azeotrope is important. In general, particularly in industrial practice, a high value of this ratio is desired. This can be achieved by selecting an entrainer which boils higher than the desired component. In laboratory azeotropic separations by batch fractional distillation, another consideration becomes important, namely, the concentration and the amount of the desired component in the distilland and the column holdup. If the amount of the component is small relative to the column holdup, an entrainer which forms a constant-boiling mixture containing a large proportion of entrainer should be selected. This requires an entrainer which boils lower than the component to be isolated. The effect of the boiling-point difference between ethanol and hydrocarbons on the concentration of the azeotrope is shown in Figure 23. If the hydrocarbon is the low-boiling material, it forms the major part of the azeotrope. Figure 24 shows a similar curve for the benzene–hydrocarbon azeotropes. It will be noted that these exist over a much narrower temperature range.

The ease of removal of the entrainer from the azeotrope is very important, since azeotropic distillation resolves a difficultly separable solution by the formation of a constant-boiling mixture which, in turn, cannot be separated by distillation. The azeotrope can be separated in a number of ways, however, such as:

(*a*) Phase separation on cooling
(*b*) Phase separation by "salting out"
(*c*) Chemical removal of entrainer
(*d*) Solvent extraction or water washing
(*e*) Second azeotropic distillation

The most desirable case is that in which the azeotrope, on cooling, separates into two layers, one rich in entrainer, which is refluxed to the fractional-distillation column, and the other rich in desired component, which is withdrawn. The latter is then subjected to a second fractional distillation to remove residual entrainer as the azeotrope. For a minimum azeotrope this operation will leave pure product in the still. In industrial practice the phase separation mentioned above is essential for a successful application of azeotropic distillation. Examples of such processes are the production of anhydrous ethanol using benzene, trichloroethylene, or cyclohexane as the entrainer,[86] and the dehydration of acetic acid with ethers or esters.[87]

Frequently, the addition of another component causes separation of the entrainer. For example, the binary azeotrope methyl ethyl ketone and water, which shows no natural separation into two layers, separates into a water-rich and a water-poor layer upon addition of a small amount of a suitable light hydrocarbon. In a similar manner the addition of salts such as sodium or calcium chloride will frequently cause phase separation by "salting out."

Phase separation can sometimes be induced by the addition of an excess of one of the constituents of the azeotrope. For example, the ternary azeotrope ethyl acetate–ethanol–water is a homogeneous liquid at room temperature. The addition of excess water will give two layers, one essentially water–ethyl acetate and the other ethanol–water saturated with ethyl acetate. The water–ethyl acetate layer at room temperature contains half as much water as the binary azeotrope; hence, on distillation, water-free ethyl acetate will be obtained as residue, with water being removed as the low-boiling binary azeotrope.

In laboratory work when recovery for reuse of the entrainer is not essential, its chemical removal is often possible. For example, in the azeotropic fractional distillation of hydrocarbons with organic acids, the latter can be removed by washing with alkali, and amines such as aniline can be removed with mineral acids. If water is a component of the azeotrope, it can be removed by suitable drying agents. In fact, the lime distillation process used in Germany prior to the development of the Keyes process for the manufacture of anhydrous ethanol was an application of this principle for breaking the water–alcohol azeotrope.

In some cases liquid–liquid extraction will be found more suitable for the removal of the entrainer. In the isolation of toluene from petroleum by azeotropic distillation with the methyl ethyl ketone–water azeotrope as entrainer for the nonaromatic constituents, the entrainer is recovered by liquid–liquid extraction with water.[88] The water phase is then fractionated to obtain the methyl ethyl ketone–water azeotrope. In other cases liquid–liquid extraction of the azeotrope with diethyl ether may remove the entrainer. In the laboratory the removal of entrainer from hydrocarbons by extraction with water can be carried out in separatory funnels. The heavier water layer is discarded and the extraction repeated, if necessary.

Another method for separating the azeotrope is to subject it to a second azeotropic distillation with a different entrainer forming an azeotrope from which it can be recovered more easily.

In addition to forming an azeotrope from which the desired compound is readily recovered, an entrainer should preferably have several other desirable characteristics. In order to be easily handled, it should be noncorrosive, nontoxic, and stable to light and heat. It should be cheap and readily available.

As mentioned above, it is desirable, but not essential in laboratory work, that phase separation of the azeotrope occur on cooling. For hydrocarbon separations, solubility of the entrainer in water is desirable.

For industrial use, low latent heat and high ratio of product to entrainer are important. The latter point has been discussed above from a laboratory viewpoint. The thermal efficiency of an entrainer affects directly the operating costs. An entrainer of higher thermal efficiency carries overhead a greater amount of product for a given heat input to the still. According to Othmer,[87] in the dehydration of acetic acid with isopropyl ether, 1425 cal.

of heat are required to vaporize the ether in order to remove one gram of water, while the similar process with ethylene chloride requires only 920 cal. These heat quantities are in addition to the 540 cal. needed in each case to vaporize one gram of water.

A general discussion of azeotropic separation and its uses has recently been presented by Othmer.[89]

D. SUMMARY

The previous discussion and a study of the available tables of azeotropes will indicate the chemical types which form azeotropes with the compounds to be separated. As guide for further selection, the following general rules are summarized:

(*a*) Select an entrainer boiling as close to the boiling point of the compound to be separated as possible.

(*b*) If there is a choice, use a selective entrainer in preference to a nonselective entrainer.

(*c*) Choose a chemically stable and heat-stable entrainer. If any doubt exists, select an entrainer whose decomposition products will not contaminate the desired product.

(*d*) Other factors being equal, the entrainer with the greatest ease of recovery should be selected. Possible recovery methods are given above.

E. EXPERIMENTAL VERIFICATION OF EFFECTIVENESS OF AN ENTRAINER

Experimental verification of the effectiveness of an entrainer for azeotropic distillation can be obtained by means of an equilibrium still such as that described earlier. It is necessary to determine the vapor–liquid

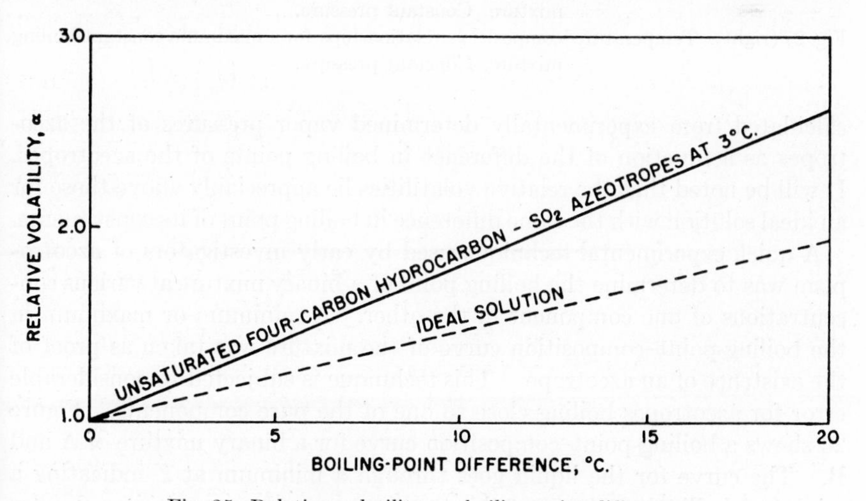

Fig. 25. Relative volatility vs. boiling-point difference.

equilibrium relationships for each component with the entrainer to establish whether an azeotrope is formed with either or both components. The difference between the boiling points of the azeotrope and the other components present is a good indication of the ease of separation of the mixture with the azeotrope. However, it is not an absolute criterion, since a better separation is frequently realized than would be predicted from the difference between the boiling points of the azeotrope and the nearest boiling component. This is illustrated by the data of Matuszak and Frey[90] on the four-carbon hydrocarbons, butenes and butanes, with sulfur dioxide as an entrainer. In Figure 25 are plotted relative volatilities α,

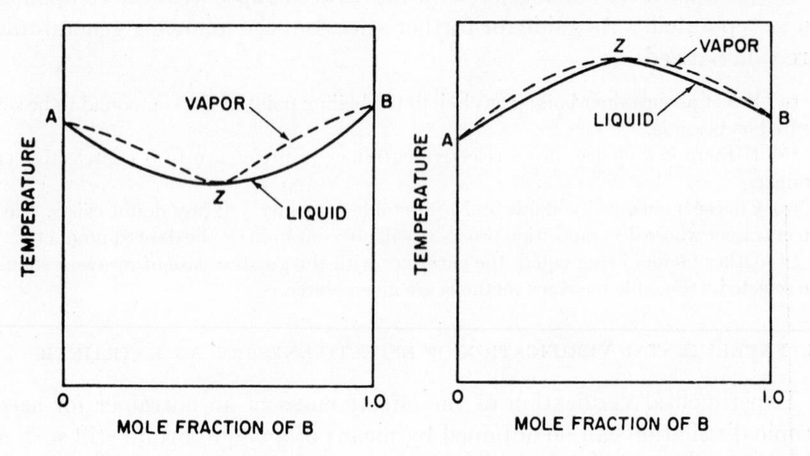

Fig. 26 (left). Temperature–composition relationships for a minimum constant-boiling mixture. Constant pressure.

Fig. 27 (right). Temperature–composition relationships for a maximum constant-boiling mixture. Constant pressure.

calculated from experimentally determined vapor pressures of the azeotropes as a function of the difference in boiling points of the azeotropes. It will be noted that the relative volatilities lie appreciably above those for an ideal solution with the same difference in boiling point of its constituents.

A quick experimental technique used by early investigators of azeotropism was to determine the boiling point of a binary mixture at various concentrations of one component in the other. A minimum or maximum in the boiling-point–composition curve of the mixture was taken as proof of the existence of an azeotrope. This technique is subjected to considerable error for azeotropes boiling close to one of the pure components. Figure 26 shows a boiling-point–composition curve for a binary mixture of A and B. The curve for the liquid goes through a minimum at Z indicating a minimum-boiling azeotrope at this temperature and composition. Similar

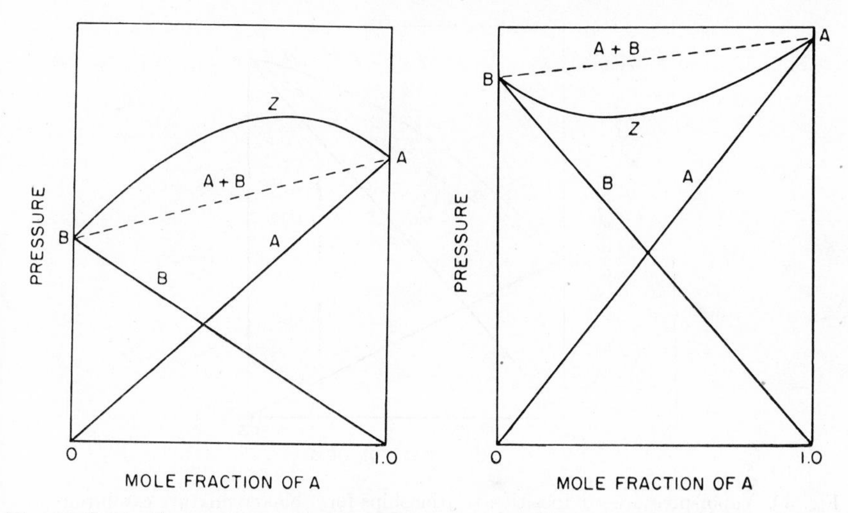

Fig. 28 (left). Vapor pressure–composition relationships for a binary mixture with a minimum constant-boiling mixture. Constant temperature.

Fig. 29 (right). Vapor-pressure–composition relationships for a binary mixture with a maximum constant-boiling mixture. Constant temperature.

curves are given in Figure 27, which shows a maximum-boiling azeotrope at Z.

Another rapid experimental technique is the determination of the vapor pressure of mixtures of the two components at a constant temperature. A maximum in the vapor-pressure curve of the binary mixture is indicative of a minimum-boiling azeotropoe while a minimum in the vapor-pressure curve of the binary mixture is indicative of a maximum constant-boiling mixture. In Figures 28 and 29 are plotted typical curves of the former and latter type, respectively. The straight lines in each figure are the partial pressures of each component of the solution calculated from Raoult's law. The sum of the ordinates of these two lines, shown dotted and designated as A + B, is the vapor pressure of the mixture predicted from Raoult's law. The actual vapor-pressure curve of the mixture in Figure 28 shows a maximum at Z, while in Figure 29, the vapor-pressure curve of the binary mixture shows a minimum at Z. Positive (or negative) deviations from Raoult's law are frequently observed for binary mixtures. Figure 30 shows a typical example of positive deviations without an azeotrope as the difference between the dotted line A + B and the curved line. Positive deviation from Raoult's law is not in itself proof of azeotrope formation, which requires that the vapor pressure curve go through a maximum. Determination of the vapor pressure as a test for azeotropism like the determination of boiling points becomes difficult for azeo-

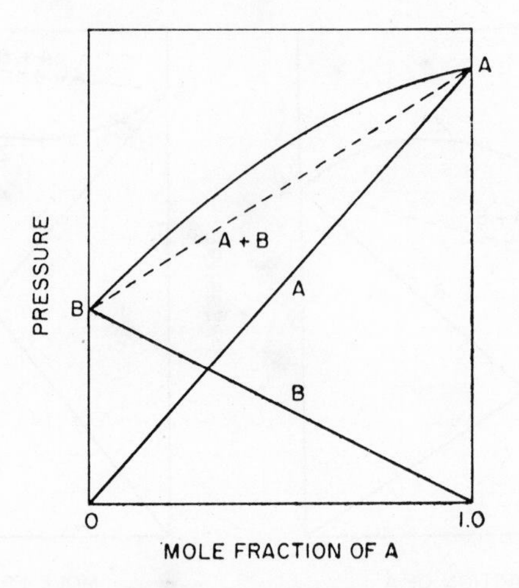

Fig. 30. Vapor-pressure–composition relationships for a binary mixture exhibiting positive deviation from Raoult's law.

tropes boiling close to the boiling point of one of the pure components of the mixture.

Unless extensive work is planned with a given entrainer, it is frequently easier to add the entrainer to the mixture and to carry out a fractional azeotropic distillation in a column of known separating power than to determine the fundamental vapor–liquid equilibria. The effect of the entrainer on the separation of the mixture will be readily observed. This technique has been used by Nelson[91] to evaluate entrainers for the separation of ethylbenzene from paraxylene.

If a column of good separating power is used and the system permitted to equilibrate at total reflux, and a small sample can be removed for analysis, it is possible to calculate the entire vapor–liquid equilibrium curve for the system by the use of the van Laar or similar equations.

4. Laboratory Apparatus and Procedure for Azeotropic Distillation

A. BATCH DISTILLATION

Azeotropic distillation has been used extensively in laboratory work because of its ease of application. Using conventional batch fractional-distillation equipment, entrainer in sufficient quantity or in excess is added to the still with the mixture to be separated. A regular analytical distillation is then carried out taking distillate fractions representing 1 or 2% of the charge. After removal of the entrainer from the distillate, the usual physical measurements such as refractive index and density or boiling point

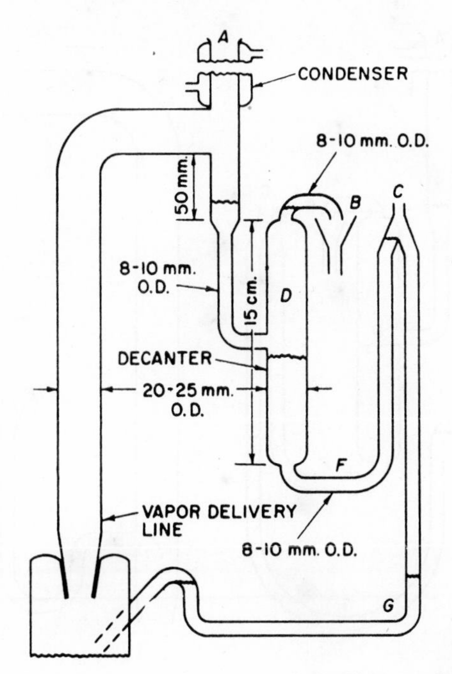

Fig. 31. Continuous decanter and distillation column.

can be made to determine the degree of purity of the entrainer-free cuts. A plot of vapor temperature at the still head versus volume per cent of charge distilled will give a good indication of the cut point between different azeotropes and excess entrainer. Conventional laboratory distillation columns suitable for this work have been described in Chapter II.

For those distillations in which the entrainer forms a separate phase in the distillate on cooling, care must be exercised in selecting the type of column head to be used. Reflux condensers with little liquid holdup and with provision for intermittent take-off of total distillate are preferred. In this way both liquid layers will be obtained as product. Examples of such column heads are the swinging-funnel, liquid-dividing type and the vapor-dividing head shown in Chapter II. If, on cooling, the entrainer is concentrated in the upper layer, the simple still head (exclusive of funnel) shown in Figure 12 may be used. The lower layer, in which the product will be concentrated, is withdrawn through stopcock *E*. When the reverse case obtains, still heads of this kind should be avoided.

Continuous separation of distillate phases with return of one phase to the column can be carried out automatically with the aid of a decanter and auxiliaries such as those shown in Figure 31. In order to return one phase to the column by gravity flow, an extension approximately 17 in. long is

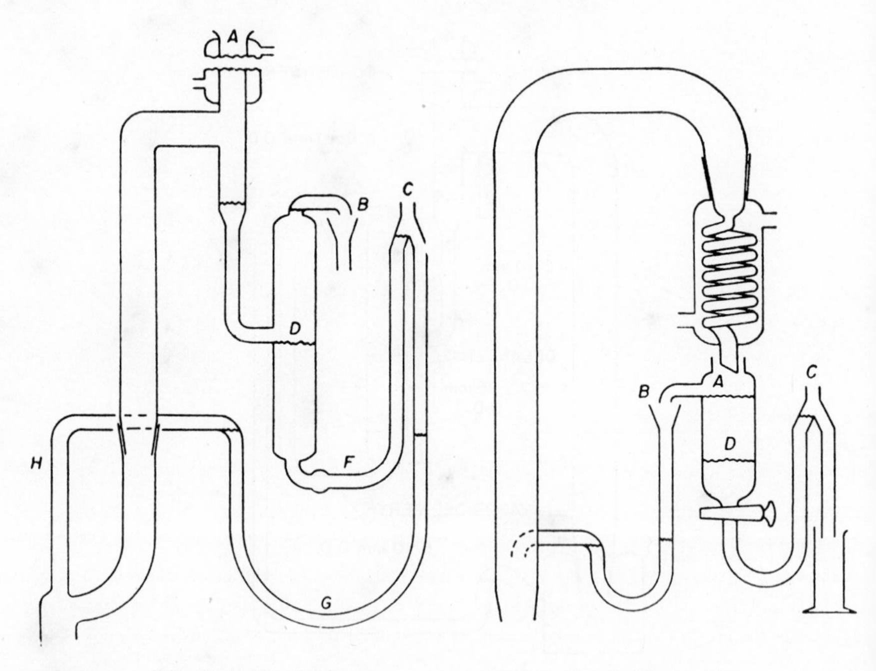

Fig. 32 (left). Alternate arrangement for setup in Figure 31.
Fig. 33 (right). Another alternate arrangement for Figure 31.

added to the top of the column to deliver the distillate vapors to an elevated condenser. The complete arrangement is shown in Figure 31 with alternate arrangements in Figures 32 and 33. The vapor delivery line is usually the same diameter as the column and is insulated or heated by electrical windings to prevent excessive refluxing. Provision must be made to vent the column as well as each decanter phase, which in the case of atmospheric-pressure distillation may be directly, to the atmosphere. These vent points are designated as *A*, *B*, and *C*, respectively, in Figures 32 and 33. Typical decanter dimensions are 15 cm. long × 2.5 cm. O.D. (6 in. × 1 in.), the delivery and overflow tubes being usually 8–10 mm. O.D. (Graduated separatory funnels of 125- and 250-ml. size have been converted into decanters by the addition of a side arm near the top.) The interfacial level in decanter *D* is determined by the difference in density of the two phases and the location of overflow point *C*. The latter can easily be adjusted if flexible plastic or rubber tubing is connected at points *F* and *C*. A glass Y- or T-tube is used for convenience at point *C*. When the material being handled attacks flexible connections of the type mentioned above so that all-glass or metal connections are necessary, semispherical ball joints at *F*, *C*, and *G* will permit adjustment of the level of *C*. Glass decanters or separators are preferred, since the level of the interface can readily be observed.

In Figure 31 the lower distillate phase is being returned through the thermometer well of a vapor-dividing head from which the valve rod and condenser have been removed. A column-feed section can also be used. Both these pieces of equipment can be purchased from commercial glass blowers as stock items. The loop in the return line at *G* provides a liquid seal so that vapors from the column cannot by-pass the condenser and escape into the atmosphere.

In Figure 32 the decanter is attached to a laboratory column of the type described in Figure 12 but from which the vent and product draw-off have been removed. The lower phase is being returned through the thermometer well at *H*.

Obviously, either the upper or lower phase may be returned to the column. In Figure 33 the upper phase is being recycled. Note that this line is vented at point *B* to permit proper operation of the decanter. The returning phase in this case is introduced through the vapor delivery tube.

Frequently, phase separation of the distillate does not occur except after considerable cooling. In such cases, it is often preferable to operate the condenser so as to cause liquefaction but not phase separation. The distillate, withdrawn while warm, will separate into two phases on further cooling. In more elaborate arrangements, two condensers are used, the first for reflux condensation, the second for phase separation of the product and recycling of the entrainer phase.

Steam Distillation. One very common form of azeotropic distillation is steam distillation. It is widely used in organic laboratory work, particularly when dealing with heat-sensitive materials. It is used for the distillation or purification of water-immiscible or slightly water-miscible materials such as aniline, glycerol, or fatty acids from cottonseed roots.

It was pointed out in the discussion of the theory of azeotropic distillation that, when two immiscible liquids are distilled and are present as separate liquid phases, each liquid will exert its own vapor pressure independent of the other so that the total pressure above the boiling solution is the sum of the individual vapor pressures. Thus, in steam distillation with a water phase present, the distillation temperature will never exceed the boiling point of water at the pressure, usually atmospheric, at which the distillation is conducted. The approximate boiling temperature can be calculated by employing this principle if the vapor-pressure data are known.

For example, if the vapor-pressure curves of toluene and water are plotted as log p vs. $1/T°K.$, straight lines are obtained. Adding vapor-pressure readings at several different temperatures and plotting these points will also result in a straight line. Where this line crosses the

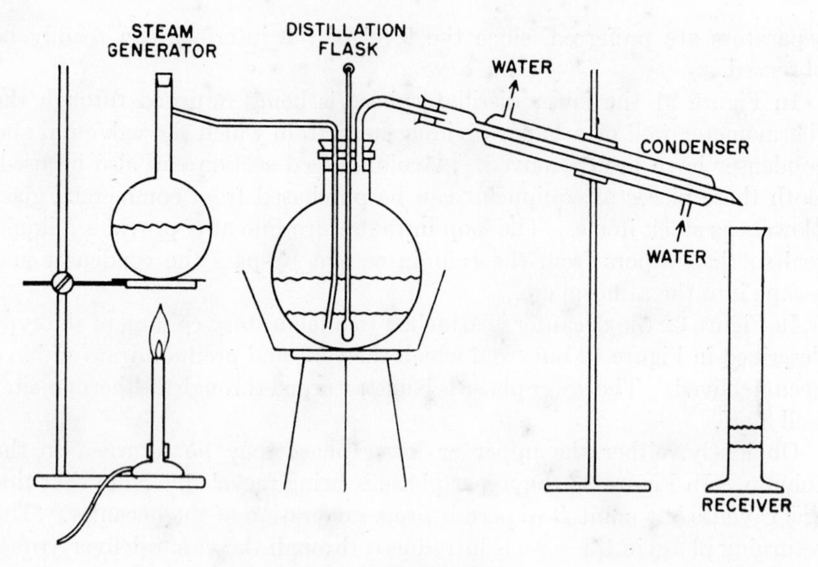

Fig. 34. Steam distillation.

760-mm. pressure ordinate will be the predicted boiling point. This intersection occurs at 84.4°C., at which temperature the vapor pressure of toluene is 337 and that of water is 423 mm. of mercury. The azeotropic boiling point reported by Horsley[82] is 84.1°C.

The molal composition of the distillate can be calculated from the above vapor pressures. The weight ratio of the two components in the distillate is given by the following equation:

$$W_A/W_B = (P_A M_A)/(P_B M_B) \tag{32}$$

where A refers to the upper-phase material, in this case toluene, and B refers to the lower-phase material, water. W, P, and M are weight, vapor pressure at distillation temperature, and molecular weight, respectively. Substituting the vapor pressures given above and the appropriate molecular weights, the following result is obtained:

$$W_A/W_B = (337)(92)/(423)(18) = 4.1 \tag{33}$$

Thus one can expect 4.1 g. toluene for each gram of water in the distillate. The predicted distillate composition is (4.1/5.1)(100) or 80.3 wt.-% toluene. The azeotropic composition reported by Horsley[82] is 86.5 wt.-% toluene.

A very useful chart for estimating the boiling points of immiscible water mixtures is given by Badger and McCabe.[92] Vapor pressures are plotted vs. temperature in the normal manner. The curve for water is plotted as 760 minus the vapor pressure of water so that the resulting curve intersects the other vapor-pressure curves at the steam-distillation boiling point at 760 mm. of mercury. Similar curves for water can be drawn for other pressure levels such as 300 or 100 mm. distillation pressure.

The use of steam distillation as a laboratory technique merely requires a source of steam, a steam delivery tube, a distillation flask, condenser, and receiver. Such an apparatus is illustrated in Figure 34. When steam is available, the steam generator may be dispensed with. Numerous modifications and improvements can be incorporated in this basic apparatus. For example, laboratory steam usually contains an appreciable amount of condensate which will rapidly fill the distillation flask with water phase. Much of this water can be eliminated by a trap or knockout flask placed just ahead of the distillation flask. Provision should be made for intermittent draining of the trap. A trap with automatic drain is described by Egly in Chapter I, Volume III, of this series.

With this arrangement shown in Figure 34, all the heat required for warming the solution and the vaporization of the distillate must be supplied by the steam which will condense in the distillation flask, gradually filling it with water phase. The latter can be reduced intermittently by draining out part of the water phase. An easier method is to supply heat to the distillation flask also, either through a steam superheater (see Egly, Chapter I, Volume III, this series) or by heating the distillation flask directly. Drains for the knockout and the distillation flask can be provided as bottom stopcocks or as suction tubes inserted through the flask stopper and extending nearly to the bottom of the flask. The latter is better practice as it is well to place all heated distillation flasks in vessels or pans of sufficient size to retain all the liquid in the distillation flask in case of breakage. This greatly reduces fire hazard in the laboratory.

The laboratory procedure for steam distillation is to charge the organic material into the distillation flask shown in Figure 34. A small amount of water may be added if desired, although condensing steam will provide an adequate water phase shortly after starting the distillation. The distillation flask should be no more than one-third full at the start of the distillation. A thermometer in the liquid phases in the distillation flask makes it possible to follow the course of the distillation. The distillation is discontinued when negligible amounts of distillate are obtained in a reasonable time such as an hour. Frequently, organic matter will be dispersed in the aqueous distillate as evidenced by a haze or white cloud in the water phase. This can usually be eliminated by adding salts such as sodium or potassium chloride to the aqueous phase.

It should be pointed out that the distillate recovered during steam distillation usually contains much more water than is predicted from azeotropic compositions. In other words, the steam is less than 100% efficient in vaporizing the organic components. The relationship between theoretical and actual distillate ratios is usually referred to as steam-vaporization efficiency and will depend upon the depth of organic phase above the water phase and the manner in which steam is dispersed in the distillation flask. The vaporization efficiency of the steam is increased as the organic phase is increased in depth to about 50 cm. It also increases as the diameters of the openings for admitting steam into the distillation flask are decreased to one millimeter. If these steps are taken to increase vaporization efficiency, a greater pressure is required to force steam into the distillation flask.

One of the simplest methods of employing steam distillation in the laboratory involves placing the organic phase and sufficient water phase in a distillation flask. The heterogeneous mixture is heated externally and the distillate condensed and collected as above. This technique is, of course, limited to those cases in which the quantity of water required for the distillation can be added to the flask at the start of the distillation.

In certain cases only a small amount of volatile material is to be recovered from a large amount of relatively nonvolatile material. In such cases an integral steam-distillation apparatus such as that just described is used but with a vertical condenser. A distillate receiver which has provision for returning water to the distillation flask is used so that the system will not be depleted in water. The oil-dilution test employed by the oil industry, in which small amounts of gasoline are distilled from lubricating oils, is an example of this type of operation. Distillate receivers suitable for this purpose may be purchased from commercial glass blowers. Such receivers are listed under oil-dilution apparatus.

The discussion thus far has been limited to steam distillation with a water phase present. Steam distillation in the absence of a water phase is widely used commercially, particularly in the petroleum industry. This type of operation is really a part of a broader technique known as distillation in the presence of an inert gas. In this case vapor pressures are still additive, but the distillation temperature will vary as the proportion of inert carrier is varied. Inert carriers which may be used are any of the common inert gases such as nitrogen, carbon dioxide, or methane, as well as steam. The last is preferred because condensation problems are simplified and water is readily available. See Chapter V.

B. CONTINUOUS DISTILLATION

For the satisfactory use of continuous azeotropic distillation considerable information about the system is necessary. This includes feed composition, percentage entrainer in azeotrope, and boiling points of azeotropes and nonazeotropes. As usually applied industrially, for example, in the manufacture of absolute ethanol or in acetic acid dehydration, a selective en-

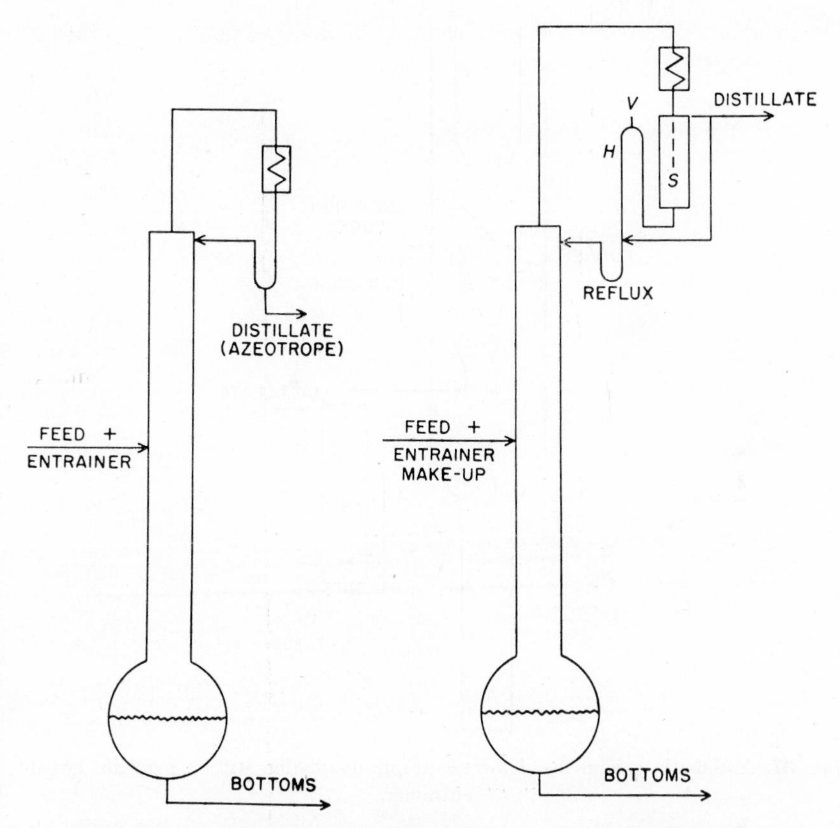

Fig. 35 (left). Continuous azeotropic distillation with miscible entrainer.
Fig. 36 (right). Continuous azeotropic distillation with partially miscible entrainer.

trainer is used which forms a minimum constant-boiling mixture. The separation in the fractionator is between the azeotrope obtained as distillate and the nonazeotrope obtained essentially pure as bottoms. In such a case the entrainer is added with the feed in amount just sufficient to form the azeotrope which is removed as distillate.

An apparatus for continuous azeotropic distillation with a miscible entrainer is shown in Figure 35. Feed and entrainer in the correct proportion are introduced at the proper point in the column. A minimum-boiling azeotrope will be obtained as distillate and segregated for later separation of the entrainer from the desired product. When a selective entrainer is used, the bottoms should theoretically be free of entrainer. In the practical case a very slight excess of entrainer ensures obtaining all the desired product azeotrope. If the entrainer boils between the azeotrope and the bottoms product, some of the entrainer may appear in the

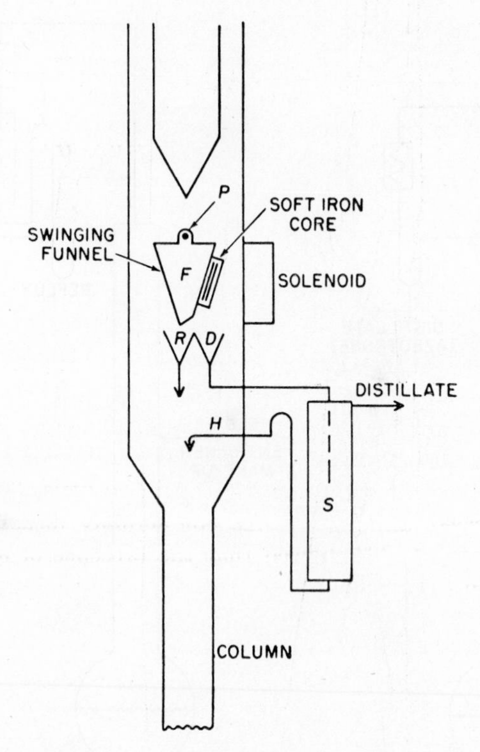

Fig. 37. Automatic column head for azeotropic distillation with a partially miscible entrainer.

bottoms if adequate stripping in the lower section of the column is not provided.

An apparatus for continuous azeotropic distillation with a partially miscible entrainer forming a minimum-boiling azeotrope is shown in Figure 36. Phase separation of the distillate occurs on cooling, and by means of a separator, *S*, the heavier entrainer phase is refluxed to the column through overflow, *H*, which is vented at *V*. A certain proportion of the light phase may have to be refluxed also in order to maintain the necessary reflux ratio. Since most of the entrainer is returned to the column, the feed introduced contains only enough entrainer to make up for that removed with the distillate product. Entrainer-free bottoms are withdrawn from the still.

The number of points of control required in the arrangements shown in Figure 36 can be decreased. A modified still-head arrangement is shown in Figure 37, in which the condenser and reflux device are inside an expanded section of the column. The reflux ratio is controlled by a swinging bucket or funnel, positioned by a solenoid, which is actuated by an electric timer not shown. The reflux ratio is really a time ratio. The column operates under conditions of total reflux, all condensate being returned to the column through funnels F and R, until the solenoid is actuated, when the funnel F is pulled to the right, pivoting on point P. All condensate then runs through H, and distillate is withdrawn. If line H is of sufficient diameter for the flow involved, it need not be vented. With this arrangement, only the feed and bottoms streams require continuous control.

C. EQUIPMENT PERFORMANCE

As in extractive distillation, little information is available on equipment performance. Guinot and Clark,[93] in discussing the continuous production of anhydrous ethanol in commercial bubble-cap plate towers, stated that, in the upper part of the column below the entrainer reflux, two liquid phases existed on several of the plates, but agitation was so vigorous that uniform dispersion of the phases was realized and little effect on plate efficiency was observed, although it was not actually measured. More recently, Schoenborn et al.[94] showed that the presence of a moderate proportion of insoluble component in the liquid made no appreciable change in plate efficiency of a laboratory bubble-cap column.

In laboratory columns of the packed variety, liquid-phase separation may have a deleterious effect on H.E.T.P. if one liquid preferentially wets the column packing.

5. Calculation of Azeotropic-Distillation Separations

In the calculation of azeotropic-distillation separations, the azeotrope can be treated as an individual component. This is illustrated by the work of Matuszak and Frey,[95] who studied the separation of the four-carbon hydrocarbons into butanes and butenes by azeotropic distillation with sulfur dioxide. Data from one of their runs have been used to plot the curve in Figure 38. The hydrocarbon mixture consisted of (*a*) *n*-butane with a trace of isobutane and (*b*) *n*-butenes with a trace of isobutene. The distillate composition is expressed on an entrainer-free basis, while the mole per cent distilled refers to the total distillate including entrainer.

The distillation was carried out isothermally at 3°C. in a laboratory vacuum-jacketed (unsilvered) glass analytical column with approximately 10 theoretical plates. The hydrocarbon in the first 56% distilled averaged 99.5% saturated hydrocarbons, while the hydrocarbon in the residue (exclusive of a trace of pentane impurity) averaged 99.4 mole-% butenes (after 82.5% distillate was removed). Shown in Figure 38 are the average sulfur dioxide concentrations in the distillate which correspond very closely to the azeotropic compositions given in Table XVII. For example,

TABLE XVII
Binary Azeotropic Mixtures of Sulfur Dioxide and Four-Carbon Hydrocarbons

Hydrocarbon	Temp., °C.	Pressure, atm.	Mole-% Hydrocarbon	Mole-% SO_2
Isobutane	3	3.17	45.1	54.9
n-Butane	3	2.65	35.6	64.4
Isobutene	3	2.24	36	64
1-Butene	3	2.37	40.7	59.3
2-Butene	3	2.05	27.7	72.3

the first distillate, which contained the saturated hydrocarbons, contained on the average 63 mole-% sulfur dioxide, which corresponds closely to the *n*-butane azeotrope when allowance is made for the azeotrope of isobutene, which contains only 54.9 mole-% sulfur dioxide. Similarly, a portion of distillate, the hydrocarbon portion of which contained 95.0 mole-% *n*-butenes, 3.4% isobutene, and 0.6% paraffins, contained 71.8 mole-% sulfur dioxide, very close to the azeotropic composition listed for 2-butene.

The separation of an azeotrope from a nonazeotrope or of two azeotropes from each other can be calculated by the conventional methods given in Chapter I, treating the azeotrope as an individual component, providing the corresponding relative volatilities are known. Most of the data on azeotropes consist of their compositions and boiling points. The use of

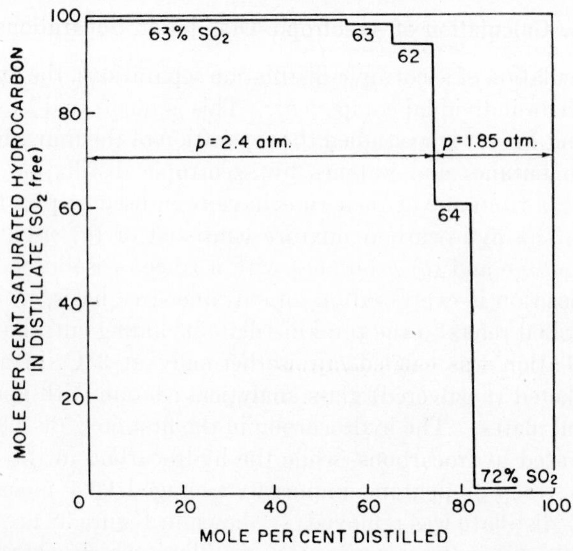

Fig. 38. Separation of butanes from butenes by azeotropic distillation with sulfur dioxide in a laboratory vacuum-jacketed glass gas-analytical column.

boiling-point differences to estimate relative volatilities, α, will in general give a conservative result. The actual separation realized during azeotropic distillation would indicate a much higher value for α than the calculated one. This was illustrated in Figure 25 for the four-carbon hydrocarbons *n*-butane, isobutane, *n*-butenes, isobutylene, with sulfur dioxide.

A. AMOUNT OF ENTRAINER REQUIRED

If the composition of the azeotrope or azeotropes is known and the approximate composition of the charge is known, the entrainer requirements can readily be estimated. For example, consider the distillation[95] plotted in Figure 38.

Basis of calculation.

(*a*) Hydrocarbon charge is 75 mole-% *n*-butane and 25 mole-% 2-butene,
(*b*) Distillation conducted isothermally at 3°C.,
(*c*) Entrainer to be used, sulfur dioxide.

Data.

n-Butane–sulfur dioxide azeotrope contains 64.4 mole-% sulfur dioxide.
2-Butene–sulfur dioxide azeotrope contains 72.3 mole-% sulfur dioxide.

Entrainer requirements per gaseous liter hydrocarbon charge.

(*a*) For *n*-butane: (750)(64.4)/(35.6) = 1350 cc. sulfur dioxide.

(*b*) For 2-butene: (205)(72.3)/(27.7) = 650 cc. sulfur dioxide.

Total for one liter of hydrocarbon gas 2000 cc. sulfur dioxide.

Thus, for theoretical entrainer requirements the charge should contain 66.7 mole-% sulfur dioxide and 33.3 mole-% hydrocarbon. The actual charge contained only 60% sulfur dioxide, which was found to be insufficient.

It is of interest to consider what results should be expected in a batch fractional distillation when various proportions of entrainer are used. For purposes of discussion a three-component mixture will be used with a high-boiling entrainer added as a fourth component, capable of forming azeotropes with each component.

(a) **Insufficient Entrainer Present to Form Azeotropes with All Components.** When this situation exists, the entrainer will appear in the distillate with the lowest boiling azeotropes until the entrainer is exhausted. Separation will then depend upon the normal volatility relationships of the remaining components.

(b) **Theoretical Amount of Entrainer Present to Form Azeotropes with All Components.** In this case the distillation will proceed as though three components were present with volatilities corresponding to those of the azeotropes. Better separation of the azeotropes will be realized than for the above case.

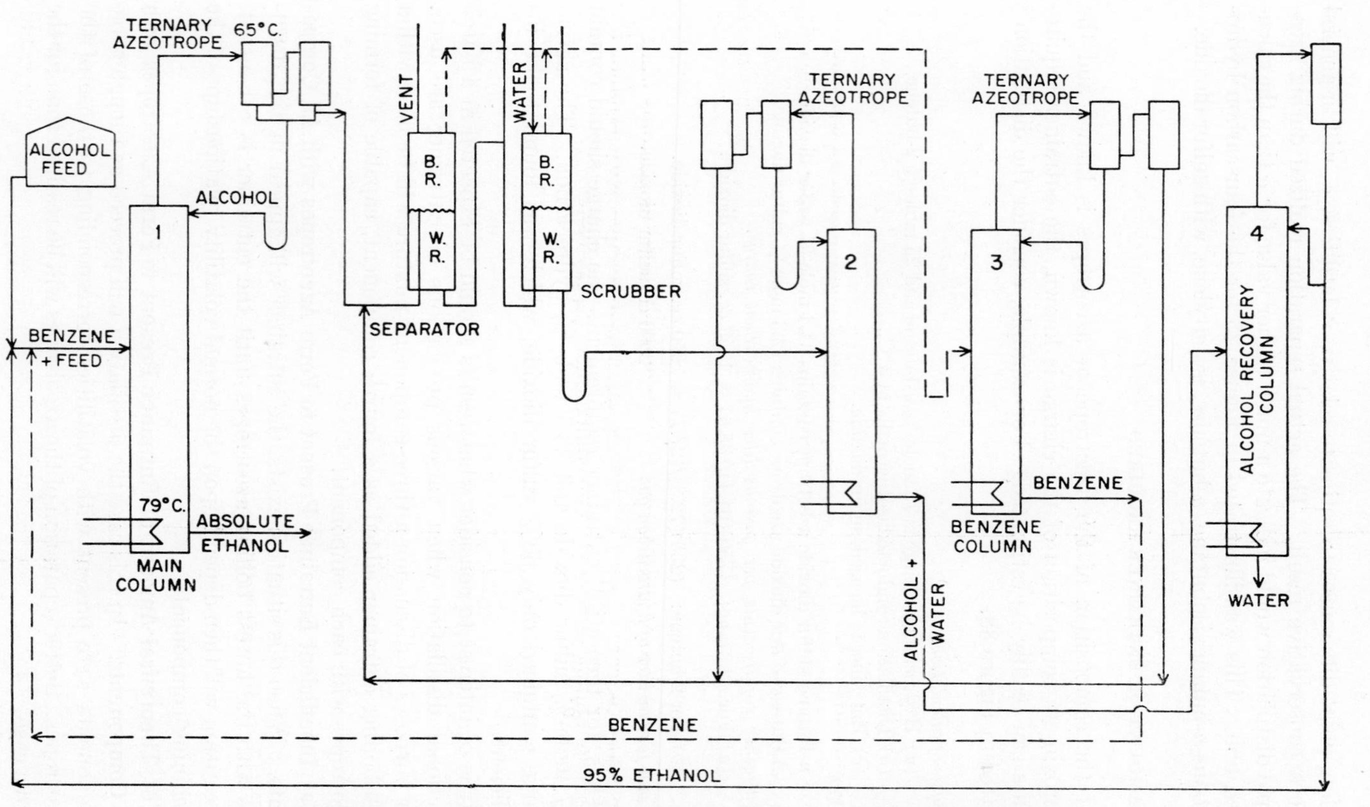

Fig. 39. Keyes process for ethanol. W. R., water-rich. B. R., benzene-rich.

(c) Entrainer Present in Excess of the Amount Necessary to Form Azeotropes with All Components. Since a high-boiling entrainer was designated, the distillation will progress with the three azeotropes being obtained successively as distillate with excess entrainer being distilled last if the distillation is carried that far. The separation of the azeotropes may be sharper than in (*b*) because of the effect of the presence of excess entrainer.

In brief, in batch azeotropic distillations the entrainer and charge will be added directly to the still in calculated proportions, and usually with a slight excess of entrainer. If the charge composition is unknown and insufficient entrainer has been added, the distillation can be stopped and additional entrainer added to the still. The distillation can then be continued after the usual equilibration time under total reflux has been allowed.

6. Example of Commercial Application of Azeotropic Distillation

While extractive distillation appears rather complicated on a laboratory scale but is relatively simple on a continuous industrial scale, azeotropic distillation is very simple to use in a laboratory batch distillation. However, the commercial applications of continuous azeotropic distillation are rather complicated. This can be seen in Figure 39, illustrating the Keyes process for the production of absolute ethanol. Ethanol (95%) and benzene entrainer are fed to column 1, where ethanol is obtained as bottoms while all the water is carried overhead as a ternary azeotrope with ethanol and benzene, boiling at 65°C. The composition (in per cent by weight) of the ternary azeotrope is as follows:

Benzene	74.1
Ethanol	18.5
Water	7.4

All the remaining equipment serves to recover benzene and alcohol carried overhead as the ternary azeotrope in column 1. On condensing, the ternary azeotrope forms two phases, which are separated in the separator. The upper, benzene-rich phase, which at 28°C. contains 85.6% (by weight) benzene, 11.6% alcohol, and 2.8% water, passes to the benzene recovery column 3, where anhydrous benzene is obtained as bottoms and the ternary azeotrope as overhead; the latter is returned to the separator.

The lower, water-rich layer flows to a scrubber, where water is added in amount sufficient to cause further benzene-phase separation. This benzene phase also goes to the benzene column. The water layer, which at 28°C. contains 40.6% (by weight) water, 51.3% alcohol, and 8.1% benzene, passes to column 2, where benzene is taken overhead as the ternary azeotrope and returned to the separator. Alcohol–water bottoms from column

2 flow to the alcohol recovery column 4, where water is removed as bottoms, and 95% ethanol is taken overhead for return to alcohol feed storage.

This process is interesting since it employs the features of distillate phase separation and phase precipitation by water addition. All heating is done by closed steam.

A. COMPARISON OF EXTRACTIVE AND AZEOTROPIC DISTILLATION

It is apparent that extractive and azeotropic distillation are quite similar in that the relative volatility of components in a solution is modified in both cases by the addition of another component in such a way as to render separation more feasible. The theoretical treatment of both systems is identical.

Extractive distillation has less of a heat load than azeotropic distillation, since the entraining agent need not be volatilized in the former case. As a result, extractive distillation is preferred for most commercial applications. On the other hand, the equipment needed for extractive distillation is somewhat more complex than that used for azeotropic distillation, and as a result, the latter is more convenient for laboratory work, particularly when batch systems are used for the separation. In addition to the lower heat requirement for extractive distillation, it usually provides for a wider choice of solvents since the practical range of volatilities is wider for a solvent than for an entrainer. Solvent and reflux rates can be set at will while volatility restrictions limit the flow rate of the entrainer and reflux in azeotropic distillation. The technique to be used in a particular separation depends upon the system to be employed and the data required. In general, extractive distillation is used in the laboratory where data are needed for the design of commercial extractive distillation processes while azeotropic distillation is used as a preparative method.

References

1. National Bureau of Standards Circular C461, U. S. Government Printing Office, Washington, D. C., 1947.
2. Fenske, Tongberg, Quiggle, and Cryder, *Ind. Eng. Chem.*, **28**, 644 (1936).
3. Tongberg, Lawroski, and Fenske, *Ind. Eng. Chem.*, **29**, 957 (1937).
4. Willingham and Rossini, paper presented before the Petroleum Division, Am. Chem. Soc. Atlantic City Meeting, 1946.
5. Huffman and Urey, *Ind. Eng. Chem.*, **29**, 531 (1937).
6. Gerster, in *Chemical Engineers' Handbook*, Perry, Chilton, Kirkpatrick, eds., McGraw-Hill Book Co., Inc., New York, 1963, Section 13.
7. Benedict and Rubin, *Trans. Am. Inst. Chem. Engrs.*, **41**, 353 (1945).
8. Dunn, Millar, Pierotti, Shiras, and Souders, Jr., *Trans. Am. Inst. Chem. Engrs.*, **41**, 631 (1945).
9. Sunier and Rosenblum, *Ind. Eng. Chem. Anal. Ed.*, **2**, 109 (1930).
10. Fleer, *J. Chem. Education*, **22**, 588 (1945).

11. Fenske, in *Science of Petroleum,* Vol. II, Dunstan, Nash, Brooks, and Tizard, eds., Oxford Univ. Press, New York, 1938, p. 1631.
12. Fenske, Carlson, and Quiggle, *Ind. Eng. Chem.*, **39,** 1322 (1947).
13. Dicks and Carlson, *Trans. Am. Inst. Chem. Engrs.*, **41,** 789 (1945).
14. Dunn, Millar, Pierotti, Shiras, and Souders, Jr., *Trans. Am. Inst. Chem. Engrs.*, **41,** 631 (1945).
15. Brunjes and Bogart, *Ind. Eng. Chem.*, **35,** 255 (1943).
16. Colburn and Schoenborn, *Trans. Am. Inst. Chem. Engrs.*, **41,** 422 (1945).
17. Anderson, Cambio, and Prausnitz, *Am. Inst. Chem. Eng. J.*, **8,** 66 (1962).
18. Prausnitz and Anderson, *Am. Inst. Chem. Eng. J.*, **7,** 96 (1961).
19. Othmer, *Ind. Eng. Chem.*, **20,** 7113 (1928).
20. Jones, *J. Chem. Eng. Data,* **7,** 13 (1962).
21. Fenske, Carlson, and Quiggle, *Ind. Eng. Chem.*, **39,** 1322 (1947).
22. Colburn, Schoenborn, and Schilling, *Ind. Eng. Chem.*, **35,** 1250 (1943); Mertes and Colburn, *ibid.*, **39,** 787 (1947).
23. Swanson and Gurster, *J. Chem. Eng. Data,* **7,** 132 (1962).
24. Quiggle and Fenske, *J. Am. Chem. Soc.*, **59,** 1829 (1937).
25. Carlson, Schubert, and Fenske, *Ind. Eng. Chem. Anal. Ed.*, **18,** 109 (1946).
26. Griswold, Andres, Van Berg, and Kasch, *Ind. Eng. Chem.*, **38,** 66 (1946).
27. Fenske, Carlson, and Quiggle, *Ind. Eng. Chem.*, **39,** 1322 (1947).
28. Updike, Langdon, and Keyes, *Trans. Am. Inst. Chem. Engrs.*, **41,** 717 (1945).
29. Staaterman, Morris, Stager, and Pierotti, *Chem. Eng. Progr.*, **43,** 148 (1947).
30. Dunn, Millar, Pierotti, Shiras, and Souders, Jr., *Trans. Am. Inst. Chem. Engrs.*, **41,** 631 (1945).
31. Prabhu and Van Winkle, *J. Chem. Eng. Data,* **8,** 14 (1963).
32. Qozati and Van Winkle, *J. Chem. Eng. Data,* **5,** 269 (1960).
33. Carlson, Smith, and Morrell, *Ind. Eng. Chem.*, **46,** 350 (1954).
34. Ramalho, Tiller, James, and Bunch, *Ind. Eng. Chem.*, **53,** 895 (1961).
35. Bunch, James, and Ramalko, *Ind. Eng. Chem. Process Design Develop.*, **2,** 282 (1963).
36. Rose, Williams, Sanders, Henry, and Ryan, *Ind. Eng. Chem.*, **45,** 1568 (1953).
37. Black, Derr, and Papadopoulas, *Ind. Eng. Chem.*, **55,** 38 (1963).
38. Tao, *Ind. Eng. Chem.*, **56,** 36 (1964).
39. Halla, Pick, Fried, and Filim, *Vapor-Liquid Equilibrium,* Pergamon Press, New York, 1958.
40. Wilson and Deal, *Ind. Eng. Chem. Fundamen.*, **1,** 120 (1962).
41. Ferguson, J. B., *J. Phys. Chem.*, **36,** 1123 (1932).
42. Pierotti, Deal, and Derr, *Ind. Eng. Chem.*, **51,** 95 (1959).
43. Deal, Derr, and Papadopoulos, *Ind. Eng. Chem. Fundamen.*, **1,** 17 (1962).
44. Tamura and Nagata, *Am. Inst. Chem. Eng. J.*, **8,** 161 (1962).
45. C. Black, *Ind. Eng. Chem.*, **51,** 211 (1959).
46. Young and Perkins, U. S. Patent 1,948,777 (1934).
47. Francis, *Ind. Eng. Chem.*, **36,** 764 (1944).
48. Dicks and Carlson, *Trans. Am. Inst. Chem. Engrs.*, **41,** 789 (1945).
49. Francis, *Ind. Eng. Chem.*, **36,** 1096 (1944).
50. *A.S.T.M. Standards on Petroleum Products and Lubricants,* D611-44T, P41-43. American Society for Testing Materials, Philadelphia, 1945.
51. Ball, *U. S. Bur. Mines Rept. Invest.*, **3721** (1943).
52. Warren, Warren, and Yarborough, *Ind. Eng. Chem.*, **51,** 1475 (1959).
53. Sheets and Marchello, *Petrol. Refiner,* **42,** 99 (1963).
54. Smith, *Ind. Eng. Chem.*, **34,** 234 (1942).
55. Varteressian and Fenske, *Ind. Eng. Chem.*, **29,** 270 (1937).

56. Ewell, Harrison, and Berg, *Ind. Eng. Chem.*, **36**, 871 (1944).
57. Hildebrand, *Solubilities*, 2nd ed., Reinhold, New York, 1936.
58. Riegel, *Industrial Chemistry*, 4th ed., Reinhold, New York, 1942, p. 283.
59. For an explanation of dipole moment, see Smyth in *Physical Methods of Organic Chemistry*. 3rd ed., Weissberger, ed., Interscience, New York, Part III, 1960.
60. Oldershaw, *Ind. Eng. Chem. Anal. Ed.*, **13**, 265 (1941). Manufactured by Glass Engineering Laboratories, Belmont, California.
61. Griswold, Andres, Van Berg, and Kasch, *Ind. Eng. Chem.*, **38**, 65 (1946).
62. Griswold and Van Berg, *Ind. Eng. Chem.*, **38**, 170 (1946).
63. Fenske, *Ind. Eng. Chem.*, **24**, 482 (1932).
64. The ratio of concentration in the distillate divided by the ratio of concentrations in the still, E.R. = $(y_1/y_2)_D/(x_1/x_2)_s$. See Fenske, in *Science of Petroleum*, Vol. II, Oxford Univ. Press, New York, 1938, p. 1631.
65. Carlson, Ph.D. Thesis, Pennsylvania State College, 1939.
66. Drickamer and Bradford, *Trans. Am. Inst. Chem. Engr.*, **39**, 319 (1943).
67. Drickamer and Hummel, *Trans. Am. Inst. Chem. Engrs.*, **41**, 607 (1945).
68. Happel, Cornell, Eastman, Fowle, Porter, and Schutte, *Trans. Am. Inst. Chem. Engr.*, **42**, 189 (1946).
69. Phillips Petroleum Co., *Petrol. Refiner*, **36**, No. 11, 295 (1957).
70. Shell Develop. Co., *Petrol. Refiner*, **36**, No. 11, 297 (1957).
71. Stone and Webster Eng. Corp., *Petrol. Refiner*, **36**, No. 11, 298 (1957).
72. Shell Develop. Co., *Petrol. Refiner*, **36**, No. 11, 299 (1957).
73. Lecat, *La tension de vapeur des Mélanges de liquides. L'Azeotropism* Lamertin, Brussels, 1918.
74. Ito and Yoshida, *J. Chem. Eng. Data*, **8**, 315 (1963).
75. Waldo and Weber, *J. Chem. Eng. Data*, **8**, 349 (1963).
76. Black, *Ind. Eng. Chem.*, **50**, 391 (1958).
77. Black, ref. 76, 403.
78. Roscoe, *Trans. Chem. Soc.*, **13**, 146 (1961); **15**, 270 (1862).
79. Merriman, *J. Chem. Soc.*, **103**, 628 (1913).
80. Nutting and Horsley, *Adv. Chem. Ser.*, **6**, 318 (1952).
81. Horsley, *Advan. Chem. Ser.*, **6**, 321 (1952).
82. Horsley, *Advan. Chem.*, **6**, (1952).
83. Ewell, Harrison, and Berg. *Ind. Eng. Chem.*, **36**, 871 (1944).
84. Othmer, *Trans. Am. Inst. Chem. Engrs.*, **30**, 299 (1933).
85. Mair, Glasgow, Jr., and Rossini, *J. Res. Natl. Bur. Std.*, **27**, 39 (1941).
86. Guinot and Clark, *Trans. Inst. Chem. Eng. London*, **16**, 189 (1933). Keyes, *Ind. Eng. Chem.*, **21**, 998 (1929). Colburn and Phillips, *Trans. Am. Inst. Chem. Engr.*, **40**, 333 (1944).
87. Othmer, *Trans. Am. Inst. Chem. Engr.*, **30**, 299 (1933).
88. Lake, *Trans. Am. Inst. Chem. Engr.*, **41**, 327 (1945). Hartley, *Petrol. Refiner*, **24**, 519 (1945).
89. Othmer, *Chemical Eng. Progr.*, **59**, No. 6, 67 (1963).
90. Matuszak and Frey, *Ind. Eng. Chem. Anal. Ed.*, **9**, 111 (1937).
91. Nelson, *Preprints, Div. Petrol. Chem. A.C.S.*, **8**, No. 1, 115 (1963).
92. Badger and McCabe, *Elements of Chemical Engineering*, 2nd ed., McGraw-Hill, New York, 1936, p. 369.
93. Guinot and Clark, *Trans. Inst. Chem. Engr. London*, **16**, 189 (1933).
94. Schoenborn, Koffolt, and Withrow, *Trans. Am. Inst. Chem. Engr.*, **37**, 997 (1941).
95. Matuszak and Frey, *Ind. Eng. Chem. Anal. Ed.*, **9**, 111 (1937).

CHAPTER V

DISTILLATION UNDER MODERATE VACUUM

R. Stuart Tipson, *Washington, D. C.*

I. INTRODUCTION

Distillation under moderate vacuum is defined as that in which the operating pressure in the system is less than atmospheric but sufficiently high that the mean free path of the vapor molecules is small relative to the gap between the distilland surface and the condensing surface. In practice, this includes all vacuum distillations performed in equipment not specifically designed for molecular distillation of the types described in Chapter VI. In the range of moderate vacuum, certain additions to, and modifications of, the equipment and procedures employed for distillation at atmospheric pressure, similar to those described in Chapter III, are necessary.

The principal advantage of distilling under diminished pressure instead of at atmospheric pressure is that the boiling point is lowered. The change in boiling point with change in pressure for benzaldehyde, for example, is shown in Figure 1. It will be noted that this diminution is much greater at lower pressures; this is because the pressure of a vapor varies logarithmically as the inverse of its absolute temperature. Many compounds which boil with decomposition at about 350°C. at 760 Torr will distil unchanged at 160–210°C. at 10 Torr. This lowering of the boiling point often permits distillation of substances which would, if distilled at atmospheric pressure, be subject to condensation, dehydration, isomerization, oxidation, polymerization, pyrolysis, or rearrangement. Commercially, distillation under moderate vacuum is used in the preparation of essential oils, fatty acids, lubricating oils, and polymerizable monomers. Vacuum distillation is also useful for heat-stable compounds that have a low vapor pressure and which boil at inconveniently high temperatures at atmospheric pressure.

In laboratory operations, simple distillation under moderate vacuum is used for removing solvents from reaction mixtures, and for lowering the concentration of a solvent to a minimum without subjecting the solute to excessive temperatures. The procedure may be used to separate a reaction product, as a distillate, from accompanying high-boiling materials, and

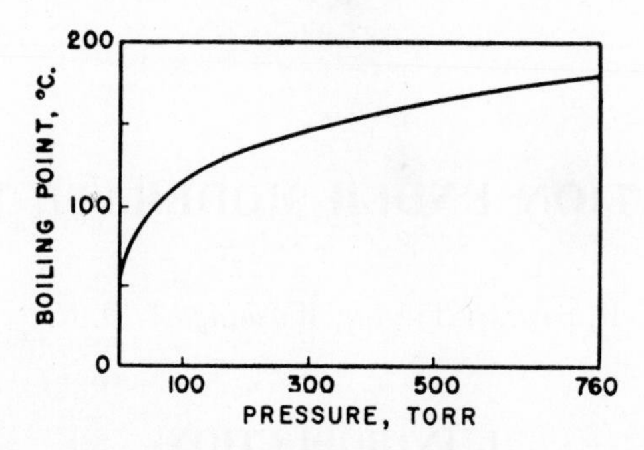

Fig. 1. Effect of pressure on boiling point of benzaldehyde.

thereby facilitate subsequent purification of the desired product by crystallization or other means. However, the major use of distillation under moderate vacuum in the laboratory is for fractionations involving the principles which operate at atmospheric pressure. The process is highly effective, provided that the pressure is precisely controlled and superheated vapor is avoided. Systems in which the relative volatility is small at atmospheric pressure but larger at lower pressures are often separable under vacuum operation.

II. THEORY

1. Fluid Flow

Moderate vacuum is arbitrarily defined as that extending from about 200 to 0.1 Torr. In this region, vapors behave essentially as at atmospheric pressure, with a gradual change toward ideality as the pressure is lowered, as is the case in the molecular stills described in Chapter VI. The density of a vapor under reduced pressure is therefore almost directly proportional to the pressure, and the molar volume is almost inversely proportional to the pressure. The latter characteristic exhibits its effects most noticeably in consideration of the flow properties. For example, a mole of vapor at 10 Torr and 100°C. has a volume of about 2300 l. compared to about 30 l. at atmospheric pressure. To force the former volume from a vapor generator through a narrow tube into a condenser in a given period of time requires energy which is expressed as "pressure drop" through the tube. To avoid this pressure drop to a significant extent, the rate of transfer must be greatly lowered, that is, the rate of distillation must be low. This requirement is a basic, operational limitation of all distillations under moderate vacuum.

2. Rectification

Distillation under moderate vacuum attains its maximum utility under rectifying conditions, just as does distillation at atmospheric pressure. That rectification over this range of pressures is possible is to be expected from the theory discussed in Chapter I, where a pressure term is not involved in the basic theory of the process of distillation. Theory and practice agree for practical equipment, within the limits imposed by pressure drop and by heat losses due to imperfect thermal insulation. The established range of pressure within which normal rectification is possible lies between atmospheric pressure (or above) and a fraction of a Torr. Properly constructed and controlled, equipment suitable for fractionation at atmospheric pressure functions equally well down to a head pressure of 40 Torr, provided that a lower throughput is used to ensure a low pressure drop through the rectifying section. This requirement practically precludes the use of plate or perforated-tray columns at the lower range of pressure, because, regardless of the rate of vapor flow, the pressure drop will be at least equal to the total depth of liquid on the trays, measured in terms of mercury. Below a head pressure of 40 Torr, packed columns having conventional construction, again with low throughput, are usable if efficiencies of 20–30 theoretical plates are acceptable. At a head pressure of 4 Torr, conventionally designed columns, using, for example, protruded packing* and providing about 15 theoretical plates, function satisfactorily with a pressure drop of only 1.5 Torr. Below about 4–5 Torr, spinning-band columns, if of adequate diameter, may be operated with very low pressure drop, but, in their present state of development, these columns are only moderately efficient unless used at very low throughputs.

Fractionating columns built and operated in accordance with the principles set forth by Kuhn,[1] Westhaver,[2] and Jantzen and Wieckhorst[3] are usable from 760 to less than 1 Torr. In accordance with the reasoning of Kuhn,[1] high efficiency can be attained, but only at very low productivity; efficiency becomes progressively lower as the pressure is reduced.

To fractionate at pressures below a few tenths of a Torr, recourse has been had to batchwise, countercurrent redistillation. In this system, simple distillations are used repeatedly; each achieves nearly one plate of separation, and many stages are cascaded to bring about reblending of intermediate fractions and ultimate separation of more-or-less pure components. Several of these stills are discussed in Chapter VI. A large amount of material is needed in these stills, and the long time required for the fractionation limits their use to fractionation of stable materials.

* For a description of protruded packing, see Chapter III.

III. APPARATUS

For a distillation under moderate vacuum, there are needed, in addition to the still, a vacuum pump, a vacuum gage, a manostat to keep the pressure constant, and suitable traps. For fractional distillation, a fraction cutter is usually required.

1. Pumps, Traps, Gages, and Manostats

Vacuum pumps are of two types: the water aspirator and the mechanical, oil-filled types. Water aspirators are commonly used for providing pressures of 10–30 Torr, the attainable pressure depending on the prevailing atmospheric pressure, the water temperature and pressure, and the condition of the pump. Because of the possibility of fluctuations in the water pressure, a trap must be connected between the receiver and the pump, to prevent back-flow of water into the receiver. Such fluctuations may also require use of a manostat. A manostat must be used when a pressure between 30 and 760 Torr is desired. In handling very volatile materials, a cold trap is connected between the receiver and the aspirator to prevent loss of the distillate. In addition, if corrosive vapors are evolved, either a glass aspirator should be used or a suitable chemical trap should be included.

The motor-driven, mechanical, oil-filled pumps produce vacua to about 1 Torr. Several types and sizes are available from scientific supply houses. The oil pump should be protected by a trap, cooled with dry ice, to prevent contamination of its oil by the low-boiling materials often present in a crude distilland.

For specific details on vacuum pumps, traps, and gages, consult the discussion on these subjects in Chapters VI and VII. Manostats for controlling the pressure over the range of moderate vacuum of 760–1 Torr are discussed in Chapter III, along with suggestions for setting up permanent vacuum systems.

2. Stills

A still consists essentially of a boiler, a head, a condenser, and a receiver. It may include a column. Stills are of two general kinds: horizontal and vertical. Combinations of the two are often employed. All glassware, preferably borosilicate type, must be strong enough to withstand the external pressure. The worker, should however, wear goggles, and place a safety-glass shield in front of the still. All stoppers must be tight; rubber stoppers may be lightly smeared with a lubricant. For high temperatures or corrosive distillands, ground-glass joints, sparingly lubricated, are preferable. To avoid lubrication, a snug-fitting plastic sleeve may be inserted in the joint. The figures in this Chapter show connections, joints, and stopcocks that are adequate for most distillands. For a more complete discussion of special seals, sealing compounds, joints, lubricants, greases, and other auxiliary materials to effect vacuum connections, the reader is referred to the discussions in Chapters III, VI, and VII on these subjects. The boiler may be heated with a water, glycerol, oil, or metal bath, or with an electric mantle.

A. HORIZONTAL STILLS

Horizontal stills have been used mainly for separation of certain mixtures of liquids of greatly different volatility, for concentration of solutions, and for batchwise, fractional redistillation.

A typical assembly due to Wendland[4] is depicted in Figure 2. At *A* is inserted a ground joint carrying a stirring rod or fine capillary tube, long enough to reach to the bottom of the distilling flask. The whole is evacuated by means of a pump, connected at *B* by stout rubber tubing to a trap and mercury manometer. The distilling flask is surrounded by a heating bath whose upper level is above the distilland level, to lessen the tendency to bump. In some cases, it may be desirable to immerse the flask as completely as possible, or to lag the neck with asbestos cord. The bath, which may be covered with an asbestos plate, is gradually heated until distillation commences, and is then kept at a constant temperature to maintain a steady, moderate rate of distillation.

Bumping frequently accompanies distillation under reduced pressure; it is a sudden, almost explosive, generation of vapor which violently agitates the distilland and which may throw part of it up into the neck of the boiler or even into the condenser. Excessive superheating of the distilland is the cause of bumping. Two-phase systems are particularly likely to bump and should therefore be avoided unless the technique of quiescent ebullition is employed. Bumping may be prevented by provision of either (*a*) quiescent ebullition from the surface of the distilland, or (*b*) a continuous source of nuclei for vaporization from inner parts of the distilland.

One method of assuring quiescent ebullition, achieved by Conners,[5] is shown in Figure 3. Its essential feature is a thermostatic valve, attached between the receiver and the pump, which opens when the temperature of the vapor falls below a predetermined setting and closes above this temperature. This permits distillation of immiscible liquids, under vacuum, without bumping. Quiescent boiling can also be carried out by the rotary still described by Craig et al.[6] and shown in Figure 4. The distilland is placed in flask *A*, which is attached by a ground joint on inlet tube *C* to receiver *B*. (Tube *C*, as depicted, is unnecessarily wide, as the conductance of a tube varies as the fourth power of its diameter.) The other neck of *B* is attached, by rubber tubing *D*, to ball joint *E* and thence to the vacuum line. For operation, evacuation is begun, the motor is started, and its speed is so adjusted that, with *A* and *B* rotating, the surface of the

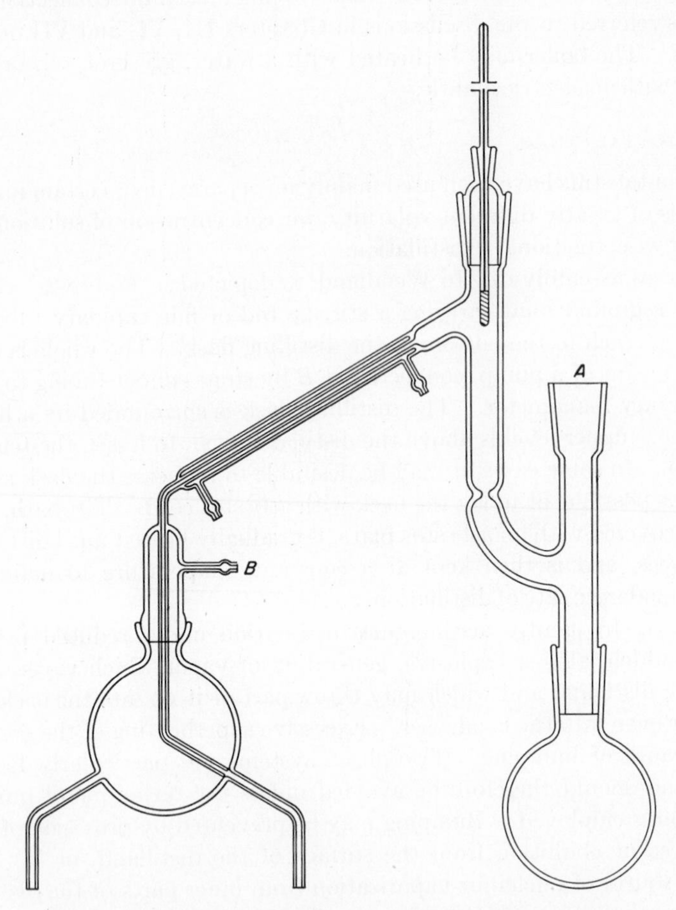

Fig. 2. Simple still for distillation under diminished pressure.[4]

liquid in *A* is not greatly disturbed. Bath *J* is then suitably heated and bath *I* is cooled with ice-water or with dry ice–chloroform. Distillation takes place rapidly without ebullition or bumping. The apparatus may also be used for evaporation or lyophilization of solutions of solids. Improved models of the rotary still have been devised[7] and several are now available commercially.

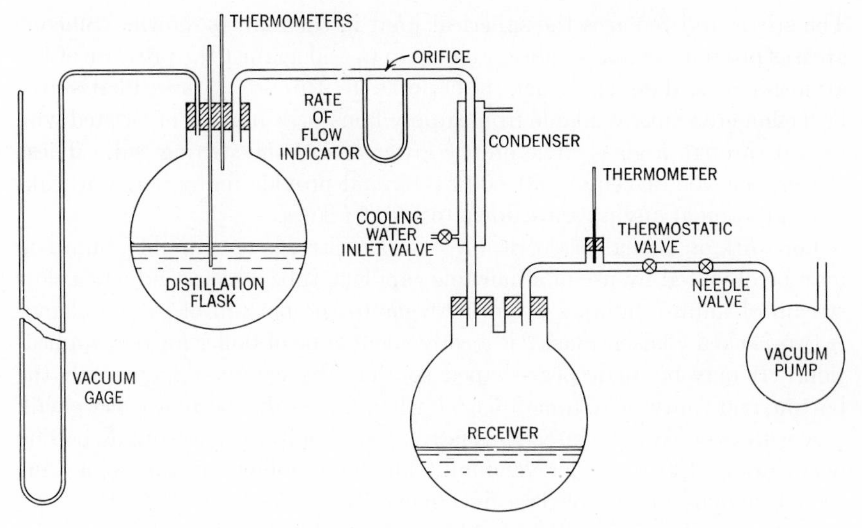

Fig. 3. Still having a thermostatic valve for quiescent ebullition.[5]

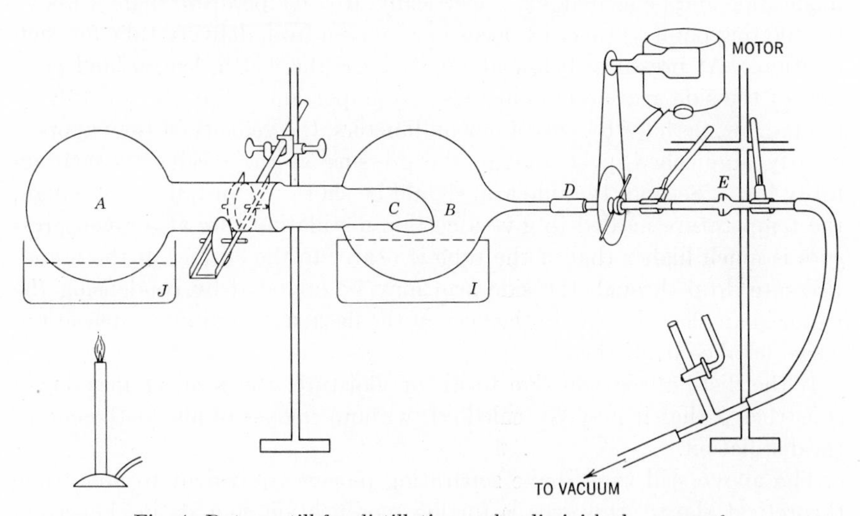

Fig. 4. Rotary still for distillation under diminished pressure.[6]

Adequate agitation of a distilland will eliminate bumping. For work on a large scale, vigorous mechanical stirring, which minimizes superheating, is often the only reliable method;[8] improved transfer of heat to the distilland results and this permits an increase in the distillation rate, a significant factor for heat-sensitive distillands. The stirrer may be magnetically operated[9] or motor-driven by a shaft through a vacuum seal, which can be constructed in the manner shown for the seal of Figure 45 of Chapter III.

The stirrer rod replaces the spherical joint in the seal, as shown. Silicone greases provide adequate lubrication, help to seal against the pressure of the atmosphere, and do not attack rubber pressure tubing. Stirrer blades may be Teflon crescents available from supply houses, or may be of twisted wire looped through a glass circle on the lower end of the stirring rod. These stirrers may be driven at 400–600 r.p.m. and provide many hours of leak-free agitation at any pressure down to about 1 Torr.

For work on a small scale, or if a suitable stirrer is unavailable, bumping may be obviated by use of a hair-fine capillary tube which conducts a slow stream of minute bubbles of an inert gas to the bottom of the distilland. A two-necked Claisen Flask[10] is a convenient type of boiler for this application. It may be made pear-shaped so that the capillary may reach the bottom and continue to function even when the residue becomes very small.

A water-cooled condenser is usually needed only for compounds boiling below about 130°C. under vacuum. For high-boiling substances, an air-cooled condenser or a cooled receiver generally suffices.

If the distillate crystallizes readily in the side arm, this tube should be made wide and be heated, e.g., electrically, to a temperature slightly above the melting point; it may be necessary to use a fresh delivery tube for each fraction. At pressures below about 15 Torr, the width, length, and position of the side arm become increasingly important. First, if this tube is too narrow, perhaps by only a few millimeters, the velocity of the vapors is greatly diminished, even though the pressure at the receiver is satisfactorily low. Second, the side arm should be short. Third, if it is too high, the temperature needed to give a certain distillation rate at a given pressure is much higher than if the tube is nearer to the surface of the liquid. Pressure drop through the side arm may be obviated by condensing the vapor in an alembic head in the neck of the flask, as in a total-condensation, variable take-off, still head.

If the distillate is sensitive to air or moisture, the receiver may be so constructed that it may be sealed off, without ingress of air, at the end of the distillation.

The above still types have separating powers equivalent to about one theoretical plate. However, a further modification consists in elongation of the neck and introduction of packing, or provision of bulbs or of a series of indentations almost meeting in the center, to give a fractionating column. The still then employs both vertical and horizontal features of condensation. The end of the elongated neck may be sealed off and provided with a sealed-in mercury well into which a thermometer may be inserted. Columns may be used with compounds which boil below about 170°C. under vacuum and which do not undergo chemical change when considerably superheated. The column may be made removable; it is then some-

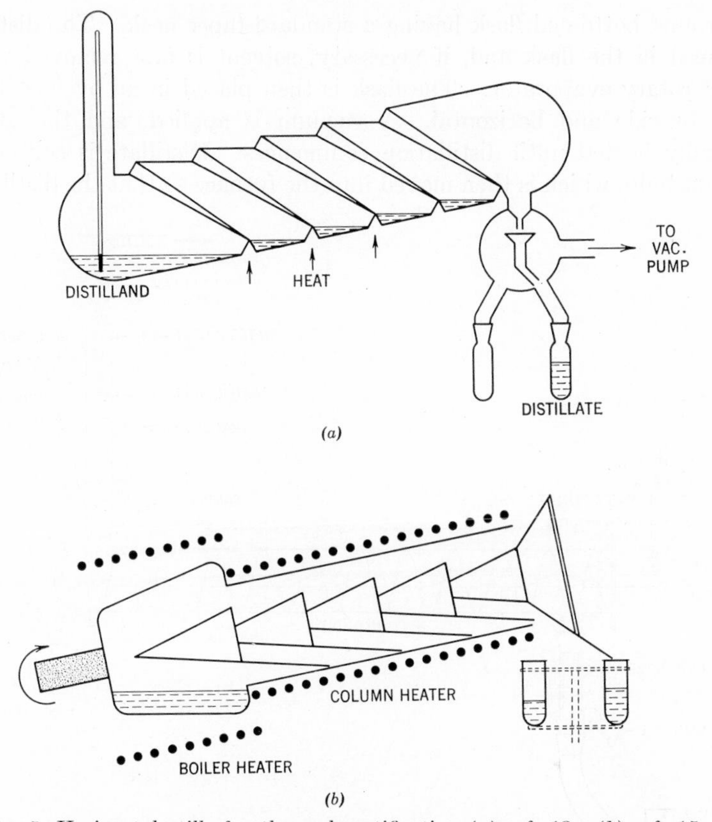

Fig. 5. Horizontal stills for thermal rectification (*a*) ref. 13; (*b*) ref. 15.

times useful in the separation of a low- from a high-boiling compound as follows: After all the low-boiling component has been distilled off and the high-boiling material has started to distil, the distillation is interrupted and the rest of the charge distilled, without a column, into a single receiver.

There has been a growth of interest in horizontal columns, mainly because of the low pressure drop they provide. The simplest design[11] consists of an evacuated, horizontal, glass tube sealed at both ends and initially containing the distilland at one end. The tube is placed inside a tubular electric heater so wound as to provide a uniform temperature gradient along the tube, the hotter end being that containing the distilland. The tube is rotated on its horizontal axis at 120 r.p.m. and the temperature of the distilland is gradually raised until slow vaporization occurs. In this way, a series of zones of distillates of different volatility is obtained.

In a related still,[12] a series of bulbs are connected together with ground-glass joints; one end is attached to the vacuum system and the other to a round-bottomed flask having a standard-taper neck. The distilland is placed in the flask and, if necessary, solvent is first removed with a Craig[6] rotary evaporator. The flask is then placed in an oven, with the bulbs outside and horizontal. A vacuum is applied, and the oven is gradually heated until distillation commences. Distillate is collected in the first bulb, which is then moved into the furnace so that the distillate is

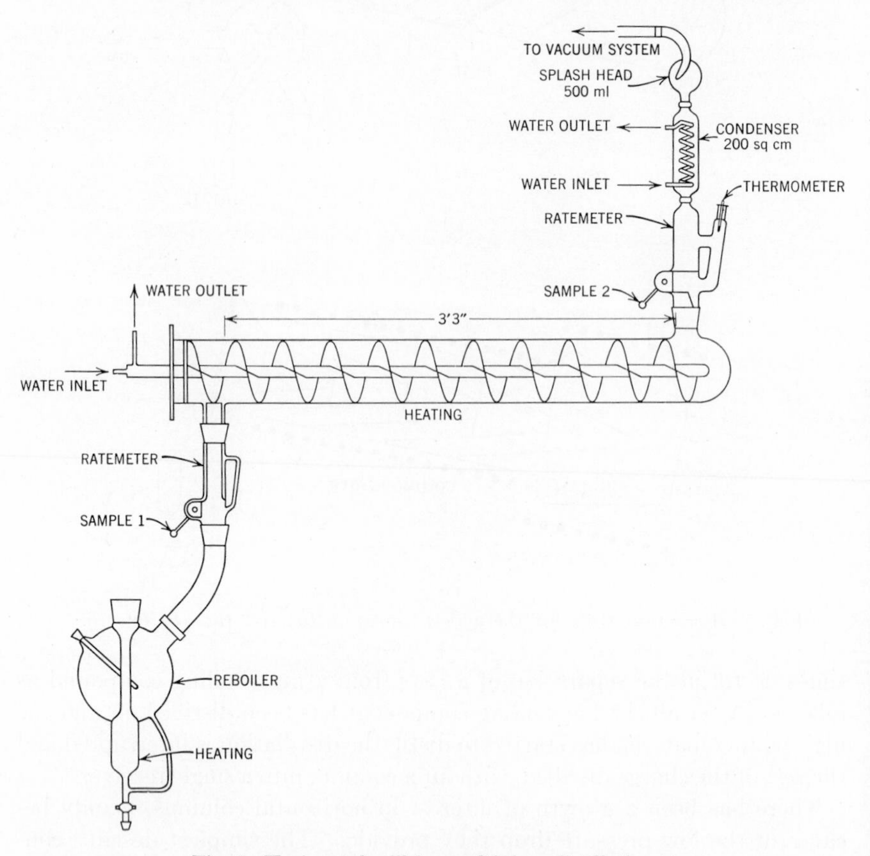

Fig. 6. Horizontal still for multiple redistillation.[16]

then condensed in the second bulb. By suitable repetition of the process, a series of fractions of distillate may be obtained.

In the still[13] shown in Figure 5*a*, an almost horizontal tube, having ten annular channels inclined at 45° to the axis of the tube, is heated electrically with four (graded) heating zones. The Ecky still is used industrially and is commercially available.[14] However, its separating power is rather low because of a high degree of diffusion in the vacuum chamber, and so a modification (Fig. 5*b*) was developed,[15] in which the column is rotated, thereby giving improved separation.

The horizontal column[16] shown in Figure 6 contains an internally cooled, copper spiral, and is electrically heated below; at a pressure of 200 Torr, it gives a low pressure drop.

In a related still,[17] a series of ten vertical columns replace the bulbs, annuli, or spirals, and are so connected as to give the effect of an almost horizontal column. The condensates move by gravity from one column to the next, and liquid is circulated by means of magnetic pumps. For a binary mixture, the still gave a separation equivalent to 13 theoretical plates.

B. VERTICAL STILLS

The main consideration in designing columns for operation under diminished pressure is a low pressure drop. Columns may be lagged with asbestos cord, or be vacuum-jacketed. In the simplest design,[3] an unpacked column is used, as shown in Figure 7. Part of the column is vacuum-jacketed and provides some fractionating effect.

High-velocity vapors exert strong tangential drag on any liquid film past which they flow. In the range of a few millimeters of mercury, this frequently becomes troublesome, and special designs must be provided to prevent the vapor from drawing a liquid film along with it. A large bulb

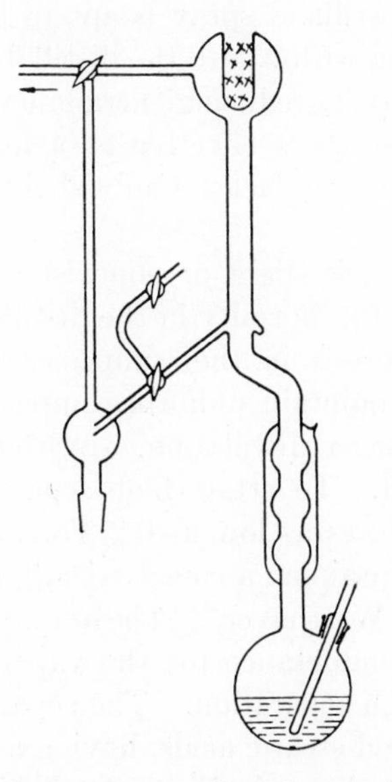

Fig. 7. A vertical, vacuum still with unpacked column.

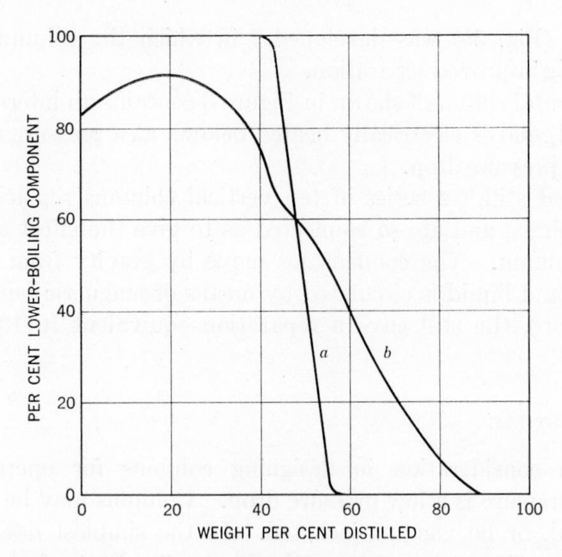

Fig. 8. Separating power of concentric-tube column at low pressure.[3] (*a*) 50/50 mixture of the methyl esters of oleic and stearic acids; 10-g. charge; difference in b.p., 3.3°C. at 0.2 Torr. (*b*) 51/49 mixture of the methyl esters of oleic and elaidic acids; 10.1-g. charge; difference in b.p., < 1°C. at 0.2 Torr.

with a ring-seal insert or annulus is a convenient device for accomplishing this. Entrainment of crude distilland presents a similar problem. If rough boiling occurs, distilland spray is apt to be thrown into the vapor stream and carried along with it into the distillate. Of the several devices that have been proposed for reducing entrainment, a simple offset or bend in the column line (Fig. 7) is effective as a mist trap. It has the advantage, which several others lack, of only slightly increasing the pressure drop.

Spontaneous ebullition is slight or nonexistent in the range of 1 to 25 Torr; this causes lack of uniformity in the distilland composition and consequent irregular variations in the composition of vapors entering the column. In order to maintain uniform composition in the distilland, as product is removed during distillation, a stirrer, of the kind previously described, may be used. To attain high separating power and low, dynamic hold-up at pressures as low as 0.2 Torr, Jantzen and Wieckhorst[3] developed a column, containing a concentrically placed tube, based on the principles of Kuhn[1] and Westhaver.[2] The annular space was 3.2 mm. wide, to provide adequate conductance for the vapor flowing at the low rate necessary for giving high separation. The separation of a mixture of the methyl esters of oleic and stearic acids, having a difference in boiling point of 2.9°C. at 0.2 Torr, is shown in Figure 8. This separation, although re-

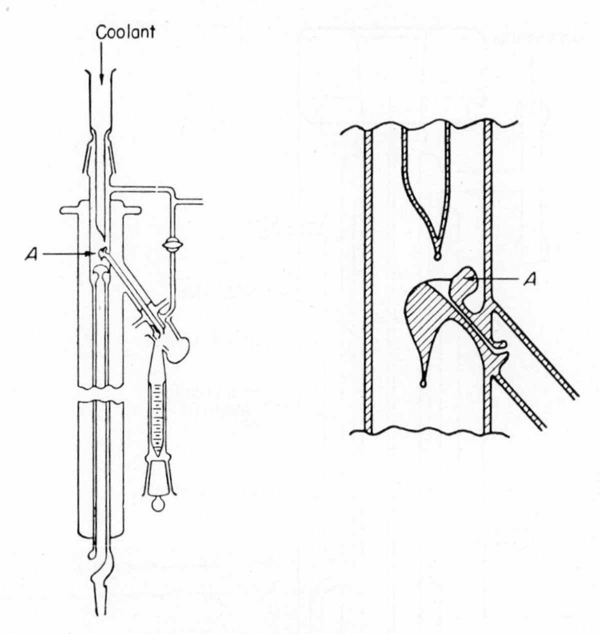

Fig. 9. Concentric-tube column.

markable, required 78 hr. for distillation of a 10-g. sample. An equally good separation of the two esters might be made by preparative, gas–liquid chromatography (G.L.C.), but the recovered esters would very probably be contaminated by significant percentages of fixed phase of the G.L.C. system. There is not, as yet, a good method for the sharp separation of high-boiling mixtures; even close-boiling, binary mixtures of the type indicated verge on the "involatile." A reasonable degree of volatility is, of course, necessary in both distillation and gas–liquid chromatography.

A concentric-tube column is shown in Figure 9. Stills[18] having fractionating efficiencies of 50 to 85 theoretical plates have been made. A column consisting of 61 parallel, vertical, unpacked tubes, each 0.4 cm. × 200 cm., permits efficient fractionation of mixtures of close-boiling components.[1]

A section of a multisection column having a low pressure drop[19] is shown in Figure 10. The vapors rise through an annulus surrounding a central tube made of 1-in. precision-bore tubing, and pass outward through twelve $^{1}/_{4}$-in. holes into an outer, condensing annulus surrounded by a concentric cooling jacket. The condensate runs down the walls into a tube that carries it to the reboiler heater; part of it is revaporized, passes in turn through three Perfo-Drip trays (a kind of sieve tray without downcomers) made of perforated, stainless-steel sheet having $^{1}/_{16}$-in. holes and 30% open area, and condenses on the water jacket in a similar column above. Below the lower

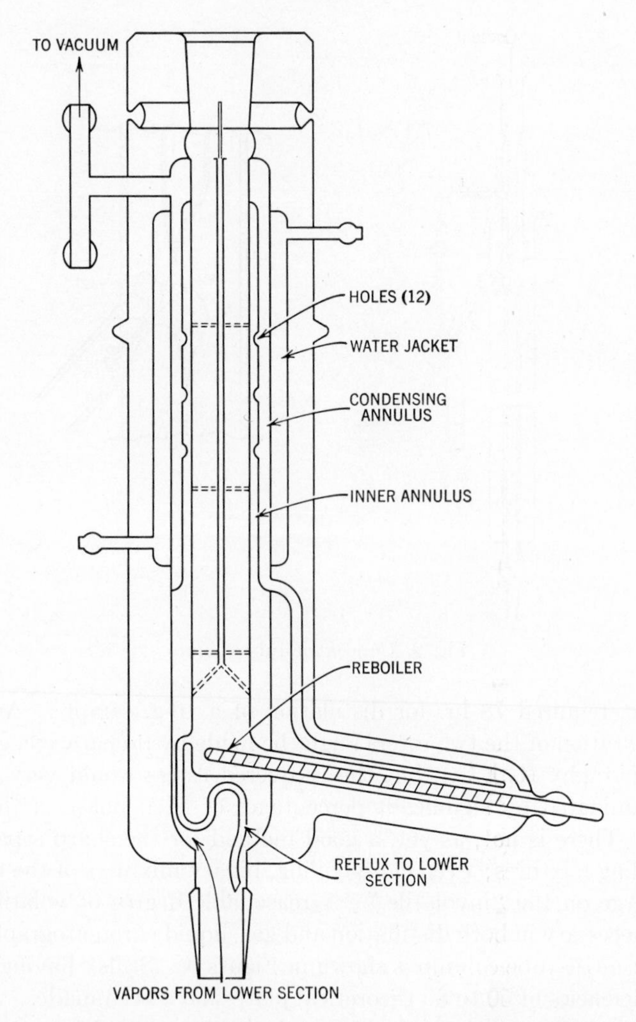

Fig. 10. Middle section of multi-section, concentric-tube column.[19]

section is connected a conventional, three-tray, Perfo-Drip column. At 50 Torr, the tray efficiencies were over 100%; at 10 Torr, they were slightly lower. The throughput was high and the pressure drop was nearly constant over the range between the load point and the flood point.

In order that equilibrium may be attained faster, mechanical agitation of the liquid and vapor in a column is advantageous. To circumvent the extremely low velocity permissible for the vapor in the Kuhn column, the normal diffusion phenomena of this type of column have been aided by use of the spinning band. This adjunct functions favorably at atmospheric

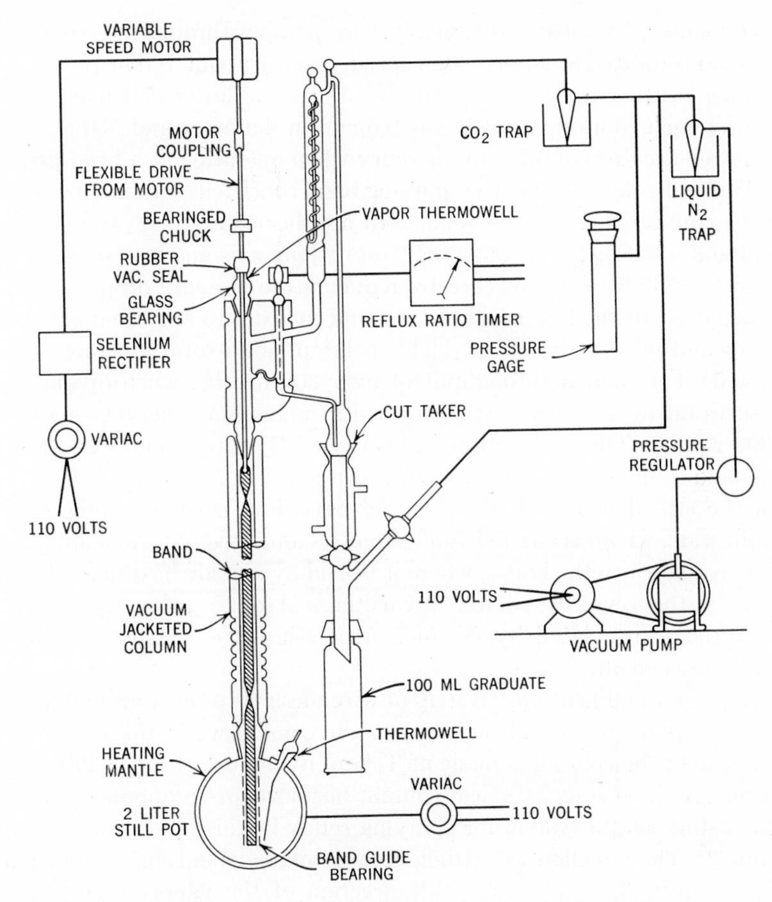

Fig. 11. Vacuum still with spinning-band column.[23]

pressure, but, at 1 to 5 Torr, it loses much of its efficacy. This may stem from the dissonance between vapor velocity and band speed at the lower pressures. Suitable test mixtures are available for testing spinning-band columns at low pressure, but these have rarely been used, and much correlative work remains to be done on the factors of rotational speed, vaporization rate, and column-wall area (where almost all of the vapor–liquid interchange occurs). Once the glamour of preparative G.L.C. has lost its luster in this field, the spinning-band column may receive renewed and deserved attention.

Spinning-band columns consist of a vertical column containing a thin, metal strip of a width slightly less than the diameter of the tube. The insert may also be a rod. It is attached to an electric motor, which is above the condenser, by means of a heavy wire passing through the condenser. The band is rotated at a fairly high speed, usually about 1000 r.p.m. Only an upper bearing is needed for the band, and its lower end may be free. The first such column,[20] which was 0.6 cm. in diameter and 550 cm. high, had a pressure drop of 0.7-mm. mercury when operating at a head pressure of 1 Torr. In this column, the spinning band consisted of a number of short lengths connected with wire links. In another column,[8, 21] the stainless-steel band was twisted through 360° on its long axis and was so rotated as to assist the flow of vapor, thereby reducing the pressure drop. A stirrer was attached to the lower end of the band in order to stir the distilland in the pot and prevent bumping. This column had a total pressure drop of only 0.04 Torr and a throughput of over 300 ml./hr. when operating at pressures below 2.5 Torr. It performed at maximum fractionating power at 300 r.p.m. The rectification efficiency of Bjorkman and Olavi's spinning-band column[22] was constant at pressures of 9 to 700 Torr.

In the still depicted (Fig. 11),[23] the band is a strip of stainless steel, $^{15}/_{32}$ in. wide, which is twisted 720° about its long axis to form a spiral, and which extends into the boiler, where it is held by a guide bearing. In stills having, at the top of the column, a vacuum seal for the rotor, the need for a stuffing box is obviated by use of a magnetic drive, and the top of the column is sealed off.[24]

In another modification,[25] a strip of wire mesh is spiraled around a shaft, and the edge of the mesh bears against the column wall; the vacuum seal at the top of the column is made of Teflon, nylon, or other self-lubricating plastic. A three-stage, vertical column has a vapor-compressing impeller in each stage and a system for spraying reflux liquid counter to the vapor stream.[26] The impellers are attached to a common axial shaft, and a static diffuser, optimal for changing the direction of the vapors with minimal loss by friction, has six helical vanes generated at a 10° angle. For testing rectification efficiencies, butyl ether–dichloroethyl ether was used at 20, 30, and 50 Torr. At 30 Torr and a rotation rate of 1520 r.p.m., the pressure drop per stage was 0.045 Torr. For a rotary, concentric-tube column having a rotor 3.9 in. wide and 50 in. high, the rotor changed laminar to turbulent flow when it was revolved at suitable speed, but at higher speeds, the efficiency fell off, possibly because of frictional heating of the vapor.[27]

Thus, numerous workers have shown interest in spinning-band columns, chiefly as a means of combining moderate fractionating power and low holdup with the requirement of a small amount of distilland. A few investigators have been chiefly interested in low pressure drop of spinning-band columns for operation at low absolute pressures (1–5 Torr). Unfortunately, there has been no common measure of column efficiency as usually understood; specific separations of high-boiling mixtures have been

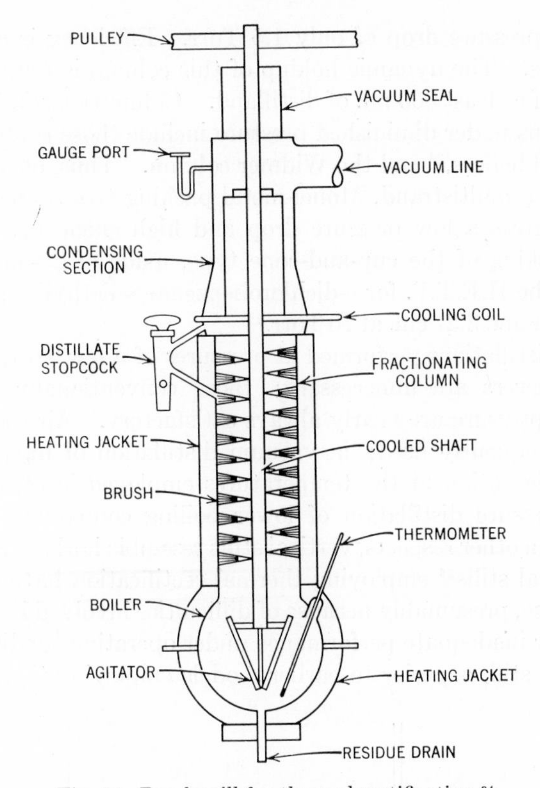

Fig. 12. Brush still for thermal rectification.[34]

the only indication of separating power. There is no indication that column efficiencies of 100 theoretical plates at 1–5 Torr pressure have yet been achieved with spinning-band columns.

Packed columns are valuable for distillation under moderate vacuum. Nearly all of the conventional types of column packing described in Chapter III are useful down to pressures of a few Torr.[28] Below this, none give efficient performance. The characteristics of packed columns under moderate vacua have been carefully determined for protruded packing.[29] Extensive data covering the pressure range of 10–760 Torr are given in Chapter III, under "Protruded Packing." The effect of pressure on permissible throughput is vividly displayed in the curves. The H.E.T.P. remains surprisingly small; this is contrary to generally accepted ideas on the effect of pressure on H.E.T.P. Throughput, on the other hand, must be low to avoid excessive pressure-drop or flooding as the operating pressure is reduced. Columns of conventional design, 28 mm. I.D. packed with 2 ft. of 0.24 in. × 0.24 in. protruded packing, may be operated at 4–5

Torr with a pressure drop of only 1.5 Torr. Efficiency is about 15 theoretical plates. The dynamic holdup of this column is fairly high, necessitating use of at least 300 ml. of distilland. Columns particularly suitable for distillations under diminished pressure include those containing special glass or metal helices,[30] and the Widmer column. Thus, over the range of 760–50 Torr, a multistrand, Monel-metal packing (Knitmesh Multifil) for the column gives a low pressure drop and high efficiency.[31] By use of Stedman packing of the cup-and-cone type, made of 25-mesh, stainless-steel gauze, the H.E.T.P. for *o*-dichlorobenzene–*p*-diethylbenzene was 1.85 cm. at 50 Torr and 3.27 cm. at 10 Torr.[32]

Even for distillations performed at pressures of a few Torr, specially designed condensers are unnecessary; those conventionally employed at atmospheric pressure are nearly always satisfactory. Air cooling is, however, more frequently used; in vacuum distillation of high-boiling compounds, condensation at the temperatures employed in conventional, atmospheric-pressure distillation of lower boiling compounds may be unnecessary. In other respects, vertical stills resemble horizontal stills.

Two vertical stills[33] employing thermal rectification have not achieved widespread use, presumably because of difficulties involved in their fabrication and their inadequate performance under operating conditions. However, a brush still, superior to earlier models employing thermal rectifica-

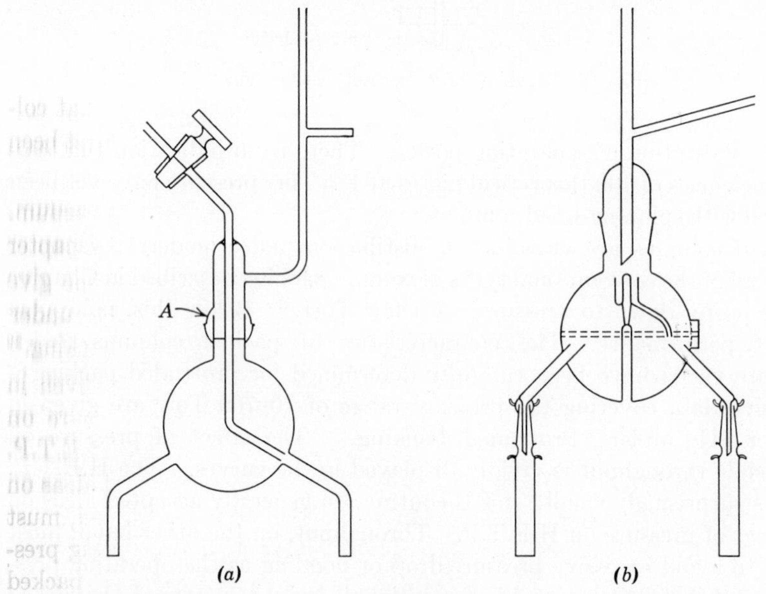

Fig. 13. Rotatable fraction-cutters. (*a*) Ball-and-socket joint[4] (*b*) magnetically actuated flow control.[32]

tion, has been devised.[34] In this still, shown in Figure 12, a rotating spiral brush having stainless-steel bristles causes the fractionation in a heated column. The distilland is vaporized in a boiler, and the vapor rises inside the vertical column. Liquid condenses on the cooled brush, which rotates at 450 r.p.m., and is flung out to the heated wall, where it is partially revaporized. Thus, continuous re-evaporation and recondensation occur

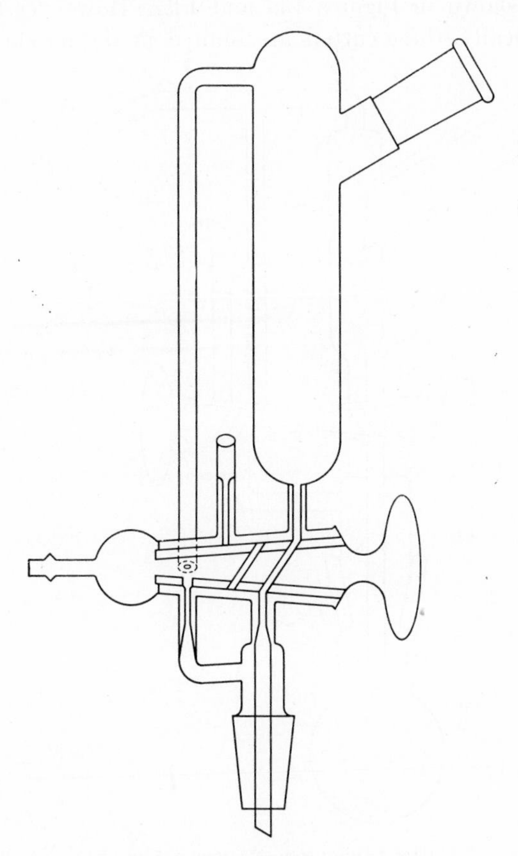

Fig. 14. "Triangle" fraction cutter.

throughout the height of the brush and column, and the most volatile fraction of the distilland works its way to the top first; here, it is condensed, and the liquid flows into a receiver. The still is operated without a head reflux, and has a capacity of 100–1500 ml. of distilland, with a distillation rate of 0.3–100 ml. of distillate per minute. The separating efficiency is from 900 to 1000% higher than that of the usual vacuum still.

C. FRACTION CUTTERS

If the hot distilland and vapor are readily oxidized, or if very precise fractional distillation is necessary, a device to permit interchange of receivers during the distillation, without interruption of the vacuum and of ebullition, must be incorporated. Fraction cutters of many designs have been devised, but, in essence, there are only three kinds. Two rotatable types[4, 32] are shown in Figures 13*a* and 13*b*. How ever they are contrived mechanically, these cutters are limited in the number of fractions

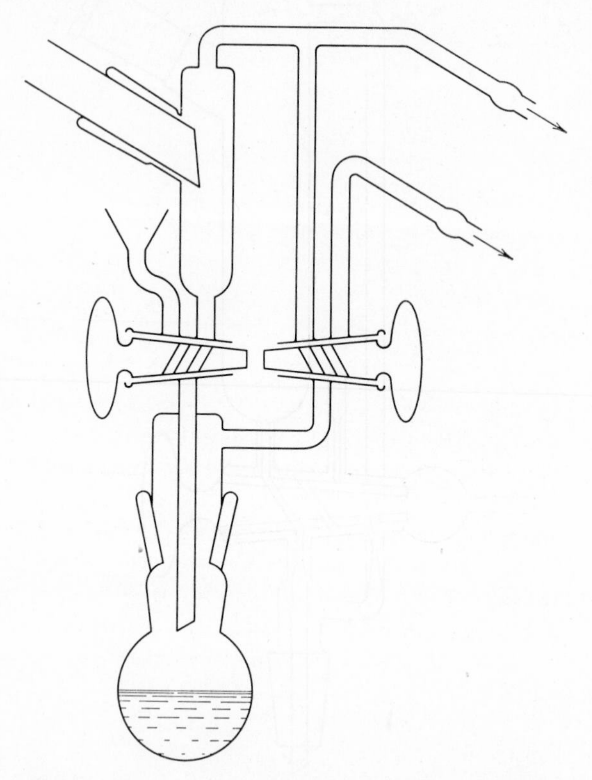

Fig. 15. Cutter having separate evacuation of receiver.[38]

they can accommodate and, for removal of accumulated cuts, interruption of a distillation may be necessary. Moreover, they may be fragile unless well constructed. In the cutter shown in Figure 13*a*, a spherical joint *A* provides ready rotation to a fresh receptacle.[4] The cutter shown in Figure 13*b* has a swivelled delivery tube to whose lower end is attached a small, permanent magnet; by moving a powerful magnet on the outside wall of the changer, the spout is centered over any one of a large number of recept-

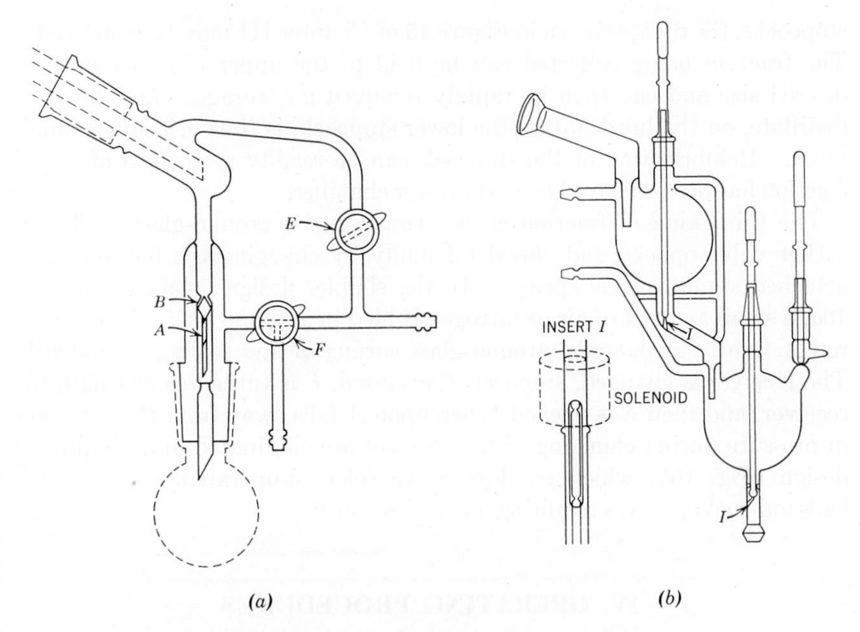

Fig. 16. Plunger fraction-cutters for vacuum distillations.[40,41]

acles.[32] In addition to those fraction cutters shown, a modified vacuum desiccator, having two side tubes, e.g., in the walls, and a central hole in the lid, may be employed.[35] A set of test tubes is arranged circularly in a rack which may be turned by means of a handle extending through a stopper in the center of the lid. The end of the condenser enters one side-arm and distillate is caused to fall into each test tube in turn. The other side-arm serves for connection to the pump. This kind of receiver changer has been mechanized to provide continuous operation and automatic withdrawal of distillate.[36] All such fraction cutters are unsatisfactory for low-boiling liquids, since all the receivers intercommunicate and there may be interchange of vapors between the fractions. Moreover, unless they are well constructed, their use may be dangerous.

The "triangle" cutters shown in Figures 14 and 15 are more ruggedly constructed and are much more suitable than the rotatable cutters when many cuts are to be taken.[37] The cutter shown in Figure 14 has the disadvantage that the pressure in the system builds up while the receiver is being changed. This deficiency has been overcome by providing a separate tube for evacuation of the fresh receiver without interruption of the distillation, as shown in Figure 15.[38] To avoid contamination of fractions by stopcock grease, Teflon cores, requiring no lubricant, even under vacuum, may be used. If these are not available, necessitating use of lubricated stopcocks, the design shown in Figure 45 of Chapter III may be employed.[39] The fraction being collected can be held in the upper chamber until of desired size and can then be rapidly removed for storage. Action of the distillate, on the lubricant on the lower stopcock, is thus held to the minimum. Relubrication of the stopcock can be readily performed after the fraction has been removed from the lower chamber.

The third kind of fraction cutter[8] consists of a ground-glass, ball-and-socket valve opened and closed manually by changing the tension in an attached stainless-steel spring. In the simpler design[40] shown in Figure 16*a*, a small amount of air or nitrogen is bled in at stopcock F, thus forcing rod A tightly against the ground-glass surface B and sealing off the still. The receiver is changed, stopcock E is closed, F is turned to evacuate the receiver, and then E is opened, whereupon A falls away from B. Changes in pressure during changing of the receiver are eliminated in an improved design (Fig. 16*b*) which employs three solenoid-operated, ground-glass, ball-and-socket valves requiring no lubrication.[41]

IV. OPERATING PROCEDURES

Operating procedures at moderately reduced pressures do not differ in any major particular from those used at atmospheric pressure. The basic requirements have been outlined in Chapter III under "Procedure." Solid distillands must be liquefied, and viscous liquids must have their viscosity lowered, by being heated to a temperature high enough to facilitate the easy escape of dissolved gases (usually air), as the pressure is diminished to the operating value; cautious heating and gradual increase of the vacuum are advisable. Successful operation then depends on the limitations imposed by the characteristics of the distilland, the distillate, the equipment, and the operating pressure.

V. INTERPRETATION OF RESULTS

Distillations performed at moderately reduced pressures (200–50 Torr), in stills of adequate separating power, may be expected to provide fractions having purities as good as, or better than, those achieved at atmospheric pressure for distillands of comparable complexity. Below 50 Torr, interpretation follows the same general approach outlined in Chapter III, but the common vagaries of column operation, the general unavailability of high separating-power, the plethora of isomers in many synthetic or natural products, the poorly defined properties frequent for the compounds of interest, and the lack of pure samples of counterparts produced from a distilland, introduce major difficulties in interpreting the results of a low-pressure distillation.

Instrumental methods in wide variety are available for quantitative measurements, but, where qualitative information is needed, instrumental methods are merely helpful; recourse must then be had to reaction mechanisms, to the reactions by which a distilland is produced, and, finally, to one's intuition, nurtured by experience.

References

1. Kuhn, *Helv. Chim. Acta*, **25**, 252 (1942); *Chem. Ingr.-Tech.*, **29**, 6 (1957).
2. Westhaver, *Ind. Eng. Chem.*, **34**, 126 (1942).
3. Jantzen and Wieckhorst, *Chem. Ingr.-Tech.*, **26**, 392 (1954).
4. Wendland, *J. Chem. Educ.*, **28**, 332 (1951).
5. Conners, *Can. J. Chem. Eng.*, **40**, 178 (1962).
6. Craig, Gregory, and Hausmann, *Anal. Chem.*, **22**, 1462 (1950); Volk, *ibid.*, **27**, 1207 (1955).
7. West, *Chem. Ind.* (*London*), **1963**, 1118; Smith, *ibid.*, **1964**, 54; Alsing, *ibid.*, **1964**, 55; Baker, Urch, and Welch, *ibid.*, **1964**, 55.
8. Birch, Gripp, and Nathan, *J. Soc. Chem. Ind.* (*London*), **66**, 33 (1947).
9. Michell, *J. Appl. Chem.* (*London*), *Suppl.* **1**, 58 (1951); Silverstein and Englert, *Chemist-Analyst*, **41**, 15 (1952); Rose and Sanders, *Anal. Chem.*, **27**, 331 (1955).
10. Amstutz, *Chemist-Analyst*, **40**, 40 (1951).
11. Bates, *Chem. Ind.* (*London*), **1958**, 1319.
12. Schrecker, *Anal. Chem.*, **29**, 1113 (1957).
13. Aldershoff, Booy, Langedijk, Philippi, and Waterman, *J. Inst. Petrol.*, **39**, 688 (1953); Ecky, U.S. Patent 2,871,250 (1959).
14. Anon., *Ind. Eng. Chem.*, **55**, 65 (1963).
15. Watt, in *Advances in Vacuum Science and Technology*, Vol. II, Thomas, ed., Pergamon Press, New York, 1960, p. 709.
16. Ellis and Suárez, *Ind. Chemist*, **37**, 281 (1961); Compare: Mair, Pignocco, and Rossini, *Anal. Chem.*, **27**, 190 (1955).
17. Madorsky, *J. Res. Natl. Bur. Std.*, **44**, 135 (1950).
18. Banks and Musgrave, *J. Appl. Chem.* (*London*), **6**, 214 (1956).
19. Myers, *Ind. Eng. Chem.*, **55**, 36 (1963).
20. Baker, Barkenbus, and Roswell, *Ind. Eng. Chem. Anal. Ed.*, **12**, 468 (1940).
21. Murray, *J. Am. Oil Chemists' Soc.*, **28**, 235 (1951); Williamson, *J. Appl. Chem.* (*London*), **1**, 33 (1951); Winters and Dinerstein, *Anal. Chem.*, **27**, 546 (1955); Nerheim and Dinerstein, *ibid.*, **28**, 1029 (1956); Rousseau, *Chim. Anal.* (*Paris*), **39**, 94 (1957); Macleod and Matterson, *Brit. Chem. Eng.*, **3**, 658 (1958).
22. Bjorkman and Olavi, *Svensk Kem. Tidskr.*, **6**, 145 (1946).
23. Lockwood, LeTourneau, Matteson, and Sipes, *Anal. Chem.*, **23**, 1398 (1951); Pease, Gilbert, and Cahn, *ibid.*, **32**, 894 (1960).
24. Foster and Green, *Anal. Chem.*, **24**, 1869 (1952).
25. Nester, *Anal. Chem.*, **28**, 278 (1956).
26. Othmer and Beattie, *Ind. Eng. Chem.*, **53**, 779 (1961).
27. Hawkins and Burris, *Anal. Chem.*, **28**, 1715 (1956); Willingham and Rossini, *J. Res. Natl. Bur. Std.*, **37**, 15 (1946).

28. Hawkins and Brent, *Ind. Eng. Chem.*, **43**, 2611 (1951); Peters and Cannon, *ibid.*, **44**, 1452 (1952); Ellis and Contractor, *J. Inst. Petrol.*, **45**, 147 (1959).
29. Cannon, Scientific Development Co., Bulletin 12A (1900).
30. Berg and Popovac, *Chem. Eng. Progr.*, **45**, 683 (1949); Myles, Feldman, Wender, and Orchin, *Ind. Eng. Chem.*, **43**, 1452 (1951); Feldman, Svedi, Connell, and Orchin, *ibid.*, **45**, 214 (1953); Gel'perin and Zelenestskiĭ, *Zh. Prikl. Khim.*, **32**, 2001 (1959); Hall, *Anal. Chem.*, **31**, 437 (1959); Norman, Haqjoo, Boot, Everitt, and Thompson, *Trans. Inst. Chem. Engrs.* (*London*), **39**, No. 6, A46 (1961).
31. Ellis, *Ind. Chim. Belge*, **25**, 35 (1960); Compare: Miskin and Qureshi, *Birmingham Univ. Chem. Engr.*, **11**, 45 (1960); Bragg, *Ind. Eng. Chem.*, **49**, 1062 (1957); Ellis and Varjavandi, *Chem. Process Eng.*, **39**, 239 (1958).
32. Mohajer, *J. Inst. Petrol.*, **47**, 212 (1961).
33. Schaffner, Bowman, and Coull, *Trans. Am. Inst. Chem. Engrs.*, **39**, 77 (1943); Bowman, U. S. Patent 2,415,411 (1947); Gulf Research and Development Co., British Patent 618,949 (1949); Byron, Bowman, and Coull, *Ind. Eng. Chem.*, **43**, 1002 (1951); Compare: Benner, Dinardo, and Tobin, *ibid.*, **43**, 722 (1951).
34. Perry and Mansing, U. S. Patent 2,586,717 (1952); Perry and Cox, *Ind. Eng. Chem.*, **48**, 1473 (1956); Perry, *ibid.*, **48**, 1479 (1956); Compare: Stevanovic, *Proc. Intern. Symp. Distn., Brighton, Engl.*, **1960**, 260; *Chem. Ingr.-Tech.*, **35**, 154 (1963).
35. Needleman, *J. Chem. Educ.*, **33**, 559 (1956); Jacobson and Miller, *Chem. Ind.* (*London*), **1957**, 1621.
36. Brown and Coles, *Anal. Chem.*, **19**, 935 (1947); Simpson and Sutherland, *ibid.*, **23**, 1345 (1951); Ulusoy, *Chem.-Ztg.*, **79**, 46 (1955); Tarbes, *Chemist-Analyst*, **42**, 308 (1960).
37. Fürst, *Chem. Tech.* (*Berlin*), **5**, 24 (1953); Radell, *J. Chem. Educ.*, **38**, 459 (1961).
38. Evans, *Chem. Ind.* (*London*), **1959**, 219.
39. Williams, private communication.
40. Sakuragi and Kummerow, *Anal. Chem.*, **26**, 620 (1954).
41. Humphlett, *Anal. Chem.*, **29**, 1241 (1957).

General References

Coulson and Herington, *Laboratory Distillation Practice*, Interscience, New York, 1958.

Krell, *Handbook of Laboratory Distillation*, American Elsevier Publishing Co., New York, 1963.

Lafferty, *Dushman's Scientific Foundations of Vacuum Technique*, 2nd ed., Wiley, New York, 1962.

Martin, *Chem. Labor u. Betrieb.*, **10**, 227 (1959).

Rose and Rose, *Distillation Literature, Index, and Abstracts, 1941–1945; 1946–52; 1953–54*, Rose and Rose, State College, Pennsylvania.

Zuiderweg, *Laboratory Manual of Batch Distillation*, Interscience, New York, 1957.

CHAPTER VI

DISTILLATION UNDER HIGH VACUUM

E. S. PERRY, *Research Laboratories, Eastman Kodak Co., Rochester, New York*

I. INTRODUCTION

The process known today as "molecular distillation" stems from the classical work of Brönsted and Hevesy[1] on the separation of the isotopes of mercury. Their resort to this method was based on the earlier work of Knudsen[2] and Langmuir[3] who showed that at very low pressures the effusion of molecules was dependent on molecular weight as well as on vapor pressure. This meant that mixtures of substances whose components have identical vapor pressures but differ in mass should be amenable to separation by molecular distillation. Brönsted and Hevesy showed that nature's distribution of the isotopes of mercury could be altered when treated by this method.

Molecular distillation is now more than a laboratory achievement. The simple device employed by Bronsted and Hevesy has passed through many variations and transformations to the modern forms of molecular stills. The pioneering efforts of Waterman,[4] Burch,[5] and especially Hickman[6] have wrought a useful tool for the chemist. Hickman's continued interest brought forth a self-contained technology which culminated in the establishment of a new industry. The molecular still permits distillation at temperatures 50–150°C. lower than those required by other vacuum stills. It provides a means of distilling organic substances having relatively high molecular weights. Heat-sensitive materials which cannot be distilled by other methods can often be successfully distilled by this method.

The term "molecular" distillation will be used in this chapter as a generic term to embrace all of the distillation processes variously known as "true molecular," "high-vacuum," unobstructed-path," "evaporative," and "short path" distillation. For an explanation of these various terms, the reader is referred to the original literature.[6,7] The following pages are devoted to a description of theory and techniques in sufficient detail to make the process readily useful to the chemist. No attempt is made to review the past developments in the field in any chronological order since such surveys are already available. A comprehensive bibliography, including scientific papers and patents, through 1941 was compiled by

Detwiler and Markley[8] and extended to 1943 by Todd[9] and through 1945 by the Roses.[10] Articles by Burch and Van Dijck[5] and by Waterman and Van Vlodrop,[4] appearing in 1939, presented the fundamental and practical aspects of the method. The review article by Hickman,[6] which was published in 1944, was the first comprehensive statement of the art. Subsequent reviews have been issued by Nieman,[11] who includes an extensive bibliography, and by Burrows.[12] The excellent compilation of theory and practice of molecular distillation, brought together under one cover by Burrows,[7] deserves special mention. And finally, an extensive compilation of all types of molecular stills, as well as industrial equipment, that has appeared heretofore in the scientific and technical literature is available in the book by P. R. Watt.[72]

This chapter is devoted to theory and to a description of laboratory molecular stills including detailed instructions for their use. In Chapter VII, the theory and practice of the equipment used to produce and measure vacuum are described.

II. THE DISTILLATION PROCESSES

1. Conventional Distillation

In the conventional distillation process the act of distillation begins at a well-defined temperature; there is a definite boiling point for each material being distilled, the process is accompanied by ebullition in the liquid phase, and the surface of the distilling liquid is located at comparatively large and variable distances from the condensing surface. The presence of the atmosphere over the boiling liquid hinders the escape of the vaporizing molecules with the net effect that the majority of them are immediately returned to the liquid phase. The evaporated molecules which enter the atmospheric phase move about in this gaseous maze with an extremely chaotic motion, due to the large numbers of collisions involved with air molecules. Their diffusion through the atmospheric phase is very slow compared to their individual velocities between collisions. This behavior, however, produces the dynamic equilibrium between vapor and boiling liquid which is responsible for the boiling point and controls the order of emergence of the individual constituents from the still. The boiling induces good turbulence in the liquid phase and the interface from which vaporization occurs is maintained substantially free of depletion of the more volatile species.

2. Molecular Distillation

In contrast, the molecular distillation process is carried out in the absence of a super-incumbent atmosphere and consequently there is neither ebullition nor a recognizable boiling point. Distillation occurs at almost any temperature and at a rate commensurate with the vapor pressure of the distilling material. The molecules of the more volatile component vaporize from a quiescent liquid surface and effuse relatively short distances through a highly rarefied space, free of physical obstruction, to a cooled surface where they condense to become the distillate. Consequently, there is no dynamic equilibrium between phases in the molecular distillation process.

The liquid phase from which vaporization takes place is extremely tranquil since no boiling occurs. The vaporization of the more volatile component from a liquid mixture, therefore, can leave the surface depleted of that species. Replenishment at the surface is achieved mostly by diffusion of the distilling species from the bulk of the liquid phase. This is normally a slow process but it is even slower in the case of the higher viscosities characteristic of the liquids usually subjected to molecular distillation.

The motion of the vaporized molecules in the rarefied atmosphere between the evaporator and condenser surfaces is of the kind described by Knudsen as "free molecular flow."[13] At these low pressures the molecules experience few collisions either with air molecules or with themselves, and travel greater distances between encounters. In conventional distillation, on the other hand, the higher pressure of the atmosphere increases the collision frequency of the molecules and, therefore, affects the progress of the process. Each kind of distillation, therefore, is characterized by the pressure of the atmosphere under which it functions.

Two important benefits result from the low pressure used in the molecular still. First, distillation is accomplished at the lowest possible temperature, and certain materials can be distilled which otherwise might be destroyed if they were distilled at normal pressure. The second is that in the molecular still the highest possible rate of distillation is achieved: the vaporizing molecules travel to the condenser in almost direct flight because collisions are reduced to the minimum.

3. The Molecular Still

In simple form the molecular still is not unlike the conventional distilling flask. Both have corresponding parts, such as boilers and condensers, which differ for the most part in their respective locations rather than in their functions. In the more sophisticated forms of either still, differences are more pronounced because of the complexities required to achieve their respective objectives. The molecular still, in any case, is complicated because of the auxiliary equipment required to produce, maintain, and measure the very low pressures needed for operation.

The molecular still must meet two important requirements to provide optimum efficiency. The spacing between the vaporizing surface and the condenser should be small and theoretically less than the "mean free path" of the distilling molecules. In operation, this space should be evacuated to a pressure so that every molecule that evaporates reaches the condenser on the first try. Ideal molecular distillation conditions are attained when the number of molecules condensing is equal to the number evaporating at any instant of time.

The molecular stills are of two general types: pot-type stills and flowing-film stills. As the name suggests, pot-type stills are those in which the material being distilled, called the "distilland," is contained as a pool of

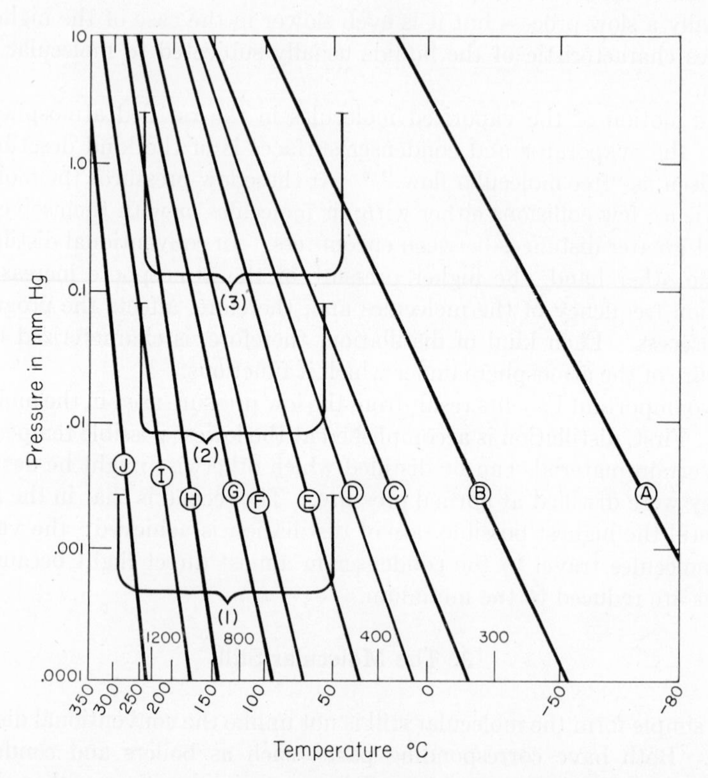

Fig. 1. Operative ranges of stills. Each bracket corresponds to a type of still: (*1*) represents a flowing-film molecular still, (*2*) a pot-type molecular still, and (*3*) a short column boiling-point still. Substances indicated by the various lines can be distilled by those stills whose brackets embrace the lines. A—water; B—ethylene glycol; C—triacetin; D—glycerol; E—di-butyl pthalate; F—di-2-ethyl hexyl pthalate; G—di-2-ethyl hexyl sebacate; H—sterols; I—coconut oil (triglycerides); J—cottonseed oil (triglycerides).

liquid in an evacuable vessel; distillation takes place from the quiescent surface of the liquid to a closely adjacent condenser.

In the flowing-film stills the distilland is made to flow as a thin film over a heated surface. If the flow is gravitational the still is known as the "falling film" type; if it is induced by centrifugal force, the name "centrifugal" still has been applied. Distillation takes place from the thin flowing film directly to a condenser which is coextensive with the vaporizing surface. These stills permit distillation from very thin films of distilland and have extended the effective range of distillation to the theoretical limit.

4. Choice of Still

At times the correct choice of vacuum still for the distillation of a mixture may involve some trial-and-error experiments. A rough guide in making a preliminary choice may be based on molecular weights. Substances in the range of 250–350 should be tried in the boiling-point still; those of higher molecular weights require molecular distillation. The upper limit of distillability is about 1200. Of course, these values will vary depending on structure and functional groups present which can cause deviations from normal behavior.

The chart of Figure 1 gives an approximate operative range for various stills. The logarithm of the vapor pressure is plotted against the reciprocal of the absolute temperature for various substances covering a wide range of pressures. Each bracket embraces the effective distillation range, pressure, and temperature for the still types indicated. A prediction of the distillability of a new substance sometimes can be made by comparison with a similar one on the chart.

The numbers inserted above the abscissas show the molecular-weight spread for the temperature range covered.

III. BASIC CONSIDERATIONS

Although molecular distillation is claimed to be a nonequilibrium process, the interpretation of its principle of operation is nevertheless based on the kinetic theory of gases. The molecular behavior in the vapor phase of the molecular still is specific and characteristic of the low pressure employed in the process. The phenomenon is referred to as "free molecular" or "Knudsen" flow and can be interpreted by the concepts of free paths and collision frequencies. As a consequence of this behavior, vaporized molecules travel the greatest possible distances and so give rise to the highest possible rate of distillation. This rate can be computed from a relationship which is founded on gas kinetics.

Some of the aspects of the theory of distillation as developed in other chapters of this volume apply to molecular distillation as well. It must be assumed that the basic laws of solution theory, such as Raoult's and Henry's laws, for example, are applicable even though there is little evidence at present to substantiate this fact. The concepts of relative volatility and activity coefficients can then be applied in molecular distillation. The basic equations of conventional distillation, such as the relative volatility equation, the Rayleigh equation and the Fenske equation, should have utility in this process.

A brief discussion of these various fundamentals will be presented in this section to show their connection with the process. Final forms of equations will be given which have practical utility within the scope of this text. More comprehensive details of the theory can be found in Dushman,[13] Loeb,[14] Glasstone and Lewis,[15] and other standard texts.

1. Mean Free Path

The individual molecules of a gas move about in the space confining them with very high velocities. Each molecule continually collides with its neighbor and produces a zigzag trajectory in its movement. It is because of this mechanism that one gas diffuses but slowly through another, although the individual velocities of each molecule are comparatively very large. The distance traveled by a molecule between two successive collisions with neighboring molecules is termed its "free path." The average distance traveled by all molecules between collisions is called the "mean free path." Its magnitude is affected inversely by the pressure of the gas; as the pressure is decreased the path increases. When the pressure is low enough so that the mean free path becomes large compared to the diameter of the container, the collisions are mainly with the walls of the container and the flow behavior of the molecules is described as "free flow," "Knudsen flow," or "molecular streaming." The maximum rate of distillation occurs when the mean free path is maximum.

The value of the mean free path can be computed by an expression deduced from the following considerations of the kinetic theory: Molecules are not geometric points, but are usually likened to spheres having finite diameters. The nature of molecules is such that as two approach one another a point is reached where repulsion sets in and a change in their direction of travel occurs. This distance of closest approach is an "effective" diameter of the molecule and is commonly referred to as the "collision" diameter. It is factually the distance separating the centers of the two molecules at this point of closest approach. The symbol σ is used to denote this distance. Two molecules are therefore in effective collision when their centers come within the distance σ of one another.

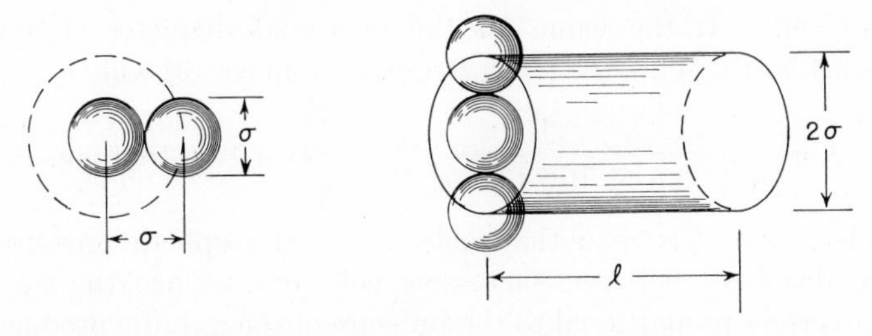

Fig. 2. Exclusion volume and mean free path. The diagram shows that there can be only one molecule in the cylinder for a collision-free passage. Each molecule, therefore, occupies a volume equivalent to $\pi\sigma^2 l$.

Consider now a unit volume of a gas in which all of the molecules but one are stationary. The molecule in motion collides with all other molecules whose centers come within a distance σ of its center. If the molecule moves a distance l cm. in one second, it will collide during each second of time with every molecule which is contained in a cylindrical volume l cm. long and $\pi\sigma^2$ cm.^{2} of cross-sectional area. This is known as the "exclusion" volume and the concept is evident from the diagram of Figure 2. The molecule in question inhabits a volume of $\pi\sigma^2 l$ cm.^{3}/sec. If n represents the number of molecules in each unit volume of the gas, then $1/n$ is the volume occupied by each molecule in the unit volume. Therefore

$$\pi\sigma^2 l = 1/n \tag{1}$$

and

$$l = 1/\pi n \sigma^2 \tag{2}$$

where l can be considered the average distance the molecule travels between successive collisions for the conditions assumed.

But, in gases, all of the molecules are in motion and to take this factor into account, eq. (2) must be corrected by the factor, $\sqrt{2}$. Equation (2) then becomes

$$\lambda = \frac{1}{\sqrt{2} n \pi \sigma^2} \tag{3}$$

where λ is now the "mean free path" of the molecule moving in a gas comprised of all molecules like itself. Therefore, λ is related inversely to the size and number of molecules of the gas.

A sample calculation of the mean free path for an oxygen molecule in a volume of oxygen gas will make the relationship more meaningful. At 0°C. and 760 mm. Hg pressure there are 6.06×10^{23} molecules per gram mole and the mole volume is approximately 22,400 cm.^{3}, or 2.5×10^{19}

molecules/cm.[3]. If the value for the molecular diameter of oxygen is taken as 3.4×10^{-8} cm., the mean free path from eq. (3) will be

$$\lambda = \frac{1}{\sqrt{2}\pi 2.5 \times 10^{19}\,(3.4 \times 10^{-8})^2} = 4.4 \times 10^{-5} \text{ cm.}$$

It is evident from this value that molecules at atmospheric pressure travel but tiny distances between successive collisions. Since the mean free path is inversely proportional to the pressure of the gas, the product of the mean free path and the pressure is constant. A molecule having a mean free path of 4.4×10^{-5} cm. at atmospheric pressure will have a mean free path of 1 cm. at 4.4×10^{-5} mm. Hg pressure.

2. Mean Free Path in Gaseous Mixtures

In the process of the molecular still, there is always present a mixture of gases comprised of the distilling molecules and the residual air molecules. This situation differs from that just described where only one molecular species was considered. The situation to be considered here will be simplified to that of two molecular species; one, the distilling molecules and the other the residual air molecules if air is assumed to consist of one molecular species.

The relationship for the mean free path of molecules in a gas composed of molecules of different kinds given by Loeb[14] can be rearranged into a more convenient form by replacing the molecular velocities with equivalents in terms of the molecular masses of the molecules. This can be done by the use of the equation of the kinetic theory

$$pv = {}^1/_3 mn\bar{c}^2 = RT \tag{4}$$

where p and v are pressure and volume of the gas; m is the mass, n is the number, and $\bar{c}^2$ is the mean-square velocity of the molecules; T is the absolute temperature and R is the universal gas constant.

In making the transformation, there results

$$\lambda_{1,2} = \frac{1}{\pi\left(\frac{\sigma_1 + \sigma_2}{2}\right)^2 n \left(1 + \frac{M_1 T_2}{M_2 T_1}\right)^{1/2}} \tag{5}$$

where $\lambda_{1,2}$ is the mean free path of molecules (1) in molecules (2); σ_1 and σ_2 are their collision diameters; M_1 and M_2 are their molecular weights; T_1 and T_2 are the kinetic temperatures associated with them and defined by eq. (4) and n is the number of molecules per cubic centimeter of the gas.

The use of eq. (5) may be shown by an example for the computation of the mean free path for di-2-ethyl hexyl phthalate in air. Molecular diameters can be computed from various properties of gases. A simple relation useful for this kind of computation is based on the assumption of spherical shapes for molecules arranged in hexagonal closest packing and Avogadro's number. The molecular diameter σ in cm. is given by

$$\sigma_{\text{cm}} = 1.32 \times 10^{-8} \left(\frac{M}{\rho}\right)^{1/3} \tag{6}$$

where ρ is the density of the liquid phase and M is the molecular weight. Insert 390 for M and 1 for ρ in eq. (6) and there results for the phthalate ester a diameter of

$$\sigma = 1.32 \times 10^{-8} \left(\frac{390}{1}\right)^{1/3} = 1 \times 10^{-7} \text{ cm.}$$

Now, the mean free path of a di-2-ethyl hexyl phthalate molecule, originating from a liquid surface at 100°C., in air at 0.001 mm. Hg pressure and 20°C. is given by eq. (5) as follows:

$$\lambda_{1,2} = \frac{1}{\pi \left(\frac{1 \times 10^{-7} + 3.4 \times 10^{-8}}{2}\right)^2 (2.5 \times 10^{19}) \left(1 + \frac{293}{373} \cdot \frac{390}{29}\right)^{1/2}}$$

Therefore, the mean free path of the ester molecule at 760 mm. Hg pressure is

$$\lambda = 8.6 \times 10^{-7} \text{ cm.}$$

But at one micron Hg pressure it will be

$$\lambda = 8.6 \times 10^{-7} \times 760 \times 10^{3} = 0.65 \text{ cm.}$$

This value for the mean free path is indeed small and would require small gap spacings in the molecular still. It will be shown later that the effective mean free paths are probably larger than these values computed by the classical equations.

3. Distribution of Free Paths

The concept of mean free path as used in the foregoing discussion represents a statistically averaged distance that any one molecule in a group will travel between collisions. In reality, every molecule in a group will travel varied distances between successive collisions, depending on chance for their individual values. Some will travel distances greater than the mean free path while others may hardly move at all between collisions. Therefore, although a mean value is envisaged from the concept of the mean free path, the paths actually traveled are not equal but may take on any value at random.

The distribution of paths for a given group of molecules, however, is of special interest to molecular distillation. The following discussion will show its significance.

Consider a group of molecules N_0 starting out at time $t = 0$, just having experienced collisions. After a given lapse of time, a fraction of the group will experience random collisions at a frequency represented by ω. The remaining ones continue to travel without collisions. Let N represent the number in this latter group at time t. Then the change in the number not experiencing collisions up to time t can be equated as follows:

$$-dN = N\omega dt\cdot$$

On integration and rearranging, the equation becomes

$$N = N_0e^{-\omega t}$$

Now, the distance traveled by a molecule at time t without experiencing a collision is l, which, in turn, is the product of the average velocity u and time t, and so

$$l = ut$$

Substituting l/u for t, we obtain

$$N = N_0e^{-\frac{\omega l}{u}}$$

The collision frequency ω can be expressed as the quotient of the average velocity u and the distance λ traveled between collisions at time t, and

$$\omega = \frac{u}{\lambda}$$

Then

$$N = N_0e^{-l/\lambda}$$

or

$$\frac{N}{N_0} = e^{-l/\lambda} \tag{6}$$

where N/N_0 is the fraction of the original group of molecules that are still traveling without suffering collisions in the distance l.

A plot of the exponential equation (6) gives the curve shown in Figure 3 where N/N_0 is plotted against the exponent l/λ. The ordinate represents that fraction of the molecules that have traveled the fraction l/λ of a mean free path, λ, without having encountered collisions. For example, when $l = \lambda$, $N/N_0 = e^{-1} = 0.368$. This means that 36.8% are still moving, free of encounters with other molecules, but $(1 - N/N_0) = 63.2\%$ have had collisions. In a molecular still, therefore, the significance of this result is that if the condenser–evaporator gap were equal to the mean free path of the distilling molecules, 36.8% of them would definitely reach the condenser without collisions, but the remaining 63.2% would not.

This result does not mean that all of the molecules in the 63.2% group will be returned to the distilland. Some of them will reach the condenser

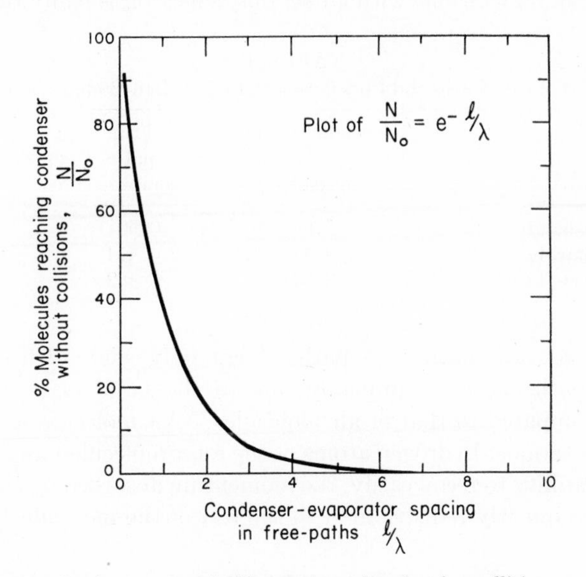

Fig. 3. Relationship between probable number of molecular collisions and evaporator condenser spacing. When $l = \lambda$, $N/N_0 = e^{-1} = 0.368$, or, 36.8% of the molecules are still moving free of encounters with other molecules.

in spite of their collisions, but certainly not all of them. Making the distillation gap smaller than the mean free path merely ensures a higher percentage of collision-free paths and consequently more distillate. This becomes more evident from the curve if other values of l/λ are considered. For a value less than unity, 0.4, for example, 67% of the molecules will reach the condenser without encounters. But for values greater than unity as, for example, 4.0, only about 2% will travel free of collision.

In practice, fortunately, the situation appears to be even better. Hickman[16] showed that distillation is less hindered by residual gas than is predicted by theory. He summed the matter up by the statement, "The residual molecules are not an independent maze through which the vapor must wander, but a movable barrier readily disturbed by distillation."

The experiments of Jacobs and Kapff[17] on the trajectories of vapor molecules cast more light on this matter. Their measurements on the impeded motion of oil molecules through residual air show that their measured "undeflected" paths are considerably greater than mean free paths computed from kinetic theory. A comparison of free paths and undeflected paths for three high-boiling organic esters is shown in Table I. In all cases the undeflected path is almost an order of magnitude greater than that computed from kinetic theory. It is obvious that the distance traveled by an oil molecule without serious deflection is many times greater

TABLE I
Comparison of Free Paths and Undeflected Paths for High-Boiling Organic Esters

Ester	Undeflected path (measured)	Free path (computed)	Ratio
Di-*n*-amyl phthalate	5.60	0.601	9.3
Di-*n*-amyl sebacate	4.41	0.474	9.3
Di-2-ethylhexyl phthalate	3.97	0.482	8.2

than its theoretical mean free path. That only slight deflections from rectilinear paths occur is probably due to the large mass of the ester molecules compared to that of air molecules. Air molecules perhaps only strike the outermost hydrogen atoms of the ester molecules, and, because of the latter's ability to recoil easily, the momentum absorbed by the hydrogen atom is subsequently redistributed to the rest of the molecule.

4. Rate of Distillation

The molecular distillation process, like conventional distillation, is comprised of several individual phenomena all occurring simultaneously to provide the end result. Four of these which are discernible and perhaps of most importance for molecular distillation are: (*1*) the rate of vaporization of molecules from the distilling surface, (*2*) the rate of condensation of vaporized molecules on the distilling surface, (*3*) the rate of condensation of the vaporized molecules on the condensing surface, and (*4*) the rate of vaporization of molecules from the condenser surface. The interrelationship of these rates may be depicted by arrows as follows:

$$\text{Vaporizer} \underset{2}{\overset{1}{\rightleftarrows}} \text{Vapor} \underset{4}{\overset{3}{\rightleftarrows}} \text{Condenser}$$

Vapor that is generated at the distilling surface should pass directly to the condenser and that which is condensed should not be induced to revaporize. In other words, to effect optimum efficiency in molecular distillation, conditions and equipment should be selected to force the process to the right. Although all of these rates are interdependent, the rate of vaporization is most fundamental since on it depend the others. This rate can be deduced theoretically from kinetic theory in an indirect manner as will be presented shortly.

Several theoretical relationships have been derived to account for the rate of molecular effusion, or vaporization under high vacuum. The equation due to Langmuir[3] is more directly applicable to the molecular distillation process than the one derived by Knudsen,[2] although both are quite similar. Langmuir used the expression to calculate the vapor pressures of metal filaments directly from their rates of vaporization in high vacuum. Since Langmuir's verification of his equation involved an experiment which more closely resembles molecular distillation than that used by Knudsen, the Langmuir form has become associated with molecular distillation.

The derivation of the Langmuir equation is based on kinetic theory with reasoning as follows: The kinetic theory postulates that there is a continuous flight of molecules from the surface of solid or liquid matter to the atmosphere surrounding it. When the system is properly confined, there is a continuous return of vapor molecules to these surfaces. The two processes proceed simultaneously and when the rate of escape is equal to the rate of return, the system is in equilibrium.

Whether liquids are boiling near their boiling points or at temperatures where their vapor pressures are in the region of a millimeter of Hg pressure, there is always equilibrium between the phases. At the lower temperatures where the vapor pressure of the liquid is less than one millimeter of Hg pressure, Langmuir suggested that the actual rate of vaporization becomes independent of the vapor surrounding it. In other words, the rate of vaporization in a high vacuum is the same as the rate of vaporization in the presence of a saturated vapor. He also considered that the rate of condensation in high vacuum is determined by the pressure of the vapor.

This saturated vapor under high vacuum can be treated as an ideal gas and its rate of return to the vaporizing surface can be deduced from the kinetic theory. It is for this return rate that the "rate equation" is deduced, although it is the rate of vaporization that is desired. But, since at equilibrium both are equal, one can be substituted for the other. It is in this indirect manner that the equation is derived.

The vapor contained in a unit cube of volume in contact with its liquid surface is assumed by the kinetic theory to be in equilibrium when one-half of the molecules are moving toward the liquid surface and the other half are moving away from it. For n molecules of mass m contained in a volume v, the quantity of vapor approaching the liquid surface will be

$$\tfrac{1}{2}mn/v, \text{ or } \tfrac{1}{2}\rho$$

where ρ = mass per unit volume or density. The average component of velocity of the molecules moving either to or from the surface is $^1/_2 u$, where u is the arithmetic mean velocity of the vapor molecules. Therefore, the mass w of vapor which strikes a unit surface of the liquid in unit time is the product of concentration and velocity, or

$$w = \tfrac{1}{2}\rho \cdot \tfrac{1}{2}u = \tfrac{1}{4}\rho u \qquad (8)$$

The density of the vapor can be expressed as a function of its pressure and temperature by means of eq. (4) because, by definition, $\rho = M/V$. Therefore

$$\rho = PM/RT \qquad (9)$$

By combining eqs. (8) and (9), the mean-velocity component becomes

$$u = 4w(RT/PM) \qquad (10)$$

From eq. (4),

$$PV = \tfrac{1}{3}mn\overline{c^2} = RT$$

which relates the pressure/volume product of a gas with the total kinetic energy of its molecules, the root mean-square velocity, $(c^2)^{1/2}$ is

$$(\overline{c^2})^{1/2} = \left(\frac{3RT}{M}\right)^{1/2} \qquad (11)$$

when M is substituted for mn. Since the mean-velocity u is related to $(\overline{c^2})^{1/2}$* as follows:

$$\frac{u}{(c^2)^{1/2}} = \frac{(8/\pi)^{1/2}}{\sqrt{3}},$$

then

$$u = (\overline{c^2})^{1/2}(8/3\pi)^{1/2} \qquad (12)$$

* In Glasstone's[15] notation, the mean-square velocity is indicated by $\overline{c^2}$. It is the average of the sum of the square of the velocity of each individual molecule, as contrasted with the square of the mean velocity u^2. The latter results by averaging the velocities of all molecules and then squaring the average. The square root of the mean-square velocity $(c^2)^{1/2}$ is therefore not equal to u; the former is equal to $(3\pi/8)^{1/2}$ or 1.085 times the latter. The foregoing analysis holds rigorously only for the equilibrium Boltzman Distribution. It is assumed for the present discussion that the disturbances of the distribution by the flow of molecules across the gap in a molecular still is negligible.

From eqs. (11) and (12), therefore,

$$u = (8RT/\pi M)^{1/2} \tag{13}$$

Finally, by combining eqs. (10) and (13), we obtain

$$w = P(M/2\pi RT)^{1/2} \tag{14}$$

which is the rate in grams per second per square centimeter at which vapor condenses on the surface of the vaporizing liquid. At equilibrium, then, eq. (14) also gives the rate of evaporation in accordance with the premise set forth at the start of the derivation.

Langmuir[3] used expression (14) to calculate the vapor pressures of pure metals by measuring the loss in weight of a filament which was maintained in vacuum at a high temperature for a definite period of time. His experimental method therefore was not one of dynamic equilibrium in the sense that the rate of evaporation from the hot filament is equal to the rate of condensation of the filament. His filaments continued to lose weight with time. The vaporizing molecules passed from the hot filament to the cold walls of the container where they condensed. The rate of return of vapor to the evaporating surface, therefore, was nil, but the rate of vaporization continued normally as if equilibrium was in existence. Langmuir's experimental verification with several metals such as tungsten, platinum, and molybdenum gave proof of the validity of the equation.

The process of the molecular still is similar to the experimental method used by Langmuir. In place of the metallic filament a thin layer of liquid is employed and the rate equation can be used to predict the rate of distillation. Discrepancies between calculated and observed rates in the molecular still are due, apart from effects such as abnormal behavior of the liquid, to effect collisions between distilling molecules and air molecules, or between like distillate molecules, which cause vapor molecules to return to the evaporator. Deviations from theoretical rates are accounted for by the use of a coefficient a as follows:

$$w = aP(M/2\pi RT)^{1/2} \tag{15}$$

This coefficient is known as the "evaporation coefficient" and is actually used as an efficiency factor to express the ratio of experimental to theoretical rates of distillation. The literature shows a great variance in the value of the coefficient. Knudsen[2] showed that mercury distilled with a coefficient near unity only when the surface of the liquid was clean. Washburn,[18] also distilling mercury in a pot-type molecular still at 0°C., found the distillation rate to be 84% of the theoretical rate.

Evidence of the validity of eq. (14) for organic molecules can be deduced from the results of Kapff and Jacobs.[19] The results of their dew-point method for the vapor-pressure determination of high-boiling esters, based on this equation, are in agreement with values obtained by Perry and Weber,[20] who used the pendulum tensimeter and theory which is free of relationships of the kinetic theory. This agreement points to the probability that coefficients of unity are possible.

Unequivocal proof of the validity of the rate equation was finally established by Hickman and Trevoy.[21] Convinced that published results on rates of evaporation of liquids were in error, mostly because of poor experimental technique, Hickman pursued the problem with new ideas while being mindful that Knudsen had been successful when using clean evaporating surfaces. Using the falling stream tensimeter with ester-type fluids whose vapor pressures were accurately known, he ably demonstrated that liquids distill with a coefficient of unity from clean new surfaces. The distillation results with 2-ethyl hexyl phthalate and 2-ethyl hexyl sebacate at 5–8 μ saturation pressure agreed within 2% of the theoretical values calculated by eq. (14) when employing the vapor pressure data of Perry and Weber.[20] At higher saturation pressures, the distillation rates decreased to about 75% of the theoretical. Hickman offered no conclusive opinion as to the cause for this latter unexpected result. He suggested the possibility of a Fraser "cloud effect" as the possible cause for the return of 25% of the evaporated molecules to the distilling stream. But since increasing the distillation gap, giving a higher ratio of condenser to evaporator surfaces, made no improvement in the distillation rates, it seemed obvious that the cloud effect could not be solely responsible for the behavior observed. The matter still remains unresolved. But the results, however, teach that molecular distillations should not be hurried since best performance is achieved at the slowest rates.

5. Characteristics of the Rate Equation

Equation (14) can be put into simplified forms which are useful to the chemist. When the value for R is taken as 8.3×10^7 dynes-cm./g. mole-°K. and P is multiplied by 1333 to convert dynes/cm.^{2} to millimeters of mercury eq. (14) becomes

$$w = \frac{P(1333)}{(6.28 \times 8.3 \times 10^7)^{1/2}} \cdot \sqrt{\frac{M}{T}}$$

or

$$w = 0.0583P\sqrt{\frac{M}{T}} \qquad (16)$$

TABLE II
Calculated Distillation Rates

	1	2	3	4	5	6
Substance	Mol. wt.	P in microns at 393°K. (120°C.)	$w = 0.0583\ P\sqrt{\frac{M}{T}}$ (g./sec./cm.²)	$m = 0.0583 \frac{P}{\sqrt{MT}}$ (mole/sec./cm.²)	$\frac{P}{\sqrt{M}}$ at 393°K.	$\sqrt{\frac{M}{T}}$ at 1 μ
Stearic acid	284	35.0	0.52×10^{-4}	0.0021×10^{-4}	2.077	0.90
Cholesterol	387	0.5	0.56×10^{-4}	0.0014×10^{-4}	0.02542	0.97
Tricaproin	387	20.0	0.60×10^{-4}	0.0016×10^{-4}	1.017	1.10
Tricaprylin	401	0.5	0.63×10^{-4}	0.0016×10^{-4}	0.02497	1.20
Tristearin	891	0.0001	0.76×10^{-4}	0.0009×10^{-4}	3.35×10^{-6}	1.32

where w is the distillation rate in g./sec./cm.[2] and P is the vapor pressure in mm. Hg.

Now by dividing both sides of eq. (16) by M, the molecular weight, the rate m is given directly in moles/sec./cm.[2], as follows:

$$m = \frac{w}{M} = 0.0583 \frac{P}{\sqrt{MT}} \tag{17}$$

Some characteristics of these equations may be demonstrated by considering them with actual values for specific substances. A list of typical substances amenable to molecular distillation is given in Table II. In the first two columns of the table are given the molecular weights and vapor pressures at 120°C. for each material. These materials cover the range of distillability in the molecular still. The figures in columns 3 and 4 show the distillation rates in grams and moles, respectively, calculated by the rate equation for 120°C. and 1 μ Hg pressure.

The equations show that the rate of molecular distillation for any substance, at any given temperature, is governed by ratio of $P/\sqrt{M}$. This means that the constituents of a mixture will distill from the liquid phase in proportion to their respective values of this ratio. The ratio of components reaching the distillate from a two-component system, for example, will be

$$\frac{p_1}{\sqrt{M_1}} \Big/ \frac{p_2}{\sqrt{M_2}} \text{ or } \frac{p_1}{p_2} \cdot \sqrt{\frac{M_2}{M_1}}$$

where p is now the partial pressure of the component. In conventional distillation, these same constituents will appear in the distillate in the ratio of their vapor pressures, namely, P_1/P_2. The separation factor in molecular distillation, therefore, should be enhanced by the value of

$$\sqrt{\frac{M_2}{M_1}}$$

over the p_1/p_2 of conventional distillation.

The significance of these quantities will be apparent from a consideration of the data in column 5 of the table. Cholesterol and tricaproin, both having identical molecular weights but widely differing vapor pressures, have $P/\sqrt{M}$ ratios of 0.025 and 1.01, respectively. The ratio of these ratios, which is 40, would suggest that tricaproin should be easily separated from cholesterol by molecular distillation. The theory predicts that they should be separable by conventional distillation as well, because their ratio of vapor pressures is also 40. Of course, these molecules will not survive the treatment of the conventional still and so their separation by this method is not possible.

Now compare cholesterol with tricaprylin. They have equal vapor pressures but different molecular weights. Since the

$$\frac{P}{\sqrt{M}}$$

ratios differ slightly, it should be possible to separate these substances by molecular distillation. But, because their vapor pressures are equal, separation by conventional distillation should not be possible even if they could withstand the thermal hazard of this method.

Finally, it is obvious that either stearic acid or tristearin should be easily molecularly distilled away from each other or from any other material listed because of their large and small values, respectively, for $P/\sqrt{M}$.

Unfortunately there is no experimental verification for the facts just deduced concerning the factor $(M_2/M_1)^{1/2}$. The fact that Brönsted and Hevesy[1] successfully concentrated mercury isotopes by molecular distillation attests to the validity of the factor. Since the isotopes are assumed to have equal vapor pressures, the separation achieved must have been due to the difference in masses. The experimental work of Trevoy[22] in comparing "projective" (molecular) distillation with "equilibrant" (conventional) distillation suggests that there are unknown factors in practice which overshadow the importance of the $(M_2/M_1)^{1/2}$ factor. His results, obtained with di-2-ethyl hexyl phthalate and di-2-ethyl hexyl sebacate, show that identical relative volatilities are obtained at temperatures below 120°C. by both methods of distillation. At higher temperatures, however, the relative volatility decreases faster for molecular distillation than for equilibrium distillation. In other words, better separation was achieved under equilibrium conditions, where the process is controlled by p_1/p_2, than for molecular distillation which is governed by

$$\frac{p_1}{p_2}\sqrt{\frac{M_2}{M_1}}$$

The advantage postulated from theory for molecular distillation is not demonstrated by these experiments. Obviously, other factors play an obscure role in this matter.

Finally, column 6 of Table II shows values of $(M/T)^{1/2}$ for the materials listed. The values for this ratio, for materials distillable in the molecular still, vary over a narrow range for a given set of conditions. This range is 0.9 to 1.3 at 1 λ Hg pressure. Because of this limited range, this ratio may be useful in some instances for estimating the approximate distilling range for new substances.

6. Distillation of Mixtures

The foregoing discussion on the rate equation has been concerned with the evaporation of pure substances. This is a situation purely of theoretical importance since the practical aspects of any distillation process must be concerned with the separation of mixtures. It will therefore be of interest to examine how some of the general theory of distillation might be applicable to systems of two or more components under conditions of molecular distillation.

A. RAYLEIGH EQUATION

The Rayleigh equation[23] relates the instantaneous composition of the distillate to that of the distilland. It is derived from a simple material balance involving only the instantaneous conditions at the head and pot of the still. The vapor–liquid equilibrium between phases that occurs in the conventional still is not implicit in the Rayleigh equation. It should therefore be applicable to the molecular distillation process as well.

The derivation and examples of the utility of the Rayleigh equation are presented in Chapter I (p. 74). The integrated form of the equation is

$$\ln S = \int \frac{dx_s}{x_d - x_s} \tag{18}$$

where S represents the total moles of distilland remaining in the still at any instant, and x_d and x_s indicate the moles of the more volatile component in the distillate and still, respectively. The integration of this basic form can be performed either algebraically or graphically. The resulting equations can be used to construct distillation curves relating either distillate composition or still composition to the total moles remaining in the still.

For ideal systems, the relationship between x_s and x_d necessary for the integration of eq. (18) is available through the relative volatility equation:

$$\frac{x_d}{1 - x_d} = \alpha \frac{x_s}{1 - x_s}$$

The relative volatility, α, for molecular distillation has the form

$$\frac{x_d}{1 - x_d} = \frac{p_1\sqrt{M_2}}{p_2\sqrt{M_1}} \cdot \frac{x_s}{1 - x_s}$$

The solutions for either x_d or x_s give

$$x_d = \frac{p_1\sqrt{M_2}\, x_s}{p_2\sqrt{M_1} - (p_2\sqrt{M_1} - p_1\sqrt{M_2})x_s} \tag{19}$$

and

$$x_s = \frac{p_2\sqrt{M_1}\, x_d}{p_1\sqrt{M_2} - x_d(p_1\sqrt{M_2} - p_2\sqrt{M_1})} \tag{20}$$

By substitution of either form into eq. (18) the integration can be performed. The resulting equations describe the change of still content with distillate or distilland composition with time. The solution of equations and the procedure for calculating distillation curves are the same as those presented in Chapter I (p. 75).

B. RATE EQUATION

Sunier[24] and Washburn[18] suggested that the evaporation of the components of a mixture in the molecular still should proceed according to the relation:

$$\frac{W_1}{W_2} = \frac{p_1\sqrt{M_2}}{p_2\sqrt{M_1}}$$

The expression represents the ratio of the rate of distillation of one component to that of another component at constant temperature. It is the basis for the relative volatility, α, in molecular distillation, which, as has already been mentioned, differs from the relative volatility of conventional distillation by the factor

$$\sqrt{\frac{M_2}{M_1}}$$

Burrows[12] has extended and expanded this aspect of the theory of molecular distillation following the classical approach used in the theory of conventional distillation. He arrived at equations for batch molecular distillation of binary systems, assuming the applicability of Raoult's law and unit activity for the components, in the forms

$$\log \frac{w_1}{q_1} = \frac{P_1}{P_2}\sqrt{\frac{M_2}{M_1}}\,\log \frac{w_2}{q_2}$$

or

$$\log \frac{w_1}{q_1} = \alpha \log \frac{w_2}{q_2}$$

where w_1 and w_2 are the instantaneous weights of components 1 and 2 remaining in the distilland, q_1 and q_2 are the initial weights of the two components, and α is the relative volatility.

He ascribed activity coefficients γ_1 and γ_2 to each component to account for deviations from Raoult's law and modified the relative volatility α as follows:

$$\alpha = \frac{\gamma_1 P_1}{\gamma_2 P_2} \sqrt{\frac{M_2}{M_1}}$$

Burrows showed the applicability of his equations and other aspects of his theory by the interpretation of some results from actual distillation data. The general applicability of these equations, however, are restricted for the present because of the lack of numerical data and information on the behavior of liquids under molecular distillation conditions. The compliance with Raoult's law of systems of the type amenable to molecular distillation has not yet been verified and the relative volatilities of systems examined have been found to vary considerably with temperatures.[21,22]

IV. MOLECULAR-STILL TYPES AND THEIR CHARACTERISTICS

1. Molecular-Still Types

Two distinct types of molecular stills have evolved. The simplest of these is the "pot-type," in which the charge for distillation is wholly contained as a pool of liquid in the boiler. Distillation takes place from the surface of the quiescent liquid to a nearby condenser. The liquid layer varies in depth during the course of the distillation and is held at the temperature of distillation for the complete duration of the process.

The second type is the "flowing-film" still of which there are two general kinds. Both are characterized by the fact that the distilland is made to flow in thin layers over a heated surface. The form in which the flow is purely gravitational is termed the "falling film" type. In the case where centrifugal force is employed to generate the film, the stills are known as "centrifugal" stills. In both types, the distilland layer is thin and the distilland is heated only while in transit over the heated surface; at all other times it can be maintained at room temperature. The liquid is heated to the distilling temperature by contact with the surface over which it flows. Distillation takes place from the liquid surface and the vapor condenses on a nearby cooled surface. Distillate and distilland are led off to appropriate reservoirs.

Typical stills of each kind are shown schematically and in photographs in the section on "Still Design."

Because of its constructional simplicity, the pot-type still has found general acceptance in the laboratory, even though the flowing-film types are more efficient and offer less thermal hazard to the distilland. Then, too, the pot-type stills can be made to accommodate very small samples which is often a necessity in experimental work. Consequently, variations in the pot-type still have been numerous, with each designer contributing some special feature or innovation for convenience to meet his particular needs. In general, few, if any, significant contributions have been made which have enhanced the performance over that of the basic style. The pot-type stills have not been of much commercial importance.

The advent of the "falling-film" type was a major advance in molecular distillation. The superior performance of the falling film still brought to light the commercial potential of molecular distillation and units of this type are used commercially.[25] The centrifugal stills which followed displaced the falling film types in some commercial operations.[26] A miniature model of the centrifugal still was also made for laboratory work and has become the standard for the distillation laboratory.[50]

The pot-type molecular still appears to satisfy the requirements for molecular distillation, but some deficiencies are inherent in its design. The physical design of the flowing-film stills obviates these difficulties which are, for the most part, concerned with the distilland layer itself. The distilling layer in the pot-type still is deep and stagnant and therefore completely unlike that of the flowing-film stills. The need for thin layers of distilland and for the renewal of the evaporating surface was sensed by the pioneers in the field. The designs of Burch's tray stills,[5] having a large ratio of surface area to depth, attest to the recognition of this need.

It was not until the experiments of Hickman and co-workers[27] on the behavior of evaporating liquids that the cause and effect of the low evaporating coefficients in pot stills were understood. This work clearly demonstrates that evaporating liquids, especially pot stills—molecular or otherwise—are inherently "torpidity" prone An evaporating surface not yielding vapor at rates commensurate with an evaporative coefficient of unity are characterized as "torpid." Torpidity is promoted by surface contamination either produced by chemical reaction of the distilling material itself or by an accumulation of foreign matter washed down into the pot by the refluxing phase. The batch-still boiler is obviously a sink for such contaminants. In contrast, the flow process of the flowing-film still provides a means of surface renewal and thus gives rise to the possibility of achieving evaporation rates approaching the theoretical.

Rapid distillation from a deep, stagnant liquid layer can induce a state of depletion of the more volatile component in the evaporating surface. Such behavior will obviously produce variable composition in the vapor. Some form of agitation in the liquid layer is therefore needed to supplement the slow diffusional process which functions to overcome this condition.

The flowing-film stills produce a turbulence in the distilling liquid because of its flow over the heated surface. Pot stills, of course, have no such turbulence, and depletion is usually minimized by distilling at low rates or by the incorporation of mechanical agitation.

The force of gravity alone, however, is not sufficient in the falling film still to overcome the forces which oppose the formation of a continuous film of distilland. The gravitational flow pattern, down the surface of a vertical tube, varies for different liquids from a uniformly continuous film to one in which the flow is in the form of streams or rivulets, leaving bare a sizable portion of the heated surface. Bare areas are undesirable, not only because they reduce the effective evaporating surface of the still, but also because they overheat and decompose the stagnant residue residing on them. Thermal degradation of this kind overburdens the vacuum pumps and usually terminates the distillation.

Much effort has been expended in attempts to resolve this problem. Many kinds of materials of construction, such as glasses, common steels, stainless-steels, chromium, nickel, aluminum, and silver, were examined for the evaporator surface. These materials were either machined from solid stock or plated. Various textured and machined surfaces, such as polished, satinized, sand-blasted, chemically etched, scored, grooved, or knurled, were used. No one combination was found satisfactory for every application. A highly polished surface appears to be a prime requisite, whereas the material of construction is of secondary importance so long as it will withstand the action of the material being distilled. Instead of allowing the distilland film to form spontaneously on the falling film evaporator, mechanical devices such as rods, blades, and brushes have been proposed to distribute the liquid in a direction normal to its gravitational flow. The centrifugal still, of course, is free of the film-formation difficulty. The surface requirement is one of smoothness of finish and inertness toward the distilling material.

2. Size and Shape of Evaporator and Condenser Surfaces

The shape and relative sizes of the evaporator and condenser of the molecular still warrant comment. The former has an influence on the effective mean free path, and the latter bears on the efficiency of the process. When distillation takes place from a flat surface to a parallel condenser, all molecules do not travel directly across the gap normal to the evaporating surface. Molecules leave the surface at all angles so that the distances traveled to reach the condenser will vary depending on the angle of departure. Only those leaving at right angles to the surface will travel a distance equivalent to the gap dimension. This behavior is interpreted by the Cosine law. Because of such distribution of directions, there can be cross collisions of molecules occurring in the gap. Such collisions can be effective in returning molecules to the evaporating surface, with a consequent loss in distillation efficiency.

Burrows[7,28] has discussed in some detail how the evaporation coefficient may be affected by the geometry of the evaporator and condenser surfaces of a molecular still. Two molecules, for example, leaving the evaporator surface from different sites at equal angles of departure, other than 90°, and traveling distances equal to the gap width, can collide at a point short of the condenser surface. For any given arrangement of evaporator and condenser surfaces, the point of collision with respect to the condenser surface will vary according to the angle of departure. For any given angle of departure, however, the point of collision can be varied and made to approach the condenser surface by a change in the geometry of the still. The further the collision takes place from the surface of the condenser, of course, the greater is the chance that the molecules may be returned to the evaporator.

Burrows showed that in a still where the evaporation takes place from a flat horizontal surface to a corresponding parallel condenser, the point of collision occurs at a greater distance from the condenser than that which would occur from a combination of curved concentric surfaces. In other words, the latter arrangement is most likely to yield a higher value for the evaporation coefficient. The effect becomes more pronounced as the diameters of the concentric surfaces become small, as for example, distillation from a falling liquid stream of the type used by Hickman and Trevoy.[21]

On the other hand, distillation from the outer concentric surface to the inner one, the reverse of the arrangement just described, gives rise to the worst possible condition. Here, collisions can occur very close to the evaporator surface and, presumably, will produce a substantial reduction in the value of the evaporation coefficient. Therefore, this arrangement of molecular still in which the condenser surface is surrounded by the evaporator surface is not desirable.

In this connection, Burrows[7] also derived an expression for the evaporation coefficient, a, based on the kinetic behavior of the molecules in the distillation gap. This involves the mean free path λ of molecules under equilibrium conditions, the distance, l, molecules travel between collisions and the gap width d. By summation of all possible probabilities by which molecules will reach the condenser—including those making the journey free of collisions as well as those which have had collisions—Burrows gave the following equation:

$$a = F + (1 - F)(2e^{-K} - e^{-2K}) \tag{21}$$

where a is the evaporation coefficient, F is the ratio of the evaporating area to the total area of condenser plus evaporator, and e^{-K} represents the quantity $e^{-(l/\lambda)}$, the fraction of molecules that reach the condenser collision-free, as discussed on p. 543. The term $e^{-(l/\lambda)}$ is modified to $e^{-(d/K\lambda)}$, where k is a factor depending primarily on the shape of the evaporator and to some extent on the shape of the condenser.

The nature of this relationship can be seen from the calculated data on Burrows given in Table III. When K is small, $^1/_4$ for example, the evapo-

TABLE III
Computed Values of the Evaporation Coefficient Using Equation (21)

K	$F = 0.5$	$F = 0.7$	$F = 0.8$
$^1/_4$	0.98	0.99	0.99
$^1/_2$	0.92	0.95	0.97
1	0.80	0.88	0.92
2	0.63	0.77	0.85
4	0.52	0.71	0.81

ration coefficient a (the fraction of molecules reaching the condenser) is near unity, whether or not the condenser area is equal to or greater than the evaporator area. As K becomes larger, it is apparent that the larger the condensing surface is made with respect to the evaporator surface (i.e., larger values of F) the more efficient the still will be in terms of the number of molecules reaching the condenser.

The agreement shown by Burrows between measured evaporation coefficient for a tray still and for a falling stream tensimeter with computed values for each still, according to eq. (21), is good.

3. Thermal Hazard

One virtue of the molecular still is its ability to distill successfully substances which are relatively involatile and/or thermally sensitive. The sensitivity of organic molecules to thermal degradation increases as the molecular size increases. Experience has taught that caution for thermal hazard becomes necessary in distillation when the molecular weight exceeds 250–300. In the molecular still, however, materials up to molecular weights of 1200 can be accommodated because the thermal hazard to which the material is subjected is greatly reduced.

Molecular distillation is preferably effected from thin layers, as already discussed. A comparison of typical film thicknesses and times of exposure at the distillation temperature for various types of stills is compiled in Table IV. The time of distillation differs markedly between stills and an

TABLE IV
Hazard of Stills

	Approx. distilland thickness[a] (mm.)	Exposure times	Pressure[b] (mm. Hg)	Temp.,[c] °C.	Relative thermal coef.[d]	Relative decompos. hazard	Hazard index[e]
Simple flask	50–100	1–5 hr.	760	360	2^{23}	1.5×10^{12}	9.4 (1 hr., 760 mm.)
Claisen flask	50–100	1–5 hr.	10	270	2^{14}	3×10^{9}	
Boiling point	50–100	1–5 hr.	0.1–1	220	2^{9}	9.2×10^{7}	5.6 (1 hr., 100 μ)
Laboratory mol. pot	10–50	1 hr.	0.001	130	1	1.8×10^{5}	3.6 (1 hr., 1 μ)
Laboratory fall. film	0.1–0.3	1 min.	0.001	130	1	3×10^{3}	1.8 (1 min., 1 μ)
Laboratory centrifugal	0.01–0.02	0.02 sec.	0.001	130	1	1	0 (1 sec., 1 μ
Industrial fall. film	1–3	2–10 min.	0.001	130	1		
Industrial centrifugal	0.03–0.06	1 sec.	0.001	130	1	5×10^{1}	

[a] Assuming similar throughput for same unit area of all stills. Data from ref. 6.
[b] Data for columns 3 through 6 taken from ref. 29.
[c] Boiling points of dibenzylphthalate.
[d] Assuming that the hazard doubles with each 10°C. rise.
[e] Data taken from ref. 30.

approximate value is given in column 2 for each type. In a cyclic molecular distillation requiring as many as 20 passes, the distilland in the falling-film still is subjected to the temperature of distillation from a fraction of a minute to 20 min.; on the centrifugal evaporator, the total time is reduced to a matter of seconds. The inferiority of the pot-type stills is evident in this comparison.

The thermal hazard imposed during distillation is a function of the time and temperatures involved. Assuming that reaction rates doubled with each 10° rise in temperature and that thermal decomposition was a chemical reaction, Hickman[29] computed relative thermal exposures for a number of stills at the boiling point of dibenzyl phthalate. These data are also given in Table IV. The centrifugal evaporator with a contact time of 0.02 sec./pass is given a relative thermal coefficient of 1 and a relative decomposition hazard of 1. The falling-film still with exposures of the order of 1 min. also has a relative thermal coefficient of unity but a relative decomposition hazard of $1/0.02 \times 60$ or 3000. The relative hazard for the simple distillation flask still reaches 1.5×10^{12}.

In a subsequent publication[30] "hazard index" was employed to assign better numerical values to thermal decomposition in stills. According to this concept, the decomposition hazard, D, is the product of time, t, in seconds and pressure, P, in microns of Hg, expressed as

$$D = t_{\text{sec}} \times P_{\mu}$$

Because the values of D become large when extended to include conventional stills, "hazard index" D is, preferably, expressed as log D or by the hazard index Dh (a convention in keeping with Sorenson's pH scale for hydrogen-ion concentrations). Thus if the centrifugal still operates for 1 sec. at 1 μ Hg pressure, it will have $D = 1$, or $Dh = 0$. The conventional Claisen flask still distilling for 1 hr. at atmospheric pressure will have a hazard index of $D = (3600 \times 76{,}000) = 2.74 \times 10^9$ or $Dh = 9.44$. Hazard indices for several types of stills and special distilling conditions are given in the last column of Table IV.

4. Fractionation

The best performance to be expected from a single act of molecular distillation is that equivalent to one theoretical plate commensurate with a relative volatility of

$$\alpha = \frac{p_1}{p_2}\sqrt{\frac{M_2}{M_1}}$$

Fig. 4. A bank of centrifugal molecular stills. The conical evaporator is clearly seen in the center of the back group of stills.

as discussed on p. 556. Complete separations are therefore not to be expected of mixtures whose components have similar vapor pressures and molecular weights. The simple molecular distillation of a mixture usually yields a series of fractions, each differing from its contiguous members but none necessarily consisting of only one component in 100% purity. As is the case in conventional distillation, enhanced separation or fractionation in the molecular still must be achieved by repetition of the process.

Fractionation in conventional distillation has long been practiced as one coordinated act in fractionating columns. The counterpart of the fractionating column has been devised for small-scale molecular distillation, but on the commercial scale molecular fractionation has been achieved by truly multiple redistillation methods. Here, several individual still units are connected together in ways to permit redistillation of distillates and residues until a desired product results. Hence, under these conditions molecular stills having the equivalent of a large number of theoretical plates will involve considerable equipment and cost.

An arrangement of individual still units to achieve enhanced separation has been described by Fraser[31] in which each distillate is fed back to join the feed of the previous still or to the feed of one still further removed. Fawcett and McCowen[32] devised several schemes for grouping stills in cascade operation in patterns resembling those employed in recrystallization. This subject was discussed in some detail by Hickman.[26] A view of a group of centrifugal stills arranged for multiple redistillation is shown in Figure 4.

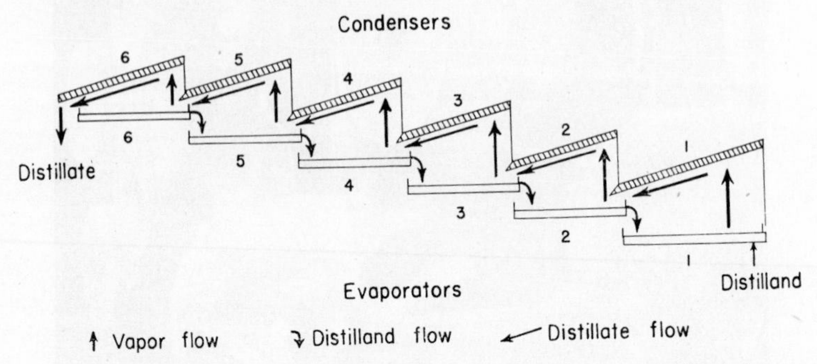

Fig. 5. Principle of multi-stage fractionation. Stream flows are indicated by arrows and condenser and evaporator surfaces are numbered. Vapor rising from evaporator 1, for example, condenses on condenser 1. The condensate flows down the inclined surface and drops off into the evaporator 2. Overflow from evaporator 2 drains into evaporator 1. At equilibrium this same process is taking place simultaneously in all units.

On the laboratory scale the principle of fractionation has been accomplished in stills comprised of composites of 10 or more stages. A variety of such stills have been described which operate on the principles of both the pot-type and the flowing-film stills.

The basis of operation for these stills is readily seen from a consideration of the sketch in Figure 5. The distillands are contained in shallow compartments in staircase fashion. Above each compartment is a saw-tooth condenser arrangement with one tooth for each compartment. The vapor rising from each compartment condenses on the opposing cold surface. Because of the reversed slope of the condenser surface, the condensate drains into the compartment of the adjacent unit one stage higher in the series. The distillands move in the opposite direction by overflow. This countercurrent flow induced by the geometry of the equipment produces distillate at the highest condenser surface and residue in the lowest compartment. The degree of separation achieved is a function of the number of stages involved. The efficiency of the still is dependent on how well each stage functions. Interdiffusion of vapor from one stage to another will reduce efficiency, as will improper mixing of overflow with the distilland in the compartment. These matters have been given due consideration in various designs of the fractionating molecular stills. Performance efficiencies of one theoretical plate per stage have been reported for these stills.

The details of construction and performance of these stills will be discussed in the section on "Still Designs."

V. STILL DESIGNS

1. General Characteristics

This section is devoted to the design of the still itself. The characteristics and requirements of the pumping system and the choice of pressure gauges are described in Chapter VII.

It is evident from the many modifications which have appeared in print that no one type of still will satisfy all the demands for molecular distillation. Although every still has its special virtues, it is impossible to describe here the numerous variations which have been proposed. Those described were selected, as being useful representatives of each type, and many others are included in the bibliography.

Any laboratory molecular still should possess the following characteristics which contribute to good performance and ease of operation.

(*1*) The condenser–evaporator distance should be less than 5 cm. and preferably less than 1 cm.

(*2*) The ratio of surface area to depth of distilland should be large.

(*3*) The renewal of the distilland surface should be continuous and rapid.

(*4*) The distilland temperature should be constant during the collection of any one fraction.

(*5*) The system should be constructed with seals and joints so tight that the pumping system will have no difficulty in maintaining a pressure of 10 μ or less.

(*6*) A cold trap interposed between still and pumps will protect the latter from contamination by volatile distillates.

(*7*) The removal of distillate without interference with continuity of distillation is desirable.

(*8*) A continuously indicating pressure gage is especially convenient.

2. Molecular Pot Stills

A. COLD FINGER TYPES

These are the simplest of all molecular stills and many versions have been proposed. A useful form made from simple tubes is shown in Figure 6. The rubber stopper is a satisfactory vacuum seal and offers no difficulty because it is not in contact with either distillate or distilland. These stills can vary in size from 1 to 2 in. in diameter for the outer tube and with $^1/_8$ to $^1/_4$ in. of annular space. A height of about 6 in. is sufficient to prevent

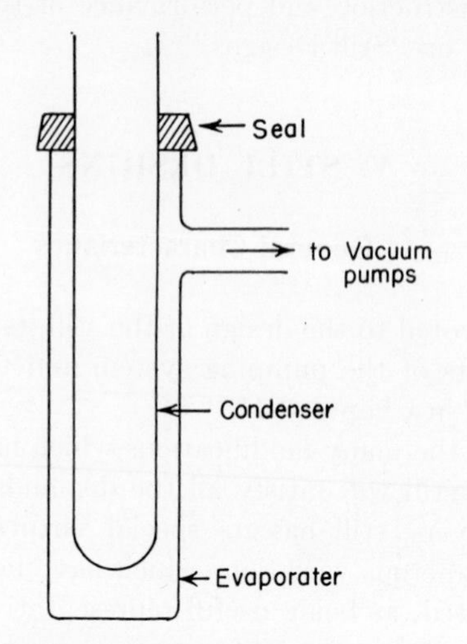

Fig. 6. Common cold-finger still.

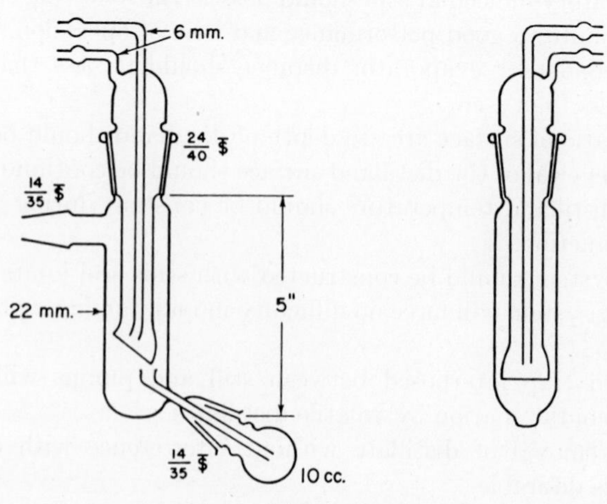

Fig. 7. Still of Riegel.

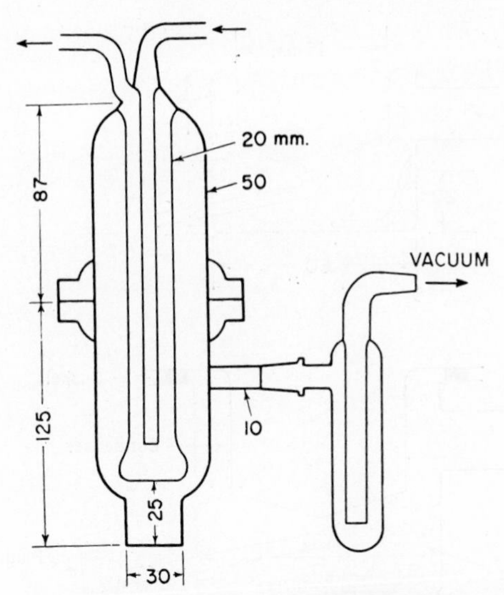

Fig. 8. Strain and Allen still.

escape of the vapor. The vacuum tubulation should be at least $^1/_2$ in. in diameter. As the size of the still is increased, however, it is best to flange both tubes so that the seal can be made by a rubber gasket. Heat is best applied by means of an oil bath and the temperature of the distilland can be assumed to be that of the bath. The smaller size is recommended for samples less than 3 g. and the larger diameter can accommodate up to 15 or 20 g.

Modifications of the cold-finger still have been described by Reigel et al.[33] and are shown in Figure 7. These stills were used in a multiple-unit assembly arranged for both macro- and micro-molecular distillation. The units themselves have unique features which might have special utility in specific applications.

Another variation of the small, cold-finger, pot-type still is that of Strain and Allen.[34] The still is constructed from flanged borosilicate glass pipe in the form shown in Figure 8. The still can be readily opened for charging the sample and for removal of distillate. A procedure is given by these authors for the distillation of very viscous materials.

B. SQUAT-TYPE POT STILLS

Some pot-type stills have been designed in a more compact form with provisions for greater capacity, larger distilling surface, and ease of removal of fractions. Many variations have been devised,[35] but the elements of two general types are shown in Figure 9. The condenser is contoured to expose

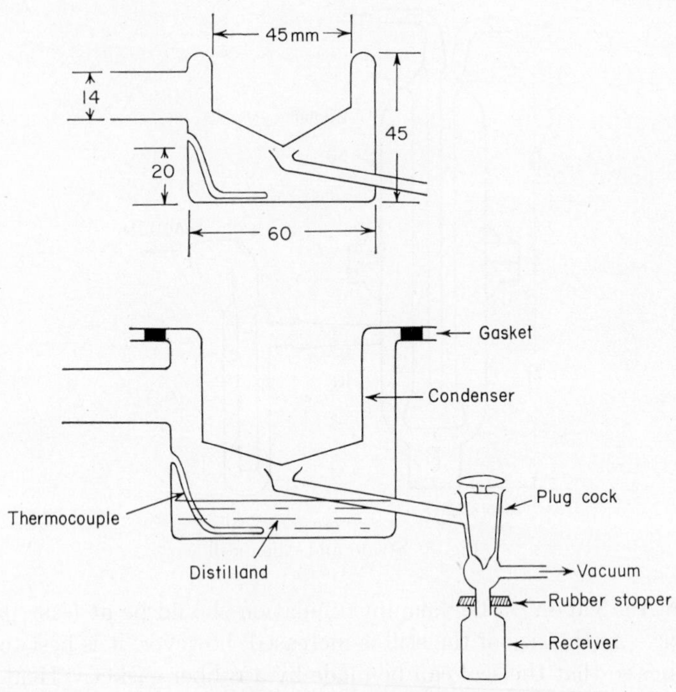

Fig. 9. All-glass stills.

a large surface to the distilling vapor, to provide a drip point to remove the distillate, and to contain the refrigerant conveniently. The all-glass unit needs no seal between condenser and pot but is inconvenient to charge and to use if the distillate is not a liquid at the temperature of the condenser. Cleaning is also difficult. The two-piece unit is free of these objections and is therefore a more versatile apparatus. The seal is no problem because of the variety of pliable polymeric materials now available for such applications. Solid distillates can be scraped off the condenser when the still is opened.

The plugcock shown, designed for vacuum application, permits the removal of any number of fractions without interfering with the distillate. Its construction allows the distillate to flow through the plug and into the receiver. These stills are bested heated by an electric element or a hot plate. The distilland temperature can be measured by means of a fine thermocouple admitted through the small well. The stills shown in Figure 9 accommodate up to 20 g. of sample. With similar stills having larger diameters, charges up to 200 g. have been used. The distillate holdup in these stills is necessarily on the large side and some intermixing of fractions must inevitably occur.

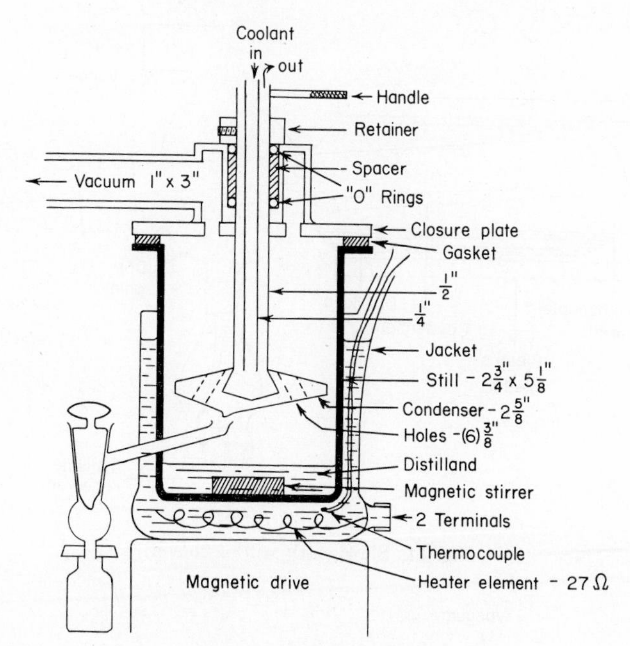

Fig. 10. Oil-jacketed still.

A useful and versatile version* of this still is shown in Figure 10. It is heated by an oil jacket which is made an integral part of the still body. The oil is heated electrically. A thermocouple measures the oil temperature close to the wall of the still pot. The condenser is made of aluminum for good heat conductivity. It is suspended from the closure plate by a tubular member through which the cooling fluid is circulated. The "O" ring seal permits rotation so that the eccentric drip point can be positioned either over the collection tube to draw off distillate or positioned elsewhere to reflux distillate. The condenser unit itself has slanting holes bored through it for passage of noncondensible gas. The vacuum take-off is made concentric with the central tube. Stirring in the distilland layer is effected by a glass-covered magnetic bar which is turned by a magnetic drive. Charges of 10–60 g. can be distilled from a unit of the size shown.

C. OTHER TYPES

A short-path, pot-type molecular still reported by Gilson[36] is shown in Figure 11. The boiler is made from glass tube to be operated in a horizontal position. The condenser is inserted a at slight angle so that the con-

* This still was designed and constructed by Mr. Dean Cox of the Kodak Research Laboratories.

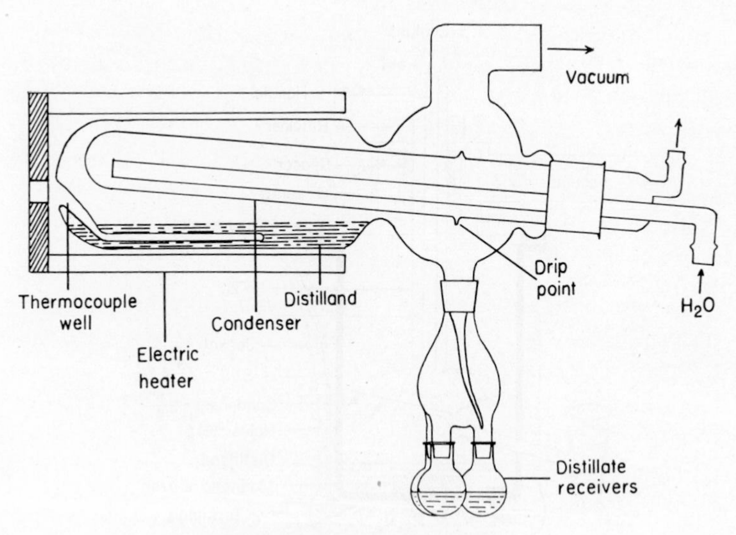

Fig. 11. Short-path still of Gilson.

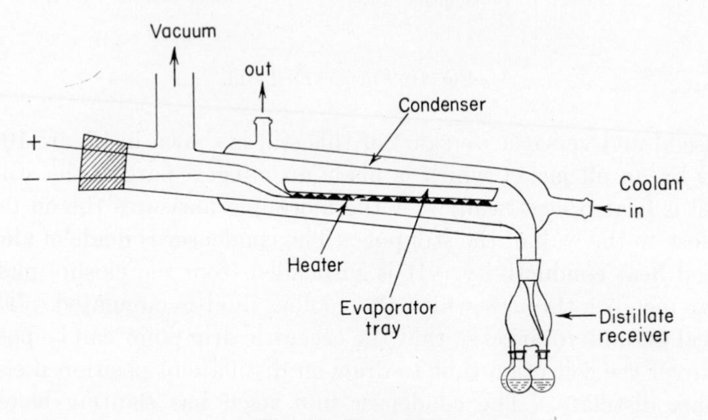

Fig. 12. Tray still.

densate will flow to the drip point and drop off into the receiver. All fittings and connections for assembly are made with standard ground-glass joints. The still pot is heated by an electrical winding and temperature is closely controlled by automatic equipment. The advantages claimed for this unit are that the still permits clear visibility of contents and thermometer, is easily assembled for operation, and that it is suitable for distilling quantities ranging from a few grams to over 100 g.

Another general form of the pot still is that known as the "tray" still. Here the distilland is contained in a shallow pan or tray. A modified version of Burch's[37] still is shown in Figure 12. The electrically heated tray, containing the distilland, is suspended within the glass tube that surrounds it. The tube serves as the condenser. The distillate drains to the collector chamber and drops off into the receivers.

Carothers and Hill[38] described another version of the tray still which they used to perform distillations and to conduct chemical reactions, such as polymerization and dehydration, as well.

D. POT STILLS FOR SMALL CHARGES

A small still suitable for the collection of two fractions has been described by Matchett and Levine.[39] The still, shown in Figure 13, is suitable for samples ranging from 0.25 to 5 g. For operation, the still, positioned horizontally, is charged through tube *E*. The still pot *C* is formed by two transverse creases, *D*, in the outer tube *A*. The inner tube *B* serves as the condenser. With the cap in position over *E*, vacuum is applied to a moderate level and the distilland is heated gently by element *H* to effect degassing. When the distillation vacuum is finally established, the still is

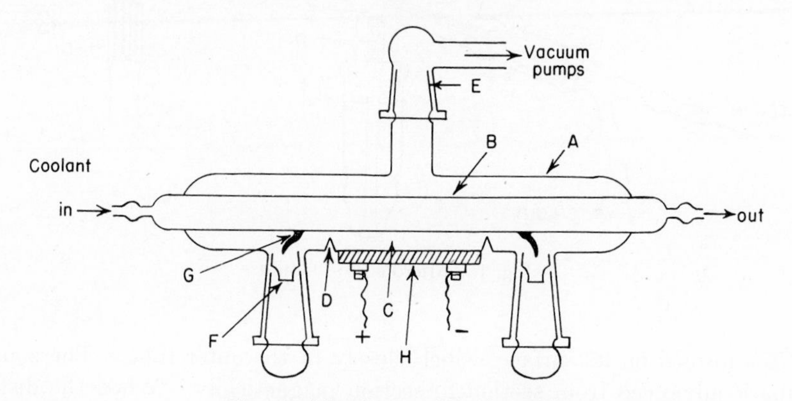

Fig. 13. Matchett and Levine still.

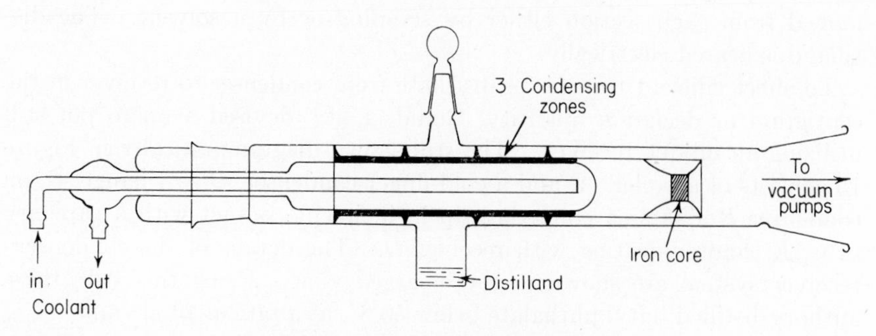

Fig. 14. Gilson semi-micro still.

tilted toward one end and the temperature is increased until distillation begins. The distillate collects on the condenser *B*, which is air- or water-cooled, and drains to the drip point *G* whence it drops into receiver *F*. When one fraction has been collected, the still is tipped toward the other end and a second fraction is collected in the same manner. The distillation can be temporarily terminated, receiver *F* changed, and after starting again, third and fourth fractions can be collected.

An all-glass still suitable for distillations on a semi-micro scale was described by Gilson.[36] It is especially useful for quantities 0.5–2.0 g. of solids or very viscous liquids. The details are shown in the diagram of Figure 14. The vapor generated from the still pot is condensed on the zones of the condenser. The condenser is zoned by means of concentric

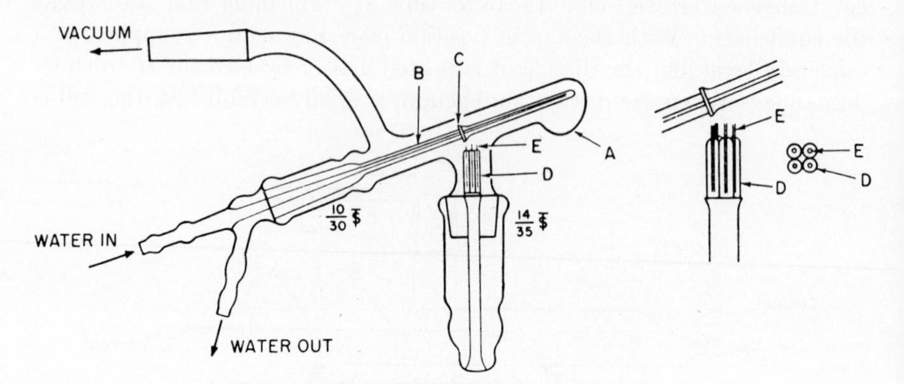

Fig. 15. Micro still of Gould.

ridges formed on its surface, which closely fit the outer tube. The zoned tube is advanced from section to section magnetically. When the distillation is completed, the zoned tube is withdrawn and the distillate is removed from each section either by scraping or by a solvent. The distilland is heated electrically.

To effect efficient transfer of distillate from condenser to receiver in the centigram or decigram quantity, Gould et al.[40] devised a micro pot still utilizing an unique receiver. The still shown diagrammatically in Figure 15 consists of a boiler, *A*, and a cold-finger condenser, *B*. A flange, *C*, on condenser *B* acts as a collecting tip in incipient contact with a capillary tube, *E*, communicating with receiver *D*. The details of the condenser–receiver system are shown in the enlarged view. Using this still, these authors distilled butyl phthalate below 50°C. at a rate of 20 μl./min.

The details for other micro stills may be found in Cheronis.[41]

3. Falling-Film Stills

The falling-film still consists of a heated vertical tubular evaporator over which distilland is allowed to flow by gravity. The flow can be either on the outside or inside surface of the tube. In either case, the distilland spreads over the entire surface in a thin film which is usually 0.1–1.0 mm. thick, depending upon the feed rate and viscosity of the distilland. The evaporator is surrounded by a closely spaced, concentric tube which serves as the condenser. This annular space is exhausted and maintained below 10 μ Hg pressure. Distilland is stored in a reservoir from which it is metered to a distributor on the evaporator column. From this point it descends the column in a continuous film. The distillate is collected in a receiver and the residue flows into a second reservoir. Some stills use only a single reservoir and recycle the distilland at a greater rate for a given period of time to ensure exposure of all the distilland.

A. A VERSATILE UNIT

A time-tested, laboratory, falling film molecular still is shown in detail in Figure 16. It gives very satisfactory performance in cyclic batch distil-

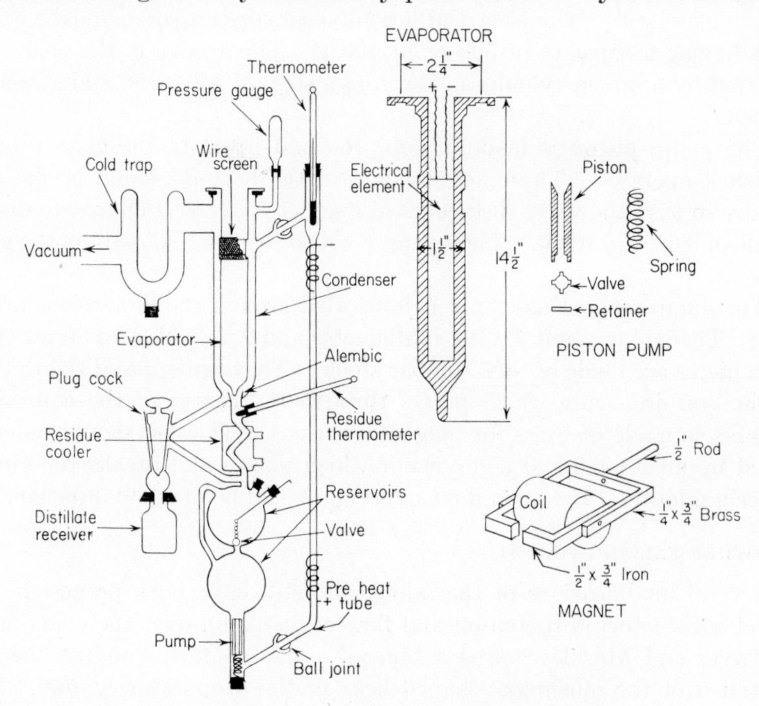

Fig. 16. A versatile falling-film still.

lation with many types of material. The condenser is made of 60 mm. tubing and is 14 in. long from top flange to the bottom of the distillate alembic. The residue cooler attached to the condenser is 35 mm. O.D. and $2^1/_2$ in. long and contains one coil of 14-mm. tubing. The reservoirs can be of any capacity; one liter has been found to be a useful size. The connecting tube between the two is valved by a $^1/_2$-in. steel ball which is controlled externally by the rod as shown. The pump housing is 12 mm. I.D. and 3 in. long. The preheat tube is 6 mm. in diameter and is connected to the still by ball joints. The upper end is enlarged to accept a thermometer and is wound with No. 20 or 22 resistance wire equivalent to 200 w. Exhausting is done through a 50-mm. tubing with a cold trap as shown. Pressure is measured by a suitable gauge. Distillate is withdrawn through the plugcock which can be positioned to allow the distillate to drop into the receiver or turned to make it pass back into the still with the residue stream. The temperature of the residue leaving the evaporator is measured by thermometer which projects into the still just below the evaporator.

The details of accessory components are also given in Figure 16. The evaporator is machined from aluminum stock and the external surface is highly polished. The upper flange is grooved to retain a gasket for sealing to the glass still. The electrical heating element is a commercial tubular unit having a capacity of 500 w. at 120 v. The groove in the column is covered by a screen cylinder made from a strip of 100-mesh stainless-steel screen.

The pump piston is made of soft iron and fitted to the glass tube in which it operates. The inner shoulder at the bottom should be flat and square so that the valve disk can seal itself effectively. The valve disk is made of 0.005-in. stock. The spring is coiled to form a loose fit in the glass tube.

The pump magnet assembly is fabricated around the dimensions of the coil. The coil is about $1^3/_4$ in. in diameter and 2 in. wide and 80 w. The pole pieces are made of soft-iron bar stock. They are screwed tightly to a $^3/_4$-in. soft iron core which passes through the center of the coil. The bracket is made of brass for magnetic reasons. The coil should be energized by an interrupted d.c. current which makes and breaks the circuit twice a minute. The on and off intervals should be of equal duration.

B. OTHER FALLING-FILM STILLS

Several modifications of the falling-film still have been proposed. To effect satisfactory distribution and flow of distilland over the evaporator, Detwiler and Markley[42] used a tapered sleeve guide to conduct the distilland over the mushroom-shaped head of the evaporator column. The entire surface of the column has a coating of fragmented glass fused to it to provide innumerable tortuous channels for the flow of distilland. Better spreading of the distilland is claimed for this method. This method was later employed by Taylor[43] in a still design in which he used a single reservoir for cyclic distillation.

Quackenbuch and Steenbach[44] surrounded the condenser with the evaporator to minimize distillate holdup. They used an assembly of glass rods which was rotated magnetically to spread the distilland over the evaporator. Other methods of redistributing distilland are the rotary blades proposed by Hickman and Perry[45] and the rolling rods of Semon.[46]

A laboratory molecular still having the evaporator surrounding the condenser is marketed as the "Rota-Film Still."[47] The unit is provided with a carbon blade redistributor to spread the distilland over the evaporator

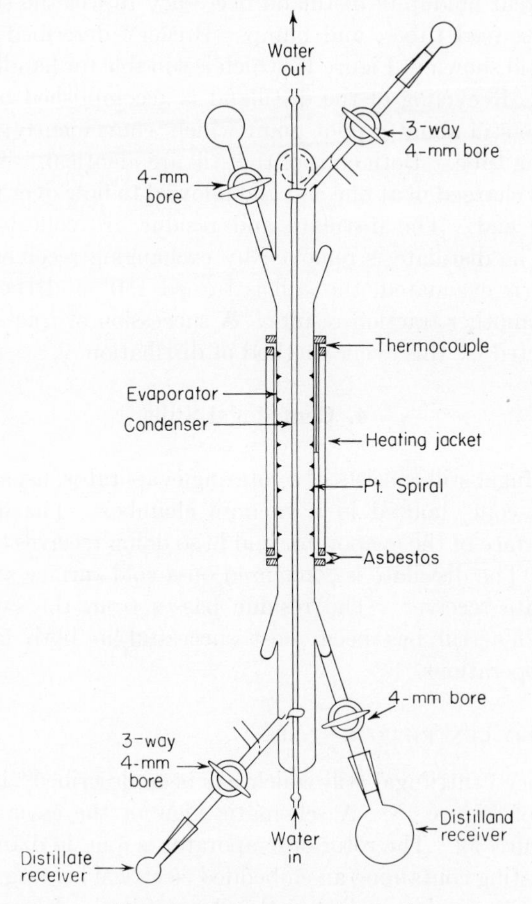

Fig. 17. Breger falling-film still

surface. Claims are made that the blade design provides a downward acceleration to the distilland to reduce thermal hazard.

Another type of falling film still utilizes a rotating steel spiral band to wipe the evaporator wall.[48] The author claims that the band serves to force the liquid downward so that a long path of travel with minimum contact time results. There are no areas therefore where the distilland can remain for any length of time and so degradation and polymerization are at a minimum. The unit is designed for cyclic batch operation and appears to be able to accommodate about 100 to 400 g. of distilland.

C. SUBMACRO FALLING-FILM STILLS

The conventional falling film stills are limited to macro-size samples of their inherent holdup of distilland necessary to wet the surface areas of the reservoirs, feed tubes, and pump. Breger[49] described the submacro falling-film still shown in Figure 17 which is suitable for handling samples as little as 4 g. Recycling of the distilland is accomplished by repeated inversion of the still about a pilot point which, conveniently, happens to be the exhausting tube. Both ends of the still are identical. The material to be distilled is charged in at one end and allowed to flow over the evaporator to the other end. The distillate and residue are collected in separate receivers. The distillate is removed by exchanging receivers. When the new receiver is evacuated, the still is turned 180° and the process is repeated, and another fraction results. A succession of fractions can therefore be collected by this cyclic method of distillation.

4. Centrifugal Stills

The centrifugal still consists of a rotating evaporator, usually in the form of a shallow cone, housed in a vacuum chamber. The distilland flows across the surface of the evaporator and in so doing receives heat from it for distillation. The distillate is condensed on a cold surface and collected in an appropriate receiver. The residue passes from the evaporator to a reservoir. This still has been most successful in both laboratory and commercial operations.

A. LABORATORY CENTRIFUGAL STILLS

A laboratory centrifugal still which has been described[50] is shown in the photograph of Figure 18. A schematic view of the essential details are shown in Figure 30. The rotor or evaporator is 5 in. in diameter and is an aluminum casting containing an embedded electrical heating element of 500 w. capacity. Power is supplied to the element by leads passing through a hollow shaft from slip rings and carbon brushes. The rotor turns on ball bearings at a speed of 1750 r.p.m. The feed pump is driven through a tiny transmission whose interchangeable gears permit a feed rate of 25–180 cc./min. The lower portion of the glass dome serves as one reservoir and a cup suspended from the pump shaft is the upper reservoir. Temperature is

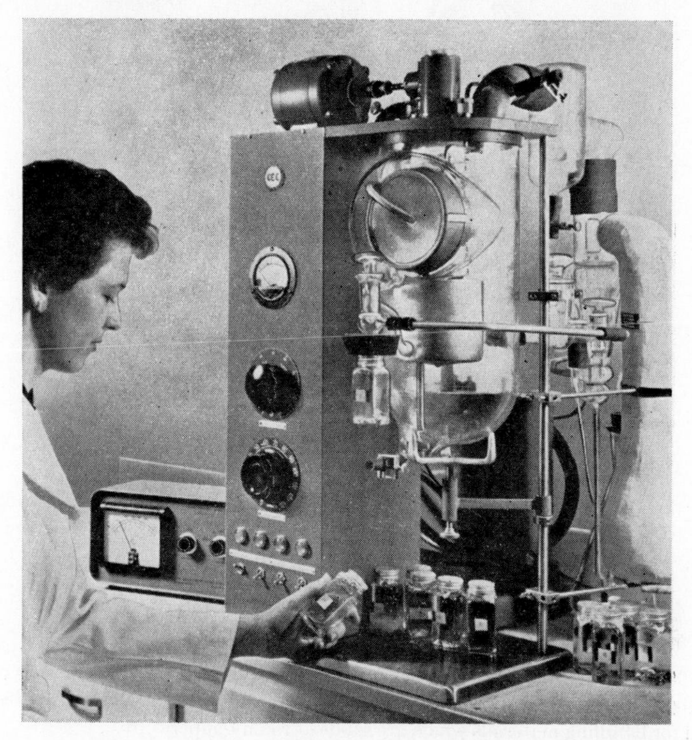

Fig. 18. Photograph of laboratory centrifugal still. The entire distillation unit is enclosed within the inverted bell jar.

measured by a thermocouple which dips into the residue-collector baffle attached to the periphery of the rotor.

The unit is available commercially.[51]

B. PILOT-SCALE CENTRIFUGAL STILL

A somewhat different design having greater capacity has been described[52] and a complete unit of this kind assembled for cyclic batch operation is shown in Figure 19. This unit, known as the CMS-14 centrifugal molecular still, is available commercially.[53] Its reservoir capacity is 5 gal. and flow rates of 2–5 gal./hr. over the evaporator are possible.

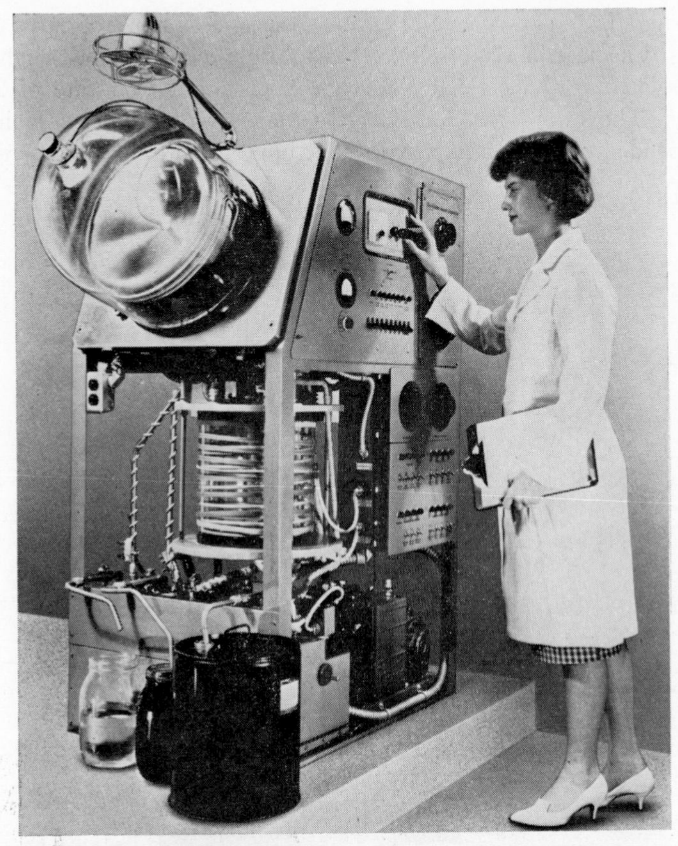

Fig. 19. Photograph of pilot-scale centrifugal still. The 14-in. evaporator is enclosed within the glass dome. The reservoirs, pipe lines, and circulating pumps are heated or jacketed for handling materials which are solids at room temperature.

5. Fractionating Stills

A. CASCADE TYPES

The principle of fractionating in molecular distillation, as described on p. 562, was employed and demonstrated by Wollner, Matchett, and Levine[54] in a simple all-glass unit having 10 stages. A number of similar fractionating stills which employ the principle of multiple redistillation but are somewhat more complex and, perhaps, more efficient have since been devised. The Wollner still shown in Figure 20 is made from a glass tube 50 mm. in diameter by 380 mm. in length. In operation it is inclined at an angle of 10° from the horizontal. The tube is ridged on top and on bottom to form two series of communicating compartments or zones. The

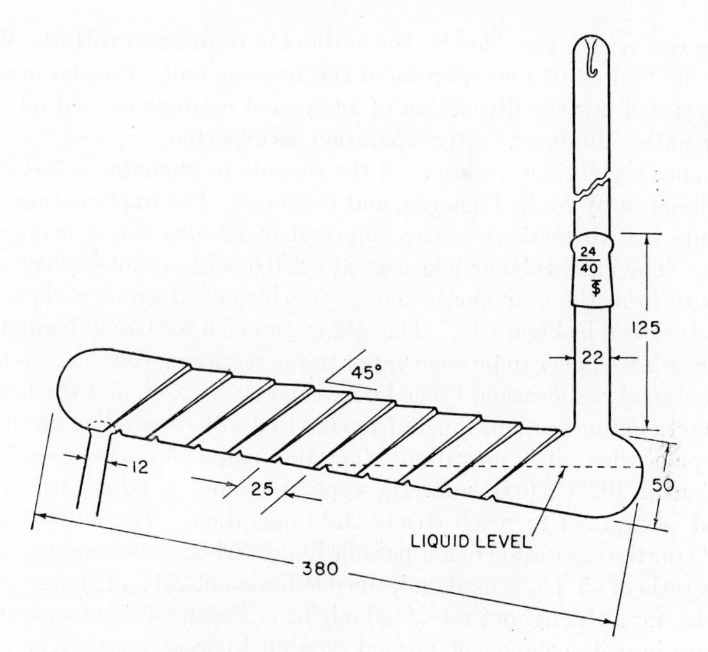

Fig. 20. Fractionating still of Wollner.

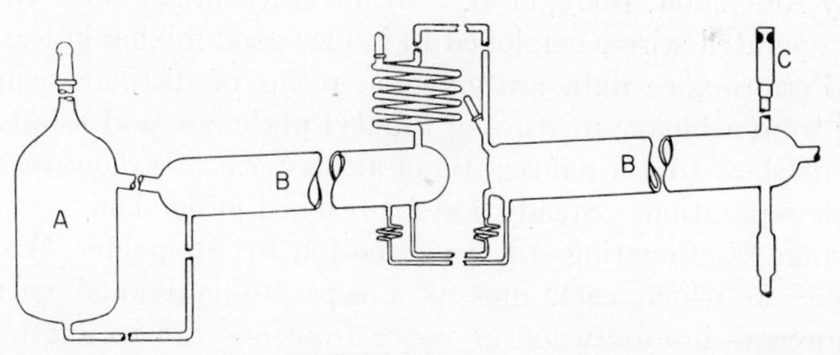

Fig. 21. Fractionating still of Mair, Pignocco, and Rossini. Vapor from the large boiler *A* feeds the first of the two fractionating sections *B*, each of which contain fittings to provide a succession of 25 still units. Connection between sections is made by means of the lower coils and the entire still is evacuated through the larger upper coil. Reflux is regulated at *C*.

upper zones are condensers and the lower ones are evaporators. The charge to be distilled is placed in the large compartment at the low end of the tube. In operation, the components of greater volatilities progressively advance upwards, stage by stage, while those of lesser volatilities regress toward the main boiler. The product leaves the unit from the top end.

The test results provided by the authors in connection with the Wollner still were limited to a comparison of the 10-stage unit with that of a single pot-type still for the distillation of acetylated marihuana "red oil." The fractionation produced better separation, as expected.

A more pretentious variation of the cascade fractionator is the 50-stage still designed by Muir, Pignocco, and Rossini.[55] The fractionating column is made in two sections, each comprised of 25 stages and connected in series. The glass tubular housings are fitted with stainless-steel components to form the individual stages. A schematic diagram of the arrangement is shown in Figure 21. The still is arranged for batch distillation by having a large boiler to provide vapor to the rectifying column as is done in conventional rectification. The boiler capacity is 2.8 l. and the holdup of the fractionating sections ranges from 0.3 to 0.44 l., depending on the angle of slope of the unit in operation. The throughput for a hydrocarbon distillation at 102°C. (0.03-mm. Hg vapor pressure) is 80 cc./hr. A 6-hr. period is required to reach steady-state operation. The authors present results for the separation of a *n*-paraffic hydrocarbon mixture of C_{18}–C_{22}. A reflux ratio of 55:1 was used, and the distillation of 2.8 l. of charge required 1900 hr. for a throughput rate of 80 ml./hr. The distillation separated the mixture into its component normal paraffin hydrocarbons. The authors claim that the apparatus can be expanded to 100 plates if needed.

A simpler 9-stage unit made of glass and metal parts has also been reported by Aldershoff, Booy, et al.[56] A novel feature of this still is a magnetically operated stirrer employed to induce good mixing in the distilland layers. Performance data are given in terms of distillate compositions resulting from a binary mixture of *n*-butyl phthalate and *n*-butyl azelate. The results show that a reflux ratio of at least 7.5:1 is required to effect a reasonable separation. Steady state is reached in one hour.

A 20-stage fractionating still was reported by Melpolder, Washall, and Alexander[57] in which each unit is a separate individual entity. This design prevents interdiffusion of vapor from one cell to another and assures good mixing in the distilland phases. The performance evaluated with a phthalate–sebacate mixture was found to be 0.8 theoretical plate per stage.

A 10-column, falling-film, molecular fractionating still was constructed by Madorsky.[58] The cascade principle was employed for the transfer of distillates from column to column; distillands were moved by tiny magnetic pistons. The author claims that the 10 columns gave a separation equivalent to 13 theoretical plates for the distillation of a binary mixture whose identity was not disclosed.

Other versions of the cascade still for fractionating in high vacuum have been reported.[59]

B. VERTICAL COLUMN FRACTIONATOR

A fractionating molecular still was devised by Perry and Cox[60] in the form of a vertical column, which utilizes the principle of the flowing film still. A detailed view of the unit is shown in Figure 22. The column is zoned to form separate stages and liquid reflux flows downward by gravity but the upward movement of liquid phase is managed by centrifugal force. The column wall is heated and serves as the evaporator for all stages. The central shaft is cooled. Vapor issuing from the evaporator surface is confined within the stage by horizontal plates and passes to the cold surface of the central shaft to condense. This condensate drains to the collector ring for each stage. Because the ring is rotating, the condensate rises by cen-

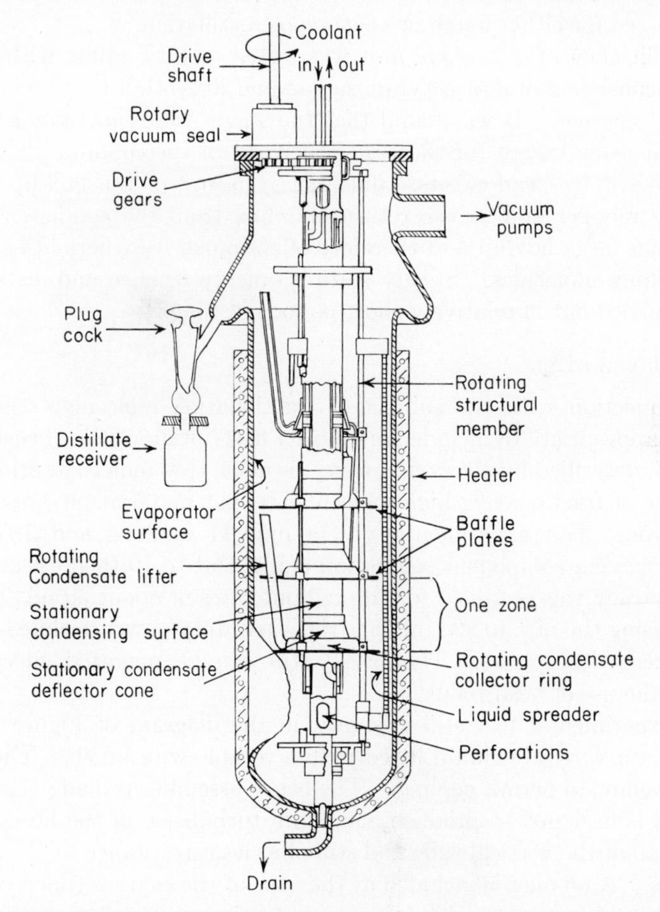

Fig. 22. Vertical fractionating still of Perry and Cox. Vapor is condensed and this liquid condensate is raised mechanically to produce countercurrent behavior.

trifugal action to the top of the evaporator one stage above. Here it joints and intermixes with the downward flowing residue from the stage above and this mixture becomes the distilland for that stage. Good mixing of the liquid streams and the maintenance of a liquid film as the evaporator are provided by the spreading device which is part of the rotating assembly used for the collector rings. A cone-shaped members is used to effect the transfer of the condensate from the cold stationary central shaft to the rotating collector rings. A small tube attached to each collector ring serves to transfer the condensate from the ring upward to the top of the next stage. The central shaft is perforated under each cone to permit passage of uncondensable vapor from each stage, through the hollow central shaft to the head of the still and then to the vacuum pumps. The unit can be employed for either batch or continuous distillation.

The efficiency of a 20-stage unit was tested at total reflux with a plate mixture consisting of di-*n*-octyl phthalate and di-2-ethyl hexyl sebacate in the usual manner. It was found that the stages were functioning at near 100% efficiency except for those at either end of the column. The latter were affected by "end-effects," due to the nature of the boil-up process from the reboiler and to the return of reflux from the condenser. This unit avoids large holdup and therefore offers much less thermal hazard to the distilling molecules. Steady state is quickly reached and distillations can be carried out in relatively short periods of time.

C. THE BRUSH STILL

In connection with the subject of fractionating molecular stills, it is perhaps appropriate to include here a brief description of the "brush still." This still, described by Perry and Cox,[61] is not a true molecular still, but it is capable of fractionating high molecular weight materials at pressures of one micron. Test experiments with a unit 11 in. long and $3^1/_2$ in. in diameter gave a component separation equivalent to 10 theoretical plates. This efficiency was obtained for throughput rates of about 50 ml./hr., but on increasing the rate to 800 ml./hr., the separatory power declined only to seven theoretical plates. The brush still can be operated successfully without the use of bead reflux.

The experimental test still is shown in the diagram of Figure 23. It consists of a vertical column fitted with a rotable wire brush. The brush shaft is hollow to permit cooling. The brush assembly is made of stainless steel and is designed to produce maximum turbulence in the liquid phase on the wall of the vertical tube and still offer least resistance to the passage of vapors. A reboiler is included at the base of the column which contains a cone-shaped stirrer to maintain concentration uniformity in the boiler liquid. The head condenser leads all condensate to the plugcock. The

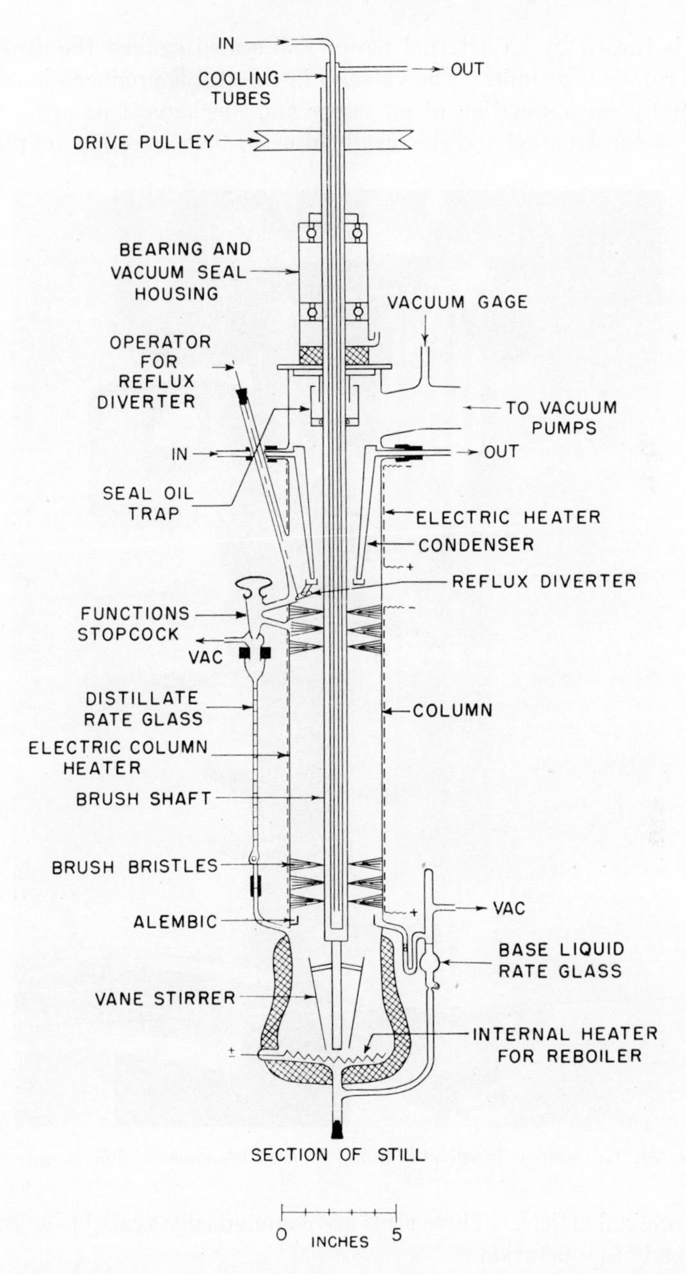

Fig. 23. The experimental brush still. Fractionation is achieved by repeated vaporization and condensation taking place along the length of the column.

brush is turned by an external motor and sealed against the atmosphere with a rotary type unit. The vacuum in the still is produced in the usual manner by a combination of oil vapor and mechanical pumps. Specific details of construction and the results of performance testing are presented

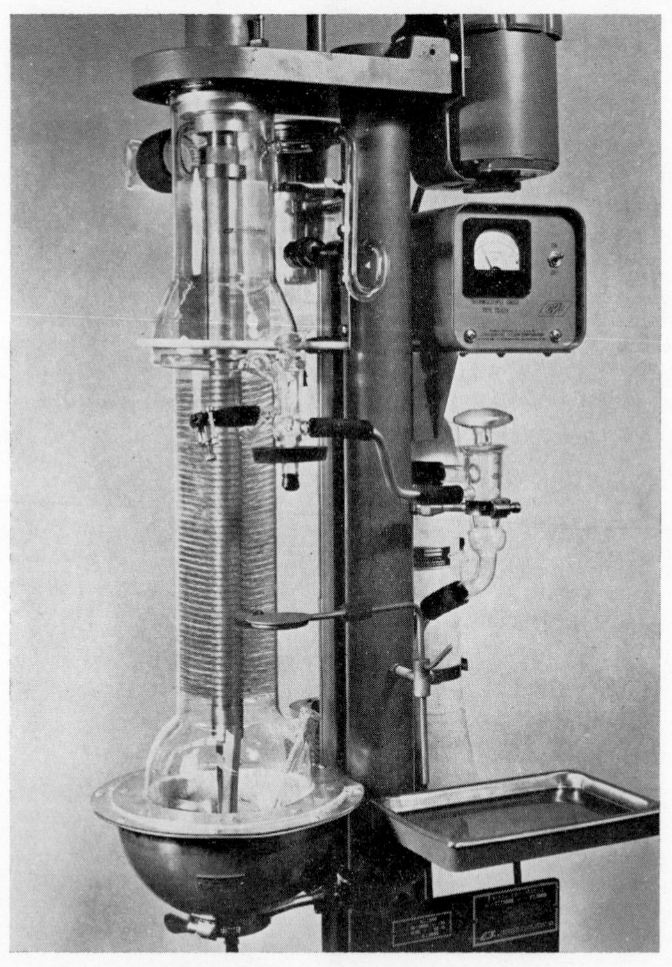

Fig. 24. Laboratory brush still unit. The brush construction is apparent.

in the original article. These stills are commercially available as complete units ready for operation.[62]

In operation, the outer column is heated and the brush shaft is cooled. The distillation process takes place in the annular space occupied by the bristles and bounded by the surfaces of the column and shaft.

The brush still offers a successful method for the fractional distillation of natural oils and other high-molecular-weight organic materials. Its high separatory power, low pressure drop, and general utility over a wide pressure range give the brush still a unique position to fill the gap between the molecular still and the vacuum fractionating column.

The performance of a laboratory unit of the kind shown on the photograph of Figure 24 has been reported by Perry[63] for the distillation of several natural oils, essential oils, and synthetic materials.

VI. DISTILLATION METHODS AND TECHNIQUES

1. Constant Temperature Versus Constant Rate

The convenience of following the course of a distillation by means of the vapor temperature, as is customary in conventional distillation, is not practical in molecular distillation. The low density and high velocity of the vapor in the gap makes the measurement of the temperature difficult. Then, too, the gap width is small so that the sensing element would be influenced by radiation from the hot and cold surfaces facing it. The progress of molecular distillation therefore is best observed by other means.

Molecular distillation can be carried out by maintaining constant either the temperature of the distillation, or the rate of distillation. When the temperature is held constant, the distillation rate is maximum at the start and continually decreases as the distillation proceeds. This behavior, of course, is a consequence of the preferential evaporation of the more volatile component and of the constant heat input to the distilland of the molecular still. When the distilland is a mixture, the composition will change, owing to the evaporation of the more volatile component, but the temperature of the distilland will remain essentially unchanged. The change in composition will produce a decrease in the vapor pressure of the distilland, thereby effecting a decrease in the evaporation rate and therefore a decrease in the distillation rate. If, however, the distillation of a single substance is considered under similar circumstances, there can be no change in composition and so the rate stays constant, as well as the temperature, throughout the entire distillation. These situations are pictured in Figure 25.

Now, in contrast, if the temperature of the distilland is continually increased during molecular distillation of a mixture so that the vapor pressure remains constant, even though the composition of the distilland is changing because of the loss of the more volatile component, the rate will remain essentially constant throughout the course of the operation. On the other hand, the distillation of a single substance under conditions of increasing temperature will produce a continual increase in the distillation rate. In other words, increasing the temperature increases the vapor pressure and consequently increases the evaporation rate. These situations are depicted in Figure 25.

In practice, the method of constant distillation rate is preferred and is used in the various distillation procedures to be described. The procedures by which molecular distillations are performed are known as batch, cyclic, analytical, multiple redistillation (fractionation), and continuous.

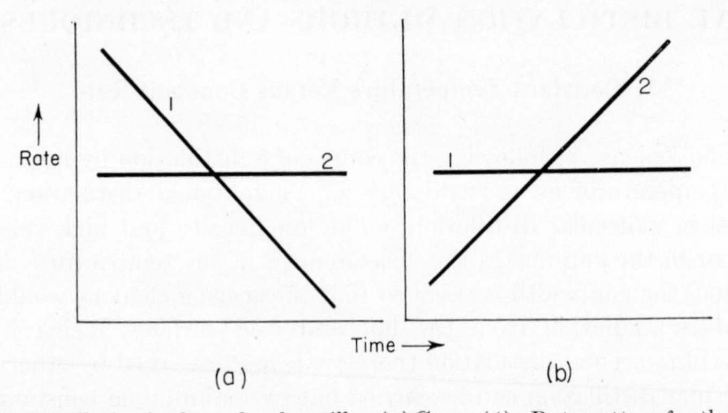

Fig. 25. Distillation in the molecular still. (*a*) Curve (*1*): Rate pattern for the distillation of a mixture at constant temperature. Curve (*2*): The corresponding behavior for the distillation of a single substance. (*b*) Curve (*1*): Rate pattern for a mixture distilling under increasing temperature. Curve (*2*): The corresponding behavior for a single substance.

The first three are the usual laboratory techniques and the remaining two are generally production methods. Fractionation by multiple redistillation is becoming more common in the laboratory as also.

In this section, the laboratory molecular distillation methods will be illustrated by typical examples.

2. Batch Distillation

The simplest batch molecular distillation is carried out in pot-type stills. The entire charge is placed in the boiler of the still and the distillate is collected in a series of fractions covering a range of temperature. The choice of still is made on the basis of the amount of material available for distillation, the physical properties of the distillates, the heat-stability of the components, the boiling range of the material, etc. A typical molecular distillation such as would be performed in a pot-type molecular still will be described as it might be done in the still of Figure 11. The still equipped for operation is shown in Figure 26. The charge is placed in the boiler of the still, the top is replaced, and the vacuum of the mechanical pump is applied. The oil bath is heated slowly, but is not allowed to exceed 100°C. The condenser is cooled by water. When degassing appears to be ending, the vapor pump is put into operation to bring the pressure down to the micron range. During this start-up period, distillate is returned to the boiler from the drip point of the condenser. When the desired distillation rate is reached by proper adjustment of the oil-bath temperature, the condenser is turned so that the distillate drops into the tube and passes to the receiver. The temperature is adjusted from fraction to fraction to

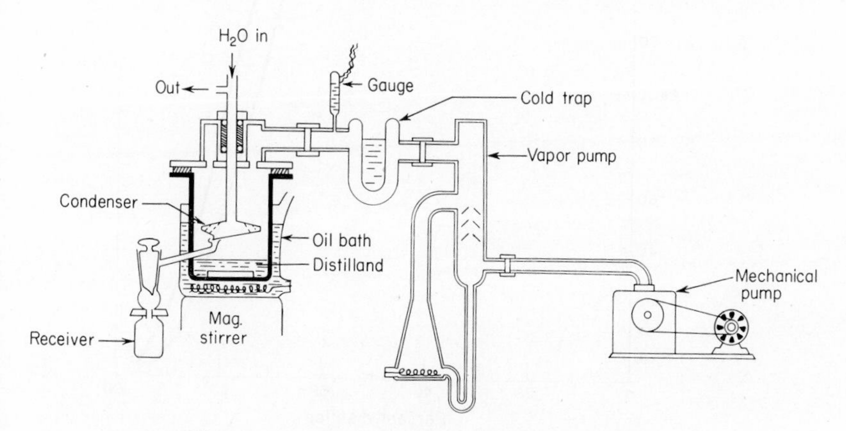

Fig. 26. A batch molecular distillation assembly.

maintain a uniform rate. The number of fractions collected will depend on the objective of the distillation. When the last fraction is removed, the heat to the boilers of the still and to the vapor pump is stopped. The mechanical pump is allowed to operate until the still cools. The vacuum is then released.

The results of a batch distillation of this kind are plotted in Figure 27. The distilland consisted of equal parts of di-2-ethyl hexyl phthalate and di-2-ethyl hexyl sebacate. The composition of each fraction in refractive-index units is plotted against the percent distilled. The two curves show the difference in separation resulting from the different rates of distillation employed. In one case the rate was 5 g./hr., in the other 17 g./hr.

A typical use of the cold-finger, pot-type molecular still is demonstrated by Quaife and Harris[64] for the quantitative removal of tocopherols from fat.

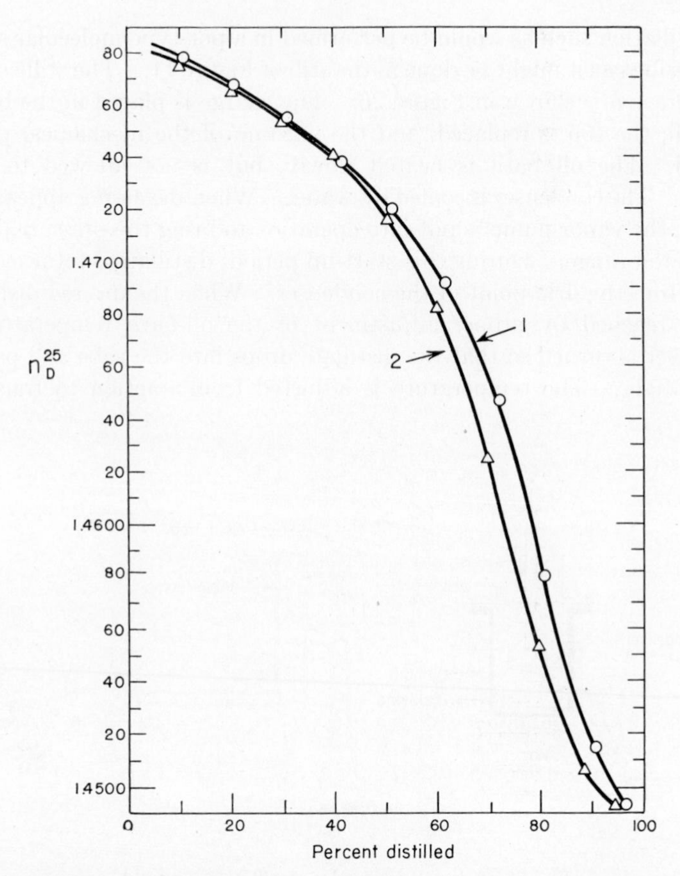

Fig. 27. Results of batch distillation. Distillation of equal parts of di-2-ethylhexyl phthalate (n_D^{25} = 1.4846) and di-2-ethylhexyl sebacate (n_D^{25} = 1.4491). Distillation rate: Curve 1, 17 g./hr.; Curve 2, 5 g./hr.

3. Cyclic Distillation

Cyclic distillation is a batch operation in the sense that all of the material to be distilled is charged to the reservoir of the still. The term "cyclic" applies to the method of segregating the residue from the distilland during each fraction. The residue from one fraction becomes the distilland for the next fraction. For each new cycle the temperature is raised to a higher level. There finally results a series of fractions, each taken at a progressively increasing temperature. The nature of the operation will be evident from the consideration of a typical example such as the distillation of a natural substance like the extract of orange peel.

Such an extract would contain the extraction solvent, terpenes, essential oils, and relatively involatile wax-like components. The extraction solvent, diethyl ether, for example, is first removed at as low a temperature as possible to avoid degradation of the essential oils. A water-pump vacuum is usually sufficient for this purpose. The terpenes are next distilled off in a "boiling point" still, again at the lowest possible temperature. The residue is then transferred to a molecular still and the essential oil and waxy components are finally separated into fractions.

At this point a brief digression to describe the boiling-point stills is not entirely out of place.

A. BOILING POINT DISTILLATION

This modification of the "alembic" still is an invaluable adjunct to the molecular still. Several variations are shown in Figure 28. It is suitable for substances which are too volatile for molecular distillation and too unstable for treatment by conventional methods. The separatory power of these stills is greater than that of the molecular still and varies with the length of the column employed. The use of a wire brush rotated to spread

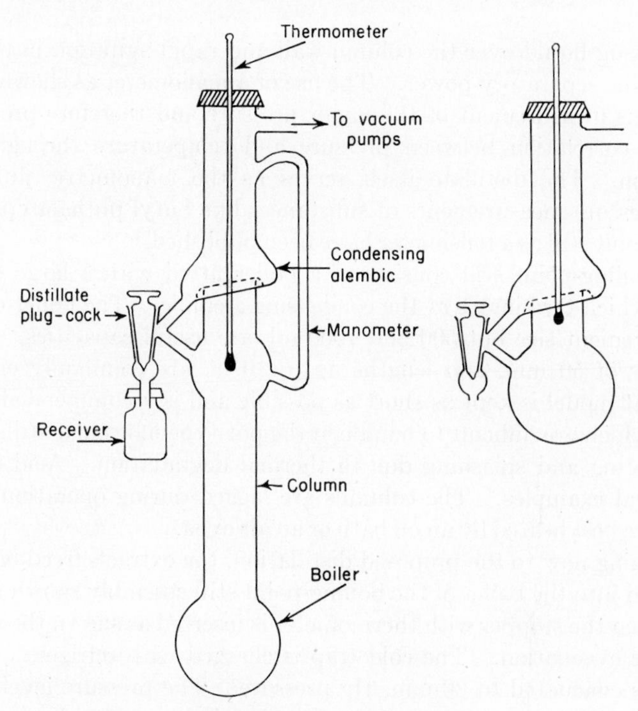

Fig. 28. Boiling-point stills.

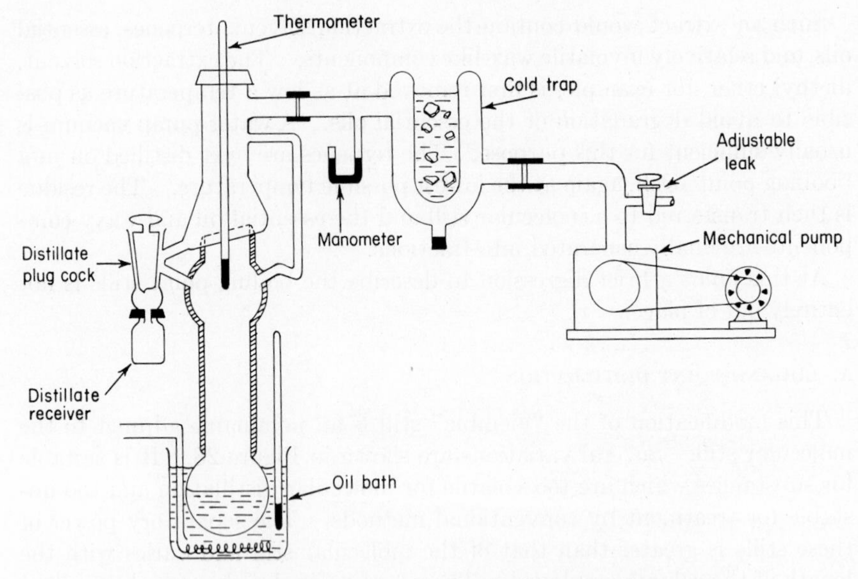

Fig. 29. A boiling-point distillation assembly.

the refluxing liquid over the column wall and rapid agitation in the boiler enhance the separatory power. The use of a manometer as shown permits continuous measurement of the vapor pressure and therefore provides an accurate correlation between pressure and temperature throughout the distillation. The distillate itself serves as the manometric fluid. The vapor-pressure measurements of substances like butyl phthalate using the boiling-point still as a tensimeter have been published.[65]

The boiling-point still consists of a boiler fitted with a large diameter column which terminates at the condensing alembic. The boiler can be of any convenient size but 500 and 1000 ml. are useful capacities. Column diameters of 50 mm. and lengths up to 10 in. are commonly employed. The squat model is kept as short as possible and is recommended for substances which are difficult to handle in the pot-type molecular stills because of sputtering and splashing due to thermal degradation. Acid chlorides are typical examples. The columns are lagged during operation and the boilers are best heated by an oil bath or an air oven.

Returning now to the proposed distillation, the extract, freed of solvent, is charged into the boiler of the boiling-point still assembly shown in Figure 29. When the stopper with thermometer is inserted as shown the system is ready for evacuation. The cold trap is charged with refrigerant and the system is evacuated to 20-mm. Hg pressure. The pressure level is maintained by adjustment of the leak device and is indicated by the manometer.

During the early stages of evacuation, the charge may boil vigorously, owing to the escape of residual solvent and dissolved gases. The volatiles are caught in the cold trap to avoid contamination of the pump fluid. As heat is applied from the oil bath, more volatiles may evolve but soon the distilland becomes quiescent and then its temperature can be raised to the point of distillation. The condensate which collects in the alembic during the early stage of distillation is returned to the column through the plugcock. When the distillation rate is established and has reached a steady state, the distillate is collected in the receiver by turning the plugcock one-half turn. The thermometer at the head of the column will indicate an almost constant value for the entire distillation because the terpene fraction distills over a very narrow range. When all of the terpene has been removed, the distillation is terminated by lowering the oil bath. The still is allowed to cool while under vacuum. The residue is then transferred to the molecular still.

B. CYCLIC DISTILLATION

Cyclic distillation of the residue from the boiling point distillation will be described for the centrifugal cyclic molecular still described on p. 577. The method and procedure are, however, equally applicable to the falling film molecular still.

The still and equipment ready for distillation are shown in the diagram of Figure 30. The residue from the boiling-point still is drawn into the lower reservoir through the tubulation at the lower end of the glass bell. This is done with the aid of the mechanical pump vacuum. The cold trap is refrigerated to freeze out any residual volatiles remaining in the residue. The feed pump is immediately put into operation to circulate the distilland over the revolving evaporator. Some heat is applied to the evaporator to assist degassing. The distilland is circulated through one or two cycles to effect complete degassing. During the final stages of degassing, the oil-diffusion pump is started. When the diffusion pump has reduced the pressure to the micron range, the rotor temperature is slowly increased until distillation begins. The first distillate is returned to the still and the temperature is adjusted to 80°C., which is the nearest 10°C. mark. When the temperature is stabilized at 80°C., the first cycle is begun. The ball valve is closed and the first fraction is collected in the receiver by opening the plugcock. As the last dregs of distilland are pumped out of the lower reservoir, the ball valve is opened, allowing the residue from the first cycle, which has collected in the upper reservoir, to flow into the lower reservoir where it then becomes the distilland for the next cycle. The first cycle is continued for an additional minute to flush the pump and the lines to the rotor. The distillate plugcock is then closed and the temperature of the rotor is increased to 90°C. While the temperature adjustment is being made, a new distillate receiver is put in place, without interrupting the distillation. When the temperature reaches 90°C., the ball valve is closed and the plugcock is opened to collect the second fraction.

These operations are repeated at each 10° interval up to 230°C. to give a series of 16 fractions. At the end of the distillation, the diffusion pump and the rotor are allowed to cool before air is admitted to the system. The residue is allowed to circulate over the rotor until the temperature drops

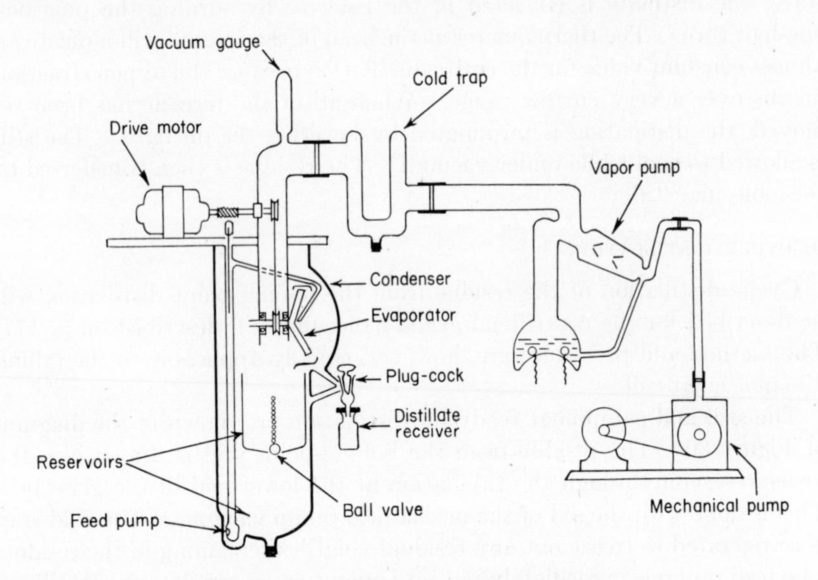

Fig. 30. A centrifugal distillation assembly.

below 100°C. The mechanical pump is then stopped and the vacuum is released. The residue is drained into a sample bottle. The still is cleaned by circulating a solvent through the system by means of the feed pump while the rotor is still warm. The rapid evaporation of the solvent floods the whole interior of the still and washes the viscous residue into the lower reservoir, from which the washings are then drained.

C. RESULTS

The results of a typical orange-oil distillation are shown in Table V. The data for the boiling-point distillation are shown in the first lines and the remaining data are for the centifugal still. The yields are calculated on the basis of a 5000-g. charge of the original oil to the boiling-point still. Thus, the terpene fraction removed at 20-mm. pressure amounted to 77%

of the charge. The residue was a yellow-to-brown semiviscous liquid having the fragrant orange-like odor of the original material.

Fractions 1 and 2 from the cyclic distillation were water-white and appeared to consist mostly of terpene material not completely removed in the boiling-point distillation. Fractions 3–7 were yellow oils, with some crystals appearing in the later ones. The remaining fractions were solids ranging from a bright yellow through orange to brown. These fractions progressively increased in hardness. The residue was a hard, brittle, black solid. The results show that 95.4% of the total charge was accounted for. The loss is due to the inherent holdup of the stills.

D. OTHER RESULTS OF CYCLIC DISTILLATIONS

The procedure of cyclic distillation is useful with many types of substances. Sometimes the purification amounts to little more than removing small quantities of impurities and color from a single substance, as, for example, a plasticizer like dioctyl phthalate. In another case, a concentrate of some specific components is required such as in the separation

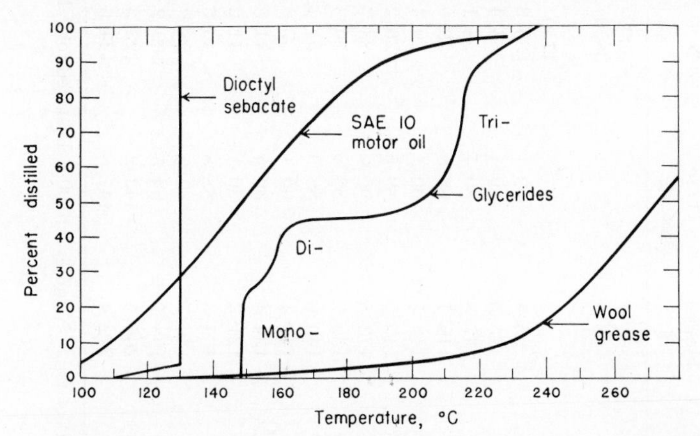

Fig. 31. Distillation curves of various substances. The complexity of natural products compared to that of synthetic materials is readily observed from the curves of the four materials shown.

of a mixture of mono-, di-, and triglycerides. Complex mixtures such as the natural oils and fats yield series of fractions which differ only slightly in composition from one to another. Typical distillation curves for materials of these kinds are shown in Figure 31 where the per cent distilled is plotted against the temperature at which the fraction was collected.

Other examples of typical cyclic distillations performed in falling film molecular stills may be found in ref. 66.

TABLE V
Separation Laboratory, Distillation Data[a]

No.	Temp., °C.	Pressure	Gross, g.	Tare, g.	Net g.	% cut	Σ %	State[d]	Color[e]
Charge[b]					5000				
A	68–80	20 mm.			3850	77.0	77.0	L	Ww
Residue					1150	23.0			
1[c]	80	250 μ	95.4	60.1	35.3	0.7	77.7	L	Ww
2	90	200	175.5	89.1	86.4	1.7	79.4	L	Ww
3	100	100	147.8	89.7	58.1	1.2	80.6	L	Y
4	110	60	118.7	88.8	29.9	0.6	81.2	L	Y
5	120	40	119.5	90.1	29.4	0.6	81.8	L	Y
6	130	25	115.7	89.5	26.2	0.5	82.3	L	Y, C
7	140	15	173.5	90.2	83.3	1.7	84.0	L	Y, C
8	150	8	139.9	89.6	50.3	1.0	85.0	S_s	Y
9	160	6	140.0	88.9	51.1	1.0	86.0	S	Y
10	170	6	147.1	90.1	57.0	1.1	87.1	S	Y
11	180	4	134.4	89.9	44.5	0.9	88.0	S	Y-O
12	190	4	121.3	90.1	31.2	0.6	88.6	S	Y-O
13	200	4	135.3	88.8	46.5	0.9	89.5	S	Y-O
14	210	4	149.7	89.9	58.9	1.2	90.7	S	O
15	220	6	198.7	89.5	109.2	2.2	92.9	S	R-Br
16	230	10	266.5	143.2	123.3	2.5	95.4	S	R-Br
Residue			272.4	147.8	124.6	2.5	97.9	S	Bl

[a] Material: Extracted Orange Peel Oil. Number: 0100. Distilled for: Product Development Lab. Date: 6-1-49. Still, Used: Molecular.

[b] Boiling point.

[c] Centrifugal.

[d] L, liquid, S_s, semisolid, S, solid.

[e] Ww, water-white. Y, yellow. O, orange. R, red. Br, brown. Bl, black. C, crystalline.

4. Analytical Distillation

The analytical molecular distillation is a systematic procedure of cyclic distillation devised by Hickman[67] for the determination of a relative boiling-point-like temperature and for the estimation of the purity of materials. This method involves the determination of the temperature at which the rate of removal, or elimination, of a constituent from a specially prepared substrate reaches a maximum. The temperature value at the maximum is a specific property of the distilling species and is designated

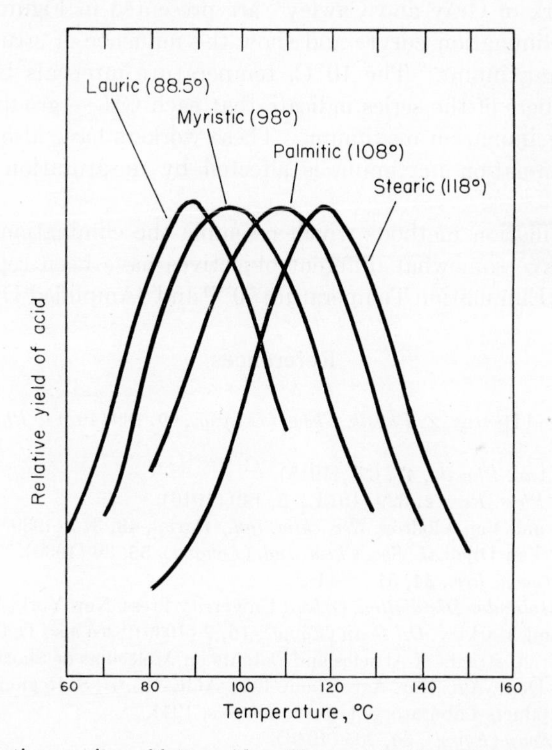

Fig. 32. Elimination maxima of fatty acids. The contribution of each methyl group can be readily seen.

the "elimination temperature." It is reproducible under controlled conditions, and substances can thereby be characterized by a temperature measurement in much the same manner as is done by the boiling point in equilibrant distillation. The procedure consists in subjecting the substance under investigation, contained in a carrier which has special distilling characteristics, to cyclic distillation. Because each successive distillation is done at a progressively higher temperature, the rate of elimination of the desired constituent increases steadily to a maximum value and then drops off. The rate of removal diminishes to zero when the constituent is completely distilled out. The variation in the concentration of the constituent from fraction to fraction, when plotted as a function of the temperature at which the fraction was distilled, resembles a probability distribution curve and is called the "elimination curve." The theoretical shape of the elimination curve for a single substance was determined mathematically by Embree.[68]

The elimination curves for some homologs of the fatty acid series taken from the work of Gray and Cawley[69] are presented in Figure 32. These are typical elimination curves and show the influence of structure on the elimination maximum. The 10°C. temperature intervals between contiguous numbers of the series indicate that each CH_2— group contributes 5°C. to the elimination maximum. These workers have also reported on how the elimination maximum is affected by unsaturation in the acid molecules.

Other distillation methods which resemble the elimination curve technique but have somewhat different objectives have been reported under the titles of "Elimination Temperature 50"[70] and "Amplified Distillation."[71]

References

1. Brönsted and Hevesy, *Z. Physik. Chem. (Leipzig)*, **99**, 189 (1921); *Phil. Mag.*, **43**, 31 (1922).
2. Knudsen, *Ann. Physik.*, **47**, 697 (1915).
3. Langmuir, *Phys. Rev.*, **2**, 329 (1913); **8**, 149 (1916).
4. Waterman and Van Vlodrop, *Rev. chim. ind. (Paris)*, **48**, 314 (1939).
5. Burch and Van Dijch, *J. Soc. Chem. Ind. (London)*, **58**, 39 (1939).
6. Hickman, *Chem. Rev.*, **34**, 51 (1944).
7. Burrows, *Molecular Distillation*, Oxford University Press, New York, 1960.
8. Detwiler and Markley, *Oil Soap (Egypt)*, **16**, 2 (1939); see also Detwiler, *ibid.*, **17**, 241 (1940); Abstracts of Articles and Patents on Molecular or Short-Path Distillation, U. S. Dept. Agr. Bur. Agr. Chem. Eng. ACE-115, U. S. Regional Soybean Industrial Products Laboratory, Urbana, Illinois, 1941.
9. Todd, *Oil Soap (Egypt)*, **20**, 205 (1943).
10. Rose and Rose, *Distillation Literature, Index and Abstracts*, **1941–1945**, Rose and Rose, State College, Pennsylvania, 1948.
11. Nieman, *Chem. Pharm. Tech. (Dordrecht)*, **9**, 21, 33, 49 (1953).
12. Burrows, *Metropolitan Vickers Gaz.*, **25**, 40 (1953).
13. Dushman, *Scientific Foundations of Vacuum Technique*, Wiley, New York, 1949, p. 90.
14. Loeb, *Kinetic Theory of Gases*, 2nd ed., McGraw-Hill, New York, 1934.
15. Glasstone and Lewis, *Elements of Physical Chemistry*, D. Van Nostrand, Princeton, New Jersey, 1960.
16. Hickman, *Chem. Rev.*, **34**, 51, 76 (1944).
17. Jacobs and Kapff, *Ind. Eng. Chem.*, **40**, 842 (1948).

18. Washburn et al., *J. Res. Natl. Bur. Std.*, **2**, 467 (1929).
19. Kapff and Jacobs, *Rev. Sci. Instr.*, **18**, 581 (1947).
20. Perry and Weber, *J. Am. Chem. Soc.*, **71**, 3720 (1949).
21. Hickman and Trevoy, *Ind. Eng. Chem.*, **44**, 1882 (1952).
22. Trevoy, *Ind. Eng. Chem.*, **44**, 1889, 1891 (1952).
23. Rayleigh, *Phil. Mag.*, **4**, 521 (1902).
24. Sunier, *J. Chem. Ed.*, **5**, 879 (1928); Sunier and Rosenblum, *Ind. Eng. Chem. Anal. Ed.*, **2**, 109 (1930).
25. Garner and MacMurray, *Ind. Chemist*, **34**, 310 (1958); see also Ref. 12, Chap. VII.
26. Hickman, *Ind. Eng. Chem.*, **39**, 686 (1947); Olive, *Chem. Met. Eng.*, **51**, 100 (1944).
27. Hickman and Trevoy, *Ind. Eng. Chem.*, **44**, 1882–1911 (1952).
28. Burrows, *Trans. Inst. Chem. Engrs. (London)*, **32**, 23 (1954); see also Ref. 12, Chap. II.
29. Hickman in *Science in Progress 4th Series*, Baitsell, ed., Yale University Press, New Haven, 1945, Chap. IX.
30. Hickman and Embree, *Ind. Eng. Chem.*, **40**, 135 (1948).
31. Fraser, U. S. Patent 2,128,223 (August 30, 1938).
32. Fawcett and McCowen, U. S. Patent 2,073,202 (March 9, 1937).
33. Reigel, Beiswanger, and Lanzl, *Ind. Eng. Chem. Anal. Ed.*, **15**, 417 (1943).
34. Strain and Allen, *Ind. Eng. Chem. Anal. Ed.*, **7**, 443 (1935).
35. Hickman and Sanford, *J. Phys. Chem.*, **34**, 637 (1930); see also Ref. 6, Fig. 6 or Ref. 29, Fig. 61.
36. Gilson, *Chem. Ind. (London)*, **739** (1950).
37. Burch, *Proc. Roy. Soc. (London)*, **A123**, 271 (1929).
38. Carothers and Hill, *J. Am. Chem. Soc.*, **54**, 1557, 1559 (1932).
39. Matchett and Levine, *Ind. Eng. Chem. Anal. Ed.*, **15**, 296 (1943).
40. Gould, Holzman, and Niemann, *Anal. Chem.*, **20**, 361 (1948).
41. Cheronis, *Micro and Semi-Micro Methods*, Vol. VI, in Technique of Organic Chemistry Series Weissberger, ed., Interscience, New York, 1954.
42. Detwiler and Markley, *Ind. Eng. Chem. Anal. Ed.*, **12**, 348 (1940).
43. Taylor, *J. Res. Natl. Bur. Std.*, **37**, 173 (1946).
44. Quackenbush and Steenbach, *Ind. Eng. Chem. Anal. Ed.*, **15**, 468 (1943).
45. Hickman and Perry, U. S. Patent 2,403,978 (July 16, 1946).
46. Semon, U. S. Patent 2,460,602 (February 1, 1949).
47. Arthur F. Smith, Inc., 201 S.W. 12 Ave., Pompano Beach, Florida.
48. Nester, *Rev. Sci. Instr.*, **31**, 1002 (1960).
49. Breger, *Anal. Chem.*, **20**, 980 (1948).
50. Biehler, Hickman, and Perry, *Anal. Chem.*, **21**, 638 (1949).
51. The CMS-5 Molecular Still, Consolidated Vacuum Corp., Rochester, New York.
52. Hickman, U. S. Patents 2,117,802 (May 17, 1938) and 2,210,928 (August 13, 1940).
53. The CMS-14 Molecular Still, Consolidated Vacuum Corp., Rochester, New York.
54. Wollner, Matchett, and Levine, *Ind. Eng. Chem. Anal. Ed.*, **16**, 529 (1944).
55. Mair, Pignocco, and Rossini, *Anal. Ed.*, **27**, 190 (1955).
56. Aldershoff, Booy, Langedijk, Phillippi, and Watterman, *J. Inst. Petrol.*, **39**, 688 (1953).
57. Melpolder, Washall, and Alexander, *Anal. Chem.*, **27**, 975 (1955).
58. Madorsky, *J. Res. Natl. Bur. Std.*, **44**, 135, 1950.
59. Madorsky, Bradt, and Straus, *J. Res. Natl. Bur. Std.*, **41**, 205, 1948; Brewer and Madorsky, *ibid.*, **38**, 129 (1947).
60. Perry and Cox, U. S. Patent 2,749,292 (June 5, 1956).
61. Perry and Cox, *Ind. Eng. Chem.*, **48**, 1473 (1956).

62. Brush Stills, Consolidated Vacuum Corp., Rochester, New York.
63. Perry, *Ind. Eng. Chem.*, **48**, 1479 (1956).
64. Quaife and Harris, *Anal. Chem.*, **20**, 1221 (1948); *Ind. Eng. Chem. Anal. Ed.*, **18**, 707 (1946).
65. Ratchford and Rehberg, *Anal. Chem.*, **21**, 1417 (1949).
66. Jewell, Mead, and Phipps, *J. Soc. Chem. Ind.* (*London*), **58**, 56 (1939).
Farmer and van den Heuvel, *J. Soc. Chem. Ind.* (*London*), **57**, 24T (1938).
67. Hickman, *Ind. Eng. Chem.*, **29**, 968 (1937).
68. Embree, *Ind. Eng. Chem.*, **29**, 975 (1937).
69. Gray and Cawley, *J. Biol. Chem.*, **134**, 397 (1940).
70. Fletcher, Insalaco, Cobler, and Hodge, *Anal. Chem.*, **20**, 943 (1948).
71. Weitkamp, *J. Am. Oil Chemists' Soc.*, **34**, 236 (1947).
72. Watt, *Molecular Stills*, Reinhold Publishing Corp., New York, 1963.

CHAPTER VII

THE VACUUM SYSTEM

J. C. HECKER, *Distillation Products Industries, Rochester, New York*

I. INTRODUCTION

In Chapter VI, attention has been directed to the design and application of high-vacuum stills. A necessary and important part of any vacuum still is the vacuum system. Under this heading are included such items as: (*1*) high-vacuum vapor pumps, and mechanical fore-pumps; (*2*) gages; (*3*) vacuum plumbing, which includes interconnecting tubes and ducts, valves, gaskets, stationary and rotating seals, etc.; (*4*) cold traps and baffles; and (*5*) accessories, which include leak detectors, sealants, etc.

To understand the working of a vacuum system, it is desirable to know the specific function of the various components, to have a knowledge of their basic design features, and to appreciate the general principles of high-vacuum production and practice. For example, as the operating pressure gets lower and lower, larger capacity pumps and larger interconnecting piping must be used. A knowledge of the derivation, application, and limitations of gas-flow formulas at reduced pressures is helpful in understanding this anomaly.

In assembling a piece of distillation equipment, the still and auxiliaries should be considered as a vacuum-distillation assembly and the component parts so designed and so sized as to perform adequately the job in hand. It frequently happens that a skillfully designed vacuum still cannot function properly because an inadequately designed vacuum system limits its performance. It is not the purpose of this chapter to present all the rules for design of laboratory vacuum systems, but to present basic fundamentals and simplified guides which may be helpful to the chemist who wishes to apply molecular or high-vacuum distillation to his problems. In a good many cases the vacuum system and accessories are larger than the still itself, that is, larger than the evaporator and condenser portion of the assembly. This is exemplified by the photographic reproductions in Figures 18 and 19 (Chap. VI). It is evident that the distillation portion is overshadowed by the auxiliary vacuum equipment. The reasons for this seemingly unbalanced relationship will become apparent as the chapter progresses.

II. DEFINITION OF TERMS

To facilitate the discussion which follows in this section, a brief definition of terms, several recurring constants, and a few basic formulas commonly used in high-vacuum distillation practice are given.

High-vacuum distillations, in general, are conducted in the 0.1 to 1000 μ region, while *molecular distillations*, in particular, are usually conducted in the 0.1 (0.0001 mm.) to 10 μ (0.01 mm.) of mercury range. The *micron*, μ, of mercury is the unit of pressure (not vacuum) which corresponds to a mercury column 0.001 mm. high and this unit has been widely adopted in high-vacuum discussions. Pressures in microns will be referred to as P with no subscript or as $P\mu$ and in microbars as $P\mu_b$. Remembering that in the c.g.s. system the unit of pressure is 1 microbar (1 dyne per cm.[2]) and that 1 atmosphere is the pressure per square centimeter exerted by a column of mercury 76 cm. high at 0°C., the relationships shown in Table I are derived.

TABLE I
Pressure Units

Atm.	Bar	$P_{mm.Hg.}$, Torr	P_{μ}, microns	$P_{\mu b}$, microbar[a]
1	1.01	760	760×10^3	1.01×10^6
0.99	1	750	750×10^3	1×10^6
1.31×10^{-3}	1.33×10^{-3}	1	10^3	1.33×10^3
1.31×10^{-6}	1.33×10^{-6}	1×10^{-3}	1	1.33
0.99×10^{-6}	10^{-6}	0.750×10^{-3}	0.75	1

[a] Same as dyne/sq. cm.

Torr, designating 1 mm. absolute pressure has been used for a number of years in German literature, and is now being used generally in this country. Also, engineers frequently use as their standard: 1 atmosphere = 29.921 in. mercury at 32°F. = 14.696 lb./sq. in.

In dealing with gas flow at reduced pressures, the rate of flow is usually expressed in one of two ways:

(*1*) *Volume per unit time*, measured at the pressure at which the volume is determined. Common units are *liters per second*, or *cubic centimeters per second*. The letter F will be used to designate flow rate, and S for pumping speeds.

(*2*) *Pressure-volume per unit time*, reduced to a selected standard unit pressure. Common units are *micron liters per second;* that is, the volume of gas flowing if the pressure were 1 micron. The letter Q will be used to express the quantity of gas flow.

The liter micron flow, Q, is constant throughout any chosen system while the liters per second, S, vary according to the pressure. This may be made clearer by thinking of micron liters as a mass which is independent of pressure, whereas volumetric flow in liters (per second) is a function of pressure. The volumetric rate of flow in liters per second is obviously related to micron liters per second as follows:

$$S = \frac{Q}{P\mu} \tag{1}$$

Large commercial vacuum installations frequently use pounds per hour to represent gas flow. The large volumes that must be pumped to handle a relatively small mass are evident from the relation for air at 25°C., where 1 lb./hr. is approximately 80,000 micron liters/sec.

Two useful expressions in dealing with gas flows at reduced pressures are *conductance* and *resistance*. Conductance is the rate of *flow per unit difference of pressure* which we shall designate as

$$F = \frac{Q}{P_2 - P_1} \tag{2}$$

and $1/F$ the resistance. The analogy follows from the electrical pattern of Ohm's law when P is compared to potential E, and Q to the current I.

$$E = IR \qquad P = Q(1/F)$$

As in electrical circuits, tubes in series have a total resistance, F, calculated as follows:

$$R = R_1 + R_2 + \dots$$

$$\frac{1}{F} = \frac{1}{F_1} + \frac{1}{F_2} + \dots$$

while tubes in parallel have the reciprocal of the resistances, or the conductances added,

$$\frac{1}{R} = \frac{1}{R_1} + \frac{1}{R_2} + \dots$$

$$F = F_1 + F_2 + \dots$$

The application of this concept will become more evident in the discussion of complete systems and in speed calculations in the molecular flow region.

The actual *speed of exhaust* of a vacuum chamber connected to a pump depends on the resistance to flow of gases through connecting tubes as well as on the speed of the pump. It can be shown that if the speed of the pump is S_p, the term, $1/S_p$, can be regarded as a resistance; and for any system having a resistance of $1/F$ up to the pump, the combined effect is

$$\frac{1}{S} = \frac{1}{S_p} + \frac{1}{F} \tag{3}$$

where S is the speed of the system. This can be rewritten as

$$S = \frac{S_p F}{S_p + F} \tag{4}$$

The "rule of thumb" to make high-vacuum connecting tubes as wide and short as possible can be clearly grasped by examining the above relationship. The effect of the resistance of connecting tubing in throttling the speed of exhaust is shown in Table II. Values of F as multiples of S_p are

TABLE II
Effect of Tubing Resistance on Speed of Exhaust

F/S_p	S/S_p
1	$^1/_2$
2	$^2/_3$
4	$^4/_5$
8	$^8/_9$
16	$^{16}/_{17}$

given and values of S, the effective exhaust speed, as a fraction of the pump speed S_p.

When the connecting tubing has a speed equal to that of the pump the resultant speed of exhaust of the vacuum chamber is half the pump speed. Even when the connecting tubing has a speed 9 times the pump speed, a reduction of 10% of the effective vapor pump capacity results. And as a corollary to the above, very little is gained in exhaust speed by increasing the size of the vacuum pump if F, the connecting tubing conductance, is not large compared to S_p, the speed of the pump. These considerations are of great importance in arriving at an efficient pumping system.

III. GAS FLOW AT REDUCED PRESSURES

1. General Discussion

The physicist is usually better acquainted with the behavior of gases at low pressures than is the chemist. The fundamental theory and mathematical analysis have been adequately covered in the literature.[1] However, a practical interpretation of the flow formulas is useful to the laboratory worker who is primarily concerned in assembling apparatus and putting it to use on a particular distillation problem. Therefore, certain liberties have been taken with the basic facts in reducing them to approximate working formulae which are sufficiently accurate for vacuum distillation applications.

Gas flow through channels at reduced pressure can be divided into three regions: *viscous*, *molecular*, and *intermediate*. This follows from the fact that at pressures in which the frequency of collision between molecules is predominant, the coefficient of viscosity as introduced in the Poiseuille law[2] is most important, whereas at lower pressures in which the frequency of collision between molecules is less frequent than that of molecules against the walls, molecular flow as defined by Knudsen[3] results. Since the type of flow changes gradually from one pressure region to another, there is the third, intermediate transitory region in which the flow is partly both. In some cases where only a rough approximation is desired, this intermediate region can be neglected.

2. Flow at Intermediate Pressures

A. GENERAL EQUATION

Knudsen[4] endeavored to arrive at an equation which would cover the three flow ranges—viscous, intermediate, and molecular. This problem was approached empirically and from a series of measurements Knudsen deduced the relation:

$$F = \alpha_1 P_{\mu b} + \alpha_2 \frac{1 + C_1 P_{\mu b}}{1 + C_2 P_{\mu b}} \text{ cm.}^3/\text{sec.} \tag{5}$$

in which $P_{\mu b}$ equals the average pressure in microbars.

$$\alpha_1 = \frac{\pi}{8\eta}\frac{r^4}{l} = \frac{\pi d^4}{128\eta l}$$

is a viscous flow factor.

$$\alpha_2 = \frac{8}{3}\frac{r}{l}\frac{A}{\sqrt{2\pi\rho_1}} = \frac{4}{3}\frac{d}{l}\frac{A}{\sqrt{2\pi\rho_1}} = \frac{4}{3}\frac{d}{l}F_0$$

is a molecular flow factor in which r equals radius, d equals diameter, and l equals length, and

$$C_1 = \frac{2r\sqrt{\rho_1}}{\eta} = 2.507\frac{r}{\lambda_{\mu b}} = 1.253\frac{d}{\lambda_{\mu b}}$$

$$C_2 = \frac{2.47r\sqrt{\rho_1}}{\eta} = 3.095\frac{r}{\lambda_{\mu b}} = 1.547\frac{d}{\lambda_{\mu b}}$$

where $\lambda\mu_b$ is the mean free path* at one microbar. Since $P\mu_b$ (microbars) = $^4/_3 P\mu$ (microns) and $\lambda\mu_b = {}^4/_3\lambda$ at 1μ, then

$$\frac{1 + C_1 P\mu_b}{1 + C_2 P\mu_b} = \frac{1 + 1.253(Pd/\lambda)}{1 + 1.547(Pd/\lambda)} = Z \tag{6}$$

in which P without a suffix signifies pressure in microns, λ the mean free path at 1 μ, and d is in centimeters.

It is to be noted that this factor, designated Z, is the same whether P and λ are expressed in units of microns or microbars as long as consistent units are employed. For air at 25°C.

$$Z = \frac{1 + 0.2461Pd}{1 + 0.3040Pd} \tag{7}$$

(There is, of course, no such thing as an air molecule, but it is convenient to assume one exists. The free path can be calculated from viscosity values.)

Converting the first term in eq. (5) from microbars to microns, and substituting Z, as defined above,

$$F = \frac{4}{3}\alpha_1 P + \alpha_2 Z \text{ cm.}^3/\text{sec.} \tag{8}$$

where P is in microns. For air at 25°C., l and d in centimeters, and pressure P in microns,

$$F = 0.177\frac{d^4}{l}P + 12.2\frac{d^3}{l}Z \tag{9}$$

$$= 12.2\frac{d^3}{l}(0.0145\, Pd + Z) \text{ l./sec.} \tag{10}$$

It is readily seen that for small values of P the first term vanishes, Z approaches unity, and F becomes equal to molecular flow for long cylindrical tubes [eq. (19)]. Also, as P becomes large, Z approaches 0.81 as the limit, and the flow reduces to viscous flow and becomes practically equal to eq. (35). (A discussion of molecular flow and viscous flow will follow in this section.)

The chart in Figure 1 relates Pd, Z, and 0.0145 Pd. For any given value of Pd, and at right angles to the vertical Pd scale, both Z and 0.0145 Pd can be read on a horizontal line and substituted in the appropriate formula at the right to arrive at the conductance of the tube in question. It is apparent both from eq. (10) and from the chart that for values of Pd greater

* See Chapter VI, p. 540, for a discussion of the mean free path.

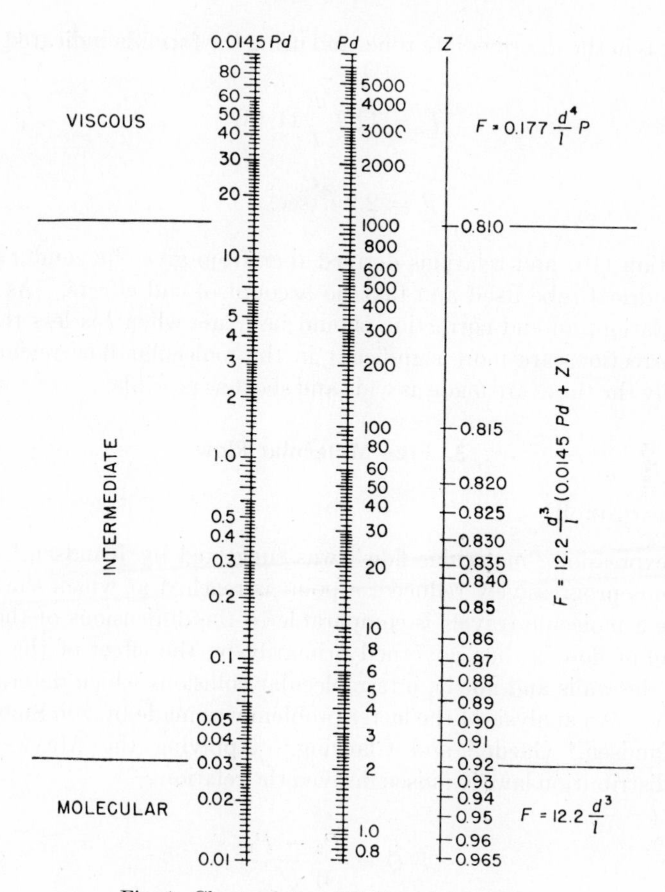

Fig. 1. Chart relating Pd, Z, and $0.0145Pd$.

than 1000 the flow is about 95% viscous, and for values of Pd less than 2 the flow is over 95% molecular. These two points have been selected as arbitrary values for separating the zones of gas flow, remembering that the numerical coefficients are for air at 25°C. Knudsen suggested that d/λ equal to or less than 0.4 be used to define molecular flow. This gives the value of Pd equal to or less than 2 which has been adopted in this Chapter.

As an illustration of the application of eq. (10) and Figure 1, assume a tube 2 cm. in diameter, 50 cm. long and air flowing through it at 25°C. at 10 μ pressure. What is the conductance of the tube? $Pd = 20$ is selected on the Pd line and Z and $0.0145\ Pd$ are read on the $Pd = 20$ horizontal line.

Pd	Z	$0.0145\ Pd$	$(0.0145\ Pd + Z)$
20	0.84	0.29	1.13

The flow is in the intermediate zone, and using the formula indicated.

$$F = 12.2 \frac{d^3}{l} (1.13)$$

$$F = 2.2 \text{ l./sec.}$$

Equation (10) and relations derived therefrom give the conductance of the cylindrical tube itself and take no account of end effects. As a strict interpretation, an end correction should be made when l is less than $50d$. Such corrections are more significant in the molecular flow region where ordinarily the tubes are made as wide and short as possible.

3. Free Molecular Flow

A. THE FACTOR, W

The expression "molecular flow" was suggested by Knudsen.[4] As the pressure is progressively reduced, a point is reached at which the average distance a molecule travels is comparable to the dimensions of the vessel. The rate of flow is then governed primarily by the effect of the collision against the walls and not be intermolecular collisions which determine the viscosity. An analysis of the latter problem was made by von Smoluchowski,[5] Knudsen,[4] Gaede,[6] and Clausing.[7] Applying the Maxwell-Boltzmann[8] distribution law, Knudsen derived the relation

$$Q = \frac{P_2 - P_1}{W\sqrt{\rho_1}} \tag{11}$$

or

$$F = \frac{Q}{P_2 - P_1} = \frac{1}{W\sqrt{\rho_1}} \tag{12}$$

where P is in microbars, ρ_1 equals density at 1 microbar, and W is a constant depending on the form and dimensions of the tube only. $W\sqrt{\rho_1}$ can be considered as a resistance since it is equal to $1/F$. The value of W can be calculated for tubes or ducts of most cross sections. For a *long* tube of length l, of varying cross section A, and perimeter H, Knudsen[4] deduced the fundamental relation

$$W = \frac{3}{16}\sqrt{2\pi}\int_0^l \frac{H}{A^2}\,dl \tag{13}$$

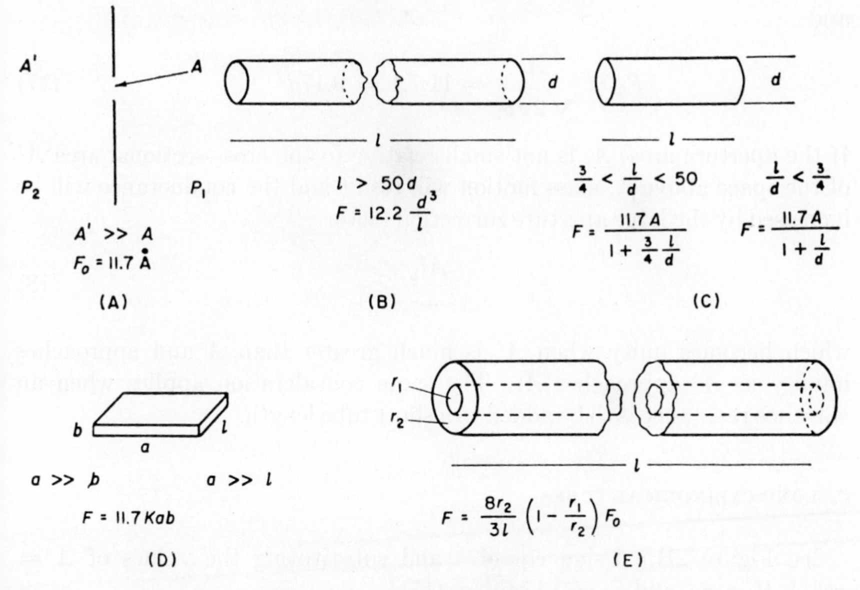

Fig. 2. Molecular flow: (*A*) aperture; (*B*) long tubes; (*C*) short tubes; (*D*) rectangular slits; (*E*) long concentric tubes.

For a duct of uniform cross section; that is, one in which H and A are not functions of the length, the value of W becomes

$$W = \frac{3\sqrt{2\pi}}{16}\frac{Hl}{A^2} \tag{14}$$

Therefore

$$F = \frac{16}{3}\frac{A}{Hl}\frac{A}{\sqrt{2\pi\rho_1}} = \frac{16}{3}\frac{A}{Hl}F_0 \tag{15}$$

The term $A/\sqrt{2\pi\rho_1}$ has been factorized separately since it will be found convenient to designate it as F_0.

B. APERTURE

See Figure 2A for the special case of $l = 0$, that is, an infinitely thin disk with an aperture of any cross section, A, which is much smaller than the area of approach,

$$W = \frac{\sqrt{2\pi}}{A} \tag{16}$$

and

$$F_0 = \frac{A}{\sqrt{2\pi\rho_1}} = 11.7A = 9.17d^2 \tag{17}$$

If the aperture area, A, is not small relative to the cross-sectional area A' of the space above it, mass motion will result and the conductance will be increased by the large aperture correction factor

$$\frac{A'}{A' - A} \tag{18}$$

which becomes unity when A' is much greater than A and approaches infinity as A' approaches A. The same consideration applies when an entrance resistance is to be added to a short tube length.

C. LONG CYLINDRICAL TUBES

See Figure 2B. Using eq. (15) and substituting the values of $A = \pi d^2/4$, $H = \pi d$, and $F_0 = 9.17d^2$ [eq. (17)]

$$F = \frac{16}{3}\frac{A}{Hl}F_0 = 12.2\frac{d^3}{l} \text{ liters/sec.} \tag{19}$$

The formulas apply only if the pipe is long. The rate at which gas can be removed from the pipe is given and no account is taken of the rate of effusion of gas into the higher pressure end. Any difficulty experienced by the molecules in finding the entrance to the pipe must be negligible compared with the difficulty of traversing the length. This will be true when

$$1 > 100r > 50d$$

D. SHORT TUBES OF UNIFORM CROSS SECTION

See Figure 2C. For tubes in which $1 < 50d$, end effects are no longer negligible in comparison to the resistance of the tube walls. One can consider the resistance as the sum of: (*1*) the resistance of the pipe inlet considered as an aperture, and (*2*) that of the pipe length itself. If W_0 is the resistance of the opening and W_t that of the tube wall,

$$W = W_0 + W_t$$

$$\frac{1}{F} = \frac{1}{F_0} + \frac{1}{F_t}$$

Substituting the value of F_t from eq. (19) and F_0 from eq. (17),

$$\frac{1}{F} = \frac{1}{9.17d^2} + \frac{1}{12.2(d^3/l)}$$

$$F = \frac{9.17d^2}{1 + \frac{3}{4}(l/d)} = \frac{11.7A}{1 + \frac{3}{4}(l/d)}, \text{ l./sec.} \tag{20}$$

Since l and d appear in the denominator as a ratio, any consistent units can be used. For example, both can be in centimeters, inches, feet, etc., as long as they are the same for any one ratio. However, for the numerical constants given, d in the numerator must be in centimeters and A in square centimeters. Equation (20) is normally sufficiently accurate for vacuum distillation calculations. For values of l/d greater than $^3/_4$, the maximum error is about 12%. It can be readily seen that when l equals 0, the expression becomes the aperture formula, and when l is much greater than d, it becomes the long tube formula.

For shorter tubes, and agreeing with the more complicated expression as derived by Clausing,[7] Kennard[9] has shown that for very short tubes the $^3/_4(l/d)$ term should be l/d, leading to the expression

$$F = \frac{11.7A}{1 + (l/d)} = \frac{9.17d^2}{1 + (l/d)}, \text{ liters/sec.} \tag{21}$$

when

$$l/d = {}^3/_4$$

If the conductance of a short noncylindrical duct of uniform cross section is desired, the same approach as used above can be made. If we substitute from equation:

$$F_d = \frac{16}{3}\frac{A}{Hl}F_0$$

in the equation

$$\frac{1}{F} = \frac{1}{F_0} + \frac{1}{F_d}$$

we obtain:

$$F = \frac{F_0}{1 + {}^3/_{16}(Hl/A)} = \text{ liters/sec.}$$

and for air at 25°C.:

$$F = \frac{11.7A}{1 + {}^3/_{16}(Hl/A)} = \text{ liters/sec.} \tag{22}$$

where A is the area in square centimeters, H and l the perimeter and length of the duct, respectively, expressed in centimeters.

Here again the denominator represents the effect of the channel walls and the numerator that of the entrance.

E. DUCTS OF NONUNIFORM OR IRREGULAR CROSS SECTION

If the value of W can not be obtained from the integral, $\int_0^l H/A^2\,dl$, of eq. (13), an estimated value of the conductance can be determined by dividing the channel into sections which will permit an approximation of the integrated value. The resistance of the sections are then added to get the total effect. An abrupt decrease in area from one section to another will introduce an entrance resistance, which, corrected by the large aperture factor, becomes

$$F_0 \frac{A'}{A' - A}$$

However, the transition from one exit section to an entrance section of the same shape and an equal (or larger) area will not require an additional entrance resistance.

F. BAFFLES, VALVES, ETC.

Only in the simplest cases is it possible to calculate with any degree of certainty the conductance of such irregular shaped channels. At best, one can calculate upper and lower limits by visualizing the channel as a duct or tube and arbitrarily selecting a reasonable value. If the conductance is critical, an experimental determination of the value is necessary.

G. COLD TRAPS

See Figures 3A and 3B. For complicated designs, the same general remarks which pertain to baffles, valves, etc., apply. However, some of the simpler designs are amenable to mathematical analysis. As an example, an approximate calculation of the conductance of a trap design shown in Figure 3A will be made. It is assumed that the gas travels equally by two parallel paths around each side of the cold thimble. For an irregularly shaped channel, from eq. (14):

$$W = \frac{3\sqrt{2\pi}}{16} \frac{Hl}{A^2}$$

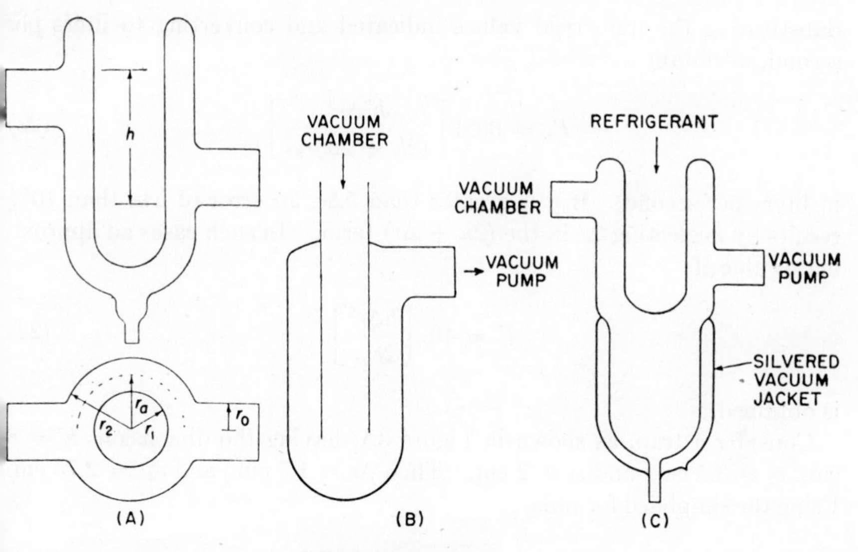

Fig. 3. Cold traps.

The axial length around each side is calculated by using the average radius:

$$r_{\text{av}} = \frac{r_2 + r_1}{2}$$

giving $l = \pi r_{\text{av}}$. The perimeter H can be approximated by assuming the channel as an inverted trough of sides h high and base $(r_2 - r_1) = \Delta r$. Or $H = 2h + \Delta r$ and the area can be assumed to be the area of section $h(r_2 - r_1)$ or $A = h\Delta r$. From eqs. (12) and (15)

$$F = \frac{1}{W\sqrt{\rho_1}} = \frac{16}{3\sqrt{2\pi\rho_1}} \frac{A^2}{Hl}$$

Evaluating the factor:

$$\frac{A^2}{Hl} = \frac{h^2\Delta r^2}{(2h + \Delta r)\pi r_{\text{av}}}$$

and hence for air at 25°C.:

$$F_t = 19{,}800 \left[\frac{h^2\Delta r^2}{(2h + \Delta r)r_{\text{av}}}\right]$$

in cubic centimeters per second. Since this is the flow around one side only, the total flow by the two parallel paths will be twice this amount.

Substituting the numerical values indicated and converting to liters per second, we obtain

$$F_t = 39.6 \left[\frac{h^2 \Delta r^2}{(2h + \Delta r) r_{av}} \right] \tag{23}$$

in liters per second. If h is greater than $5\Delta r$, an error of less than 10% results by neglecting Δr in the $(2h + \Delta r)$ term. In such cases an approximate value of

$$F = 40. \left[\frac{h \Delta r^2}{2 r_{av}} \right], \tag{24}$$

is obtained.

Consider a trap, as shown in Figure 3A, having the dimensions $h = 8$ cm., $r_2 = 3.5$ cm., and $r_1 = 2$ cm. Then $\Delta r = 1.5$ cm., and $r_{av} = 2.75$ cm. Using the simplified formula

$$\frac{h \Delta r^2}{2 r_{av}} = \frac{8 \times 1.5^2}{2 \times 2.75} = 3.27$$

hence, the trap has a conductance 40 times this number or about 130 l./sec.

A gas molecule entering the trap from the upsteam side arm of radius r_0 will "see" an opening of area approximately $A = 2r_0 \cdot \Delta r$. To determine whether an entrance resistance, F_0, need be added to F_t, the value of A should be compared with the upstream area, $A' = \pi r_0^2$. As long as A is much greater than A', no allowance for F_0 need be made, or, in this particular case, as long as

$$2\pi r_0 \Delta r \geq \pi r_0^2$$

or

$$2\Delta r \geq r_0$$

For the example being considered, $2\Delta r = 3$, which is greater than $r_0 = 2.5$; therefore no entrance resistance, $1/F_0$, need be added. In those cases in which there is a reduction in area on leaving the downstream side of the trap an entrance resistance should be added in computing the resistance from the trap shell to the next point downstream.

The conductance of a trap of the general design shown in Figure 3B has been calculated by Dushman.[10] It should be observed that the conductance for all cold traps will be lower at a lower temperature, T, by the factor $\sqrt{T/273}$. The average temperature of the gas in passing through the trap can be approximated from the temperature of the refrigerant being used.

H. ELBOWS AND BENDS

Klose[11] determined rates of flow of gases at low pressures and concluded that F depends only on the total length of path and on the values of r for different sections. The introduction of bends or elbows has no appreciable effect. Therefore, in the high-vacuum flow region it is usually sufficient to consider the effective length of an elbow or a bend as its axial length. However, Sheriff[12] indicates that each bend requires the addition of one tube diameter to the length, l, in the conductance formula.

I. SLITS OF RECTANGULAR SECTION

See Figure 2D. For tubes with rectangular section, $a \gg b$ and $a \gg l$, Clausing[7] has arrived at the relation

$$F = 3.638Kab\sqrt{T/M} \text{ liters/sec.} \tag{25}$$

and for air at 25 °C.:

$$F = 11.7Kab \text{ liters/sec.} \tag{26}$$

Values for K as a function of l/b appear in Table III.

TABLE III
Slits—Values of K as a Function of l/b

l/b	K	l/b	K
0	1.0	1.5	0.6024
0.1	0.9525	2.0	0.5417
0.2	0.9096	3.0	0.4570
0.4	0.8362	4.0	0.3999
0.8	0.7266	5.0	0.3582
1.0	0.6848	10.0	0.2457

J. CONCENTRIC TUBES

See Figure 2E. For a long annular space we can again apply the general equation (15) for conductance:

$$F = \frac{16}{3}\frac{A}{Hl}F_0$$

The area A is the open space between the two cylinders, or $\pi(r_2^2 - r_1^2)$. The perimeter H is the combined circumferences of the inside diameter of the outside shell and the outside diameter of the inside core, or $2\pi(r_2 + r_1)$. Therefore,

$$\frac{A}{Hl} = \frac{1}{2l}\left(1 - \frac{r_1}{r_2}\right) \quad F = \frac{16}{3}\frac{\pi(r_2^2 - r_1^2)}{2\pi(r_2 + r_1)}\frac{F_0}{l} = \frac{8r_2}{3l}\left(1 - \frac{r_1}{r_2}\right)F_0$$

$$= x\frac{r_2}{l}F_0, \text{ liters/sec.} \quad (27)$$

Values of

$$x = \frac{8}{3}\left(1 - \frac{r_1}{r_2}\right) \text{ as a function of } \frac{r_1}{r_2}$$

are given in Table IV. For air at 25°C.:

$$F_0 = 11.7A = 11.7\pi(r_2^2 - r_1^2) \quad (28)$$

TABLE IV

Concentric Tubes—Values of x as a Function of r_1/r_2

r_1/r_2	x	r_1/r_2	x
0	2.67	0.6	1.07
0.1	2.40	0.7	0.80
0.2	2.13	0.8	0.53
0.3	1.86	0.9	0.266
0.4	1.60	1.0	0
0.5	1.33		

If the concentric tubes are short, $l < 50\Delta r$, the value of A/Hl as derived above can be substituted in the short tube formula equation (20) or (21). It is of interest to note that if the concentric tube is a falling-film still or similar device where the gas is formed or liberated between the surfaces, no end correction is necessary. Also, if the still is being pumped equally at both ends, and the gas liberation is uniform along the length, it can be assumed that half the length is being evacuated equally in both directions.

It is to be remembered that free molecular flow predominates when the mean free path is large compared to the dimensions of the opening. As stated previously, for cylindrical tubes as long as

$$Pd \leq 2 \text{ or } \lambda \geq 2.5d$$

molecular formulas are accurate to within 5% for air at 25°C. Also, when numerical values are given they apply only to air at 25°C. unless otherwise stated. Since the density is proportional to the molecular weight, the value of the conductance for other gases at other temperatures can be found by multiplying F or F_0 by

$$\sqrt{29/M}\sqrt{T/273}$$

where T is in degrees Kelvin. The temperature correction is to be considered in calculating the conductance of cold traps.

4. Viscous Flow

A. LAMINAR REGION

The flow of gas in the viscous laminar flow (nonturbulent) region is governed by Poiseuille's law.[13]

Referring again to eq. (5), it can be seen that the second term becomes negligible at higher pressures. When Pd is greater than 1000, the flow is over 95% viscous.

The formula reduces to

$$F = \frac{\pi r^4}{8\eta l} P_{av} = \frac{\pi d^4}{128\eta l} P_{av} \text{ liters/sec.} \tag{29}$$

which is one way of expressing Poiseuille's law, where P_{av} is the average pressure along the tube.

The more familiar expression for viscous laminar flow is

$$m = \frac{\pi}{16\eta}\frac{r^4}{l}\frac{P_2^2 - P_1^2}{RT} \tag{30}$$

in which m is moles/sec.; n, coefficient of viscosity in poises at temperature T; r, radius of the tube in centimeters; l, length of the tube in centimeters; P_2, pressure at inlet in microbars; and P_1, pressure at outlet in microbars. If V is the rate of flow in cubic centimeters per second at pressure P:

$$PV = mRT$$

and substituting m from eq. (30)

$$PV = \frac{\pi}{16\eta}\frac{r^4}{l}(P_2^2 - P_1^2) \tag{31}$$

Since $P_2^2 - P_1^2 = (P_2 + P_1)(P_2 - P_1)$, and also $(P_2 + P_1)/2$ equals the average pressure P_{av}, eq. (31) becomes

$$PV = \frac{\pi}{8\eta}\frac{r^4}{l}P_{av}(P_2 - P_1) = Q \tag{32}$$

or

$$F = \frac{Q}{P_2 - P_1} = \frac{\pi r^4}{8\eta l} P_{av} \text{ liters/sec.} \tag{33}$$

which is identical with the expression [eq. (29)] deduced from the general formula of Knudsen.

As shown previously, when Pd exceeds 1000 eq. (9) becomes $F = 0.177 (d^4/l)P$, in which F is in liters per second per unit pressure drop. In dealing with forepressure lines, one can often tolerate pressure drops of 10 to 20%. Since $F = Q/(P_2 - P_1)$, Q, the quantity flowing at a pressure difference $P_2 - P_1$ microns, becomes:

$$Q = 0.177 \frac{d_4}{l} P(P_2 - P_1) \text{ micron liters/sec.} \tag{34}$$

in which d is diameter in centimeters; l, length in centimeters; P, average pressure in microns, $(P_2 + P_1)/2$; P_2, inlet (higher) pressure in microns; P_1, outlet (lower) pressure in microns. It is obvious from the factor d^4/l, that a much greater effect is obtained from a change in diameter than by altering the length. Doubling the diameter is equivalent to shortening the length 16 times.

As an illustration of the use of eq. (34), let us consider a tube 1 cm. diam. and 10 cm. long which is to conduct air at 25°C. at an average pressure of 100 μ under a pressure drop of 10 μ, or $P_2 = 105\ \mu$, and $P_1 = 95\ \mu$. The value of d^4/l becomes $l^4/10 = 0.1$, and $P(P_2 - P_1) = 100 \times 10 = 1000$. This leads to a value of 17.7 micron liters/sec.

As pointed out previously, it is sometimes desirable to express flow rates in terms of the volume of gas flowing per second at the prevailing average pressure P. Equation (34) becomes

$$S = \frac{Q}{P} = 0.177 \frac{d^4}{l} (P_2 - P_1) \text{ liters/sec.} \tag{35}$$

where P_2 and P_1 are in microns and d and l in centimeters.

In the example given above, the 17.7 micron liters/sec. is equivalent to 0.177 liters/sec. at 100 μ. The two expressions *micron liters per second* and *liters per second* should offer no difficulties if the conversion from one to the other is considered as a gas compression or expansion using 1 micron as the standard base pressure. We have selected the *micron* as our unit of pressure and the *micron liter* follows naturally.

Equation (35) can be rearranged to give a convenient expression for estimating the size of a fore vacuum line when the mechanical pump speed and length of connecting tubing are known. Assume a vessel is to be connected by a length of tubing 100 cm. long to a mechanical pump with a speed, S_p, of 2 liters/sec. (a Cenco Hyvac 14 has a rated capacity of 2.3 liters/sec. at 100 μ). The speed of 2 liters/sec. is at the pump inlet and with a finite pressure drop does not equal S in eq. (35). It can be shown that with pressure drops of less than 20% between the mechanical pump and the vessel, an error of less than 10% results if the pump speed, S_p, is substituted for S. The maximum error of 10%, with a top arbitrary limit of a 20% reduction, is usually well within the limits of other errors in estimating pipe sizes.

Rearranging eq. (35), and for the special case when $\Delta P = P_2 - P_1$ and $\leq 0.2 P_1$:

$$\Delta P = 5.64 \frac{l}{d^4} S_p \leq 0.2 P_1$$

or

$$d^4 \geq 28.2 \frac{l S_p}{P_1} \tag{36}$$

giving a general expression for determining diameters of fore-pressure lines, of length l centimeters, conducting air at 25°C. at the fore-pump intake pressure P_1 microns, into a fore-pump of capacity S_p liters per second, and for pressure drops of less than 20%. Substituting the selected values of l = 100 cm., S_p = 2.3 liters/sec., and P = 100 μ, the diameter should be no smaller than 2.74 cm. to keep the pressure drop or reduction in speed below 20%.

B. TURBULENT REGION

The equations derived so far from Poiseuille's law are applicable only for *viscous laminar flow*. However, in normal vacuum practice and for a properly designed distillation vacuum system, turbulent flow rarely, if ever, occurs. This can be shown by an examination of the conditions which lead to turbulence. It was first demonstrated by Reynolds[14] that if a certain critical velocity, μ_c, is exceeded, the pressure drop as calculated by the Poiseuille equation is too small. A dimensionless number, R, called he "Reynolds number," was defined which is used to determine the transition value of laminar to critical velocity.

$$\mu_c = \frac{R\mu}{\rho r} = \frac{2R\eta}{\rho d}$$

For glass, R has a value of 1000 and for metal between 400 and 500.[15]

Using the value 1000 and substituting for air at 25°C. a value of η = 1.845×10^{-4}, and a value of $\rho = 1.56 \times 10^{-9}$ g./cubic cm., at 1 μ pressure, one obtains

$$\mu_c = \frac{2.366 \times 10^5}{d} \text{ cm./sec.} \tag{37}$$

The velocity is also equal to the volume of gas flowing per second divided by the area, or

$$\mu_c = \frac{Q}{\pi a^2} = \frac{4Q}{\pi d^2} \tag{38}$$

Combining eqs. (37) and (38),

$$\mu_c = \frac{4Q}{\pi d^2} = \frac{2.366 \times 10^5}{d} \tag{39}$$

Therefore, at the critical velocity, Q = 185,000 d, micron liters per second where d is the diameter in centimeters.

Perhaps a better understanding of this value can be obtained by referring to Table V where Q for a tube 1 cm. in diameter is converted to liters per second, F. Comparing the speeds with some of the more common laboratory and industrial mechanical pumps, it can readily be seen that turbulent flow may occur at the initial stage of exhaust for small diameter tubes, but becomes less likely as the pressure is lowered.

TABLE V

Critical Flow Rate (Laminar to Turbulent Flow) as a Function of P for Tubes 1 cm. in Diameter

P_μ	$P_{mm.}$	F
1	0.001	185,000
10	0.01	18,500
100	0.1	1,850
1000	1.0	185
10,000	10.	18.5

IV. VACUUM PUMPS

1. Backing Pumps or Fore-pumps

Not many years ago, to the organic chemist a vacuum pump brought to mind a water aspirator. The *laboratory-size water aspirator* serves its useful purpose for Buchner funnel filtrations or Claisen flask distillations, but generally is not suitable for high-vacuum distillations. The laboratory water aspirator has a pumping capacity of the order of 20 cc./sec. producing an ultimate vacuum of from 8 to 12 mm. mercury, depending on the water temperature and pressure. Compared to this is the smallest Cenco mechanical pump, the "Hyvac S/4," which has a rated speed of about 170 cc./sec., and the Welch "Disto-pump 1399" mechanical pump with a speed of about 500 cc./sec. at 100 μ.

A. MECHANICAL ROTARY PUMPS

Rotary oil-sealed mechanical pumps are used almost exclusively for laboratory and pilot plant operations. These pumps and others which exhaust against atmospheric pressure are used as the primary vacuum pump, commonly referred to as a "backing pump" or "fore-pump," and capable of maintaining intake pressures of 0.1 to 2 mm.

The basic features and operating principles of one type of rotary pump, as given by Sullivan,[16] follow. Certain features are common to all these pumps (Fig. 4).

"A rotor R rotates inside a stator X. Line or area of contact G, between rotor and stator, and contact K, between vane V and stator, divide the volume between rotor and stator into two chambers (in pumps with two vanes instead of one this volume is divided into three chambers). Through the motion of the rotor one chamber is expanding and the other contracting. The expanding chamber is connected to the intake, I, of the pump and the contracting chamber to the exhaust, E. Oil films at G and K seal the pump. A valve D, usually, but not in all pumps, spring loaded, seals the contracting chamber against a flow of gas inward. This valve is oil sealed.

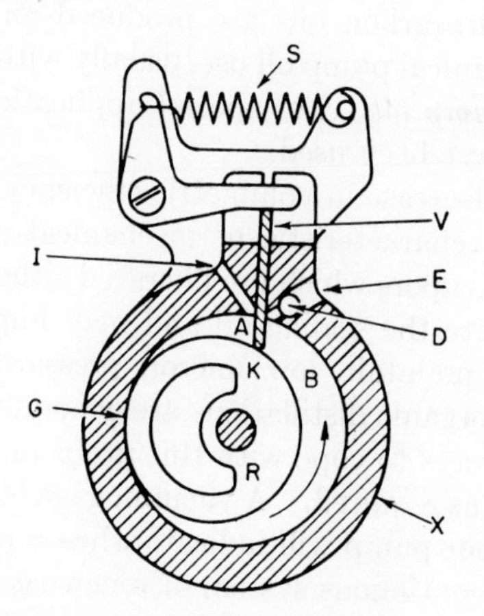

Fig. 4. Cenco Hyvac pump.

The free air displacement of a rotary oil-seal pump is a function of the volume between the rotor and the stator and the number of revolutions the rotor makes in unit time. In single-vane pumps the free air displacement, expressed in liters per second, liters per minute, or cubic feet per minute, is the product of the number of revolutions of the rotor per time unit and the volume between the rotor and stator (Fig. 4). A sliding, oscillating seal is provided for the vane in the top section of the stator."

Even though mechanical pumps with fresh uncontaminated oil can produce vacuums in the low micron range, as a practical matter single-stage rotary pumps find their most extensive use in distillation as backing pumps above the 0.1 to 1.0 mm. (100–1000 μ) region. In general, their pumping efficiency falls off appreciably with decreasing pressure, particularly below 100 μ. Multistage mechanical pumps have been designed to lower the ultimate vacuum and at the same time increase the volumetric efficiency at lower pressures. However, with the improved designs of vapor pumps now available, it is considered good distillation practice to rely on vapor-jet or vapor-condensation pumps to maintain vacuums below 0.1 to 1 mm. and in combination with mechanical pumps or ejectors to compress from there to atmospheric pressure. This is even more apparent when one considers that it is not uncommon for a small laboratory still to require a pump with a speed of 50 to 100 liters/sec. in the 1–10 μ range. A vapor-jet pump compressing from 2 to 200 μ can reduce the mechanical pump size 100 times.

All mechanical rotary vacuum pumps are sealed with a low vapor pressure lubricating oil. In new pumps a sealing oil with a viscosity in the range of SAE 20 to 30 is commonly used. As the pump wears and the clearances gradually increase, a heavier oil in the range of SAE 20 to 30 can be substituted. Hydrocarbon oils are produced and sold under various trade names for mechanical pump oil use, usually with the descriptive name *mechanical vacuum pump oil.* For special applications, sealing oils other than hydrocarbons have been used.

In addition to the decrease in volumetric efficiency with lower pressures, which is an inherent characteristic of mechanical pumps resulting from clearance limitations, vapors which are liberated either before or during the distillation contaminate the sealing oil and may impair the pump's operation. Attempts to maintain low micron pressures with a mechanical pump when used for organic distillations are generally futile.

There are several ways to cope with this problem. One simple method is to change pump oil as required. A vacuum gage between the mechanical pump and the oil-vapor pump will indicate when a change is needed. On large installations, a continuous system of renewing the sealing oil and reclaiming the contaminated oil by suitable means has been successfully used.

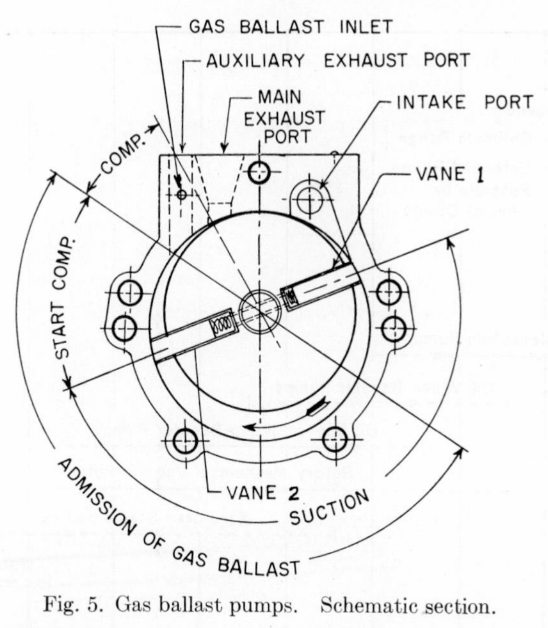

Fig. 5. Gas ballast pumps. Schematic section.

Cold traps, which will be discussed later, assist materially in condensing volatile contaminants which would otherwise reach the fore-pump.

Gaede[17] proposed a mechanical pump modification that would admit air during the discharge compression cycle of a rotary mechanical pump. The effective concentration or partial pressure of the contaminating vapor is reduced to a degree such that for many vapors, condensation can be prevented. Rotary pumps incorporating this principle are known as "vented-exhaust" or as "gas ballast" pumps. The pumping characteristics of such pumps have been described by Power and Kenna.[18] Although as low a permanent gas pressure cannot be achieved, pressures of a few tenths of a millimeter with a single stage pump can be maintained. Vapor-jet pumps are available that will readily operate into these fore-pressures.

There are a number of mechanical pumps on the market incorporating the vented-exhaust or the gas ballast principle. Two examples of laboratory size models are the Dist-O-Pump (Welch Manufacturing Company), and the Hyvac S-14 (Central Scientific Company).

Figure 5 illustrates the end view of the exhaust stage of a Hyvac pump provided with the gas ballast feature. The operation is explained as follows:

The pumping cycle begins as Vane No. 1 passes the intake port. A crescent-shaped volume is formed which is terminated as Vane No. 2 passes the intake port. The formation of this volume draws gas from the intake stage which becomes trapped between the

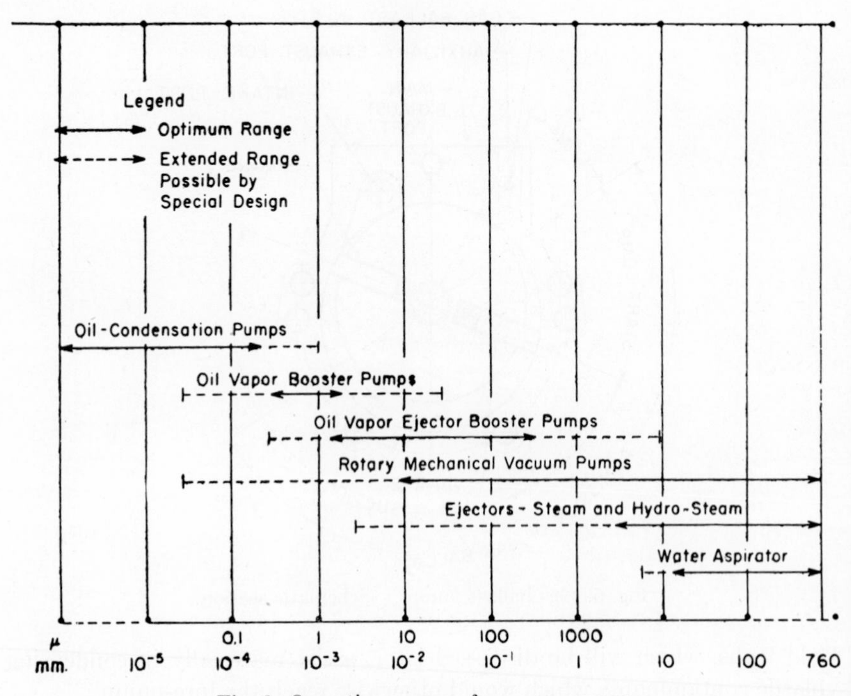

Fig. 6. Operating ranges of vacuum pumps.

two vanes. When Vane No. 1 has just passed the auxiliary exhaust port or gas ballast inlet, air is permitted to enter the volume between the two vanes as a result of the difference in pressure. Vane No. 2 then compresses the gas slightly above atmospheric pressure in order to lift the exhaust valve. A steel check ball in the gas ballast valve body shown in Figure 5 prevents gases from exhausting through the air inlet hole during the compression cycle.

On large installations, multistage steam ejectors or hydrosteam ejectors are used as backing pumps. Vapors as well as "permanent gases" are readily handled by ejectors, thereby eliminating the contamination problem.

A diagrammatic representation of the ranges covered by pumps discussed in this chapter is shown in Figure 6.

B. STEAM AND WATER EJECTORS

Vapor-ejector forepumps are usually operated with high-pressure steam (60 to 250 p.s.i.g.), although other actuating vapors have been tried.[19] A typical single-stage ejector is shown in Figure 7.[20] Such units are joined in series to produce almost any degree of vacuum from atmospheric to pressures in the micron region. A five-stage ejector can be made to produce a

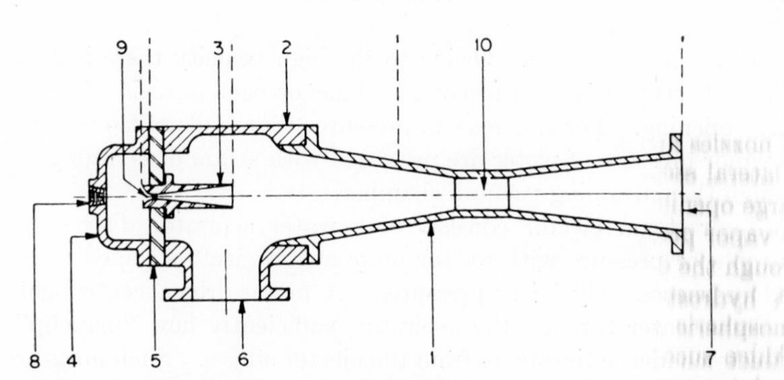

Fig. 7. Basic one-stage steam-ejector assembly: (*1*) diffuser; (*2*) air chamber; (*3*) steam nozzle; (*4*) steam chest; (*5*) nozzle plate; (*6*) suction; (*7*) discharge; (*8*) steam inlet; (*9*) nozzle throat; (*10*) diffuser throat.

"shut-off" vacuum of between 25 and 50 μ. As a matter of steam conservation, intercondensers are interspersed between some of the stages. In such cases, to remove the condensed steam to the atmosphere, the ejectors and condenser are generally placed about 34 ft. above a water basin, sometime called a "hotwell," into which the end of a barometric leg is submerged. When such height is not available, the water can be removed by a discharge pump which requires about an 8- to 10-ft. head for its operation. By and large, the barometric leg is the more common choice.

Barometric condensers are generally used on four- and five-stage ejectors, sometimes on three stages, and rarely on small two-stage assemblies. Commercial-size steam ejectors are ordinarily too large for laboratory application. However, small units can be made which find many applications in vacuum distillation.

Steam jet ejectors operate on a mass-velocity principle. The propelling steam expands adiabatically through a divergent nozzle, converting its pressure energy to kinetic energy. The mass of high-velocity steam is directed through a mixing chamber and into a convergent–divergent diffuser. In passing through the mixing chamber the steam entrains a definite mass of gas or vapor being evacuated. In imparting velocity to the gas, the steam is slowed down, and the resultant mass enters the diffuser where the kinetic energy is converted to pressure which is considerably higher than that in the vacuum chamber. There is no condensation of actuating vapors during the compression cycle. The high expansion ratio of the steam in a four- or five-stage ejector may accelerate the steam to Mach numbers of 9 to 11. The cooling effect from this expansion in many cases produces ice on the nozzle mouth as well as in the diffuser throat. The ice formation alters critical dimensions and interferes with the ejector's operation. The condition is alleviated by adding steam jackets to the nozzles and diffusers. Owing to the high velocity there is practically no lateral escape of steam or entrained gas or back diffusion from the discharge opening. For this reason, pressures thousands of times lower than the vapor pressure of water are produced with steam discharging into and through the entraining vacuum chamber.

A hydrosteam ejector consists of a water aspirator discharging into atmospheric pressure with one or more steam ejectors joined in series to produce successively lower pressures. A motor-driven centrifugal pump circulates water through the aspirator, sufficiently new "makeup" being added to condense the steam from the ejector stages. Such units are compact, relatively free from trouble, and are useful for degassing purposes as well as backing units for oil-booster pumps.

2. Oil-Vapor Pumps

A. GENERAL

Mercury-vapor pumps are not as common in organic high vacuum distillation as oil-vapor pumps and therefore consideration will be given only to pumps using organic compounds as boiler fluids. A description of mercury pumps is given by Dushman[1] and their construction is discussed by Barr and Anhorn.[21]

Since molecular distillations are conducted generally at pressures in the 0.1–10 μ region, a standard condensation pump which relies principally on the diffusion principle is in most cases not entirely applicable. The terms "condensation pump" and "diffusion pump" are used synonymously, although the present-day high-vacuum pumps are more nearly of the condensation type, as designed by Langmuir,[22] than of the diffusion type as proposed by Gaede.[23]

B. CONDENSATION PUMPS

In the discussion of steam-ejector pumps it was pointed out that the actuating vapor (steam) was not condensed during the compression cycle. As distinct from this, a condensation pump relies on the fundamental principal that the actuating vapor, after having imparted its momentum to the gas molecules, is rapidly condensed, the condensing zone being maintained sufficiently low that no appreciable re-evaporation and hence random motion of the oil vapor takes place. Therefore, the primary difference between the operation of a condensation pump and an ejector pump is that in a condensation pump the gas molecules acquire a forward momentum as a result of collision with oil-vapor molecules, whereas in the ejector pump the gas is entrained in a high-speed steam and rapidly moved along with it

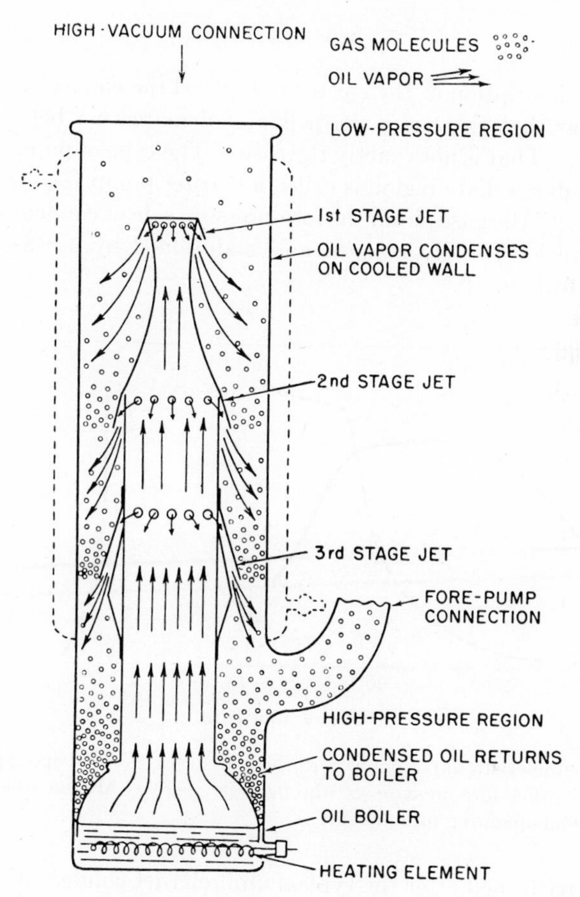

Fig. 8. Schematic section, oil condensation pump.

into a compression zone. One could be considered particle motion and the other mass motion.

A section of a typical oil-condensation pump is shown in Figure 8. One or more stages operate from a common boiler, which may or may not have partitioning zones depending on whether the pump is fractionating or non-fractionating. The actuating fluid is vaporized from the boiler, the vapors conducted to vapor-directing jets by appropriate chimneys, and the vapors projected in the fore-pressure direction. Molecules diffusing into the steam are propelled forward. The oil vapor condenses on the cold wall and returns to the boiler to repeat the cycle. More efficient operation is obtained from multistage pumps, and, when extremely high vacuums are needed, fractionating pumps are used.

C. BOOSTER PUMPS

From the description of the ejector pump and the condensation pump, it would appear that there is a sharp line of demarcation between the two mechanisms. That is not exactly the case. The type of pump which operates in the intermediate region is called a booster pump because it was first used to "boost" the gases from the fore-pressure side of condensation pumps to a pressure level easily reached and maintained by a reasonable sized mechanical fore-pump.

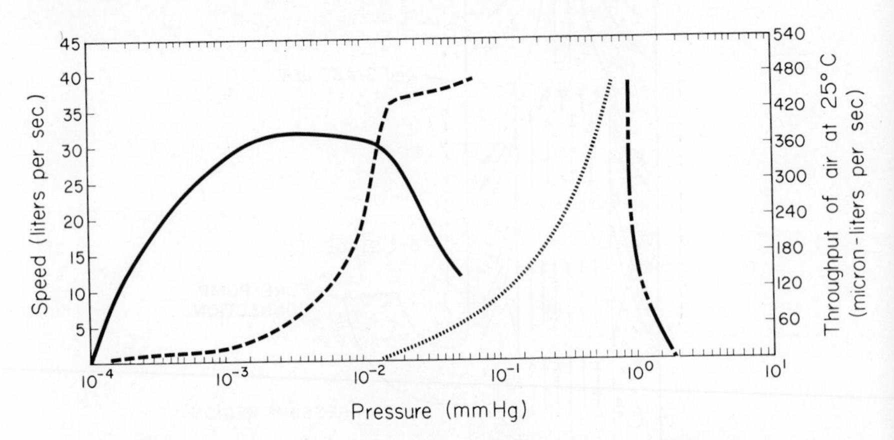

Fig. 9. Characteristic vapor pump performance curves. (——) Speed pressure curve. (— — — —) Limiting fore-pressure vs. throughput. (— —) Micron liters throughput. (| | | | |) Normal operating fore-pressure.

A pump patterned after the typical umbrella-jet condensation pump but altered to give maximum speed in the 10^{-3}–10^{-4} mm. mercury range has been designed. A typical pump of this type is similar to the one shown in Figure 8. Characteristic performance curves are given in Figure 9. Such pumps are modified condensation pumps and as such have an inherent upper limit to their optimum operating range, usually a top limit of a micron or two.

D. OIL-VAPOR EJECTOR PUMPS (DIFFUSION EJECTOR PUMPS)

Oil-vapor pumps have been designed which combine the principles of the ejector and condensation pumps and are capable of optimum performance in the range of 1 μ to several millimeters of mercury. An example is shown in Figure 10. This type of pump is generally preferred to the umbrella-jet type for distillation work above 1 μ. Performance curves similar to those in Figure 9 will indicate their optimum pumping range. Laboratory-size

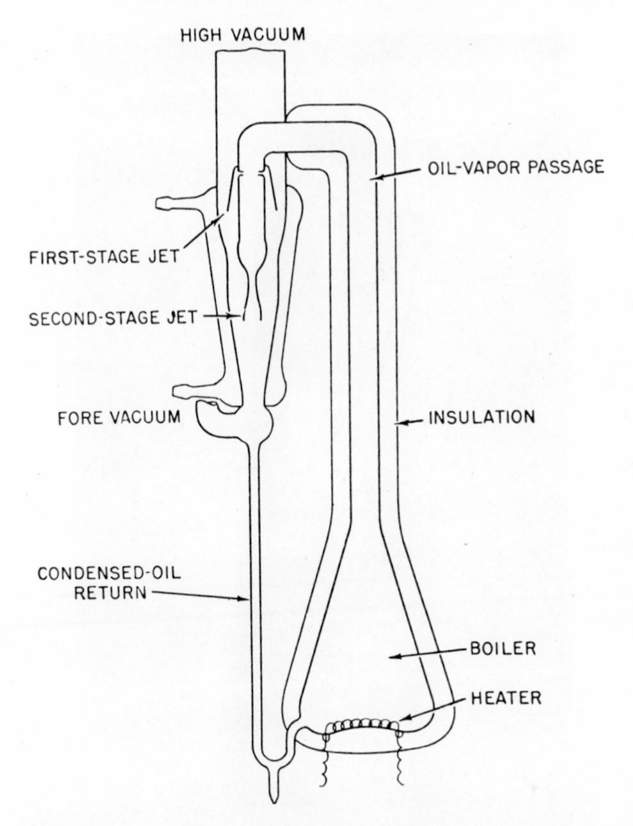

Fig. 10. Glass booster pump (vapor ejector) cross section.

pumps of the type shown in Figure 10 have speeds of 25–30 liters/sec. in the 1–10 μ range.

A photograph of a commercially available glass booster pump made by Consolidated Vacuum Corporation is shown in Figure 11.

E. SELECTION OF VAPOR PUMP—PERFORMANCE SPECIFICATIONS

It is obvious that an oil-vapor pump should be chosen whose maximum or, at best, optimum range covers the anticipated operating pressure of the vacuum still. To assist in this choice we can deduce from the previous discussions that three values can be used to define the relative performance of vacuum pumps:

1. Ultimate Vacuum. This is the lower limit of pressure which may be attained in a finite time in a closed vessel connected to the pump. With most types of pumps the ultimate vacuum depends on the fore-pressure as well as on the vapor pressure of the actuat-

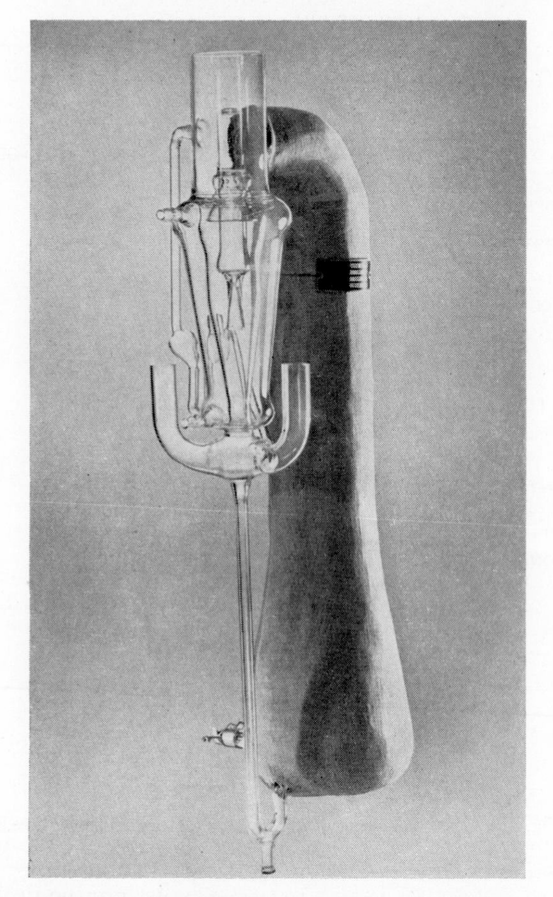

Fig. 11. Glass booster pump (vapor ejection).

ing oil. In actual measurement its value will also depend on whether a refrigerated trap is used and if so, on its temperature.

2. Speed—Usually Expressed in Liters per Second. One value of the speed is usually not sufficient to characterize pump performance. Curves such as shown in Figure 9 indicate whether the pump has a broad or narrow pumping zone and also the effect of fore-pressure on the capacity. The speed can be expressed mathematically as:

$$-(dP/dt) = (S/V)(P - P_0)$$

in which P is the pressure at any time, t; P_0, the ultimate vacuum attainable by the pump; V, the volume of the space being evacuated; and S, the pump speed.

3. Exhaust Pressure or Fore-pressure Breakdown—Both Dynamic and Static. As indicated in Figure 9, there is a definite limit to which vapor pumps can compress gas. They do not discharge to atmosphere directly but require a "fore-pump" or "backing pump." The fore-pressure into which a vapor pump can discharge the compressed gas is a characteristic of the design and type of pump, and, in general, the maximum fore-pressure will result under zero throughput, or at the so-called static fore-pressure. It is important in evaluating a pump to compare values on a comparable basis—dynamic under load, and static under no load. Within limits the fore-pressure breakdown is related to the heat input to the pump boiler.

There are several ways of measuring the speeds of pumps and certain precautions must be taken to obtain reliable values.[24] Unless one is equipped to make and to interpret the measurements it is probably just as well to rely on the values of an accredited manufacturer.

There are other less tangible but equally important factors in selecting a pump for vacuum-distillation application, such as:

(*1*) The ability of the pump to handle semicondensible or other contaminants which may reach the pump during a distillation.

(*2*) Operating efficiency, which is usually of secondary importance in laboratory work but should not be overlooked for larger installations.

(*3*) Maintenance, which includes the durability of the pump as well as its ease of inspection and cleaning.

F. LIQUIDS FOR OIL-VAPOR PUMP BOILERS

The proper choice of an operating fluid for vapor pumps depends on one or more of the following characteristics:

(*1*) *Stability* of the fluid on prolonged heating at a boiler temperature (and pressure) necessary to produce copious vapor ebullition.

(*2*) *Vapor pressure* in the range necessary to permit the production of the desired ultimate vacuum.

(*3*) *Physical properties* such as being fluid at the temperature of the condenser, wetting ability, and viscosity. It is also desirable that the fluid have a low heat of vaporization, although this is not a critical property.

(*4*) *Relative unreactivity* to permanent gases (particularly oxygen), metals, water, and vapors which may be released during the distillation and eventually reach the pump.

Even though the specifications seem rather stringent, usually one or more fluids can be found which are satisfactory. In Table VI are listed some of the more common fluids with the properties relevant to making a pump-oil choice. When mixtures are given, such as hydrocarbons, the vapor pressure is governed principally by that of the lightest constituent.

Laboratory oil-vapor pumps are ordinarily not made fractionating or self-purifying since it is a relatively easy matter to change the pump oil as desired. However, on large installations for continuous operation it is advantageous to have the pumps fractionating. Arrangements should be provided for removing heavy tars or residues which collect in the boiler, as well as the light ends which are continuously swept toward the fore-pressure region by the gas flow through the system.

An oil-vapor pump is relatively foolproof. However, there are certain *operating precautions* that should be taken. In general, pump oils, even

TABLE VI
Oil-Vapor Pump Fluids

Material	Pressure ranges in mm. Hg.				
	10^{-5}	10^{-4}	10^{-3}	10^{-2}	10^{-1}
Organic esters					
Di-2-ethyl phthalate (Octoil)[a]	←———	------------			
Amyl phthalate	————	————	————	------------	
Di-butyl phthalate		————	————	————	------------
Hydrocarbons					
Apiezon[b] oil B	←———	------------			
Apiezon oil A	←———	————	------------		
Litton[c] oil	←———	————	------------		
Convoil[a] 10	————	————	————	------------	
Chlorinated hydrocarbons					
Aroclor[d] 1248	————	————	————	------------	
Convaclor[a] 8		————	————	————	------------
Organosilicon compounds					
Silicone[e] DC 702	←———	————	------------		

———— optimum operating vacuum region
------------ permissible extended range
←——— lower pressures obtainable.

[a] Consolidated Vacuum Corporation, Rochester, New York.
[b] James G. Biddle Company, Philadelphia, Pennsylvania.
[c] Litton Engineering Laboratories, Grass Valley, California.
[d] National Research Corporation, Cambridge, Massachusetts.
[e] Dow Corning Corporation, Midland, Michigan.

though organic liquids, can stand considerable abuse. This is no excuse, however, for their being mistreated when a little reasonable care will greatly extend the life of the oil. It is good practice to cool the pump boiler to 50 to 100°C. below normal operating temperature before exposing the fluid to air. And it is generally desirable to boil or distill the pump fluid at pressures not greatly in excess of the normal operating boiler pressure. For condensation-pump fluids this is in terms of tenths of millimeters of mercury pressure and, for oil ejector booster pump oils, in terms of centimeters and tens of centimeters. Thermal switches or pressure-operated switches can be incorporated to give automatic protection to the boiler fluid. The heat input to the boiler should be adjusted according to the manufacturer's recommendation for optimum performance. The mere darkening of a pump fluid is no reason for a change to fresh oil. Color, of itself, is no criterion of ability of an oil to pump well. The need for change should be governed principally by the performance of the pump, both as to ultimate vacuum and to speed. A dark, messy-looking fluid may behave even better than the original charge, whereas a clear, colorless fluid contaminated with a light-boiling, difficult to remove contaminant may be ready for discarding. Occasionally during the degassing cycle or during the removal of the light fractions, constituents reach the pump and condense on the cold diffuser wall. This is particularly true when solvents have been used for cleaning the still between runs. Also, the cooling water should be turned off during exposure of the pump to atmospheric pressure, since moisture from the air might otherwise condense on the cold inner walls of the pump when the humidity is high. The fluids can sometimes be successfully purged of low-boiling contaminants or water by boiling the fluids for several minutes with the cooling water off. This operation must be watched closely to make sure the liquid is not all vaporized into the fore-pressure arm. Also, in the case of a water-cooled glass pump, the condenser should be kept full of water so that excessive thermal shock and breakage will not occur when cold water rushes against the glass seals.

V. VACUUM GAGES

1. General

A chart of the various gages which cover the pressure ranges encountered in high-vacuum distillation is given in Fig. 12. From the list one might think that a "foolproof" gage could be selected upon which full reliance could be placed and that readings as indicated by a pointer on a dial could be accepted as the "true" pressure. This is not always the case. Most vacuum gages rely on an indirect method of determining the pressure and do not determine the density directly nor "count" the number of molecules per unit volume. It is helpful to have an understanding of the principles of operation and precautions to be taken in the use of the gages which have been accepted as most practical. In interpreting gage readings one should know whether condensible gases or vapors affect the readings, and whether the sensitivity depends on the nature of the gases or vapors being measured.

2. Fore-Pressure Gages

The U-tube mercury manometer (or an open tube submerged in a well) and the *Bourdon*-type gage are used for fore-pressure measurements from atmospheric pressure down to about 10 mm. Such gages are relatively trouble-free and their accuracy is sufficient for indicating the degree of vacuum during the evacuation cycle. A special Bourdon gage[25] is available which can be used in the range of 1–20 mm. If greater sensitivity is required, an oil manometer can be used. A nonviscous, low-vapor-pressure organic fluid, usually a diffusion-pump oil, is used to fill the tube. The

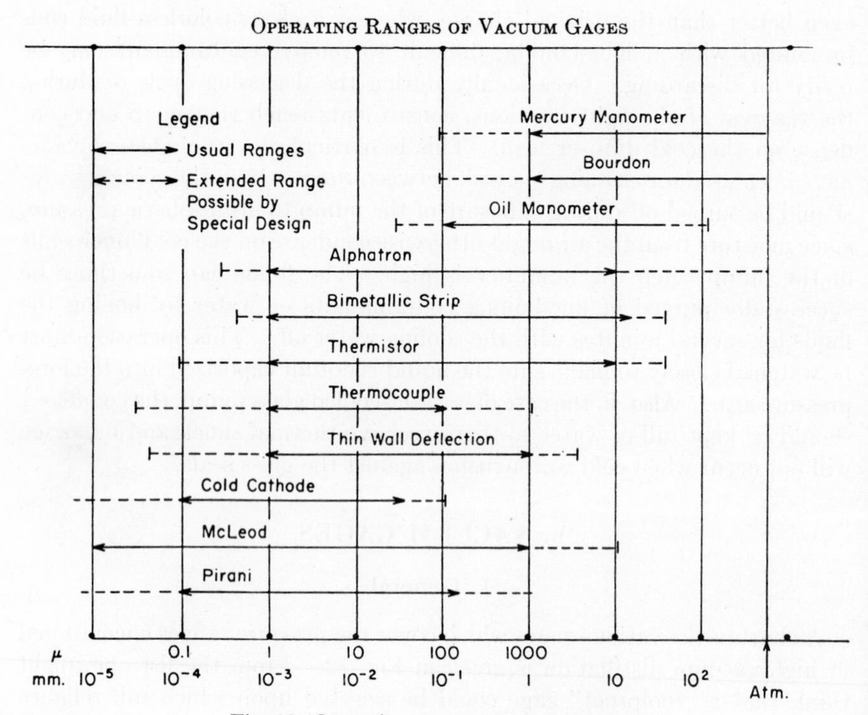

Fig. 12. Operating ranges of vacuum gases.

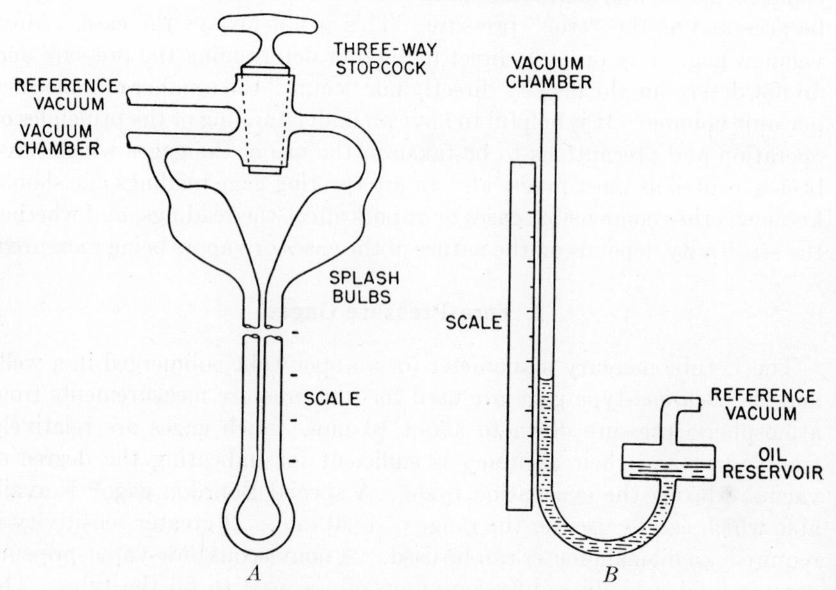

Fig. 13. Oil manometers: (*A*) U-tube: (*B*) single-tube well.

level difference in actual measured millimeters can be converted to millimeters mercury by multiplying scale Δ mm. by density of oil/density of mercury. It is sometimes convenient to make a scale calibrated directly in millimeters of mercury. In this case one scale division in millimeters of mercury equals density of mercury/density of oil. The reference vacuum can be a small rotary mechanical pump which will give an ultimate vacuum of 25 μ or less. In Figure 13A is shown a U-tube model with a stopcock arrangement for equalizing the pressure in the two limbs during "pump-down" or "outgassing" periods. In Figure 13B the volume of the well is made large relative to the volume of the measuring tube, so that a fixed scale can be used. Oil-filled manometers must be "outgassed" each time they are exposed to atmospheric pressure. This is done in a matter of minutes and is usually not objectionable, particularly if the system is to be maintained under vacuum for an extended period of time. The oil manometer is relatively free from trouble, measures total pressure, and is most useful in the range of 0.1–20 mm. The range has been extended by the use of a sloping U-tube in place of a vertical arrangement.[26]

The bench-mounted *McLeod* gage is generally not a practical instrument for high-vacuum distillation application. A portable tilting type[27] or a gage with an adjustable closed end is useful as a fore-pressure measuring device. The errors in regard to condensible vapors which are inherent in the standard McLeod gage are not avoided by the simplified designs. However, these instruments are portable and very convenient to use. A similar device called a Vacustat is described by Yarwood.[28]

3. Fine-Pressure Gages

Of the gages listed in Figure 12, those which have received greatest acceptance for high-vacuum distillation measurements below 100 μ are: Pirani, thermocouple, cold-cathode (Alphatron), and portable McLeod. The characteristics of these gages are shown in Table VII.

The Pirani and thermocouple gages depend on the change of heat conductivity with pressure, which at low pressures, increases linearly with pressure. Such gages, in general, are operated in such a manner as to maintain a constant energy input to the warmed element. The element consists of a filament or ribbon of some metal (such as tungsten, nickel, or platinum) which has a high temperature coefficient of resistance and which is not attacked by the gases or vapors to be measured at the temperature involved. As the pressure is raised and lowered, the hot element will lose heat at a varying rate and thereby suffer a temperature change. Therefore, such gages resolve themselves into means of measuring the temperature of the hot element. In the thermocouple type, the temperature is determined by means of a thermocouple spot-welded to the heated element.

TABLE VII
Vacuum Gages for Molecular Distillation

Type	Principle	Useful range	Advantages	Disadvantages
Pirani	Loss of heat from hot wire proportional to pressure	0.1 μ to 0.3 mm.	(*1*) Portable (*2*) Continuous reading (*3*) Attach directly to apparatus	(*1*) Filament contamination causes zero shift; must be periodically recalibrated (*2*) Sensitivity depends on nature of gas or vapor present
Thermocouple	As above except thermocouple junction used	0.1 μ to 0.1 mm.	(*3*) Attach directly to apparatus	(*1*) As for (*2*) above (*2*) Less sensitive than Pirani
"Alphatron"	Positive ion current proportional to pressure; radium capsule source of electrons	0.1 μ to 10 mm.	(*1*) Attach directly to apparatus (*2*) Attach directly to apparatus (*3*) Attach directly to apparatus (*4*) Wide range	(*1*) Precautions attending use of radium; not serious if operating instructions are carefully followed
Portable McLeod	Compresses known volume to known PV	0 to 5000 μ	(*1*) Portable (*2*) Convenient	(*1*) Intermittent reading (*2*) Hg contamination (*3*) Pressure readings are low if condensible vapors present

In the resistance type, the Pirani being an example, the temperature is determined by measuring the change in resistance, or the potential[29] is measured which must be supplied to the *Wheatstone* bridge to keep the resistance and hence the temperature of the wire constant. The change in length can also be used for this purpose.

A schematic diagram of a resistance-wire gage, Pirani type, and calibration plots are given in Figures 14 and 15, respectively. A Wheatstone-bridge arrangement is used for measuring the resistance changes. To compensate for room-temperature and bridge-voltage variations, a second tube duplicating as closely as possible the characteristics of the measuring

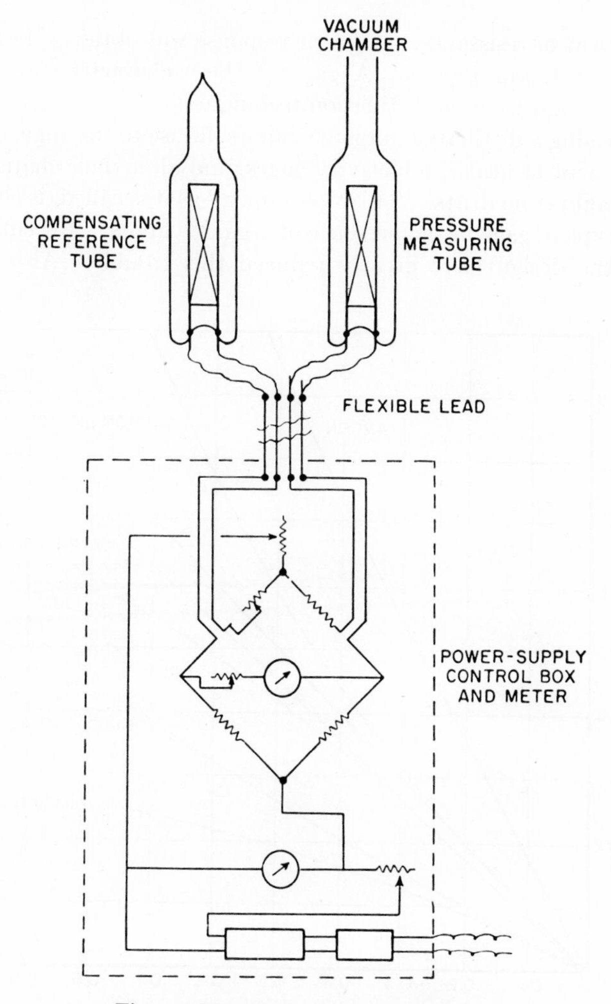

Fig. 14. Pirani gage (wiring diagram).

tube is sealed off at an extremely low pressure and balances the opposing arm of the bridge circuit. The calibration of the gage is dependent on the thermal conductivity of the gas in the system.

A photograph of a commercially available hot wire (Pirani) gage made by Hastings-Raydist Incorporated is shown in Figure 16. An improved model of a thermocouple gage made by Consolidated Vacuum Corporation is shown in Figure 17.

A thermistor-type of gage has been described by Becker, Green, and Pearson.[30] These semiconductor elements have a high negative temperature coefficient of resistance. A linear response was obtained in a vacuum gage between 1 and 1000 μ. A gage of these characteristics would be adaptable to high-vacuum distillation technique.

In performing a distillation, organic vapors diffuse to the gage, deposit on the hot element of heat-conductivity gages, and alter their characteristics. The gage calibration drifts. This "zero shift," as it is called, is characteristic of this type of gage in the presence of organic vapors. Recent improvements in the design have greatly reduced this trouble. Also, the gage

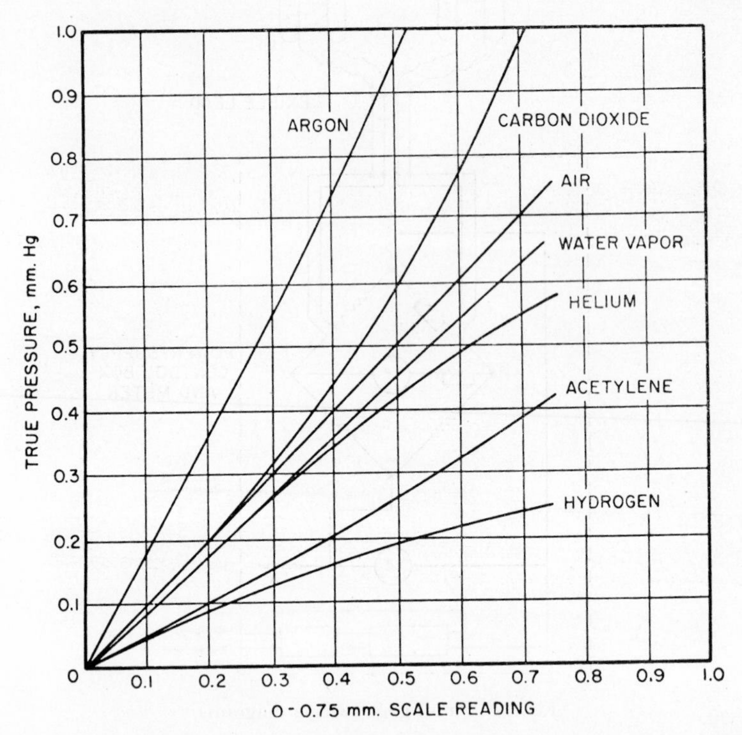

Fig. 15. Calibration curves for various gases with Pirani gage, type PG-1A, Distillation Products Industries. Bridge voltage 3 v.

contamination can be lessened by attaching the gage to the downstream side of a cold trap or baffle, although this is likely to give readings lower than actually exist in the evaporating zone.

If the Pirani or thermocouple gage is to be relied on for periods of weeks or months, a means for a periodic calibration against a "standard" gage or on a test rack should be provided. A test rack can be assembled from the following essential components:

(*1*) A condensation pump capable of producing 10^{-4} mm. or lower.
(*2*) A mechanical backing pump.
(*3*) A cold trap with outlets for attaching a gage or gages.
(*4*) A McLeod gage which can be read to a micron in the range of 1–20 μ.

One or more gages along with the McLeod is attached to a high-vacuum manifold connected to the condensation pump. Several points on the faulty gage scale are checked against the McLeod readings, and the zero

Fig. 16. Pirani gage (Hasting–Raydist, Inc.).

adjustment reset accordingly. The pressure can be adjusted by admitting a small continuous amount of air through an adjustable leak valve. A short piece of thick-walled rubber tubing with a fine wire inserted through the opening and with a screw pinch clamp compressing the tubing against the wire makes a simple, satisfactory, adjustable leak valve.

The *Alphatron* developed by Downing and Mellen[31] operates on the ionization-gage principle, the ionization being produced by alpha particles as distinct from electron bombardment in the hot-filament gage. This gage is rugged and suffers little from contamination. However, since the gage contains a radium source, certain precautions have to be taken in the use of this instrument. This is not a serious consideration if the manufacturer's operating instructions are followed.

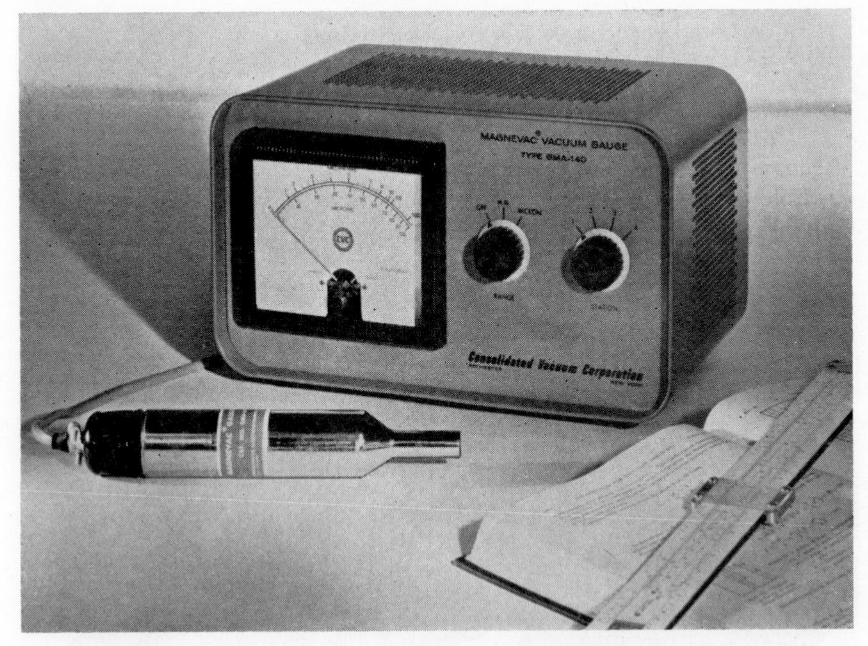

Fig. 17. Pirani gage (Consolidated Vacuum Corp.).

Gages should be connected as near the distilling zone as possible to obtain an indication of the true pressure. Contamination difficulties sometimes necessitate their being placed away from the still, but in such cases allowance should be made for possible pressure drops between the gage and the distilling zone.

VI. COLD TRAPS AND BAFFLES

As pointed out previously, during most distillations of organic materials, vapors which are dissolved as impurities in the original material, or vapors generated by thermal decomposition during the distillation, often fail to condense in the still. This is particularly true when the condensing zone is kept warm to assist the flow of viscous condensates, or to prevent the precipitation of solids from saturated solutions. If vapors so liberated from the distilland are not condensed by some cooling means between the still and the condensation pump, they are likely to be wholly or partially condensed or absorbed on the cold condensing zone of the pump.

Since the vacuum attainable by a condensation pump depends on the vapor pressure of the operating fluid, it is obvious that the performance of the pump will be impaired in proportion to the type and amount of contaminating vapor that reaches it. Annoying "bumping" of the boiler usually accompanies a contaminated pump, which also affects the speed and degree of vacuum attainable. With the heat input adjusted properly and with fresh pump fluid in the boiler, evolution of vapor takes place without the bumping and bubble formation which ordinarily accompany a boiling liquid.

In addition to protecting the pump, one frequently wishes to examine all the constituents of the distilling liquid and therefore endeavors to trap any vapors which do not condense in the still. Of the many shapes and forms of cold traps, the one shown in Figure 3A is particularly suited for high-vacuum distillation.

The refrigerants most commonly used are liquid nitrogen, liquid air, or powdered dry ice. Since liquid air has a varying composition, resulting from the faster vaporization of nitrogen, its temperature[32] may vary between about −183 and −196°C. Liquid nitrogen is now readily available in commercial quantities and is preferable to liquid air since a more constant lower temperature of about −195°C. is obtained, and, in addition, the possible explosion hazard of liquid air is obviated. An imploding trap containing liquid air can produce an explosive reaction when connected to a condensation pump or to a still containing hot oxidizable organic compounds.

A liquid-nitrogen trap can effectively remove water vapor, carbon dioxide, and relatively heavy organic vapors. However, such gases as ethane, ethylene, methane, and carbon monoxide have appreciable vapor pressures at liquid-nitrogen temperatures and are not adequately trapped. By reducing the pressure over liquid nitrogen, lower temperatures can be produced, as shown in Table VIII.

TABLE VIII
Temperature Versus Pressure of Common Refrigerants

Pressure, mm	760	76	7.6	0.76
N_2[a]	−196°C	−210°C.	−220°C.	−227°C.
CO_2[b]	−78°C.	−103°C.	−12°C.	−137°C.

[a] *International Critical Tables*, Vol. III, McGraw-Hill, New York, 1928, p. 204.
[b] Ref. a, p. 207.

In cases in which the extreme low temperature of liquid nitrogen is not needed, a trap temperature of −78°C. can be produced with solid carbon dioxide. The vapor pressure of water at dry-ice temperature is about 1 μ, and since molecular distillations are generally performed in the low-micron region, water vapor cannot be effectively removed by a dry-ice trap. To provide better heat transfer between the dry ice and the trap wall, a liquid, such as acetone, alcohol, or *butyl Cellosolve*, is added to the powdered dry ice to form a mush.

As shown in Figure 20, it is common practice to have two cold traps. In performing a distillation, it is advisable to delay cooling the traps until a pressure of around 100 μ is reached. However, if it is known or suspected that the still charge contains solvents or volatile contaminants, the second trap is chilled and a pre-evacuation or degassing period is allowed. At the end of this period the vacuum is broken and the trap warmed and drained before the actual distillation is begun. If the solvents or vapors are excessive, both traps can be filled during the degassing cycle and drained before attempting to attain the desired distilling vacuum. In any case, it is advisable to fill the trap between the vapor pump and mechanical pump first. After a vacuum of around 100 μ is reached, the vapor pumps are turned on and the trap between the still and vapor pump is filled. If this trap is filled when the pressure is high, vapors which are condensed at this high pressure will be *slowly* liberated as the vacuum gets better, prolonging the time needed to attain the ultimate distilling vacuum.

If copious quantities of liquid materials are being collected in the cold thimble, a bottom vacuum-jacketed section is added, as in Figure 3C. The re-evaporation which would occur as liquid drops to the bottom of the trap is lessened if the vacuum flask is added. A short piece of heavy-wall rubber tubing, with pinch clamp, connected to a small bottle permits the periodic draining of collected fluids and their removal to the atmosphere.

The conductance or "speed" of cold traps of the general design shown in Figure 3B has been discussed by Dushman.[1] It should also be observed that at temperatures lower than 25°C. the conductance will be lower than at 25°C. The conductance will be

$$F\sqrt{T/298}$$

in which T is the temperature of the refrigerated trap and F its conductance at 25°C.

For liquid nitrogen at -196°C. (77°K.), the conductance for any gas is $\sqrt{77/298} = 0.52$ times that for the same gas at 25°C.

An obstruction or series of obstructions in the vapor path which will induce multiple collisions of the molecules with a surface maintained sufficiently cold to condense the impinging vapor molecules is called a *baffle*. A right-angle bend or a cold trap could be considered specific baffle designs. In some instances a baffle is used to prevent the condensation pump oil from diffusing upstream into other parts of the apparatus. A baffle designed by Morse, Humphreys, and Watson[33] is shown in Figure 18A. The inner container for refrigerant is surrounded by two helical ramps fastened to the

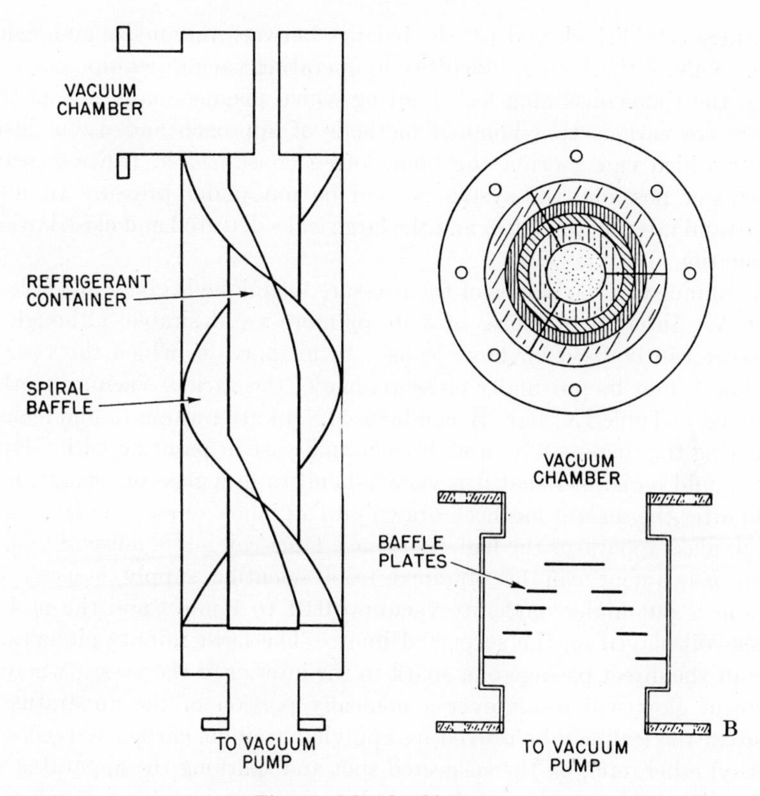

Fig. 18. Metal cold traps.

cold thimble. Another common type of baffle is shown in Figure 18B. The conical stack of washers of decreasing diameters has tubing fastened thereto, through which cold water or a suitable refrigerant can flow. In some instances, when continuous operation is desired, the tubing becomes the expansion zone of a *Freon* compressor system.

Mechanical baffles, as distinct from cold traps, are not commonly used in small laboratory installations. Their importance in pilot-plant and commercial installations is apparent.

VII. LEAK DETECTION

As vacuum stills are made more complex, the chance for leaks increases. Systems which are assembled with gasketed joints, metal welds, rotating seals, and so on are rarely absolutely tight. A certain amount of air in-linkage is usually tolerated, the degree depending on (*1*) the standard of tightness established, and (*2*) the balance between pump size and leakage rate. One of the trying difficulties in operating vacuum equipment is too often the time-consuming leak hunting which plagues many an operator. There are various time-honored methods of approach and useful instruments which can shorten the hours often consumed in fruitless search. Whenever possible, the system should be put under pressure (if it can withstand internal pressure) and the large leaks detected and closed prior to evacuation.

A summary of variations of the pressure technique is given in Table IX, Part A. Internal pressures of 5 lb. or more are desirable, although less pressure can be used for large leaks. In instances in which the vessel or system cannot be put under pressure, one of the various vacuum methods outlined in Table IX, Part B, can be used. In attempting to find leaks by smearing the suspected area with vacuum grease or painting with Glyptal, one should remember that it is very difficult to fuse glass or repair a metal weld after the sealant has been drawn into a pinhole or small crack.

For glass apparatus the high frequency Tesla-coil is still a useful tool. A hand instrument can be obtained from scientific supply houses. The system is put under moderate vacuum (0.01 to 1 mm.) and the probe of Tesla-coil played on the suspected joint. The most minute pinholes will permit the direct passage of a spark to the interior of the vessel, whereas a uniform glow will result over a nonleaky portion of the apparatus. If desired, the leak can be proved by applying acetone, carbon tetrachloride, diethyl ether, etc., on the suspected spot and sparking the apparatus with the coil. A characteristic glow of the vapor used will result when the solvent is drawn into the vacuum chamber. Compounds containing chlorine give a greenish glow and hydrocarbons, diethyl ether, and water vapor a greenish-gray glow, while air gives a red or pink discharge. Precautions should be taken in using a high-frequency discharge, for an intense spark can itself puncture a hole in thin glass. The outgassing of a glass system can be accelerated by intermittently ionizing the gas by means of a high-frequency discharge. Obviously, the spark test cannot be used for metal equipment.

The halogen-ion detector[34] (see Table IXB) is more sensitive than the soap-bubble test. It is based on the observation that heated platinum shows a sharp increase in positive ion emission when in contact with a gas or vapor containing halogens. In using the device the system is put under a positive pressure of a halogen-bearing gas or a mixture of such gas and air. The gas escaping through a leak is drawn by means of a self-contained fan into and through the sensitive element. If it is not practical to put the system under a positive pressure, the sensitive element can be sealed in the vacuum system, probably in the fore-pressure line, and the system probed with

TABLE IX
Leak Detection Methods

Internal fluid	Probe	Response	$\mu \times l \times$ sec.$^{-1}$	Remarks
		A. Pressure		
1. Air–N	Immersion	Bubbles	0.5	Vessel built to withstand internal pressure. Water tank for submergence. Area to be observed under good light for at least 5 min. Occluded air on outer surface troublesome
2. Air–N	Soap film	Bubbles	0.5	As above. Also soap solution which forms tough, persistent bubbles
3. Air–N	Flame	Wavering	500	Draft-free room
4. Air–N	Sound	Hissing	500	Low background noise level
5. Acidic gas: CO_2, SO_2, HCl	Ammonia	Visible fumes	0.5	Vessel must withstand corrosive action of pressure gas
6. Ammonia	Acidic gas	Visible fumes	0.5	As above
7. Liquid	Sight	Wet exterior surface	50	Low-viscosity liquid, water, kerosene, etc. Added dye sometimes aids detection
8. Organic halide	Halide torch	Visible flame color change	0.5	Vessel to withstand internal gas pressure. Draft-free room. Subdued illumination to observe flame color change
9. Helium	As for 1–4	As for 1–4	5	As for 1–4
10. Hydrogen	As for 1–4	As for 1–4	5	As for 1–4; also explosive hazard

(*continued*)

TABLE IX (*continued*)

B. Vacuum

Instrument[a]	Probe	Response	$\mu \times l \times$ sec.$^{-1}$	Useful op. range (μ)	Remarks
1. HF (external electrode	Tesla-coil	Hole shows up as bright-color "pip"	—	50–1000	Can be used on glass only—thin glass may be punctured by discharge
2. HF (internal electrode)	$(CH_3)_2CO$, CH_3OH, CO_2, H_2, CH_4	Visible change in color of discharge	—	100–1000	Residual gas or vapor confusing—results indefinite
3. P	$(CH_3)_2CO$, CH_3OH, CCl_4, H_2, CH_4	Fluctuation in apparent pressure reading when leak is bathed with probe gas	1–100	5–200	Useful on small systems. Response slow on large volumes (>150 l.). A steady pressure reading should be established before probing begins
4. P	Vacuum putty, vacuum grease, castor oil, etc.	Decrease in pressure when leak covered	1–100	5–200	As above. Leak should be permanently sealed after finding. Grease or putty temporary expedient only
5. P (2 gages used; 1 trapped, 1 untrapped)	$(CH_3)_2CO$, CH_3OH, CCl_4	Probe gas condenses on trapped gage giving out-of-balance reading	1–10	5–200	As for 3
6. A	Gaseous hydrocarbons, H_2, CO_2	As for 3	1–10	<0.5	As for 3
7. P	Gaseous hydrocarbons, H_2, CO_2	Compare rate of rise in backing space with probe gas as against air in-leakage rate of rise	5–10	5–200	Pressure buildup in fore-pressure volume with fore-pump valved off. Time consuming, extensive outgassing required. Method discontinuous

8. P	As for 7	As for 7 except for primary vacuum chamber	5–10	5–200	As for 7. Pressure buildup in primary vacuum chamber when valve closed to pump
9. A	As for 7	As for 8	5–10	1–1000	As for 7
10. P	Air	Rate of rise	1–100	5–200	Time-consuming, extensive out-gassing required. Indicates leak present but not its location. Useful for isolating general location of leak in complicated system by segregating and testing one portion at a time
11. A	Air	Rate of rise	1–100	1–1000	As for 10
12. Optical spectrometer	Any gas giving bright visible spectrum compared to air's	Instantaneous visible change	0.1–1	1–1000	Unreliable—"clean-up" of discharge tube slow
13. Ionization gage with palladium diffusion barrier	Hydrogen	Rapid for small volumes; sluggish for large	5–10	1–200	Practical for small volumes <100 liters
14. Halogen-ion detector	Halogen-containing gas or vapor	Rapid	1–100	Vacuum or atmosphere	Can be used with vessel under pressure of halogen gas or vapor. Escaping gas detected. Or vessel under reduced pressure with detecting element in vacuum line
15. Mass spectrometer (helium leak detector)	Helium	Instantaneous	<0.01	1–500	Very fast method. Testing system must be properly designed to obtain quick "clean-up" of helium and quick response. Best known method to date

[a] P = Pirani or thermocouple, A = Alphatron, and HF = high-frequency discharge.

halogen-bearing gas. When a leak is approached, the halogen gas is "sucked" through the leak and quickly detected by the platinum electrode. As an alternate location, the device could be attached to the discharge post of the mechanical fore-pump, with suitable means being provided to trap out entrained oil globules, and the same probing procedure followed. Typical halogen compounds which can be used are chloroform, carbon tetrachloride, and Freon. An amplifier can be substituted for the microammeter and the sensitivity of the instrument increased.

A simple and less sensitive halogen detector is an acetylene burner or gas bunsen burner, equipped with a copper plate supported in the flame. The air intake to the burner is through a rubber hose which is moved about near the suspected leak, as above. Halogen-bearing gas or vapor escaping through the leak of the system under pressure is drawn into the flame, imparting a bright green color from the reaction of the halide with the hot copper plate.

The varying sensitivity with composition of gases of the *Pirani* or thermocouple gage can be put to practical use in leak hunting. The sensitivity is highest for gases of high thermal conductivity, such as hydrogen and helium, and lowest for "heavier" gases. Therefore, if a gas or vapor which is either "lighter" or "heavier" than air is played on a suspected leak while the system is under vacuum, a leaky spot will produce a sharp deflection of the Pirani gage. Either natural or illuminating gas can be used in place of hydrogen or helium as a probe gas. Also, propane, acetone, or carbon tetrachloride vapor sprayed onto the suspected joint has been used. This method is limited to peaks of such size that a vacuum of between 5 and 200 μ can be established, which is the most useful range of the Pirani gage for this purpose. Thermocouple gages can be used for this purpose, although the Pirani is more sensitive.

The most sensitive of all instruments for detection of leaks is the mass spectrometer *helium detector*.[35] A modification of the original mass spectrometer of Aston and Dempster[36] "tuned" to helium ions affords the basis for the detecting instrument. If a singly charged positive ion of molar mass M is accelerated by a negative potential gradient of E volts and projected into a magnetic field of strength of H gauss, it is bent into a circular path of radius r centimeters, according to the relation

$$r^2 = 2070(EM/H^2)$$

This follows from the fundamental relationship

$$e/m = 2E/H^2r^2$$

Therefore, for a fixed value of E and H, ions of different mass will have different radii. Electrons from an ion source, on striking helium and other

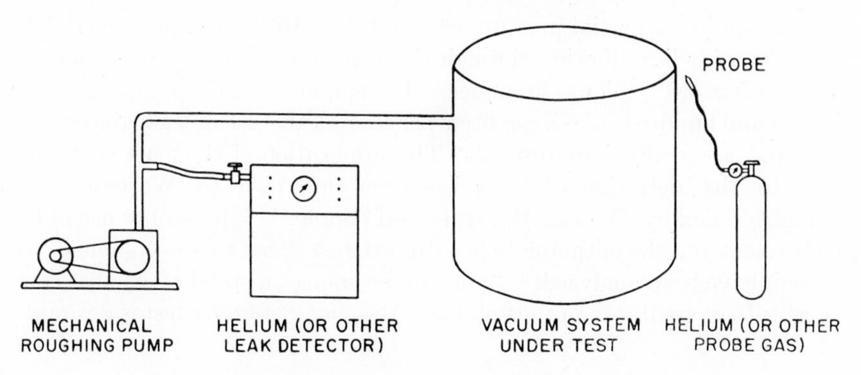

Fig. 19. Typical leak detector-vacuum system arrangement.

gas atoms, knock out electrons thereby forming positive ions. By means of a strong potential gradient, the positive ions are quickly pulled from the ionizing zone, both to accelerate them in a path at right angles to the field, as well as to remove them from the high electron density where recombination with electrons might occur. In passing through the magnetic field, the ions are sorted out according to their mass and charge. A collector plate is placed to receive only the helium ions, which when present cause a positive current to flow through an amplifier circuit, and thence to a meter.

Figure 19 shows an arrangement of a vacuum system and a leak detector. The leak detector has self-contained vacuum pumps which maintain a pressure lower than that needed for the suspect system during test. The system under test is first exhausted with its own fore-pump and, when the pressure is sufficiently low, the throttle valve admitting gas from the system to the leak detector is opened. The degree of opening will depend on the vacuum in the system under test. A fine jet of helium is played on the suspected joints. A "squealer" device can be hooked into the circuit to permit one person to hunt leaks at locations where the meter is not readily watched.

Helium was chosen for the probe gas for the following reasons:

(*1*) Helium is a rare gas in the atmosphere (1 part in 200,000); therefore a low background level is established.

(*2*) The helium ion has a distinct and individual location on the ion spectrum and thereby eliminates the possibility that an ion of any other gas might be mistaken for helium.

(*3*) Its rate of diffusion through the leaks and through the vacuum systems is rapid, being exceeded only by hydrogen.

(*4*) It is plentiful and readily available in this country.

The instrument will detect one part helium in 200,000 parts of air and, on occasion, this can be increased several times. Under such dilutions the helium has a partial pressure of about 5×10^{-11} mm. mercury. The quantity of helium flowing through the spectrometer tube corresponds to about 1.5×10^{-6} micron liters/sec. In comparison with pumping speeds in tens and hundreds of micron liters per second, the size of leaks that can be detected are really infinitesimal. The application of the mass spectrometer to the detection of leaks has been described by Worcester and Doughty[37] and by Thomas, Williams, and Hipple.[38] The proper use of the instrument and the optimum balance of exhaust speed versus volume of the system have been analyzed.[39] For rapid response, a speed of exhaust comparable to or greater than the volume of the chamber under test is desirable.

VIII. VACUUM FITTINGS

Even though it is desirable to eliminate as many temporary joints as possible, rubber-tubing connections and rubber-gasket flanged joints have their place in assembling vacuum-distillation equipment. In *joining glass tubes*, rubber tubing can be successfully used (see Fig. 20A). *Small-diameter* (<1 cm. O.D.), good quality, heavy-wall, rubber tubing is recommended. A standard red rubber or elastic synthetic tubing with $^3/_{16}$-in. I.D. and a $^1/_2$-in. O.D. is adaptable to 8-mm. O.D. glass or metal tubing.

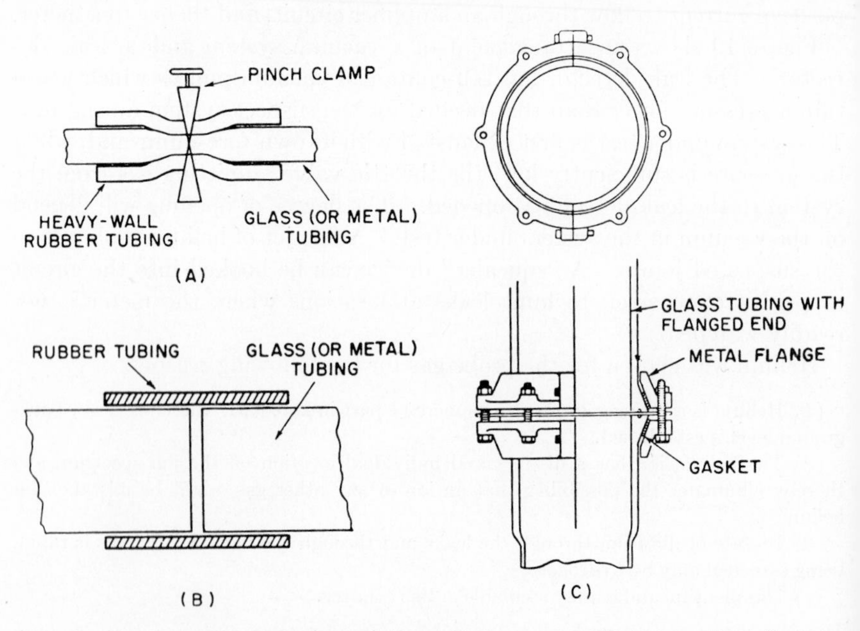

Fig. 20. Glass-to-glass connections: (*A*) small diameters; (*B*) intermediate diameter; (*C*) large diameter.

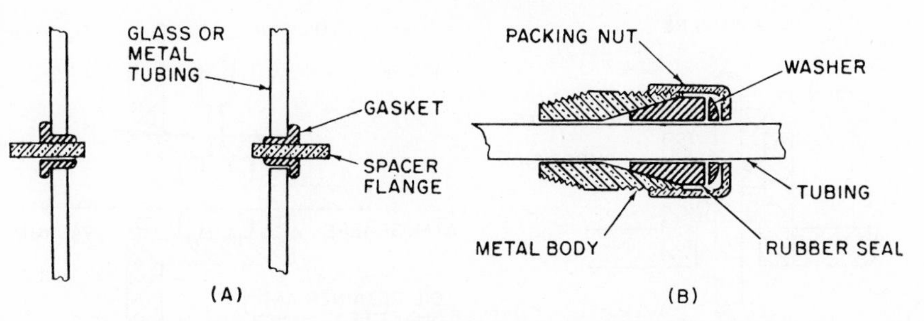

Fig. 21. Glass-to-metal joints: (*A*) small tubing; (*B*) large tubing.

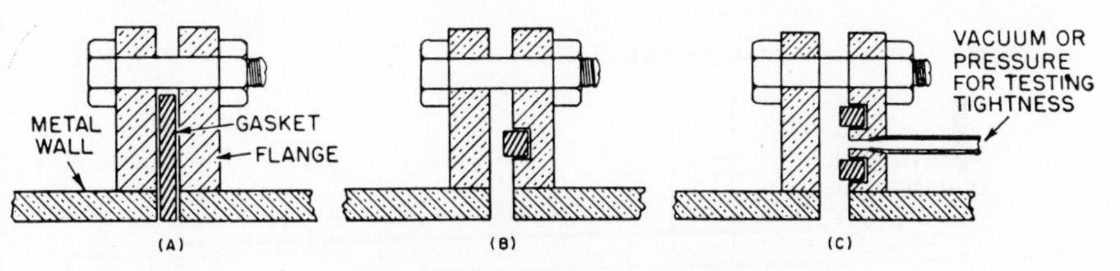

Fig. 22. Metal flange-gasket assemblies.

The wall thickness should be such that the tubing will not collapse when vacuum is applied. By leaving a gap of a half inch or so between the two ends of the tubes being joined, a pinch clamp can be used to seal off sample bottles, gages, condensate from a cold trap, etc.

For joining tubes of *intermediate diameter* (Fig. 20B), between 1 and 5 cm., rubber tubing of 2–3 mm. wall thickness can be used. There should be no gap between the ends of the tubes, or the tubing may "suck in." In both this case and that of the smaller diameter tubes, the inner diameter of the rubber tubing should be in the range of 5–15% smaller than the outer diameter of the tube over which it slips. The elasticity of the tubing will determine the amount of stretch that can be accomplished; the tighter the better. In general, soft rubber (durometer <45) is to be preferred to the harder grades (durometer >45). The inside of the rubber sleeves and the outside of the joining tubes should be smeared with castor oil, vacuum grease, or another low-vapor-pressure lubricant. This serves the double purpose of lubricating the parts, thereby making the tube insertion easier, and sealing the minute air gap between the rubber sleeve and the tube. In general, all rubber joints should be made with a sealing lubricant or "vacuum grease."

For *large diameters* (I.D. >5 cm.), standard flanged joints as shown in Figure 20C are recommended. These can be obtained commercially in various sizes. Rubber or synthetic gasket material of durometer hardness

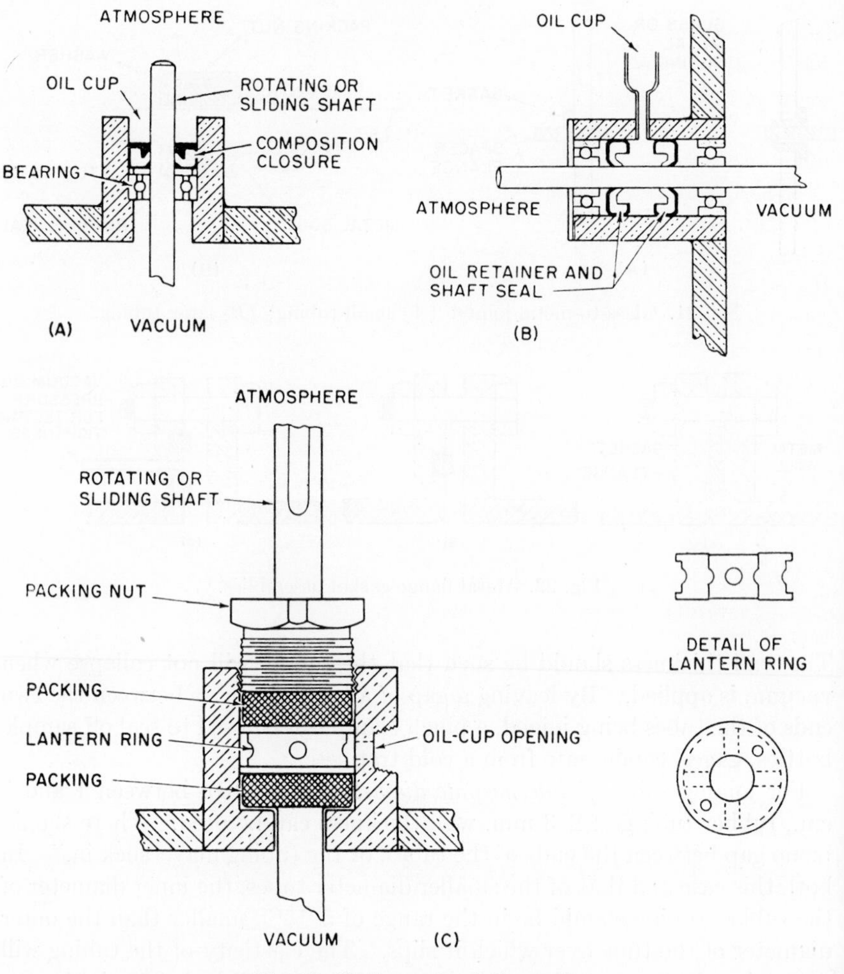

Fig. 23. Sliding and rotating seals.

between 50 and 70 is generally used. Also, the scheme shown in Figure 21B is applicable.

In making *glass-to-metal joints*, a gasket or rubber-tubing connection of some sort is commonly used. The refinement of a graded glass-to-metal seal is rarely used in assembling high-vacuum distillation apparatus. Glass tubes can be joined to metal tubes by the scheme shown in Figure 20A or 20B. An assembly shown in Figure 21B can be used for inserting glass tubes, such as a Pirani gage, into a metal chamber. Modifications of this general scheme have been described elsewhere.[40] A rubber section is squeezed by a compression nut against the tube and the side wall, thus sealing both surfaces. For large diameters, a gasket joint such as shown in Figure 21A can be used. The metal flange can be the base of a vacuum chamber or a separating washer between a glass-to-glass, metal-to-glass, or metal-to-metal section. A special molded gasket is ordinarily used for this purpose.

Flanged metal joints can be made in many different ways. Some of the common patterns are shown in Figure 22. With reasonable care in assembly and alignment the simpler designs are frequently satisfactory. Plain *flat-surface flanges* can be used successfully if the surfaces can be drawn up with uniform tightness against a lubricated gasket. A flange with a *single recessed groove* into which is inserted a square or rectangular gasket is a refinement over the flat surface. A *double recessed groove* is a further refinement. The inner gasket provides the vacuum seal, while the outer one forms a confined space which can be evacuated with an auxiliary vacuum pump, air pressure or probe gas pressure applied therein, and the response of the vacuum gage on the system noted. This is particularly helpful in leak hunting in complicated systems with many flanged joints.

Typical examples of *sliding and rotating shaft seals* are shown in Figure 23. In all cases it is advantageous to have an oil reservoir on the atmospheric side of the seal. For a vertical mounted shaft, as shown in Figure 23A, sufficient height is allowed on the bearing and seal housing to afford space for an oil pool above the oil-retainer seal. For horizontally mounted shafts (Figs. 23B and 23C) a double seal or packing is commonly used with an oil-filled space between the two.

The circular gaskets of round cross section known as "O" rings can be adapted to the examples given and to many other designs. The manufacturer gives information on the proper selection of sizes for any particular application.

As a final precaution, *dry joints frequently leak.* If it is undesirable to lubricate the mating surfaces, as a second choice the edge to the atmosphere should be oiled or smeared with a suitable vacuum grease.

Fore-pressure lines are generally of such size that standard pipe can be used. In making up *threaded joints* on standard pipe, it is advisable to smear the threads with a sealing compound, preferably of a nonhardening type. After the joint is tightly drawn together the contact between the two pieces can be coated with Glyptal if the joint is found to be leaky on test. A well made threaded joint can be tight and is considerably simpler than welded pipeline construction.

In selecting *valves* for metal systems, the choice will depend to some extent on the pressure region in which they are to be used. If a valve is to be inserted in the high-vacuum line (0.1–10 μ), a valve with low impedance should be selected, that is, one in which very little reduction in cross-sectional area takes place when the valve is open. Some impedance in the fore-pressure line can be tolerated. Valves whose packing glands have been replaced by a sylphon bellows arrangement have decreased the possibility of leaks from that source. When *glass stopcocks* are used, one should select those with large bores and preferably with oil-sealing cup arrangement attached.

IX. INTEGRATED SYSTEMS

Having discussed the basic components which go into a distillation system, we can now consider the construction of a typical laboratory assembly. Let us refer to Figure 24 and take the example of a batch pot still with an outer tube 12 cm., an inner tube 6 cm. in diameter, and a distance of 12 cm. between the base of the inner tube and the side-arm vacuum connection. It would be nice to know the total gas load so that a speed of exhaustion could be mathematically determined. Since there are many factors involved, such as liberation of dissolved gases, thermal decomposition, and air in-leakage, a quantitative value of the gas load is rarely known for all the samples which will be examined. A few trial runs

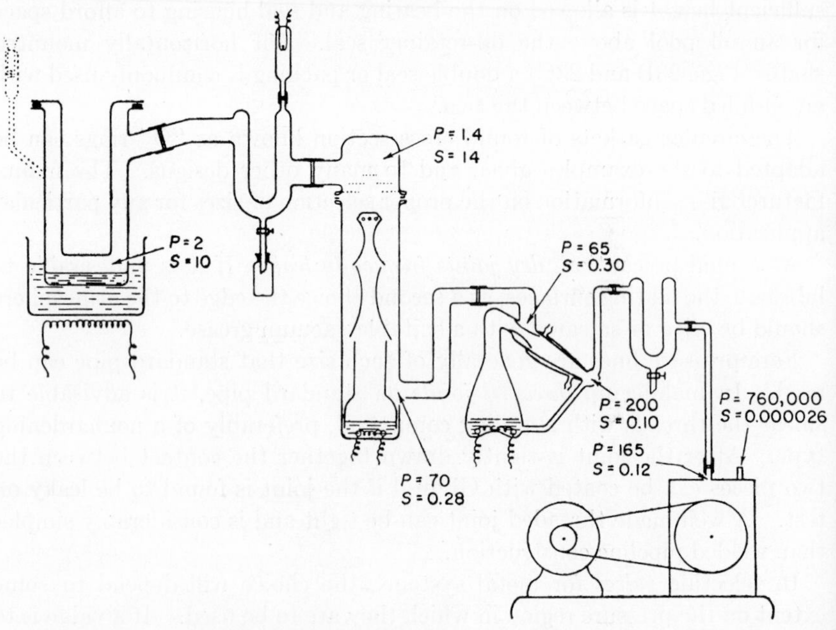

Fig. 24. Typical pressure–gas flow relationship in a distillation system. *P*, pressure in microns of mercury. *S*, gas flow in liters per second.

in a given piece of equipment will soon establish whether sufficient pumping capacity is available at the distilling zone. Pressure measurements at the still will give a direct indication of the effective pumping speed.

Lacking data or experience, a first approximation can be made by providing a still of evaporating surface of A square centimeters, with a speed of exhaust of approximately $1/4\ A$ micron liters/sec. In the example chosen, the still has an evaporating area of about 80 cm.^{2} and, by the rule of thumb above, an exhaust speed of 20 micron liters/sec should be available at the still. Furthermore, if we assume the distillation will be done at 2 μ, a speed of 10 liters/sec. would be equivalent to 20 micron liters/sec.

As experience is gained, sizes of pumps and connecting tubing can be estimated for any given size still without a complete mathematical analysis of every detail of gas flow through the system. However, as an exercise in demonstrating a method of approach and the effect of tubing and obstructions in high-vacuum systems, an analysis of the distillation train in Figure 24 is presented. As a simplification, it is assumed that the gas is air at 25°C. and the numerical formulas as given in an earlier section apply. First of all, dissolved air liberated from the still contents will find resistance in entering the space between the condensing tube and the outside wall. Since the upstream area, A', is not large compared to the downstream area, A, the aperture conductance [eq. (18)] is

$$F_1 = F_0 \frac{A'}{A' - A}$$

$$F_0 = 11.7A = 11.7\pi(5^2 - 3^2) = 590$$

$$\frac{A'}{A' - A} = \frac{25}{25\pi - \pi(25 - 9)} = \frac{25}{9} = 2.8$$

Hence

$$F_1 = 590 \times 2.8 = 1650 \text{ liters/sec.}$$

The gas will next find resistance in passing between the walls of the still and the condenser. The conductance along this concentric path is

$$F_2 = 11.7A(r_2/l)x = 590 \times {}^5/_{12} \times 1.07 = 262 \text{ liters/sec.}$$

Molecules will find little difficulty in entering the side arm from the still; the area of approach is comparable to the area of the opening. Therefore, the so-called long-tube formula will apply (even though $l < 50d$) since no end correction need be included.

$$F_3 = 12.2(d^3/l) = 12.2(125/12) = 127 \text{ liters/sec.}$$

Proceeding next to the trap, we can use eq. (24) for the design shown in Figure 3B. Hence,

$$F'_4 = 130 \text{ liters/sec.}$$

This is the conductance at 25°C. If the trap is to be filled with dry ice, and assuming the gas flowing through is at the temperature of the cold thimble, −78°C., the conductance will be $\sqrt{195/298} \times 130$, or

$$F_4 = 105 \text{ liters/sec.}$$

In flowing from the trap to the side tube, no end resistance need be considered since the area of approach is comparable to the tube entrance area. The connecting tubing between the trap and the pump dome has

$$F_5 = 12.2(d^3/l) = 12.2(125/10) = 153 \text{ liters/sec.}$$

The dome shown will have a negligible resistance. However, were a baffle included an additional reduction in speed of 50 to 80% could be expected. For this example, we shall assume that the pump either with or without a baffle is a unit with a speed of S_B liters per second. Having established the conductance of the various components between the evaporating surface and the oil booster pump, we can now arrive at a size required to fulfill the prescribed condition of 10 liters/sec. at the distilling zone. Solving for F in the equation $1/F = 1/F_1 \ldots 1/F_5$:

F_n	$1/F_n$
1 = 1650	0.0006
2 = 262	0.0038
3 = 127	0.0078
4 = 105	0.0095
5 = 153	0.0065
Total	0.0282

gives

$$F = 35.5 \text{ liters/sec.}$$

Since the speed of exhaust, S_s, has been estimated to be 10 liters/sec. the required speed of the oil-booster pump, S_B, can be obtained from the relationship:

$$\frac{1}{S_s} = \frac{1}{S_B} + \frac{1}{F} \quad \text{or} \quad \frac{1}{S_B} = \frac{1}{S_s} - \frac{1}{F} = 0.1 - 0.0282 = 0.0718$$

or

$$S_B = 13.9 \text{ liters/sec.}$$

Therefore, a booster pump (or pump plus baffle) with a speed of 13.9 liters/sec. will exhaust 10 liters/sec. from the distilling zone through this interconnecting system. A reduction in effective speed of 39% through interconnecting tubes and baffles is not unusual in high-vacuum practice.

From the specifications and performance curves of the pump selected, the fore-pressure into which the gas will be compressed can be determined. For this example we shall take 70 μ. Up to the first oil-vapor pump intake, the flow is essentially molecular, but after passing through the pump and being compressed to a fore-pressure value of 70 μ into a tube 1.4 cm. in diameter, the flow is in the intermediate zone, $Pd = 98 > 2$. In compressing the gas, the volume flow rate decreases to 1.4/70 of its value on entering the pump, or to 0.28 liter/sec. In contrast to this the micron liter flow rate of 20 micron liters/sec. is constant throughout the system (less any air in-leakage along the path or decomposition vapors from the oil-vapor pumps).

Assuming the first oil-vapor booster pump is connected to a second oil-vapor booster pump by a 20-cm. length of 1.4-cm. I.D. tubing, from eq. (10) and Figure 1 we can calculate that the conductance would be about 3.7 liters/sec. The second vapor pump, size S_E, can be determined from

$$\frac{1}{S} = \frac{1}{S_E} + \frac{1}{F} \quad \text{or} \quad \frac{1}{S_E} = \frac{1}{S} - \frac{1}{F} = \frac{1}{0.28} - \frac{1}{3.7} = 3.57 - 0.27 = 3.30$$

or

$$S_E = 0.30 \text{ liter/sec.}$$

the required speed of the oil-vapor ejector pump.

From the specifications of the pump selected, the fore-pressure against which it will operate can be determined. For this example, assume that in going through the pump the gas is compressed to about 200 μ, thereby reducing the volumetric flow rate to about 0.10 liter/sec. Assuming we use a 30-cm. length of 8-mm. tubing to join the second vapor pump to the mechanical pump, the Pd factor then becomes 160 and $F = 0.65$ liter/sec. The pump size is determined as before from

$$\frac{1}{S_M} = \frac{1}{S} - \frac{1}{F} = \frac{1}{0.10} - \frac{1}{0.65}$$

or

$$S_M = 0.12 \text{ liter/sec.}$$

the required mechanical pump speed to remove the gases to the atmosphere. As an indication of the size of rotary pump, a Cenco Hyvac has a speed of 0.10 liter/sec. and a Cenco Megavac a speed of 0.30 liter/sec. in the 200 μ pressure region.

If the oil-vapor pump could compress gas to twice the fore-pressure, a fore-pump of only half the size would be necessary. There have been efforts made along this line during the past several years, resulting in the design of oil-vapor ejector booster pumps which will operate into fore-pressure in the 1–10 mm. mercury range. Also, oil-vapor pumps have been developed which combine the action of the first and second oil-vapor pumps, one such pump replacing two. A pump of this general design is shown in Figure 9.

As a generalized summary, an approach to the design of a laboratory high-vacuum distillation system can be made along these lines:

(*1*) Calculate or estimate the evaporating area in A square centimeters and thereby establish an exhaust speed of $^1/_4$ A micron liters/sec. Determine the operating vacuum μ, and establish the liters per second by dividing $^1/_4$ A micron liters/sec. by μ, the pressure in microns.

(*2*) Lay out the interconnecting piping, trap, etc., between the still and the oil-vapor pump. Calculate the resulting conductance and the pump size required. If less than 50% of the rated pump speed is utilized, open up the vacuum lines to cut down the resistance.

(*3*) Select an oil-vapor pump with optimum pumping characteristics at the desired operating vacuum, and preferably one with a high fore-pressure breakdown.

(*4*) Continue as in (*2*) for the next stage of interconnecting piping, and so on to the mechanical fore-pump.

As a practical matter, for both vapor and mechanical pumps the next largest sized pump available is used in each case, the extra capacity being useful for shortening pump-down time and for handling traces of unpredictable air inleakage. In fact, after having arrived at the speed required at the still from (*1*), a vapor pump having at least 50% more speed can be chosen and the connecting tubing between the still and pump so chosen to maintain the desired conductance.

A schematic diagram, as in Figure 20, on which one can mark the various pertinent data, the flow rates, and the pressures at different points—the latter depending in large part on the pumps selected—will be of assistance in making an overall evaluation of any comtemplated system.

References

1. Dushman, *Scientific Foundations of Vacuum Technique*, 2nd ed., Wiley, New York, 1962, Kennard, *Kinetic Theory of Gases*, McGraw-Hill, New York, 1938, Chaps. 3 and 8; Loeb, *Kinetic Theory of Gases*, 2nd ed., McGraw-Hill, New York, 1934, Chap. 7; Taylor, *A Treatise on Physical Chemistry*, 3rd ed., Van Nostrand, New York, 1942, p. 174.
2. Poiseuille, *Société Philomathique de Paris Bulletin*, 28, 77 (1938); *Compt. Rend.*, **11**, 961, 1041 (1840); **12**, 112 (1841); **15**, 1161 (1892); Loeb, Ref. 1, p. 230.
3. Knudsen, *Ann. Physik.*, **28**, 75, 999 (1909), and subsequent papers, Loeb, Ref. 1, p. 290; Taylor, Ref. p. 168.
4. Knudsen, *Ann. Physik.*, **28**, 75 (1909), and subsequent papers.
5. von Smoluchowski, *Bull. Acad. Krakau*, **1903**, 143; Hagenbach, *Poggendorf's Ann.*, **109**, 835 (1860); Brillouin, *Lecons sur la Viscosité*, Paris, 1907.
6. Gaede, *Ann. Physik*, **41**, 289, 337 (1913).
7. Clausing, *Ann. Physik*, **12**, 961 (1932).
8. Maxwell, *Phil. Mag.*, **19**, 22 (1860); Boltzmann, *Sitzber. Akad. Wiss. Wien.*, **74**, 503 (1876).
9. Kennard, *Kinetic Theory of Gases*. McGraw-Hill, New York, 1938, pp. 306–308.
10. Dushman, *Scientific Foundations of Vacuum Technique*, Wiley, New York, 1949, pp. 105–110.
11. Klose, *Physik. Z.*, **31**, 503 (1930); *Ann. Physik*, **11**, 73 (1931).
12. Sheriff, *J. Sci. Instr.*, **26**, 42 (1949).
13. Poiseuille, *Société Philomathique de Paris Bulletin*, **28**, 77 (1838); *Compt. Rend.*, **11**, 961, 1041 (1840); **12**, 112 (1841); **15**, 1161 (1892); Loeb, *Kinetic Theory of Gases*, 2nd ed., McGraw-Hill, New York, 1934, p. 230.
14. Taylor, *A Treatise on Physical Chemistry*, 3rd ed., Van Nostrand, New York, 1942, p. 177.
15. Ruckes, *Ann. Physik*, **25**, 983 (1908); McAdams, *Heat Transmission*, 2nd ed., McGraw-Hill, New York, 1942, Chap. 5.
16. Sullivan, *Rev. Sci. Instr.*, **19**, 1 (1948).
17. Gaede, British Patent, 475,840.
18. Power and Kenna, *Vacuum*, **5**, 35 (1957).
19. Work and Haedrich, *Ind. Eng. Chem.*, **31**, 464 (1939).
20. *Standards of Heat Exchange Institute*, Steam Jet Ejector and Vacuum Cooling Section, Part 1, Steam Jet Ejectors, Heat Exchange Institute, New York, 1938, p. 4.
21. Barr and Anhorn, *Scientific and Industrial Glass Blowing and Laboratory Techniques*, Instruments Publishing Co., Pittsburgh, Pennsylvania, 1949, pp. 161–178.
22. Langmuir, *Gen. Elec. Rev.*, **19**, 1060 (1916); *J. Franklin Inst.*, **182**, 719 (1916).
23. Gaede, *Ann. Physik*, **46**, 357 (1915); *Z. tech. Physik*, **4**, 337 (1923).
24. Dayton, *Ind. Eng. Chem.*, **40**, 795 (1948); Dushman, *Scientific Foundations of Vacuum Technique*, Wiley, New York, 1949, pp. 105–110.
25. Latham, Power, and Dennis, *Vacuum*, **2**, 33 (1952).
26. Hickman, *Nature*, **187**, 405 (1960).
27. Hickman, "High Vacuum with the Polyphenyl Ethers—A Self-contained Technology," in *Proc. 2nd. Intern. Congr. on Vacuum Techniques*, Washington, 1961, Pergamon Press, in press.
28. Wallace and Tiernan Products, Inc., Belleville, New York.
29. Hickman, *Chem. Rev.*, **34**, 82 (1944).
30. Flosdorf, *Ind. Eng. Chem. Anal. Ed.*, **17**, 198 (1945).
31. Yarwood, *High Vacuum Technique*. 2nd rev. ed., Wiley, New York, 1945, p. 39.

32. Dushman, *Scientific Foundations of Vacuum Technique.* Wiley, New York, 1949, p. 317.
33. Becker, Green, and Pearson, *Trans. Am. Inst. Elec. Engrs.*, **65**, 711 (1946).
34. Downing and Mellen, *Rev. Sci. Instr.*, **17**, 218 (1946); *Electronics*, **19**, 142 (1946).
35. Dodge and Dunbar, *J. Am. Chem. Soc.*, **49**, 591 (1927).
36. More, Humphreys, and Watson, *Rev. Sci. Instr.*, **8**, 263 (1937).
37. Dushman, *Scientific Foundations of Vacuum Technique*, 2nd ed., Wiley, New York, 1962.
38. Ochert and Steckelmacher, *Vacuum*, **2**, 125 (1952).
39. Pirani and Yarwood, *Principles of Vacuum Engineering*, Chapman & Hall, London, 1961.
40. White and Hickey, *Electronics*, **21**, 100 (1948).
41. Nier, Stevens, Hustralid, and Abbott, *J. Applied Phys.*, **18**, 30 (1947); Jacobs and Zuhr, *ibid.*, **18**, 34 (1947).
42. Aston, *Phil. Mag.*, **38**, 707 (1919); Dempster, *Phys. Rev.*, **11**, 316 (1918).
43. Worcester and Doughty, *Trans. Am. Inst. Elec. Engrs.*, **65**, 946 (1946).
44. Thomas, Williams, and Hipple, *Rev. Sci. Instr.*, **17**, 368 (1946); *Westinghouse Engr.*, **6**, 108 (1946).
45. Jacobs and Zhur, *J. Applied Phys.*, **18**, 34 (1947).
46. Lauritsen and Lauritsen, *Rev. Sci. Instr.*, **19**, 919 (1948).

General References

Dushman, *High Vacuum*, General Electric Co., Schenectady, 1922.

Newman, *The Production and Measurement of Low Pressures*, Van Nostrand, New York, 1925.

Dunoyer, *Vacuum Practice*, Van Nostrand, New York, 1926.

Goetz, *Physik und Technik des Hochvakuums*, Friedrich Vieweg and Sohn Akt.-Ges., Braunschweig.

Kaye, *High Vacua*, Longmans, Green, London, 1927.

Wien and Harms, *Handbuch der Experimental Physik*, Vol. 4, Akademische Verlagsges, Leipzig, 1930, pp. 413–461.

Harnwell and Livingood, *Experimental Atomic Physics*, McGraw-Hill, New York, 1933, Appendix B.

Espe and Knoll, *Werkstoffkunde der Hochvakuumtechnik*, Springer, Berlin, 1936.

Holland-Merten, *Die Vakuumtechnik*, (industrial) G. A. Koenig, Erfurt.

Mönch, *Vakuum technik im Laboratorium*, Edwards Brothers Inc., Lithoprint 1944, 1937.

Hoag, *Electron and Nuclear Physics*, Van Nostrand, New York, 1938, pp. 354–386.

Strong, *Procedures in Experimental Physics*, Prentice-Hall, Englewood Cliffs, New Jersey, 1943, pp. 93–187.

Farkas and Melville, *Experimental Methods in Gas Reactions*, MacMillan, New York, 1939, pp. 42–102.

Reilly and Rae, *Physico-Chemical Methods*, Vol. I, Van Nostrand New York, Chapter VII, and pp. 573–582.

Yarwood, *High Vacuum Technique*, 2nd ed., Chapman and Hall, London, 1945.

Jnanananda, *High Vacua*, Van Nostrand, New York, 1947.

Martin and Hill, *A Manual of Vacuum Practice*, Melbourne University Press, Melbourne, 1947.

Reilly and Rae, *Physico-Chemical Methods*, Vol. III, Van Nostrand, New York, 1948, pp. 457–491.

Sanderson, *Vacuum Manipulation of Volatile Compounds*, Wiley, New York, 1948.
Spangenberg, *Vacuum Tubes*, McGraw-Hill, New York, 1948, pp. 747–810.
Bachman, *Techniques in Experimental Electronics*, Wiley, New York, pp. 1–67, 89–140.
Guthrie and Wakerling, eds., *Vacuum Equipment and Techniques*, McGraw-Hill, New York, 1959.
Dushman. *Scientific Foundations of Vacuum Technique*, 1st ed., Wiley, New York, 1949.
Calvin, Heidelberger, Reid, Tolbert, and Yankwich, *Isotopic Carbon*, Wiley, New York, 1949.
Barr and Anhorn, *Scientific and Industrial Glassblowing and Laboratory Techniques*, Instruments Publishing Co., Pittsburgh, 1949.
Jaeckel, *Kleinste Drucke, Ihre Messung und Erzeugung*, Springer-Verlag, Berlin, 1950.
Holland-Merten, *Handbuch der Vakuumtechnik*, Wilhelm Knapp, Halle.
Mönch, *Hochvakuumtechnik*, R. A. Lang Verlag, Berlin-Charlottenburg.
Normand et al., *Vacuum Problems and Techniques*, TID-5210, Office of Technical Services, Dept. of Commerce, Washington 25, D. C.
Weissberger, ed., Technique of Organic Chemistry Series, *Distillation*, Vol. IV, Interscience, New York, 1951, pp. 463–602.
Kohl, *Materials Technology for Electron Tubes*, Reinhold, New York, pp. 433–452.
Berl, ed., *Physical Methods in Chemical Analysis*, Vol. II, Academic Press, New York, pp. 333–386.
Davy, *Industrial High Vacuum*, Pitman and Sons, London.
Reimann, *Vacuum Technique*, Chapman and Hall, London, 1952.
Graves and Froman, *Miscellaneous Physical and Chemical Techniques of the Los Alamos Project*, McGraw-Hill, New York.
Marton, ed., *Advances in Electronics*, Vol. V, Academic Press, New York, 1953, pp. 213–246.
Yarwood, *High Vacuum Technique*, 3rd ed., Wiley, New York, 1955.
Kirk and Othmer, eds., *Encyclopedia of Chemical Technology*, 1st ed., Vol. 14, Interscience, New York, pp. 503–536.
Holland, *Vacuum Deposition of Thin Films*, Wiley, New York, 1956.
Leck, *Pressure Measurement in Vacuum Systems*, Reinhold, New York, 1957.
Auwärter, *Ergebnisse der Hochvakuumtechnik und der Physik dünner Schichten*, Wissenschaftliche Verlagsgesellschaft M.B.H., Stuttgart.
Bunsha, *Vacuum Metallurgy*, Reinhold, New York, 1958.
Diels and Jaeckel, *Leybold Vakuum-Taschenbuch für Laboratorium und Betrieb*, Springer-Verlag, Berlin/Gottingen/Heidelberg.
Morand and Roy-Pochon, *Traité Pratique de Technique du Vide*, Association Nationale de la Recherche Technique, Paris.
Flügge, ed., *Handbuck der Physik* Band XII Thermodynamik der Gase, Springer-Verlag, Berlin/Gottinger/Heidelberg; pp. 515–608, Allgemeine Vakuumphysik (in German); pp. 609–663, Production and Measurement of Ultra-high Vacuum (in English).
Monch, *Neues und Bewährtes aus der Hochvakuumtechnik*, VEB Wilhelm Knapp Verlag, Halle (Saale), 1959.
Barrett, ed., *Progress in Vacuum Science and Technology*, Pergamon Press, New York.
Cable, *Vacuum Processing in Metalworking*, Reinhold, New York, 1960.
Bunshah, ed., *Transactions of the 1959 Vacuum Metallurgy Conference*, New York University Press, New York.
Thomas, ed., *Advances in Vacuum Science and Technology*, 2 vols. Pergamon Press, New York.

Delafosse, Mongodin, and Boutry, *Les Calculs de la Technique du Vide,* Société Francaise des Ingénieurs et Techniciens du Vide, Paris, 1961.

Dushman, in *Scientific Foundations of Vacuum Technique,* 2nd ed., Lafferty, ed., Wiley, New York, 1962.

Burrows, *Molecular Distillation*, Oxford Univ. Press, London, 1960.

Roth and Roth, *Brit. Chem. Engng.*, **5**, 392 (1960).

Cenco Vacu-Rule, No. 94008. Central Scientific Co., Chicago.

Vacuum Calculator. F. J. Stokes Corporation, Philadelphia.

Van Atta, *The Design of High Vacuum Systems,* General Engineering Co. (Radcliffe) Ltd.

Watt, *Molecular Stills,* Reinhold, New York, 1963, Appendix A-1.

Pirani and Yarwood, *Principles of Vacuum Engineering,* Chapman & Hall, London, 1961.

Transactions of the National Vacuum Symposium, Pergamon Press, New York, 1954–1961; Macmillan Co., New York, 1962–1963.

CHAPTER VIII

SUBLIMATION

R. Stuart Tipson, *Washington, D. C.*

I. INTRODUCTION

When crystals vaporize without melting and the vapor, upon cooling, condenses directly to crystals, the process is called *sublimation*. The initial solid is the *sublimand*, and the product is the *sublimate*. The procedure of vaporizing a *melt* and directly condensing the vapor to crystals will be called *quasisublimation*. Theoretically, any compound which distils without decomposition may also be sublimed at appropriate temperature and pressure; however, sublimation may be immeasurably slow, even under optimal conditions, if the vapor pressure of the crystals is very low.

An important difference between distillation and sublimation lies in the fact that, in sublimation, vapor molecules reach the solid–gas interface principally by a peeling-off of surface layers; whereas, in distillation, this is supplemented to a much greater extent by diffusion and convection in the liquid distilland. Moreover, sublimation as a fractionation procedure suffers from the supposed impossibility of producing reflux. In distillation, the liquid condensate can flow by gravity, and it is therefore possible to bring about countercurrent, contact distillation or a series of multiple redistillations. It appears that no satisfactory countercurrent, contacting, vertical sublimator has been devised, presumably owing to the mechanical difficulties involved. Fractional recrystallization by repeated single sublimations may be compared with repeated fractional recrystallization from a solvent (see Volume III, Chapter VI, this series).

Direct crystallization from the gas phase may be much more efficient than distillation; *e.g.*, volatile impurities which would be dissolved in a *liquid* condensate, but which are not dissolved or appreciably adsorbed by the *crystalline* sublimate, can be removed. Thus, separation of volatile crystallizable compounds from relatively nonvolatile substances, and from volatile substances which do not condense under the conditions of the sublimation, is often readily accomplished. Separation of compounds which are of comparable vapor pressure is usually not readily achieved because of the necessity for repeated single sublimations, and even this treatment may not suffice. When applicable, sublimation may give a high yield of very pure, crystalline product, and the process is often rapid.

II. GENERAL CONSIDERATIONS

The vapor pressure, p, of a pure heat-stable compound increases with the temperature in accordance with the Clausius-Clapeyron equation[1]

$$dp/dT = L/TV$$

where L is the latent heat of sublimation, V the difference in volume between vapor and solid, and T the absolute temperature.

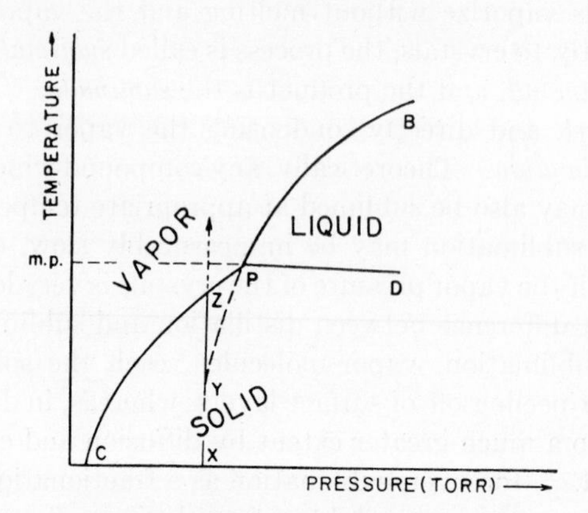

Fig. 1. Effect of pressure on subliming point (CP), melting point (PD), and boiling point (PB).

In the phase diagram (Fig. 1), the curve CP depicting the relation between temperature and vapor pressure,[2] at equilibrium between the solid and its vapor, is known as the *sublimation curve;* its upper limit is the triple point, P, at which solid, liquid, and vapor coexist in equilibrium. At P, the latent heat of sublimation[3] of the solid is equal to the latent heat of fusion plus the latent heat of evaporation of the liquid.

On heating at atmospheric pressure, a solid will eventually melt and then boil if the vapor pressure is less than 1 atm. at the melting point; it will sublime if the vapor pressure reaches 1 atm. at a temperature below the melting point. Thus, if X (Fig. 1) is 760 mm., the crystals sublime at Z. For example, the triple point of cyanogen iodide[4] is at 146°C. and 993 mm.; hence, it may be readily sublimed at 760 mm. Below the triple-point pressure, a substance is not stable in the liquid state. Curve PY represents the behavior of the supercooled liquid.

Depending on the information available, the vapor pressure at any particular temperature, T, may be estimated by means of the Clausius-Clapeyron equation or the following empirical formulas. In a univariant system, the vapor pressure, p, is approximately[5] given by

$$\log p = 7.53 - (2.95T_s + 4.59T_k)T$$

where T_k is the boiling point and T_s the melting point, or[6]

$$(1/\beta) \log \pi = n \log \theta + C\theta(\theta - 1)(1 + a^3 - 2\,\theta)(2\,\theta + a - 1)^{-3}$$

where π is ratio of vapor pressure at the temperature T to the vapor pressure at the triple point; n and C are constants; β is ratio of heat of sublimation to heat of liquid vaporization at the triple point, θ is ratio of temperature T to the triple-point temperature; and a is $[(2\,T_c/T_t) - 1]^{1/3}$, where T_c and T_t are the critical and triple-point temperatures, respectively.

The temperature at which the vapor pressure equals 760 mm. is often referred to as the *subliming point.* It is as characteristic of a substance as the melting point and may be changed by the presence of another gas. Unlike the melting point, but like the boiling point, it may vary enormously with the pressure in the system. The temperature at which *deposition of sublimate becomes noticeable* is often recorded in the literature. This may not be the true subliming point, since under the conditions employed, the vapor pressure of the solid may never reach 760 mm. The value observed may also depend on the apparatus used. For example, sublimation of indigo did not occur[7] when the distance between sublimand and condensing surface was 2.5 cm., but when it was 0.01–0.1 mm., a sublimate collected.[8] The practical subliming point has been defined[7] as the lowest temperature at which a sublimate discernible under the microscope is obtained when the substance is maintained for twenty minutes at that temperature in a standard, specified apparatus (see Fig. 6 and Table II). Ten minutes was chosen[9] as the time period in determining the subliming points of certain amino acids under vacuum. In a group of 700 organic compounds, the difference between the subliming point and the melting point increased linearly with increase in the melting point.[10]

In order to *melt* a compound which sublimes at atmospheric pressure, it must be heated at elevated pressure. For example, hexachloroethane[11] melts at 187°C. At 185°C., it has a vapor pressure of 1 atm. Hence, it readily vaporizes without melting, and, on cooling, the vapor crystallizes without first giving liquid (see Fig. 1). On heating under pressure, hexachloroethane melts and distils. The vapor pressures of a number of compounds at the melting point are given in Table I. Measurement of sublimation pressures follows the principles and techniques of vapor-pressure measurements in general.[12]

TABLE I
Vapor Pressure of Some Organic Compounds at the Melting Point

Compound	Melting point, °C.	Vapor pressure at melting point, mm. Hg
Toluene	−95	0.001
p-Nitrobenzaldehyde	106	0.01
Benzoic acid	120	6
Naphthalene	79	7
Acetic acid	16.4	9.45
Hydroquinone	169	14.1
Benzene	5.5	36
Camphor	179	370
Hexachloroethane	187	800
Acetylene	−81.5	912
Cyanogen iodide	146	993
Carbon dioxide	−57	5.1 atm.

The heat of sublimation, *i.e.*, the energy required to overcome the cohesive forces of the crystal and transform it to vapor, depends on the nature of the compound. In general, each chemical group contributes to the *intermolecular* forces according to its location in the molecule, its polarity, and its contribution to the van der Waals attraction, particularly its ability to form co-ordinate links, *e.g.*, hydrogen bonds. A few average values[13] are: —COOH, 8970; —OH, 7250; $=CH_2$ and $—CH_3$, 1780; and $—CH_2—$, 990 cal. Energy supplied to overcome molecular cohesion also increases the *internal* vibration in the molecule, and if, at any bond, the vibrational energy exceeds the binding energy, the bond will break and the molecule decompose.[14] Theoretically, *any* substance can be sublimed or distilled unchanged if the energy which the molecules must acquire, to overcome the cohesive forces and reach the condensing surface, does not exceed the heat of disruption of the least stable bond.

In order to obtain maximum velocity of sublimation, the surface area of the sublimand should be as great as possible, *i.e.*, the material should be finely powdered.[15] This may also reduce the retarding action of less volatile impurities and the danger that a dust of impure material, arising from decrepitation[16] caused by the presence of mother liquor or solvent of crystallization, may reach the condensing surface. The sublimand should be spread in a thin layer, except in entrainer sublimations with thorough permeation by the entrainer. It may well be agitated mechanically. The distance from sublimand surface to condenser surface should be short.[17]

Direct formation of crystals from the vapor phase depends on the properties of the compound, the presence of nuclei at the condensing surface, the pressure, and the temperature of the sublimand and sublimate, respectively. Such simple symmetrical molecules as quinone, anthracene, and naphthalene readily yield beautifully crystalline sublimates. In sublimation, as in crystal growth from solution, the *number, shape, and size of the resulting crystals* depend on the rate of nucleus formation[18] relative to that of crystal growth and on the rate at which material is supplied. Hence, sublimation of pure crystals may be directed toward the preparation of many small crystals or of a few large ones. In common practice, three kinds of sublimate are encountered: cake, powder, and macrocrystalline sublimates. Whereas some substances, *e.g.*, menthol, benzoic acid, and naphthalene, readily yield individual crystals no matter what the conditions are, other compounds are difficult[19] to obtain in this form.

The rate of condensation[20] obviously depends on the rate at which the vapor is supplied to the condenser and on the temperature difference between the condenser walls and vapor. On striking a solid surface, a vapor molecule may either condense or rebound. Under vacuum, the ratio[21] of the number striking to the number condensing is close to unity for nonpolar molecules such as naphthalene, but for benzoic acid (dipole moment 0.8×10^{-18} e.s.u.), it is probably less than 0.3, and for camphor (dipole moment 2.95×10^{-18} e.s.u.), its value is only 0.17. The condensing molecules may not be immediately frozen into immobility, but probably move more or less freely in a layer on the condensing surface for a short time. The lower the condenser temperature, the more rapidly will the particles be arrested. Consequently, to avoid the deposition of amorphous or microcrystalline material, the temperature of the condensing surface should not be too low. The most perfect crystals will, in general, result if the temperature of the cooling surface is only slightly below the melting point, *i.e.*, the maximum compatible with direct condensation to crystals. This is important in the microsublimation of compounds to get discrete euhedral crystals of measurable angles.[22] Slow growth is conducive to perfection of shape. Formation of hard coatings may result if the condenser temperature is considerably below the melting point. Thus, water cooling, as compared with air cooling, usually favors deposition of a hard coating of sublimate difficult to remove.

It is obvious that the thickness of the sublimate coating on the walls, and therefore the shape and relative size of the condenser, will affect the character of the sublimate. Installation of baffles impedes passage of the vapor through the condensing chamber and increases the condensing surface. Brushes or swinging hammers are employed industrially for removal of deposits from the condensing surfaces. The introduction of a cold gas into the condensation chamber often causes rapid condensation and deposition of snowlike sublimates.

III. TYPES OF SUBLIMATION

1. Simple Sublimation

Simple sublimation, involving diffusion of the vapor to the condensing surface at atmospheric pressure, is limited to substances with a relatively high vapor pressure. In order that direct crystallization from the vapor may occur, the temperature and pressure at the condensing surface must lie below the triple-point temperature and pressure.

2. Entrainer Sublimation

One way of bringing about sublimation of a substance which, on heating, would ordinarily melt and then boil, is to introduce an inert gas or vapor as an *entrainer*, so that the partial pressure of the sublimand vapor is brought below the triple-point pressure and the sublimand vapor is swept along with the entrainer. On suitable cooling, the vapor will then crystallize directly, without first liquefying. Thus, *d*-camphor (triple point 179°C., 370 mm.) is readily sublimed below 179°C. in a current of air at atmospheric pressure. This entrainer technique was suggested by Liebig.[23] It is particularly useful for heat-sensitive compounds with fairly low vapor pressure. With respect to volatile impurities, the function of the entrainer is, in a sense, similar to that of the solvent in recrystallization from solution.[24] In such processes, when the entrainer is saturated and diffusion in the solid state is not the rate-limiting step, the time t (hours) required for transfer of weight W of volatile substance in the sample taken is[25]

$$t = [W \times 760 \times 22.4 \times (1 + aT)]/vMR$$

where a is the thermal coefficient of expansion of gases, T the temperature (°C.) in heating chamber, v the vapor tension (in mm.) of the substance at T°, M is molecular mass of the substance, and R the rate of entrainer flow (in liters per hour). The entrainer must be well distributed over the sublimand surface or, preferably, permeate the finely divided powder. The more intimately it comes into contact with the sublimand, the greater the rate of vaporization up to a certain value.

The choice of the entrainer depends on the chemical and physical properties of the sublimand. Thus, *air* may be employed as the entrainer for benzoic acid,[26] phthalic anhydride, or naphthalene,[27] which are inert to oxygen. For the sublimation of salicylic acid, a 6% *carbon dioxide plus air* mixture is used. Sublimation in *steam* may be employed for substances, *e.g.*, 2-naphthol, camphor, benzanthrone,[28] or anthracene, which melt above 100°C. and are practically insoluble in and not decomposed by water. A dry sublimate may be obtained directly, with water vapor at atmospheric pressure as the entrainer, if the condenser is kept above 100°C. The same principle may be employed with other entrainers.

The temperature of the entering entrainer should be close to the vaporization temperature of the sublimand. If the entrainer temperature is lower, the vapor is cooled and premature condensation results. If the entrainer temperature is much higher, the vapor becomes superheated and the advantages of low-temperature vaporization of compounds unstable to heat may be lost. In practice, *slight*[29] superheating, to prevent premature crystallization before the vapor reaches the condenser, is advisable. In the sublimation of salicylic acid, maximal dispersion of the powdered sublimand is ensured[30] by whirling it with an inert gas, *e.g.*, air, nitrogen, or carbon dioxide, to form a cloud; this is then treated with additional inert gas hot enough to effect sublimation. Alternatively, the powder may be directly treated with hot entrainer[31] so that the substance is volatilized while it is being suspended.

Entrainer sublimation usually gives feathery flakes, a fine light crystalline powder, or a fluffy snowlike sublimate ("flowers"). Crystallization occurs in the vapor space of the condenser rather than on its walls, because the entrainer transfers heat from the vapor to the walls and tends to whirl up crystallization nuclei. The greater the percentage of entrainer, the greater is the likelihood of "snow" formation.

3. Vacuum Sublimation

Sublimation of heat-sensitive compounds frequently becomes possible if the pressure in the system is reduced, and vacuum sublimation is often the most convenient method for isolating or purifying an organic compound. If often takes but a few minutes to liberate a volatile compound from nonvolatile substances which may otherwise be difficult to remove. Although oxalic acid tends to decompose to formic acid and carbon dioxide on sublimation at 760 mm., it is readily sublimed[32] at 10 mm. The conditions of molecular distillation—a high vacuum in which the distance from sublimand to condenser is less than the mean free path of the vaporizing molecules—often give excellent results with compounds of low vapor pressure. The theory and equipment for sublimation in a high vacuum are closely related to those for molecular distillation (see Chapter VI). Quinine,[33] morphine,[33] maleic acid,[34] and D-glucose[35] may be sublimed under moderately high vacuum without decomposition, and dipentaerythritol[36] is best purified in this way. Lauric acid sublimes[34] at 22°C., myristic acid at 27°C. palmitic acid at 32°C., stearic acid at 38°C., alizarin[37] at 45°C., and strychnine[37] at 103°C. Table II shows the effect of diminished pressure on

TABLE II
Effect on Sublimation Point Caused by Diminishing the Pressure[a] Rate of Sublimation

Compound	M.p., °C.	Sublimand temp., °C.	Sublimation temp., °C., obs. At 760 mm.	At 0.5–1 mm.	Rate of sublimation at 0.5 to 1.0 mm.[b] Time, hr.	Sublimate yield, %
Naphthalene	79	50	36–38	25	0.5	86.2
Iodoform	119	75	43–45	30–34	0.5	96.7
Caffeine (anhyd.)	233	150	72–74	36–39	0.5	99.9
Theobromine	348	210	146–149	110–114	0.5	99.8
Benzoic acid	120	80	43–45	25	0.75	99.9
Hexamethylene-tetramine	—	90	45–47	25	0.75	99.3
Quinine (anhydrous)	175	165	157–160	99–103	1.0	99.3
2-Naphthol	122	75	43–45	33–35	1.25	99.6
Saccharin	224	150	84–86	59–63	1.5	99.9
Acetanilide	113	70	56–58	34–36	2.25	99.8
Cinnamic acid	132	90	58–60	52–56	2.25	99.7
DL-Alanine	295	180	135–137	59–63	2.25	99.6
Phthalic anhydride	129	80	50–52	27–30	2.5	99.5
Coumarin	68	50	40–42	30–33	2.75	100
Urea	132	95	59–61	49–52	3.25	99.2
Barbital	188	115	66–68	43–46	3.25	99.6
Vanillin	80	55	47–49	33–35	4.0	99.5
Anthracene	215	100	77–79	28–31	5.0	99.1
Cholesterol	145	130	No sub.	38–40	7.0	99.5
Alizarin	285	180	71–73	34–38	9.0	99.7
Isatin	200	110	78–80	47–50	10.0	99.7
Cinchonine	260	170	164–167	82–86	19.25	99.6
Acetylsalicylic acid	135	105	77–80	52–55	21.0	99.7
Cocaine	96	85	No sub.	48–51	35.0	99.6
Atropine	114	95	No sub.	60–64	42.0	99.2

[a] Based on Hoffman and Johnson, *J. Assoc. Offic. Agr. Chemists*, **13**, 367 (1930). Compare Illari, *Chem. Abstr.*, **25**, 2880; *Ann. Chim. Applicata*, **21**, 127 (1931); Eder, *Schweiz. Wochschr.*, **51**, 228, 241, 253 (1913); Hortvet, *J. Assoc. Offic. Agr. Chemists*, **6**, 481 (1923); Hubacher, *Ind. Eng. Chem., Anal. Ed.*, **15**, 448 (1943).

[b] Condenser temperature about 20°C.

the sublimation point of a number of compounds. Most of the α-amino acids are sublimable[38] under high vacuum, without decomposition. The preparation of thin films of such polar compounds as purines, pyrimidines, and amino acids by sublimation onto quartz slides in a molecular still has been used to prepare samples for the study of their ultraviolet absorption spectra.[39]

Compounds which distil at atmospheric pressure may be sublimed under suitable vacuum. Naphthalene, which melts at 79°C. and has a boiling point of 218°C. at 760 mm., sublimes rapidly at 70°C. at 13 mm. The vapor pressure of 2-naphthol at its melting point (122°C.) is 2.5 mm.; hence, for sublimation, the system is evacuated to a pressure below 2.5 mm.

If simple vacuum sublimation of compounds having a low vapor pressure is slow, judicious admission of an *entrainer* may speed up the process, just as it speeds up simple sublimation. Introduction of entrainer will tend to increase the pressure in the system.

4. Quasisublimation

Some compounds, such as camphene hydrate,[40] have been first obtained in crystalline form only by crystallization from the vapor derived from the *melt.* Presumably, nonvolatile impurities are left behind during the treatment, and volatile impurities, retarding crystallization from the melt or from a solvent, do not hinder crystallization from the vapor phase. Depending on the chemical and physical properties of the compound, any of the above-mentioned methods used for sublimation may prove successful.

It is a common industrial procedure to melt the crystals, vaporize the liquid, and recrystallize the compound directly from the vapor phase. When a substance with a fairly high triple-point pressure, such as camphor (triple point 179°C., 370 mm.), is heated in a vertical sublimator—for instance, a basin covered with a cold glass funnel—the heavy vapor lies on the substance, the partial pressure over the compound rises to the triple-point pressure, and it melts and eventually boils. However, if the hot vapor near the condensing surface is diluted with hot air, so that the partial pressure remains below the triple-point pressure, the vapor condenses directly to crystals on the condenser. Similarly, on boiling certain substances in a retort, sublimate is observed above the vapor during the period while vapor is still rising and some air remains in the retort. As soon as the air has been expelled, the vapor condenses as liquid in the neck of the retort. However, if the vapor is passed into a large chamber containing hot air, sublimate again forms until the point is reached at which the partial pressure of the vapor exceeds the triple-point pressure, when it again condenses as liquid. In order that direct condensation to crystals may be accomplished, it is necessary that the partial pressure of the condensing vapor be reduced below the triple-point pressure. This may be brought about by diluting the vapor. Except that the material is first melted, the procedure is similar to entrainer sublimation (see Sec. III-2). A process combining entrainer quasisublimation with rapid condensation in the presence of additional cold entrainer has been described[41] for compounds whose vapor pressure in the solid state is less than 10 mm. (see Sec. IV-2B).

IV. DESIGN AND OPERATION OF SUBLIMATORS

A sublimator is essentially a chamber in which a temperature difference can be maintained between two surfaces. The sublimand is placed on the hotter surface, and the sublimate collected on the cooler surface, which may be situated *above, to one side of, or below* the vaporizing surface. The main advantage of the horizontal sublimator is that, with proper use, sublimate cannot possibly return to the sublimand vessel. The kind of apparatus chosen is determined by such factors as (*1*) the stability of the sublimand on heating; (*2*) its vapor pressure and ease of vaporization; (*3*) the size of the sublimand sample; (*4*) the relative importance of obtaining the maximum possible yield of sublimate; and (*5*) the physical form of sublimate desired. Certain pieces of equipment designed for distillation can be used, with little or no modification, for sublimation; in this category are some of the molecular stills (see Chap. VI).

The sublimand may be heated[42] by any of the methods described in Chapter II of the present volume and in Chapter I, "Heating and Cooling," in Volume III of this series. Care should be taken that the temperature is not too high in relation to the pressure in the system. Especially under high vacuum, the sublimand may exhibit a behavior reminiscent of a boiling liquid, *viz.*, a dancing movement of the individual particles[43] or a vibration of the whole sublimand mass,[44] because it has been so heated that the vapor pressure of the compound locally exceeds the pressure existing in the apparatus. To avoid transfer of dust of crude sublimand to the condenser surface, a plug of glass wool or other porous medium may be inserted between the vaporizing and condensing surfaces.

Cooling devices will be considered individually, since the choice depends on such factors as the physical form desired for the sublimate.

1. Vertical Sublimators

A. SIMPLE SUBLIMATION

Air-Cooled Condenser. Perhaps the simplest method[45] of subliming a small sample is to place a thin layer on a glass plate resting on an asbestos sheet heated with a microflame. A second glass plate, which acts as condenser, is tilted 0.5–1.5 mm. above the sublimand by means of a support, 3–4 mm. high, inserted under one end. In determining the minimum temperature at which a visible sublimate results, it has been recommended[46] that the sublimand be heated electrically for close temperature control and that the condensing surface be placed 0.01–0.1 mm. from the sublimand surface. As a rule, the sublimation is better conducted in an enclosed space. Thus, one may place the sublimand on a watch glass, cover it with another watch glass, and heat the lower glass gradually.[47] The two glasses may be of the same size, ground to fit each other at the edges, and held together by means of a metal clamp.[48] A filter paper may be placed between the glasses to catch falling sublimate. For sublimation in an inert gas or *in vacuo*, the whole apparatus must be enclosed.

One of the first uses of microsublimation[49] was the systematic examination and identification of such alkaloids as strychnine, morphine, and atropine. A little of the material under study was placed in a depression in a platinum foil, covered with a glass slip, and then cautiously heated. The apparatus was later improved[50] by using a sublimation cell composed of a glass ring supported by a glass disk and covered with another glass disk or, preferably, a microscope slide, so that the sublimation might be observed under the microscope.[51] The cell was placed on a brass plate bored to accept a thermometer and heated with a microflame or electrically. The first fractional microsublimation,[52] of a mixture of alizarin, flavopurpurin, and isopurpurin, was conducted in such a cell having a lead ring. An asbestos ring was used in subliming caffeine from an alcoholic potash extract of tea leaves.[53] To diminish the chance of crystallization on the walls, a brass ring, 1 cm. in diameter and 1 mm. high, was recommended[54] for compounds which do not attack the alloy. In another design,[55] cylindrical wells of various depths and diameters are drilled in the top of the metal heating block; sublimand may be placed in each and covered with a glass slide. A modification known as the "apophorometer"[56] consists of an electrically heated platinum ribbon on which the sublimand is placed; this is encased in two watch glasses ground to fit. The whole may be enclosed in another vessel for sublimation in an inert gas or under diminished pressure. A rather similar apparatus[57] has a built-in, circular thermometer for measuring the temperature of the sublimand. Certain organic dyes may be detected by microsublimation[58] in an apparatus of this kind.

For work on a somewhat larger scale,[59] the lower vessel may be a porcelain dish, and a funnel or beaker may be employed as the condensing surface. A covered porcelain crucible, heated in a sand bath, has also been used.[60] If the sublimate shows a tendency to fall off the condenser into the sublimand, a sheet of paper or cardboard, punctured with pinholes, should be placed between the lower and upper vessels. A modification[61] of this device employs a steam coil for heating a moist sublimand, and a dry sublimate results.

Larger amounts may sometimes be sublimed by spreading the substance evenly on the bottom of an Erlenmeyer flask, loosely stoppering it, and immersing it to a depth of an inch in a heated oil bath. Salts of organic bases,[62] *e.g.*, *N*-methyl-α-pyridone hydrochloride, have thus been sublimed. A test tube may be used in a similar way. To avoid contamination of sublimate by residual sublimand during withdrawal at the end of the sublimation, a snugly fitting second test tube[63] of slightly smaller diameter, whose bottom has been cut off (Fig. 2), may be inserted. The sublimate is deposited on the walls of the inner tube. Another solution to this problem is

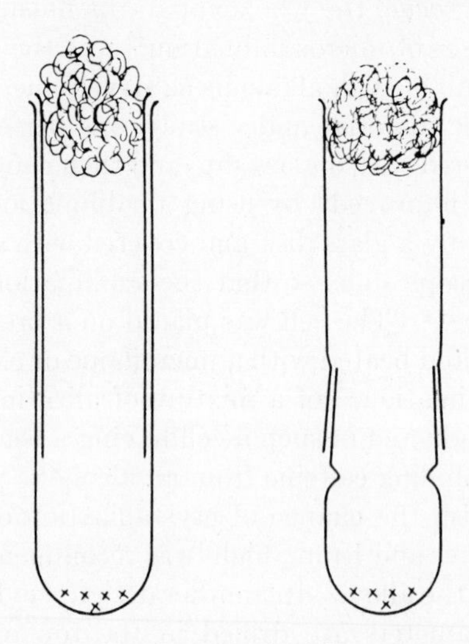

Fig. 2. Simple vertical sublimators.[63,64]

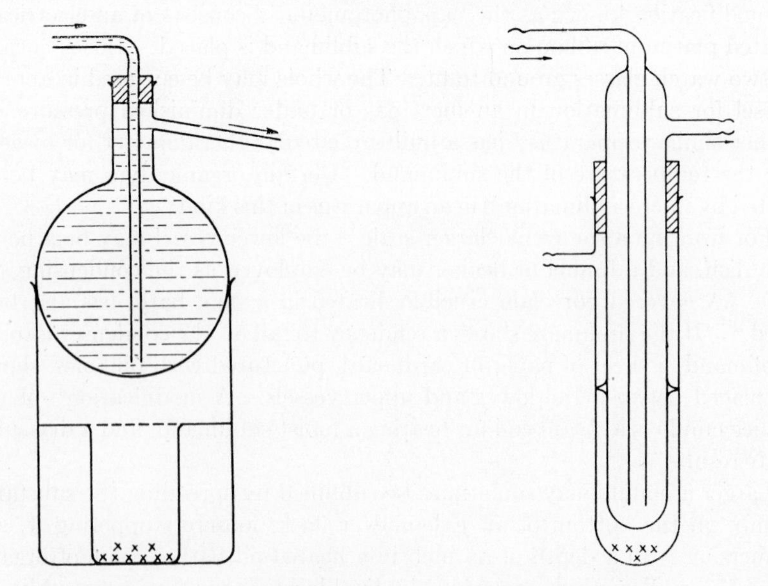

Fig. 3 (left). Vertical sublimator with liquid-cooled condenser.[68]
Fig. 4 (right). Vertical sublimator with liquid-cooled condenser.[69]

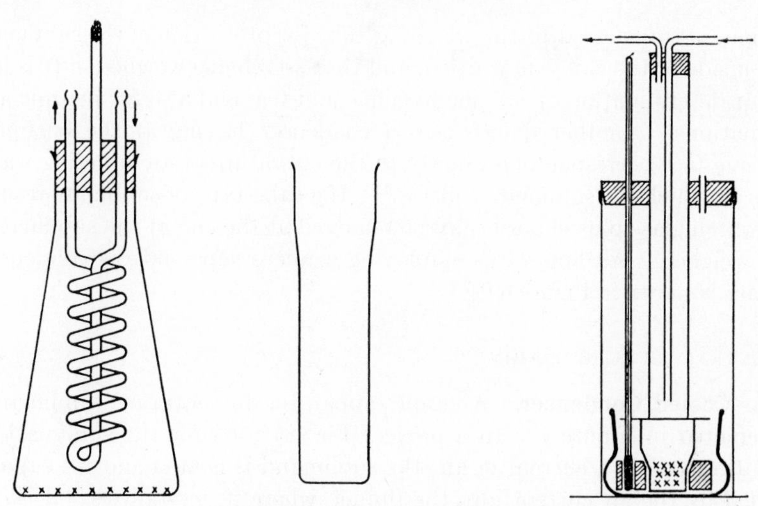

Fig. 5 (left). Vertical sublimator with liquid-cooled condenser.[70]
Fig. 6 (right). Vertical sublimator with liquid-cooled condenser.[72]

the use[64] of a ground-glass joint as shown in Figure 2. The tube is recommended for use in the determination of benzoic acid by sublimation.

Liquid-Cooled Condenser. If the temperature of the condensing surface might rise to the melting point of the sublimate, it becomes necessary to cool it. Cooling is also indicated for quantitative experiments and for sublimations at room temperature. For micro work,[65] it may be sufficient to put a drop of water or a damp cloth on a flat glass plate or watch glass used as the condensing surface. Xanthine bases were thus readily sublimed from plant materials. Pieces of dry ice may also prove satisfactory as coolant.

For prolonged sublimations and for those on a macro scale, a stream of cold liquid[66] is preferable for cooling. In an early device,[67] a "cold-finger" condenser is inserted through the neck of a conical funnel which rests on the rim of a vessel containing the sublimand. The rim serves to collect liquid condensate, and a porous plate resting on the dish catches any dislodged sublimate. Depending on the sublimand, a seal between rim and funnel may be provided by mercury, paraffin wax, or plaster of Paris. The apparatus is readily modified for entrainer or vacuum sublimation. A simpler form[68] is depicted in Figure 3. If a test tube is used as the subliming vessel (Fig. 4), three glass prongs[69] may be sealed onto the tubular condenser to prevent contact with the walls of the tube on withdrawal. For quantitative work with small amounts, the sublimate is washed off the condenser, the solution evaporated to dryness, and the residue weighed. For direct weighing of the sublimate,[70] the apparatus shown in Figure 5 was developed. The condenser consists of a spiral tube which, after the sublimation, is transferred to the weighing tube for protection of the sublimate. The inside of the coil is now dried, and the assemblage weighed. It is useful for determination of caffeine in coffee and tea, and also for benzoic acid estimations. Another device uses a condenser having at the bottom a concave face corresponding exactly to the curvature of an adhering watch glass on which the sublimate collects.[71] If a cake-type of sublimate results, the watch glass plus deposit may be removed at the end of the sublimation and weighed. An apparatus employing a microscope slide as condensing surface is shown in Figure 6.[72,73]

B. ENTRAINER SUBLIMATION

Air-Cooled Condenser. A simple apparatus for entrainer sublimation is depicted in Figure 7. In a device (Fig. 8) used for the sublimation[74] of anthracene in a current of air, the sublimand is heated and its vapor is carried by the air current into the funnel, where it crystallizes. 2-Naphthol was sublimed[75] in the apparatus shown in Figure 9 at the rate of almost

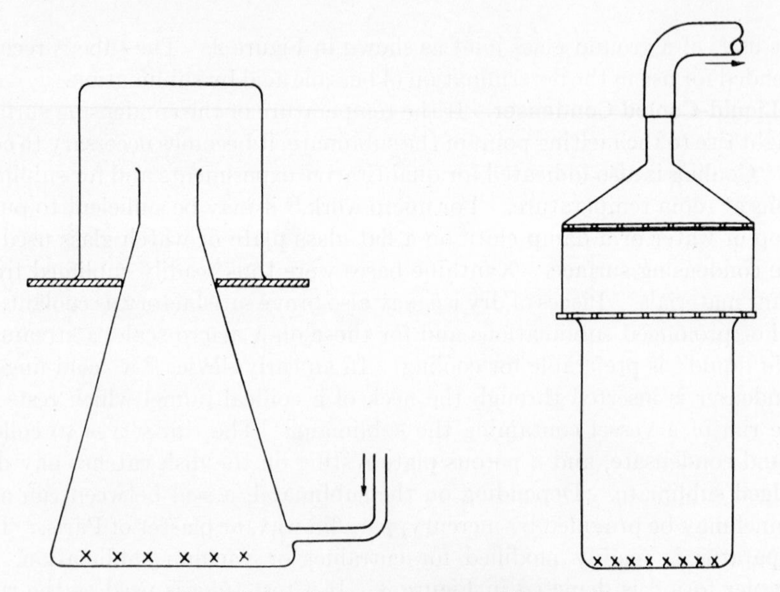

Fig. 7 (left). Vertical entrainer sublimator.[73]
Fig. 8 (right). Vertical entrainer sublimator.[74]

1 g./min. It was heated until almost molten and a current of air passed over its surface either by air pressure on the flask side-tube or by suction at the upper end of the condensing tube. The latter was plugged with cotton to minimize loss of sublimate.

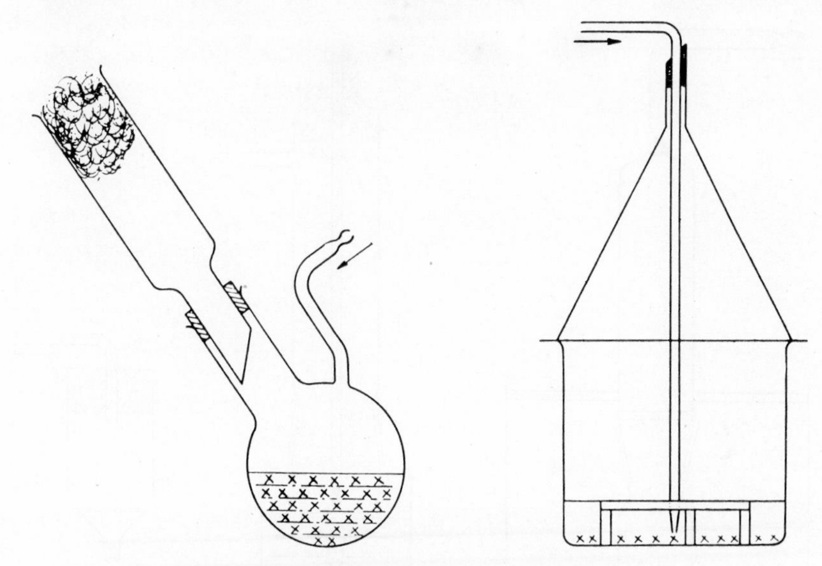

Fig. 9 (left). Vertical entrainer sublimator.[75]
Fig. 10 (right). Vertical entrainer sublimator.[76]

The apparatus shown in Figure 10 was designed for the sublimation of[76] compounds difficult to vaporize. A vigorous stream of entrainer is passed through the tube and over the heated sublimand. The sublimate collects on the inner walls of the funnel and between two sheets of paper. The lower of these is supported on a glass tripod, the upper between beaker and funnel.

Liquid-Cooled Condenser. Devices of this kind are not shown, since they differ from those just described only by the presence of a liquid-cooled condenser (see Sec. IV-1A) above the sublimand surface.

C. VACUUM SUBLIMATION

The techniques and equipment for producing moderate and high vacua are discussed in Chapters V and VI.

Air-Cooled Condenser. Probably the simplest apparatus consists of a flask, containing the sublimand, which is evacuated and sealed and then gradually heated with a free flame. The method appears to have been first employed[77] for the sublimation of indigo at 30 to 40 Torr. Urea was similarly sublimed.[78] In a related device,[79] a small temperature gradient between sublimand and sublimate (for slow growth of well shaped crystals) was ensured by placing a sealed, evacuated tube containing the sublimand in a vertical tube containing a layer of mercury and a layer of a

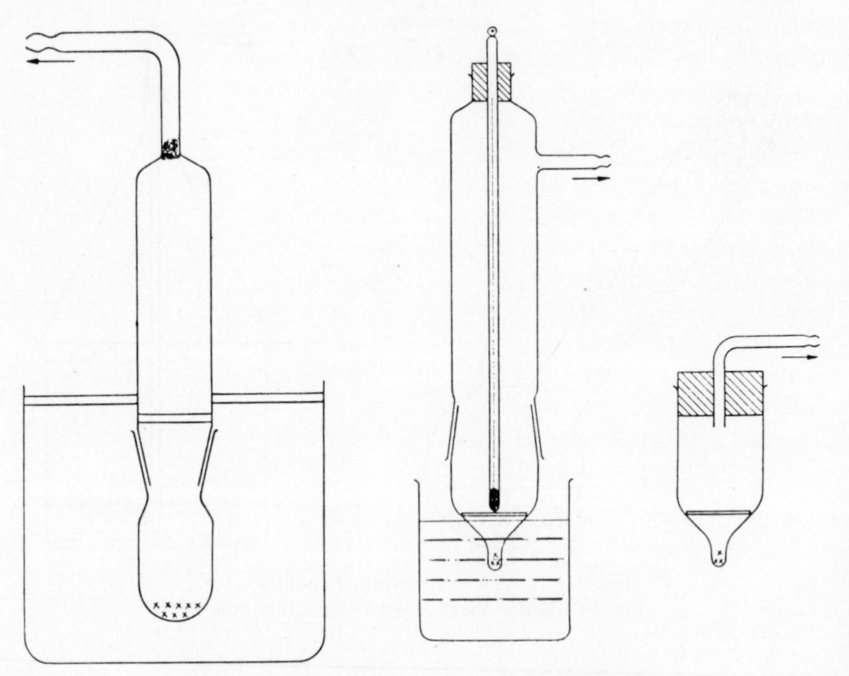

Fig. 11 (left). Vertical vacuum sublimator.[82]
Fig. 12 (right). Vertical vacuum microsublimator.[83]

liquid boiling at the temperature chosen for condensation of sublimate. The outer tube was placed under a reflux condenser and was heated until the liquid was boiling, thus heating the mercury and sublimand to a temperature slightly above the sublimate temperature.

Another simple device is a vertical tube, heated in an oil bath[80] or in a well bored in a metal block,[81] and connected to a vacuum pump. The sublimate collects on the cooler walls of the tube, but is often difficult to remove. If hanging deposits are formed, they may be dislodged by slight vibration and will fall back onto the residue. A loose asbestos plug may therefore be inserted in the tube so that it is a few millimeters inside the heating block. Owing to the much greater volatility of certain nitriles, they were readily separable from the related amides in this apparatus at 0.1–1 Torr., pressure, at temperatures near the melting points.

So that the sublimate might be readily accessible after the sublimation, a ground-glass joint has been used to connect the condenser with the vaporizer. To catch falling deposits of sublimate, a porous asbestos plate was interposed between it and the sublimand (Fig. 11). It may be omitted if the sublimate collects as a hard deposit. The sublimand, plate, and ground joint were heated in an air bath. The advantage of heating the joint is that if leakage, either accidental or deliberate (see Sec. IV-1D), occurs there, the entering entrainer is at the same temperature as the sublimand. In this apparatus,[82] such compounds as indigo, and mono- and di-bromoquinizarin,[83] which by other methods sublime with difficulty and considerable loss, were readily sublimed. An apparatus of 25-mm. internal diameter suffices for the sublimation of 1–4 g.; one 60 mm. wide was used for the sublimation of 13 g. of indigo in 3 hr. The device is also useful for fractional sublimations of compounds of different volatility, and for determination of the sublimation temperature. The color of the vapor and its spectroscopic absorption may be readily ascertained. For quantitative sublimations, the two parts of the apparatus may be weighed before and after a sublimation. Incidentally, the apparatus is also useful for the determination of solvent of crystallization.

In high-vacuum work, the ground joint must be greased and preferably not heated. It should therefore be placed[84] near the top of the tube, where it is unlikely to become clogged with sublimate. This apparatus is useful if two sublimates are expected. For example, on subliming a mixture of benzoic acid plus *o*-benzoylbenzoic acid, each formed a separate band on the cool part of the tube and could be scraped out separately. Quantitative separation of certain types of compound could be made at 10 μ provided that the temperature of the sublimand was very accurately controlled (see Sec. V). A thermostatically controlled heating block, drilled to accept tubes of several different diameters, was therefore designed.

Although vacuum microsublimation was first employed many years ago,[85] the sublimate was not collected on a microscope slide and was therefore not always suitable for microscopic examination. In order to overcome this problem, a microscope slide was bent at right angles near each end,[86] to form legs, and placed over the sublimand in a horizontal tube, which was then evacuated and heated in the under section of a modified Pregl heating block. The sublimate then collected on the under side of the microscope slide. By providing a suitable opening near the sublimand end of the tube, provision could be made for admission of a slow stream of dry entrainer. In a somewhat similar apparatus,[87] sublimate is collected on a microscope slide held 0.1 to 0.01 mm. above the surface of the sublimand, which is heated electrically. It may be used under vacuum or with an atmosphere of inert gas. An excellent device[88] for the sublimation[89] of 0.5 mg. of material onto a slide or round cover glass is that shown in Figure 12.

Liquid-Cooled Condenser. *External Cooling.* Vertical, vacuum sublimation with external cooling[90] of the condensing surface may be conducted by placing the sublimand in a small test tube which is covered with a piece of parchment paper or a porous plate and then inserted in a large test tube. This is evacuated, and heated below while being cooled above.

The apparatus may be used either for micro- or macro-sublimations. If the evacuating tube is replaced by a drying tube, it may also be employed for sublimation at atmospheric pressure. Related devices,[91] in which the sublimate may be collected on a cover glass or may be prevented by means of a wire screen from falling back into the crude sublimand, have been described.

Another form for direct sublimation onto a microscope cover glass consists[92] of an electrically heated, thermostatically controlled metal cylinder on which is placed a glass ring containing the sublimand, a glass slip, and a water-cooled metal cylinder. By changing the glass slip periodically, fractional microsublimation may be obtained.

For sublimation on a larger scale,[93] a dish containing the sublimand was placed on a small electric heater inside a vacuum desiccator having a side tube for evacuation. The heater wires passed through the side tube and the desiccator lid was cooled with a stream of cold water, so that sublimate collected on the inside of the lid.

Internal Cooling. One of the simplest devices for vacuum sublimation consists[94] of a test tube cooled, for example, with running water and placed inside a larger test tube containing the sublimand. When the larger tube is evacuated and heated, the sublimate collects on the smaller tube, but some of it is likely to drop off when the inner tube is removed, unless the deposit is compact. An apparatus of this kind has been employed[95] for the simultaneous vaporization and irradiation of ergosterol to give a sublimate containing vitamin D.

The sublimator may be provided[96] with a ground-glass joint; it is then useful for fractional sublimations. A similar tube, having a flat bottom on which the sublimand is spread in a thin layer, is valuable for quantitative microsublimation. The distance from sublimand to condenser tip is only 10 mm. This device has been employed for the estimation of 2-methyl-1,4-naphthoquinone, acetylsalicylic acid, phenacetin, phenobarbital, nicotinamide, salol, and sulfanilamide in pharmaceutical tablets. Other components, *e.g.*, starch, sucrose, lactose, talcum, magnesium stearate, L-cystine, and D-glutamic acid, do not sublime at 150°C. and 10 μ.

In the apparatus[97] shown in Figure 13, the rubber stopper and innermost glass tube may be removed if it is desired to cool the condensing surface to a low temperature, *e.g.*, with dry ice–chloroform. An apparatus of this kind has been found suitable[98] for the sublimation of 100-g. samples of certain compounds at 0.025 mm. It has also been used[99] in the preparation of gas-free liquids, by quasisublimation of the liquid onto the condenser, cooled with dry ice–ether. The dissolved gases are not condensed but are drawn off and separately collected. The sublimate is then melted, allowed to drop back into the still, and again quasisublimed. It is essential that the temperature of the condenser be low enough that the vapor shall condense directly as solid, since, were liquid to condense, it might redissolve some of the undesired gaseous impurities. Furthermore, the vapor pressure of the sublimate must be negligible at the temperature of the condenser, so that loss of sublimate shall be inappreciable.

A microsublimator of this same type is provided[100] with a small well for the sublimand. It is alleged that the sublimate is then deposited on the bottom of the condenser instead of on the walls of the still and the upper part of the condenser. A similar sublimator,[101] having a vacuum-jacketed cooling element is suitable for semimicrosublimations involving use of dry ice, liquid ammonia, or liquid nitrogen as coolant. With such a sublimator,[102] cholesterol has been sublimed from blood lipides at 88°C. and 0.003 μ.

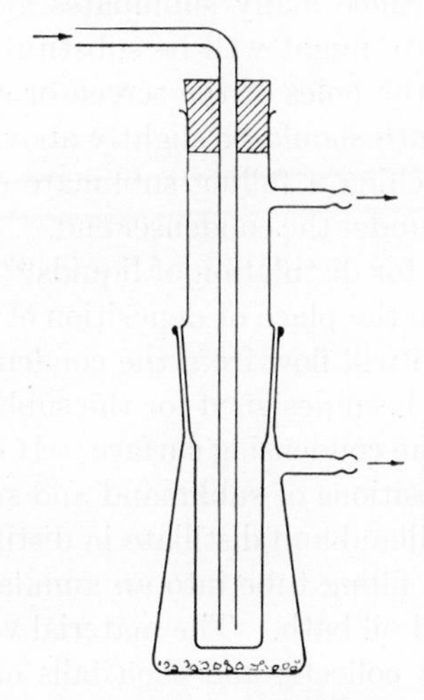

Fig. 13. Vertical vacuum sublimator with liquid-cooled condenser.[97]

If sublimators having ground-glass joints are to be used under very high vacuo, it is necessary to lubricate the joints with special grease,[103] and danger arises that the sublimate may become contaminated with the grease during the sublimation or on withdrawing the condenser at the end of the sublimation. An apparatus having a large flange joint[104] instead of a tapered joint was therefore devised (Fig. 18, Chap. VI). This was later simplified[105] by providing a sublimand well which could be heated in an oil bath and by sealing the water-cooled condenser into the upper dome (Fig. 19, Chap. VI). In another modification,[106] an electric hot plate was employed and the dome was replaced by a tightly fitting iron cover through which passed a tubular condenser, arranged horizontally. Beneath this was placed a glass condenser plate for collection of sublimate.

So that the distance between condenser and sublimand, surface might be adjustable to suit the particular sublimand and to avoid the danger of contamination by grease inherent in the use of tapered ground-glass joints, it is recommended[107] that a rubber stopper placed on a stout glass flange be employed instead of a ground joint. Furthermore, a Pyrex glass cloth may be employed to catch any falling sublimate, and the condenser may be pushed down until it is almost touching this glass cloth. The condenser is bulb shaped to deter deposition of sublimate in the upper parts of the still. A rather similar, but perhaps less flexible, design has also been described.[108] Onto the edges of the condenser, having a convex lower surface, are sealed three small pieces of glass rod. These are bent inward at right angles to form a support for a metal screen fine enough to catch all crystals falling on it. Since many sublimates attack metal, a sealed-in, coarse sintered-glass plate might well be substituted for the metal screen. To avert deposition in the holes of the screen or sintered glass, the upper surface of the heating bath should be slightly above the level of the screen. Simpler devices for catching a falling sublimate consist of a watch glass sealed onto or mounted under the condenser end.

Certain stills suitable for distillation of liquids[109] require modification for use as sublimators, since the place of deposition of a sublimate must be accessible whereas a liquid will flow from the condensation area to an accessible point. A still has been designed for the sublimation[110] of compounds which readily drop off the condensing surface. It consists essentially of an alembic in which the positions of sublimand and sublimate are the reverse of those normal for distilland and distillate in distillation. The sublimand is introduced through a filling tube into an annular receptacle surrounded by an electrically heated oil bath. The material volatilizes and strikes the cooling surface; here it collects, and then falls off into the receiver, not back into the sublimand. Material which collects as large crystals falls off readily and the operation need not be interrupted. The cooling surface is entirely surrounded by warm space so that sublimate collects at no other part of the apparatus. The short distance between the annulus and the condenser is advantageous.

For very difficultly volatilizable compounds it is essential that the condensing surface be close to the surface of the sublimand. The gap should be large enough to accommodate the flow of uncondensed vapor, arising from decomposition and leaks, and yet be small enough to be commensurate with the mean free path of the sublimand vapor molecules. For rapid pumping, the side arms for connection to the evacuating system should be wide. Molecular stills (see Chap. VI) may be employed for fractional sublimation of a mixture whose components differ in volatility or molecular size, or both. Thus, a thin layer of the sublimand is spread on the bottom of the sublimator[111] and the condensing surface, only 2–3 mm. from the solid, is cooled with running water or dry ice–acetone. The sublimator is then evacuated to less than 10^{-6} Torr. mercury. Under these conditions, dibenz[*a,h*]anthracene (m.p., 260°C.) sublimes readily at 140°C. and slowly at 100°C. A still of this kind has been employed in the study of pyrolysis of high polymers.[112] A number of such sublimators, macro or micro, may be attached[113] to a manifold, 40 mm. in diameter, maintained at 10^{-5} mm. and provided with an auxiliary degassing line maintained at 10^{-3} mm. If the sublimators are electrically heated, sublimations may be allowed to run for long periods of time without attention.

The microsublimator described by Eder[114] (see Fig. 12) has been modified in a number of ways, *e.g.*, by encasing most of the thermometer with a water-cooled condenser on which sublimate collects.[115] The thermometer bulb reaches into the sublimand in the small well. With this device, it was possible to determine the "initial temperature of sublimation," *i.e.*, the temperature at which sublimate was first observed at a given pressure while the temperature was being raised 1°C. per minute. When two such condensers were placed in the ends of a U-tube, containing the sublimand and bearing a ground joint at each end, a device for fractional macrosublimation was obtained. With the system suitably evacuated, one condenser was kept cold until all of one component had sublimed. Then this section was closed off and the other condenser was cooled, the temperature of the sublimand being gradually raised until sublimation of the second component was appreciable.

In another variation,[116] the thermometer is replaced by a water-cooled tubular condenser. The apparatus is useful for the qualitative sublimation of plant constituents. A simpler form, with no ground joint, was also described. By flattening the lower end of the condenser,[117] and touching it with a drop of anhydrous glycerol, a cover glass could be made to adhere. The sublimand was placed in the small well. Alternatively, this was filled with sand or fine iron filings on which was placed a copper foil or small glass dish containing the sublimand; with this arrangement, the well could be dispensed with. By changing the glass disk before each rise in temperature, it was found possible to conduct fractional microsublimations for microchemical characterization.

In a modification,[116] the lower end of the condenser is curved downward and is placed over an annulus which serves for the collection of any liquid condensate, formed, for example, in treatment of plant products. The bulb containing the sublimand is inserted in an electrically heated oil bath so that the middle of the ground, restricted neck is level with the oil surface. If no liquid condensate forms but some sublimate collects on the walls of the upper part, this restricted neck may, after the sublimation, be

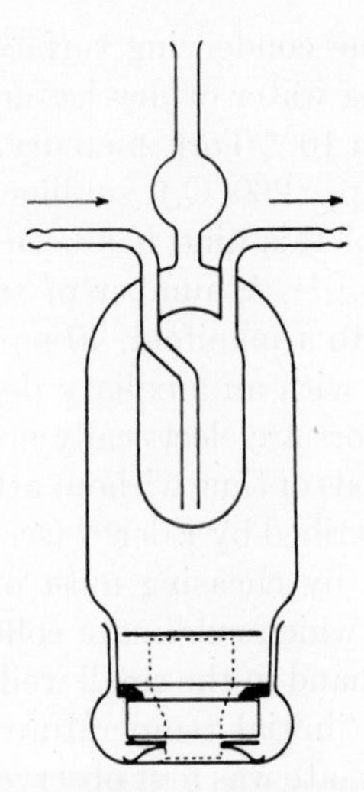

Fig. 14. Vertical vacuum sublimator with liquid-cooled condenser.[118]

plugged with a ground-glass stopper so that the sublimate may be dissolved out. Should the sublimate tend to collect as hanging deposits, a metal gauze or perforated disk may be placed on the annulus. If a small sample of sublimate is desired for microscopic examination, a microscope cover glass may be placed across the annulus, just below the end of the condenser.

Figure 14 depicts an apparatus which may be used[118] for quantitative or qualitative macrosublimations and for microsublimation onto a microscope slide. Glass dishes of various sizes, containing the sublimand, may be placed on a spring support. For microsublimations, a glass capsule having a narrow base is placed in the central hole in the spring support. If desired, a porous diaphragm, *e.g.*, 100-mesh platinum gauze, may be placed on the dish. The disadvantage of this apparatus is that the sublimate must be washed off the condenser. For comparative results, two such sublimators may be heated in the same bath, cooled with the same cooling system, and evacuated by the same pump.

D. ENTRAINER VACUUM SUBLIMATION

Air-Cooled Condenser. If a poorly fitting ground-glass joint is deliberately employed in the apparatus previously described[119] for vacuum sublimation (Fig. 11), hot air enters the sublimator, is directed onto the surface of the sublimand, and acts as entrainer. The simple apparatus shown in Figure 15, used[120] for purification of phthalimide and benzoic acid by repeated sublimation, consists of a suction flask attached to a glass funnel inverted over a dish in which the material is heated. For the sublima-

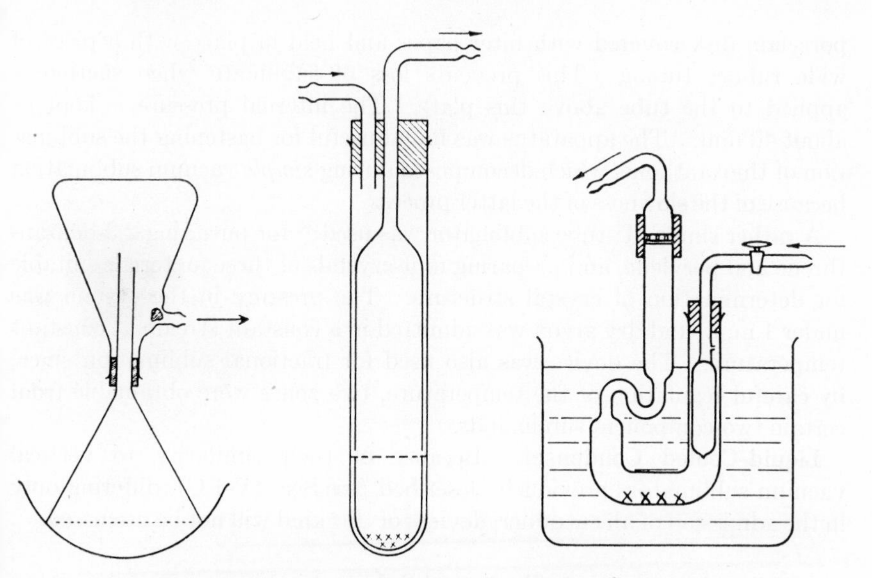

Fig. 15 (left). Vertical entrainer–vacuum sublimator.[120]
Fig. 16 (center). Vertical entrainer–vacuum sublimator.[121]
Fig. 17 (right). Vertical entrainer–vacuum sublimator.[123]

tion of small quantities, a watch glass may be used; for larger amounts, the funnel may be placed on a piece of perforated cardboard or aluminum sheet resting on a porcelain dish containing the material. For continuous sublimation, use of a strong, arched aluminum disk, packed on the funnel with premoistened asbestos paper, is recommended. A small cotton wad is placed in the side tube of the suction flask to minimize loss on evacuating.

In the apparatus[121] depicted in Figure 16, the entrainer is admitted at any desired speed and the center tube is used for connection to the vacuum pump. A piece of paper or other porous material is placed as shown, to prevent sublimate from falling onto the sublimand and to prevent spattering of sublimand onto the sublimate. In a related sublimator,[122] the upper tube is packed with an adsorptive substance and is held at the vapor temperature. Adsorption occurs and the separation is effected as with a chromatogram.

An excellent device[123] for preventing sublimate from falling back into the sublimand consists of a double bend in the tube between the two as shown in Figure 17. Sublimand is introduced into the U-tube through its straight limb and is heated in an air bath or oil bath. The entrainer enters through a baffle system inserted in the straight limb; this prevents the formation of vortices which would carry sublimate against the direction of the entrainer current. At the top of the bent limb is placed a perforated porcelain disk covered with filter paper and held in place with a piece of wide rubber tubing. This prevents loss of sublimate when suction is applied to the tube above this plate. The internal pressure is kept at about 40 mm. The apparatus was found useful for hastening the sublimation of thioxanthone, which decomposed during *simple* vacuum sublimation because of the slowness of the latter process.

A rather similar U-tube sublimator was used[124] for purifying 2,3-benzanthrene and perylene, and preparing unit crystals of these materials suitable for determination of crystal structure. The pressure in the system was under 1 mm., and dry argon was admitted in a constant stream at constant temperature. The device was also used for fractional sublimation since, by careful regulation of the temperature, two zones were obtainable from certain two-component sublimands.

Liquid-Cooled Condenser. Because of their similarity to vertical vacuum sublimators previously described (see Sec. IV-1.C), differing only in the admission of an entrainer, devices of this kind will not be discussed.

2. Horizontal Sublimators

Retort-type sublimators differ from *distillation* devices of this kind in that the tube connecting the vaporizing chamber with the condensing chamber must be short, wide, and readily cleanable, so that the possibility of clogging is minimized. For preference, this tube should be maintained at such a temperature that no crystallization occurs in it. The condensing tube or chamber must also be wide and voluminous.

A. SIMPLE SUBLIMATION

Air-Cooled Condenser. The simplest form is a horizontal tube sealed at one end. The sublimand is placed near the sealed end and heated; the sublimate collects in the cooler, unsealed end. Thus, trioxymethylene was readily sublimed[125] in a bomb tube heated in a furnace, with the unsealed end projecting from the furnace. The apparatus has been improved by using a standard-taper or spherical ground-glass joint for connecting the vaporizer to the cylindrical, horizontal condenser.

Enlarging the sealed end of the tube to give a true retort permits the sublimation of relatively large amounts of material. The retort side-arm may be inserted[126] in the neck of a bell jar resting on a glass plate. The sublimate collects in a porcelain dish. The apparatus may also be employed for vacuum sublimation if the bell-jar rim is carefully ground to fit the supporting glass plate. Industrially, to prevent blocking by sublimate, the connecting tube extends down into the vaporizer, is enlarged where it leaves this chamber, and is heat-insulated outside the vaporizer.[127] The condensing chamber may be equipped with a rotating drum from which the sublimate is mechanically scraped, in fractions, into a receiver.

For microsublimation, the sublimand is introduced[128] into a glass tube, *e.g.*, 200 mm. long and of 7 mm. external diameter, closed at one end. The closed end is placed in a metal block having a thermometer in another hole. The block is heated with a microburner, and it is possible to observe, with some precision, the temperature at which sublimation into the cool part of the tube becomes noticeable. After sublimation is complete, the section of the tube containing the sublimate is cut off, and the sublimate removed. A substance containing moisture may be heated to 120°C. and the water which condenses at *a* (Fig. 18) may be evaporated by means of the microflame *c*. With extremely small samples,[129] the microtube is then drawn out to a finer bore at *b* and the temperature of the block is gradually raised until sublimation occurs and the sublimate collects at *b*.

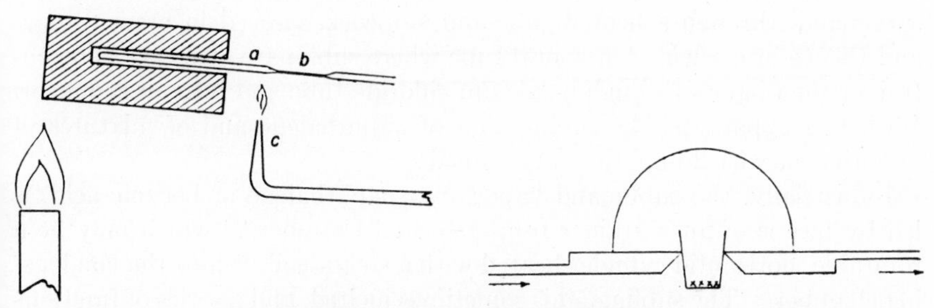

Fig. 18 (left). Horizontal microsublimator.[129]
Fig. 19 (right). Horizontal sublimator with liquid-cooled condenser.[130]

Liquid-Cooled Condenser. A simple horizontal sublimator[130] which may be cooled with running water is shown in Figure 19. The sublimand is placed in a crucible which rests in the hole of the annulus and is covered with an inverted dish, funnel, or beaker.

Very readily sublimable compounds may be sublimed[131] in a desiccator heated above by means of an electric light bulb held in place with plaster of Paris. The sublimand is placed in a beaker. A second beaker may contain phosphorus pentoxide for desiccation; normally, it should be removed prior to sublimation. The top of the desiccator may be insulated, and the bottom and walls, which serve as the condensing surface, appropriately cooled.

B. ENTRAINER SUBLIMATION

Air-Cooled Condenser. The simplest device of this kind consists[132] of a long tube to one end (*A*) of which is attached the source of entrainer,

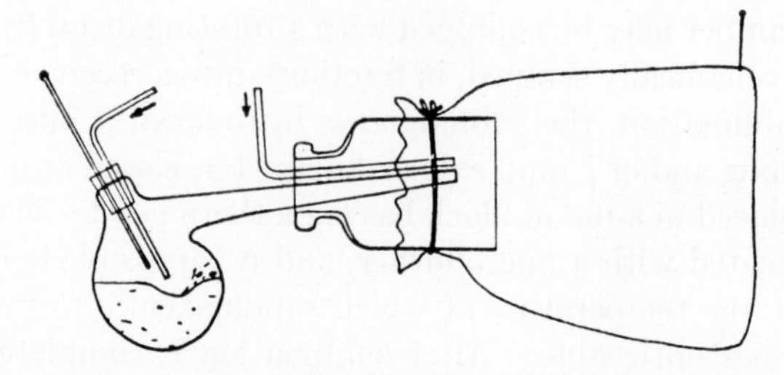

Fig. 20. Horizontal entrainer quasisublimator with air-cooled condenser.[136]

to the other a bubble counter. The sublimand is placed in the tube near *A* and is suitably heated. The sublimate collects in the cooler end of the tube.

In another apparatus,[133] the sublimand is placed in a spiral glass tube which is then inserted in a thermostat kept just below the melting point. The air current enters through soda lime and drying tubes, passes over the sublimand, through a heated tube and stopcock encased in brass tubing, and thence into a wide horizontal tube where sublimate collects. The entrainer then passes through a calcium chloride tube and into an aspirator. With this apparatus, the sublimation of naphthalene and of mixtures of naphthalene with 2-naphthol was studied.

Industrially, the sublimand vapor, *e.g.*, naphthalene or benzoic acid, is led by means of an entrainer from a heated chamber,[134] which may be a rotatable, horizontal cylinder heated with a steam coil,[135] into the condensing chamber. The sublimand is sometimes melted, and a series of fractions of sublimate may be collected.

The simplest form of horizontal semimicrosublimator consists of a straight glass tube into which is introduced a boat containing the sublimand. A current of air or other indifferent gas is then passed through the tube, which is heated under the boat and cooled beyond it. Entrainer microsublimation may be conducted as previously described (see Sec. IV-2A), except that a longer tube, having a capillary constriction for the first third of its length, is used. Next to the constriction is placed a layer of asbestos and then the sublimand. Both ends of the tube are left open and protrude from the block. The end nearer the sublimand is connected to the source of inert gas.

For entrainer quasisublimation, with cooling by means of cold air, the compound is placed[136] in a retort and heated until molten, but not boiling, *e.g.*, until its vapor pressure is about 100 mm. The vapor is blown, by means of compressed air directed onto the surface of the melt, into a widemouth bottle whose bottom has been removed (Fig. 20). A cotton bag is tied over the end of this receiver, and the mouth of the bottle is stuffed with cotton to prevent escape of material. The aerated vapor tends to con-

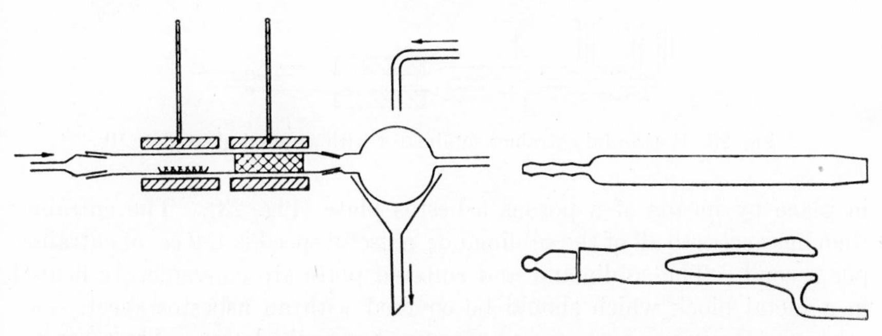

Fig. 21 (left). Horizontal entrainer sublimator with liquid-cooled condenser.[137]
Fig. 22 (right). Horizontal entrainer sublimator with liquid-cooled condenser.[140]

dense as a mist, but a current of air, chilled by passage through a copper coil immersed in ice water, is directed into the receiver and a fluffy, crystalline product results. Naphthalene, heated to about 140°C., and benzoic acid, heated to about 170°C., are readily purified in this way.

Liquid-Cooled Condenser. A simple apparatus[137] for entrainer sublimation, having a water-cooled condenser, is shown in Figure 21. The sublimand is heated by means of an aluminum block and the stream of vapor is heated with a second block before passing into the condensing vessel. The physical character of the sublimate can be varied by changing the speed of the stream of dry entrainer. A sublimator of this kind may be assembled[138] from a drying pistol plus a few supplementary pieces. A rather similar steam sublimator[139] has been described.

A horizontal sublimator, suitable for quantitative sublimation[140] (Fig. 22), consists of a vaporizer tube and a condensing tube. A plug of glass wool is stuffed into the narrow end of the vaporizer, the sublimand is introduced, a plug of glass wool is inserted into the wide end, and the whole weighed. It is then attached to the condensing tube which is cooled with a stream of ice water, a slow current of dry air is drawn through, by suction on the side arm of the condensing tube, and the vaporizer is heated electrically. After sublimation is complete, the condensing tube is detached, dried, and weighed. Camphor, naphthalene, and benzoic acid sublimed readily in this apparatus, giving a 99–100% recovery. A convenient rate of entrainer flow was found to be 1.3 liters per hour.

The maximum speed of sublimation cannot be attained with the entrainer sublimators so far discussed, because the entrainer tends to pass only over the surface of the sublimand and does not become completely saturated with its vapor. This may be overcome[141] by a sealed-in, coarse sintered-glass plate interposed between sublimand and sublimate. The finely powdered sublimand is loosely packed on one side of the plate and held

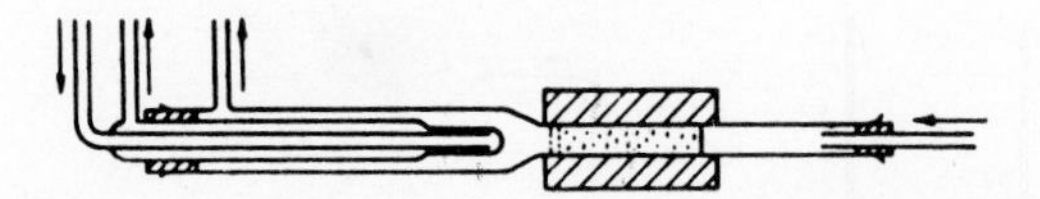

Fig. 23. Horizontal entrainer sublimator with sintered-glass plate.[141]

in place by means of a porous asbestos plate (Fig. 23). The entrainer then has access to all of the sublimand; a useful speed is 1–2 cc. of entrainer per second. The sublimand and sintered plate are conveniently heated in a metal block which should be covered with an asbestos sheet, since otherwise the upper part might not get as hot as the lower. The temperature is preferably kept some 10°C. below the melting point. The condensing tube may be closed with a solid rubber stopper and cooled externally with running water instead of by an inserted condenser as shown. Efficient cooling is essential in quantitative work.

C. VACUUM SUBLIMATION

The horizontal vacuum sublimator is essentially a retort having a cooled condenser; the pressure in the apparatus is diminished, by means of a pump, until below the triple-point pressure of the sublimand. The maximum effect is obtained if the material in the retort is only just below the melting point.

Air-Cooled Condenser. Sublimators of this kind may be conveniently grouped according to whether the source of heat is stationary, movable, or graded.

Stationary Source of Heat. The sublimand is shaken down into the closed end of a tube[142] which is then held horizontal and tapped until the compound spreads out into a horizontal layer. After the tube has been evacuated and the open end sealed, the end containing the sublimand is placed horizontally in a furnace, so that the other end projects into the open air. The sublimate then collects in this cooler part of the tube. To ensure a constant temperature for the sublimand in smaller scale work, the sublimand end of the tube may be enclosed in a heating jacket[143] containing a liquid of suitable boiling point. The liquid is heated to boiling, under reflux (Fig. 24). An Abderhalden dryer may be used for this purpose.

In early experiments on sublimation at pressures of about 0.001 mm., an all-glass apparatus devoid of ground joints was employed.[144] In case the sublimand might not have been thoroughly dry and free from volatile impurities, a condensing or absorption trap was connected[145] between the sublimate receiver and the pump. Quinine sublimed readily at a bath temperature of 170–180°C. Morphine, indigo, alizarin, anthracene, chrysene, camphoric acid, caffeine, theobromine, and codeine were also sublim-

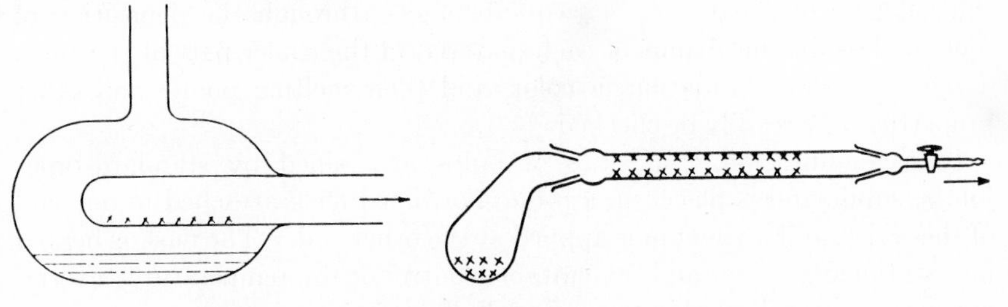

Fig. 24 (left). Horizontal vacuum sublimator.[143]
Fig. 25 (right). Modified retort for vacuum sublimation.[146]

able in this apparatus. The sublimator was improved[146] by the introduction of two ground-glass joints, as shown in Figure 25. This rendered it capable of being readily disassembled, a feature of particular value in fractional sublimation employing a stationary source of heat. The retort is so shaped that it can be heated in any kind of bath, including a hot-air oven. The joint by which it is attached to the condensing tube, and the first few inches of the latter, should also be heated. At pressures of 0.5–17 mm., such compounds as alizarin and indigo were sublimed quantitatively. The apparatus was also found useful for the preparation of certain acid anhydrides from the corresponding acids, *e.g.*, maleic anhydride from maleic acid.

A sublimator of totally different design,[147] useful for macrosublimations, is shown in Figure 26. It consists of a large bell jar carefully ground to fit a glass plate. The joint is never heated and may be lubricated, since sublimate does not come in contact with it. On the glass plate rests a large crystallizing dish which serves as receiver for the sublimate. A hole is bored in this plate for introduction of the evacuating tube. Two corresponding holes are bored in the plate and this dish, through which are passed wires for an electric heater supported by a wide glass tube which prevents access of sublimate to the wires. The bottom is cut out of a glass crystallizing dish; this is then inverted and placed on the hot plate to prevent sublimate from reaching the latter. In the hole in the crystallizing dish is placed a platinum or glass dish containing the sublimand. In subliming such compounds as salicylic acid, it is important that the material should not come in contact with metal. The apparatus gives rapid, efficient sublimation of such compounds as naphthalene and benzoic acid.

Movable Heating Zone. By slowly and uniformly moving the sublimand end of a horizontal, tubular sublimator into the heating zone,[148] *e.g.*, a tubular electric heater, or by periodically moving the source of heat back along the tube,[149] *e.g.*, about 6 cm. each time, preferably with simultaneous increase in temperature by a few degrees, it has been found possible to obtain some degree of separation of two substances, through the deposition of more-or-less distinct bands of each material in the cooler part of the tube. These may show gradation in color, and their melting points and other properties may readily be checked.

In a modification,[150] a series of bulbs are joined by standard-taper joints, sublimand is placed in a round-bottomed flask attached to one end of the series, and a vacuum is applied at the other end. The flask is heated in a stationary heater and, by suitable control of the temperature, a series of fractions are collected in the various bulbs.

Zone sublimation has been achieved in a horizontal tube (Fig. 27) having, at each end, a close-fitting graphite plunger attached to a central, stainless-steel rod passing through an O-ring seal.[151] The space between

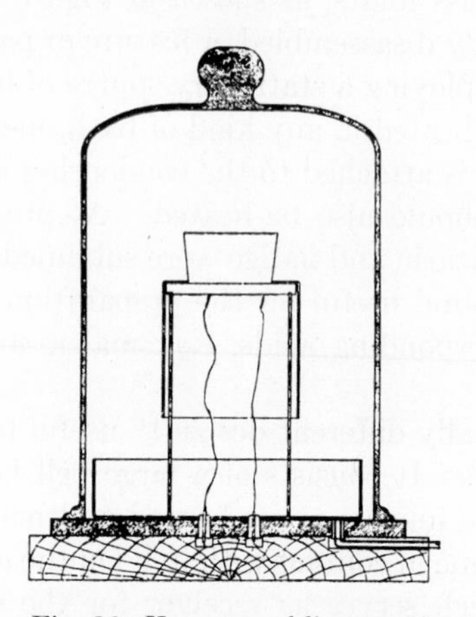

Fig. 26. Vacuum sublimator.[147]

the plungers is packed solid with the sublimand, and the tube is evacuated at both ends, between the plungers and seals. An annular heater surrounding a section of the tube is slowly moved from one end of the sublimand to the other. At the beginning, the plunger at the heated end is moved away from the sublimand by a distance equal to the width of the annulus; this part in the sublimand then moves along with the annulus until it reaches the other end, whereupon, the plunger at that end is pushed in until it touches the sublimand. After each pass, the zone moves by one zone width. Impurities may collect at either end, depending on their relative volatilities.

Graded Heating Zone. By use of a graded heating zone,[149,152] most readily obtained electrically, a great improvement in fractional sublimation results. Sublimand is volatilized at the closed end of the tube and the

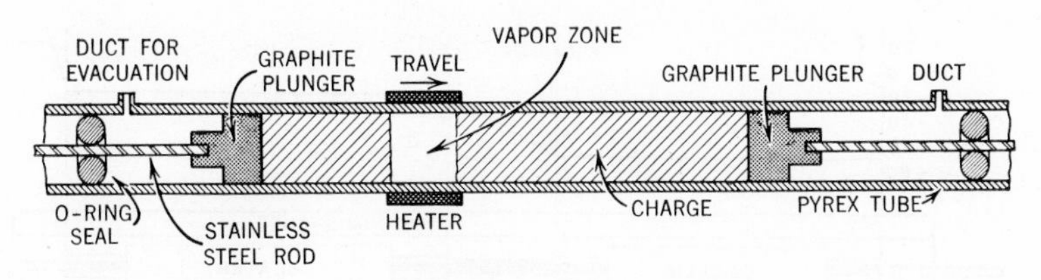

Fig. 27. Apparatus for vapor zone-refining.[151]

vapor is allowed to condense fractionally by controlling the heat throughout the length of the tube.

Liquid-Cooled Condenser. *External Cooling.* Quasisublimation, followed by true sublimation, has been used in freeing a sublimable substance from dissolved[153] gas, and in separation[154] of 3 substances normally gaseous at room temperature (Chap. IV). The mixture of gases is cooled until liquid, *e.g.*, in a vessel cooled in liquid nitrogen contained in a Dewar flask. The two more volatile gases are then allowed to vaporize off partly and are collected as liquid in a second cooled vessel. This liquid is again allowed to vaporize and the vapor is condensed to *solid* in a third cooled vessel. Finally, this solid is sublimed under diminished pressure, the occluded gaseous impurity being mainly removed in the process. Quasisublimation has also been employed[155] for isolation of crystalline *p*-xylene sublimate from a liquid mixture of *m*- and *p*-xylenes at a pressure below 10^{-6} Torr. mercury. A long evacuated glass tube containing the mixture was slowly and uniformly pulled through a temperature gradient maintained by a thermostat system. The temperature of the hot end was $-15°$C. and that of the cold end was $-70°$C. In this way, crystals of the *p*-xylene were obtained in the warm end, and liquid *m*-xylene plus some *p*-xylene was distributed along the gradient (see Fig. 28).

In a simple sublimator,[156] the sublimand is placed near the closed end of a tube, and the other end is surrounded by a cooling jacket. A vacuum is applied, and the tube is slowly pushed through a heater having a linear temperature gradient. An apparatus[157] for sublimation under diminished pressure is shown in Figure 29. It consists of a brass temperature-equalizer A, with thermometer well E, and a large cavity into which fits tube C, whose upper portion is cooled by the cylindrical water jacket B. Inside C rests a removable glass sleeve D. C is closed by a rubber stopper carrying a glass tube connected to the vacuum pump. The sublimand is placed on the bottom of C; on heating A, it volatilizes and is collected on sleeve D. The temperature at which sublimation starts may be accurately determined, and the sublimate may be removed intact on sleeve D. The constituents of a sublimable mixture may be removed in stages in a fractional sublimation, D being replaced with a replicate at each stage.

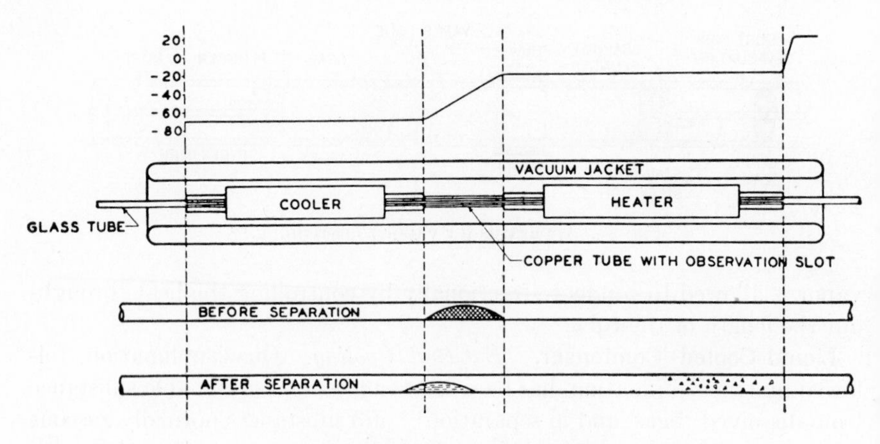

Fig. 28. Horizontal sublimator.[155]

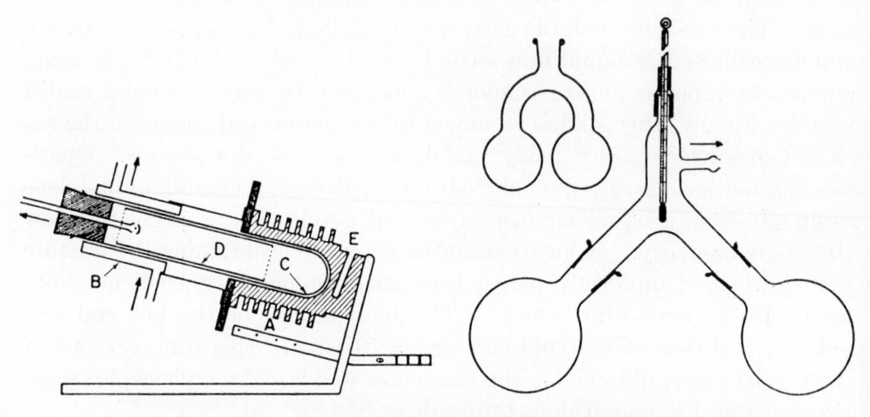

Fig. 29 (left). Vacuum sublimator with liquid-cooled condenser.[157]
Fig. 30 (right). Vacuum sublimator with liquid-cooled condenser.[158]

The horizontal vacuum device[158] shown in Figure 30 is not subject to clogging of the delivery tube. Loss on repeated sublimation is eliminated. The sublimand is placed in one flask, vacuum is applied, and the sublimand is gently heated until sublimate collects in the other flask, which is cooled by running water or dry ice–chloroform. If resublimation is necessary, the flask which had held the sublimand may now be replaced by a clean flask to act as condenser, and the compound resublimed, reversing the direction of vapor flow. Should it be desired to collect two fractions of sublimate without releasing the vacuum, the two-bulb flask shown may be used as the receiver; by turning it through 180° and cooling it, either bulb may be used as condenser.

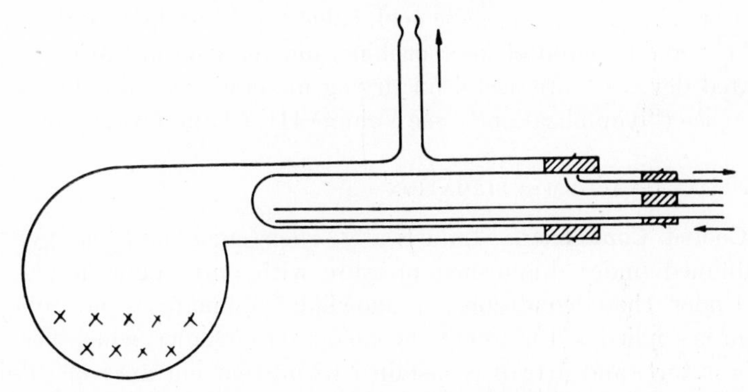

Fig. 31. Horizontal vacuum sublimator with liquid-cooled condenser.[159]

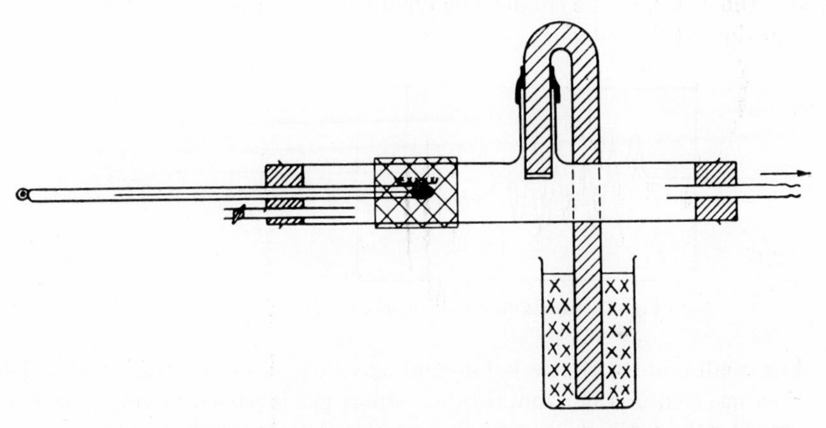

Fig. 32. Horizontal vacuum microsublimator with liquid-cooled condenser.[160]

Equipment of this kind may also be employed for sublimation of ice—the so-called "freeze-drying" (see Volume III, Chapter VIII, this series).

Internal Cooling. A self-explanatory design[159] of horizontal vacuum sublimator is shown in Figure 31. The apparatus has been modified[160] (Fig. 32) so that the temperature and pressure may be accurately measured. The condenser consists of a bent metal rod, one end of which is inserted into the sublimator and held in place by air-tight rubber tubing; the other, longer end dips into a receptacle containing a freezing mixture. To the flat end of the rod inside the sublimator is fixed a cover glass by means of a drop of glycerol. The sublimand is placed in a small platinum boat held onto the thermometer bulb with platinum wire. The thermometer may be pushed in or out as desired. The part of the tube to be heated is encased in copper gauze and then heated with a microflame. After 10 min. at 25 mm., good yields of sublimate were obtained with tartaric and succinic acids at 60°C.; citric acid, malic acid, gallic acid, morphine, and narcotine at 100°C.; and D-mannitol, apomorphine, and veratrine at 140°C.

Related devices[161] are useful for drying materials by subliming out the water as ice ("lyophilization"—see Volume III, Chapter VIII, this series).

D. ENTRAINER–VACUUM SUBLIMATION

Air-Cooled Condenser. Industrially, such compounds as pyrogallol are sublimed under diminished pressure with only slight admission of air. Under these conditions, a snowlike sublimate is not obtained. Vacuum is applied at the top of the condenser chamber, which lies alongside the retort, and a trap is installed to prevent entrance of sublimate into the vacuum pump. Pivoted baffles are arranged horizontally, one above the other, in the condensing chamber, which is provided with a discharge door at the bottom.

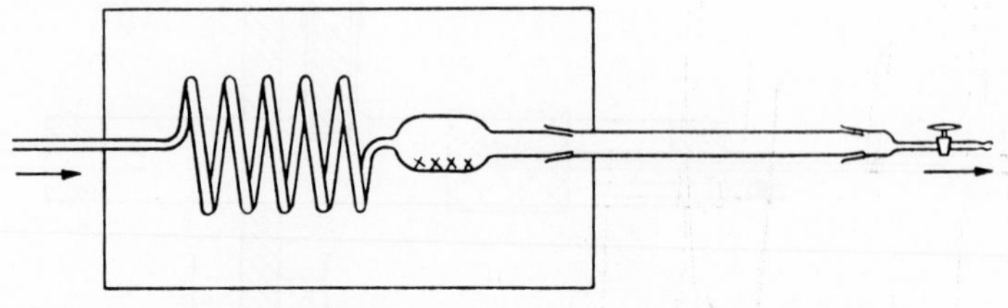

Fig. 33. Horizontal entrainer–vacuum sublimator.[163]

For small-scale work, the sublimand may be placed in a small boat which is then inserted in a horizontal tube. Inert gas is passed in very slowly at one end of the tube, its speed being regulated, *e.g.*, with a stopcock. Suction is applied at the other end of the tube. The section containing the sublimand is then gradually heated in an air bath or by means of a tubular electric heater;[162] sublimate collects in the cool end, to which suction is applied.

A *preheated* entrainer is employed in the apparatus[163] shown in Figure 33, which is particularly useful for hastening the sublimation of difficultly volatilizable compounds. A thin layer of sublimand is spread in the wide section of the tube which, together with the coil and the first ground joint, is heated in a hot-air bath. For the sublimation of compounds which are so readily decomposable that they may only be exposed to the minimum sublimation temperature for a short time, a kind of "flash" sublimation may be employed. The dry, finely powdered sublimand is added periodically in small portions, without breaking the vacuum, from a receptacle connected above the vaporizing chamber by means of a ground-glass joint. Additions of sublimand should be started after the apparatus has been

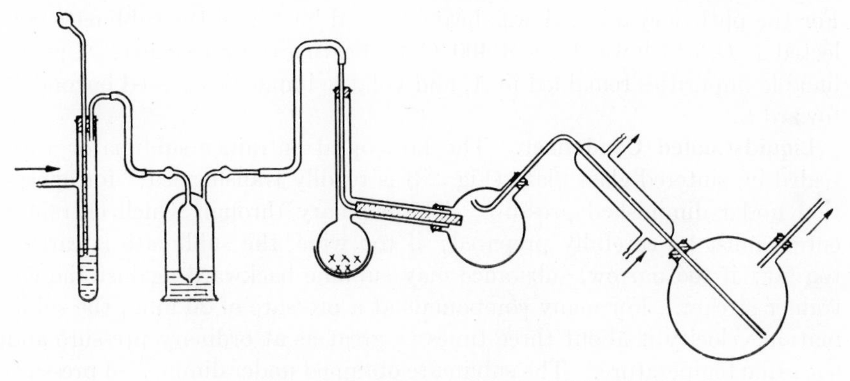

Fig. 34. Horizontal entrainer–vacuum sublimator.[164]

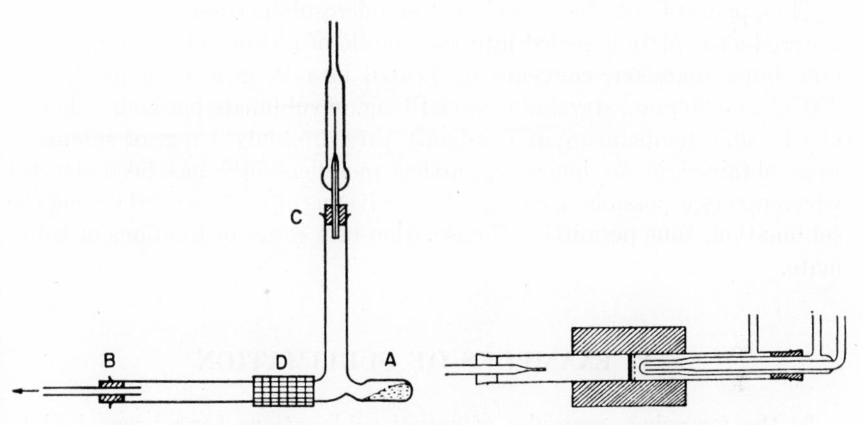

Fig. 35 (left). Entrainer–vacuum sublimation at high temperature.[165]
Fig. 36 (right). Horizontal entrainer–vacuum microsublimator with liquid-cooled condenser.[166]

evacuated and heated to the desired temperature. The device[164] shown in Figure 34 ensures complete condensation by cooling the entrainer with a water-cooled Liebig condenser after most of the sublimate has been deposited in the air-cooled chamber. The entrainer may be prepurified, and its rate of flow is readily regulated.

An apparatus (Fig. 35) made from the hardest glass is useful[165] for materials which do not melt but are sublimable at high temperatures, *e.g.*, phthalocyanins. Crystals over 1 cm. long were prepared by this means for x-ray study. The sublimand is introduced, through *B*, into *A*, and the apparatus then fitted together as shown. A pump and gage are attached at *B*, and a stream of inert gas, *e.g.*, carbon dioxide, enters through the capillary at *C*, preventing deposition of sublimate in the vertical arm.

For the phthalocyanins, *A* was heated to red heat, and the sublimate collected at *D*, which was kept at 400°C. by heating the wire gauze. Unsublimable impurities remained in *A*, and volatile impurities passed beyond *D* toward *B*.

Liquid-Cooled Condenser. The horizontal entrainer–sublimator with sealed-in, sintered-glass plate (Fig. 23) is readily transformed[166] for operation under diminished pressure. The capillary through which entrainer enters must be carefully prepared; if too wide, the sublimate is carried too far; if too narrow, substance may sublime backward against the entrainer stream. For many compounds at a pressure of 20 mm., the sublimation velocity is about three times as great as at ordinary pressure and the same temperature. The sublimate obtained under diminished pressure is compact, whereas at ordinary pressure it is fluffy.

The apparatus has been modified for microsublimation (Fig. 36). The sintered-glass plate is sealed into the middle of a tube, 14 cm. long, of 12 mm. outer diameter, conveniently heated in a Pregl heating block. At 230°C. and 20 mm., strychnine gave 13 mg. of sublimate per hour, whereas at the same temperature and ordinary pressure, only 4 mg. of sublimate were obtained in an hour. A further modification[167] has been devised which makes it possible to change the receiver as often as desired during the sublimation, thus permitting the isolation of a series of fractions of sublimate.

V. EXAMPLES OF SUBLIMATION

In the foregoing, examples of actual sublimations have been cited to illustrate the various devices and procedures. A few others, mostly of an analytical nature, are appended. Examples of direct sublimation of a compound from crude, natural product are the following: separation of caffeine from dried coffee or tea leaves, ferulic acid from asafetida, santonin from artemisia, gentisin from gentian root, hydrastine from hydrastis rhizome, and cinnamic acid from Sumatra benzoin.[168] Cantharidine may be sublimed from the dried cantharides insect or from powdered American blister beetles,[169] particularly after moistening with chloroform plus sufficient hydrochloric acid to render the material distinctly acid. The sublimate obtained from glycosides usually consists of the aglycon; if the glycoside is moistened with mineral acid prior to sublimation, the sublimate is almost certain to be the aglycon. This may often be employed as a rapid, simple means of identification[170] for the glycoside.

Many alkaloids are readily sublimed under vacuum.[171] Such pharmacologically active substances as caffeine, strychnine, morphine, barbituric acid, and phenacetin injected into animals are recoverable from the central nervous system by sublimation.[172] Fatty acids, cholesterol, and cholesterol esters may be sublimed from blood, brain, etc. In some cases, it may be necessary to prepurify the material. For instance, in determining vanillin in vanilla beans[173] by vacuum sublimation, the compound is extracted into a solvent, and the residue sublimed after evaporation of the solvent. This method is also said to be preferable in estimating the caffeine in coffee. A similar procedure is used in the determination of saccharin in foods,[174] *e.g.*, ice cream. Extraction with ethyl ether, and evaporation of the latter, gives a material from which the saccharin may be sublimed. Benzoic acid in ketchup may be similarly determined. Sublimation has also been applied to steroids,[175] amino acids and peptides,[176] dyes,[177] and metalloporphyrin complexes.[178]

Sublimation of ice is a useful procedure[179] for drying substances at low temperature. The stability of biological products is greatly enhanced by thorough drying under such conditions.[180] Palatable dehydrated milk, fruit juices, and meat[181] may be prepared.[182] At temperatures of -60 to -85°C., the rate of vaporization of ice[183] is 10^{-4} to 10^{-6} g. per square centimeter per second. Thus, for example, blood plasma or serum should be desiccated[184] below -10°C. until practically no moisture remains, and finally freed from residual traces while the temperature is allowed to rise to $+37$°C.

In fractional sublimation, some degree of preferential vaporization and recrystallization at any given pressure may be effected by close control and graded change of the temperature of the heating and cooling surfaces, provided that there is a pronounced difference in vapor pressure of the components of the starting mixture. Thus, caffeine is separable from theobromine by fractional sublimation. Sublimation has also been used in separating the nitration products of aminopyridines,[185] the *N*-trifluoroacetylated esters of amino acids and peptides,[186] and the metal derivatives of 8-quinolinol.[187]

With a stationary source of heat, the temperature of the retort may be gradually raised, and successive fractions of sublimate collected. These are progressively poorer or richer in the desired compound. If a horizontal tubular still is used, a movable heating zone (see Sec. IV-2C) may lead to the same result. Thus, after no more sublimate collects in the cool end of the tube, the temperature of the heater may be raised, the cold end of the tube moved farther from the heater, and a second fraction of sublimate collected.[188] At the end of the sublimation, the various fractions may be carefully scraped out by means of a long metal spatula, or the tube may be cut. An industrial method of achieving fractional sublimation is to heat the mixture gradually, *e.g.*, electrically, and collect a series of sublimates on a moving condensing surface.[189] Progressive condensation may also be brought about by passing the vapor through a series of condensers at successively lower, constant temperatures. Industrially,[190] in the separation of such mixtures as anthraquinone plus anthracene, or phthalic anhydride plus naphthalene, this may be achieved by dividing the boxlike condensing chamber, through which the vapors pass, into sections by means of parallel gauze screens from which accumulated crystals may periodically be shaken by the impact of swinging weights; each section is provided with a cooled baffle. Alternatively, the condensing chamber may be cylindrical and subdivided into a series of concentric cylinders[191] by gauze screens on which travel brushes for removal of crystals. The chambers increase in capacity from the center out, and the vapors are led first into the innermost chamber, which may actually contain the vaporizer. The purest product collects in the innermost chamber, the impurest fraction in the outermost, or vice versa.

The following examples illustrate fractional *vacuum* sublimation. 1-Hydroxyanthraquinone (0.200 g.) gave 0.165 g. of sublimate after 0.33 hr. at 130°C. and 9 μ; the same weight of 2-hydroxyanthraquinone gave only 0.063 g. of sublimate after 24 hr. at the same temperature and pressure. Hence, on keeping a mixture of the two isomers at 100°C. and 10 μ, the sublimate[192] was essentially the 1-hydroxy compound, which was collected and removed. The temperature of the sublimand was then raised to 180°C. and the sublimate consisted mainly of the 2-isomer. Separation was much sharper than by fractional recrystallization from a solvent. Similarly, salol is readily and almost quantitatively separated from a 50:50 mixture with phenacetin by first subliming out the former at 35°C. and 11 μ for 2 hr., and then subliming the latter at 120°C. and 13 μ for 0.25 hr. Again, certain soft drinks contain[193] both benzoic acid and saccharin; sublimation at 45–55°C. and 1–2 mm. during 3 hr. gives the benzoic acid, which is collected and weighed; treatment at 145–160°C. and 1–2 mm. during 3 hr. then gives the saccharin.

Proper control of the *pressure* in the system will also aid in fractionation. For example, a series of sublimates may be isolated at progressively lower total pressures, the temperature of sublimand and condenser being kept constant.

Fractional microsublimation is useful in the examination of drugs[194] and in pharmacognosy[195] and toxicology.[196] Thus, the characters of the crystalline sublimates from many drugs have been ascertained, and the behavior of mixtures of two, three, or more components has been studied.[197] Of 92 such mixtures, 61 were completely recognized by this method.

References

1. Hume-Rothery, *Phil. Mag.*, **28**, 465 (1939). Milosavlévić, *Chem. Abstr.*, **41**, 4347, 5766; *Compt. Rend.*, **224**, 731, 1345 (1947). Compare Elgin et al. *Chemical Engineers' Handbook,* McGraw-Hill, New York, 1950, p. 624.
2. Ramsay and Young, *Trans. Roy. Soc. London,* **175**, 37 (1884). Strübin, *Chem. App.*, **16**, 139 (1929).
3. Wolf and Weghofer, *Z. Physik. Chem.*, **B39**, 194 (1938). Dunken and Wolf, *ibid.*, **B38**, 441 (1938). Kitaĭgorodskiĭ, *Chem. Abstr.*, **40**, 6929; *Acta Physicochim. U. R. S. S.*, **21**, 379 (1946).
4. Ketelaar and Kruyer, *Rec. Trav. Chim.*, **62**, 550 (1943).
5. van Liempt, *Z. Anorg. Allgem. Chem.*, **111**, 280 (1920).
6. Duclaux, *Compt. Rend.*, 214, 78 (1942). Compare Verschaffelt, *Chem. Abstr.*, **21**, 1907; *Bull. Classe Sci. Acad. Roy. Belg.*, **12**, 644 (1926).
7. Hoffmann and Johnson, *J. Assoc. Offic. Agr. Chemists,* **13**, 367 (1930).
8. Kempf, *Z. Anal. Chem.*, **62**, 284 (1923).
9. Brown, *Trans. Roy. Soc. Can., Sect. III,* **26**, 173 (1932).
10. Kofler and Doser, *Die Chemie,* **55**, 13 (1942). Kofler and Kofler, *Mikro-Methoden zur Kennzeichnung Organischer Stoffe und Stoffgemische,* Universitäts-verlag Wagner, Innsbruck, 1948.
11. Staedel, *Ber.*, **11**, 1735 (1878).
12. Coolidge, *J. Am. Chem. Soc.*, **45**, 1637 (1923); **46**, 680 (1924). Coolidge and Coolidge, *ibid.*, **49**, 100 (1927). Compare Thomson, "*Determination of Vapor Pressure,*" in Weissberger, ed., *Physical Methods of Organic Chemistry,* 3rd ed., Interscience, New York, Part I, 1959, Chap. IX.
13. Dunkel, *Z. Physik. Chem.*, **138**, 42 (1928). Meyer and Mark, *Der Aufban der hochpolymeren Organischer Naturstoffe,* Akadem. Verlagsgesellschaft, Leipzig, 1930, p. 32. Hill, *Science,* **76**, 218 (1932). Meyer, *Natural and Synthetic High Polymers,* Interscience, New York, 1942; 2nd ed., 1950.
14. McDonald, *J. Franklin Inst.*, **221**, 103 (1936).
15. Hulett, *Z. Physik. Chem.*, **37**, 385 (1901).
16. Richards, *Z. Physik. Chem.*, **46**, 189 (1903).
17. Kraft and Dÿes, *Ber.*, **28**, 2583 (1895). Krafft and Weilandt, *ibid.*, **29**, 1316, 2240 (1896).
18. Kaischew and Stranski, *Z. Physik. Chem.*, **B26**, 317 (1934). Langmuir, *Phys. Rev.*, **2**, 329 (1913); **8**, 149 (1916); *J. Am. Chem. Soc.*, **38**, 2221, 2250 (1916); *Trans. Faraday Soc.*, **17**, 607, 621 (1921–1922). Volmer et al., *Z. Physik.*, **5**, 31, 188 (1921); **7**, 1, 13 (1921); *Z. Physik. Chem.*, **102**, 267 (1922).
19. Eder and Haas, *Mikrochemie, Emich Festschr.*, 43 (1930).
20. Langmuir, *Phys. Rev.*, **2**, 329 (1913); *J. Am. Chem. Soc.*, **35**, 122 (1913). See Miyamoto, *Trans. Faraday Soc.*, **29**, 794 (1933); Herzfeld, *J. Chem. Phys.*, **3**, 319 (1935).
21. Alty, *Proc. Roy. Soc. London,* **A161**, 68 (1937).
22. Shead, *Proc. Oklahoma Acad. Sci.*, **15**, 86 (1935); **16**, 87 (1936).
23. Liebig, *Ann.*, **101**, 49 (1857). Compare Jaeger, U. S. Patent 1,852,782 (1932); James, *Chem. Ind. (London)*, **34**, 595 (1949).
24. See Volume III, Chapter VI, this series.
25. Fuller, *Chemist-Analyst,* **29**, 6 (1919).
26. Cole, *Chem. Abstr.*, **17**, 1483; U. S. Patent 1,445,870.

27. Société pour l'exploitation des Procédés Abderhalden, *Chem. Abstr.*, **23**, 3034; French Patent 649,974 (1928). See also, Jackson, *Chem. Abstr.*, **17**, 1355; U. S. Patent 1,446,564; Timbrol Pty., Ltd., *Chem. Abstr.*, **33**, 5710; Australian Patent 107,040 (1939).
28. Lyford, *Chem. Abstr.*, **22**, 1255; U. S. Patent 1,662,070.
29. Field, *Chem. Abstr.*, **22**, 1366; U. S. Patent 1,662,056.
30. Comte, *Chem. Abstr.*, **29**, 1438; U. S. Patent 1,987,282.
31. Livingston, *Chem. Abstr.*, **29**, 1438; U. S. Patent 1,987,301.
32. Klein and Werner, *Z. Physiol. Chem.*, **143**, 141 (1925).
33. Krafft and Weilandt, *Ber.*, **29**, 2240 (1896).
34. Hansen, *Ber.*, **42**, 210 (1909).
35. Hill, *Science*, **76**, 218 (1932).
36. Ebert, *Ber.*, **64**, 114 (1931).
37. Kempf, *Z. Anal. Chem.*, **62**, 284 (1923).
38. Werner, *Mikrochemie*, **1**, 33 (1923).
39. Scott, Sinsheimer, and Loofbourow, *Science*, **107**, 302 (1948). Compare Christ, Burton, and Botty, *ibid.*, **108**, 91 (1948).
40. Aschan, *Ber.*, **41**, 1092 (1908).
41. Robertson, *J. Chem. Educ.*, **9**, 1713 (1932). Alzikovich, *Chem. Abstr.*, **42**, 3744; *J. Appl. Chem., USSR*, **20**, 460 (1947).
42. Krafft and Bergfeld, *ber.*, **38**, 254 (1905). McDonald, *J. Franklin Inst.*, **221**, 103 (1936). Beckmann, *Naturwissenschaften*, **9**, 305 (1921). Kempf, *Z. Anal. Chem.*, **62**, 284 (1923). Karrer and Rosenberg, *Helv. Chim. Acta*, **5**, 575 (1922). Hubacher, *Ind. Eng. Chem., Anal. Ed.*, **15**, 448 (1943).
43. Krafft and Dÿes, *Ber.*, **28**, 2583 (1895). Arctowski, *Z. Anorg. Chem.*, **12**, 417 (1896).
44. Spring, *Z. Physik. Chem.*, **15**, 65 (1894).
45. Oddo, *Gazz. Chim. Ital.*, **23**, 313 (1893). Tunmann, *Schweiz. Wochschr. Pharm.*, **48**, 749 (1910); *Chem. Abstr.*, **5**, 2695; **6**, 924, 2629; *Apoth. Ztg.*, **26**, 344, 812 (1911); **27**, 494, 507, 515 (1912); *Chem. Abstr.*, **6**, 916; *Ber. Pharm. Ges.*, 21, 312 (1912).
46. Kempf, *Z. Anal. Chem.*, **62**, 284 (1923).
47. Gorup-Besanez, *Ann.*, **93**, 265 (1855).
48. Kolbe, *Handwörterbuch der reinen und angewandten Chemie*, Vieweg, Braunischweig, 1850, Suppl., Lfg. 1–4, p. 425.
49. Helwig, *Das Mikroskop in der Toxikologie. Beitrage zur mikroskopischen und mikrochemischen Diagnostik*, Zabern, Mainz, 1865. Compare Pfeil, *Angew. Chem.*, **54**, 161 (1941).
50. Guy, *Pharm. J.*, **8**, 719 (1866–1867); **9**, 10, 58, 106, 195, 370 (1867–1868). Waddington, *ibid.*, **9**, 409 (1867–1868). Blyth, *J. Chem. Soc.*, **33**, 313 (1878); *Ber.*, **11**, 996 (1878). Lüdy, *Chem. Abstr.*, **27**, 2; *Pharm. Zentralhalle*, **73**, 209 (1932).
51. Kofler, *Pharm. Monatsh.*, **13**, 81 (1932); *Chem. Abstr.*, **26**, 3871; *Arch. Pharm.*, **270**, 293 (1932). Schürhoff, *Chem. Abstr.*, **26**, 4507; *Arch. Pharm.*, **270**, 363 (1932). Deininger, *Pharm. Ztg.*, **78**, 362 (1933). Kofler and Doser, *Die Chemie*, **55**, 13 (1942).
52. Schunck and Roemer, *Ber.*, **13**, 41 (1880).
53. Kley, *Rec. Trav. Chim.*, **20**, 344 (1901).
54. Shead, *Proc. Oklahoma Acad. Sci.*, **16**, 87 (1936). Rosenthaler, *Chem. Abstr.*, **27**, 451; *Apoth. Ztg.*, **47**, 1358 (1932).
55. Fischer, *Chem. Abstr.*, **32**, 4276; *Deut. Apoth.-Ztg.*, **53**, 361 (1938).

56. Joly, *Proc. Roy. Irish Acad.*, **2**, 38 (1891); *Phil. Mag.*, **25**, 301 (1913); **27**, 1 (1914); *Chem. News*, **107**, 241 (1913). Fletcher, *Chem. Abstr.*, **7**, 3580; *Sci. Proc. Roy. Dublin Soc.*, **13**, 460 (1913).
57. Fuchs, *Mikrochim. Acta*, **2**, 317 (1937).
58. Kutzelnigg, *Mikrochim. Acta*, **3**, 33 (1938).
59. Michel, *Chem.-Ztg.*, **36**, 138 (1912).
60. Fischer and Hepp, *Ber.*, **22**, 357 (1889).
61. Koehler, *Chem.-Ztg.*, **39**, 122 (1915).
62. Decker, *J. Prakt. Chem.*, **155**, 28, 222 (1893).
63. Llewellyn, *Chem. News*, **97**, 198 (1908).
64. Henville, *Analyst*, **61**, 104 (1936).
65. Nestler, *Z. Untersuch. Nahr. Genussm.*, **4**, 289 (1901); **5**, 245 (1902); **6**, 408 (1903); *Ber. Deut. Botan. Ges.*, **19**, 350 (1901). Frank, *Z. Untersuch. Nahr. Genussm.*, **6**, 880 (1903).
66. Landolt, *Ber.*, **18**, 56 (1885). Philippe, *Chem. Abstr.*, **6**, 3342; **8**, 1073; **10**, 1059; *Mitt. Lebensm. Hyg.*, **3**, 41 (1912); **4**, 351 (1913); **6**, 177, 233 (1915); **7**, 37 (1916). Müller-Hoessly, *ibid.*, **6**, 251 (1915). van Zijp, *Pharm. Weekblad*, **64**, 916 (1927). Jacquemain, *Bull. Soc. Chim. France*, **53**, 633 (1933).
67. Hertkorn, *Chem.-Ztg.*, **16**, 795 (1892). Nicolaysen, *ibid.*, **25**, 1031 (1901).
68. Morton, *Laboratory Technique in Organic Chemistry.* McGraw-Hill, New York, 1938, p. 215, Fig. 116.
69. von Fellenberg, *Chem. Abstr.*, **26**, 4733; *Mitt. Lebensm. Hyg.*, **23**, 97 (1932).
70. Exner, *J. Assoc. Offic. Agr. Chemists*, **1**, 208 (1915).
71. Benvegnin, *Chem. Abstr.*, **21**, 1033; *Mitt. Lebensm. Hyg.*, **17**, 315 (1926). Compare Philippe, *ibid.*, **3**, 41 (1912).
72. Hoffmann, Jr., and Johnson, *J. Assoc. Offic. Agr. Chemists*, **13**, 367 (1930).
73. Northey, private communication. Compare Fieser, *Experiments in Organic Chemistry*, Heath, New York, 1935, p. 232.
74. Robertson and Deakers, *J. Chem. Educ.*, **9**, 1717 (1932).
75. Bailey, *Ind. Eng. Chem., Anal. Ed.*, **12**, 194 (1940).
76. Baeyer and Fraude, *Ann.*, **202**, 164 (1880).
77. von Sommaruga, *Ann.*, **195**, 302 (1879).
78. Bourgeois, *Bull. Soc. Chim.*, **7**, 45 (1892).
79. Burkardt, *Anal. Chem.*, **26**, 1255 (1954).
80. Kaufmann, Medina, and Zapata, *Anal. Chem.*, **32**, 192 (1960).
81. Ashley et al., *J. Chem. Soc.*, **1942**, 103.
82. Riiber, *Ber.*, **33**, 1655 (1900). Compare Gettler, Umberger, and Goldbaum, *Anal. Chem.*, **22**, 600 (1950). Hausmann, *ibid.*, **26**, 619 (1954).
83. Liebermann and Riiber, *Ber.*, **33**, 1658 (1900).
84. Hubacher, *Ind. Eng. Chem., Anal. Ed.*, **15**, 448 (1943).
85. Rosenthaler, *Ber. Pharm. Ges.*, **21**, 338, 525 (1911). Compare Tunmann, *ibid.*, **21**, 312 (1911); Joly, *Phil. Mag.*, **25**, 301 (1913).
86. Schoeller, *Z. Angew. Chem.*, **35**, 506 (1922).
87. Kempf, *Z. Anal. Chem.*, **62**, 284 (1923). Kofler and Dernbach, *Mikrochemie*, **9**, 345 (1931). Fischer, *ibid.*, **15**, 247 (1934). Compare: Opfer-Schaum, *Pharmazie*, **2**, 540 (1947); *Suddeut. Apoth.-Ztg.*, **89**, 269 (1949). Maher, *Science*, **117**, 529 (1953). Petrucci and Weygandt, *Anal. Chem.*, **33**, 275 (1961).
88. Eder, *Chem. Abstr.*, **7**, 2832; *Schweiz. Wochschr.*, **51**, 228, 241, 253 (1913).
89. Eder, *Arch. Pharm.*, **253**, 14, 17 (1915). Wagenaar, *Chem. Abstr.*, **21**, 675; *Pharm. Weekblad*, **64**, 10 (1927); Eder and Haas, *Mikrochemie, E ich Festschr.*, **1930**, 43;

Eder, *Chem. Abstr.*, **8**, 398; *Vierteljahrsschr. Naturforsch. Ges. Zurich*, **57**, 291 (1912); *Chem. Abstr.*, **6**, 1204; *Apoth.-Ztg.*, **26**, 831 (1911). Buchi, Perlia, and Strebel, *Pharm. Acta Helv.*, **28**, 109 (1953).
90. Sckworzow, *Z. Angew. Chem.*, **20**, 109 (1907).
91. Viehoever, *J. Assoc. Offic. Agr. Chemists*, **6**, 473 (1923).
92. Clarke and Hermance, *Ind. Eng. Chem., Anal. Ed.*, **11**, 50 (1939).
93. Noyce, *Anal. Chem.*, **22**, 1581 (1950).
94. Nicolaysen, *Chem.-Ztg.*, **25**, 1031 (1901). Breusch, *Z. Physiol. Chem.*, **227**, 242 (1934).
95. Whittier, U. S. Patents, 2,106,779 and 2,106,780 (1938). Compare Milas, U. S. Patent 2,117,100 (1938).
96. Hubacher, *Ind. Eng. Chem., Anal. Ed.*, **15**, 448 (1943).
97. Viehoever, *J. Assoc. Offic. Agr. Chemists*, **6**, 473 (1923). Compare: Erdos, *Mikrochem. Mikrochim. Acta*, **36/37**, 417 (1951). Duncanson, *J. Chem. Soc.*, **1952**, 1753. Gross and Grodsky, *J. Am. Chem. Soc.*, **77**, 1678 (1955). Dufour and Pariaud, *Bull. Soc. Chim. France*, **1955**, 419.
98. Tiedemann, *Wiss. Veröffentl. Siemens-Konzern*, **5**, 229 (1926).
99. Hibben, *Bur. Std. J. Res.*, **3**, 97 (1929).
100. Riegel et al., *Ind. Eng. Chem., Anal. Ed.*, **15**, 417 (1943); see Fig. 17, Chap. VI.
101. Marberg, *J. Am. Chem. Soc.*, **60**, 1509 (1938).
102. Koehler, Hill, and Fearney, *Federation Proc.*, **7**, No. 1, Part 1, 165 (1948).
103. Burch, *Proc. Roy. Soc. London*, **123A**, 271 (1929). Morton et al., *Ind. Eng. Chem., Anal. Ed.*, **11**, 460 (1939). Bailey, *ibid.*, **14**, 177 (1942).
104. Carothers and Hill, *J. Am. Chem. Soc.*, **54**, 1557 (1932).
105. Strain and Allen, *Ind. Eng. Chem., Anal. Ed.*, **7**, 443 (1935).
106. Bailey, *Ind. Eng. Chem., Anal. Ed.*, **14**, 177 (1942).
107. Morton et al., *Ind. Eng. Chem., Anal. Ed.*, **11**, 460 (1939).
108. Nelson, *Ind. Eng. Chem., Anal. Ed.*, **14**, 153 (1942).
109. Hickman and Sanford, *J. Phys. Chem.*, **34**, 637 (1930); see Fig. 15, Chap. VI.
110. Kleipool, *Chem. Weekblad*, **43**, 123 (1947). Compare Koehler, *Chem. Ztg.*, **39**, 122 (1915).
111. McDonald, *J. Franklin Inst.*, **221**, 103 (1936). Compare Helin and Vanderwerf, *Anal. Chem.*, **21**, 1284 (1949).
112. Madorsky and Straus, *Chem. Eng. News*, **26**, 948 (1948).
113. Riegel et al., *Ind. Eng. Chem., Anal. Ed.*, **15**, 417 (1943).
114. Eder, *Schweiz. Wochschr.*, **51**, 228, 241 (1913).
115. Illari, *Chem. Abstr.*, **25**, 2880; *Ann. Chim. Applicata*, **21**, 127 (1931).
116. Viehoever, *J. Assoc. Offic. Agr. Chemists*, **6**, 473 (1923).
117. Werner, *Mikrochem.*, **1**, 33 (1923). Klein and Werner, *Z. Physiol. Chem.*, **143**, 141 (1925). Compare Malissa, *Mikrochem. Mikrochim. Acta*, **34**, 393 (1949).
118. Hortvet, *J. Assoc. Offic. Agr. Chemists*, **6**, 481 (1923).
119. Riiber, *Ber.*, **33**, 1655 (1900).
120. John and Fischl, *J. Prakt. Chem.*, **110**, 282 (1925).
121. Diepolder, *Chem.-Ztg.*, **35**, 4 (1911).
122. Kofler, *Monatsh.*, **80**, 694 (1949).
123. Christopher, *Proc. Chem. Soc.*, **27**, 236 (1911).
124. Hertel and Bergk, *Z. Physik. Chem.*, **B33**, 319 (1936).
125. Tollens, *Ber.*, **15**, 1828 (1982).
126. Wright, *Chem. News*, **103**, 138 (1911).
127. Bayer and Co., German Patents 332,196; 334,669; 343,319 (1919).

128. Pregl, *Quantitative Organic Microanalysis,* Translation by Fyleman. Churchill, London, 1924, p. 176.
129. Benedetti-Pichler, *Ind. Eng. Chem., Anal. Ed.,* **2,** 309 (1930).
130. Brühl, *Ber.,* **22,** 238 (1889). Tseng and Hu, *Chem. Abstr.,* **28,** 5718; *Science Quart. Natl. Univ. Peking,* **4,** 327 (1934).
131. Cornog and Olson. *Ind. Eng. Chem., Anal. Ed.,* **11,** 551 (1939).
132. Volhard, *Ann.,* **261,** 380 (1891). Hönigschmid and Birckenbach, *Ber.,* **55,** 4 (1922). Compare: Pino and Zehrung, *J. Chem. Educ.,* **31,** 476 (1954). Melhuish, *Nature,* **184,** 1933 (1959).
133. Perman and Davies, *J. Chem. Soc.,* **91,** 1114 (1907).
134. Andrews, Conover, John, and Ruth, Brit. Patent 179,991 (1921); *Chem. Zentr.,* **93,** 839 (1922); Selden Co., Swiss Patent 93,810 (1921).
135. Cole, *Chem. Abstr.,* **17,** 1483; U. S. Patent 1,445,870.
136. Robertson, *J. Chem. Educ.,* **9,** 1713 (1932). Compare Aĭzikovich, *J. Appl. Chem. USSR,* **20,** 460 (1947).
137. De Bruijn, *Chem. Weekblad,* **37,** 249 (1940). Compare Abrahamson, *Anal. Chem.,* **25,** 203 (1953).
138. Adickes, *Chem. Abstr.,* **38,** 2853; *Chem. Tech.,* **15,** 173 (1942).
139. Craig, *Ind. Eng. Chem., Anal. Ed.,* **9,** 56 (1937).
140. Fuller, *Chemist-Analyst,* **29,** 6 (1919).
141. Soltys, *Mikrochemie, Emich Festschr.,* **1930,** 275.
142. Volhard, *Ann.,* **261,** 380 (1891). Knocke, *Ber.,* **42,** 206 (1909).
143. Krafft and Bergfeld, *Ber.,* **38,** 254 (1905). Hansen, *ibid.,* **42,** 210 (1909).
144. Krafft and Weilandt, *Ber.,* **29,** 1316, 2240 (1896); **32,** 1623 (1899). Krafft and Dÿes, *ibid.,* **28,** 2853 (1895).
145. Compare Biltz, *Ber.,* **45,** 3662 (1912).
146. Kempf, *Ber.,* **39,** 3722 (1906); *Chem.-Ztg.,* **30,** 1250 (1906); *J. Prakt. Chem.,* **78,** 201 (1908). Compare Smith, *Anal. Chem.,* **20,** 1252 (1948).
147. Morey, *J. Am. Chem. Soc.,* **34,** 550 (1912).
148. Elbe and Scott, *Ind. Eng. Chem., Anal. Ed.,* **10,** 284 (1938).
149. Morton et al., *Ind. Eng. Chem., Anal. Ed.,* **11,** 460 (1939).
150. Schrecker, *Anal. Chem.,* **29,** 1113 (1957). Compare Flaschenträger, Abdel-Wahhab, and Labib, *Mikrochim. Acta,* **1957,** 390.
151. Weisberg and Rosi, *Rev. Sci. Instr.,* **31,** 206 (1960).
152. Almquist, *J. Biol. Chem.,* **120,** 635 (1937). Morton et al., *Ind. Eng. Chem., Anal. Ed.,* **11,** 460 (1939). Hickman, *ibid.,* **14,** 250 (1942). Compare Bates, *Chem. Ind. (London),* **1958,** 1319. Schmidt, *Mikrochim. Acta,* **1959,** 406. Sugisawa and Aso, *Chem. Ind. (London),* **1961,** 781.
153. McKelvy and Taylor, *Natl. Bur. Std. U. S., Sci. Technol. Papers,* **18,** 679 (1923).
154. Gray, *J. Chem. Soc.,* **87,** 1606 (1905).
155. Elbe and Scott, *Ind. Eng. Chem., Anal. Ed.,* **10,** 284 (1938).
156. Thomas, Sanborn, Mukai, and Tebbens, *Anal. Chem.,* **30,** 1954 (1958).
157. Hedley, *Chem. Ind.* (London), **44,** 752 (1925).
158. Bolstad and Dunbar, *Ind. Eng. Chem., Anal. Ed.,* **15,** 464 (1943).
159. Prins, *Chem. Weekblad,* **9,** 343 (1912). Freudenberg et al., *Ann.,* **494,** 57 (1932). Helin and Vanderwerf, *Anal. Chem.,* **21,** 1284 (1949).
160. Wagenaar, *Z. Anal. Chem.,* **76,** 224 (1929); **79,** 44 (1930); *Chem. Abstr.,* **24,** 993; *Pharm. Weekblad,* **66,** 1121 (1929).
161. Campbell and Pressman, *Science,* **99,** 285 (1944). Compare Pomes and Irving, *ibid.,* **101,** 22 (1945). Strickler and Schaffer, *ibid.,* **107,** 71 (1948); Holzman, *ibid.,* **111,** 550 (1950).

162. Pitha, *J. Chem. Educ.*, **23**, 403 (1946).
163. Kempf, *Chem.-Ztg.*, **42**, 19 (1918).
164. Gutbier and Payer, *Chem.-Ztg.*, **48**, 807 (1924).
165. Barrett, Dent, and Linstead, *J. Chem. Soc.*, **1936**, 1719.
166. Soltys, *Mikrochemie, Emich Festschr.*, **1930**, 275.
167. Hurka, *Chem. Abstr.*, **37**, 3302; *Mikrochem. Mikrochim. Acta*, **30**, 193 (1942).
168. Van Itallie, *Pharm. J.*, **112**, 31 (1924). Compare Zapotocky and Harris, *J. Am. Pharm. Assoc., Sci. Ed.*, **38**, 557 (1949).
169. Viehoever and Capen, *J. Assoc. Offic. Agr. Chemists*, **6**, 489 (1923).
170. Fischer, *Chem. Abstr.*, **32**, 722; *Arch. Pharm.*, **275**, 516 (1937).
171. Botolfsen and Paulssen, *Bull. Soc. Chim. France*, **1946**, 390.
172. Keeser and Keeser, *Chem. Abstr.*, **24**, 5066; *Arch. Exptl. Pathol. Pharmakol.*, **147**, 360 (1930).
173. Hortvet, *J. Assoc. Offic. Agr. Chemists*, **8**, 559 (1925).
174. Oakley, *J. Assoc. Offic. Agr. Chemists*, **28**, 298 (1945).
175. Lemberger et al., *J. Am. Pharm. Assoc., Sci. Ed.*, **43**, 338 (1954).
176. Gross and Grodsky, *J. Am. Chem. Soc.*, **77**, 1678 (1955).
177. Kunze, *Textil-Praxis*, **11**, 160 (1956).
178. Erdman, Ramsey, and Hanson, *Science*, **123**, 502 (1956).
179. Flosdorf and Webster, *J. Biol. Chem.*, **121**, 353 (1937). Flosdorf and Mudd, *J. Immunol.*, **34**, 469 (1938). Flosdorf, Stokes, and Mudd, *J. Am. Med. Assoc.*, **115**, 1095 (1940). Flosdorf, Hull, and Mudd, *J. Immunol.*, **50**, 21 (1945). Flosdorf, *Drug Cosmetic Ind.*, **57**, 188 (1945); *J. Chem. Educ.*, **22**, 470 (1945); *Modern Packaging*, **19**, No. 3, 133, 164 (1945). Bradish, Brain, and McFarlane, *Nature*, **159**, 28 (1947). Bradish, *Chem. Products*, **10**, 60 (1947). Meryman, *Science*, **130**, 628 (1959).
180. Craigie, *Brit. J. Exptl. Pathol.*, **12**, 75 (1931). Elser, Thomas, and Steffen, *J. Immunol.*, **28**, 433 (1935). Flosdorf and Mudd, *ibid.*, **29**, 389 (1935). Reichel, U. S. Patent 2,066,302 (1936). Scherp, Flosdorf, and Shaw, *J. Immunol.*, **34**, 447 (1938). Flosdorf, Boerner, Lukens, and Ambler, *Am. J. Clin. Pathol.*, **10**, 339 (1940). Mudd and Flosdorf, *New England J. Med.*, **225**, 868 (1941). Beckett, *J. Sci. Instr.*, **28**, Suppl. 1, 66 (1951).
181. Flosdorf, *Meat*, **22**, No. 5, 27, 58 (1945).
182. Flosdorf, *Food Inds.*, **17**, 22, 98, 100, 102, 104, 106, 108 (1945); *Chem. Eng. Progr.*, **43**, 343 (1947); *Freeze-Drying (Drying by Sublimation)*, Reinhold, New York, 1949; *Biological Applications of Freezing and Drying*, R. J. C. Harris, ed., Academic Press, New York, 1954.
183. Miescher and Tschudin, *Chem. Abstr.*, **40**, 2720; *Helv. Phys. Acta*, **18**, 456 (1945).
184. Flosdorf and Mudd, "*Large Scale Desiccation of Blood Substitutes from the Frozen State*," in Mudd and Thalhimer, eds., *Blood Substitutes and Blood Transfusion*, Thomas, Springfield, 1942.
185. Pino and Zehrung, *J. Am. Chem. Soc.*, **77**, 3154 (1955).
186. Weygand, Geiger, and Swodenk, *Angew. Chem.*, **68**, 307 (1956).
187. Charles and Langer, *J. Phys. Chem.*, **63**, 603 (1959).
188. Kempf, *J. Prakt. Chem.*, **78**, 213 (1908).
189. Fletcher, *Chem. Abstr.*, **8**, 1942; Brit. Patent 29,537 (1912).
190. Andrews, U. S. Patents 1,324,716; 1,324,717 (1919). The Selden Co., Selden, and Selden, *Chem. Abstr.*, **16**, 1341; Brit. Patent 173,723 (1920). *Chem. Abstr.*, **16**, 2242; Brit. Patent 174,013 (1920). Gibbs, *Chem. Abstr.*, **18**, 1071; U. S. Patent 1,484,260.

191. The Selden Co., Selden, and Selden, *Chem. Abstr.*, **16**, 2242; Brit. Patent 173,789 (1920). Adams, *Chem. Abstr.*, **18**, 2; U. S. Patent 1,470,950.
192. Hubacher, *Ind. Eng. Chem., Anal. Ed.*, **15**, 448 (1943).
193. Oakley, *J. Assoc. Offic. Agr. Chemists*, **28**, 298 (1945).
194. Dezani, *Chem. Zentr.*, **1916**, 1044; *Giorn. Farm. Chim.*, **64**, 394 (1915). Seifert, *Chem. Abstr.*, **35**, 2673; *Deut. Apoth.-Ztg.*, **55**, 576, 584 (1940); *Chem. Abstr.*, **37**, 2882; *Deut. Apoth.-Ztg.*, **56**, 600 (1941).
195. Kandersteg, *Chem. Abstr.*, **38**, 2787; *Schweiz. Apoth.-Ztg.*, **82**, 61, 81 (1944).
196. Bichsel, *Med. Tech. Bull.*, **7**, 103 (1956).
197. Weismann, *Chem. Abstr.*, **29**, 8237; *Pharm. Acta Helv.*, **10**, 125 (1935).

General References

Gambill, "Find Heat of Fusion and Sublimation," *Chem. Eng.*, **65**, 147 (1958).

Kofler, L., and Kofler, A., *Mikro-Methoden zur Kennzeichnung organischer Stoffe und Stoffgemische*, Universitätsverlag Wagner, Innsbruck, 1948.

Nord, "Sublimation," *Chem. Eng.*, **58**, 157 (1951).

Stull, "Vapor Pressure of Pure Substances. Organic Compounds," *Ind. Eng. Chem.*, **39**, 517 (1947).

Vernon, "Sublimation," in *Chemical Engineers' Handbook*, McGraw-Hill, New York, 1950, pp. 660–665.

Vogel, "Die heterogenen Gleichgewichte," in Masing, ed., *Handbuch der Metallphysik*, Vol. II, Akadem. Verlagsgesellschaft, Leipzig, 1937. Reproduced by Edwards, Ann Arbor, 1944.

Wilke, "Sublimation: Its Applications in Chemical Processing," *Chem. Inds.*, **63**, 34–38, 122, 124 (1948).

CHAPTER IX

CONTINUOUS DISTILLATION

Frederick E. Williams, *Hercules Powder Co.*

I. INTRODUCTION

Two general modes of operation are used in fractional distillation. The older of these and the one most commonly practiced in the laboratory and widely used in industry is batch distillation. Continuous distillation, by contrast, is very largely a process of large-scale industry. It is universally used in petroleum technology to produce a large variety of products from crude petroleum; in large-scale chemical production it is used to isolate more or less pure compounds, as in the phenol and ethylene glycol manufacture; in some industries, such as tall oil refining, it is necessarily used to minimize thermal hazard to the material being fractionated. While the common characteristic of these uses is large-scale operation, a definite requirement is that the composition of the feed to a continuous fractionation unit exhibit only moderate variations in composition. The latter characteristic makes it possible to determine fairly accurately and to build a column of the required separating efficiency for a specific separation under prescribed operating conditions, to determine operating costs and finally, capital outlay.

In batch distillation, a quantity of material is charged to the still pot of a fractionating column and subjected to the procedure discussed in Chapter II to separate more or less completely the components of the feed in accordance with their boiling points. Batch distillation is not, in a general sense, a steady-state operation, since the composition of the contents of the still pot and of the material moving up and down the column is continuously changing.

In contrast to batch operation, continuous distillation is ideally, and in practice closely approaches, a steady-state operation. Material of constant composition to be fractionated is fed at a constant rate directly into the column and flows downward against a rising stream of vapor generated at a uniform rate in the still-pot (generally designated as a reboiler). Vapor reaching the top of the column enters a condenser where it is liquefied; part of this liquid is returned to the top of the vapor–liquid contacting section as reflux, and part is withdrawn as product, as in batch distillation. Since the feed is continuously introduced into the column, and only a portion of the feed is taken off as distillate, the balance is removed continuously from the reboiler as bottoms product. The net result of this operation is to split the feed into a distillate of the more volatile components, and into a bottoms of the less volatile components. In its simplest form, a continuous column splits a feed into a distillate and a bottoms product; the composition of these two products is determined by the separating power of the column, the reflux ratio used, and the fraction of the feed entering each product. For example, a mixture of benzene, toluene, and higher aromatics can be continuously fractionated into pure benzene distillate and bottoms of the remaining aromatics plus a small percentage of benzene, or substantially complete removal of benzene from the feed can be effected if a small amount of toluene is allowed to pass into the distillate; theoretically if not practically, an infinity of splits can be obtained.

As a laboratory technique, continuous distillation has been used much less than batch distillation owing to the greater simplicity of the latter, and to its utility for analytical purposes. Furthermore, continuous distillation was for a long time considered to be impractical on a small scale, a belief which was more or less valid until adequate metering devices were developed for small-scale operations; these and the many developments in laboratory batch distillation during the period 1930–1950 were the necessary precursors of equipment for continuous laboratory distillation.

Interest in continuous distillation on a laboratory or pilot plant scale has arisen for several reasons. Increasing application of continuous distillation in industrial processing makes it highly desirable to use this type of processing during the laboratory and pilot plant stages in a development program. Recoverable yields and product quality of a process can be measured under conditions closely approaching those expected in large-scale operation. If the efficiency of the laboratory equipment is properly determined, the operation will provide a crosscheck on the column efficiency and operating conditions calculated as being necessary for satisfactory large-scale operation.

In some instances, thermal sensitivity of a material being processed may require the use, in the laboratory or pilot plant, of continuous distillation to minimize thermal hazard, the advantage here stemming from the greatly reduced time that material is held at a given temperature in continuous distillation as compared with batch distillation.

Lloyd[1] has discussed continuous distillation as a laboratory technique; he suggests that it is an excellent means of purifying mixtures containing small amounts of low boilers and high boilers in a large fraction of desired product. The low boilers are more efficiently removed by continuous fractionation than by batch fractionation, and the desired product can be recovered with good yield from high boilers with a somewhat lower average reflux ratio by using continuous distillation rather than batch distillation. Higher quality in the desired product can usually be expected with continuous than with batch operation.

Ellis[2] has given an excellent discussion of batch versus continuous distillation as applied to the separation of phenol and cresol mixtures.

II. THEORY

Continuous distillation is a steady-state operation amenable to theoretical treatment as discussed in Chapter I. Binary mixtures are easily handled by the method indicated, but for multicomponent mixtures, calculations for a particular separation become difficult, although modern computer methods allow such computations to be made in reasonable time. The basic graphic procedure for calculating the requirements for separating a multicomponent mixture was devised by McCabe-Thiele.[3] Much additional work has been done to simplify handling these problems; this work has been discussed in great detail by Gilliland and Robinson,[4] and most recently by Hengstebeck.[5] Although calculated requirements for a separation may be highly dependable, incorrect vapor pressure data, departures from laws of solutions, introduction of simplifying assumptions, unmeasurable interactions among components, vagaries of column design (particularly plate efficiency), and different plate efficiencies for different components of a given mixture, endow the best calculations with a significant amount of uncertainty. This may lead to expensive overdesign of a plant column, or unsatisfactory underdesign. This uncertainty appears to be a hazard of the art.

For laboratory or pilot plant continuous columns, overdesign is the lesser evil. If a packed column is involved, its separating power may be readily changed by adding or removing short packed sections. For general use, a continuous column should certainly have high separating power to make the location of the feed point less critical. On the other hand, a correctly located feed point makes full use of available plates, and permits use of a minimum reflux ratio during a particular separation. And there is always the possibility that a feed may have physical characteristics which will not allow a column to exhibit its normal plate efficiency or its expected H.E.T.P.; in these circumstances the "extra" efficiency will be welcome.

III. EQUIPMENT

In its simplest though not most desirable form, a continuous still is readily constructed from a batch column by providing a tubulation in the

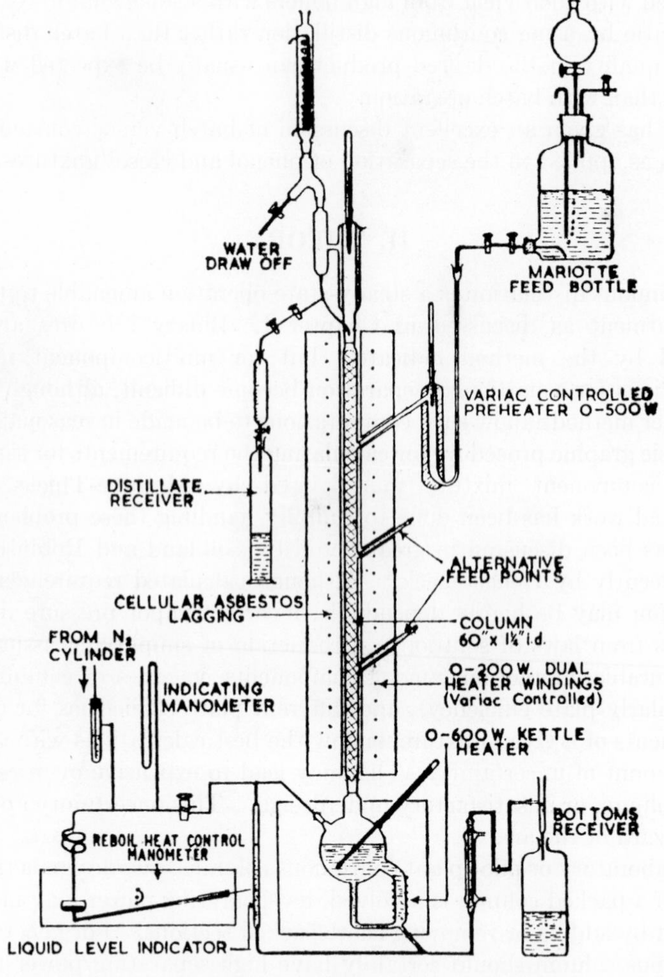

Fig. 1. All glass continuous distillation column.[1]

column for feed introduction at a point about one-third to one-half the distance from the still-pot to the condenser, and by putting an outlet tubulation in the still-pot for bottoms removal. Feed, suitably preheated, is introduced directly into the column, vapor is generated by heating the still-pot, and distillate is removed by a timer arrangement, or otherwise, as in batch operation. A somewhat improved version of this type of column is shown in Figure 1. Boil-up rate is controlled by the back-pressure manometer, and level control in the still-pot depends on a simple overflow arrangement which is adjustable to compensate for the slightly higher pressure in the reboiler as compared with that outside of the column. Severe bumping in the reboiler, by momentarily increasing the reboiler pressure, may force out excessive amounts of the reboiler liquid; in the arrangement shown in the figure, bumping is less likely to occur than in a simple round-bottom flask conventionally heated.

1. Column Construction

Column construction and sizing and internal vapor–liquid contacting arrangements for continuous columns for laboratory operation are quite similar to those used in batch operation. Fairly complete data for liquid and vapor capacity of columns packed with protruded packing are given in Chapter II. Several diameters and various operating pressures are included in the data. If vacuum-jacketed columns are used, two or more jacketed sections of suitable length for the desired separating power may be stacked in series, with tubulations blown into the connecting pieces as ports for the introduction of feed. Feed ports are similarly introduced between sections if the construction uses heat-loss compensating jackets.

The feed port divides a continuous column into two sections; the part of the column above the feed port is called the rectifying section and functions to minimize the concentration of higher boiling components of the feed in the distillate, and forces them into the bottoms product. The part of the column below the feed port is called the stripping section, and functions to force the lower boiling components of the feed into the distillate, and to minimize their concentration in the bottoms product.

As a general rule, a continuous column should be fed at a point where the composition of the liquid flow down the column is the same as the feed composition; otherwise, plates or their equivalents near the feed point are to some extent wasted. On the other hand, the possible number of feed points is limited; hence the practical procedure for laboratory operation is to use a larger number of plates than theoretically necessary to make a separation in order that the location of the feed port be less critical.

Column internals may be dump packings, bubble-caps, or perforated plates. There is some tendency to prefer the last two types since their large-scale counterparts are widely used in industry; dump packings have been found satisfactory, however, and have some advantage in that, where necessary, some adjustment of column efficiency can be effected by removal of some packing from a section, or by addition of another partly or fully packed section.

For general laboratory use, it is preferable to build a column efficient enough to take care of difficult separations. Feed ports at points one-third, one-half, and two-thirds of the distance between the bottom and top of the packed area will generally provide enough variation in the feed point to give good fractionation. In some easy separations an efficient column will be "loafing" to some extent, but efficiency will be available when it is needed.

2. Reboilers

Unlike its counterpart (the still-pot) in batch stills, the reboiler of a continuous column functions primarily as a vapor generator; its capacity is therefore secondary and need have only the volume consistent with providing adequate heat transfer surface for a desired rate of vapor generation, and a liquid surface consonant with easy vapor disengagement. In glass, some compromise will be necessary among these requirements since conventional electrical heating mantles provide only low heat flux for a given size flask. If the projected heating area of the flask is always covered with liquid, as it should be, the reboiler hold-up will be large relative to reboiler vapor generating capacity. Highet[6] has circumvented this limitation of commercial heating mantles by use of a reboiler of the thermal circulation type shown in Figure 1. High heat flux is possible and permissible in this design since the rapidly evolving vapor creates a pumping action to circulate liquid through the vapor generating area. Greater vapor generating capacity can be attained by using two or three heating arms instead of a single arm with a 600-watt heater, as diagrammed. This arrangement is especially favorable when temperature-sensitive materials are being evaporated; the larger heat exchange surface of a multiple-arm arrangement will permit a lower temperature at the liquid-heater interface for a given evaporation rate than is possible with the single arm.

Cylindrical reboilers mounted with their longitudinal axis horizontal provide a large vapor disengagement surface in a relatively small volume of liquid. For example, a cylindrical reboiler 4 in. in diameter and 12 in. long can be operated with only 500 ml. of liquid, yet will have a vapor disengagement surface of 42 sq. in., and can, with a little ingenuity, be fitted with an 800-watt heater of about 50 sq. in. area.

In metal construction the same reasoning holds. Rugged strip heaters are available, which may be purchased contoured to fit the lower horizontal external surface of cylindrical reboilers. Since these strip heaters generally dissipate about 10–15 watts per sq. in., it may be necessary to sacrifice low reboiler hold-up to obtain the desired evaporation rate.

If a reboiler is to be used in a continuous carrier distillation where dry steam is sparged through the liquid in the reboiler to bring about evaporation, a cylindrical reboiler should be mounted vertically to provide (at the sacrifice of low hold-up) a depth of liquid sufficient to insure good efficiency in the use of the steam. A finite time is necessary for the steam to become saturated with organics; hence the necessity for a relatively deep layer of liquid. This arrangement has been used satisfactorily in an all-metal construction;[7] the reboiler was 3.5 in. in diameter, and was fitted with eight 350-watt strip heaters. Evaporation rates of 6–7 liters/hr. of cumene and similar hydrocarbons were achieved; when steam carrier is used, the permissible evaporation rate is considerably lower because the steam is generally a large fraction of the total allowable vapor flow through the column.

It is apparent that for a given design of reboiler, residence time of the bottom product will be a function of feed rate, and of the fraction of the feed being removed as bottoms. With conventional designs, short residence time is impossible to achieve in all circumstances. It has been suggested[8] that an evaporator consisting of a closely fitting spinning band rotating at a few hundred r.p.m. inside an externally heated vertical cylinder provides excellent heat transfer characteristics and low residence time. This idea has been demonstrated in the Vacu-Film Processor,[9] and it can undoubtedly be adapted as a reboiler for laboratory continuous distillation.

Reboilers for pilot plant continuous distillation can be steam-heated multitube heat exchangers of suitable design and size. Hold-up in this type of equipment may be larger than desired for certain operations.

3. The Condenser System

The condenser system of a continuous distillation column may exactly duplicate a type used in batch operation; an example used by Highet is shown in Figure 1. A vapor or liquid dividing system of the type used in batch distillation, functioning through the action of a timer, will provide a more reliable control of product rate than will the stop-cock control used in Figure 1.

A more elegant but more complex condenser system consists of a simple tubular condenser in which all vapors issuing from the top of the column are liquefied and then pass to a primary distillate receiver near floor level. Two streams are drawn from this receiver by suitable pumps; one is the product stream, and the other is the reflux stream. The volume of the latter is equal to the product stream multiplied by the numerical value of the desired reflux ratio. The reflux stream is preheated to the temperature prevailing at the head of the column, and discharged onto the top of the packed section. By the simple expedient of maintaining the feed, reflux and product rate at prescribed values, and by maintaining a constant level in the primary distillate receiver the behavior of the column can be readily determined; shifts of distillate level indicate improper heat input to the reboiler and the direction of the shift indicates the adjustment to be made in heat input to the reboiler.

This type of operation assumes accurate foreknowledge of the feed composition (determined by a small-scale batch fractional distillation or, more probably, by gas–liquid chromatography), and assumes that the split between distillate and bottoms can be prescribed. When a distillate of high purity is being sought but is not being produced in the quantity expected, the reflux ratio can be increased, and the fraction of feed taken as distillate can also be increased until the expected yield is obtained, or until it is apparent that the separating power of the column will not provide the expected yield in the purity described.

4. Column Insulation

Insulation of continuous columns follows the same practice used with batch columns. Heat-loss compensating jackets are more likely to be used than are vacuum jackets. It is well to have a sufficient number of these along the length of the column to permit a reasonable gradient of compensation to be maintained in accordance with the temperature gradient naturally occurring in the column.

5. Special Equipment for Continuous Distillation

Since a continuous fractionating column is a totally dynamic system, its operation is most reliable when several items of equipment not required in batch fractionation units are used.

While they are not entirely essential, as will be indicated later, metering pumps to feed the column, to return reflux to the column, and to discharge distillate to storage, are desirable for the most satisfactory operation of continuous columns. Unless these three pumps operate with high reliability, the basic characteristic, steady-state during the operation, will not be attained.

Several manufacturers* produce pumps suitable for small-scale and pilot plant continuous distillation operations. The piston type pump appears to be the most practical, since it is usable at pressures up to several hundred pounds; it is available in capacities to cover a wide variety of pump rates, and is available in multiple units to handle the three streams to and from the column and to provide a fourth pump for metering water to a steam generator for carrier distillation.

The relative capacities required of the three pumps will vary consider-

* Hills-McCanna Co., Chicago, Illinois. Milton Roy Co., Philadelphia, Pennsylvania. Research Appliance Co., Box 307, Allison Park, Pennsylvania.

ably; generally the reflux pump should have the largest capacity, especially if a large fraction of a feed is being taken as distillate at a high reflux ratio. For example, if 80% of a feed is being withdrawn as distillate at a 10:1 reflux ratio, the reflux pump will be required to pump 8 times as much

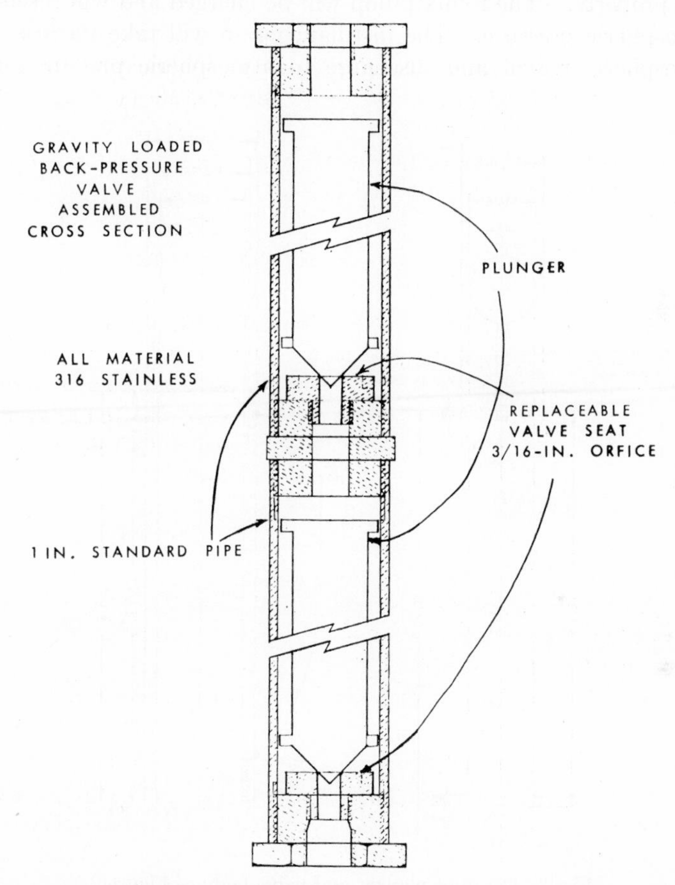

Fig. 2. Gravity loaded back-pressure valve. Silver soldered externally at top, middle, and bottom to prevent air leakage.

liquid as the feed pump. On the other hand, the distillate pump will never have to pump at as great a rate as the feed pump.

In some operations, an additional pump, one which is completely independent of the three or four previously discussed, may be used to withdraw bottoms product from the reboiler, on the command of a suitable level control, and discharge it to storage. For this purpose, the pump operates intermittently as required to maintain a uniform level in the reboiler.

The capacity of this pump should be in moderate excess of any expected bottoms rate.

Operation of a continuous distillation unit at reduced pressure requires total absence of air leakage into any of the several pumps if they are to operate properly. The reflux pump will be charged and will discharge at subatmospheric pressure. The distillate pump will take its feed from a subatmospheric region and discharge to atmospheric pressure, usually,

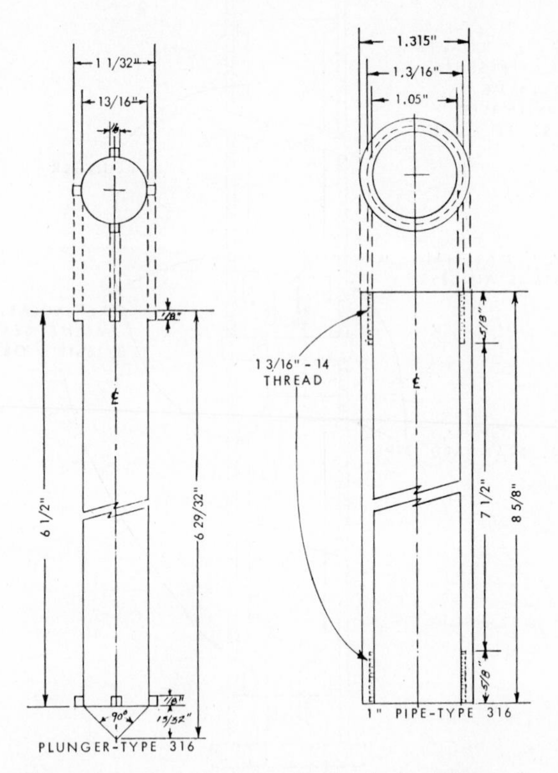

Fig. 3. Detail of plunger and valve body of Figure 2.

although at low rates better operation may prevail if the discharge is made into the pressure of the system. The feed pump is preferably fed from a source at atmospheric pressure; to prevent uncontrolled flow of feed into the column when it is operating at subatmospheric pressure, a spring-loaded or gravity-loaded back-pressure valve (see Figures 2 and 3) is installed in the discharge line from the feed pump. The weight of the plummets resting on the $^3/_{16}$ in. orifices requires a pressure of 34 lb./sq. in. to initiate liquid flow.

To ensure a leak-proof pumping system, it may be necessary to eliminate residual leakage with soft soldered joints. Some of the newer sealants* appear to do well in this service.

Hard metal gaskets in demountable check valves may have to be replaced by aluminum alloy or copper gaskets. Leakage of air into the pump cylinder through the packing gland is most readily prevented by evacuating to system pressure a lantern ring area between two units of flexible packing in the piston stuffing box;[10] this arrangement and the hydrostatic head on the discharge side of the pump will prevent any leakage.

6. Preheaters

In continuous distillation, two streams of liquid continuously enter the column; both the feed and the reflux at their source are below the temperature of the column at the point of their entrance into the column, and unless they are preheated to column temperature, a portion of the vapor rising from the reboiler will condense to provide from its latent heat the heat necessary to bring the liquid streams to column temperature. This condensation will introduce a significant error in the measured reflux ratio, and may cause unfavorable operating behavior.

Suitable preheaters should be installed on the feed and reflux return lines to add the necessary heat to these streams. The preheaters are electrical resistance windings of asbestos-covered nichrome wire which may be wound directly on glass lines or on metal lines covered by two layers of cross-wound, thin asbestos tape. Adequate thermal insulation should be provided for the preheaters; 85% magnesia pipe insulation functions well. When feed and reflux rates are sizeable, as they may be in larger installations, feed and reflux lines should be of such diameter and length as to provide the necessary heat transfer surface. Rough calculation will indicate the amount of heat needed for preheat. Close adjustment of the power dissipated in the preheaters can be obtained by use of variable transformers. Thermocouple wells immediately outside the feed and reflux discharge ports in the respective lines are necessary to indicate the proper feed and reflux temperatures, which should match those of the column at the entrance points. Above 100°C., steam-heated preheaters can be used but less readily than electric types.

In addition to the preheaters to heat feed and reflux to column temperature, the several pumps and their check valves have to be heated to temperatures sufficiently high to prevent solidification or development of unmanageably high viscosity of materials being pumped. Steam-heated pumps and check valves are available from some manufacturers for this

* Permacel, U. S. Highway No. 1, New Brunswick, New Jersey.

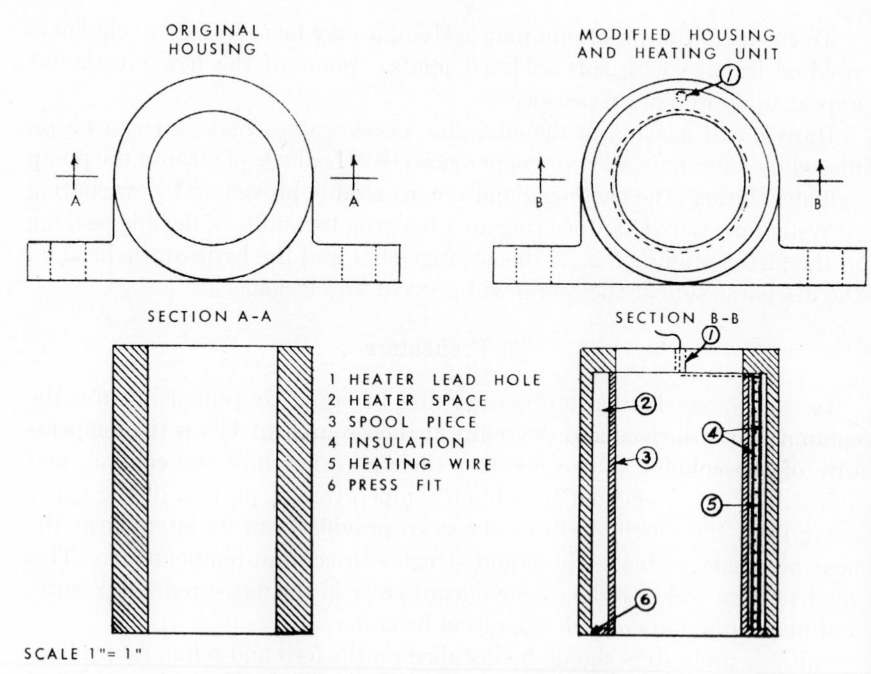

Fig. 4. Electrically heated pump housing.

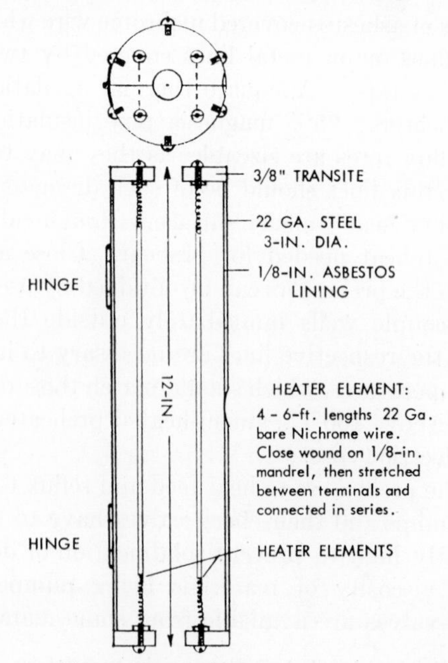

Fig. 5. Pump check-valve heater.

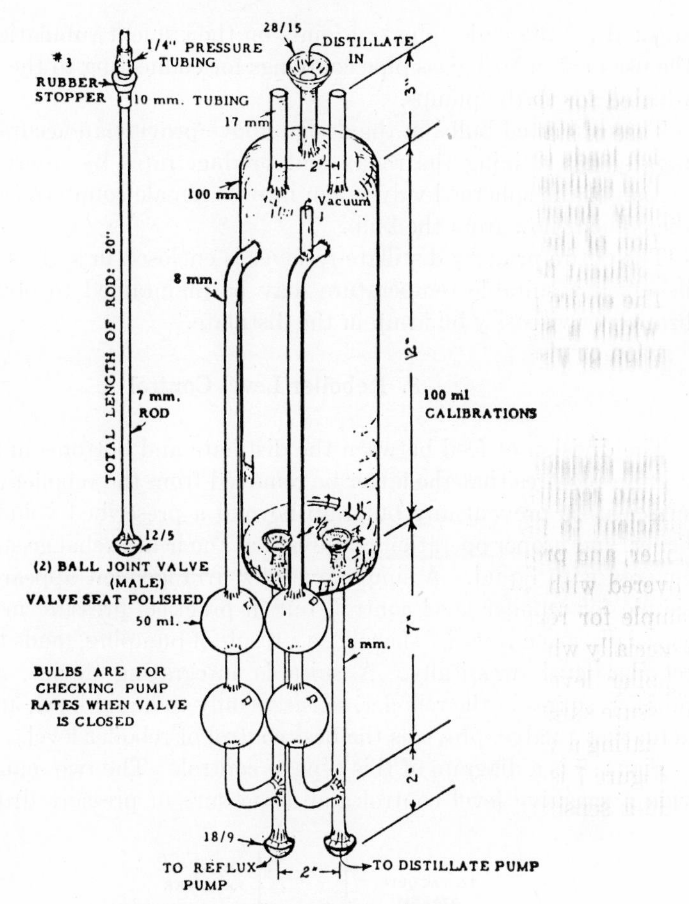

Fig. 6. Primary distillate receiver.

purpose, but the total set-up of valves, pressure regulators, and traps to provide the necessary range of temperatures is rather burdensome.

One manufacturer's* pumps and check valves can be heated electrically by the arrangement shown in Figs. 4 and 5. One end of the pump heater winding is connected to the grounded pump body; the other end is "hot." The controlling variable transformer must therefore be properly connected.

7. Primary Distillate Receiver

The primary distillate receiver mentioned earlier is made of glass as shown in Figure 6. Short sections of $^1/_4$-in. glass pipe flanges may be sub-

* Hills-McCanna Co., Chicago, Illnois.

stituted for the male spherical joints on the effluent tubulations to permit the use of standard glass pipe couplings for connecting to the metal tubing which leads to the pumps.

The calibrated bulbs in the design above provide an accurate means for rapidly determining the reflux and product rates by inserting the male section of the spherical valve stem into its female counterpart, and timing the effluent flow from the bulb.

The entire primary distillate receiver is enclosed in a glass-fronted oven in which a suitable temperature may be maintained to obviate crystallization or viscosity build-up in the distillate.

8. Reboiler Level Control

The division of feed between the distillate and bottoms in a continuous column requires that the latter be removed from the reboiler at a rate just sufficient to prevent any build-up beyond a prescribed volume in the reboiler, and proper operation requires that the heat exchange surface remain covered with liquid. A simple overflow arrangement appears temptingly simple for reboiler level control, but in practice, pressure in the column, especially when it varies sharply as a result of bumping, tends to change the reboiler level drastically. A suitable integrating device, insensitive to pressure surges in the reboiler, sensitive only to liquid level, and capable of actuating a valve, provides the best control of reboiler level.

Figure 7 is a diagram of this type of control. The two manometers provide a sensitive level control and a measure of pressure drop across the

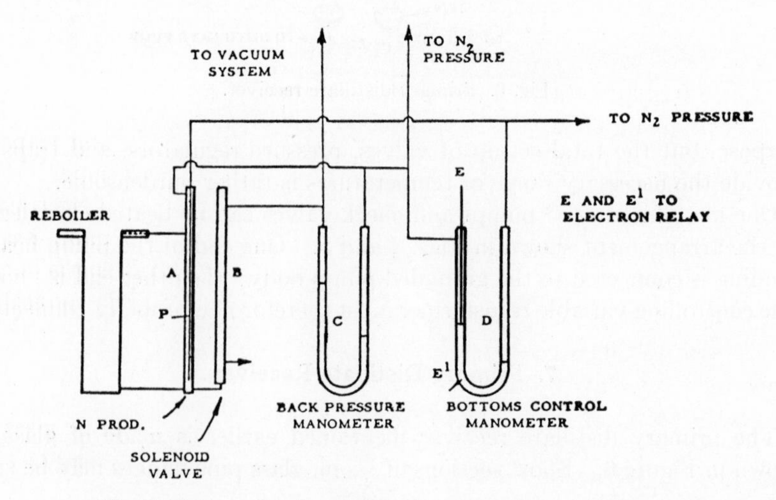

Fig. 7. Bottoms level control and pressure-drop manometers.

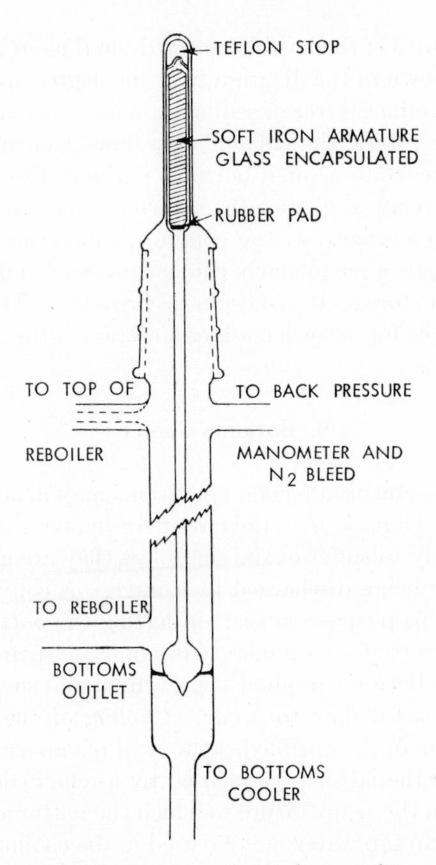

Fig. 8. Glass bottoms discharge valve.

column. Liquid in the level control manometer is ethylene or propylene glycol containing about 1% of dissolved sodium nitrate. This solution is sufficiently conducting to actuate an electronic relay when contact occurs between the liquid and the adjustable electrode. The electronic relay energizes the solenoid valve which opens briefly to allow a small portion of reboiler liquid to discharge until contact in the level control manometer is broken.

Another effective type of level control for all-glass equipment consists of a magnetically operated glass valve of the construction diagrammed in Figure 8. The valve is operated intermittently by a timer of the type used for control of reflux ratio. Once the on–off ratio of the timer is adjusted for a given rate of effluent flow, only occasional slight adjustment of the "off time" is necessary to maintain the proper reboiler level. Obviously, since the valve is flooded, the stem must be raised only slightly from the seat if wide departures of the level from the desired point are to be avoided. The Teflon plug shown in the diagram fixes the degree of opening.

If the bottoms product is free of sediment, which may cause malfunctioning of pump check valves, the effluent may flow from reboiler to the bottoms cooler and thence to a small bottoms pump. The latter is actuated by the electronic relay and operates intermittently to remove bottoms product directly to storage. If the column is operating at reduced pressure, use of a pump is a particularly convenient way to discharge bottoms product directly to storage at atmospheric pressure. The pump arrangement is most suitable for use when a large fraction of the feed is being taken as bottoms product.

9. Bottoms Cooler

The reboiler temperature in some operations may attain a level of 250–275°C. or higher. Organic materials at these temperatures are unsafe to handle and are likely to suffer oxidation unless they are greatly reduced in temperature before being discharged to storage. A convenient and automatic control for this purpose consists in letting the bottoms product discharge through a compact coil submerged in a liquid of such boiling point that solidification of the bottoms product is prevented and sufficient mobility is retained for the desired flow to occur. Cooling of the bottoms stream occurs by conversion of its sensible heat to heat of vaporization of the bath liquid; vapor from the latter is condensed by a reflux condenser attached to the bath. When the temperature to which the bottoms are cooled is not critical, cold or warm tap water may be used in the cooling bath, the water entering and leaving through suitable connections on the body of the bath. A single bath of proper construction can be used with both types of cooling.

10. Simplified Continuous Stills

In the preceding discussion considerable emphasis has been put on the auxiliaries used with a continuous column if it is to meet the requirement of wide utility and ease of operation under a wide variety of conditions. Simpler arrangements of equipment and controls have been used. Highet[6] has developed the arrangement shown in Figure 1. Aside from the continuous feed arrangement with its preheater, and the simplified version of the bottoms effluent control, this column is quite similar to a conventional batch column, and can be used as such by closing the feed port and bottoms discharge line.

Feed rate to the column is controlled by two stopcocks in series; Highet suggests a pump as an alternative. Excessive discharge rate of the bottoms

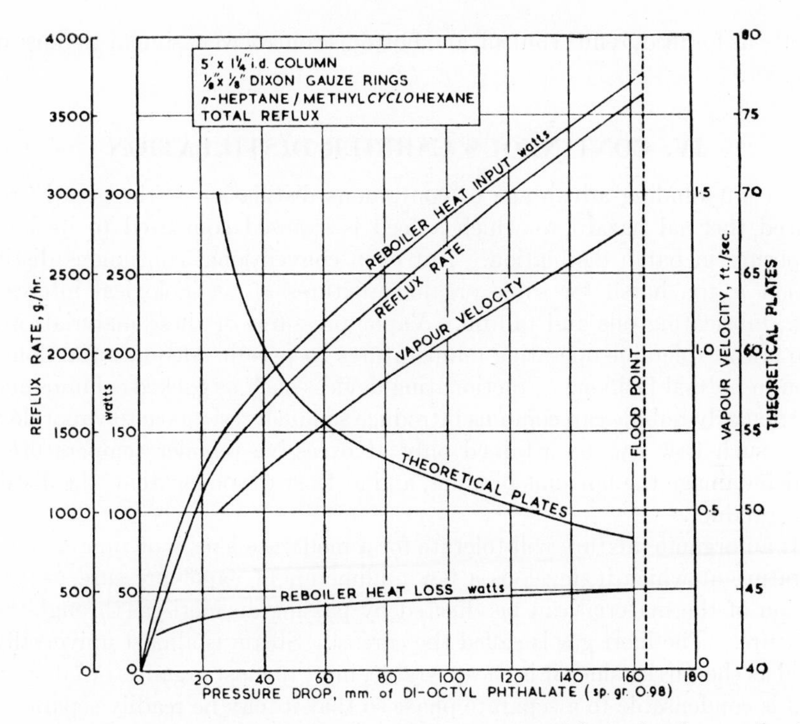

Fig. 9. Characteristics of column of Figure 1 measured during batch operation.[1]

as a result of bumping appears to be minimized by use of a capillary line to the bottoms cooler. Direct return of reflux to the column without preheating the liquid to column temperature may introduce some variation in the behavior of the column. Precise control of the reflux ratio is difficult in the arrangement shown in Figure 1. This problem may not be significant as long as the ratio is great enough to make a prescribed separation.

Figure 9 gives considerable information, experimental and calculated, about the column (as a batch column) under conditions of total reflux. Additional data is given in the original paper on the use of the column in the continuous mode of operation to separate the two isomers of di-isobutylene. From the known relative volatility of the two isomers, and the reflux ratio used in the operation, the Lewis equation shows that there were 24 theoretical plates above the center feed point and 28.5 theoretical plates below the feed, for a total of 52.5 plates. This is in good agreement with 50 theoretical plates measured at total reflux at comparable boil-up rates.

Beribauer et al.[11] discuss bench scale continuous distillation techniques as used for various refining and petrochemical investigations. The columns were vacuum-jacketed Oldershaw perforated plate columns;

methods for feed, reflux control, and bottoms control were similar to those of Highet.[6]

IV. CONTINUOUS CARRIER DISTILLATION

An outstanding advantage of continuous distillation is the greatly reduced thermal hazard to which a feed is exposed compared to its long exposure in batch distillation. But even conventional continuous distillation is too harsh for some organic mixtures of technological interest, e.g., lubricating oils and tall oil. Vapor pressures of these materials are too low at tolerable operating temperatures to permit adequate fractionation in normal fashion. Fractionating devices such as packed columns and particularly bubble cap columns introduce so much resistance to vapor flow that such flow can be attained only at excessive reboiler temperatures, which damage the bottoms product, and at least to some extent, the distillate product.

If an organic mixture will tolerate for a moderate length of time a temperature at which it develops a few millimeters of vapor pressure, evaporation of the material can be effected by passing an inert gas through the mixture. The inert gas is called the carrier. Steam is almost universally used as the carrier since it is cheap, stable, inert to most organics of interest, and is condensable to a separate phase so that it may be readily separated from most organic materials.

If the steam is 100% effective in its evaporating effect, the amount of steam required is given by the equation

$$\frac{W_0}{W_w} = \frac{M_0 P_0}{M_w(P_t - P_0)}$$

where W_0 = weight of organics; W_w = weight of steam; M_0 = molecular weight of organics; M_w = molecular weight of steam; P_t = total pressure in reboiler; P_0 = vapor pressure of reboiler contents.

It is apparent that by keeping P_0 as high as possible and P_t as low as possible, the steam requirements are minimized and become zero when P_t and P_0 are equal. The vapor load on a column used in carrier distillation is generally high (in moles) owing to the steam, and the liquid load will tend to be low. On the other hand, if a packed column is operated conventionally at a pressure of only a few millimeters (as measured in the reboiler), both vapor and liquid load will likely be very low. In a bubble cap column, the pressure in the reboiler cannot be lowered below a value equivalent to the total depth of liquid on the plates plus the pressure at the top of the column, regardless of the vapor flow.

Operation of a continuous carrier column is not greatly different or much more complex than that of a conventional unit. The reboiler temperature can be controlled automatically at a prescribed temperature; the evaporation rate is then controlled by the rate of steam injection into the reboiler liquid.

Separation of the steam and organics is readily accomplished by passing the effluent vapors from the column through a warm condenser to liquefy the organics at a temperature at which their vapor pressures are insignificant, but at which water will not condense (50–55°C. for a column operating at 50 mm. pressure). The steam carrying some entrained organics then passes through a warm entrainment separator, and then to a cold condenser to be liquefied. Organics draining from the warm condenser and entrainment separator pass by way of a U-tube to a distillate receiver to be withdrawn as product and reflux. The U-tube precludes passage of steam into the distillate receiver where unwanted condensate might form.

A small pilot plant continuous distillation unit suitable for conventional or carrier operation has been described.[7] The column proper is 4 in. in diameter and is packed with 10 ft. of 0.24 × 0.24 protruded packing supported at the bottom of the column on a 60° cone of $^{1}/_{8}$-in. wire screen. The column is center fed. Its efficiency is estimated from the measured efficiency of an identical column with 5 ft. of packing to be about 25 theoretical plates. Efficiency tests were made during fractionation by carrier operation of a mixture of 33% of palmitic and 67% of stearic acid, each of which was 99.5% pure.

The entrainment separator for carrier distillation consisted of a 36-in. length of 4-in. tubing packed with 24 in. of protruded packing supported on a 60° cone of wire screen. Steam and entrainment enter tangentially just below the cone; effluent steam leaves similarly and passes to the cold condenser. The entrance and exit tubes are 2 in. in diameter. The entrainment separator is heated externally by passing the "cooling" water from the warm condenser through a winding of $^{1}/_{4}$-in. copper tubing wound around the body of the separator.

This unit, as described,[7] has been modified to the extent that the cumbersome Dowtherm-heated feed and reflux preheaters have been replaced by resistance heaters on the feed and reflux lines as described under "Equipment" in this chapter.

Steam is generated by pumping distilled water at a controlled rate into a 40-ft. coil of $^{3}/_{8}$-in. copper tubing in a steam chest operating at about 75 p.s.i.g. The steam leaving the coil passes through an electrically heated line directly into the reboiler through a sparge ring at the bottom. Steam efficiency is high. The method for metering steam as used here is far superior to use of a flow meter and utility steam, particularly for low rates of flow.

This column has been unusually satisfactory and useful for both continuous carrier distillation and conventional continuous distillation.

V. OPERATING PROCEDURE

Inasmuch as a continuous distillation is a steady-state operation, a practical operating procedure requires that this condition be attained at the earliest possible time after start-up. To this end, the feed rate during start-up may be set at a somewhat higher value than will be used later during operation, and the boil-up rate is made as high as possible, but below flooding conditions, to produce internal (until the column is heated) and then external reflux until the dynamic hold-up of the column is satisfied. At this time, the feed rate may be gradually reduced to its prescribed value, care being exercised always to hold the reboiler level near its predetermined value. From this point on, operations consist in adjusting the vaporization rate in the reboiler to be thermally equivalent to the reflux and distillate necessary to provide the desired quantity and quality of overhead product.

A major help in the operation of a continuous column is an accurate analysis of the feed to indicate the possible splits and the one desired between overhead product and bottoms product. Selection of the split should precede any operation. Such analysis can be made by analytical batch distillation, or by the much more rapid gas–liquid chromatography.

As was noted earlier, a continuous column of adequate separating power operated at a sufficiently high reflux ratio can separate a pure component (barring azeotrope formation) from a volatile mixture; somewhat less than 100% of the pure component can be recovered as pure product, however. To isolate all the component from a mixture requires that some of the next higher boiling component be taken overhead with a loss in purity of the distillate. In a comparable batch distillation, pure component can be recovered until column hold-up, separating power of the column, and reflux ratio no longer permit pure component to be recovered. At this time, a mixture (break cut) of the pure component and next higher boiler begins to be produced; this change shows up as an increase in vapor–liquid equilibrium temperature, and serves as a more or less adequate guide for the batch operation. On the other hand, in a continuous distillation, the overhead product represents a certain proportion of the feed, and the vapor–liquid equilibrium temperature at the head of the column will be a function of the overhead composition. This may vary from a substantially pure component to a mixture of two or more components. The bottoms product composition will be changed at least quantitatively, and generally qualitatively, from that of the feed since qualitative change is a minimum objective of almost any distillation.

A suitable control point is frequently difficult to choose for a continuous column. For laboratory or pilot plant columns, it is usually possible to provide a batch of feed of uniform composition. This feed can be fed at a uniform rate to a column operating at a constant reflux ratio with a constant proportion of the feed being removed as distillate. The criterion of proper column operation is whether or not the overhead and bottoms products meet the prescribed compositions and is based on analyses of these products.

Gas–liquid chromatography will usually provide a quick analysis for this purpose. If a column of adequate separating power is being used, an increase of reflux ratio for a given split of the feed will tend to reduce lower boilers in the bottoms, and deplete the overhead of higher boilers. If the bottoms product is substantially free of prescribed low boilers, then a reduction of reflux ratio may be possible and still permit the desired quality of distillate and bottoms to be produced.

Any change of reflux ratio, or change in the split will entail several hours of operation to bring about a new steady state. Nothing can be done to shorten this time since the rate of attainment of steady state is a function of the material being fractionated, the equipment, and the operating conditions.

Since only two products, overhead and bottoms, may be taken from a continuous column at one time,* isolation of an intermediate product from a feed will require that, during a first distillation, lower boiling components be removed as distillate and a bottoms be produced which becomes the feed for a second distillation. During the second distillation, the desired product is collected as distillate, and a new bottoms is produced. On a large scale, two columns would generally be used in such an operation, although the same procedure can be used in laboratory continuous distillation.

A continuous distillation of the carrier type is operated below atmospheric pressure at an automatically controlled reboiler temperature sufficiently high to produce a significant vapor pressure (at least a few millimeters) in the reboiler liquid. Steam at a measured rate is sparged through the reboiler liquid to bring about evaporation of the reboiler contents. Heat requirements for the reboiler are those necessary to supply normal heat losses and heat of vaporization of the organic materials; the steam, even when somewhat superheated, supplies little or no latent heat for evaporation.

The vapor load on the column is usually quite high in carrier distillation owing to the carrier steam; the permissible liquid load is generally less than for a noncarrier operation. Separation of the organics and steam is effected

* Side streams are not considered in this discussion.

by the condensation of the former in a warm condenser operated at a temperature 10° to 15° above the dew point of a steam at the column pressure. Uncondensed steam then passes through an entrainment separator to remove suspended organics, and passes to a cold condenser to liquefy the steam and traces of organics (usually present) having finite vapor pressures at a temperature of the entrainment separator. These organic materials can usually be readily separated from the water phase as a homogeneous liquid and pumped or otherwise returned to the top of the entrainment separator to act as a scrubbing liquid to aid in removal of entrainment from the steam. In other respects, operation of the column is similar to a noncarrier distillation. The method previously mentioned, in which the total organic condensate is collected in a primary distillate receiver and subsequently split into a product and reflux streams, is unusually effective with carrier distillations.

Two somewhat obvious rules should be followed in feed preparation: (*1*) suspended matter in the feed should be minimized by passing it through a 100-mesh screen before it enters the metering system; and (*2*) suspended water in a feed should be kept at a minimum by proper settling. Remaining suspended water as well as dissolved water may appear with the distillate as a separable phase. This should be removed by a suitable separator before the organics are returned to the column as reflux, or taken from the column as product.

Despite close adherence to rule (*1*), certain complex feeds may precipitate insolubles on the plates or in the packing below the feed port as a result of solubilizing lower boilers being removed as distillate. The column may be partially plugged eventually as a result of the build-up of insolubles. A gradual increase of pressure drop over that normally found for a particular set of operating conditions indicates such a build-up.

References

1. Lloyd, *Petrol. Refiner*, **29**, 135 (1950).
2. Ellis, *Chem. Process Eng.*, **34**, 193, 280 (1953).
3. McCabe and Thiele, *Ind. Eng. Chem.*, **17**, 605 (1925).
4. Gilliland and Robinson, *Elements of Fractional Distillation*, McGraw-Hill, New York, 1950.
5. Hengstebeck, *Distillation—Principles and Design Procedure*, Reinhold, New York, 1961.
6. Highet, *Chem. Ind.* (*London*), **1950**, 783.
7. Williams, in *Vacuum Symposium*, Pergamon Press, New York, 1956.
8. Spurlin, private communication.
9. Arthur F. Smith, Rochester, New York.
10. Hills-McCanna Co., Chicago, Illinois.
11. Beribauer, Oakley, Porter, Staib, and Stewart, *Ind. Eng. Chem.*, **49**, 1673 (1957).

CHAPTER X

PILOT PLANT DISTILLATION

DONALD E. ORGEN, *Celanese Corporation of America*

I. INTRODUCTION

It is necessary to determine exactly what is the purpose of a pilot plant distillation unit before the design and construction can be started. This is the most obvious and logical first step. Unfortunately, it is not always taken. What data are to be obtained from the distillation or what role will the distillation play in the pilot plant? After giving the matter some thought, it may be decided that the pilot plant distillation unit is not needed at all. The pros and cons of pilot plants and pilot plant distillation units are discussed briefly by Scheibel,[1] Holliday,[2] and Grothe.[3]

Pilot plant distillations are generally carried out for three reasons or objectives: (*1*) product preparation, (*2*) process demonstration, and (*3*) distillation scale-up data. A pilot plant distillation may not be required if none of these three objectives exist in a particular case.

The significance of the product preparation objective is self-explanatory. If one of the purposes of a pilot plant is to prepare a quantity of product for evaluation, it is necessary to include a pilot plant distillation to separate that product from the reactants and obtain the required product purity. Often the main purpose of the pilot plant is to produce a product in sufficient quantity to determine its market acceptability and potential. In this case an adequate distillation unit would probably be a critical part of the pilot plant.

Process demonstration is another legitimate reason for a pilot plant distillation. It is not, or should not be, concerned with the feasibility of a distillation separation of the main products. The feasibility of this separation should have been established in laboratory equilibrium stills or distillation columns. Rather, the distillation should be concerned with trace components which may accumulate slowly in a recycle reactants system and eventually poison the reaction. By utilizing the pilot plant distillation unit in the same manner as the proposed commercial distillation unit in the process, some assurance is obtained that a build-up of a trace impurity can be prevented if the commercial column is equal to or better than the pilot plant column. If a trace component build-up is discovered, the pilot plant distillation will be useful in identifying this component and thereby indicating methods for its removal.[4]

The third and most controversial reason for a pilot plant distillation is distillation scale-up data. Many claim that a more accurate design of a commercial column can be obtained by using vapor–liquid equilibrium data and the operating data for commercial columns than from the scale-up of a pilot plant column.[1] This is undoubtedly true in most cases. However, there are times when pilot plant data are desirable. For example, pilot plant data are needed when considerable fouling or a chemical reaction occurs in the distillation column. Then it becomes necessary to determine the optimum feed plate location to minimize fouling or to obtain the specified reaction. These data are best obtained in a pilot plant.

Once it is decided that a distillation unit is necessary for a particular pilot plant, the question is what type of unit is needed? The natural tendency is to think in terms of continuous distillation units for pilot plants. This is unfortunate because in many instances a batch distillation unit is better suited to a particular pilot plant. The factors that must be considered in choosing between a batch and continuous distillation unit are:

(*1*) Process demonstration
(*2*) Number of products
(*3*) Thermal degradation
(*4*) Volume of material to be distilled
(*5*) Feed composition variability
(*6*) Cost

For a complete process demonstration, it is obvious that when the commercial process will use continuous distillation units, the pilot plant must have a continuous distillation unit; when a batch distillation unit is to be used commercially, the pilot plant must have a batch distillation unit. If the distillation operation is not required in the process demonstration, then factors (*2*)–(*5*) will determine which form of distillation unit should be used.

Batch distillation units are favored when there are a large number of products and by-products to be separated and where a relatively inexpensive unit is required. Although the batch units generally are less expensive than the continuous unit because of lower instrument costs, labor costs are higher because of the number of manual operations required in this intermittent distillation. A further advantage of the batch distillation is its ability to handle wide variations in feed composition.

Continuous distillation units are favored when there is a large volume of product and where there is a thermal degradation problem. Another advantage is the ability to fit the continuous distillation unit into a continuous pilot plant. Products can be distilled shortly after they leave a reactor and the recycle streams can be sent back to the reactor automatically. The use of a batch distillation unit with a continuous pilot plant necessitates the storage of large quantities of recycle streams for use in the pilot plant when the distillation unit is being cleaned and recharged.

All of these factors must be weighted and a choice made between the batch and continuous distillation unit. In some pilot plants, both batch and continuous distillation units may be employed. Once the choice is made, the distillation unit can be designed.

II. DESIGN

A pilot plant distillation unit must be designed to perform the required separation at the required rate. It is necessary that the design of the distillation unit receive the same attention as the design of the reactor in the pilot plant. It is not necessary, however, to obtain a definitive design as is done with a commercial unit. A pilot plant distillation unit must be designed with a sufficient safety factor so that it will be able to perform a more difficult separation than is initially contemplated. Substantial safety factors can be employed in pilot plant distillation design because the incremental cost is generally a moderate one. It must be emphasized, however, that some unit design calculations must be made to insure that the unit will at least make the required separation.

1. Batch Distillation Design

A. COLUMN DESIGN

The basis for designing a batch distillation unit to distill a set quantity of liquid in a set time is outlined by Bogart.[5] The McCabe–Thiele method is used to determine the number of theoretical plates required. An equation developed by Bogart is used to determine the vapor rate, and therefore, the distillation column diameter needed to complete the distillation within a given interval. Bogart's equation is based on a constant overhead product composition. The reflux ratio is varied during the distillation to maintain the constant overhead product composition. At the start of the distillation, the reflux ratio is low because of the high concentration of the more volatile component in the reboiler. The reflux ratio is steadily increased to maintain the purity of the distillate as this component is depleted in the reboiler. Several illustrations of this design method are given in the literature.[6–8]

The following procedure is followed in this design:

(1) The vapor–liquid equilibrium diagram is plotted on XY coordinates.

(2) The total reflux and minimum reflux lines are drawn on this diagram.

(3) An initial operating line of twice the minimum reflux ratio (external reflux ratio) is drawn on the diagram. This is the maximum reflux ratio which will be used in the distillation. It will be sufficient to separate the key components at the end of the distillation.

(4) The number of theoretical plates necessary to give the required product with this reflux ratio is graphically determined by the McCabe–Thiele method. These are the number of theoretical plates which will be used in the column since they represent the number required to make the most difficult separation, i.e., at the end of the distillation. The actual number of plates is calculated from the plate efficiencies and the safety factor employed.

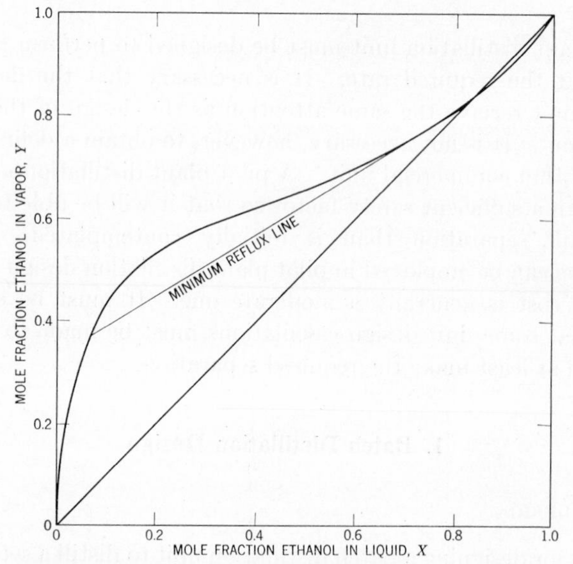

Fig. 1. Vapor–liquid equilibrium of ethanol–water system—minimum reflux line for batch distillation.

(5) The vapor rate is calculated by the Bogart equation. The column diameter is determined from this rate and the vapor handling capacity of the plates or packing.

This procedure is used in the design example which follows.*

Example—Design of a Batch Distillation Column.

Basis:

4,000 gallons per day of 70% ethanol is separated into an overhead fraction containing 92.42 wt.-% ethanol and a bottoms fraction containing 2.8 wt.-% ethanol. The actual distillation time is 20 hr./day.

* The symbols used throughout this chapter are the AIChE-ASA standard symbols as used and defined in Chapter I.

TABLE I

Vapor–Liquid Equilibrium of Ethanol–Water System

Mole Fraction of Ethanol	
Liquid phase, x	Vapor phase, y
0	0
0.018	0.179
0.021	0.199
0.033	0.272
0.050	0.353
0.054	0.3375
0.085	0.411
0.106	0.458
0.124	0.470
0.125	0.488
0.135	0.484
0.176	0.514
0.230	0.542
0.288	0.570
0.315	0.571
0.321	0.572
0.385	0.612
0.403	0.619
0.403	0.625
0.440	0.633
0.514	0.658
0.556	0.675
0.602	0.695
0.643	0.713
0.673	0.735
0.689	0.741
0.805	0.814
0.840	0.850
0.894	0.894
0.926	0.917
0.987	0.985
1.0	1.0

Calculate the column diameter and number of bubble cap trays needed to perform this distillation.

Data:

Molecular weight of ethanol	46.1
Molecular weight of water	18.0
Specific gravity of 70 wt.-% ethanol solution	0.871

The vapor–liquid equilibrium diagram for the ethanol–water system is given in Figure 1. This diagram is constructed from the data of Jones[9] and Bloom[10] which are combined and shown in Table I.

The design superficial vapor velocity in the bubble cap column is assumed equal to 2.0 ft./sec. so that the design can be compared directly to Bogart's design which used that value. Actually, 5–12 ft./sec. superficial vapor velocities are generally used.[11]

Calculation:

First, convert feed and product compositions to mole fractions.

$$\text{Total feed} = (4000 \text{ gal.})(0.1337 \text{ ft.}^3/\text{gal.})(62.4 \text{ lb./ft.}^3)(0.871) = 29{,}000 \text{ lb.}$$

$$\text{Ethanol in feed} = \frac{(0.70)(29{,}000 \text{ lb.})}{46.1 \text{ lb./lb. mole}} = 440 \text{ lb. moles}$$

$$\text{Water in feed} = \frac{(0.30)(29{,}000 \text{ lb.})}{18.0 \text{ lb./lb. mole}} = 484 \text{ lb. moles}$$

$$\text{Total number of feed moles} = S_0 = 440 + 484 = 924 \text{ lb. moles}$$

$$\text{Mole fraction of ethanol in feed} = \frac{440 \text{ lb. moles}}{924 \text{ lb. moles}} = 0.476$$

$$\text{Ethanol in 100 lb. of overhead product} = \frac{(0.9242)(100 \text{ lb.})}{46.1 \text{ lb./lb. mole}} = 2.00 \text{ lb. moles}$$

$$\text{Water in 100 lb. of overhead product} = \frac{(0.0758)(100 \text{ lb.})}{18.0 \text{ lb./lb. mole}} = 0.421 \text{ lb. moles}$$

$$\text{Mole fraction of ethanol in overhead product} = \frac{2.00 \text{ lb. moles}}{(2.00 + 0.421) \text{ lb. moles}} = 0.826$$

In like manner, the mole fractions are calculated for the bottoms product. A tabulated summary of the mole fractions is given in the following table.

	Mole fraction of ethanol	Symbol
Feed	0.476	x_{s0}
Overhead product	0.826	x_{Dc}
Bottoms product	0.011	x_s

The minimum reflux line is obtained from the McCabe–Thiele diagram in Figure 1. The minimum reflux line in batch distillation is the line connecting the 45° diagonal at the overhead composition and the equilibrium line at a point whose x coordinate is equal to the bottoms composition.

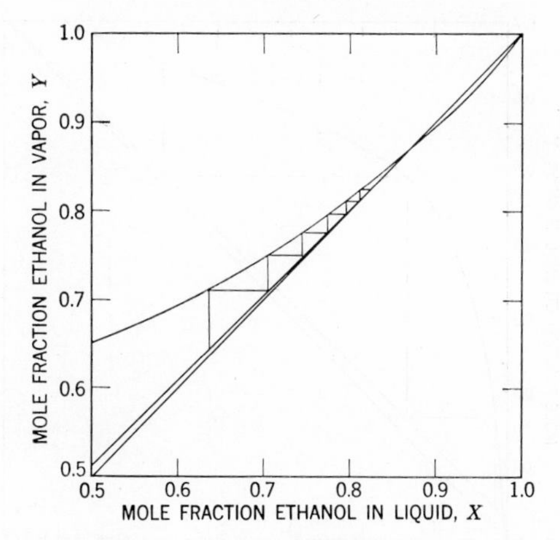

Fig. 2. Calculation of theoretical plates—batch distillation.

Since the equation of the operating line is

$$y_{n-1} = \frac{L}{V} x_n + \frac{D}{V} x_D$$

the internal reflux ratio, L/V, is calculated from the slope of the operating line. The external reflux ratio, L/D, is calculated from

$$L/D = \frac{L/V}{(1 - L/V)}$$

In Figure 1, the slope of the minimum reflux operating line is equal to 0.880. Therefore,

$$L/D = \frac{0.880}{1 - 0.880}$$
$$= 7.34$$

The maximum reflux ratio which is used in the distillation is equal to twice the minimum reflux ratio.

$$\text{Maximum Reflux Ratio} = (2)(7.34)$$
$$= 14.7$$

The operating line slope is calculated from

$$L/V = \frac{L/D}{1 + \mathrm{L/D}}$$
$$= \frac{14.7}{1 + 14.7}$$
$$= 0.936$$

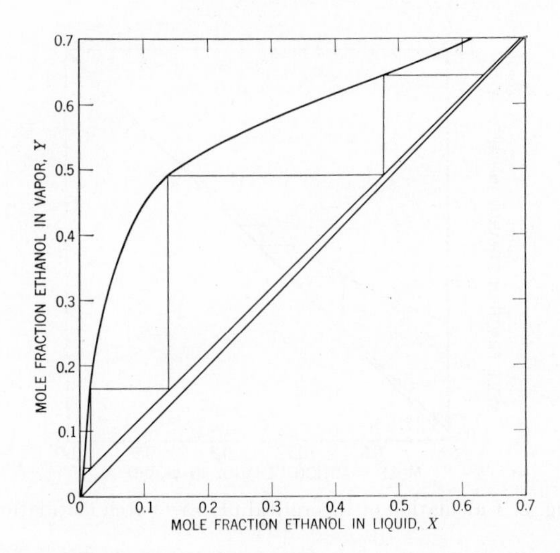

Fig. 3. Calculation of theoretical plates—batch distillation.

Using this operating line, the number of theoretical plates are obtained by the McCabe–Thiele method as shown in Figures 2 and 3. Ten theoretical plates are the number required.

The McCabe–Thiele graphic method does not strictly apply in this distillation because of the different molar heats of vaporization of ethanol and water, 9400 and 9729 cal./g. mole, respectively, at their normal boiling points. The operating lines on the McCabe–Thiele diagram are calculated on the assumption of constant molar overflow which means the liquids must have the same molar heat of vaporization. However, the difference of the heats of vaporization between ethanol and water is not critical in this case since Bogart[5] calculated the same number of theoretical plates for this separation after correcting for the difference in the molar heat of vaporization.

The Bogart equation must be solved in order to obtain the vapor rate needed to distill the feed in the specified time, θ,

$$\theta = \frac{S_0(x_{Dc} - x_{s0})}{V} \int_{x_{sF}}^{x_{so}} \frac{dx_s}{(1 - L/V)(x_{Dc} - x_s)^2}$$

Since the overhead product is being held constant by varying the reflux ratio, the two variables in the integral are L/V and x_s. To integrate this function, operating lines having different L/V values are drawn on the vapor–liquid equilibrium diagram and the McCabe–Thiele method is used to determine the x_s value with a ten theoretical plate column (Fig. 4). A graphical integration of a plot of x_s vs. $[(1 - L/V)(x_{Dc} - x_s)^2]^{-1}$ gives the

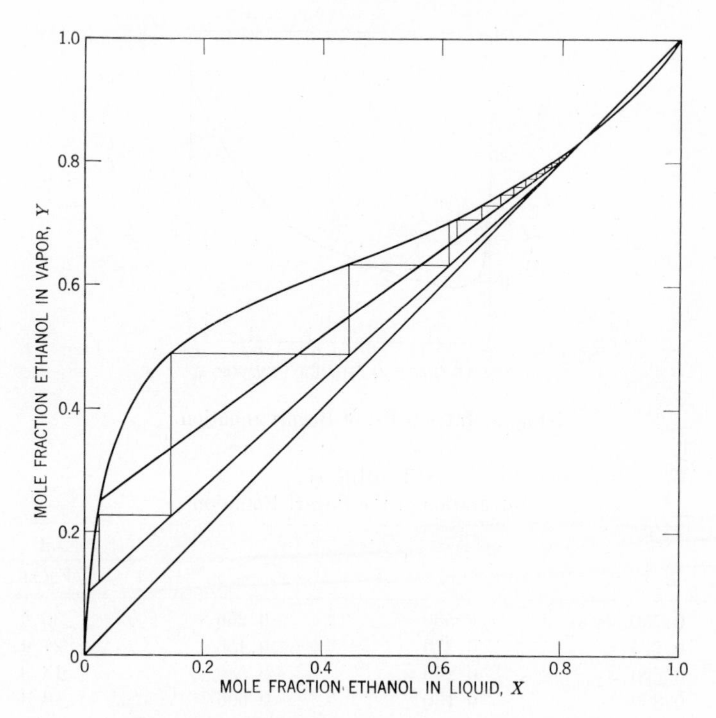

Fig. 4. Calculation of x_s for Bogart equation.

value of the integral. A tabulation of the calculations are in Table II and the graphical integration is shown in Figure 5.

Substitution of the calculated and known values into the Bogart equation gives

$$20 = \frac{(924)(0.826 - 0.476)(8.83)}{V}$$

$$V = 143 \text{ lb. moles/hr.}$$

At 760 mm. Hg pressure, the overhead temperature is 173°F., and the vapor volume is

$$\text{Vapor volume} = \frac{(143 \text{ lb. moles/hr.})(359 \text{ ft.}^3/\text{lb. mole})(173 + 460)\ ^\circ\text{R.}}{(3600 \text{ sec./hr.})(32 + 460)\ ^\circ\text{R.}}$$

$$= 18.4 \text{ ft.}^3/\text{sec.}$$

The column diameter is calculated from the vapor volume and the specified superficial vapor velocity.

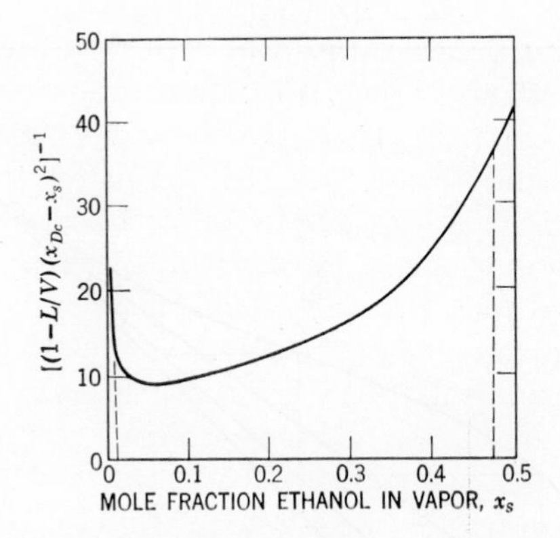

Fig. 5. Integration of Bogart equation.

TABLE II
Integration of the Bogart Equation

L/V	x_s	$x_{Dc} - x_s$	$\dfrac{1}{(1 - L/V)(x_{Dc} - x_s)^2}$
0.750	0.560	0.266	56.4
0.775	0.370	0.456	21.4
0.790	0.240	0.586	13.9
0.800	0.130	0.696	10.3
0.840	0.025	0.801	9.8
0.875	0.012	0.814	12.1
0.936	0.005	0.821	23.2

$$\text{Superficial vapor velocity} = \frac{\text{Vapor volume}}{\text{Cross-sectional column area}}$$

$$2.0 \text{ ft./sec.} = \frac{18.4 \text{ ft.}^3/\text{sec.}}{(\pi/4)(D^2)}$$

$$= 3.42 \text{ ft. or } 41.1 \text{ in.}$$

This value compares closely to the more rigorously calculated value of 38.4 in. obtained by Bogart.

B. REBOILER

The two most important criteria in designing the reboiler are the volume of distilland and the boil-up rate. The volume of distilland determines the volume of the reboiler and the boil-up rate determines the heat transfer area of the reboiler. The volume of distilland and the boil-up rate should be large enough to separate products as rapidly as they are made by the pilot plant. It must be recognized that a batch distillation unit requires time to charge the reboiler, attain equilibrium, and clean the unit after the distillation is completed, in addition to the actual distillation. The time needed for these operations will vary depending upon the products and the skill of the operator. The size of the reboiler, therefore, will depend upon the production rate of the pilot plant and the per cent of distillation time that can be attained each day. The amount of liquid charged to the reboiler should not exceed $^{2}/_{3}$'s of its capacity. This will allow sufficient vapor space above the liquid for thermal expansion. Therefore, with the previous example, the reboiler volume would be (3/2)(4000 gal.) or 6000 gals.

Sufficient heat transfer area must be allotted to the reboiler to obtain the maximum vapor rate calculated for the column. For example, in the previous calculation the vapor rate was calculated as 143 lb. moles/hr. in order to perform the separation in the required time. Since the column diameter was determined by this vapor rate, this is the maximum vapor rate that the column can accommodate. Therefore, the heat transfer area of the reboiler will be calculated from this vapor rate.

It can be seen from McAdams,[12] that the overall coefficient of heat transfer, U, is greater than 200 B.t.u./(hr.)(ft.^{2})(°F.) for a large number of boiling liquids. This value, therefore, can be used to give a conservative estimate of the amount of heat transfer area required. The following example illustrates the calculation for the batch distillation column designed in the previous section.

Example—Design of the Reboiler Heat Transfer Area

Basis:

Vapor rate = 143 lb. moles/hr. (Assume this is 100% water)
Available steam pressure = 150 p.s.i.a. (Steam temperature = 358°F.)
Bottoms boiling point = 212°F.
Heat of vaporization of water = 970 B.t.u./lb.

Calculations:

$$\text{Heat load} = (143 \text{ lb. moles/hr.})(18 \text{ lb./lb. mole})(970 \text{ B.t.u./lb.}) = 2.5 \times 10^6 \text{ B.t.u./hr.}$$

$$A = \frac{q}{U\Delta T}$$

where A = heat transfer area, ft.^{2}; q = heat transfer rate, B.t.u./hr.; U = overall coefficient of heat transfer, B.t.u./ft.^{2} hr. °F.; ΔT = temperature difference, °F.

$$A = \frac{2.5 \times 10^6 \text{ B.t.u./hr.}}{200 \text{ B.t.u./hr. ft.}^2 \text{ °F. } (358\text{–}212)\text{°F.}} = 86 \text{ ft.}^2$$

This heat transfer area could be supplied by a Model VT 1261[13] standard model vertical reboiler whose overall dimensions are 12.75 in. O.D. by 4 ft. long. This reboiler has a heat transfer area of 99 sq. ft. which should be ample for this distillation.

Assuming 99 sq. ft. is a good size, would a larger size, for example, 167 sq. ft. be better? It is likely that the larger size reboiler would create problems in boil-up rate control that would not exist with the smaller reboiler. Changes in the reboiler steam temperature or distilland temperature would cause larger changes in the heat input as the heat transfer area is increased. As is the case with excessive heat transfer area reboilers, the heat input and therefore the vapor rate would oscillate considerably as the boil-up rate controller attempts to adjust the reboiler temperature to exactly the right value. For example, if the distilland has an overall heat transfer coefficient of 400 B.t.u./hr.-ft.^{2} °F. instead of the 200 assumed in the design, the steam pressure to the reboiler would have to be reduced to decrease the temperature difference between distilland and steam in the equation

$$q = UA\Delta T$$

With the 99 sq. ft. reboiler, this T would be reduced to

$$\begin{aligned} \Delta T &= q/UA \\ &= (2.5 \times 10^6 \text{ B.t.u./hr.})(400 \text{ B.t.u./hr.-ft.}^2 \text{ °F.})(99 \text{ ft.}^2) \\ &= 63\text{°F.} \end{aligned}$$

This corresponds to a steam pressure of 45 p.s.i.a.

With the 167 sq. ft. reboiler, this T would be reduced to

$$\begin{aligned} \Delta T &= (2.5 \times 10^6 \text{ B.t.u./hr.})/(400 \text{ B.t.u./hr.-ft.}^2 \text{ °F.})(167 \text{ ft.}^2) \\ &= 37\text{°F.} \end{aligned}$$

This corresponds to a steam pressure of 30 p.s.i.a.

Since the boil-up rate in the column is controlled by the steam pressure in the reboiler, what is the change in heat input due to a steam pressure correction of 1.0 p.s.i.a.? At 45 p.s.i.a., the steam temperature decreases 1.4°F. for the 1.0 p.s.i.a. pressure decrease, while at 30 p.s.i.a., the temperature decreases 2.0°F. The heat input decrease at 45 p.s.i.a. is equal to

$$\begin{aligned} q &= (UA\Delta T)_2 - (UA\Delta T)_1 = UA(\Delta T_2 - \Delta T_1) \\ &= (400 \text{ B.t.u./hr.-ft.}^2\text{-°F.})(99 \text{ ft.}^2)(-1.4\text{°F.}) \\ &= -55{,}400 \text{ B.t.u./hr.} \end{aligned}$$

The heat input decrease at 30 p.s.i.a. is equal to

$$q = -133{,}600 \text{ B.t.u./hr.}$$

These calculations show that the heat input to the column becomes more sensitive to small changes in reboiler temperature as the area of the reboiler is increased. Therefore, the reboiler must be approximately the right size for the planned distillation and should not be of an arbitrary large size. However, if the reboiler purchased is too large, the heat transfer area can be reduced by blanking some of the tubes.

C. PRODUCT RECEIVERS

In the design of the product receivers the quantity and type of products must be considered. For a batch distillation, it is best to have a separate receiver for each product rather than a single receiver from which the products are pumped to their storage tanks. Separate receivers reduce the amount of contamination of the succeeding products. The material of construction and the design pressure of the receivers must be in accord with the products and the operating pressure. Cooling or heating must be supplied to the receiver if the product is a low boiling material or a solid at ambient temperatures. Provisions must also be made to clean out the receiver periodically.

2. Continuous Distillation Design

A. SEPARATION SCHEME

A separation scheme must be chosen before the actual design of a specific column can be started. If more than two components are to be separated in a reasonable pure state, more than one continuous distillation column must be employed. For example, if three components are to be separated in a pure state, two columns must be used. Two separation schemes are possible in this instance as shown in Figure 6. Case I separates components A, B, and C into A and B as overhead and C as bottoms in the first column, and A as overhead and B as bottoms in the second column. Case II separates A as overhead and B and C as bottoms in the first column and B as overhead and C as bottoms in the second column. The number of possible separation schemes increases quite rapidly as the number of feed components increases. For example, there are five separation schemes for four feed components, 14 separation schemes for five feed components, and 42 separation schemes for six feed components. It is important, therefore, to decide where the splits will be made between components.

Two general principles guide the selection of the separation scheme: (*1*) "The advantages of minimum quantities for difficult separations," and (*2*) "The advantage of the 50-50 split".[14] The aim of these principles is to minimize the amount of heat required to make the separations of the com-

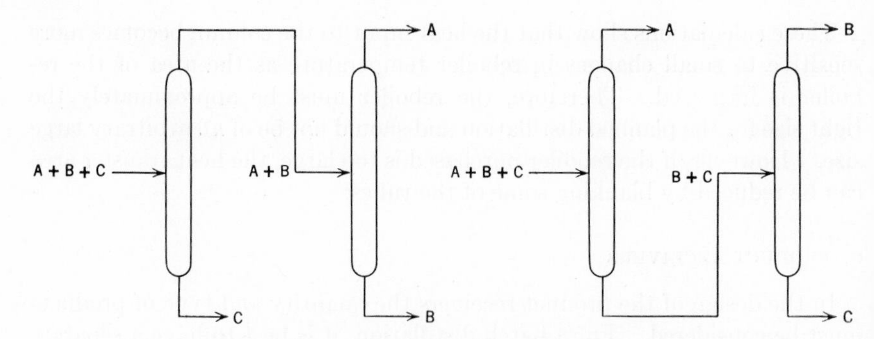

Fig. 6. Continuous distillation separation scheme.

ponents in the distillation columns. Although the cost of the heat may not be a major item in the pilot plant, it could be a critical item for the commercial plant. The proper choice should be made in the pilot plant to insure the proper one being made in the commercial plant.

The first principle, "the advantage of minimum quantities for difficult separation," is based on the fact that higher reflux ratios are required for difficult separations than for easy separations. Therefore, by making the easy separations first, there will be a smaller quantity of feed to be vaporized at the high reflux ratios required for the difficult separation.

The second principle, "The advantage of the 50-50 split," rests on the economy of using the column heat to make the maximum separation in both halves of the column. When a 50-50 split is made, the heats required for the top and bottom halves of the column are equal and proportional to the number of moles of overhead product. Therefore, all of the heat is essentially used twice to separate the overhead from the bottoms. However, with unequal splits, half of the column has higher heat requirements than the other half. Part of the heat, therefore, is being wasted in part of the column.

These two principles are only rough guides to the method of choosing the separation scheme. Occasionally they will contradict each other and the amount of heat required for each scheme must be calculated to determine the lower heat requirement scheme. The principles are useful, however, in eliminating many uneconomical separation schemes.

B. COLUMN DESIGN

The basic McCabe–Thiele diagram is used to determine the number of theoretical plates required in a continuous distillation column. However, it is necessary to determine the operating lines, and therefore, the reflux ratio before the McCabe–Thiele method can be employed. The usual procedure is to determine the minimum reflux ratio and then use a reflux ratio which is 1.1–2 times the minimum.

An example of the calculation procedure is given below using the same base conditions used in the batch distillation design calculations given earlier.

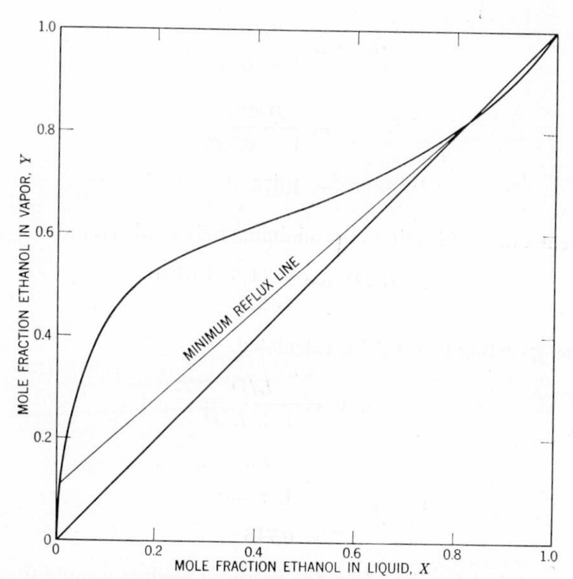

Fig. 7. Minimum reflux line for continuous distillation.

Example—Design of a Continuous Distillation Column.

Basis:

4000 gallons per day of 70 wt.-% ethanol is separated into an overhead fraction containing 92.42 wt.-% ethanol and a bottoms fraction containing 2.8 wt.-% ethanol. The feed to the column is at its boiling point. The distillation unit is operating 24 hr./day.

Calculate the column diameter and the number of bubble cap trays needed to perform this distillation.

Data:

Ethanol Mole Fractions

$$x_F = 0.476$$
$$x_D = 0.826$$
$$x_w = 0.011$$

Feed rate = 29,000 lb./day

The vapor–liquid equilibrium diagram is given in Figure 7.

Calculations:

First, the minimum reflux ratio operating line is determined graphically in Figure 7. The equation of the operating line is

$$y_{n-1} = \frac{L}{V} x_n + \frac{D}{V} x_D$$

and, therefore, the minimum internal reflux ratio is equal to the slope of this operating line. From Figure 7, $L/V = 0.626$.

The external minimum reflux ratio, L/D, is calculated from

$$L/D = \frac{L/V}{1 - L/V}$$

$$= \frac{0.626}{1 - 0.626}$$

$$= 1.672$$

If an actual reflux ratio of 1.5 times the minimum reflux ratio is used:

$$(L/D)_{\text{actual}} = (1.5)(1.672)$$
$$= 2.5$$

To obtain the operating line, L/V is calculated.

$$L/V = \frac{L/D}{1 + L/D}$$

$$= \frac{2.5}{1 + 2.5}$$

$$= 0.715$$

The operating line is determined from the overhead product composition and the slope of this operating line. The operating line for the column below the feed plate can be constructed from the "q" line and the operating line above the feed plate.[15,16] The "q" lines are shown in Figure 8. "q" is defined as the total heat to convert one mole of feed to saturated vapor divided by the molar latent heat. The "q" line has a slope of $q/(q - 1)$ and crosses the 45° diagonal at the feed composition point. The operating line below the feed plate is a straight line connecting the bottoms composition point on the 45 diagonal and the point of intersection of the "q" line and the operating line above the feed plate.

With the two operating lines established, the number of theoretical plates are obtained by the McCabe–Thiele method as shown in Figure 9. A total of 15 theoretical plates are required for the separation. The actual number of plates will depend upon the efficiency of the plate and the safety factor employed. If a plate efficiency of 70% is assumed and a 30% safety factor[17] is used, a total of 28 actual plates would be needed in the 1.5 times minimum reflux case and a total of 21 actual plates in the 2.0 times minimum reflux case.

The column diameter is calculated from the vapor rate. From the data given, it is calculated that 20,100 lb./day or 437 lb. moles/day of ethanol and 1650 lb./day or 91.7 lb. moles/day of water are the overhead product. However, the vapor rate in the column is given by

$$V = (\text{External reflux ratio} + 1)D$$
$$= (2.5 + 1)(528.7 \text{ lb. moles/day})$$
$$= 1852 \text{ lb. moles/day}$$

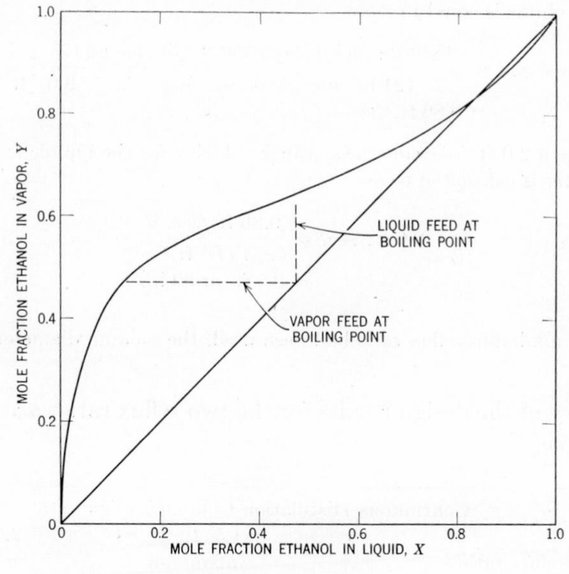

Fig. 8. "q" lines.

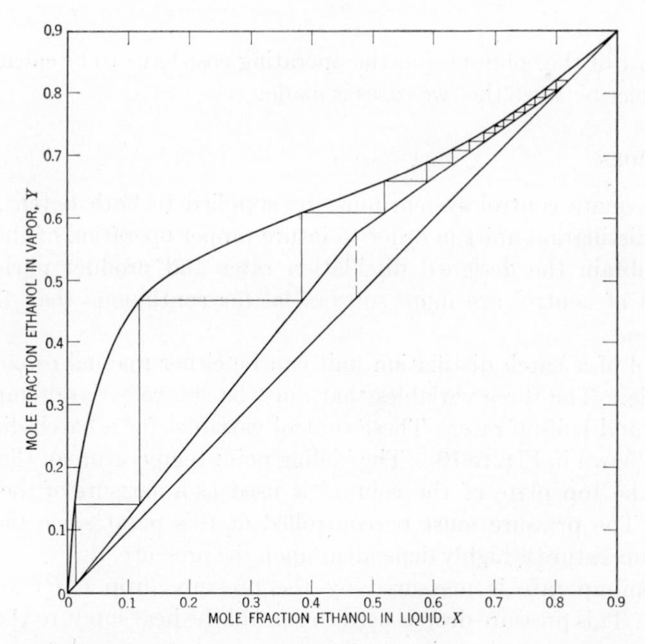

Fig. 9. Calculation of theoretical plates—continuous distillation.

The vapor volume is equal to

$$\text{Vapor volume} = \frac{(1852\ \text{lb. moles/day})(359\ \text{ft.}^3/\text{lb. mole})(173 + 460)°\text{R.}}{(24\ \text{hr./day})(3600\ \text{sec./day})(32 + 460)°\text{R.}}$$
$$= 9.86\ \text{ft.}^3/\text{sec.}$$

If we assume a 2.0 ft./sec. superficial vapor velocity for the bubble cap column, the column diameter is calculated from

$$2.0\ \text{ft./sec.} = \frac{9.86\ \text{ft./sec.}}{(\pi/4)(D^2)\text{ft.}^2}$$
$$= 2.5\ \text{ft. or } 30\ \text{in.}$$

If twice the minimum reflux ratio had been used, the column diameter would be 34 inches.

A summary of the design results for the two reflux ratios are given in the following table.

Continuous Distillation Column Design

Reflux ratio	1.5 times minimum	2.0 times minimum
No. of theoretical plates	15	11
No. of actual plates	28	21
Column diameter, in.	30	34

The cost of the columns and the operating cost have to be calculated before a choice between the two cases is made.

C. CONTROLS

An adequate control system must be supplied to both batch and continuous distillation units in order to insure proper operation of the column and to obtain the designed distillation rates and product purity. The problems of control are more substantial for continuous than for batch distillation.

Control of a batch distillation unit can be either manual or completely automatic. The three variables that must be controlled are temperature, pressure and boil-up rate. These control variables for a batch distillation unit are shown in Figure 10. The boiling point temperature of the product leaving the top plate of the column is used as a measure of the product purity. The pressure must be controlled at this point since the boiling point temperature is highly dependent upon the pressure.

The boil-up rate is measured by the pressure drop (ΔP) across the column. This pressure drop is used to control the heat input to the reboiler and thereby regulate the boil-up rate.

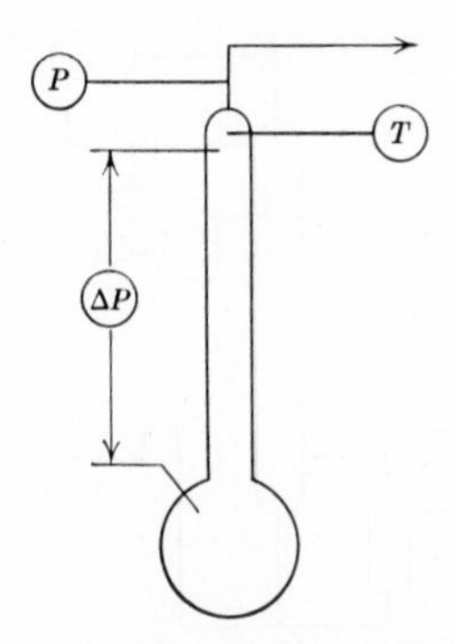

Fig. 10. Control variables for batch distillation.

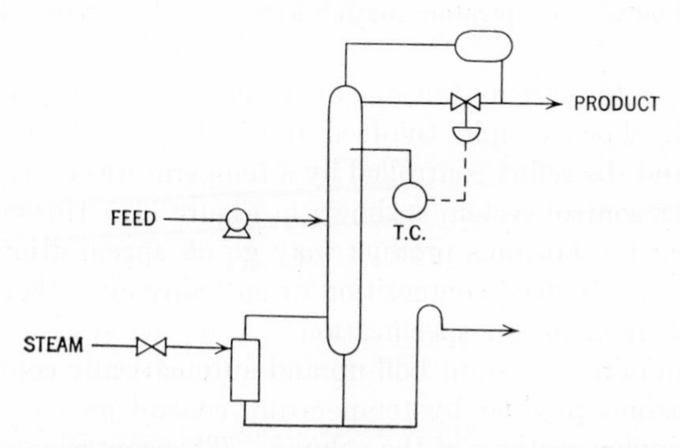

Fig. 11. Continuous distillation column control—overhead product temperature controls the reflux ratio. T.C., temperature controller.

The overhead temperature is used to vary the reflux ratio and subsequently to maintain product purity. The distillation is completed when the reflux ratio has reached a predetermined maximum value. If more than one product is taken overhead, the controlling temperature of the reflux ratio controller must be adjusted at each cut point.

The batch distillation unit can also be operated at constant reflux ratio. In this instance, the overhead product purity decreases continuously as the overhead is removed. At an overhead temperature necessary to give the needed purity for the accumulated overhead product, the column is either switched to total reflux or the product receivers are changed. Once again, the control temperature setting must be adjusted at each cut point.

Although a continuous distillation unit can also be operated manually, better results are obtained with automatic controls. There are many control systems which can be used with a continuous distillation unit.[18,19] Most of these systems are too intricate and require too much detailed design for use in a pilot plant distillation unit. Common practice, even in com-

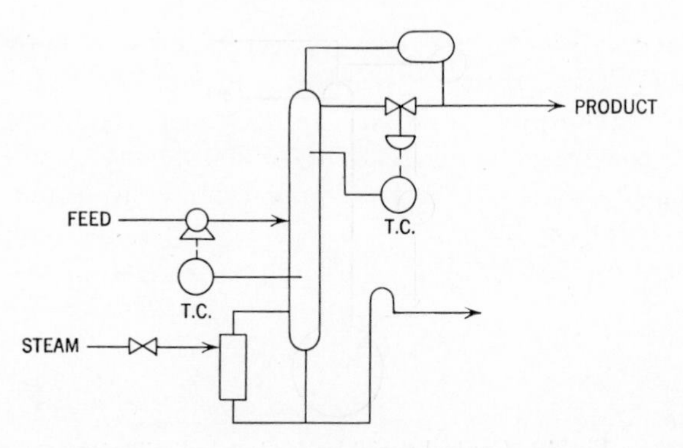

Fig. 12. Continuous distillation column control—overhead product temperature controls reflux ratio and bottoms temperature controls feed rate. T.C., temperature controller.

mercial units, is to place all but one of the controllable variables on fixed-value control. For example, the feed and boil-up can be placed on fixed rate control and the reflux controlled by a temperature control point in the column. This control system is shown in Figure 11. However, with this control system the bottoms product may go off specification if there are slight changes in the feed composition or enthalpy even though the overhead product remains on specification. A better system would be to manually maintain a constant boil-up and automatically control the overhead and bottoms product by temperature control points in the enrichment and stripping sections of the column. This control system is shown in Figure 12. The upper temperature control point controls the reflux ratio and the bottom temperature control point controls the feed rate to the column. Bertrand and Jones[14] point out that there is the danger of accumulating an intermediate boiler in the middle of the column when the overhead and bottoms composition are controlled. Care must be exercised, therefore, in choosing the proper temperature control points and in insuring the absence of an intermediate boiling point component between the designed overhead and bottoms product. If such an intermediate boiling point component is present, it will be necessary to change the temperature control value, and take this component as an overhead or bottoms product to be separated in a subsequent distillation.

III. EQUIPMENT

Distillation units can be purchased as a package unit or the individual components can be purchased and combined into the complete unit. The advantage of obtaining a package unit is that the combination of equipment has been tested and found to operate successfully with other distillations. Time is saved therefore, by eliminating much of the "debugging" and modifications of pilot plant equipment. Of course, it may be necessary to purchase and construct individual components because of specific distillation requirements. Also, it may be less expensive to obtain these components individually if the distillation control equipment needs are not as extensive as those generally supplied with package units.

1. Package Units

Batch distillation package units can be obtained from several sources. One barrel size package unit[20] for vacuum distillation is described in the literature. This unit is designed for charges up to two barrels although smaller units are available for charges of 1–50 liters. An important feature of these stills is that the performance is almost identical from the 1 to 400 liter or 2 barrel unit. This particular unit, the Sarnia Hivac still, is a single distillation plate unit. The flask or distillation pot is a spherical stainless steel vessel similar to the usual laboratory still pot.

Although the unit only performs a simple one plate batch distillation, it contains many good features. The flask is charged and discharged through a pipe which leads to the bottom of the flask. This eliminates the need to move the heavy still pot. A thermowell is placed within $^1/_4$ in. of the bottom of the flask to indicate the liquid temperature. It is possible therefore, to obtain liquid temperatures even when most of the liquid has been distilled overhead. The flask is heated with a 12 to 25 kw. electrical heating mantle which contains 3 to 6 220 v. heaters to provide a heat density of about 15 w./sq. in. and give a rapid heat-up. The actual heat input during the distillation is controlled by a variable autotransformer which is actuated by the pressure drop across the column, i.e., the boil-up rate. The distillation charge can be cooled rapidly by an internal water cooling coil thereby decreasing the nonproductive cooling down period of the unit. Steam can also be used in this coil to aid in the heating up of the charge. The distillation head (Model A Hivac) is a vacuum jacketed glass unit which contains an elbow bend designed to entrain liquid and return it to the still pot. The vapors from the side arm enter the condensing zone which contains a large surface area glass cooling coil. The condensed liquid is collected in a vacuum receiver. The temperature is measured at the top of the distillation head. It is important that the temperature and pressure measurements are made at the same point since pressure gradients can occur in the distillation column which may cause errors in calculating the atmospheric equivalent temperature. These errors could be sizeable at the low pressure used in this unit (50 μ to 50 mm. Hg).

Temperatures are measured by iron-constantan thermocouples of 26- to 30-gage wire enclosed in a thin glass wall tube. The vacuum gage used is the tensimeter which employs the boiling point of a pure compound to indicate the pressure. The tensimeter does not operate well below 200 μ; therefore a McLeod gage must be used at these low pressures.

Although the batch unit described has only one plate it is a simple matter to interpose a column between the still pot and the condenser. However, it would not be possible to obtain the same high vacuums with a column in the unit because of the pressure drop across the column. Either a liquid or vapor dividing head can be used. The columns are vacuum jacketed glass Oldershaw or packed columns. The entire package unit may be purchased from the H. S. Martin Co. of Evanston, Illinois.

A combination reactor distillation pilot plant unit is available from the Doyle and Roth Manufacturing Co. The reactor-distillation flask is available in a range of sizes from 5 to 100 gal. These units are designed to carry out a reaction and distill the products directly from the reactor vessel. The 100 gal. still pot is designed for full vacuum or 50 p.s.i.g. at 600°F., while the 15 gal. still pot is designed for full vacuum or 150 p.s.i.g. at 600°F. All of these units can be equipped with a 7-ft.-long packed distillation column mounted on the reactor vessel or still pot.

The column diameter increases with the size of the reactor still pots. The 15 gal. reactor still pot has a $4^1/_2$ in. diam., schedule 10, 316 SS column and the 100 gallon reactor has a 8 in. diam. column. Each column has two or more sections of electrical heaters to maintain adiabatic conditions in the column. This electrical heating is placed on a sheet jacket which is separated from the column wall by a $^1/_4$ in. air space. An additional jacket is placed over the heating coils and the entire vessel is insulated with 3 in. magnesia block and a steel metal casing. The entire column and reactor still pot is constructed of 316 SS. With the 100 gal. model, two 50 gal. capacity product receivers are supplied.

The unit comes complete with all controls and indicating instruments. These include a 12 point temperature indicator, rotameters, voltage regulator, pressure indicator, low level liquid controller, pressure indicator controller, and accessories. All electrical equipment is Class I, Group D (explosion proof). The total cost for these package units varies from $13,000 to $20,000. Other companies, such as the York Process Equipment Corp. and the Artisan Industries Inc., construct complete package distillation units for specific needs.

All of the package units described are batch distillation units. It does not seem likely that a continuous distillation unit could be purchased off the shelf since the conditions under which this distillation is carried out and the requirements of the column, pumps, and receivers are myriad. It is

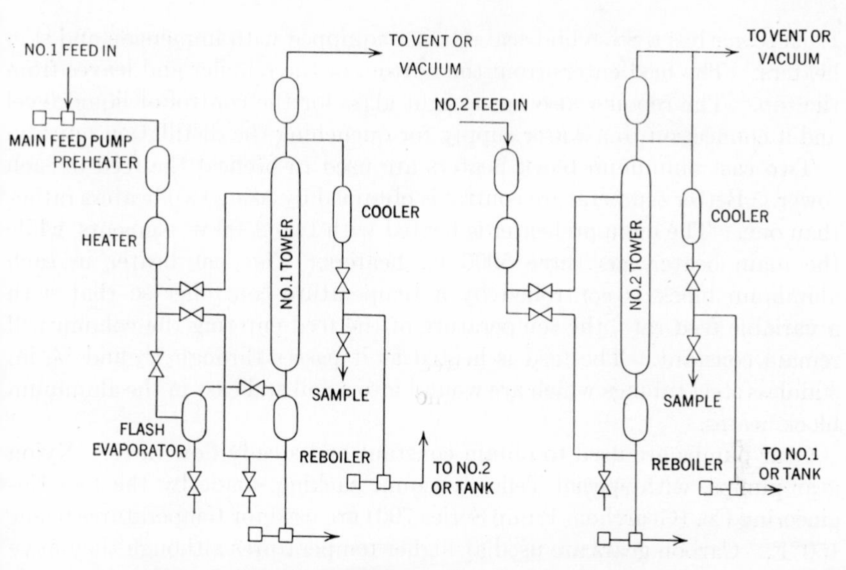

Fig. 13. Versatile continuous pilot plant distillation unit.

not practical to have one continuous distillation package unit that will operate under all conditions. However, Chemet Engineers, Inc. (Pasadena, California) does offer three standard continuous distillation units. However, most continuous distillation units purchased as a package unit are designed specifically for the application.

A versatile continuous pilot plant distillation unit is described by Cooke.[21] This semiautomatic unit with electrical heating is capable of handling 100 to 10,000 gal. of distilland. A schematic diagram of this unit, which can be operated by a single man, is shown in Figure 13. Two 54-in. packed columns are used; one having a $5^1/_2$ in. diameter and the other a $4^1/_4$ in. diameter. The larger column can handle 70 lb./hr. and the smaller column 40 lb./hr. at 50% vaporization of crude oil. Nominal capacity of the installation is about 5 bbl./day. Lower rates would be obtained if the units were run under vacuum. The two towers can be operated in series or parallel, and at atmospheric pressure or under vacuum. The feed can enter the column from the top, the middle, or the bottom. The towers are made of vacuum jacketed glass and enclosed by glass fiber jackets to provide adiabatic operation and as a safety measure against column breakage. The towers are packed with either 0.24 or 0.16 in. protruded SS packing and give the equivalent of 10–15 theoretical plates at total reflux. Of course, the total number of plates can be increased by adding another section to the column or the number of theoretical plates can be decreased by only partially filling the column. The reflux ratio is manually set with a timer.

Each tower has a SS cylindrical reboiler equipped with immersion and skin heaters. The feed enters from the bottom of the reboiler and leaves from the top. The reboiler also has a sight glass for the control of liquid level and a connection to a water supply for quenching the distillation quickly.

Two cast aluminum block heaters are used to preheat the feed to each tower. Better temperature control is obtained by using two heaters rather than one. The main preheater is heated with two 2500 w. elements, while the main heater has three 5000 w. heaters. The last heater in each aluminum block is controlled by a temperature controller so that with a variable feed rate, the temperature of the feed entering the column will remain constant. The feed is heated as it passes through $^3/_8$ and $^1/_4$ in. stainless steel tubings which are wound into a coil and cast in the aluminum block heater.

Gear pumps are used to obtain constant and steady flow rates. Nylon gear pumps, with special Teflon vacuum packing, made by the Eco Engineering Co. (Gearchem Pump Series 700) are used for temperatures below 150°F. Carbon gears are used at higher temperatures although they have been found to be very fragile. These pumps can be used for vacuum distillation as well as atmospheric distillations. The main feed pump is driven by a variable speed dc motor connected to a hydraulic transmission. This combination of variable speed motor and variable speed transmission is used to provide flexibility in pumping viscous and nonviscous liquids at widely different rates.

The distillate product is usually collected by gravity flow. However, when operating under vacuum or when very large overhead fractions are taken, a pump must be used. The pump is activated by a liquid level detector installed in the side arm of each rundown cooler. These level detectors are of the simple light beam type. When the liquid level rises in the side arm the pump motor speed is increased about 25%. When the liquid level drops, the lower pumping rate is restored. It is necessary to manually set the pump to that speed which is required to remove the overhead product and then allow the liquid level controller to speed up the pump if the product collection increases.

The liquid level in the reboiler is controlled by a capacitance liquid level controlling device and a variable speed pump. The pump is mounted directly on the base plate in the reboiler bottom thereby eliminating a suction line.

A novel bottoms removal system is used for vacuum operation. As shown in Figure 14, the bottoms liquid is pumped continuously through a back pressure regulator and is recycled to the reboiler. A solenoid valve can then be used to remove product from the line. The liquid level controller is used to operate this solenoid valve. Viton, a fluorocarbon elastomer, is used for the pressure regulator diaphragm for temperatures above 350°F.

Vacuum is supplied by a mechanical pump. The vacuum in the system is measured by a tensimeter which uses the boiling point of a pure compound to indicate pressure. The vacuum controller operates a solenoid bleed valve. A manual bleed valve is used as a coarse control to hold the pressure just below that desired for operation. Fine control is then supplied by the solenoid bleed valve.

A 50% ethylene glycol inhibited with Nacap maintained at −30°F. is used as the refrigerant. A 10 H.P. compressor with a capacity of 30,000 B.t.u./hr. is used to cool the 250 gal. of refrigerant.

Other pilot plant distillation units are described in the literature. Carpenter and Helwig[22] give a detailed description of the design and construction features of continuous fractionating columns including packed column from 2.5 to 12 in. in diameter and up to 25 ft. in height. Distillation systems for high pressure, atmospheric, and vacuum operations are shown, including many specific details of the construction of reboilers, condensers, preheaters, etc.

A combination batch and continuous fractionating column is described by Kiguchi.[23] This unit can handle 5–17 gal. batch distillations and 0.5–10 gal./hr. continuous distillations. Operating conditions can vary from 5 mm. Hg to 600 p.s.i.g. pressure and 10–750°F. temperature.

2. Columns

A. PACKED COLUMNS

Packed columns are used most often in pilot plant distillations. The reason for this choice is the simplicity, flexibility, and low cost of packed columns in the small diameter sizes. Any pipe, either metal or glass, can be used as a packed column. It is only necessary to put a flange and a packing support in a pipe to convert it to a packed column. The packing height can be varied to increase or decrease the number of theoretical plates. Additional lengths of pipe and packing can easily be added to the column to increase the separation power. It is also easier to clean a packed column since the packing can be discarded, the empty pipe cleaned, and new packing put in the column within a short time.

A wide variety of packings are available for these columns. These include steel Pall rings, ceramic and carbon Intalox saddles, ceramic, carbon, or steel Raschig rings, and protruded packing. The Pall rings are used where high capacity and efficiency are needed and corrosion is not an important factor. Ceramic Intalox saddles are used where high capacity and efficiency and resistance to corrosion are needed. Carbon packings are used for high temperatures in nonoxidizing atmospheres or where extreme thermal shock is encountered. Raschig rings are used because of their low cost. Protruded packing is used where efficiency is needed for atmospheric and vacuum distillations. However, the cost of protruded packing is higher than the other packings.

Some general rules for using packing are given in the table below.[24]

Liquid Redistribution and Packing Size

Packing	Liquid redistribution, column diameters	Packing size, column diameters
Raschig rings	$2^1/_2$–3	$^1/_{30}$
Intalox and Berl saddles	5–8	$^1/_{15}$
Pall rings	5–10	$^1/_{10}$–$^1/_{15}$

The Raschig rings are much poorer in distributing the liquid in the column. Hence the liquid redistribution sections must be used more often and the packing size must be smaller.

Raschig rings and Intalox and Berl saddles should be packed wet. Although it is not necessary to wet pack Pall rings, it will aid in randomizing the pack.

The height equivalent to a theoretical plate (H.E.T.P.) for several types of packing are given in the following table.[25]

H.E.T.P. For Packing

System	Packing	H.E.T.P., ft.	Optimum superficial vapor velocity, ft./sec.
Ethanol–water	1.4 in. Raschig rings	0.82	4.8
	1 in. Raschig rings	0.64	3.6
	0.32 in. Raschig rings	0.3	2.3
	1 in. Saddles	0.64	5.5
Benzene–toluene	0.32 in. Raschig rings	0.48	1.6
Benzene–ethylene Dichloride	0.32 in. Raschig rings	0.3	1.5

B. PLATE COLUMNS

Plate columns are also used in pilot plant distillations. For atmospheric and vacuum distillations down to 200 mm. Hg pressures, the most widely used plate column is the Oldershaw column. This column has a high and fairly constant efficiency with a good throughput rate. These

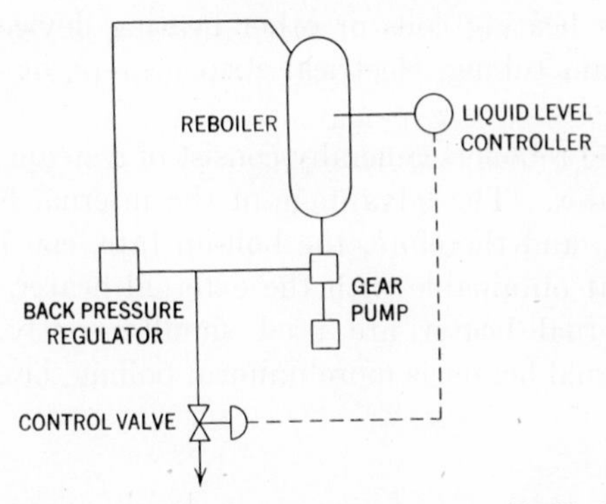

Fig 14. Bottoms removal system for vacuum distillation unit.

glass, vacuum jacketed, Oldershaw columns are available at sizes from 1 to over 5 in. in diameter from the H. S. Martin Co.

The minimum vapor velocities on several different plate columns can be estimated from the data of Arnold, Plank, and Schoenborn.[26] Minimum air velocities of 24–44 ft./sec. are required through the plate holes to maintain stable bubbling when the hole diameters are 0.025 to 0.373 in. and the free areas are 3.9 to 11.5% of the column area.

An inexpensive plate column is reported by Myers.[27] This column contains removable sieve trays which do not have downcomers. Instead, the liquid intermittently drips downward through the same holes that allow the vapor to pass upward. The plates are drilled and tapped in the center and are screwed on to the central rod in the column. The tray spacing, therefore, can be varied at will. As in the case of the packed columns, any pipe can be used for this column. Since the sieve plates have $^1/_4$ in. holes, these trays are applicable for fouling operations or for high surface tension liquids.

3. Reboilers

There are essentially three types of reboilers:

(*1*) Externally heated
(*2*) Internally heated
(*3*) Circulating reboiler contents through an external heater

An externally heated reboiler is generally limited to the smaller batch distillation units because of the rapid decrease of heating surface to reboiler volume as the volume increases above 10 gal. A major advantage of the external reboiler heater is its isolation from the distilland. If the interior surface of the reboiler becomes fouled, it can be easily cleaned because it is not obstructed by heating coils or other heating devices. The external heater can be steam tubing, electrical strip heaters, or electrical heating coils.

Internally heated reboilers generally consist of a steam coil or an electrical immersion heater. The advantage of the internal heater is that the heat transfer area, and therefore, the boil-up rate, can be increased considerably over that obtainable with the external heater. Frequently, an external and internal heater are used simultaneously. An additional benefit of the internal heater is more uniform boiling, i.e., less tendency to bump.

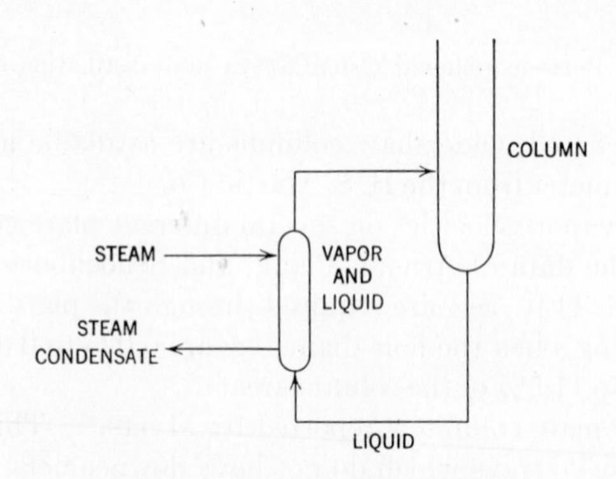

Fig. 15. Thermosyphon reboiler.

Circulation of the reboiler contents through an external heat exchanger is generally used in continuous distillations. The most common system is the thermosyphon reboiler which is shown in Figure 15. A shell and tube heat exchanger is placed in parallel with the column, and the shell side is heated with steam. The liquid in the heat exchanger tubes rises as it is heated because of its decrease in density with increasing temperature. Boiling in the tubes also aid in propelling the liquid up and out of the heat exchanger into the distillation column. Additional liquid flows into the heat exchanger from the column to replace the liquid which has boiled and flowed into the column. With a sufficient reboiler temperature, very high flow rates can be obtained which yield excellent heat transfer rates.

4. Reflux Splitters

Two approaches are possible with reflux splitters:

(*1*) Laboratory type reflux splitters with constant reflux ratio

(*2*) Industrial type reflux splitter systems with variable reflux ratio control

The simplest approach is to use the laboratory type reflux splitter with a constant reflux ratio. The constant reflux splitter can be manually adjusted to give various reflux ratios. However, with this type of reflux splitter, it is not a simple matter to have the critical column variable control the reflux ratio. Automatic shut-off controllers are available which will put a column on total reflux when a set overhead or bottoms temperature has been reached. Either a liquid splitter or a vapor splitter can be used with this system.

An industrial type reflux splitter system generally employs a temperature at some point in the distillation column to control the reflux ratio. This system can be employed on either batch or continuous distillation units.

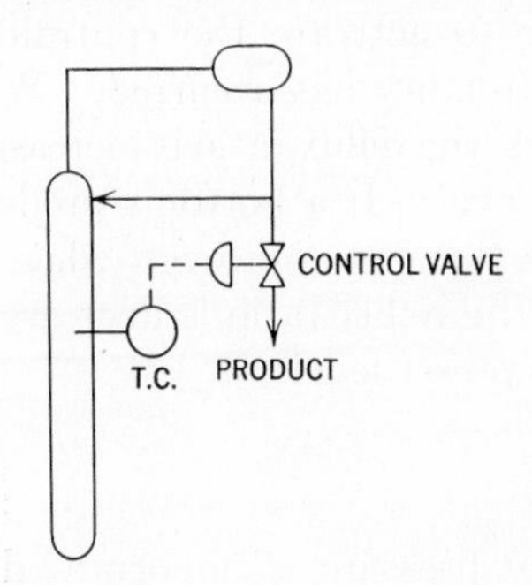

Fig. 16. Industrial reflux splitter system. T.C., temperature controller.

In a continuous distillation column, the temperature control point is located at a point in the column where there is a rapid change in temperature with plate composition. In batch distillation, the overhead temperature is generally used as the control point.

One type of industrial reflux splitter system is shown in Figure 16. The overhead condensate flows directly from the overhead condenser into the column. The amount of overhead withdrawn as product is controlled by the temperature at the control point in the column. An automatic valve is opened to collect product when the temperature reaches or falls below the specified value.

5. Control Equipment

There are three variables which are controlled in most pilot plant distillations: temperature, pressure, and boil-up rate. In addition, continuous distillation columns require control of the feed and product flow rates. The purpose and technique of control are described in the following sections.

A. TEMPERATURE

The purpose of temperature control is obviously to obtain the desired product in a sufficient yield and purity. In a batch distillation, the temperature of the overhead product is monitored by a thermocouple which places, through a controller, the column on total reflux when a preset temperature is reached. The overhead temperature can also be used to vary the reflux ratio in a batch ditillation so that the maximum yield of product can be obtained.

In continuous distillation, the temperature of a point in the column is chosen to control the reflux ratio. The point chosen is one where there is a significant change in temperature with composition. This change in temperature must occur to activate the control instrument before any serious effect in product quality has occurred. When the temperature of the control point increases, the reflux ratio is increased to bring the temperature back to the preset level. If a bottoms product is desired, the same techniques are used. In this case, however, when the temperature of the control point decreases, the reflux ratio is decreased to bring the bottoms temperature back to the preset level.

B. PRESSURE

The control of column pressure is important due to its effect on the liquid's boiling point. For this reason it is important that the pressure at the temperature control point also be controlled. The technique of vacuum control is shown in Figure 17. The pressure is controlled by the

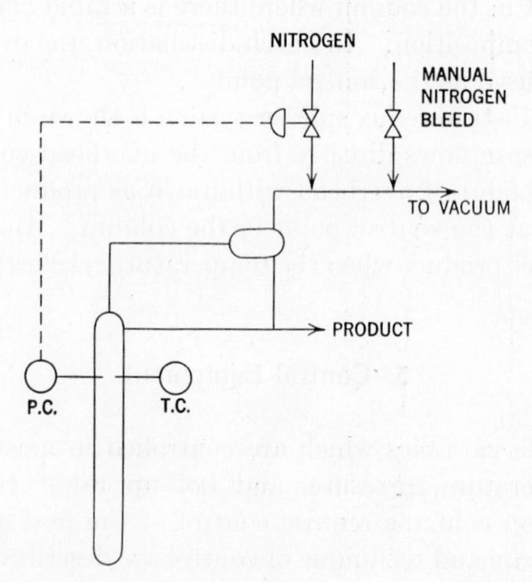

Fig. 17. Vacuum control. T.C., temperature controller; P.C., pressure controller.

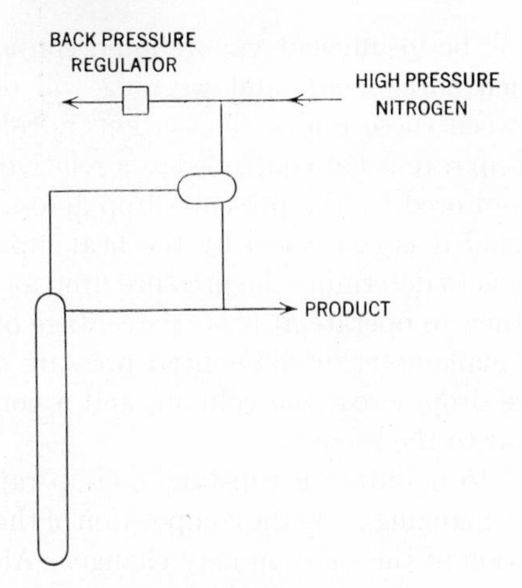

Fig. 18. Pressure control.

use of a constant and intermittent air bleed. The constant air bleed is adjusted so that the column will operate somewhat below the design pressure. The intermittent air bleed, controlled by the pressure in the column, is used to bring the column up to the design pressure.

In pressure distillations, the technique shown in Figure 18 is used. Nitrogen or another inert gas is constantly flowing into the top of the condenser and through a back pressure regulator to maintain a constant column pressure. The nitrogen is at a slightly higher pressure than the design distillation pressure to insure a slow flow of nitrogen through the system. If there is not a constant flow of nitrogen through the back pressure regulator, the pressure can fluxuate and thereby cause erratic column operation.

It is not as important in pressure distillation, as in vacuum distillation, to control the pressure at the same point as the temperature control point. In vacuum distillation, fluctuations of 5–10 mm. Hg would cause a large change in boiling point at an absolute pressure of 50 mm. Hg. However, a fluctuation of 50–100 mm. Hg would cause very little change in boiling point at 100 p.s.i.g.

C. BOIL-UP RATE

The importance of boil-up rate control is to maintain column operating stability and efficiency and to obtain product at the fastest rate practical. The boil-up rate, i.e., the vapor rate in the column must be kept within certain limits. Above the upper limit, flooding will occur in a packed column and excessive entrainment will occur in a plate column. Below the lower limit, there will be insufficient vapor–liquid contacting in a packed column to give much enrichment, and weeping will occur in the plate column. Even between these limits, fluctuations in column performance can occur if the boil-up rate is not controlled at a relatively constant value.

Boil-up rate is monitored by the pressure drop across part or all of the distillation column and it is controlled by the heat input to the reboiler. The usual procedure is to determine the pressure drop at the flooding point of the column and then to operate at some percentage of this boil-up rate (e.g., 70–90%). A manometer or differential pressure cell is used to determine the pressure drop across the column, and a controller is used to control the heat input to the reboiler.

The heat required to maintain a constant boil-up rate in a batch distillation is constantly changing. As the composition of the reboiler changes, the heat of vaporization of the solution may change. Also, as the reboiler temperature increases, the heat losses to the surroundings increase. The rate of heat input to a batch distillation, therefore, generally must be increased gradually as the distillation proceeds. If the heat input rate is not increased, the distillation rate would slow down and the column could possibly become inoperable.

6. Insulation

Batch and continuous distillation columns should have sufficient insulation to prevent excessive condensing of vapor on the column walls. Excessive condensation in the column increases the reflux ratio in the lower portions of the column, which inefficiently adds to the separating power of the column. However, it also seriously reduces the product rate of the column. It is necessary, therefore, to put insulation around the column to allow it to operate in an essentially adiabatic manner. In most larger diameter columns, the usual insulation materials such as fiber glass and asbestos, are sufficient to prevent excessive condensation. In smaller diameter columns, a vacuum jacketed column is usually sufficient. However, in many applications it is necessary to use insulation and a column heater to maintain adiabatic operations. This is most often the case in small diameter columns operating under vacuum. Under these conditions, the heat transfer surface to vapor volume ratio is large so that large heat losses can occur per unit volume of vapor in the column. Also, since the vapor is at a reduced pressure, its mass per unit volume and therefore its total heat content is reduced. A small amount of heat loss will condense a large percentage of the vapor under these conditions and thereby make the column inoperable.

In a continuous distillation, a manually controlled column heater can most readily be used since a relatively constant temperature profile is obtained and maintained in the column. Heat losses, therefore, should be constant.

In a batch distillation, a differential temperature controller can be used to maintain low heat losses. This controller is set to maintain a set temperature difference between the column and the jacket.

IV. OPERATION

1. Start Up

Start up of a pilot plant batch distillation is essentially the same as a laboratory batch distillation. The distillation feed is pumped into the reboiler and the column and reboiler are purged with nitrogen or another inert gas. The charge is heated while the column is on total reflux. With some packings, it may be desirable to flood the column to properly wet the packing. When the proper overhead temperature has been reached, and the column is operating at the designed boil-up rate, the distillation products can be collected.

With a pilot plant continuous distillation, steady-state conditions must prevail before the products can be collected. The usual technique is to charge the reboiler with the feed and start heating the reboiler. Additional feed may be pumped into the column during this heat-up period to maintain a constant liquid level in the reboiler. Once the design boil-up rate is reached, feed is added and product is withdrawn continuously into a slop container until the design conditions are attained. After operating for a period of time under these steady-state conditions, product can be collected.

2. Steady State

Steady-state column operation applies mostly to continuous distillation since almost everything is constantly changing in batch distillation. However, even in batch distillation, the boil-up rate and pressure should be kept at a constant value. During the steady-state distillation period, it is necessary to keep the controlled variables within their specified limits for continuous distillation columns. If the control system is properly designed, sudden changes in the feed composition will not upset the column operations a great deal. However, it must be recognized that drastic changes in feed composition will necessitate some changes in the variable set points of even well-designed control systems.

3. Shut Down

The usual shut-down procedure for a continuous distillation column is quite simple. The product and feed streams are stopped and the heat is turned off. Nitrogen or another inert gas is used to blanket the column during the cooling period to prevent air from being drawn into the column and possibly forming an explosive mixture with the hot vapors.

The shut down for the batch distillation is the same as for a laboratory batch distillation. The product take-off is discontinued and the heat is turned off. Nitrogen or another inert gas is used to blanket the column during the cooling period. It is sometimes necessary to pump out the bottoms from the reboiler while it is still hot because of a high viscosity or a high freezing point bottoms.

V. SAFETY

The handling of large quantities of hot combustible liquids and vapors in pilot plant distillations requires that considerable thought be given to safety. Since at times combustible liquids and vapors must be handled, air must be prevented from mixing with these combustibles. Also, a source of ignition must be prevented from coming in contact with the combustible vapors in the event an explosive mixture is accidently formed.

Preventing air from contacting the column contents is accomplished by purging the column with nitrogen or another inert gas. With low boiling or hot feeds, the column should be purged before the feed is added to the reboiler. During the distillation, an inert gas should be added to the top of the condenser to prevent air from entering the column during pressure fluctuations. As stated in the previous section, it is quite important to use this inert gas purge during the cooling period.

Preventing a source of ignition from contacting an explosive mixture is accomplished by using, whenever possible, steam heating, explosion proof electrical equipment, and air purging nonexplosion proof electrical equipment. In most pilot plants, the most convenient and the safest heating method is steam. Pneumatic control equipment, intrinsically safe, and explosion proof electrical control equipment should be used whenever possible. When it is not possible to obtain explosion proof electrical equipment, e.g., electrical heaters, these should be placed in a container which is purged with air. If it is possible for the combustible vapors to enter this container, it should be purged with an inert gas.

Other safety hazards involved are the breakage of glass columns, overpressuring of the column, peroxide formation or concentration, and incompatibility of the cooling media and distillation charge. All large glass parts in a distillation unit should be considered as likely to rupture.

Shields should be placed around these parts to contain flying glass. Quite often the normal insulation around the glass column and reboiler is sufficient to prevent flying glass.

When distilling materials which form peroxides or other thermally unstable compounds, an analysis of the feed should be done to insure that the unstable materials will not be concentrated to such a degree as to pose a serious hazard. If the concentration is too high, the feed should be treated to reduce or remove this unstable compound before distillation.

The compatibility of the cooling media and the feed should always be checked. More than one accident has occurred because the condenser cooling media reacted violently with the distillation feed. Condensers sometimes develop leaks and allow the feed and cooling media to come in contact with each other. This could result in an explosion if the two are not compatible.

References

1. Scheibel, *Ind. Eng. Chem.*, **50**, 579 (1958).
2. Holliday, *Brit. Chem. Eng.*, **7**, 117 (1962).
3. Grothe, *Chem. Eng.*, **63**, 239 (1956).
4. Martin, *Petrol. Refiner*, **39**, 161 (1960).
5. Bogart, *Trans. Am. Inst. Chem. Eng.*, **33**, 139 (1937).
6. Block, *Chem. Eng.*, **68**, 87 (1961).
7. Molyneux, *Chem. Process Eng.*, **41**, 43 (1960).
8. Molyneux, *Chem. Process Eng.*, **41**, 98 (1960).
9. Jones, Schoenborn, and Colburn, *Ind. Eng. Chem.*, **35**, 666 (1943).
10. Bloom, Clump, and A. H. Koeckert, *Ind. Eng. Chem.*, **53**, 829 (1961).
11. Lowenstein, *Ind. Eng. Chem.*, **53**, 44A (1961).
12. McAdams, *Heat Transmission*, 3rd ed., McGraw-Hill, New York-London, 1954.
13. Doyle and Roth Manufacturing Co., Inc., Standardized Heat Transfer Equipment, Data Book No. 1152, p. 5.
14. Harbert, *Petrol. Refiner*, **36**, 169 (1957).
15. Norman, *Absorption, Distillation and Cooling Towers*, 1st ed., Wiley, New York, 1961, pp. 105–106.
16. Gilliland, *Elements of Fractional Distillation*, 4th ed., McGraw-Hill, New York-London, 1950, pp. 125–127.
17. Parkins, *Chem. Eng. Progr.*, **55**, 60 (1959).
18. Bertrand and Jones, *Chem. Eng.*, **68**, 139 (1961).
19. Parkins, *Chem. Eng. Progr.*, **55**, 60 (1959).
20. Cooke, *Ind. Eng. Chem.*, **55**, 36 (1963).
21. Cooke, *Ind. Eng. Chem.*, **54**, 47 (1962).
22. Carpenter and Helwig, *Ind. Eng. Chem.*, **42**, 571 (1950).
23. Kiguchi, *Ind. Eng. Chem.*, **46**, 1363 (1954).
24. Eckert, *Chem. Eng. Progr.*, **57**, 54 (1961).
25. Norman, *Absorption, Distillation and Cooling Towers*, Wiley, New York, 1961, p. 302.
26. Arnold, Plank, and Schoenborn, *Chem. Eng. Progr.*, **48**, 633 (1952).
27. Myers, *Ind. Eng. Chem.*, **50**, 1671 (1958).

CHAPTER XI

AUTOMATION IN DISTILLATION

THEODORE J. WILLIAMS, *Monsanto Company, St. Louis, Missouri*

I. INTRODUCTION

The automatic control of distillation columns has always been a popular subject in the process control literature. This popularity has greatly increased in recent years as computers and more sophisticated mathematical techniques have made it possible to study theoretically as well as experimentally some of the more complex aspects of the subject. However, the many possible configurations of distillation columns and the tremendous number of variables involved in specifying their operation have to date made it impossible to provide a completely integrated picture of all aspects of column control. There is thus room for many more experimental and mathematical studies of further aspects of the problems involved.

In keeping with the stated purpose of this volume, this chapter will review and collect the most popular present-day practices in plant distillation column control as reinforced and modified by recent studies of the subject. Special attention will be given to special purpose computers and other devices for overall column control integration and for elimination of the effect of uncontrollable upsets.

An extensive bibliography of the most important recent and background literature on the subjects of distillation column control and their dynamic behavior in the face of various upset conditions is also included as the last section.

II. DEFINITION OF THE DISTILLATION COLUMN CONTROL PROBLEM AND A BASIC RECOMMENDED CONTROL SCHEME

As has been brought out in earlier chapters (particularly Chap. IX), a typical plant continuous distillation column is designed to carry out the separation of a feed stream of a certain specified rate and composition to a desired degree of purity of heads or of bottoms product or both. This is to be carried out with the aid of a heating medium and a cooling medium of known characteristics and amounts. Provided the design is properly carried out and provided no changes occur in the properties and/or rates of feed and of heating and of cooling mediums, the column will continue to make it desired separation indefinitely.

Unfortunately, such stable operation is not the case in practice and a control system must be provided. It will be of greater or less complexity and sophistication depending upon the severity of the upsets to be expected and the degree of exactness required in the composition and rate of the output streams from the column. To provide the control system necessary, the following subjects must be considered simultaneously by the designer:

(*a*) Designation of those column external variables where uncontrollable variations or upsets may be anticipated during the operation of the column along with a selection of the proper internal variables whose alteration may compensate for such upsets.

(*b*) Choice of the optimum methods and locations for detection of the occurrence of an upset and of the degree to which its correction has been accomplished by a manipulated variable.

(*c*) Design of the proper automatic control system to convert the detected error arising from an upset into the required corrective action by the manipulated column variable. Such a design must consider the several possible methods of applying these corrections in light of the economics of the plant operation involved. It would then pick the economic optimum configuration for the control task desired.

1. The Variables of the Distillation Process

For purposes of our discussion here, the variables of the distillation process can be divided into five groups as follows:

(*a*) *Design Variables* such as the number of plates or separation stages required, the physical characteristics of the mixture to be separated, and other such factors established by the original statement of the design problem and the final physical design configuration involved. Since these factors are unalterable by the control function, they will not be considered further here.

(*b*) *External Independent Variables* or those parameters of column operation encompassed by the feed stream and the ambient conditions of operation. These variables are the ones which introduce upsets into the distillation system.

(*c*) *Internal Independent Variables* or those additional column operating parameters which may be designated. With the external independent variables first mentioned, the internal variables serve to completely specify the operation of the column. These are then the variables which are to be manipulated in order to correct for the presence of upsets in the external variables.

(*d*) *Semi-Independent Variables of Column Operation* or those variables of column design or operation which are only rarely changed but whose manipulations may have a decided effect upon column operation.

(*e*) *Dependent Variables* or all other parameters of column operation which may be measured or calculated for use in determining column control error or response to a given correction.

2. Classification of the Variables of a Distillation Column

For any distillation column, only seven independent operating variables are needed to define its operation.

(*a*) *External Independent Variables*
- (*1*) Feed rate
- (*2*) Feed composition
- (*3*) Feed temperature or feed quality
- (*4*) Ambient pressure of operation
- (*5*) Ambient temperature of operation

(*b*) *Internal Independent Variables*
- (6,7) Two of the following five quantities:
  - Overhead product composition (complete)
  - Bottoms composition (complete)
  - Boil-up rate–feed rate ratio
  - Feed split or distillate-bottoms ratio
  - Vapor rate–liquid rate ratio

(*c*) *Semi-Independent Variables of Column Operation*
- (*1*) Location of feed tray
- (*2*) Column reflux temperature

For a binary mixture, the overhead product and bottoms composition is given by the mole fraction of only one component. For a multicomponent mixture of n components, the mole fraction of $n - 1$ components must be specified. This condition is assumed to prevail here, where the overhead or bottoms composition is considered.

The semi-independent variables of feed tray location and of reflux temperature can affect distillation column control. However, in distillation theory these are secondary factors usually considered noncritical. For simplification, at this stage of our discussion, it is assumed that the optimum feed tray location has been chosen and that the reflux is returned at its boiling point. They will be discussed more fully later. Thus proper choice of the seven main variables will permit determination of all of the dependent variables for any given mixture such as:

(*d*) Dependent Variables
- (*1*) Liquid composition. Bottoms, each plate, distillate.
- (*2*) Vapor compositions at each plate or location in the column.
- (*3*) All unspecified flow rates. Liquid, vapor, distillate take-off, bottoms take-off.
- (*4*) Temperatures at each location in column.

These dependent variables are, of course, interrelated through the thermodynamic laws governing the vapor–liquid equilibria of the mixture and by the material balance requirements of the column itself. Figures 1 and 2 show the location and interrelation of each of these variables.

The basic problem in distillation control can now be resolved into three parts: determining which two of the five possible internal independent variables should apply, which method is most direct for sensing variations in independent variables specified as constants, and how the displaced

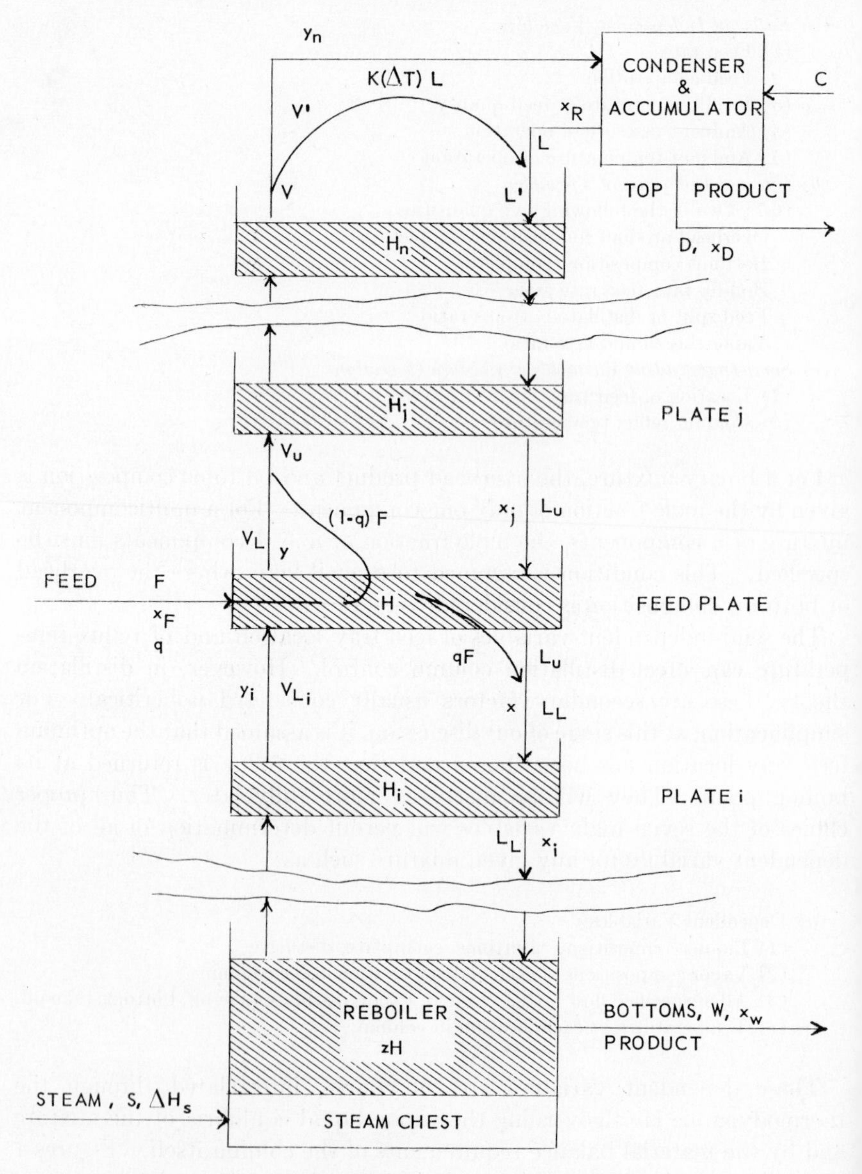

Fig. 1. The variables of column operation.

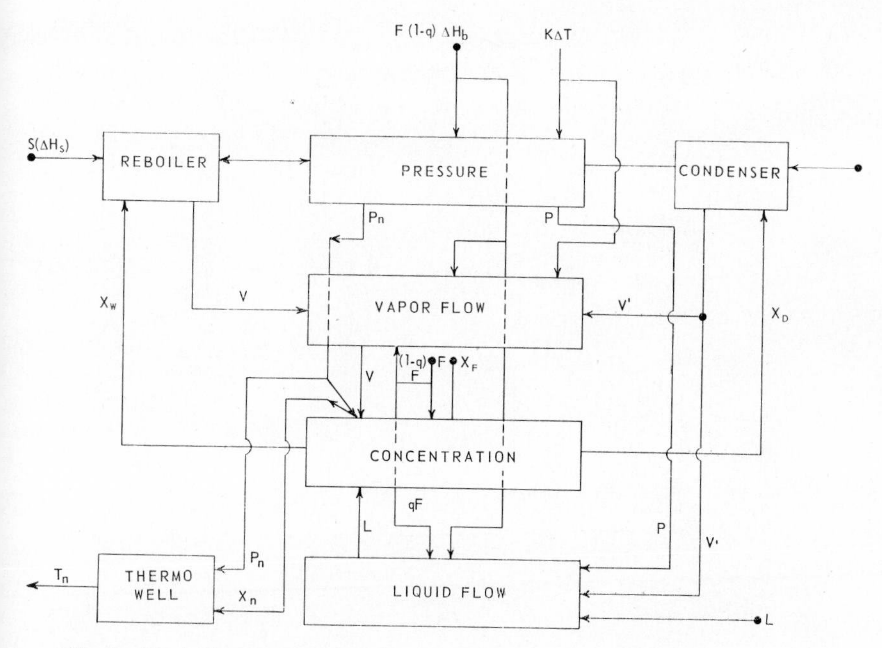

Fig. 2. Block diagram showing interrelation of column operating variables.[45]

variable can be restored to its chosen operating value through adjustment of the controlled system. If the internal variables are to be truly independent, it is absolutely necessary that the boil-up rate be specified as the ratio of the respective steam rate to the feed rate rather than as simply that variable's rate of flow alone.

3. Classes of Distillation Control

On the basis of these statements, several schemes for distillation column control may be suggested (Table I and Figure 3).

Because of the instrumentation system chosen for each control scheme, certain internal independent variables should be selected. In Table I, these systems are arranged in order of increasing flexibility to illustrate the development of an optimum system.

The scheme of Figure 3A, requiring a constant feed composition, is the simplest example possible and seems entirely unrealistic in most plant situations. This method has been called inferential or environmental control,[33] and succeeds only when it can prevent all upsets originating from external sources from reaching the column. Here flow controllers alone are sufficient to maintain steady operation because only boil-up rate and distillate take-off rate need be kept constant.

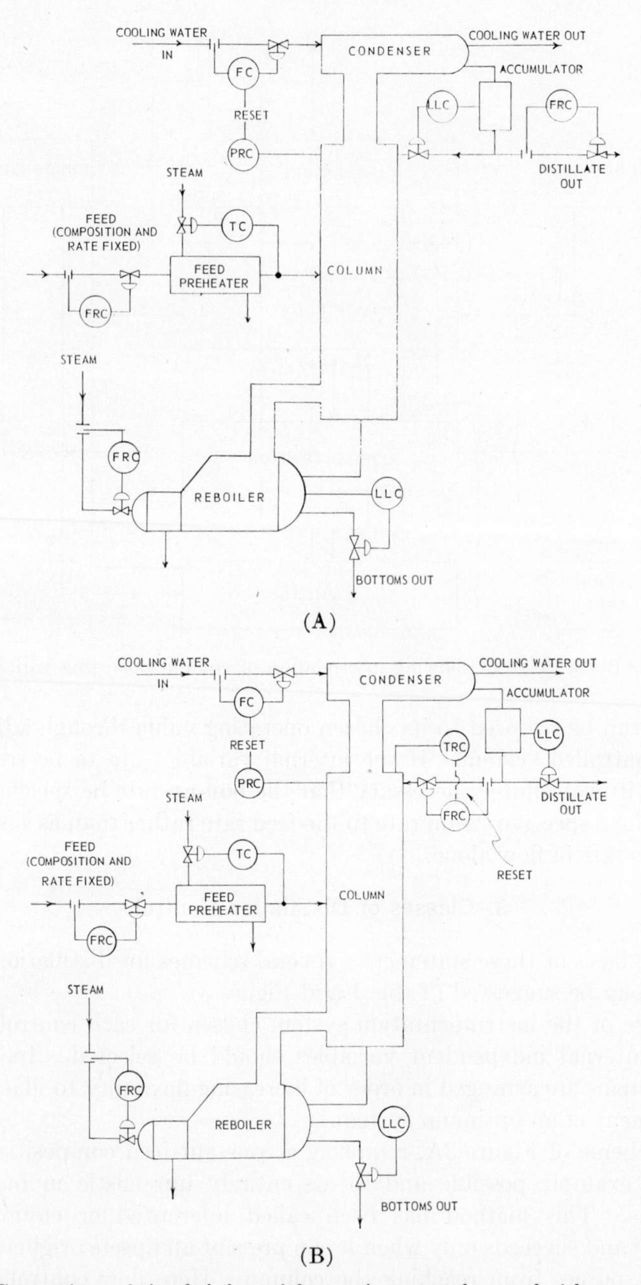

Fig. 3. Comparison of simple inferential or environmental control with proposed, more sophisticated schemes. (A) Original arrangement. (B) This allows for smoother control of heads composition but constant feed still required. (See also p. 771.)

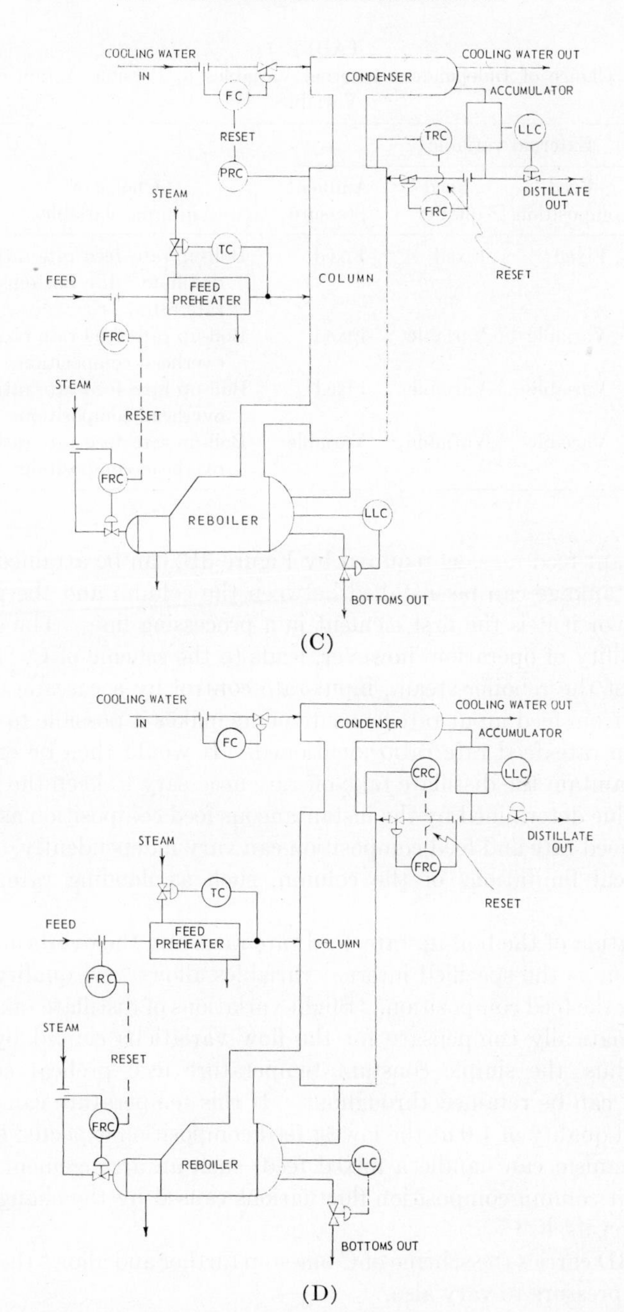

Fig. 3 (*continued*). (C) Ratio of boil-up rate to feed rate permits some flexibility. (D) Composition detection of heads sample allows ultimate degree of control.

TABLE I
Relation of Choice of Independent Internal Variables to Possible Action of External Variables

External variable					
Feed rate	Feed composition	Feed quality	Ambient pressure	Choice of internal variables	Refer to Fig. 3
Fixed	Fixed	Fixed	Fixed	Boil-up rate–feed rate ratio, distillate rate—bottoms-rate ratio	A
Fixed	Variable	Variable	Fixed	Boil-up rate–feed rate ratio, overhead composition	B
Variable	Variable	Variable	Fixed	Boil-up rate–feed rate ratio, overhead composition	C
Variable	Variable	Variable	Variable	Boil-up rate–feed rate ratio, overhead composition	D

A constant feed rate, as required by Figure 3B, can be attained either if sufficient tankage can be installed between the column and the preceding plant unit or if it is the first element in a processing line. The desire for true flexibility of operation, however, leads to the scheme of C. Here the resetting of the reboiler-steam, input-rate control by a cascade controller operating from feed input rate measurements makes it possible to maintain the boil-up rate–feed rate ratio mentioned. It would then be easily possible to maintain the distillate take-off rate necessary to keep the feed split at that value determined by the instantaneous feed composition as it varies. Thus the feed rate and feed composition can vary independently, as long as the physical limitations of the column, such as flooding rate, are not exceeded.

Designation of the boil-up rate–feed rate ratio and the overhead product composition as the specified internal variables allows feed quality to vary along with the feed composition. Slight variations of distillate take-off rate will automatically compensate for the flow variations caused by quality shifts. Thus, the simple constant temperature feed preheat control of Figure 3A can be retained throughout. If this temperature can be set to give a feed quality of 1.0 at the lowest feed composition expected and if the feed mechanism can handle a mixed feed, such an arrangement helps to smooth out column composition fluctuations caused by the change in feed composition itself.[64]

Figure 3D carries the scheme of C one step further and allows the ambient operating pressure to vary also.

This simplifies the control of cooling water, but makes the use of temperature alone as a composition detector impossible. In such a situation some device must be used which measures composition directly or measures another composition-sensitive but non-temperature-sensitive property, because temperature will vary drastically with pressure.

Thus, boil-up rate–feed rate ratio and overhead product composition are specified as the optimum internal variables for control. Is this really so? The present situation allows the bottoms take-off rate to be determined by an auxiliary level controller in the reboiler. Thus a constant heat transfer area is maintained in the reboiler and boil-up rate control can be tied directly to steam input rate. Any other scheme would result in level fluctuations with corresponding heat transfer area variations in the reboiler. Thus the steam rate and/or pressure would have to vary in a complex manner to maintain the boil-up rate at its established value.

Bottoms composition may be used as an independent variable, but because pot volumes are usually ten or more times greater than plate holdups, bottoms composition can vary only at a correspondingly slower rate than any plate compositions. Thus a much greater sensitivity can be attained with overhead product composition as the independent variable, even when the bottoms is the desired product.

Table II and Figure 4 summarize the resulting recommended basic control scheme and the main and subsidiary control functions included. Alternate methods for accomplishing some of these functions and methods of circumventing several of the assumptions necessary in using the overall

TABLE II
Summary of Recommended Control Scheme

Main control functions	
Designated independent internal variable	Method of determining and regulating required variation
Overhead product composition	Sampled by dependent variable near top of column and maintained as constant as possible by resetting reflux rate controller
Boil-up rate–feed rate ratio	Variations of feed rate detected by flow controller and used to reset steam input rate controller previously set at some intermediate rate for task at hand
Required subsidiary controls	
Subsidiary variable	Method of control
Feed temperature	Feed preheater on feed line
Bottoms take-off rate	Level control on reboiler
Pressure (where necessary for temperature elements)	Variation of condenser cooling water rate
Distillate take-off rate	Level control on accumulator

control scheme above will be discussed in the succeeding sections. In addition, the control of column auxiliaries such as economizer-heat exchangers will be discussed. Also, some of the newer computer control schemes for anticipatory or feed forward control will be mentioned.

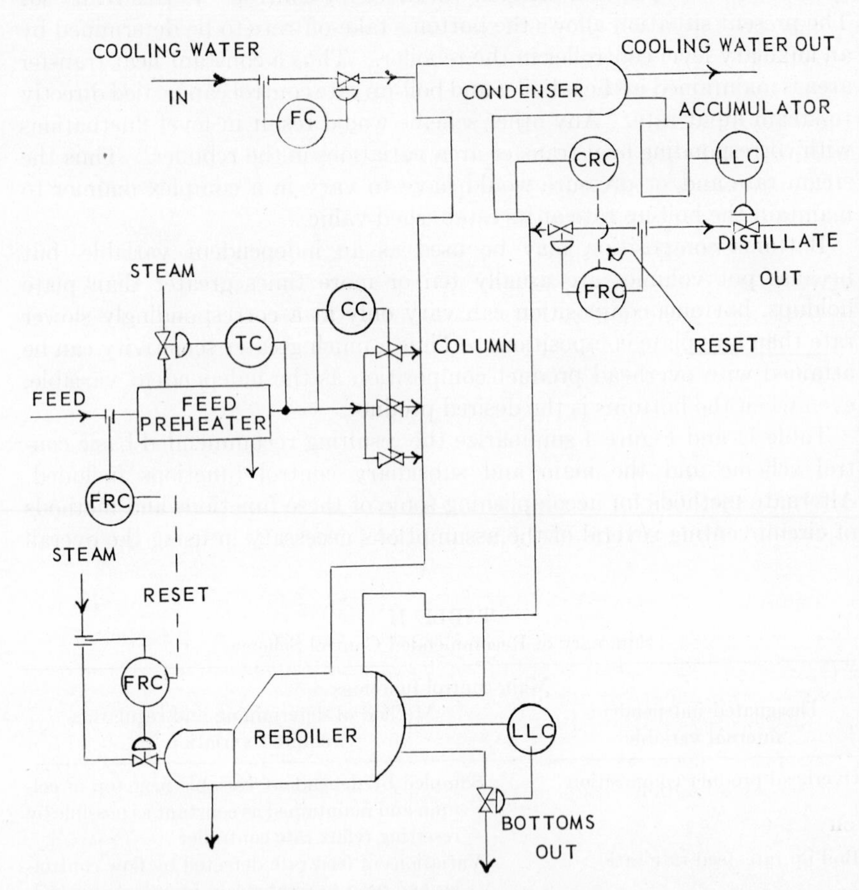

Fig. 4. The ultimate control scheme for a distillation column embodies results of theoretical studies to give automatic control.

It should be noted that the above recommended control system applies best for those cases where the feed is entered cold or at its bubble point. When appreciable vapor is present in the feed, control of the column overheads becomes much more sensitive. When this occurs, a feed-forward control of reflux may become important. Section VI describes the control systems involved when this is desired.

4. Ranges of Control Operation, Design Limits, etc.

The designer must bear in mind when considering column control systems that the allowable ranges of variation of the manipulated variables are often quite small. For example, a column may be designed to have a reflux rate which is 1.15–1.25 times the minimum. In addition, the corresponding vapor rate may be 85–90% of its allowable maximum. Therefore, rate fluctuations for control purposes are limited to ±15–20% of the base values by column pinch conditions on the one hand and by column flooding on the other. Violation of either limit can cause a severe decrease in the separating ability of the column and thus a violent composition upset. Further, column controls are not usually designed to counter pinch and flooding upsets—another reason for scrupulously avoiding their occurrence. A very careful design of fluid flow lines and their constituent valves along with the judicious use of limiting devices on the control instruments themselves will, however, effectively accomplish this requirement. Such limiting devices will not be shown on the figures of this chapter but will be understood as being present.

III. INSTRUMENT CHARACTERISTICS AND THEIR EFFECT UPON DISTILLATION COLUMN CONTROL

The previously discussed control scheme was derived under the assumption that perfect detecting and controlling instruments were available. For example, the requirement for top plate composition sampling imposes a severe requirement on analyzer performance for a column making a very close separation, particularly if a multicomponent mixture is involved. It is therefore necessary for us to consider the nature of the instrument shortcomings which may arise and the remedies which may be required to circumvent them.

1. Effect of Dead Space in Samples

Perhaps the most common instrument error to be considered is that of dead space, or the region within which the instrument cannot detect that an error has occurred in the measured variable. Figure 5A, B shows two means by which dead space can occur, while Figure 6A, B shows the effect of such an instrument error on the response of a controller.

When an instrument with dead space is used in a top plate sampling situation on a distillation column, the error in column output is nearly equal to instrument dead space as shown in Figure 7. However, when the

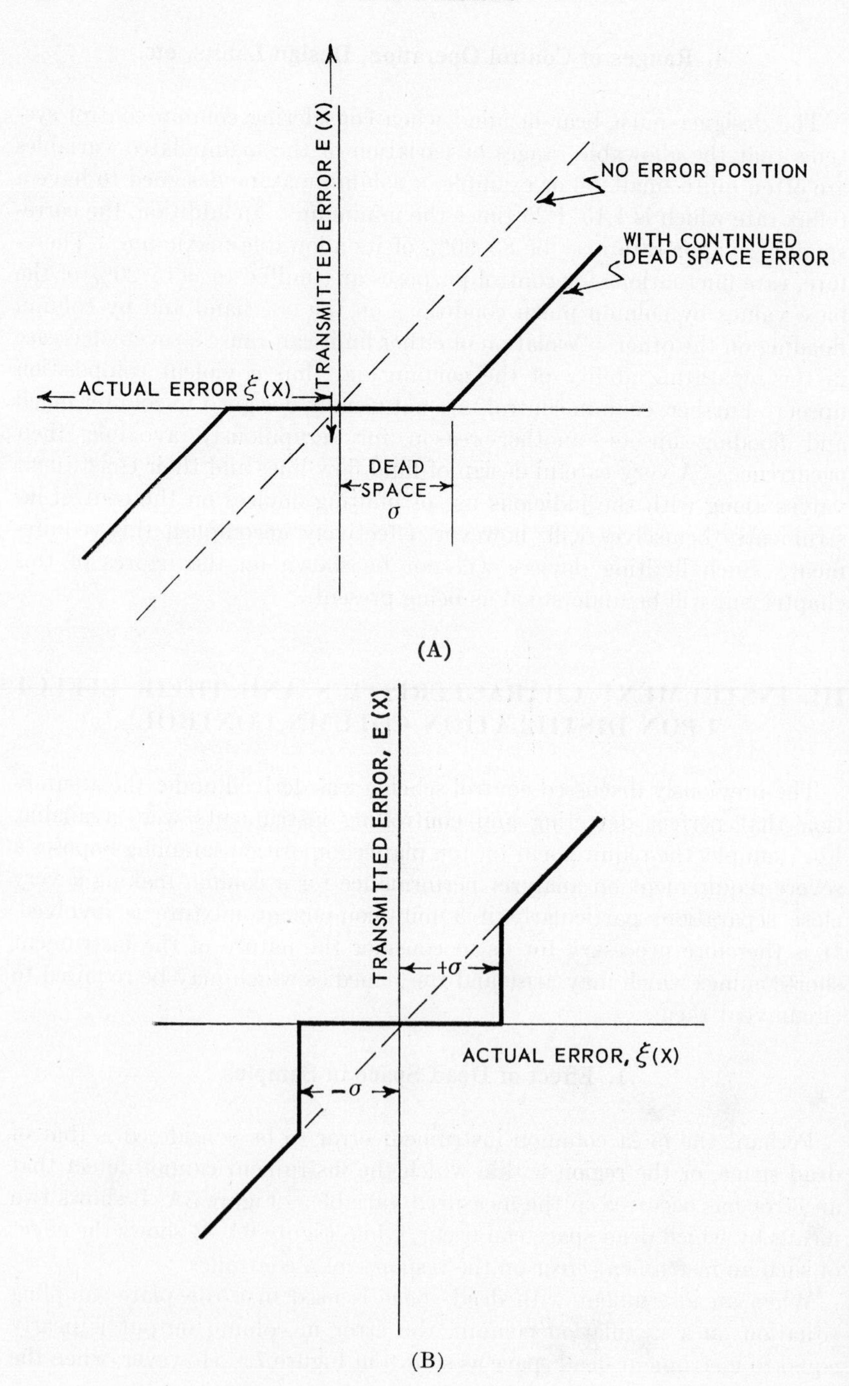

Fig. 5. A dead space exists when sampling device is unable to detect small deviations of sample variable from set point.

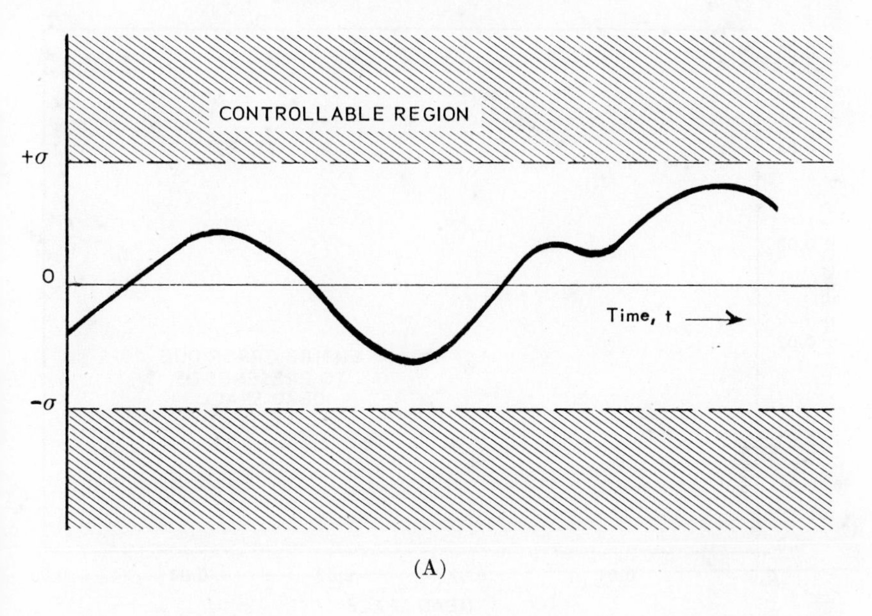

(A)

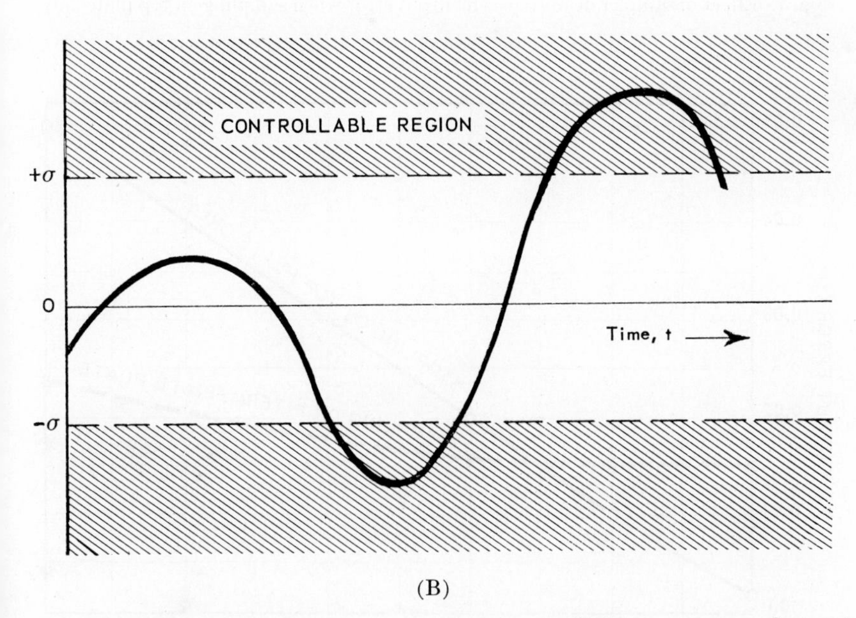

(B)

Fig. 6. (A) The quality of the product cannot be specified to any more refinement than the dead space of the control system will allow. (B) The process may build up sufficient inertia to drive the value of the sampled variable a considerable distance beyond the dead space. Too severe correction thereafter may result in oscillation.

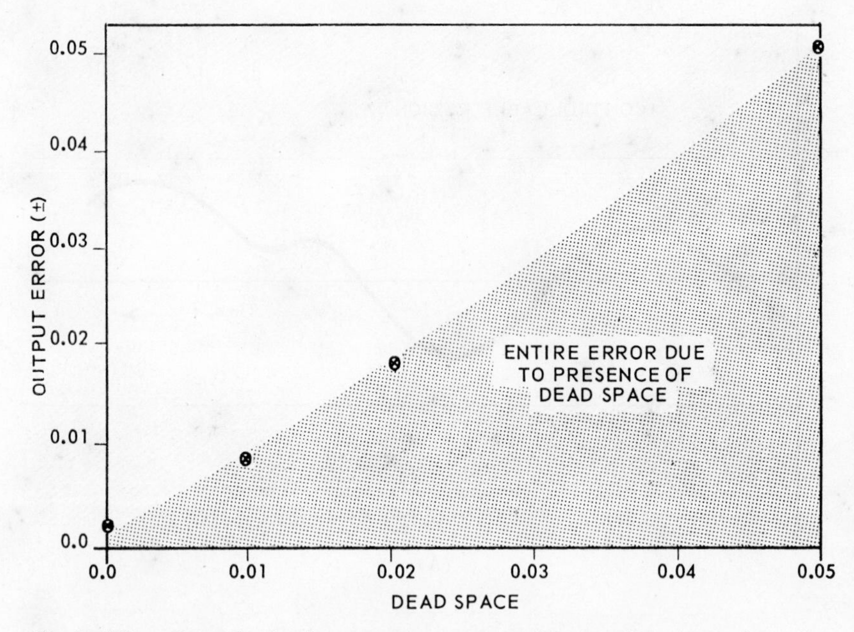

Fig. 7. Effect of sampler dead space on output error when sampling on top plate only.

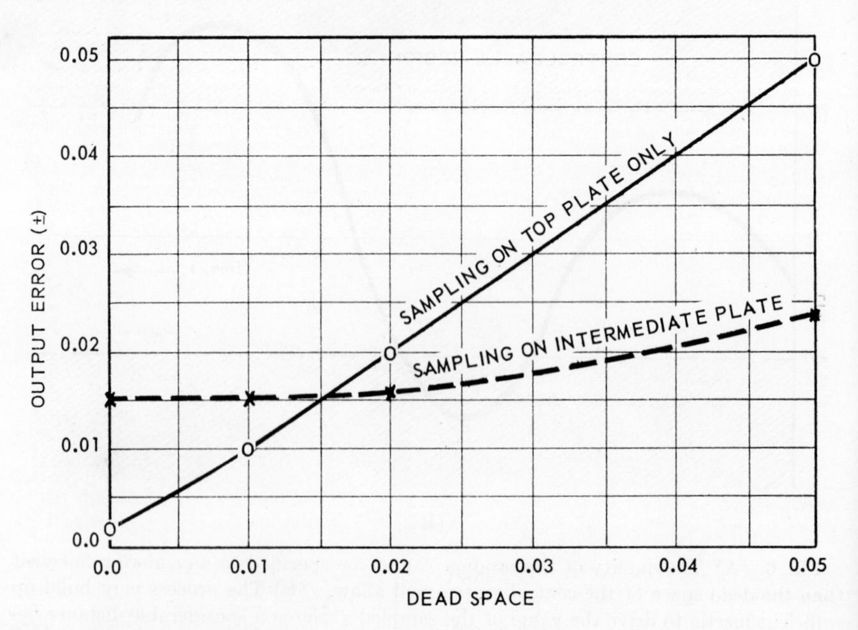

Fig. 8. For a dead space of less than 0.015 mole fraction, top plate sampling is best.

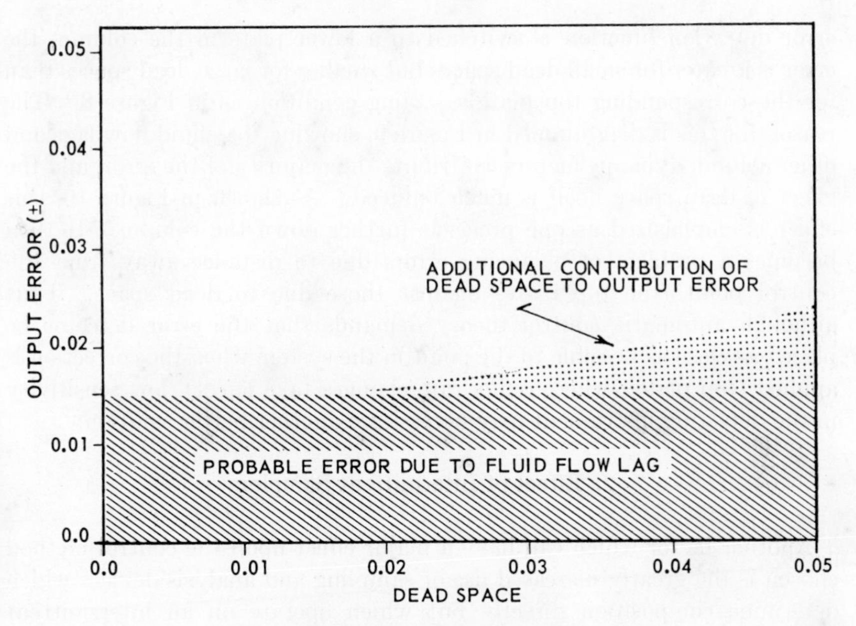

Fig. 9. Sampling on intermediate plate only.

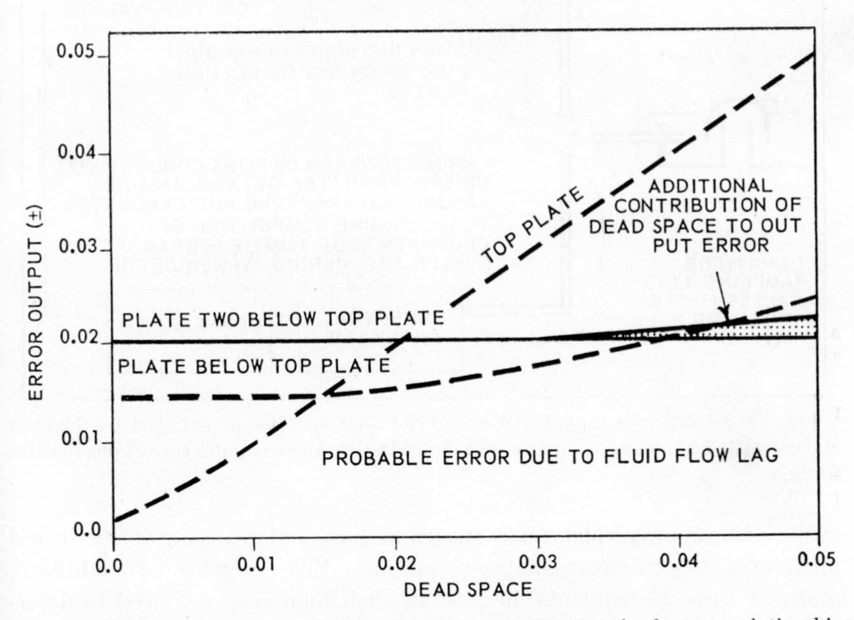

Fig. 10. Effect of use of succeeding plates on output error–dead space relationship.

error detection function is switched to a lower plate in the column, the error is greater for small dead spaces but smaller for large dead spaces than for the corresponding top plate sampling condition as in Figure 8. The reason for this is diagrammed in Figure 9, showing that fluid flow lags and other column dynamic factors contribute the majority of the error, and the effect of dead space itself is much reduced. As shown in Figure 10, this effect is emphasized as one proceeds further down the column. It then becomes a problem of balancing errors due to distance away from the control point (the top plate) against those due to dead space. Thus although automatic control theory demands that the error detector be placed as close as possible to the point in the system when the correction is applied (top plate—where reflux rate changes take effect), low sensitivity in the detecting instrument may necessitate another better solution.

2. Effect of Intermittent Samplers

Another factor which can have a major effect upon the control method chosen is the greatly increased use of sampling and analysis devices which determine composition directly but which operate on an interrmittent

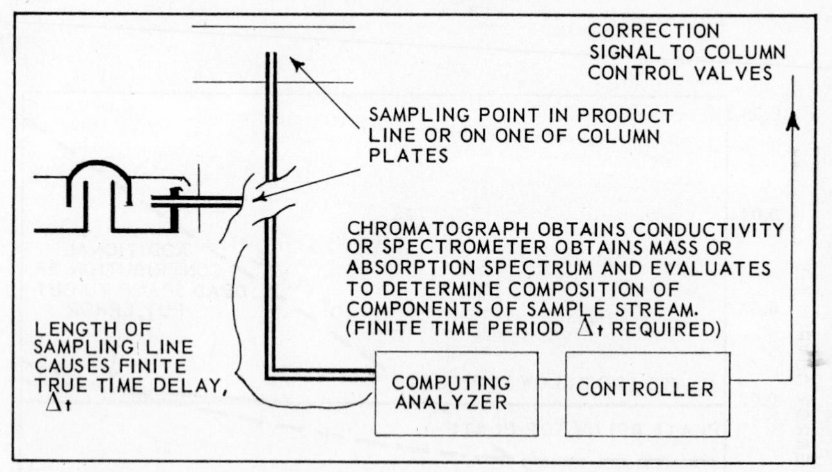

Fig. 11. Details of sampling system. Controller operates as detected by analyzer and associated computer, compares with desired value, and computes corrections to valve settings.

cycle. Chromatographs, mass spectrometers, and scanning infrared and ultraviolet spectrometer analyzers fall into this category. In addition, many of these instruments, because of their high cost, are used to determine the output at several different sampling points through a time-

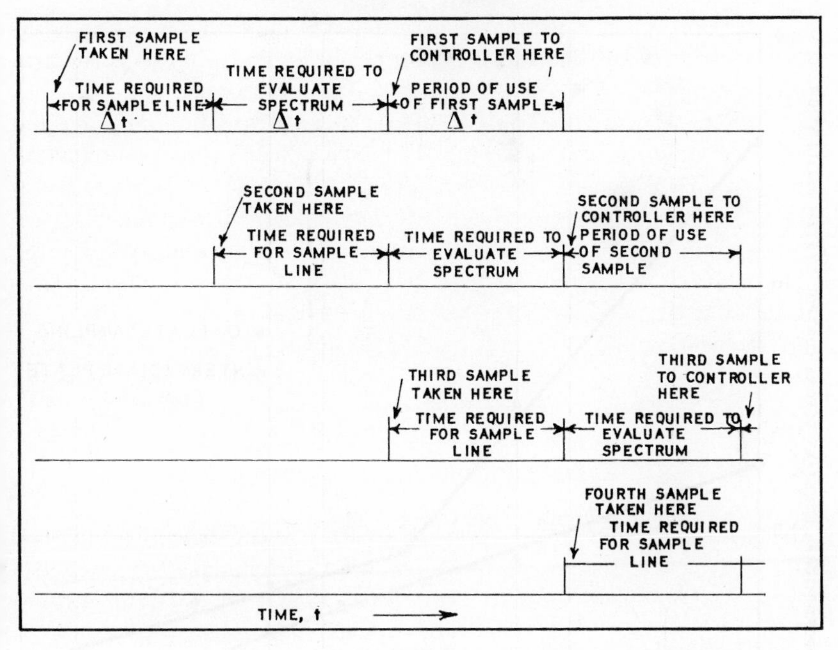

Fig. 12. Time relationship of events in operation of intermittent sampling device.

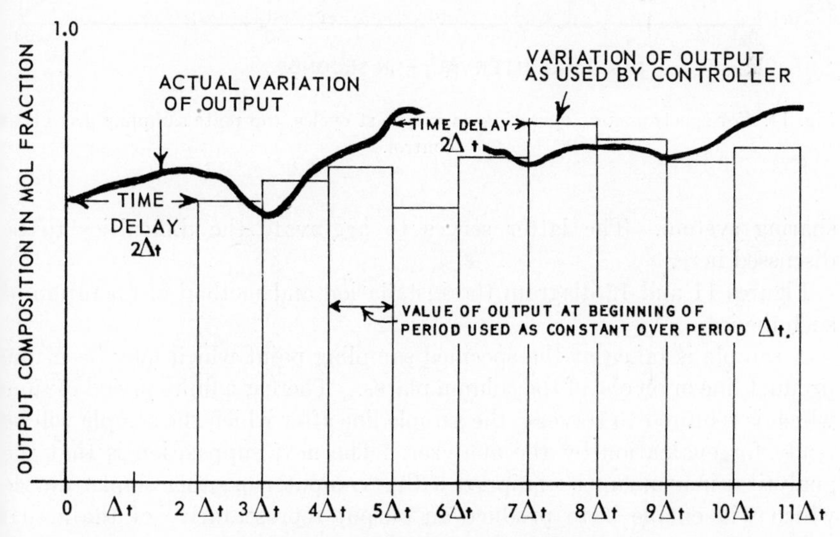

Fig. 13. Comparison of real output of process and that actually used by the controller operating with an intermittent sampler.

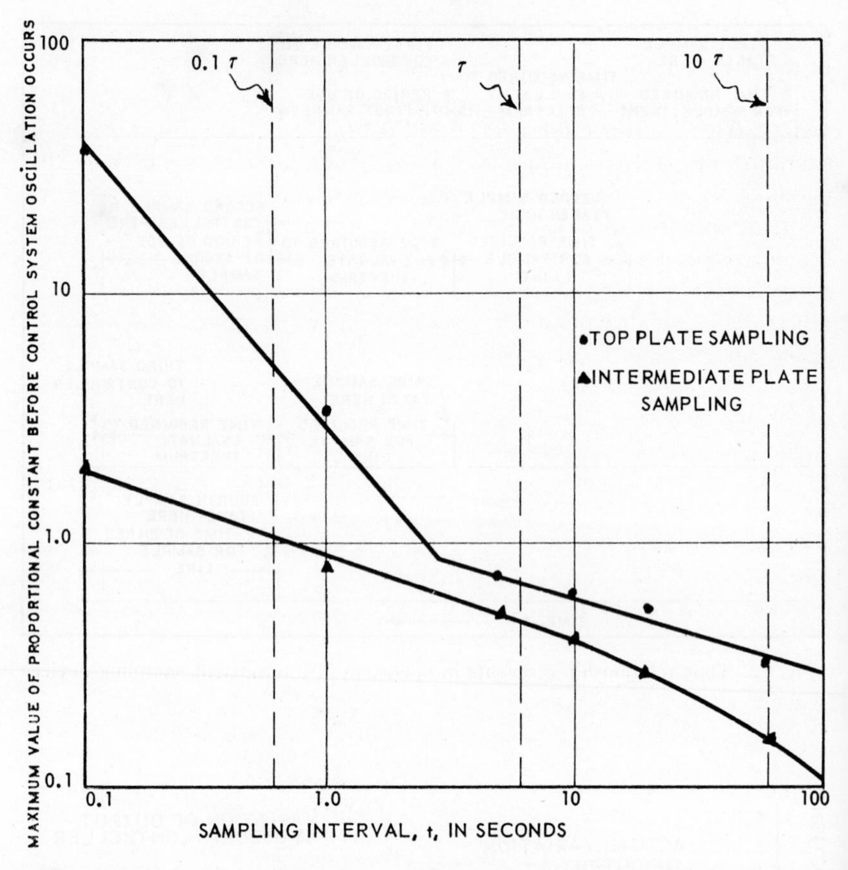

Fig. 14. For spectrometers operating on very fast cycles, top plate sampling gives best control.

sharing system. The latter serves to aggravate the difficulties to be discussed here.

Figures 11 and 12 diagram the installation and method of operation of such devices.

A sample is taken at the specified sampling point which may be in the product line or on one of the column plates. There is a finite period of time which is required to traverse the sample line after which the sample will be ready for evaluation by the analyzer. The next supposition is that the analytical instrument is equipped with a computer or other similar device which will enable it to produce an output representative of the actual composition of the sample stream rather than to give merely its per cent absorption at various frequencies or other representative signal. This process of obtaining the primary instrument indication and of converting it to signals representative of actual composition will require another definite period of time. Therefore, the composition of the stream will be available to the controller for determination of output error and for the computation of the required control correction only after a period of time which is the sum of the two periods just mentioned.

In addition, because the instrument or its associated computer can operate only upon one sample at a time, the controller must make use of the result from each discrete sample as a constant for that period of time necessary for the instrument and its associated computer to complete their operation. Figure 13 diagrams this situation. For purposes of completeness, it will be assumed that the periods of time entailed in sample-line true-time lag and in analyzer plus computer operation are the same. This is done for convenience only and is not an absolutely necessary assumption. It is necessary to know only the total-line delay involved and the sampling interval or rate of sample-taking which is used.

In order to show the effects of an increasing sampling interval, the maximum proportional constant allowable with each of a series of sampling intervals, which still gives a stable response, is plotted against the corre-

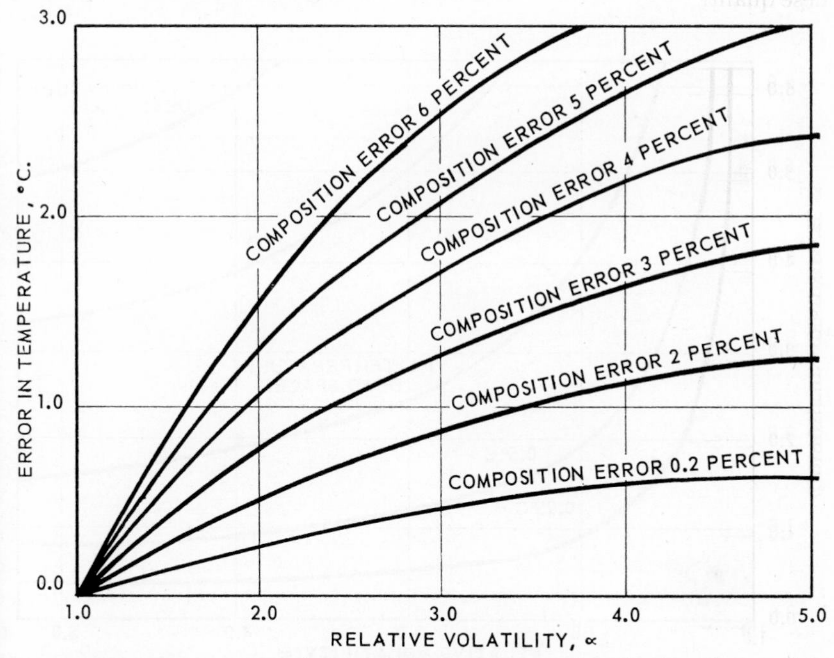

Fig. 15. Pressure must be closely controlled, if temperature is to be the primary column variable detected by the sampler.

sponding sampling interval for top plate sampling and for intermediate plate sampling in Figure 14. It can be seen from these plots that the permissible value of the proportional constant falls rapidly until a sampling interval of about one-half the basic-column time constant, τ, or three seconds for this example is reached. After this point the rate of decrease is less as sampling interval increases. However, the permissible value of the proportional constant is now much smaller.

This same point has been previously brought out in a study of other systems. It is a common control system rule that the maximum sampling interval should be less than one-half the system time constant when expressed in the same units of time. Thus, the maximum sampling interval in our distillation example test column should be three seconds or less since most time lags in the system were six seconds.

3. Use of Alternate Methods of Detecting Composition Changes

As has been mentioned several times previously, the primary output specification in distillation is generally the composition of the heads and bottoms products. Therefore, every effort should be made to sample these quantities directly and to use the resulting information as the primary

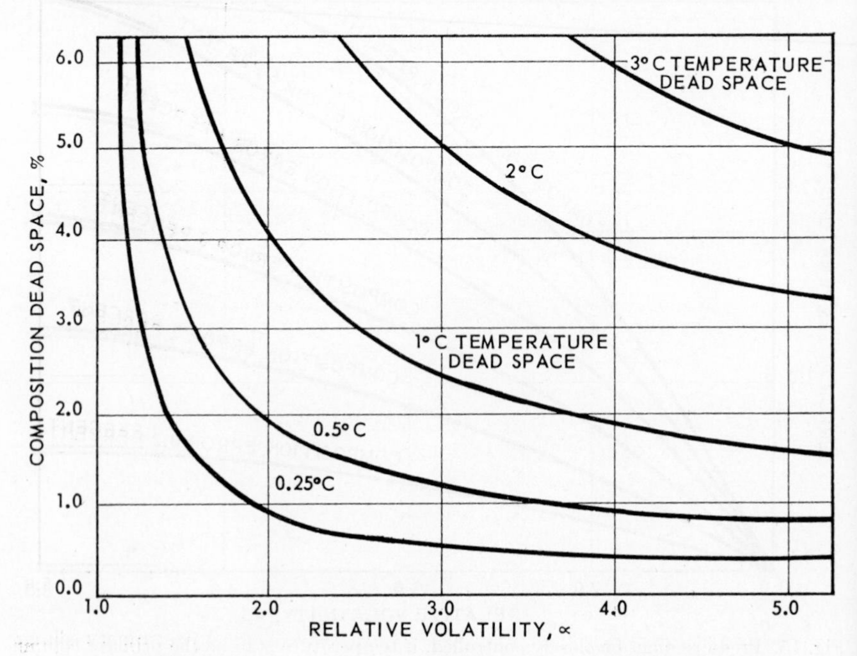

Fig. 16. Relationship of temperature dead space to composition dead space.

control activation method. However, as just discussed, the available analytical instruments may not have the necessary sensitivity or may need too much time to carry out the required analysis. Finally, suitable instruments may not even exist.

It is necessary then to detect another property which is related to composition and which can substitute for it in developing the presence of errors

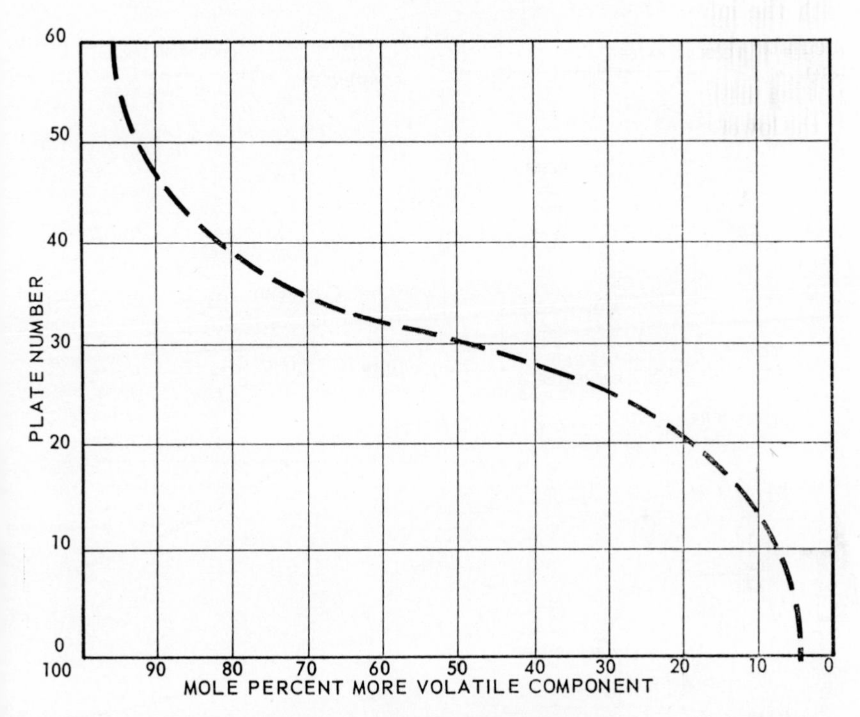

Fig. 17. Composition variation and resulting temperature variation is highest on intermediate plate of a distillation column.

in column composition. The most commonly chosen property for this purpose is temperature. Figure 15 relates the boiling point, i.e., tray temperature variation to the resulting composition variation for various relative volatilities of binary mixtures. It is therefore necessary to maintain a very close control of column pressure, if temperature is to be the primary column variable detected by the sampler for control purposes. Otherwise, another property must be used for satisfactory results. Figure 16 emphasizes this by relating the composition dead space to temperature dead space for various volatilities.

Because of the nature of most vapor–liquid equilibria, there is a much greater variation of composition and hence of temperature on the intermediate plates of the column as is shown in Figure 17. This, combined with the information already shown concerning the effect of dead space errors, makes the choice of an intermediate plate a natural for a temperature sensing instrument, providing one is willing to accept the much higher value of the lower limit on control error.

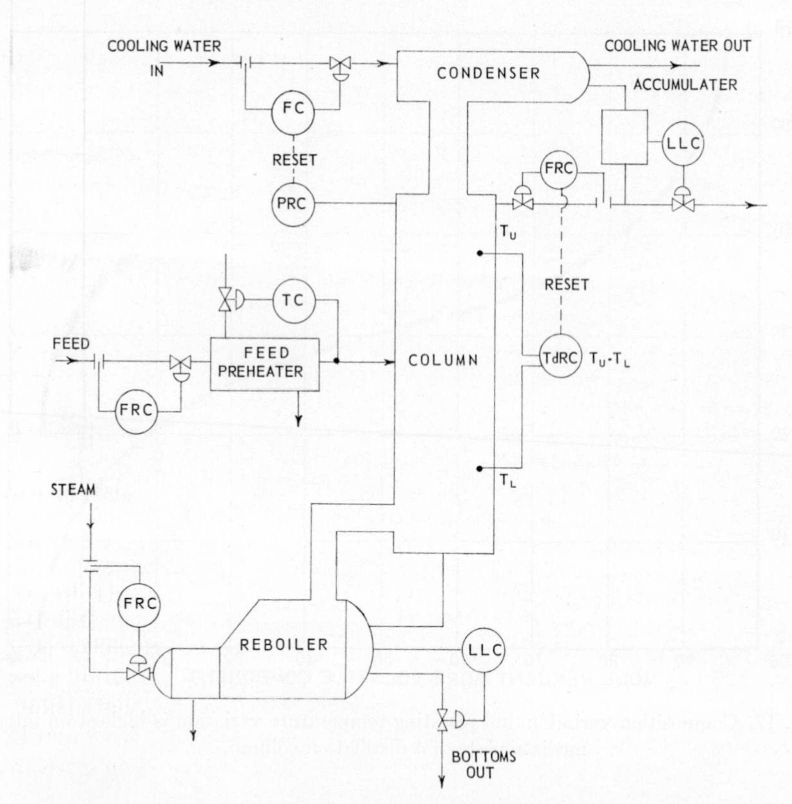

Fig. 18. Temperature difference measurement for distillation column control.

In case a sufficient control of pressure to prevent undesirable excursions of temperature is not possible, or if variable amounts of subsidiary components are present which might affect the temperature–composition relationship, the use of a temperature difference measurement is often satisfactory (Fig. 18). It should be noted, however, that this method is subject to dynamic variations arising in both ends of the column and, therefore, is mainly a steady-state control device.

IV. COLUMN DYNAMICS AND THEIR EFFECT UPON COLUMN AUTOMATIC CONTROL

1. Some General Considerations Regarding Dynamics and Control

As was indicated previously, control systems for distillation columns are generally designed on the basis of the steady-state performance of the column with sensitivities or degree of variation of control variables at selected points checked by trial-and-error, steady-state calculations. Such a procedure is entirely satisfactory for establishing such sensitivities provided no reversal of the direction of response occurs during an operating transient. It is also necessary that some other method be available for determining the control modes to be employed and the proper settings of the gains of each of these modes.

TABLE III

General Conclusions Regarding Column Control Systems to Compensate for Dynamic Effects

(*1*) The rate control mode or derivative mode is generally ineffective in distillation column control. Therefore, only proportional band and reset or integral control should be employed.

(*2*) Where one can sample compositions on the top plate of the column continuously, very high gains of proportional control or low proportional bands can be employed. In this case integral or reset control is not necessary.

(*3*) As the composition sampling point is moved further away from the top plate location, the allowed gain rapidly decreases because of the response lags introduced by the intervening plates between sampling and control point. In this case, integral or reset control must be added to secure a satisfactory control action.

(*4*) In the presence of dead space, of intermittent sampling, or when considering large, slow-responding columns care must be taken to limit the gain of the integral control mode, i.e., use very long reset times, to avoid an oscillatory response of the control system.

(*5*) Level controls, particularly in reboilers, and in accumulators which are used to feed succeeding columns, should be set to give a relatively slow response and a correspondingly wide variation of their own levels. This will prevent rapid changes of heating area in reboilers. It will also help prevent the propagation of an oscillatory behavior on to succeeding columns.

(*6*) Level controls used to regulate the flow of fluid streams, such as bottoms flow to succeeding columns, should be used in cascade. That is, the fluid stream should have its own tightly regulated flow control loop whose set point is changed as gradually as possible by the level controller.

(*7*) Where more than one possible control element location is available for control of a particular variable, that one which gives the fastest response should be selected. A tentative evaluation of relative response rates can be obtained by the methods given in Part 3 of this Section.

Rosenbrock[53] has stated that, in general, binary columns are always monotonic in their response, i.e., no reversal of response is possible. This has been shown to be generally true except for some very special start-up conditions.[47] Therefore, sign reversal should be no problem for such columns. However, recent work shows that sign reversal can often occur in certain sections of multicomponent columns during the transient period while recovering from an upset condition.[40] Thus, a controller might possibly give the opposite control correction temporarily and aggravate the upset condition of the column. Such occurrences can be prevented by a proper choice of sampling location to avoid the region of sign reversal of the sampled variable.

In general, the exact information necessary to make the decisions required above can only be obtained from a detailed study of the dynamics of the column conducted either experimentally or through theoretical computations on analog or digital computers. However, numerous studies of this type have been conducted in the past and some general conclusions can be given concerning these topics.[5,6,9,10,20,21,25,34,44,45,48,49,57,59,60,63,64,66] Table III collects these for the benefit of the reader. In addition, approximate mathematical models[41] of distillation columns have been formulated which can give an excellent indication of the magnitude and form of the response of the column composition (and other related variables) under various upsets and imposed input functions. These are given in the following sections.

2. Derivation of Mathematical Models of Dynamic Systems

Before entering upon a discussion of the dynamic effects of column control, it may be well to define some of the mathematical expressions which have become associated with such discussions. Particularly important here are the concepts of the first-order transfer function, the higher order transfer function, dead time, and various combinations of these to give more complex cases.

A. THE FIRST-ORDER TRANSFER FUNCTION

The first type of operating characteristic to be taken up is that which is exemplified by an ordinary binary mixing process, the *first-order transfer function*. Consider the simple apparatus of Figure 19 and assume that the kettle gives complete mixing at all times. Now let us further assume that pure component 1 has been flowing into the kettle. Suddenly the feed composition is changed so that now pure component 2 is being introduced at the same rate as previously used for component 1. The resulting com-

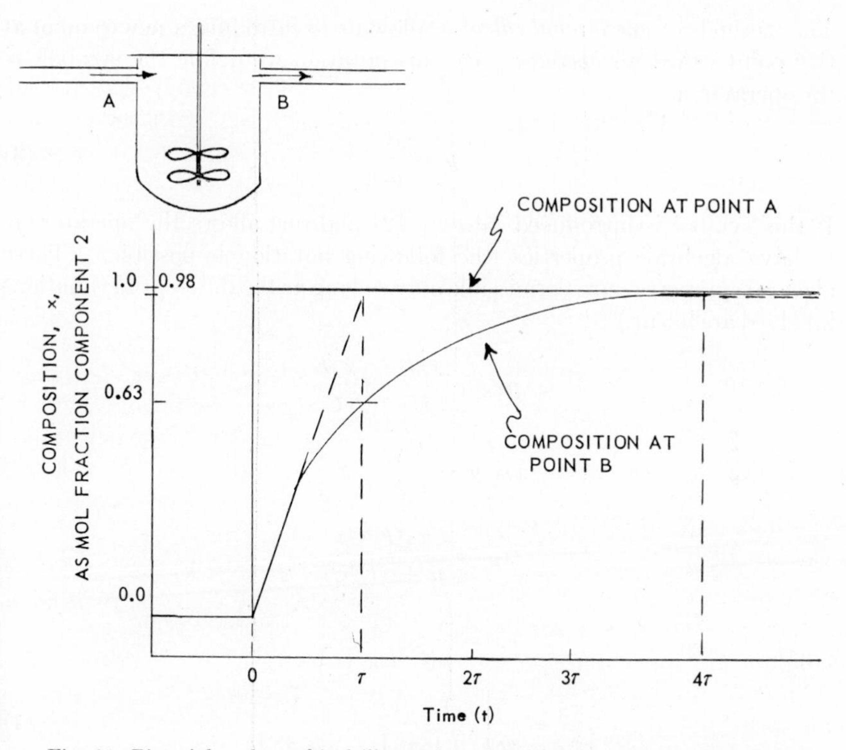

Fig. 19. Pictorial and graphical illustration of a first-order transfer function.

position of the entering stream at point A has been plotted in the graph of Figure 19 as the mole fraction of component 2 and thus shows a sharp jump to pure component 2 at zero time or at the beginning of the experiment. This sudden change in the value of the composition of the entering stream at point A is known as a *step-function.*

We can now write a differential equation expressing the composition appearing at point B as follows:

$$\frac{dx_B}{dt} = (x_A - x_B)\frac{F}{C} \tag{1}$$

where x_A and x_B are the compositions at points A and B, respectively. F is the flow rate into the kettle, and C is the capacity of the kettle, both in consistent units. Equation (1) may be rearranged as follows:

$$\frac{dx_B}{dt} + \frac{x_B F}{C} = \frac{x_A F}{C} \tag{2}$$

The methods of *operational calculus* allow us to introduce a new symbol at this point called an *operator*. By this notation we define the symbol, p, the operator, as

$$p = \frac{d}{dt} \tag{3}$$

If this symbol is introduced into eq. (2) and one allows the operator, p, to have algebraic properties, the following notation is possible. (These algebraic properties are permissible only so long as the differential equations involved are linear.)

$$px_B + \frac{x_B F}{C} = \frac{x_A F}{C}$$

$$x_B\left(p + \frac{F}{C}\right) = x_A \frac{F}{C}$$

$$x_B = \frac{x_A(F/C)}{p + (F/C)}$$

$$x_B = \frac{x_A}{p(C/F) + 1}$$

$$\frac{x_B}{x_A} = \frac{1}{p(C/F) + 1} = \frac{1}{\tau p + 1} \tag{4}$$

The expression $1/(\tau p + 1)$ is called a *first-order transfer function* and the symbol $\tau = C/F$ is called the *time constant* of the process of mixing in the vessel. It can be seen that the quantity, τ, has units of time equivalent to the units of time used in expressing the flow rate into and out of the kettle. The expression $1/(\tau p + 1)$ is also called the equation of a *single-capacity system* since there is only one place available for storage of the material flowing in at point A, the capacity, C, of the kettle itself.

The solution of eq. (1) by classical means gives the expression

$$x_B = (1 - e^{-(F/C)\,t})x_A \tag{5}$$

or

$$x_B = (1 - e^{-t/\tau})x_A \tag{5a}$$

e is here the base of the Naperian or natural logarithms.

If the expression is plotted, the curve labeled "composition at Point B" on Figure 19 is obtained. Some interesting points concerning the quantity τ can be obtained from this graph. Consideration of eq. (1) shows that the initial rate of change of x_B is equal to F/C. Therefore, if the initial slope

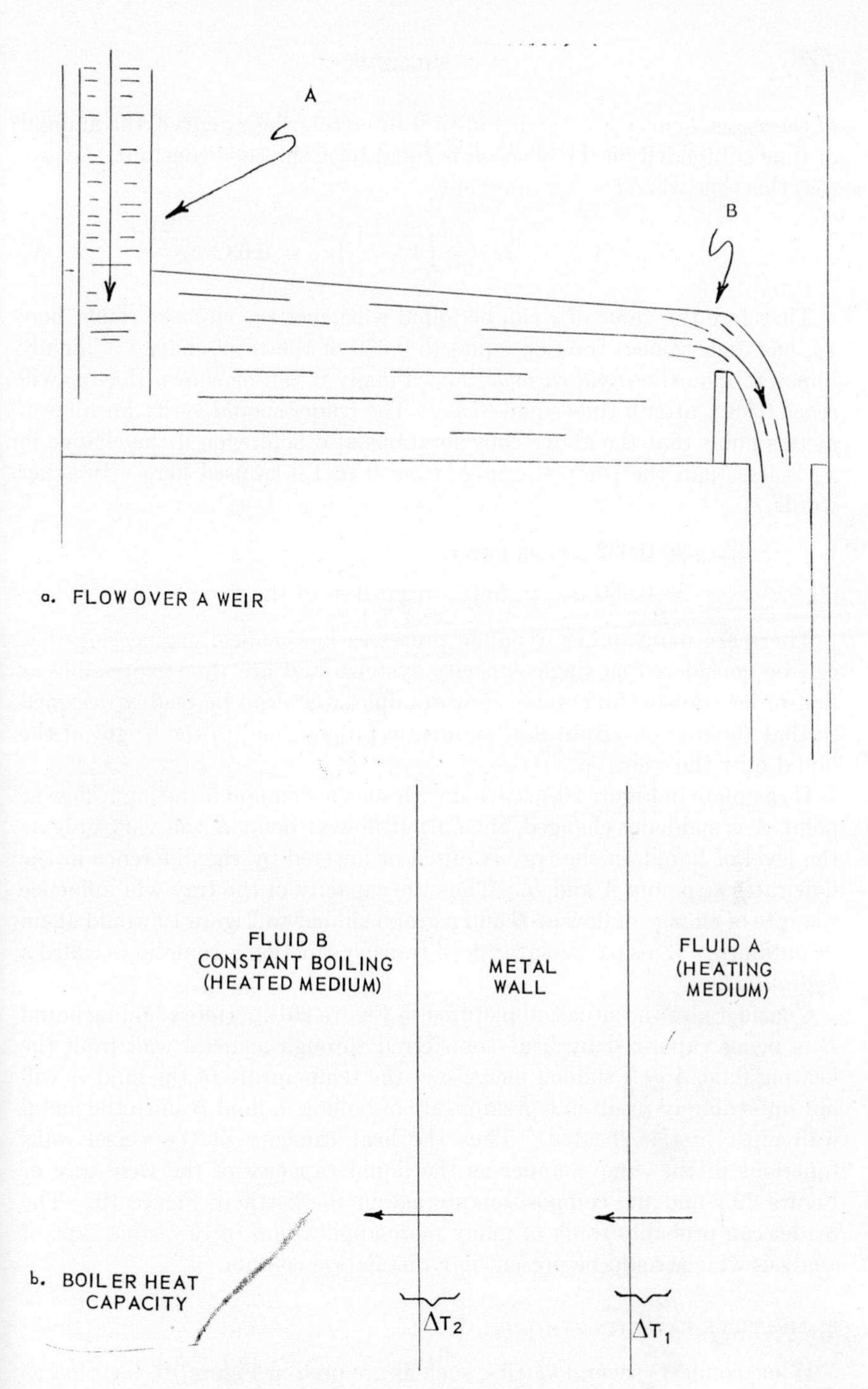

Fig. 20. Other examples of first-order transfer functions.

of the x_B vs. t curve is extended until it intersects the x_A curve, the amount of time subtended on the abscissa is equal to τ, the time constant. In eq. (5a) this time when $t = \tau$ means that

$$x_B = (1 - e^{-1})x_A = \left(1 - \frac{1}{e}\right)x_A = 0.632\ x_A \tag{6}$$

Therefore the value of τ can be found whenever the *output variable*, here x_B, has undergone a fraction equal to 0.632 of the total change originally imposed upon the *input variable*, x_A. Finally it can be shown that x_B will reach $0.98x_A$ after a time equal to 4τ. The reader should verify for himself at this point that the above considerations also hold even if the change in x_A is less than the complete range from 0 to 1.0 as used here. In other words,

$$\begin{aligned} \Delta x_B &= 0.632\ \Delta x_A \text{ in one } \tau, \\ &= 0.980\ \Delta x_A \text{ in four } \tau \text{ regardless of the size of } \Delta x_A \end{aligned}$$

There are many other dynamic processes in chemical engineering that can be considered as single-capacity systems and are thus expressible as first-order transfer functions. For example, weirs can be readily designed so that the rate of output flow is directly proportional to the height of the liquid over the weir.

If the plate in Figure 20A is fitted with such a weir and if the input flow at point A is suddenly changed, the output flow at point B will vary only as the level of liquid on the tray is raised or lowered by the difference in the flow rates at points A and B. Thus the capacity of the tray will influence the rate of change of flow at B and a graph similar to Figure 19 would again be obtained. This particular type of transfer function is sometimes called a *hydraulic lag.*

Consider also the situation pictured in Figure 20B. Here a boiling liquid B is being vaporized by heat transferred through a metal wall from the heating fluid A. A sudden increase in the temperature of the fluid A will not immediately result in a greater rate of boiling in fluid B since the metal wall must first be heated. Thus the heat capacity of the vessel walls functions in the same manner as the liquid capacity of the weir tray of Figure 20A and the composition storage in the kettle of Figure 19. The reader can probably think of many more applications of this same type of analysis which would be present in a distillation column.

B. MULTIPLE-CAPACITY SYSTEMS

If one connects several kettles, such as are used in Figure 19, together as in Figure 21, one obtains a simple representation of a *multiple-capacity*

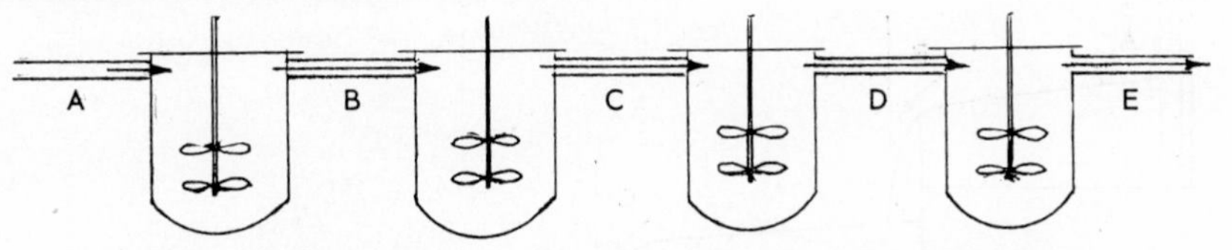

Fig. 21. Multiple-capacity systems, higher order transfer functions.

system and one represented by a *higher order transfer function.* By an analogy similar to eq. (4), the composition x_C can be represented as a function of composition x_B as follows:

$$x_C = \frac{x_B}{\tau_B p + 1} \tag{7}$$

but from eq. (4),

$$x_B = \frac{x_A}{\tau_A p + 1} \tag{4}$$

Therefore since we have allowed ourselves to perform algebraic operations on the operator p,

$$x_C = \frac{\left(\frac{1}{\tau_A p + 1}\right) x_A}{\tau_B p + 1} = \frac{x_A}{(\tau_A p + 1)(\tau_B p + 1)} \tag{8}$$

and

$$\frac{x_C}{x_A} = \frac{1}{(\tau_A p + 1)(\tau_B p + 1)} \tag{8a}$$

Equation (8a) is a second-order transfer function since this same system is represented classically by the following differential equation which is second order.

$$\frac{d^2 x_C}{dt^2} + 2\left(\frac{F}{C}\right)\frac{dx_C}{dt} = \left(\frac{F}{C}\right)^2 (x_A - x_C) \tag{9}$$

By a similar development it can be shown that the output composition at point E, x_E, is related to the input composition, x_A, by the relation:

$$\frac{x_E}{x_A} = \frac{1}{(\tau_A p + 1)(\tau_B p + 1)(\tau_C p + 1)(\tau_D p + 1)} \tag{10}$$

$$= \frac{1}{(\tau p + 1)^4} \tag{10a}$$

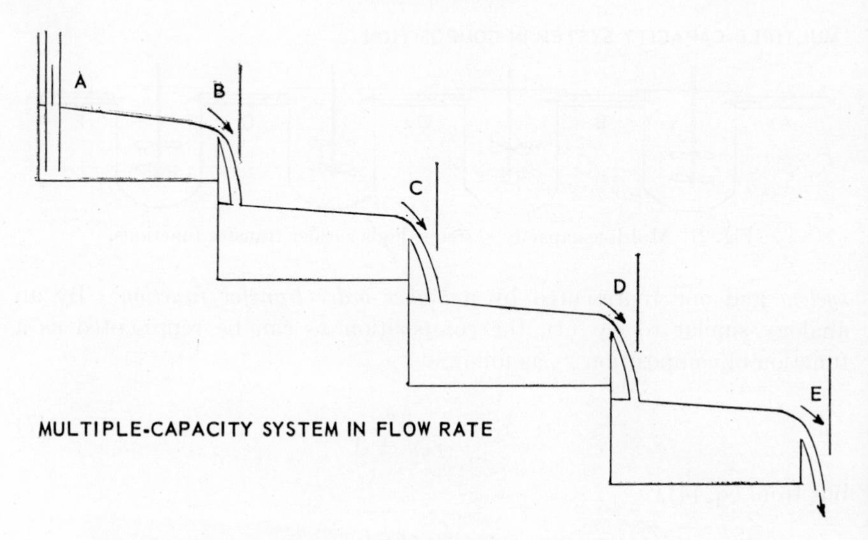

Fig. 22. Multiple-capacity systems, higher order transfer functions.

if all τ's are equal. This, of course, gives a fourth-order differential equation by classical means.

The flow system of Figure 22 when treated by similar methods will give the flow rate ratio F_E/F_A, again as a fourth-order transfer function:

$$\frac{F_E}{F_A} = \frac{1}{(\tau_A'p + 1)(\tau_B'p + 1)(\tau_C'p + 1)(\tau_D'p + 1)} \tag{11}$$

Thus many second- and higher order transfer functions can be considered as combinations of several first-order systems. Graphs of either of these examples when plotted as in Figure 19 will appear as shown in Figure 23.

It is possible also to have second- or higher order transfer functions which are not factorable completely into simple first-order expressions. Thus it is possible to have expressions such as

$$\frac{x_N}{x_A} = \frac{1}{p^n(\tau_1 p + 1)(\tau_2 p + 1)\ldots} \tag{12}$$

or

$$\frac{x_N}{x_A} = \frac{1}{p(\tau_1 p + 1)(\tau_2{}^2 p^2 + \xi p + 1)\ldots} \tag{13}$$

where

$$\xi \neq 2\tau$$

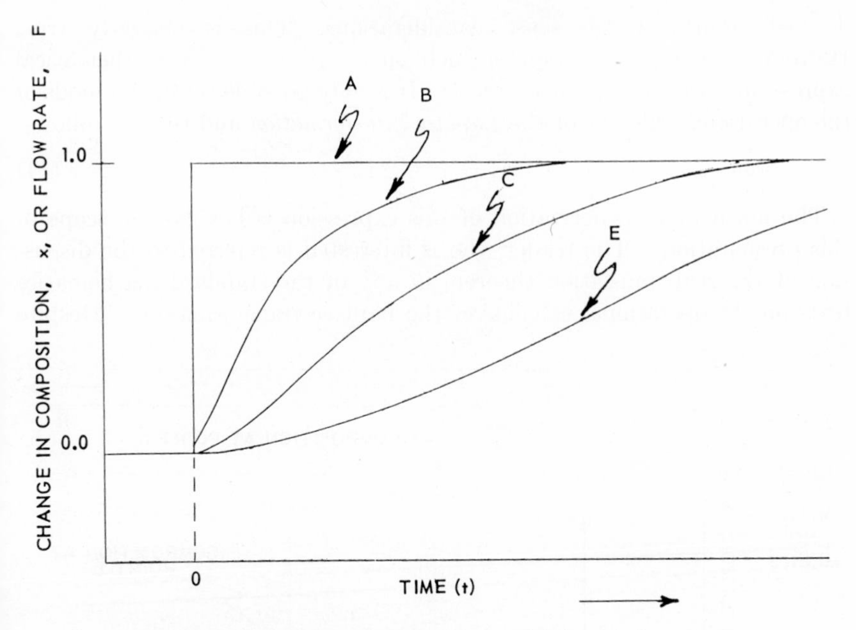

Fig. 23. Graphical representation of a multiple capacity system.

Many hydraulic and pneumatic devices are of the type of eq. (13).[1] These equations can be derived, as was the first-order transfer function, by writing the differential equation of the process; substituting the operator, p, for each d/dt in the equation; solving for the ratio of the output variable to the input variable; and then factoring the resulting expression. Since such expressions are very hard to evaluate by ordinary mathematical means, the expression is often assumed to fall under the category of eq. (10) or (12).

The types of expressions first considered are also known as *exponential time delays* with the first-order transfer function also being called a *simple time delay.*

C. TRUE-TIME DELAYS OR DEAD TIMES

Another type of time delay is also of major importance in considering the dynamics of petroleum and chemical processes. This is the concept of *true-time delay* or *dead time* or the time required to traverse a long pipe or a piece of apparatus wherein it is assumed that no mixing occurs. An example of this is "plug flow" through a long pipe or a condenser. Figure 24 gives a graphical representation of such an event. The reader will probably consider this as a ridiculously simple concept and one readily derived from common sense considerations. This is perfectly true. However, the representation of such an occurrence by a mathematical expression is difficult in the extreme. It is only possible by the methods of the operational calculus or the *Laplace transformation* and then as follows:

$$x_A = e^{-pT_{DT}} x_B \tag{14}$$

The mathematical derivation of this expression is beyond the scope of this presentation. The reader who is interested is referred to the discussion of the real-translation theorem in any of the standard mathematics texts on the operational calculus or the Laplace transformation. Despite

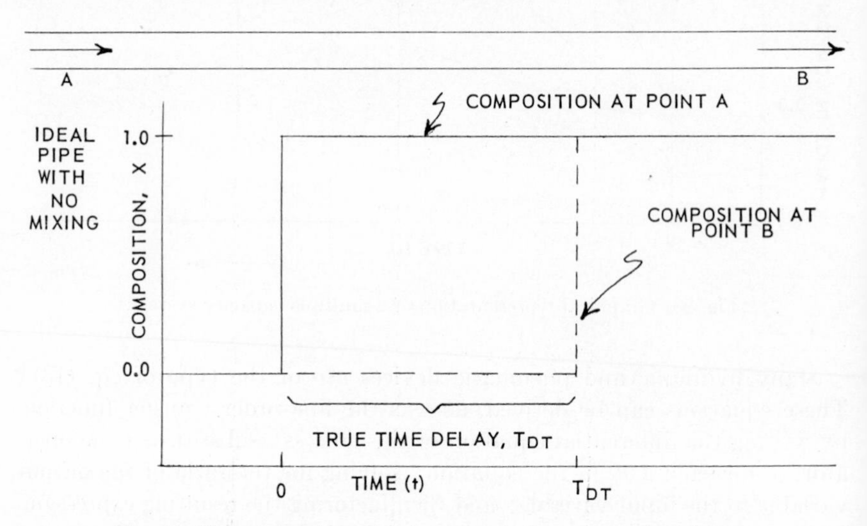

Fig. 24. Pictorial and graphical representation of true time delay.

the very great importance of such an expression in describing the process dynamics of the various components of a refinery, with their long pipe lines and large holdups, its inclusion in an equation makes the solution of the resulting equation almost impossible by conventional, that is classical means, except for the very simplest cases. These equations are, however, readily solvable by modern computing machines, such as the electronic differential analyzer, so a remedy to our dilemma is at hand.

D. GENERAL CASE

The actual process found in the refinery or chemical plant is, of course, neither purely an exponential time delay nor completely a true time delay. Figure 25 discusses one possible occurrence and shows how it may be approximated by a combination of one true time delay and one exponential

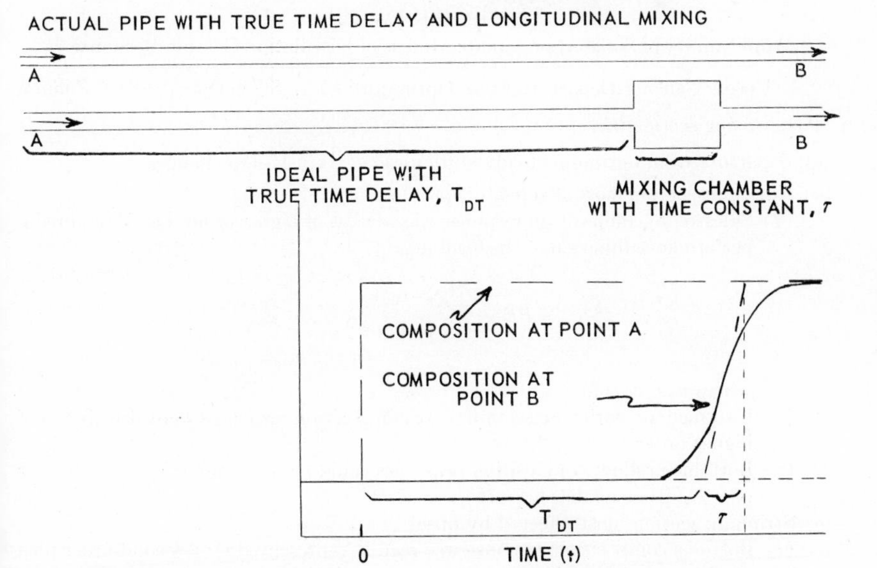

Fig. 25. Representation of an actual process by a combination of simpler ideal characteristics.

time delay. The resulting dynamic equation for the composition at point B as a function of that at point A would be

$$x_B = \frac{e^{-pT_{DT}} x_A}{\tau p + 1} \tag{15}$$

if we again permit algebraic manipulations of these expressions.

3. Approximate Mathematical Models and Responses of Distillation Columns

Exact mathematical modes of distillation columns are extremely complicated if all contributing factors are taken into account.[4,50,62] However, approximate models of the form just discussed are often very helpful in postulating the column's response to certain types of upsets, in designing proper control systems, and in postulating new types of control.

These approximate models, sometime called transfer functions, or performance functions, usually have the form

$$PF = \frac{O}{I} = \frac{Ke^{-T_{DT}p}}{(\tau_1 p + 1)(\tau_2 p + 1)} \tag{16}$$

TABLE IV

Applicability of Some Approximate Models of Distillation Column Response

I. Upsets Causing Departure From Optimum Steady-State Operation of Column

A. Pasteurizing section present on column

1. All departure from optimum steady-state upsets except boilup changes

(*a*) Enriching section most affected by upset

(*1*) Sidestream composition response was alwaps of higher order, i.e., it required a performance function of the form [eq. (17)]

$$PF = \frac{Ke^{-T_{DT}p}}{(\tau_1 p + 1)^n}$$

where $n > 2$, commonly $n = 4$ or 5.

(*2*) Intermediate enriching section plate composition responses were also always of higher order.

(*3*) Bottoms product composition responses could be represented by second-order plus deadtime models [eq. (16)]

(*b*) Stripping section most affected by upset

(*1*) Bottoms composition response was readily represented by a second-order plus deadtime model [eq. (16)].

(*2*) Intermediate stripping section plate composition responses were always of higher order as defined above [eq. (17)].

(*3*) Enriching section responses could be represented by pseudo first-order models —no deadtime [similar to eq. (4)].

$$PF = \frac{K}{(\tau p + 1)}$$

2. Boilup changes—departure from optimum steady-state

(*a*) Sidestream composition

(*1*) Large upsets—higher order plus deadtime [Equation (17)].

(*2*) Small upsets—second-order plus deadtime [Equation (16)].

(*b*) Intermediate plate compositions—higher order plus deadtime [eq. (17)].

(*c*) Bottoms composition—second-order plus deadtime [eq. (16)].

B. No pasteurizing section on column—all upsets

1. Enriching section most affected by upset

(*a*) Overhead composition response could be represented as a second-order plus deadtime system [eq. (16)].

(*b*) Intermediate tray composition responses were always of higher order [eq. (17)].

(*c*) Bottoms composition response, second-order plus deadtime [eq. (16)].

2. Stripping section most affected by upset

(*a*) Responses same as reported above.

II. Upsets Resulting in Return to Optimum Steady-State Operation of Column

Responses of all sections of the column could be readily approximated by a first-order response with no deadtime [eq. (4)].

or

$$= \frac{Ke^{-T_{DT}p}}{(\tau_1 p + 1)^n} \tag{17}$$

where PF = performance function; O = output response; I = input function; T_{DT} represents equivalent deadtime; τ_1, major time constants; τ_2, minor time constant; K, proportionality constant or scale factor; e, base of Naperian logarithms; and p, differential operator.

Table IV presents the results of an investigation to determine the approximate models for a number of different column configurations and operating conditions.[41]

A. THE CONCEPT OF "CHANGE OF INVESTORY" TIME

In order to lend a unifying factor to the models just presented, an overall concept of column response is necessary. Such a concept is that of the "change of inventory" time in the column. If one defines this function as follows:

$$T_{\text{INV}} = \frac{(\text{INV})_f - (\text{INV})_i}{(F_\nu x_{F_\nu} - F_i x_{Fi}) - (D_\nu - D_i)x_{Di} - (W_\nu - W_i)x_{Wi}} \tag{18}$$

where INV = inventory of component in question in column at time considered; f = refers to final steady-state condition of column; i = refers to initial steady-state condition of column; ν = refers to conditions at time just after step change upset.

The T_{INV} value is, of course, a pseudo first-order time constant considering the whole column holdup as a first-order mixing stage. That it works for higher order systems is due to the fact that the 60% response points of these systems (important in the approximate model developing formulas used here) is almost coincidental with the 63.2% (One Time Constant) point for the first-order system.

Table V extends the overall rules for approximation model order given in Table IV to predict the best ratios of major and minor time constants and of dead times and their relation to Change of Inventory time for each upset condition studied. The rules of Tables IV and V should be applicable to any column operating under conditions similar to those covered in the study.[41] They should also be applicable to other types of upsets provided the very definite hysteresis effect of the column response is taken into account for input functions requiring a two-sided response.

As mentioned earlier, the hysteresis effect on column response noted here is due to the immediate "pinch relieving" action of the column whenever more favorable column operating parameters are imposed. Since a pinch

TABLE V

Ratio of Time Constants and Deadtimes for Approximate Models of Distillation Column Response

I. Upset causing departure from optimum column separation

A. Boilup change

(*1*) Second-order plus deadtime models

$$\tau_1 = 3\tau_2 = 3T_{DT}$$

$$\Sigma\tau + T_{DT} = T_{\text{INV}}$$

Of equivalent product takeoff upset (i.e., same change in product composition)

(*2*) Higher order plus deadtime models

$$T_{DT} = {}^3/_2 \Sigma \tau_n$$

$$\Sigma\tau_n + T_{DT} = T_{\text{INV}} \text{ as above}$$

B. Input flow or composition or output flow upset

(*1*) Second-order plus deadtime model

$$\tau_1 = 4\tau_2 = ({}^4/_3)T_{TD}$$

$$\Sigma\tau + T_{DT} = T_{\text{INV}}$$

(*2*) Higher order plus deadtime model

$$T_{DT} = {}^3/_2 \Sigma \tau_n$$

$$\Sigma\tau + T_{DT} = T_{\text{INV}}$$

II. Upset causing return toward optimum column separation

$$T_{DT} = 0$$

First-order model sufficient

(*1*) Bottoms most affected

$$\tau = \left[\frac{H_R + H_{C_L}}{H_T}\right] T_{\text{INV}}$$

(*2*) Tops most affected

$$\tau = \left[\frac{H_A + H_{C_U}}{H_T}\right] T_{\text{INV}}$$

where H_R = reboiler holdup; H_{C_L} = holdup of lower column section less reboiler; H_A = accumulator holdup; H_{C_U} = holdup of upper column section less accumulator; H_T = total holdup.

is normally confined to one or the other end of the column and since by far the greatest changes in column composition occur there in the early part of the transient, it would seem that only the pinched end of the column should be considered in computing Change of Inventory time and the resulting column time constant. This has been done in Table V with excellent results. It should be noted in passing that while the initial transient for the pinch relieving case is fast, the overall equilibration time or total response time is at least as long as that for the pinch generating transient.

For cases where more than one upset is applied to the column at any one time, the "change of inventory" time can be computed for the combined transient in the same manner as for a single transient. If it is further assumed that the higher order response will predominate, the form of the resulting multiple transient can also be established.

B. PHYSICAL MEANING OF THE APPROXIMATE MODELS

Since the distillation column is a true higher order system, there is little reason to suspect a physical meaning for the values of the parameters developed in the approximation models derived here. The "change of inventory" time does have a physical meaning as a pseudo first-order time constant for the complete holdup of the column. It thus serves as a unifying concept between the real and approximate models for the column.

TABLE VI

Sketching Graphs of the Transient Response of Distillation Columns

(*1*) From steady-state calculations determine:

$$K = \frac{\text{Column output composition change}}{\text{Input variable upset magnitude}}$$

(*2*) From steady-state calculation determine the Change of Inventory Time, T_{INV}, according to eq. (18).

(*3*) Enter Tables IV and V and determine the performance function type.

(*4*) If a first-order response is indicated sketch the response similar to Figure 4.

(*5*) If a second-order plus deadtime response is indicated, follow the instructions of Figure 26.

(*6*) If a higher response ($n > 2$) is indicated, follow the instructions of Figure 27.

Likewise, the modification of the "change of inventory" time for the half-column case to develop the response time for the pinch relieving transient condition in the column is also based upon a physical occurrence in the column and again serves to base the approximations on true operating reality for the column. The "change of inventory" time, different for different sized upsets, adequately compensates for much of the nonlinearity present in the response of a distillation column to differing magnitude upsets.

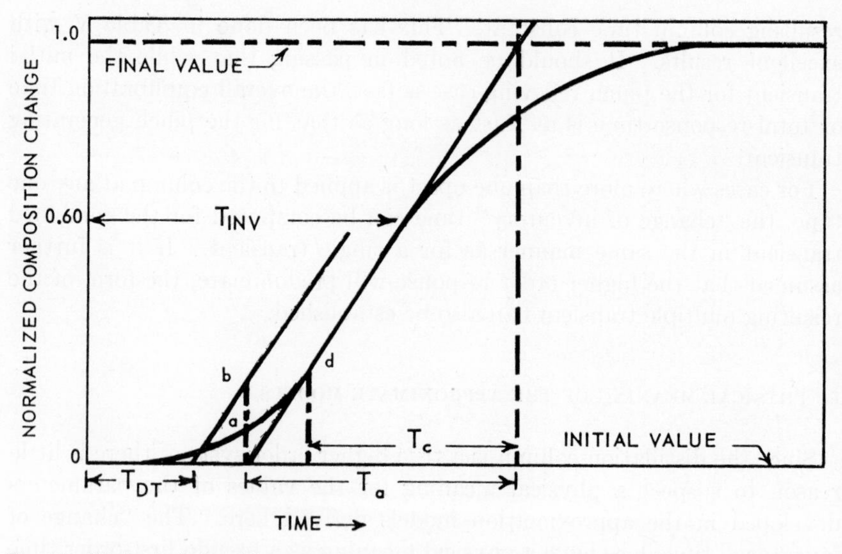

Fig. 26. Method of sketching transient response of column for second-order performance function.

(*1*) Determine value of:

$$x = \frac{\tau_1}{\tau_2}$$

$$T_c = \tau_1 + \tau_2$$

$$f(x) = (1 + x)(x)\frac{x}{(1 - x)}$$

$$T_a = \frac{T_c}{f(x)}$$

(*2*) Draw asymptotic line determined by value of T_a and T_{INV} as in sketch above.

(*3*) Plot T_{DT} point.

(*4*) Draw line parallel to asymptote through point of T_{DT}.

(*5*) Determine point *b* immediately above intercept of initial value line and asymptote

(*6*) Lay off T_c and T_a and determine location of point, *d*, on asymptote.

(*7*) Locate point, *a*, equal to $1/e$ times value of point, *b*.

(*8*) Sketch transient curve of column response from origin, through point *a*, coincident to asymptotic line at point *d* and asymptotic to final value line in form similar to this figure.

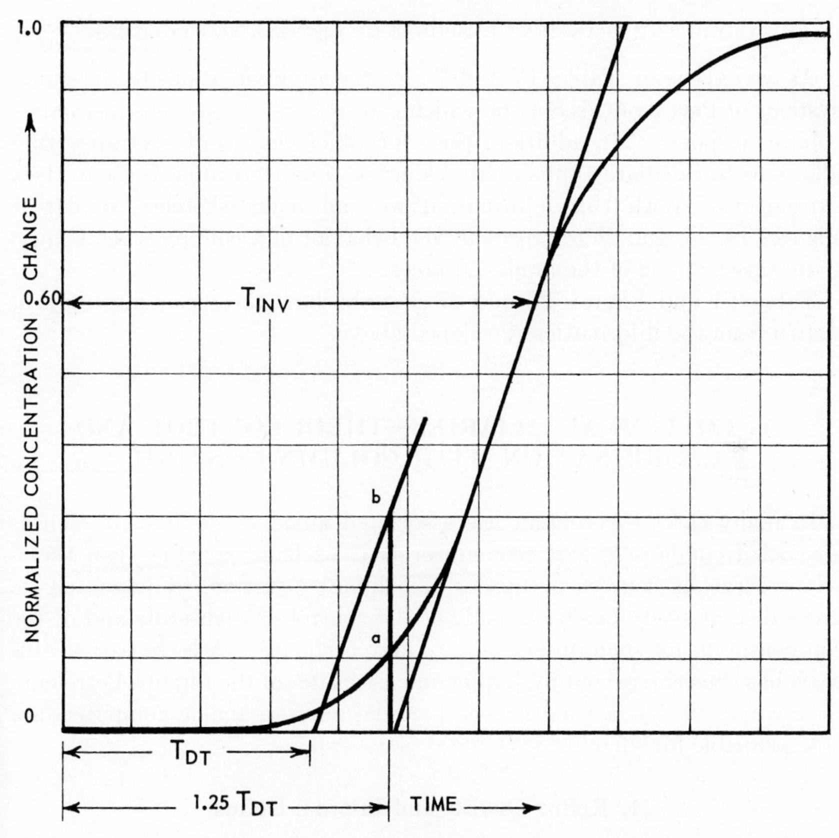

Fig. 27. Method of sketching transient response of column for higher order performance functions.

---

1) Determine T_{INV} and T_{DT} according to the formulas in Table V.

(*2*) Locate the T_{DT} point and the intercept of the asymptote line at 1.25 T_{DT} on the initial value line.

(*3*) Draw the asymptote line through the T_{INV} and 1.25 T_{DT} point.

(*4*) Locate point *b* by drawing a line through the T_{DT} point parallel to the asymptote.

(*5*) Locate point *a* at $1/e$ of point *b*.

(*6*) Draw the transient curve through point *a*, coincident with the asymptote at approximately 0.40, and eventually asymptotic to the final value. The shape of the curve will closely resemble figure.

C. SKETCHING THE TRANSIENT RESPONSE OF DISTILLATION COLUMNS

As we have seen, Tables IV and V give the approximations to the simple systems of Part 2 of this Section which can be used to represent distillation column response. In addition, the concept of change of inventory time allows us to calculate approximate values of time constants to use in these expressions. With this information we can make sketches similar to Figures 19, 23, and 25 to represent the behavior of a column when subject to an upset of one of the input variables.

Table VI and Figures 26 and 27 describe how these sketches may be drawn from the information developed above.

V. COLUMN AUXILIARIES—THEIR CONTROL AND COORDINATION WITH COLUMN CONTROL

In many cases the column has associated auxiliary equipment such as air-cooled condensers and economizer heat exchangers which can themselves serve as sources of upsets in column operation. Fortunately, a great deal of study has been made of the control of such units and of the compensation for such upsets as they may originate. A large part of this work has been carried out by Lupfer and associates of the Phillips Petroleum Company.[36–39] As a result, several special purpose analog computers are now available for such tasks.

1. Reflux Quality and Internal Reflux

While practically all theoretical work in distillation is carried out under the assumption that the reflux enters the top plate at the boiling point of the material on the plate, it is well known that the majority of operating columns must actually use a reflux which is much colder than the top-plate boiling temperature. A study of the transient and automatic control aspects of continuous distillation should therefore determine what effect such a condition may have on the response of the column.

In the ideal, steady-state example, the top-plate vapor rate, the reflux rate, and the distillate take-off rate, are related by the equation

$$V = L + \mathrm{D} \tag{19}$$

If the reflux is cold, a certain fraction of original vapor flow is condensed in heating the reflux to the plate temperature.

Therefore, again in the steady state

$$V' = V - fL = L + D \tag{20}$$

where fL is the amount of vapor condensed in heating the reflux and f may be termed the reflux condensation factor. This factor is a function of the heat capacity, heat of vaporization, and boiling point of the reflux material as well as its actual temperature prior to entrance onto the top plate.

$$f = \frac{(T_b - T_R)C_p}{\Delta H_b} \tag{21}$$

where ΔH_b is the heat of vaporization, T_b is the boiling point, T_R is the reflux temperature, and C_p is the heat capacity. Figure 28 relates f to reflux temperature for several typical hydrocarbon materials at 1 atm. ambient pressure. Similar graphs can readily be constructed for other materials and conditions.

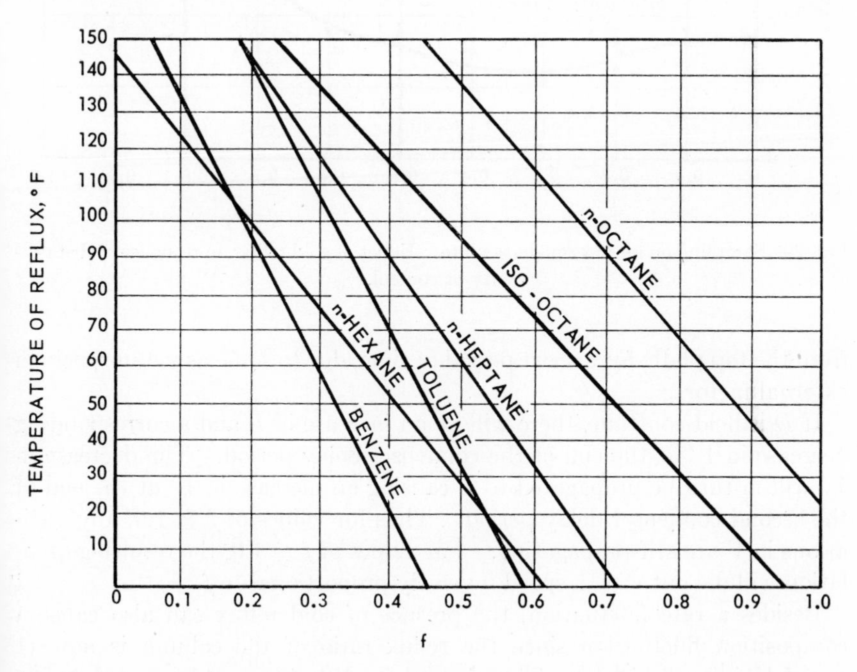

Fig. 28. Values of reflux condensation factor for various reflux temperatures and typical heads products.

Equation (20) will not be correct during a period of transient operation since the values of V, L, and D cannot be related directly in algebraic equation form because of the finite period of time required for the reflux material to flow through the condenser and associated lines. As an example of this, consider a column which is operating in the steady state according to eq. (20). Let us now allow a sudden increase to occur in the vapor rate

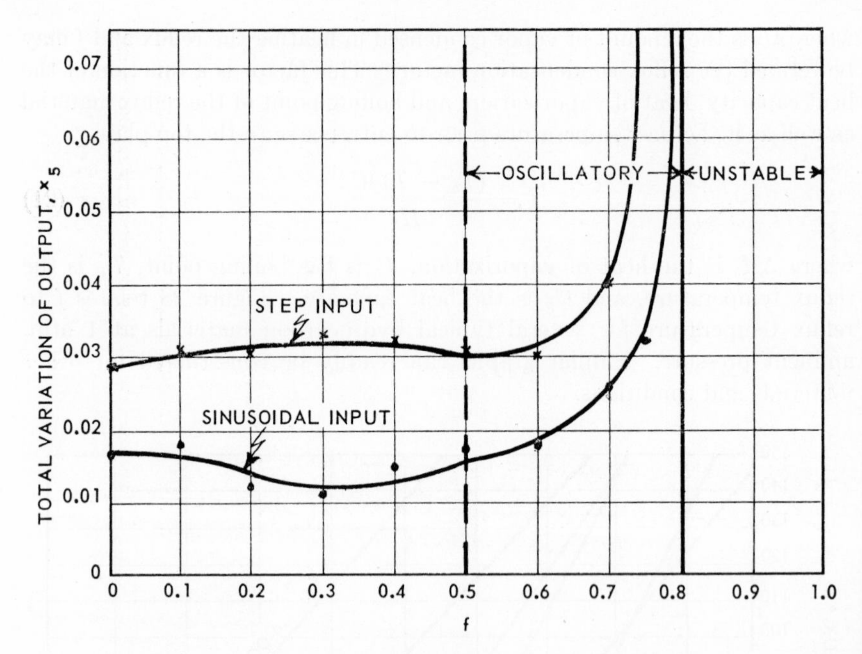

Fig. 29. Sampling on an intermediate plate. Effect of cold reflux on response and stability of control.

from the top plate, for a short period of time, due to some as yet unspecified external factor.

If D is held constant, there will be an increase in L and a corresponding decrease in V' at the end of the condenser delay period. The decrease in V' will in turn be propagated to L causing an increase in V' at the end of the second condenser delay period. Thus for values of $f \geqq 1.0$, any variations in V are self-propagating. For values of $f \leqq 1.0$, the resulting oscillation will die out with a speed inversely proportional to f.

Besides a rate fluctuation, the presnce of cold reflux can also cause a composition fluctuation since the reflux ratio of the column is now $(1 + f)L/D$ instead of L/D. Therefore, the value of D must be varied during the transient fluctuation discussed previously if the heads composition is to be maintained reasonably constant.

With this in mind, let us show an example of the effect which cold reflux can have on the controllability and control response of a column subjected to various methods of automatic control. For this purpose, a five-plate column simulated on an analog computer was utilized.[64] Both top-plate and intermediate-plate (plate 4) samplings were investigated. The optimum controller setting as previously developed for each case was used.

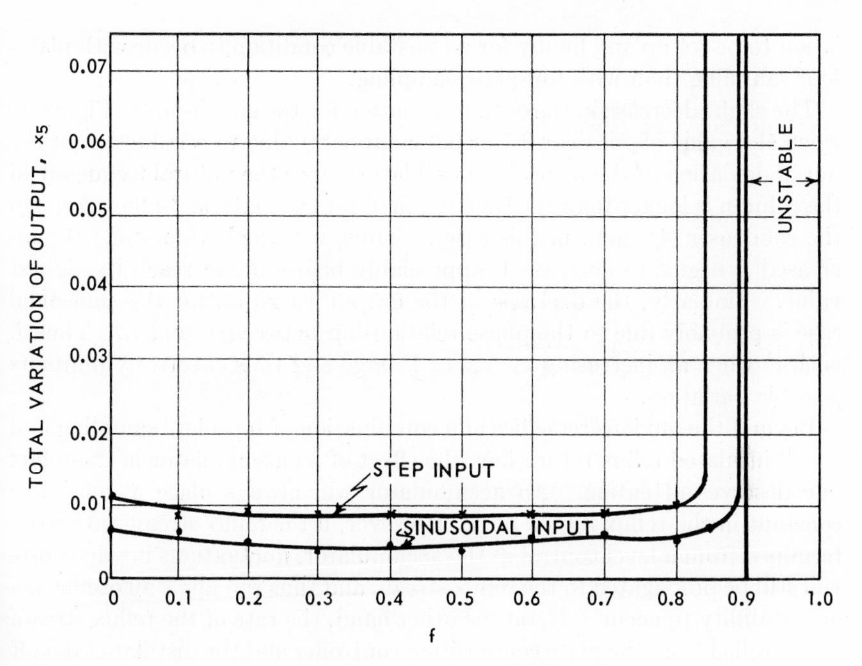

Fig. 30. Sampling on top plate.

It was assumed that the external influence which caused a change in the vapor rate was a composition change of ± 0.12 mole fraction in the feed to the column. Since the feed was assumed to be at constant temperature, this corresponded also to a vapor rate change in the column—i.e., q varies between 0 and 1.0 for $\alpha = 5.0$ as assumed here. Both a step variation and a sinusoidal variation with a frequency of 1 cycle in 10 min. were used.

Figures 29 and 30 show the results obtained. The total variation of top-plate composition (x_5) was chosen as the parameter which gave the best comparison between step and sinusoidal inputs. It is to be remembered, however, that the output composition variation caused by a step input quickly assumes a much smaller steady-state value after an initial large deviation. It is the initial large deviation that is plotted here.

The increased stability and smaller variation present with the top-plate sampling example is due to the fact that it can immediately detect the effect of a rate change through its accompanying composition change and can then make the proper adjustment in the distillate take-off rate to compensate. The fourth plate sampler on the other hand is handicapped by the presence of the exponential time delay of the top plate which hinders the detection of the composition changes that are occurring and the application of the proper corrections. It is thus much easier for an oscillation to be set up and finally for an unstable condition to occur with plate-four sampling than with top-plate sampling.

The slight decrease in the output variation for the step input of Figure 30 when the value of f is near 0.5 or 0.6 is probably due to a reduction of the initial deviation of the developing oscillation since the natural frequency of the column is longer than the time required for the material to flow through the condenser ($^1/_2$ min. in this case). Thus, with high values of f the increased L begins to decrease V appreciably before it can reach its highest value. Similarly, the decrease in the output variation for the sinusoidal case is probably due to the phase relationship between V and L. Thus L is large when an increasing x_F makes V large and thus effectively limits its possible variation.

Beyond the obvious remedies of a combination of top-plate sampling and a well insulated reflux return line, the effect of an accumulator in the reflux line deserves attention. An accumulator will always place a long time constant in the reflux return line. However, if the reflux stream rate is determined from a level control in the accumulator, fluctuations in vapor rate will still be propagated to the reflux stream and thus can allow an oscillation or instability to occur. If, on the other hand, the rate of the reflux stream is controlled from the plate composition controller and the distillate take-off comes from the level control of the accumulator, vapor rate fluctuations cannot be propagated and the described events cannot occur. Thus a control scheme similar to that of Figure 3B will effectively prevent these fluctuations from occurring.

A. CONTROL TO MAINTAIN A CONSTANT INTERNAL REFLUX

One of the special devices developed by Lupfer and associates involves a small analog computer designed to compensate for the upset caused by a cold reflux by regulating external reflux in such a way as to keep internal reflux constant. Thus the column never sees the effect of a cold reflux and the upsets described in the previous paragraphs cannot occur. This is, of course, a superior method to the feedback type of compensation required with the control system of Figure 3B. It has performed admirably in many plant installations.

The internal reflux flow rate in the column, L', can be obtained from the external reflux flow rate, L, as follows:

$$\begin{aligned} L' &= L(1 + f) \\ &= L(1 + K\Delta T), \end{aligned} \tag{22}$$

where

$$K = C_p/\Delta H_b \tag{23}$$

The computed value of internal reflux is continuously compared with the preset desired value of this quantity and corrections made in the external rate, L, until L' is equal to the set point value.

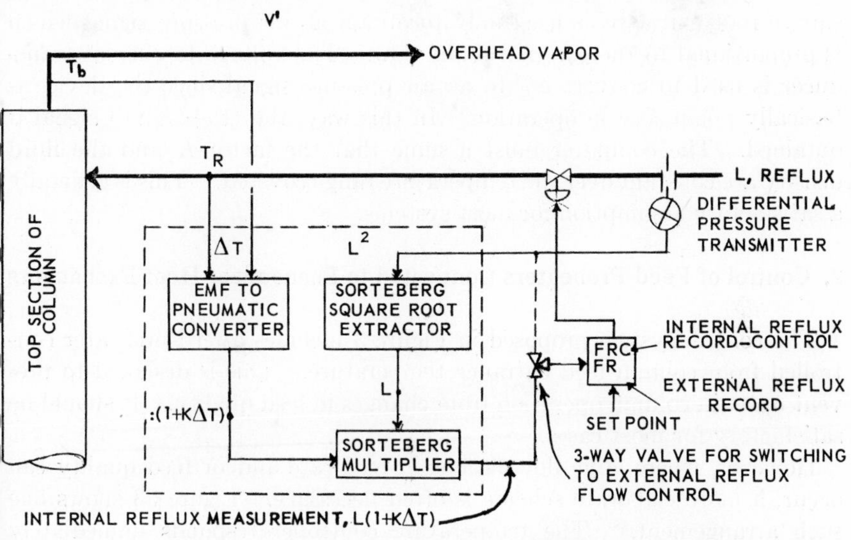

Fig. 31. Block diagram of a simple pneumatic analog computer for control of internal reflux flow.

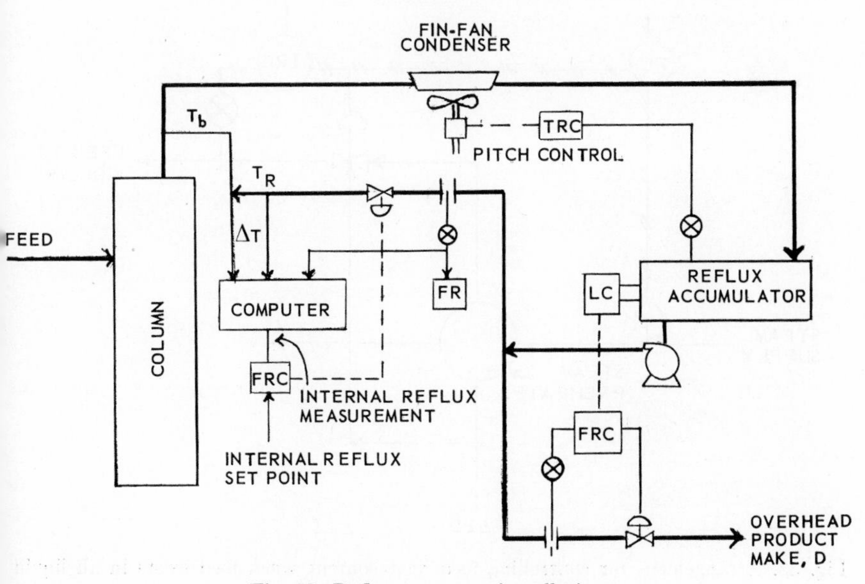

Fig. 32. Reflux computer installation.

Several different types of computers have been marketed for this purpose. That originally developed by Lupfer and Berger[36] is shown in Figures 31 and 32. As shown in Figure 31, there is only one major computing component required for the solution of eq. (22). This is the multiplier. The square root extractor is used only to obtain an air pressure signal which is proportional to the external reflux flow. The voltage to current transducer is used to convert ΔT to an air pressure signal since the device is basically pneumatic in operation. In this way, the $(1 + K\Delta T)$ signal is obtained. The computer must assume that the factor K and the fluid density are constant over the temperature range covered. This is generally a satisfactory assumption for most systems.

2. Control of Feed Preheaters Connected to Economizer Heat Exchangers

The control system proposed in Figure 3 includes a feed-preheater controlled from column feed entrance temperature. This is designed to prevent upset in column operation from changes in feed quality. It should be satisfactory for most cases.

However, where large fluctuations in feed rate and/or feed quality can occur, a more elaborate scheme is often necessary. Figure 33 shows one such arrangement.[38] The temperature controller responds immediately to position the three-way valve to provide rapid corrections to feed tem-

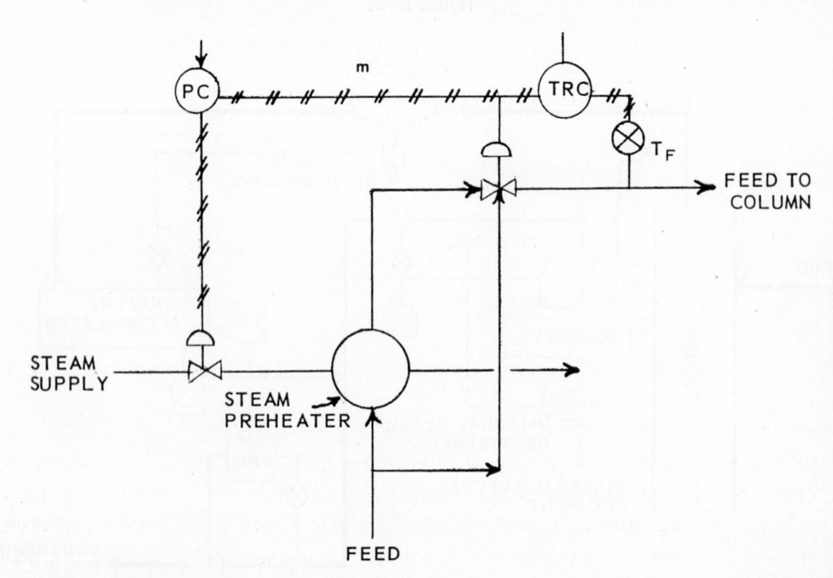

Fig. 33. Arrangement for controlling feed heat content when feed exists in all liquid phase.

perature. In addition, by acting through the pressure controller of the preheater, it gradually varies the overall fluid temperature. As a result, the three-way valve is returned to its midpoint position from which it can move in any necessary direction to correct the next upset which is detected.

Where partially or completely vaporized feeds are being used and particularly when bottoms product flows are used as feed preheat fluids for

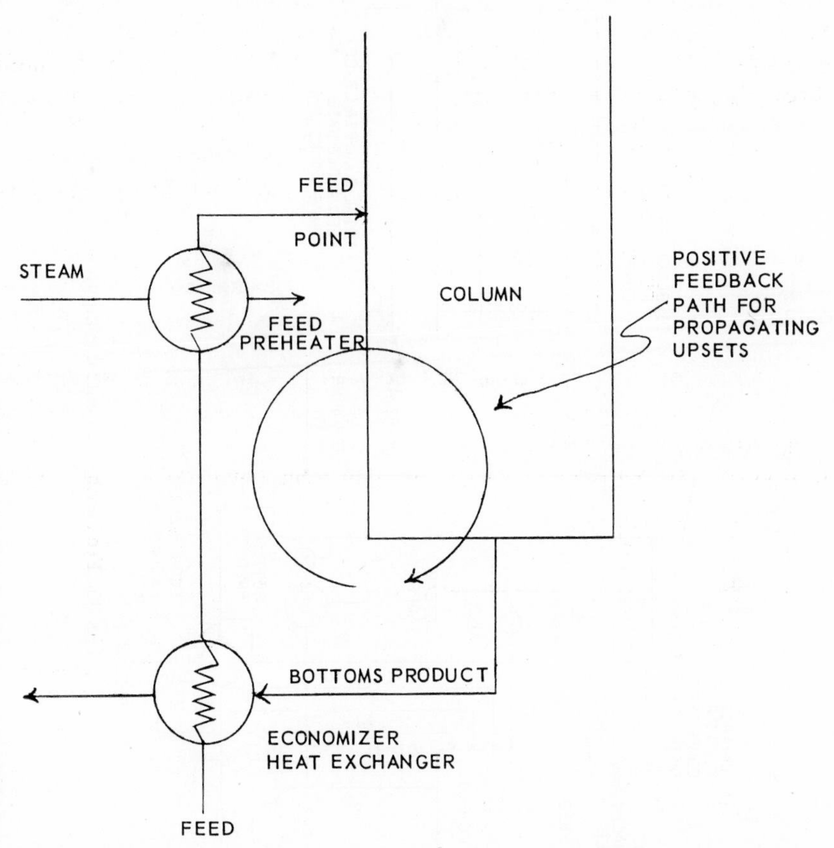

Fig. 34. Propagation of upsets in columns equipped with heat economizer exchangers.

heat economy purposes, an even more elaborate scheme is required for smooth control and the prevention of upset propagation. As is shown in Figure 34, the economizer heat exchanger provides a positive feedback path for propagating upsets just as occurred with the subcooled reflux discussed above. In order to correct this possible source of difficulty, the Phillips Petroleum group has devised another analog computer type controller.[38] This device (Fig. 35) maintains a continuous monitoring of the enthalpy

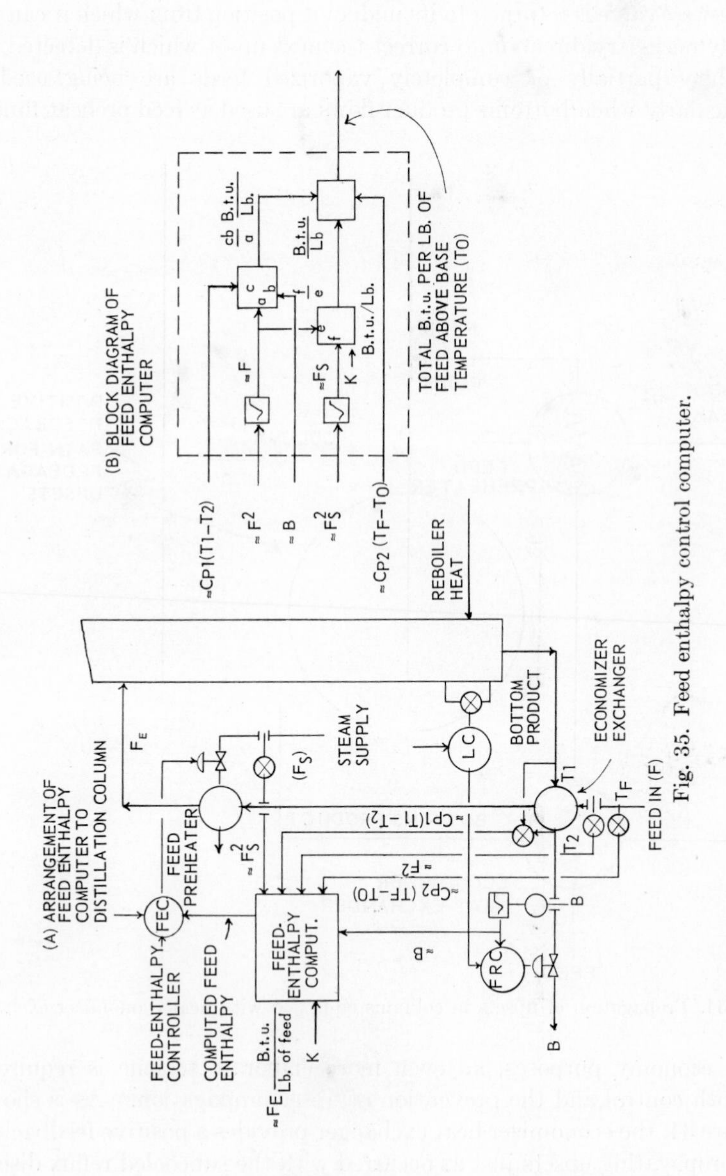

Fig. 35. Feed enthalpy control computer.

rather than the temperature of the feed and controls the steam flow to the feed preheater to maintain this enthalpy constant.

To carry this out, it must measure the rate and temperature drop of the bottoms product stream through the economizer condenser. This, combined with a knowledge of the rate and initial temperature of the feed, will give the enthalpy content of the feed at the entrance to the preheater. Knowing the desired enthalpy content for column entry, it is then a relatively simple matter to compute the rate of steam entry to the preheater necessary to supply this required heat addition.

VI. SOME ADVANCED TOPICS IN DISTILLATION COLUMN CONTROL

1. Optimum Feed Plate Location

One of the semi-independent variables of column operation is feed plate location. If feed composition does not vary greatly, one feed plate location is sufficient. However, for some possible wide variations of feed composition "pinches" and a corresponding reduction in column separating capacity may occur beyond the capacity of the control system to correct. Thus some sort of automatic feed plate changes would be desirable. Figure

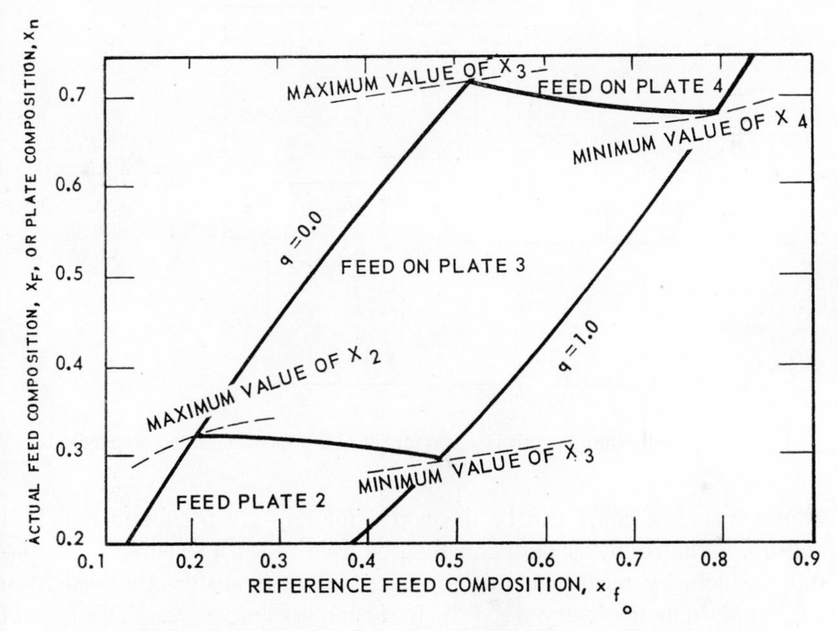

Fig. 36. Best feed plate location depends on feed quality as well as composition.

36 shows a sample chart of the optimum feed plate locations for a small column. Feed plate location is a function of the feed quality as well as the comparison of the actual feed composition to the reference or median feed composition. While the particular case shown here is for a five-plate

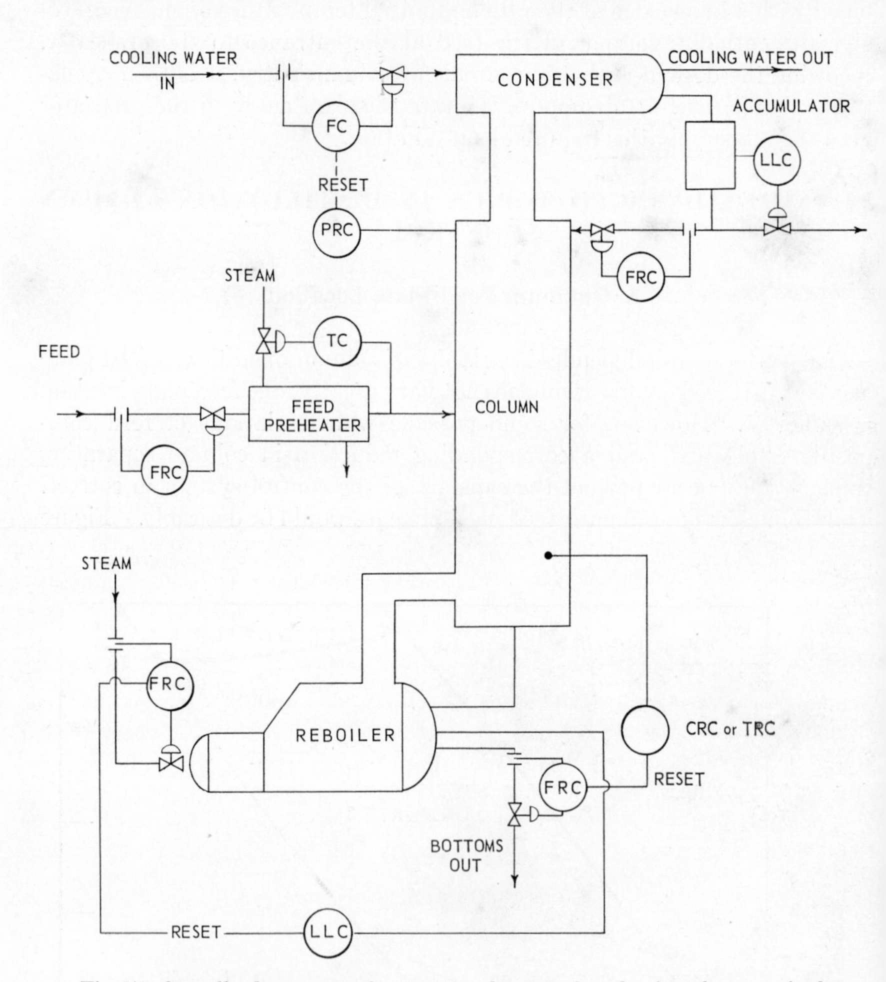

Fig. 37. Overall column control system for the case of predominately vapor feeds.

column,[48] such a chart can be developed for any given column and feed mixture. The resulting data can then be used to set a solenoid type controller which, by means of quick-opening valves, transfers the feed from plate to plate as necessary when the feed composition varies. This type of control is included in the recommended control system of Figure 4.

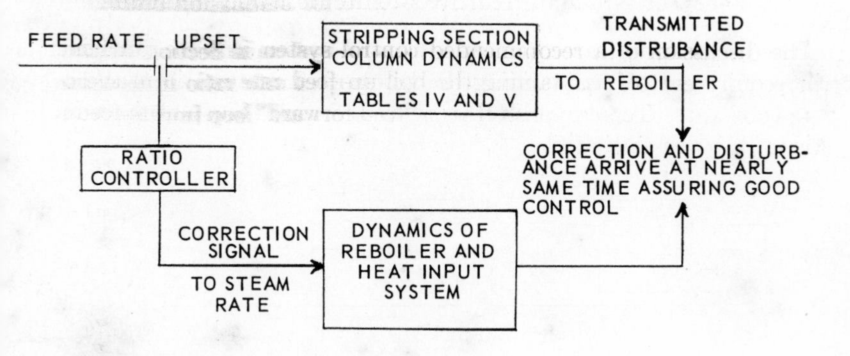

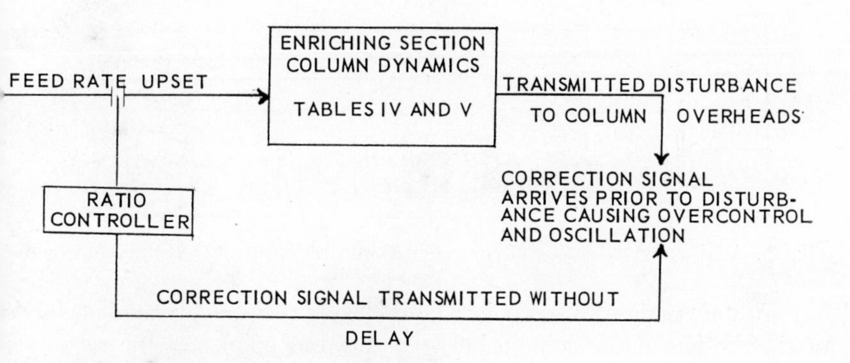

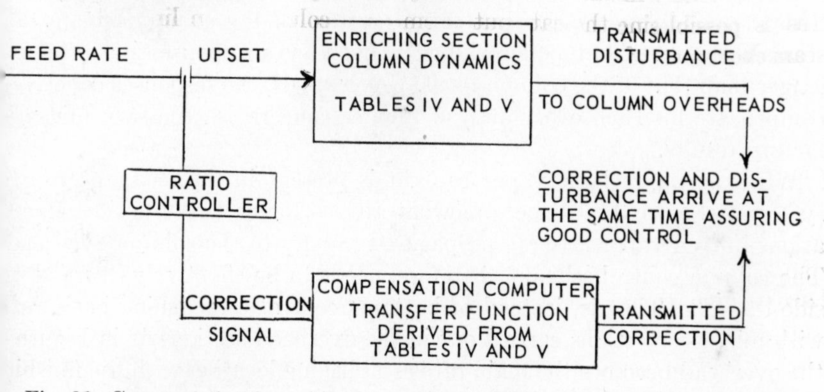

Fig. 38. Compensation for column dynamics in feed forward control systems.

2. Feed Forward and Predictive Control for Distillation Columns

The discussion of a recommended control system in Section I includec the requirement of maintaining the boil-up–feed rate ratio in the columı as a constant. To accomplish this, a "feed forward" loop from feed rate t stream rate was included.

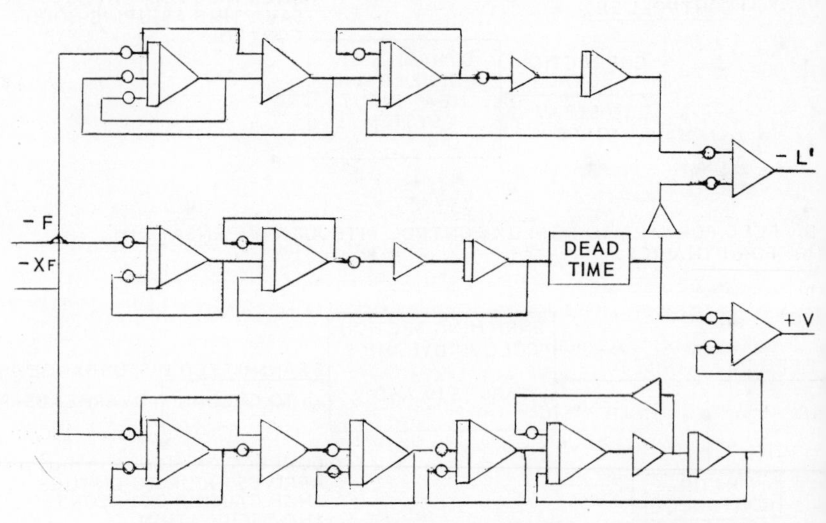

Fig. 39. Analog representation of controller compensation used by Rippin and Lamb.

Part 3 of Section IV has pointed out the approximate dynamic behavio of the section of the column between the feed point and the reboiler i terms of the equivalent dead time and the probable rate of change of re sponse at the bottom of the column. No provision for accounting fo these dynamics is included in the control system proposed in Figure 4 This is possible since the heat input system of the column (steam line steam chest, metal of reboiler wall, etc.) itself has a response time as long o longer than that of the column itself. As a result, the responses effectivel compensate for each other and no further concern is necessary for satis factory results.

When an appreciable vapor content is present in the feed, the contro system of Figure 3 must be somewhat altered for best results since fluctu ations in feed vapor rate are propagated rapidly to the column overheads The column control scheme, therefore, needs to be effectively "turned up side down." That is, instead of bottoms control establishing basic rate with minor corrections carried out in the overhead sections as in Figure the overhead becomes the main rate establishing location with the finishin control applied in the bottoms. Figure 37 diagrams such a control systen

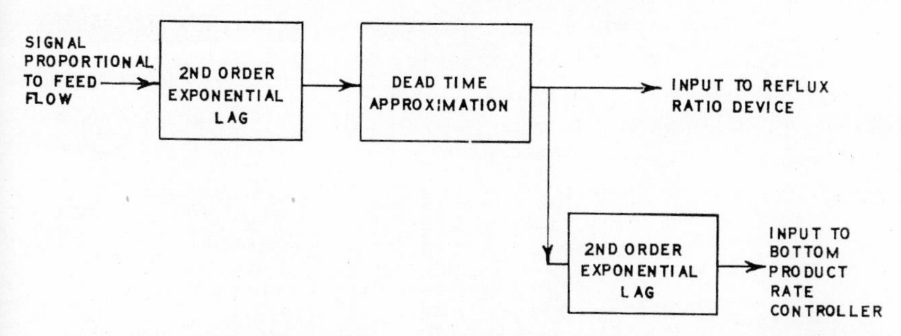

Fig. 40. Compensating transfer functions used by Lupfer and Parsons[37] for feed forward control compensation.

Since a delay in control response does not occur in the overhead section of the column as in the reboiler, an external compensation to parallel the normal column transfer function must be added to assure good control. Figure 38 diagrams the basis for such action.

The forms of the compensating transfer functions for use in feed forward control of reflux have been postulated by Rippin and Lamb[46] and by Lupfer and Parsons.[37] Table VII gives the transfer functions as developed by Rippin and Lamb, while Figure 39 presents an analogue computer diagram designed to use these to compensate for the effects of both feed rate and feed composition.

TABLE VII

Summary of Controller Transfer Functions Used by Rippin and Lamb[46]

Transfer function	Time constants	
$\frac{L'}{x_F} = \frac{(1 + \tau_1 S)}{(1 + \tau_2 S)(1 + 2\xi_3\tau_3 S + \tau_3^2 S^2)}$	$\tau_1 = 1.075$ $\tau_2 = 1.5$ $\tau_3 = 0.17$	$\xi_3 = 0.8$
$\frac{V}{x_F} = \frac{(1 + \tau_1 S)}{(1 + \tau_2 S)(1 + \tau_3 S)^2(1 + 2\xi_4\tau_4\pi + \tau_4^2 S^2)}$	$\tau_1 = 9.1$ $\tau_2 = 1.78$ $\tau_3 = 0.50$ $\tau_4 = 0.10$	$\xi_4 = 0.7$
$\frac{L'}{F} = \frac{e^{-\tau_1 S}}{(1 + \tau_2 S)(1 + 2\xi_3\tau_3 S + \tau_3^2 S^2)}$	$\tau_1 = 0.25$ $\tau_2 = 0.667$ $\tau_3 = 0.667$	$\xi_3 = 1.1$

Lupfer and Parsons used only feed rate information, but used it for correction of both reflux rate and bottoms product take-off rate. Figure 40 shows a block diagram of the compensating network which they used. Note that these transfer functions or performance functions are nearer in form to those predicted in Tables IV and V than are those of Rippin and Lamb although either would probably give satisfactory results.

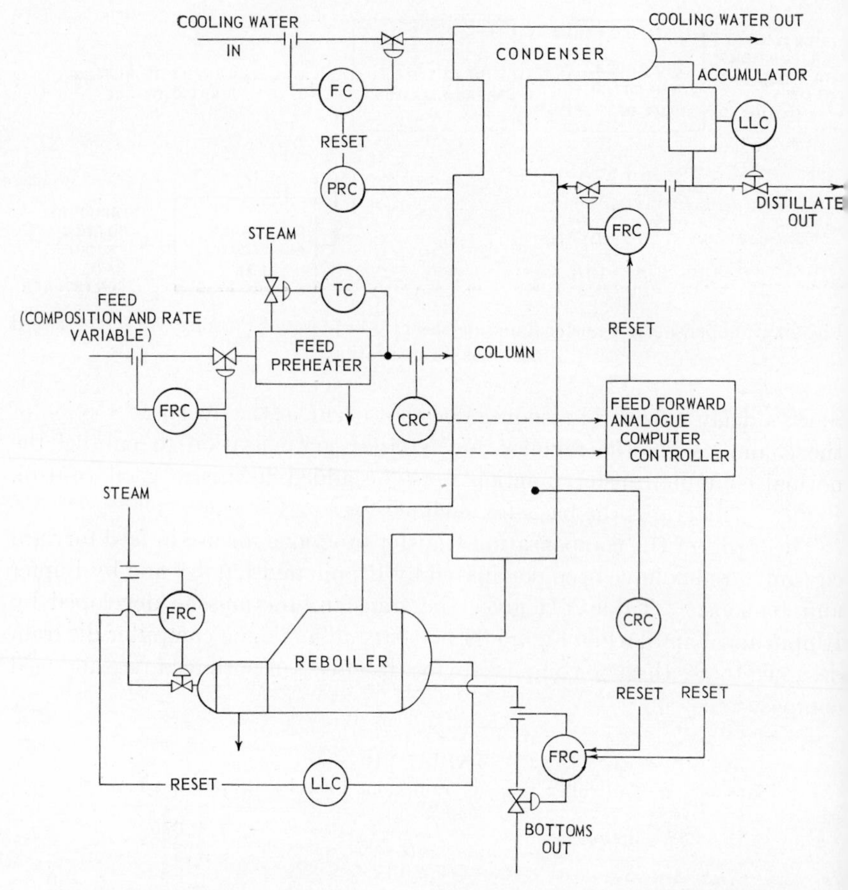

Fig. 41. Overall feed forward control system for predominately vapor feeds.

Figure 41 shows the control system of Figure 37 modified to include the compensating computer functions just discussed. Computer functions to compute the deadtime approximations required in each of the devices mentioned above are given in the text on analog computer use by Johnson.[31]

3. Some Additional Proposals for Column Control Devices

In a recent article Haines[26] proposed several additional applications of analog computer controllers for distillation column use. While it is not known that any of these devices actually exist at the time of this writing each of them is worthy of active consideration for the purpose shown.

A. PUMPAROUND HEAT REMOVAL

Frequently, it is necessary to remove excess heat from a fractionating column to maintain column flow rates and assure proper separation. If pumparound heat removal is employed, this operation in theory can be controlled with an analog computer (Fig. 42). In this type of operation, a trim cooler is ordinarily employed for adjusting the amount of heat removed, inasmuch as temperatures and flow rates of the main coolant stream normally depend upon operations elsewhere in the plant.

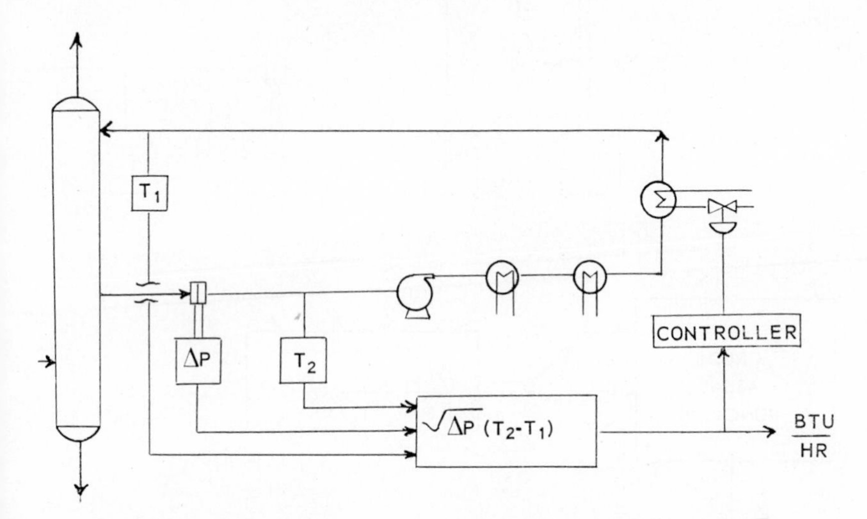

Fig. 42. Analog computer for control of pumparound heat removal.

Even though the trim cooler is automatically regulated by appropriate temperature controls, the amount of heat removed from the tower may not remain constant. Temperature of pumparound leaving the tower, temperature of pumparound returning to the tower, and its flow rate, can be measured but they are not the primary variables. However, if fed into an analog computer that calculates the rate of heat removal, these variables will control the operation. The computer output goes to a conventional controller which adjusts the quantity of heat removed by the trim cooler.

B. BOTTOMS CUTPOINT

When cutting deeply into a crude oil for maximum output, the still operator attempts to maintain a specified flash zone temperature to obtain a constant bottoms flow rate. The number of different crudes to be run and feed rate changes to the atmospheric still complicates the operator's

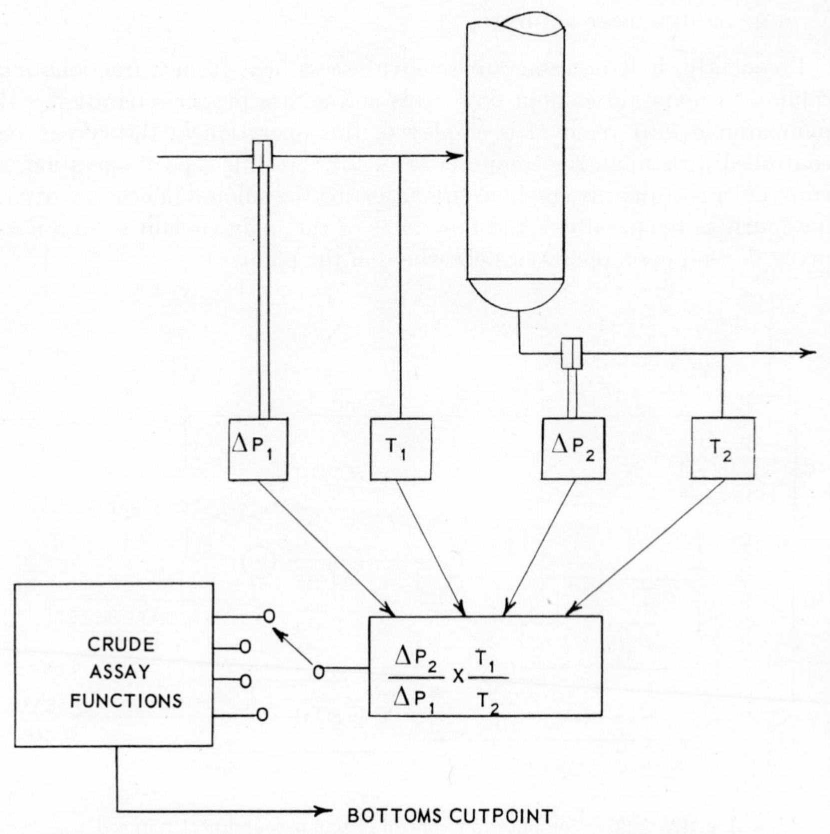

Fig. 43. Analog computer for cut-point control of bottoms of crude columns.

problems. The job is even more complicated if flow measurements are not temperature or density compensated.

One analog system has been proposed (Fig. 43) where the compensated bottoms flow is divided by the compensated total crude flow for calculating per cent bottoms. The computer automatically uses the correct assay curve previously set on a crude selector switch and reads out bottoms cut-point.

C. CAPACITY CONTROL

Analog computers may be used to manipulate the overall operating capacity in fractionation towers. One such instrument, diagrammed in Figure 44, computes the actual vapor rate from measured product and reflux rates, the vapor capacity as a function of measured pressure, and the per cent of vapor capacity actually utilized. The computed percentage is

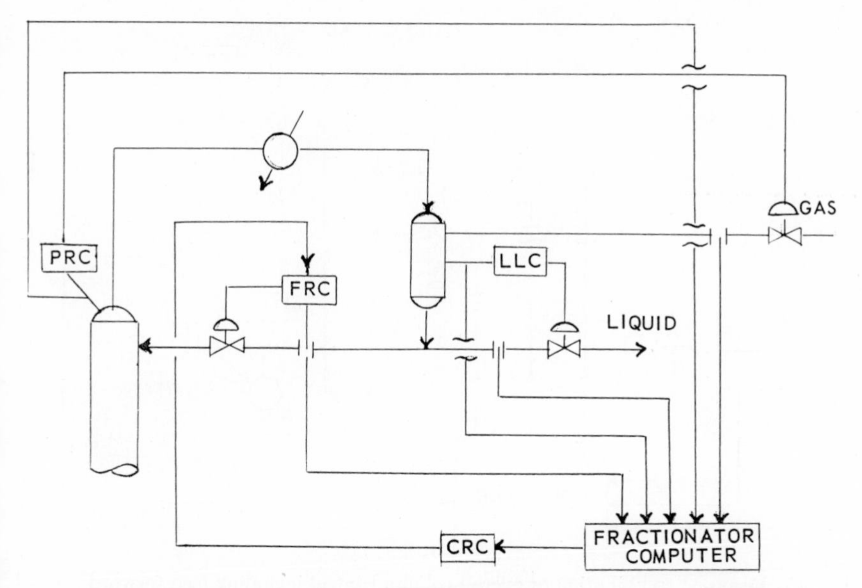

Fig. 44. A proposed analog computer for control of column capacity.

recorded and can be used to control the tower to any desired percentage of capacity.

D. OVERALL COLUMN CONTROL INCLUDING FEED FORWARD CONTROL

Analog computers should be suitable for a combination of feed forward and overall column control, where the computer automatically changes the feed plate location, reboiler temperature, and reflux ratio set point.

A feed stock analysis and a feed stock temperature measurement is taken and fed into the computer, which has previously been instructed on the steps it must take for different feed compositions and temperatures. In this application, the computer receives advance notice that a different feed stock will shortly enter the tower and makes changes accordingly, keeping tower upsets to a minimum.

Figure 45 presents a block diagram of the computer and instrumentation which would be required for such a device.

It should be noted that analog computers have been specified for the complex control devices recommended in each case above. However, should a digital computer be present for other plant control tasks in the same unit as the distillation column under consideration, this computer can be programmed to carry out any of the functions discussed above. On the other hand, there probably is not enough justification in any of them to

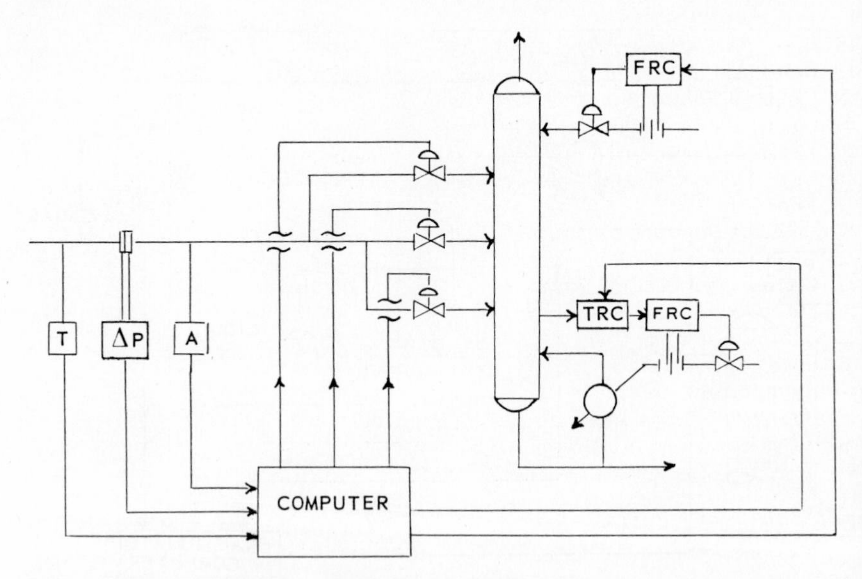

Fig. 45. Proposed combination of overall column control including feed forward control by means of special purpose computer.

warrant using a special digital computer in place of the analog suggested if the digital computer is not already justified for another task.

References

1. Anisimov, *Automatic Control of Rectification Processes,* Consultants Bureau, New York, 1957.
2. Ankel and Hengst, *Regelungstechnik,* **6,** 361 (1958).
3. Archer, *Brit. Chem. Eng.,* **5,** 88 (1960).
4. Archer and Rothfus, *Chem. Eng. Progr. Symp. Ser.,* **57,** No. 36, 2 (1961).
5. Armstrong and Wilkinson, *Trans. Inst. Chem. Eng.* (*London*), **35,** 352 (1957).
6. Armstrong and Wood, *Trans. Inst. Chem. Engrs.,* (*London*) **39,** 65 (1961).
7. Armstrong and Wood, *Trans. Inst. Chem. Engrs.* (*London*), **39,** 80 (1961).
8. Aikman, *ISA J.,* **3,** 412 (1956).
9. Baber, Edwards, Harper, Witte, and Gerster, *Chem. Eng. Progr. Symp. Series,* **57,** No. 36, 148 (1961).
10. Baber and Gerster, "Experimental Transient Response of a Pilot-Plant Distillation Column. Part II Response to Liquid and Vapor Rate Perturbations," Paper presented before the 54th Annual Meeting, American Institute of Chemical Engineers, New York, December, 1961.
11. Bauer and Orr, *Chem. Eng. Progr.,* **50,** 312 (1954).
12. Berger and Campbell, *Chem. Eng. Progr.,* **51,** 348 (1955).
13. Berger and Short, *Ind. Eng. Chem.,* **48,** 1027 (1956).
14. Bertrand and Jones, *Chem. Eng.,* **68,** No. 4, 139 (1961).
15. Bogenstatler and Hengst, *Chem. Ing. Tech.,* **31,** 425 (1959).

16. Boyd, *Petrol. Refiner*, **27**, 533, 594 (1948).
17. Broadhurst, *Trans. Soc. Instr. Technol.*, **8**, 1 (1956).
18. Campbell, *Process Dynamics*, Wiley, New York, 1958.
19. Coulter, *Petrol. Refiner*, **31**, No. 12, 137 (1952).
20. Davidson, *Trans. Inst. Chem. Engr.*, **34**, 44 (1956).
21. Day, *Plant and Process Dynamic Characteristics*, Butterworths, London, 1957, pp. 29–55.
22. Endtz, Janssen, and Vermuelen, *Plant and Process Dynamic Characteristics*, Butterworths, London, 1957, pp. 170–200.
23. Fourroux, Karasek, and Wightman, *ISA J.*, **7**, No. 5, 76 (1960).
24. Fraade, *Regelungstechnik*, **9**, 269 (1961).
25. Gilliland and Mohr, *Chem. Eng. Progr.*, **58**, No. 9, 59 (1962).
26. Haines, *Ind. Eng. Chem.*, **52**, 662 (1960).
27. Harbert, *Petrol. Refiner*, **35**, No. 11, 151 (1956).
28. Hassett, *Brit. Chem. Eng.*, **5**, 95 (1960).
29. Hengst and Meier, *Regelungstechnik*, **3**, 219 (1955).
30. Hoyt and Stanton, *Petrol. Refiner*, **32**, No. 10, 115 (1953).
31. Johnson, *Analog Computer Techniques*, McGraw-Hill, New York (1956).
32. Keating and Townsend, *Proceedings of the Joint Symposium on Instrumentation and Computation*, J. M. Pirie, ed., The Institution of Chemical Engineers, London, 1959, p. 29.
33. Kiguchi and Ridgway, *Petrol. Refiner*, **35**, No. 12, 179 (1956).
34. Lamb, Pigford, and Rippin, *Chem. Eng. Progr. Symp. Ser.*, **57**, No. 36, 132 (1961).
35. Lloyd, Ayers, and Karasek, *Anal. Chem.*, **32**, 698 (1960).
36. Lupfer and Berger, *ISA J.*, **6**, No. 6, 34 (1959).
37. Lupfer and Parsons, *Chem. Eng. Progr.*, **58**, No. 9, 37 (1962).
38. Lupfer and Oglesby, *Ind. Eng. Chem.*, **53**, 963 (1961).
39. Lupfer and Oglesby, *ISA J.*, **8**, No. 11, 53 (1961).
40. Moczek, Otto, and Williams, "Control of a Distillation Column for Producing High-Purity Overheads and Bottoms Streams," Paper presented at the 142nd National Meeting, American Chemical Society, Atlantic City, New Jersey, September 11, 1962.
41. Moczek, Otto, and Williams, "Approximation Models for the Dynamic Response of Large Distillation Columns," Paper presented at the Second IFAC Congress, Basle, Switzerland, August 27–September 4, 1963.
42. Parkins, *Chem. Eng. Progr.*, **55**, No. 7, 60 (1959).
43. Powell, *ISA J.*, **5**, No. 4, 32 (1958).
44. Rademaker and Rijnsdorp, *World Petrol. Congr., Proc. 5th New York*, **1959**, Paper 5, Section VII.
45. Rijnsdorp and Maarleveld, "Use of Electrical Analogues in the Study of the Dynamic Behaviour and Control of Distillation Columns," *Symposium on Instrumentation and Computation in Process Development and Plant Design*, pp. A63ff, Institution of Chemical Engineers, London, May, 1959.
46. Rippin and Lamb, "A Theoretical Study of the Dynamics and Control of Binary Distillation," Paper presented before the 53rd Annual Meeting, American Institute of Chemical Engineers, Washington, D. C., December, 1960.
47. Rose, Johnson, and Williams, *Ind. Eng. Chem.*, **48**, 1173 (1956).
48. Rose and Williams, *Ind. Eng. Chem.*, **47**, 2284 (1955)
49. Rosenbrock, *Trans. Inst. Chem. Eng. (London)*, **35**, 347, 361 (1957).
50. Rosenbrock, *Brit. Chem. Eng.*, **3**, 364, 432, 491 (1958).

51. Rosenbrock, *Trans. Inst. Chem. Engrs.*, (*London*) **38,** 279 (1960).
52. Rosenbrock, Tavendale, Storey, and Challis, *Automatic and Remote Control*, Vol. 4, Coales, Ragazzini, and Fuller, eds., Butterworths, London, 1961, pp. 303–311.
53. Rosenbrock, *Trans. Inst. Chem. Engrs.*, (*London*) **40,** 35 (1962).
54. Rosenbrock, *Chem. Eng. Progr.*, **58,** No. 9, 43 (1962).
55. Tyler, *Chem. Eng. Progr.*, **58,** No. 9, 51 (1962).
56. Uilti, *Petrol. Refiner*, **29,** No. 3, 130 (1950).
57. Voetler, and Armstrong *Plant and Process Dynamics Characteristics*, Butterworths, London, 1957,pp. 73–100.
58. Wherry and Berger, *Petrol. Refiner*, **37,** No. 5, 219 (1958).
59. Wilkinson and Armstrong, *Chem. Eng. Sci.*, **7,** 1 (1957).
60. Wilkinson and Armstrong, *Plant and Process Dynamic Characteristics*, Butterworths, London, 1957, pp. 56–72.
61. Williams, *Ind. Eng. Chem.*, **50,** 1214 (1958).
62. Williams, T. J., "The Status of Studies of the Dynamics of Mass-Transfer Operations—A Review and Commentary," paper presented before the 47th National Meeting, American Institute of Chemical Engineers, Baltimore, Maryland, May, 1962.
63. Williams and Harnett, *Chem. Eng. Progr.*, **53,** No. 5, 220 (1957).
64. Williams, Harnett, and Rose, *Ind. Eng. Chem.*, **48,** 1008 (1956).
65. Williams and Lauher, *Automatic Control of Chemical and Petroleum Processes*, Gulf Publishing Company, Houston, Texas, 1961.
66. Wood and Armstrong, *Chem. Eng. Sci.*, **12,** No. 4, 272 (1960).
67. Woods, *Control Eng.*, **5,** No. 5, 91 (1958).

SUBJECT INDEX

D

E

F

G

H

I

J

K

L

M

N

O

T